Yovanna Neri (Medical Ass.)

PEARSON

ALWAYS LEARNING

Career Prep

Second Custom Edition

CSK 100 – Study Skills
CMF 95 – Math Fundamentals
CAT 150 – Anatomy, Physiology, and Terminology

PIMA
MEDICAL
INSTITUTE

Taken from:
Medical Terminology: A Living Language, Fifth Edition
by Bonnie F. Fremgen and Suzanne S. Frucht

*Keys to Success: Building Analytical, Creative,
and Practical Skills*, Brief Sixth Edition
by Carol Carter, Joyce Bishop, and Sarah Lyman Kravits

Math Basics for the Health Care Professional, Third Edition
by Michele Benjamin Lesmeister

Cover Art: Courtesy of PhotoDisc/Getty Images and Stockbyte/Getty Images.

Taken from:

Medical Terminology: A Living Language, Fifth Edition
by Bonnie F. Fremgen and Suzanne S. Frucht
Copyright © 2013, 2009, 2005, 2002, 1997 by Pearson Education, Inc.
Published by Prentice Hall
Upper Saddle River, New Jersey 07458

Keys to Success: Building Analytical, Creative, and Practical Skills, Brief Sixth Edition
by Carol Carter, Joyce Bishop, and Sarah Lyman Kravits
Copyright © 2012, 2009, 2006, 2003, 2001, 1999 by Pearson Education, Inc.
Published by Prentice Hall

Math Basics for the Health Care Professional, Third Edition
by Michele Benjamin Lesmeister
Copyright © 2009 by Pearson Education, Inc.
Published by Prentice Hall

This special edition published in cooperation with Pearson Learning Solutions.

All trademarks, service marks, registered trademarks, and registered service marks are the property of their respective owners and are used herein for identification purposes only.

The information, illustrations, and/or software contained in this book, and regarding the above-mentioned programs, are provided "As Is," without warranty of any kind, express or implied, including without limitation any warranty concerning the accuracy, adequacy, or completeness of such information. Neither the publisher, the authors, nor the copyright holders shall be responsible for any claims attributable to errors, omissions, or other inaccuracies contained in this book. Nor shall they be liable for direct, indirect, special, incidental, or consequential damages arising out of the use of such information or material.

Pearson Learning Solutions, 501 Boylston Street, Suite 900, Boston, MA 02116
A Pearson Education Company
www.pearsoned.com

Printed in the United States of America

4 5 6 7 8 9 10 V363 16 15 14 13

000200010271290567

SB

ISBN 10: 1-256-52542-1
ISBN 13: 978-1-256-52542-4

Contents

Medical Terminology: A Living Language
by Bonnie F. Fremgen and Suzanne S. Frucht

CSK 100
Study Skills

Taken From:

Keys to Success: Building Analytical, Creative, and Practical Skills, Brief Sixth Edition
by Carol Carter, Joyce Bishop, and Sarah Lyman Kravits

BRIEF CONTENTS

Quick Start to College, with coverage of some basic information you need at the beginning of your coursework, is designed to help you feel more in control as you start this important journey toward the achievement of a college education. As you read, consult your college handbook and/or website to learn about the specific resources, policies, and procedures of your college.

Start by learning what your college expects of you—and what you have a right to expect in return as a consumer of education. Continue on to explore the people and resources that can assist you while you are enrolled. Finally, consider the financial aid possibilities that can help you pay for it all.

What your college **expects of you**

If you clarify what it means to be a college student right at the start, you will minimize surprises that may be obstacles later on. What is expected of you may be different from anything you encountered in high school or in other educational settings. Because expectations differ from college to college, use the material that follows as general guidelines.

Follow procedures and fulfill requirements

Understanding and following college procedures will smooth your path to success.

Registration

Registration may take place through your school's computer network, via an automated phone system, or in the school gym or student union. Scan the college and website and consider key factors as you make your selections.

- ▶ Core/general requirements for graduation
- ▶ Your major or minor or courses in departments you are considering
- ▶ Electives that sound interesting, even if they are out of your field

Once you choose courses, but before you register, create a schedule that shows daily class times to see if the schedule will work out. Meet with your advisor for comments and approval.

Graduation and curriculum requirements

Every college has degree requirements stated in the catalog and website. Make sure you understand those that apply to you, such as the following:

- ▶ Number of credits needed to graduate, including credits in major and minor fields
- ▶ Curriculum requirements, including specific course requirements
- ▶ Departmental major requirements

School procedures

Your college has rules and regulations, found in the college handbook and on the website, for all students to follow, such as the following common procedures:

Letter grade	A	A−	B+	B	B−	C+	C	C−	D+	D	F
Numerical grade	4.0	3.7	3.3	3.0	2.7	2.3	2.0	1.7	1.3	1.0	0.0

▶ *Adding or dropping a class.* If you find that a course is not right for you or that there are better choices, adding or dropping courses should be done within the first few days of the term. Withdrawals after a predetermined date, except those approved for special cases, usually receive a failing grade.

▶ *Taking an incomplete.* If you can't finish your work due to circumstances beyond your control—an illness or injury, for example—many colleges allow you to take a grade of Incomplete. The school will require approval from your instructor and you will have to make up the work later.

▶ *Transferring schools.* Research the degree requirements of other schools and submit transfer applications. If you are a student at a community college and intend to transfer to a 4-year school, take the courses required for admission to that school. In addition, be sure all your credits are transferable, which means they will be counted toward your degree at the 4-year school.

Understand your school's grading system

When you receive grades, remember that they reflect your work, not your self-worth. Most schools use grading systems with numerical grades or equivalent letter grades (see Key QS.1). Generally, the highest course grade is an A, or 4.0, and the lowest is an F, or 0.0.

In every course, you earn a certain number of college credits, called *hours*. For example, Accounting 101 may be worth three hours. These numbers generally refer to the number of hours the course meets per week. When you multiply each numerical course grade by the number of hours the course is worth, take the average of all these numbers, and divide by the total number of credit hours you are taking, you obtain your **grade point average**, or GPA.

GRADE POINT AVERAGE (GPA)

A measure of academic achievement computed by dividing the total number of grade points received by the total number of credits or hours of coursework taken.

Learn the minimum GPA needed to remain in good standing and to be accepted and continue in your major. Key QS.2 shows you how to calculate your GPA. You can also use Web resources such as www.back2college.com/gpa.htm to calculate your GPA electronically.

Make the most of your school's computer system

A large part of college communication and work involves the computer. In a given day you might access a syllabus online, e-mail a student, use the Internet to tap into a library database, write a draft of an assignment on a computer, and send a paper draft to an instructor electronically. *Get started right away.* Register for an e-mail account and connect to the college network. In addition, register your cell phone number with the school so you can get emergency alerts.

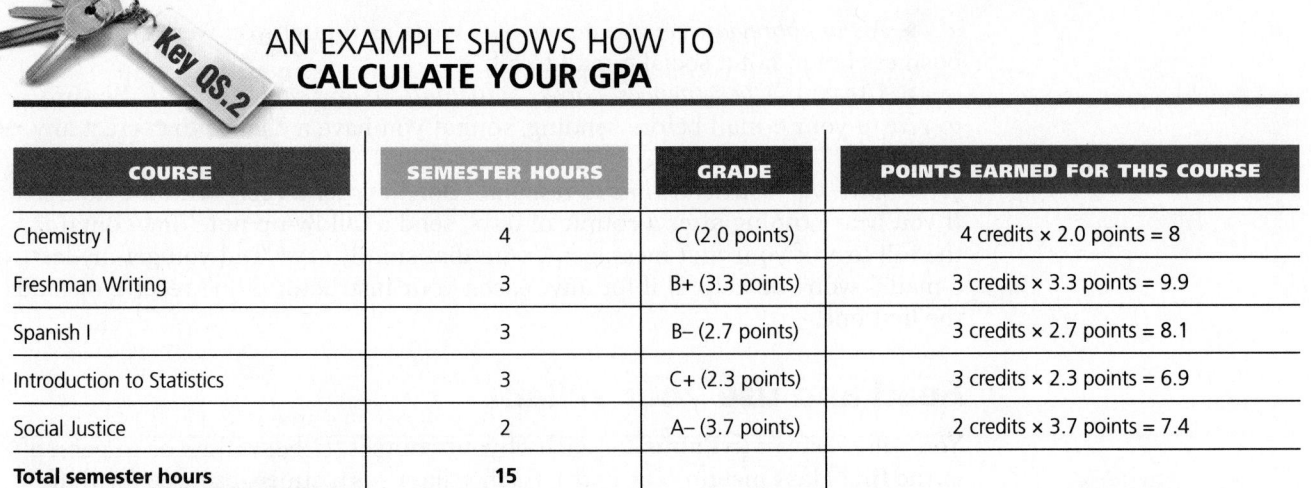

AN EXAMPLE SHOWS HOW TO
CALCULATE YOUR GPA

COURSE	SEMESTER HOURS	GRADE	POINTS EARNED FOR THIS COURSE
Chemistry I	4	C (2.0 points)	4 credits × 2.0 points = 8
Freshman Writing	3	B+ (3.3 points)	3 credits × 3.3 points = 9.9
Spanish I	3	B– (2.7 points)	3 credits × 2.7 points = 8.1
Introduction to Statistics	3	C+ (2.3 points)	3 credits × 2.3 points = 6.9
Social Justice	2	A– (3.7 points)	2 credits × 3.7 points = 7.4
Total semester hours **Total grade points for semester**	**15**		**40.3**

GPA for semester (total grade points divided by semester hours): 40.3 divided by 15 = 2.69
Letter equivalent grade: C+/B–

▶ *Use the system.* Communicate with instructors and fellow students using e-mail. Browse the college website. Search databases at the college library. If you don't know how, find someone to show you.

▶ *Save and protect your work.* Save electronic work periodically onto a primary or backup hard drive, CD, or flash drive. Use antivirus software if your system needs it.

▶ *Stay on task.* During study time, try to limit Internet surfing, instant messaging, visiting MySpace and Facebook, and playing computer games.

One of the most important directives for college students communicating via computer is to *follow guidelines* when contacting instructors via e-mail. When you submit assignments, take exams, or ask questions electronically, rules of etiquette promote civility and respect. Try these suggestions the next time you e-mail an instructor:

▶ *Use your university account.* Instructors are likely to delete unfamiliar e-mails from their overloaded e-mail inboxes. Helen_Miller@yourschool.edu will get read—but disastergirl@yahoo.com may not.

▶ *Don't ask for information you can find on your own or bother your instructor with minor problems.* Flooding your instructor with unnecessary e-mails may work against you when you really need help.

▶ *Write a clear subject line.* State exactly what the e-mail is about.

▶ *Address the instructor by name and title.* "Hello Professor Smith" or "Hi Dr. Reynolds" is better than "Hey."

▶ *Be clear and comprehensive.* First, state your question or problem and what you want to achieve. For example, "In my essay, I believe I covered the key points. I would like to meet to discuss your critique." Next, if necessary, support your position, using bullet points if you have a number of support statements. Finally, end by thanking the instructor and signing your full name.

▶ *Avoid abbreviations and acronyms.* Write as though you were crafting a business letter, not a social e-mail to a friend.

▶ *Use complete sentences, correct punctuation, and capitalization.* Be sure to reread your e-mail before sending, so that you have a chance to correct any mistakes.

▶ *Give the instructor time to respond.* Don't expect a reply within 2 hours. If you hear nothing after a couple of days, send a follow-up note that contains the full text of your first message. A note that simply says "Did you get my last e-mail?" won't be helpful if for any reason your instructor didn't receive or read the first one.

Read and use your syllabi

You will receive a **syllabus** for each of your courses, either online or in person at the first class meeting (or both). Each syllabus is a super-resource for that course, providing the following information:

SYLLABUS
A comprehensive outline
of course topics and
assignments.

▶ Focus and goals of the course
▶ Required and optional reading, with a schedule of when that reading is covered
▶ Dates of quizzes and exams and due dates for assignments
▶ The instructor's grading system and components of your final grade
▶ Your instructor's policy regarding latecomers and missed class meetings
▶ How and when to connect with your instructor in person, by phone, or online
▶ Important college-wide policies such as the academic integrity policy

You might consider each syllabus as a "contract" between you and your instructor, outlining what your instructor expects of you (readings, assignments, class participation) as well as what you can expect from your instructor (availability, schedule of topics, clarification of grading system).

Put this super-resource to use by reading syllabi thoroughly and referring to them throughout the term. When you have a question, look for an answer in your syllabus first before contacting your instructor. Marking up your syllabus will remind you of responsibilities, as will "backdating"—noting in your written or electronic planner the interim goals to achieve by particular dates in order to complete assignments. For example, if you have a fifteen-page paper due on October 12, you would enter dates in September and October for goals such as topic chosen, first draft, and final draft. Key QS.3 shows a portion of an actual syllabus with important items noted.

Get involved

Extracurricular activities give you a chance to meet people who share your interests and to develop teamwork and leadership skills as well as other skills that may be important in your career. In addition, being connected to friends and a supportive network of people is one of the main reasons people stay in school.

Some freshmen take on so many activities that they become overwhelmed. Pace yourself the first year. You can always add activities later. As you seek the right balance, consider this: Studies have shown that students who join organizations tend to persist in their educational goals more than those who don't branch out.[1]

ENG 122 Spring 2007

Instructor:	Jennifer Gessner
Office Hours:	Tue & Thur 12:30–1:30 (or by appointment) in DC 305
Phone:	303-555-2222
E-mail:	jg@abc.xyz

How to connect with the instructor

Required Texts: *Good Reasons with Contemporary Arguments,* Faigley and Selzer
A Writer's Reference, 5th ed., Diana Hacker

Required Materials:

Books and materials to get ASAP

- a notebook with lots of paper
- a folder for keeping everything from this class
- an active imagination and critical thinking

Course Description: This course focuses on argumentative writing and the researched paper. Students will practice the rhetorical art of argumentation and will gain experience in finding and incorporating researched materials into an extended paper.

Writer's Notebook: All students will keep, and bring to class, a notebook with blank paper. Throughout the semester, you will be given writing assignments to complete in this book. You must bring to class and be prepared to share any notebook assignment. Notebook assignments will be collected frequently, though sometimes randomly, and graded only for their completeness, not for spelling, etc.

Course coverage, expectations, responsibilities

Grading:

How grades are determined for this course

- Major Writing Assignments worth 100 points each.
- Final Research Project worth 300 points.
- Additional exercises and assignments range from 10 to 50 points each.
- Class participation: Based on the degree to which you complete the homework and present this in a thoughtful, meaningful manner in class.
- Attendance: Attendance is taken daily and students may miss up to three days of class without penalty, but will lose 5 points for each day missed thereafter.
- Late work: All work will lose 10% of earned points per class day late. No work will be accepted after five class days or the last class meeting.

Final Grade: The average of the total points possible (points earned divided by the total possible points). 100–90% = A; 89–80% = B; 79–70% = C (any grade below 70% is not passing for this class).

Academic Integrity: Students must credit any material used in their papers that is not their own (including direct quotes, paraphrases, figures, etc.). Failure to do so constitutes plagiarism, which is illegal, unethical, <u>always recognizable</u>, and a guaranteed way to fail a paper. The definition of plagiarism is "to steal and use (the writings or ideas of another) as one's own."

Reflects school's academic integrity policy

Week 4

Topic of that day's class meeting

2/1	<u>The Concise Opinion.</u>
	HW: Complete paper #1 Rough Draft (5–7 pages double-spaced)
2/3	How Professionals Argue
	HW: <u>Read Jenkins Essay (p 501 of *Good Reasons) and</u> <u>Rafferty Essay (p 525)</u>; compare argumentative style, assess and explain efficacy of arguments.

Notice of due date for paper draft

Notice of reading assignments to complete

Week 5

2/15	Developing an Argument
	Essay Quiz on Jenkins and Rafferty Essays
	HW: Chap 5 of *Good Reasons;* based on components of a definition of argument, write a brief explanation of how your argument might fit into this type.
2/17	Library Workday: Meet in Room 292
	PAPER #1 DUE

Notice of quiz

Notice of final due date for paper

Source: Jennifer Gessner, Community College of Denver.

Connect with people and resources

During your first weeks of school, as you navigate through what may seem like a maze of classes and business offices it is important to know that instructors, administrators, advisors, and a range of support staff are available to help. Groups and organizations also provide support and opportunities to broaden your experience. Tap into the various resources at your school.

Instructors and teaching assistants

The people who teach your courses—instructors and teaching assistants—are your most available human resources at college. You see them from one to five times per week and interact with them more directly than with any other authority on campus. They see your work and, if your class size is small, they hear your ideas and consequently may get to know you quite well. Instructors are potential resources and necessary allies in your education.

What kind of help might you seek from an instructor or teaching assistant?

- Clarification on material presented in class
- Help on homework
- Information about how to prepare for a test
- Consultation on a paper you are working on
- Details about why you received a particular grade on a test or assignment
- Advice about the department—courses, majoring—or related career areas

When you want to speak personally with an instructor for longer than a minute or two, choose your time carefully. Before or after class is usually not the best time for anything more than a quick question. When you need your instructor's full attention, there are three ways to get it: make an appointment during office hours, send e-mail, or leave voice-mail messages.

- *Office hours.* Instructors keep regular office hours, generally appearing on your syllabus or posted on instructors' office doors and on instructors' or departmental Web pages. Always make an appointment for a meeting. Face-to-face conferences are ideal for working through ideas and problems (for example, deciding on a term paper topic) or asking for advice (for example, looking for guidance on choosing courses in the department).

- *E-mail.* Use e-mail to clarify assignments and assignment deadlines, to ask questions about lectures or readings, or to clarify what will be covered on a test. Using the e-mailing guidelines presented earlier in Quick Start will increase the likelihood of receiving a positive response. Instructors' e-mail addresses are generally posted on the first day of class and may also appear in your handbook or syllabus.

- *Voice mail.* If something comes up at the last minute, you can leave a message in your instructor's voice mailbox. Make your message short but specific ("This is Rick

Jones from your 10 o'clock Intro to Psychology class. I'm supposed to present my project today, but have a fever of 102 degrees"). Avoid calling instructors at home unless they give specific permission to do so.

If you are taking a large lecture course, you may have a primary instructor plus a *teaching assistant* (TA) who meets with a small group of students on a regular basis and grades your papers and exams. You may want to approach your TA with course-related questions and problems before approaching the instructor. Because TAs deal with fewer students, they may have more time to devote to specific issues.

Academic advisors

In most colleges, every student is assigned an advisor who is the student's personal liaison with the college. (At some schools, students receive help at an advising center.) Your advisor will help you choose courses every term, plan your overall academic program, and help you understand college regulations, including graduation requirements. He or she will point out possible consequences of your decisions ("If you put off taking biology now, you're facing two lab courses next term"), help you shape your educational goals, and monitor your academic progress.

Although you are responsible for fully understanding graduation requirements—including credit requirements—and choosing the courses you need, your advisor is there to help you with these critical decisions. You will most likely be required to meet with your advisor once each term; however, you can schedule additional meetings if and when you need them.

Mentors

You may find a (mentor) during college who can give you a private audience for questions and problems and advice tailored to your needs, as well as support, guidance, and trust. In return, you owe it to a mentor to respectfully take advice into consideration. A mentor might be your advisor, an instructor in your major or minor field, or a resident assistant (RA). Some schools have faculty or peer mentoring programs to match students with people who can help them.

> MENTOR
> A trusted counselor or guide who takes a special interest in helping you reach your goals.

Tutors and academic centers

Tutors can give you valuable and detailed help on specific academic subjects. Most campuses have private tutoring available, and many schools offer free peer tutoring. If you feel you could benefit from the kind of one-on-one work tutoring can give, ask your instructor or your academic advisor to recommend a tutor. If your school has one or more academic centers, you may be able to find one there. *Academic centers,* including reading, writing, math, and study skills centers, centers, offer consultations and tutoring to help students improve skills at all levels.

Administrators

Every college needs an administrative staff to operate smoothly and efficiently. One of the most important administrative offices for students is the office of the dean of student affairs, which, in many colleges, is the center for student services. Staff members there can answer your questions or direct you to others who can help. You will also encounter

- The *bursar's office* (also called the office of finance or accounting office) issues bills for tuition and room and board and collects payments from students and financial aid sources.
- The *financial aid office* helps students apply for financial aid and understand the eligibility requirements of different federal, state, and private programs (see Chapter 9 for more details on financial aid).
- The *registrar's office* handles course registration, sends grade reports, and compiles your official *transcript* (a comprehensive record of your courses and grades). Graduate school admissions offices require a copy of your transcript, as do many prospective employers.

Student-centered services

Colleges provide a host of services that help students succeed in college and deal with problems that arise.

- *Academic computer center.* Most schools have computer facilities that are open daily, usually staffed by technicians who can assist you. Many facilities also offer training workshops.
- *Student housing or commuter affairs office.* Residential colleges provide on-campus housing for undergraduate students. The housing office handles room and roommate placement and deals with special needs (for example, an allergic student's need for a room air conditioner) and problems. Schools with commuting students may have transportation and parking programs.
- *Health services.* Generally including sick care, prescriptions, routine diagnostic tests, vaccinations, and first aid, college clinics are affiliated with nearby hospitals for emergency care. In addition, psychological counseling is sometimes offered through health services or at a separate facility. Many colleges require proof of health insurance at the time of registration.
- *Career services.* Helping students find part-time and full-time jobs, as well as summer jobs and internships, career offices have reference files on careers and employers. They also help students learn to write resumés and cover letters and search job sites on the Internet; these offices sponsor career fairs and provide space for employers to interview students on campus.
- *Services for disabled students.* For students with documented disabilities, federal law requires that assistance be provided in the form of accommodations ranging from interpreters for the hearing impaired to ramps for students in wheelchairs. If you have a disability, visit this office to learn what is offered, and remember that this office is your advocate if you encounter problems.
- *Veterans' affairs.* The veterans' office provides services including academic and personal counseling and current benefit status, which may affect tuition waivers.

Resources for minority students

Minority includes students of color; gay, lesbian, and bisexual students; and students from underrepresented cultures or religious backgrounds. Along with activities that appeal to the general student population, most colleges have organizations and services that support minority groups, including specialized student associations, cultural centers, arts groups with a minority focus, minority fraternities and sororities, and political action groups.

Many minority students seek a balance, getting involved with members of their group as well as with the college mainstream. For example, a student may join the Latino Students Association as well as clubs for all students such as the campus newspaper or an athletic team.

You are beginning the journey of your college education and lifelong learning. The work you do in this course will help you achieve your goals in your studies, your personal life, and your career. Psychologist Robert J. Sternberg, the originator of the successful intelligence concept that is the theme of *Keys to Success*, has said that those who achieve success "create their own opportunities rather than let their opportunities be limited by the circumstances in which they happen to find themselves."[2] Let this book and this course help you create new and fulfilling opportunities on your path to success.

KEYS TO SUCCESS

chapter 1

Welcome to College

Growing Toward Success

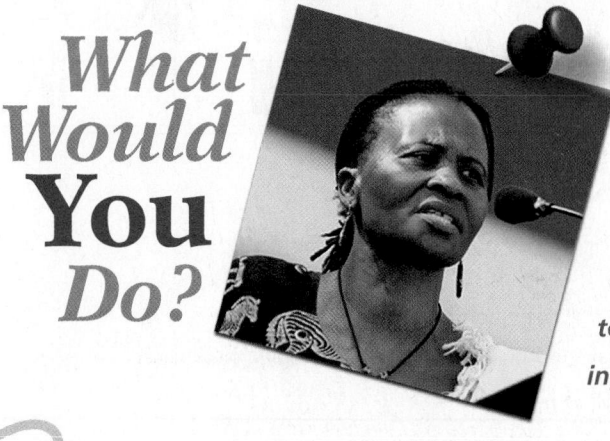

What Would You Do?

Think about this problem as you read, and consider how you would approach it. This chapter jump-starts your entry into the college experience, with information on how to make the transition and gather the ingredients for success.

Jo Luck runs a group called Heifer International, which aims to combat poverty and hunger through training, livestock donation, and other services. In the late 1980s, Ms. Luck encouraged a group of women in a Zimbabwe village to follow their dreams.

One of the women, a cattle herder named Tererai Trent, wrote down four goals on a scrap of paper: to study abroad, earn a B.A. degree, then a master's, and finally a doctorate. She put the paper in a tin and buried it under a rock in the pasture. Having endured abuse from her husband and years of hard work raising the five children born since her marriage at age 11, she hoped education would change her life. To prepare for college, she took correspondence courses paid for with money she made working for Heifer and other organizations. Eventually she applied to and was accepted by Oklahoma State University, moving with her family to the United States with support from Heifer and the fundraising efforts of family and friends.

Despite satisfying her first goal, Trent faced more struggle ahead. Her family lived in a trailer and often went hungry. She continued to endure beatings and was nearly expelled for missing tuition payments. With support from OSU she pressed on to earn her B.A., but her husband fell ill with AIDS and required her care around the clock as she began work toward her master's degree. (To be continued . . .)[1]

Throughout this book, you will meet people like Tererai who have worked through issues to achieve academic, career, and life goals. Whether you have something in common with these people or not, they will expand your perspective and inspire you to move ahead on your own path. You'll learn more about Tererai, and revisit her situation, within the chapter.

In this chapter, you'll explore answers to these questions:

ANALYTICAL   CREATIVE   PRACTICAL

STATUS *Check*

▶ *How prepared are you for college?*

For each statement, circle the number that feels right to you,
from 1 for "not at all true for me" to 5 for "very true for me."

▶ I feel ready to handle college-level work.	1 2 3 4 5
▶ I can identify how college culture differs from high school and the workplace.	1 2 3 4 5
▶ I am aware of what it takes to succeed in today's technology-driven, ever-changing workplace.	1 2 3 4 5
▶ I believe my intelligence can increase as a result of my effort.	1 2 3 4 5
▶ I use a combination of critical, creative, and practical thinking to reach a goal.	1 2 3 4 5
▶ I believe that success demands hard work and practice no matter what my talents are.	1 2 3 4 5
▶ I can explain the value of acting with academic integrity in college.	1 2 3 4 5
▶ I am able to perceive my own emotions accurately as well as those of others.	1 2 3 4 5
▶ I relate effectively to others and can work successfully in a team.	1 2 3 4 5
▶ I know that I will need to learn throughout my life to succeed in the workplace.	1 2 3 4 5

Each of the topics in these statements is covered in this chapter. Note those statements for which you circled a 3 or lower. Skim the chapter to see where those topics appear, and pay special attention to them as you read, learn, and apply new strategies.

REMEMBER: *No matter how prepared you are to succeed in college, you can improve with effort and practice.*

"Successfully intelligent people . . . have a can-do attitude. They realize that the limits to what they can accomplish are often in what they tell themselves they cannot do, rather than in what they really cannot do."

—Robert Sternberg

Where are you now—and where can college take you?

Think about how you got here. Are you going to college straight from high school or its equivalent? Or are you returning after working one or more jobs or completing a tour of duty in the armed forces? Do you have life skills from experience as a partner or parent? No matter what your background or motivation, you have enrolled, found a way to pay for tuition, signed up for courses, and shown up for class. You have earned this opportunity to be a college student.

If you are wondering how this or any other college course will make a difference for you, know that your experience in this course and during this term has the potential to:

▶ Allow you to discover more about how you learn and what you want
▶ Build academic skills as well as transferable life skills
▶ Help you set and reach your most important goals
▶ Increase your ability to relate effectively to others and work together

Now that you *have* the opportunity, you need to *use it*. This book, and your course, offer tools that will help you grow and achieve your goals, perhaps

student profile

Zack Moore
University of Rhode Island, Kingston

About me:

I major in communications, have added a business minor, and play wide receiver on the URI (University of Rhode Island) football team. Although I have some great mentors in several fields, I am not sure what my career choice will be. I hope to play football for as long as possible, but when I am done on the field, I might like to become a motivational speaker, open a warehouse-style gym, or help my grandfather run Horseless Carriage Carriers, his automobile transportation business.

What I focus on:

Ever since I was a toddler, my parents encouraged me to interact with as many people as possible. My life experiences have brought me in contact with people of many backgrounds, ages, races, and beliefs. I've developed an ability to carry on a conversation with practically anyone about practically anything. I like to think that I make as great an impact on people I meet as they often do on me.

Two years into my college career, I find it interesting to look back at how far I have come since arriving at summer football camp before my freshman year. Not only have I learned a lot in the classroom, but daily interactions with classmates, professors, teammates, coaches, roommates, and others in the college community have shaped me in ways that I would never have anticipated.

To me, college is a place where I am exploring who I am, gaining a better understanding of what makes others tick, and figuring out who I will be when I enter the professional world.

What will help me in the workplace:

While I don't know exactly what I will do with my life, I believe that the communication, social, and emotional skills I am developing each day will help me succeed in whatever career I choose.

---

beyond what you've ever imagined. You will be able to make the most of them—if you start by believing that you can grow.

When a high jumper or pole vaulter gets over a bar of a certain height, someone raises the bar so that the athlete can work toward a new goal. The college experience will "raise the bar" for you with tougher instructors, demanding coursework, and fellow students whose sights are set high. Others' goals and expectations are only part of the picture, though. College is a place where *you* can raise the bar to reach your personal aspirations, whatever they might be. As amazing as Tererai Trent's story is, know that you don't have to live in poverty halfway across the world to want to make changes for the better. Think about how you want to improve *your* life. This book and course will challenge you to set the bar to the height that's right for you.

First, however, begin your transition to college by looking at the present— the culture of college, what you can expect, and what college expects of you.

Then, consider the future—what a college education means for you in the workplace and life.

The culture of college

Whatever your age or stage of life, knowing what to expect in college will help you to transition more successfully. You are likely to experience most or all of the following aspects of college culture (spend some time with your college's student handbook to get informed about details specific to your school).

■ *Independent learning.* College offers you the chance to learn with a great deal of freedom and independence. In exchange, though, instructors expect you to function without much guidance. This culture requires strong self-management skills. You are expected to make the following—and more—happen on your own:

▶ Use syllabi to create, and follow, a schedule for the term (see Quick Start to College)
▶ Navigate course materials electronically (if your school uses an online course management system such as BlackBoard)
▶ Get to class on time with the materials you need
▶ Complete text and other reading with little to no in-class review of the reading
▶ Set up and attend study group meetings
▶ Turn in projects and coursework on time and be prepared for exams
▶ Get help when you need it

■ *Fast pace and increased workload.* The pace of each course is typically twice as fast as high school courses and requires more papers, homework, reading, and projects. Although demanding, learning at this speed can also energize and motivate you, especially if you did not feel inspired by high school assignments. The heavy, fast-paced workload demands more study time. For each hour spent in class, plan two to three hours of study and work time outside of class. For example, if you are in class for nine hours a week, you need to spend at least twice that number each week studying and working outside of class time.

■ *Challenging work.* Although challenging, college-level work offers an enormous opportunity to learn and grow. College texts often have more words per page, higher-level terminology, and more abstract ideas compared to high school texts. In addition to difficult reading, college often involves complex assignments, challenging research papers, group projects, lab work, and tests.

■ *More out-of-class time to manage.* The freedom of your schedule requires strong time management skills. On days when your classes end early, start late, or don't meet at all, you will need to use the open blocks of time effectively as you juggle other responsibilities, including perhaps a job and family.

■ *Diverse culture.* Typically, you will encounter different ideas and diverse people in college. Your fellow students may differ from you in age, life experience, ethnicity, political mindset, family obligations, values, and much more. Also, if you commute to school or attend class with others who do, you may find it challenging to connect with others.

■ *Higher-level thinking.* You'll be asked to move far beyond recall in college. Instead of just summarizing and taking the ideas of others at face value, you will interpret, evaluate, generate new ideas, and apply what you know to new situations (more on thinking skills later in this chapter).

You are not alone as you adjust. Look for support resources, including instructors, academic advisors, mentors, other students, or tutors; technology such as the Internet, library search engines, and electronic planning aids; and this book (see Quick Start to College for more information on resources). Seek help from campus officials, as when Tererai asked Oklahoma State University personnel to help her with housing and finances. And to give meaning to your efforts in college, consider how your efforts will serve you in the workplace.

Getting through the day-to-day activities of college demands basic computer know-how as well as an understanding of the school's research and communication technology.
© iStockPhoto

Your place in the world of work

Although this is likely to be one of your first courses, it can lay the foundation for career exploration and workplace skill development. You will learn to distinguish yourself in a global marketplace, in which North American workers often compete with workers from other countries. Thomas Friedman, author of *The World Is Flat*, explains how the digital revolution has transformed the working environment you will enter after college:

> It is now possible for more people than ever to collaborate and compete in real time with more other people on more different kinds of work from more different corners of the planet and on a more equal footing than in any previous time in the history of the world—using computers, e-mail, networks, teleconferencing, and dynamic new software.[2]

These developments in communication, combined with an enormous increase in knowledge work such as Internet technology and decrease in labor-based work such as factory jobs, mean that you may compete for information-based jobs with highly trained and motivated people from around the globe. The working world, too, has raised the bar.

What can help you achieve career goals in this new "flat" world?

■ *College degree.* Statistics show that getting a degree increases your chances of finding and keeping a highly skilled, well-paying job. College graduates earn, on average, around $20,000 more per year than those with a high school diploma (see Key 1.1). Furthermore, the unemployment rate for college graduates is less than half that of high school graduates (see Key 1.2).

■ *21st century skills.* Taking a careful look at what the current workplace demands of workers and what it rewards, education and business leaders have founded an organization called the Partnership for 21st Century Skills. Together these leaders developed the Framework for 21st Century Learning shown in Key 1.3, delineating the categories of knowledge and skills that successful workers need to acquire.

Looking at this framework, you will see that success in today's workplace requires more than just knowing skills specific to an academic area or job. Author Daniel Pink argues that the ability to create, interact interpersonally, generate ideas, and lead diverse teams—skills all found in the Framework for 21st Century Learning—will be more and more important in the workplace. Because coursework traditionally focuses more on logical and analytical skills, building your interpersonal and creative skill set will require personal initiative from you. Often, these skills can be developed through in-class collaboration and teamwork as well as volunteer work, internships, and jobs.[3]

DIGITAL REVOLUTION
The change in how people communicate brought on by developments in computer systems.

KNOWLEDGE WORK
Work that is primarily concerned with information rather than manual labor.

MORE EDUCATION
IS LIKELY TO MEAN **MORE INCOME**

Median annual income of persons with income 25 years old and over, by gender and highest level of education, 2009

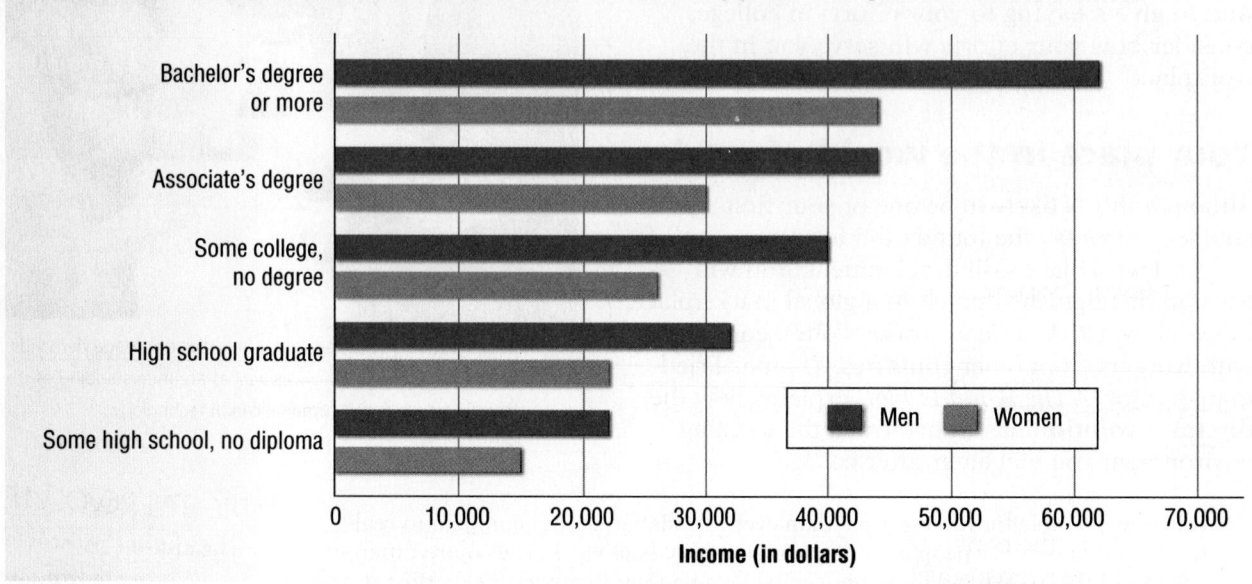

Source: U.S. Census Bureau, "Income, Poverty, and Health Insurance Coverage in the United States, 2009," *Current Population Reports,* Series P60-238, September 2010.

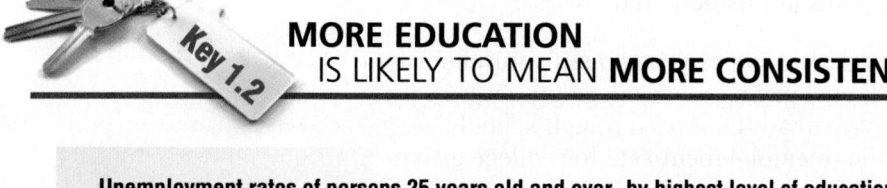

MORE EDUCATION
IS LIKELY TO MEAN **MORE CONSISTENT EMPLOYMENT**

Unemployment rates of persons 25 years old and over, by highest level of education, 2009

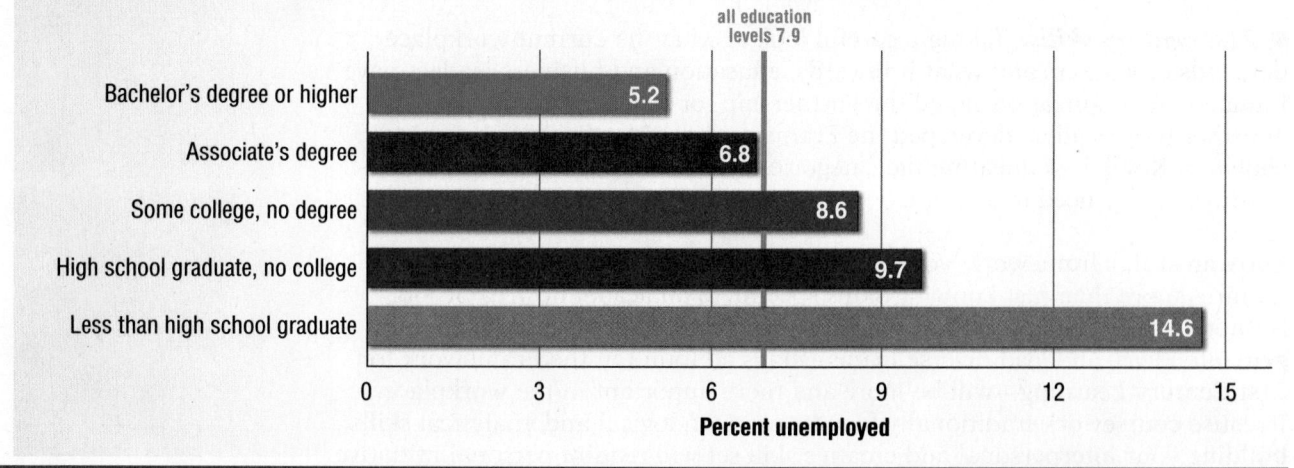

Source: U.S. Department of Labor, Bureau of Labor Statistics, Office of Employment and Unemployment Statistics, "Current Population Survey," May 2010.

THE **FRAMEWORK FOR 21ST CENTURY LEARNING**
SHOWS WHAT YOU NEED TO SUCCEED

CORE SUBJECTS AND 21ST CENTURY THEMES	LEARNING AND INNOVATION SKILLS
• Global Awareness • Financial, Economic, Business, and Entrepreneurial Literacy • Civic Literacy—Community Service • Health Literacy	• Creativity and Innovation • Critical Thinking and Problem Solving • Communication and Collaboration
INFORMATION, MEDIA, AND TECHNOLOGY SKILLS	**LIFE AND CAREER SKILLS**
• Information Literacy • Media Literacy • ICT (Information, Communications, and Technology) Literacy	• Flexibility and Adaptability • Initiative and Self-Direction • Social and Cross-Cultural Skills • Productivity and Accountability • Leadership and Responsibility

Source: Adapted from Partnership for 21st Century Skills Framework, www.p21.org/index.php?option=com_content&task=view&id=254&Itemid=120.

As you read the content and do the exercises in *Keys to Success,* you will grow in every area of this framework. There are links between these 21st century skills and what you will be reading and doing in the weeks to come, and the Personal Portfolio activity at the end of each chapter indicates which 21st century skills it builds. In fact, the three thinking skills that take focus in this text—analytical, creative, and practical—are all included within the framework. These three thinking skills will help you achieve your most important goals because they are critical to delivering what the world needs workers to do.

How can successful intelligence help you achieve your goals?

How do you define *intelligence?* Is an intelligent person someone who excels in high-level analytical courses? A successful professional in science or law? Or a person who scores well on standardized tests such as IQ (intelligence quotient) tests? The idea of using an IQ test to gauge intelligence and predict success is based on the belief that each person is born with a fixed amount of intelligence that can be measured. However, cutting-edge researchers such as Robert Sternberg and Carol Dweck have challenged these ideas.[4]

When test anxiety caused Sternberg (a psychologist and dean of students at Tufts University) to score poorly on IQ and other standardized tests during elementary school, he delivered what was expected of him—very little. However, his fourth-grade teacher turned his life around when she expected more. Sternberg has conducted extensive research supporting his sense that traditional intelligence measurements lock people into poor performance and often do not reflect their potential.[5]

Stanford psychologist Carol Dweck also had a life-changing experience when, as a young researcher, she conducted an experiment to see how elementary school children coped with failure. She gave students a set of puzzles that grew increasingly difficult. To her surprise, certain students welcomed the tough puzzles and saw failure as an opportunity. "They knew that human qualities, such as intellectual skills, could be cultivated through effort. And that's what they were doing—getting smarter. Not only weren't they discouraged by failure, they didn't even think they were failing. They thought they were learning."[6] Dweck's research since then has focused on the potential for increasing intelligence and the attitude that fosters that potential (more on that attitude later in the chapter).

The research of Sternberg, Dweck, and others suggests that intelligence is *not* fixed; people have the capacity to increase intelligence as they learn. In other words, *you can grow what you are born with*. Studies in neuroscience support this perspective, showing that the brain can develop throughout life if you continue to learn. Recent brain research shows that when you are learning, your brain and nerve cells (neurons) are forming new connections (synapses) from cell to cell by growing new branches (dendrites).[7] These increased connections then enable the brain to do and learn more.

The three thinking skills

How can you unlock your potential and achieve your important goals in college, work, and life? According to Sternberg, it takes three types of thinking: analytical (critical), creative, and practical. He calls this combination *successful intelligence*,[8] and he illustrates it with a story.

Two boys are walking in a forest. They are quite different. The first boy's teachers think he is smart, his parents think he is smart, and as a result, he thinks he is smart. He has good test scores, good grades, and other good paper credentials that will get him far in his scholastic life.

Few people consider the second boy smart. His test scores are nothing great, his grades aren't so good, and his other paper credentials are, in general, marginal. At best, people would call him shrewd or street smart.

As the two boys walk along in the forest, they encounter a problem—a huge, furious, hungry-looking grizzly bear, charging straight at them. The first boy, calculating that the grizzly bear will overtake them in 17.3 seconds, panics. In this state, he looks at the second boy, who is calmly taking off his hiking boots and putting on his jogging shoes.

The first boy says to the second boy, "You must be crazy. There is no way you are going to outrun that grizzly bear!"

The second boy replies, "That's true. But all I have to do is outrun you!"[9]

This story shows that successful goal achievement and problem solving require more than book smarts. When confronted with a problem, using *only* analytical thinking put the first boy at a disadvantage. On the other hand, the second boy *analyzed* the situation, *created* options, and took practical *action*. He knew his goal—to live to tell the tale—and he achieved it.

How thinking skills move you toward your goals

Sternberg explains that although those who score well on tests display strong recall and analytical skills, they are not necessarily able to put their knowledge to work.[10] No matter how high you score on a library science test, for example, as a librarian you will also need to be able to devise useful keyword searches (creative thinking) and communicate effectively with patrons and other librarians (practical thinking). Of course, having *only* practical "street smarts" isn't enough either. Neither boy in the bear story, if rushed to the hospital with injuries sustained in a showdown with the bear, would want to be treated by someone lacking in analytical skills.

What do each of the three thinking skills contribute to goal achievement?

■ *Analytical thinking.* Commonly known as *critical thinking,* analytical thinking starts by engaging with information through asking questions and then proceeds to analyzing and evaluating information, often to work through a problem or decision. It often involves comparing, contrasting, and cause-and-effect thinking.

■ *Creative thinking.* Creative thinking concerns generating new and different ideas and approaches to problems, and, often, viewing the world in ways that disregard convention. It often involves imagining and considering different perspectives. Creative thinking also means taking information that you already know and thinking about it in a new way.

■ *Practical thinking.* Practical thinking refers to putting what you've learned into action to solve a problem or make a decision. Practical thinking often means learning from experience and emotional intelligence (explained later in the chapter), enabling you to work effectively with others and to accomplish goals despite obstacles.

Together, these abilities move you toward a goal, as Sternberg explains:

> Analytical thinking is required to solve problems and to judge the quality of ideas. Creative intelligence is required to formulate good problems and ideas in the first place. Practical intelligence is needed to use the ideas and their analysis in an effective way in one's everyday life.[11]

The following example illustrates how this works.

The goal-achieving thinking skills of Tererai Trent

▶ She *analyzed* her experience and abilities to determine what she was capable of accomplishing. She analyzed her circumstances to determine a course of action she could manage.

▶ She *created* a dream plan—to live in the United States and pursue a B.A., master's, and PhD.

▶ She took *practical action* to gain admittance to college, pay for her family to move to the United States, and care for her family while attending classes.

Why is developing successful intelligence so important to your success?

1. *It improves understanding and achievement, increasing your value in school and on the job.* People with critical, creative, and practical thinking skills are in demand because they can apply what they know to new situations, innovate, and accomplish their goals.

2. *It boosts your motivation.* Because it helps you understand how learning propels you toward goals and gives you ways to move toward those goals, it increases your willingness to work.

3. *It shows you where you can grow.* Students who have trouble with tests and other analytical skills can see the role that creative and practical thinking play. Students who test well but have trouble innovating or taking action can improve their creative and practical skills.

Chapter 4—the chapter on thinking—goes into more detail about all three skills.

Although thinking skills provide tools with which you can achieve college and life goals, you need **motivation** to put them to work and grow from your efforts. Explore a mindset that will motivate you to vault over that bar (and then set a higher one).

> MOTIVATION
> A goal-directed force that moves a person to action.

GET ANALYTICAL!

Define Your "College Self"

Making the most of the opportunities that college offers starts with knowing, as much as you can, about who you are and what you want. Analyze your "college self" using questions like the following to think through your personal profile. Write and save your description to revisit later in the course.

What is your student status—traditional or returning, full- or part-time?

_____

_____

How long are you planning to be in your current college? Is it likely that you will transfer?

_____

_____

What goal, or goals, do you aim to achieve by going to college?

_____

_____

_____

_____

What family and work obligations do you have?

_____

_____

What is your culture, ethnicity, gender, age, lifestyle?

_____

_____

What is your current living situation?

_____

_____

What do you feel are your biggest challenges in college?

_____

_____

_____

_____

What do you like to study, and why does it interest you?

_____

_____

_____

_____

How can a "growth mindset" motivate you to persist?

Different people have different forces or *motivators*—grades, love of a subject, the drive to earn a degree—that encourage them to keep pushing ahead. Motivators can change with time and situations. Your motivation can have either an external or internal *locus of control*—meaning that you are motivated either by external factors (your parents, circumstances, luck, grades, instructors' feedback, and so on) or internal factors (values and attitudes).

Often, you will be motivated by some combination of external and internal factors, but internal motivation may have a greater influence on success. Why? Although you cannot control what happens around you, you *can* control your attitude, or *mindset*, and the actions that come from that mindset. Based on years of research, Carol Dweck has determined that the perception that talent and intelligence can develop with effort—what she calls a *growth mindset*—promotes success. "This view creates a love of learning and resilience that is essential for great accomplishment," reports Dweck. People with a growth mindset "understand that no one has ever accomplished great things—not Mozart, Darwin, or Michael Jordan—without years of passionate practice and learning."[12]

By contrast, people with a *fixed mindset* believe that they have a set level of talent and intelligence. They think their ability to succeed matches what they've been born with, and they tend to resist effort. "In one world [that of the fixed mindset], effort is a bad thing. It . . . means you're not smart or talented. If you were, you wouldn't need effort. In the other world [growth mindset], effort is what *makes* you smart or talented."[13]

For example, two students do poorly on an anatomy midterm. One blames the time of day of the test and her dislike of the subject, whereas the other feels that she didn't study enough. The first student couldn't change the subject or meeting time, of course, and didn't change her approach to the material (no extra effort). As you may expect, she did poorly on the final. The second student put in more study time after the midterm (increased, focused effort) and improved her grade on the final as a result. This student knows that "smart is as smart does."

You don't have to be born with a growth mindset. *You can build one.* "You have a choice," says Dweck. "Mindsets are just beliefs. They're powerful beliefs, but they're just something in your mind, and you can change your mind."[14] One way to change your mind is through specific actions that demonstrate your beliefs. Such actions include being responsible, practicing academic integrity, facing your fears, and approaching failure as an opportunity to learn and improve.

Build self-esteem with responsible actions

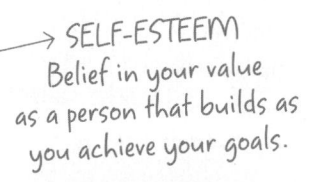

> SELF-ESTEEM
> Belief in your value as a person that builds as you achieve your goals.

You may think that you need to have a strong sense of (self-esteem) to take action toward your goals. In fact, the reverse is true. Taking responsible action builds strong self-esteem because it gives you something to be proud of. Your actions change your thinking. Basketball coach Rick Pitino explains: "If you have established a great work ethic and have begun the discipline that is inherent with that, you will automatically begin to feel better about yourself."[15]

A growth mindset helps you build self-esteem because it encourages you to put forth effort. If you know you have the potential to do better, you will be more likely to try. A research study of employees taking a course in computer training supports this idea. Half the group, told their success depended on innate ability, lost confidence by the end of the course. By contrast, the other half, told their skills could be developed through practice, reported a good deal *more* confidence after they had completed the same course and made, in many cases, the same mistakes.[16]

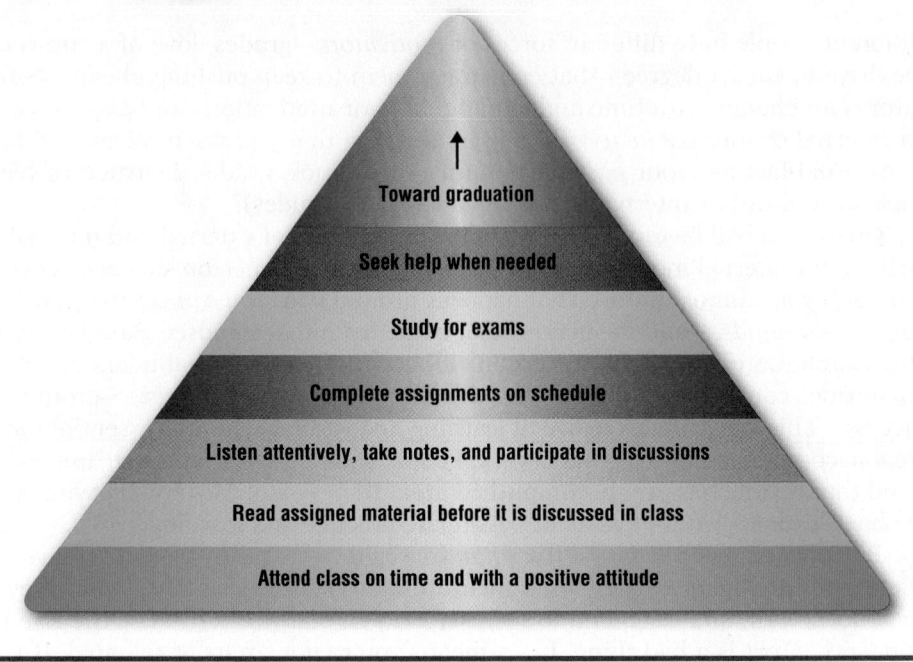

↑
Toward graduation

Seek help when needed

Study for exams

Complete assignments on schedule

Listen attentively, take notes, and participate in discussions

Read assigned material before it is discussed in class

Attend class on time and with a positive attitude

Even simple responsible actions can build the foundation for powerful self-esteem. What actions will you take to build your confidence? Consider using Key 1.4 as a starting point for ideas. Taking daily responsible actions such as these will help you to succeed in any course. Your efforts will enable you to grow no matter what your starting point.

Practice academic integrity

Having (academic integrity) means valuing learning and ensures an education based on *ethics* (your sense of what is right to do) and hard work. Find your school's code of honor or academic integrity policy in your student handbook, school website, or in your syllabus. Read it thoroughly so you know exactly what it asks of you. When you enrolled, you agreed to abide by it.

The Center for Academic Integrity, part of the Kenan Institute for Ethics at Duke University, defines *academic integrity* as a commitment to five fundamental values:[17]

ACADEMIC INTEGRITY
Following a code of moral values in all aspects of academic life—classes, assignments, tests, papers, projects, and relationships with students and faculty.

▶ *Honesty.* Honesty defines the pursuit of knowledge and implies a search for truth in your classwork, papers and lab reports, and teamwork with other students.

▶ *Trust.* Trust means being true to your word. Mutual trust—between instructor and student, as well as among students—makes the exchange of ideas possible.

▶ *Fairness.* Instructors must create a fair academic environment where students are judged against clear standards and in which procedures are well defined.

▶ *Respect.* In a respectful academic environment, both students and instructors accept and honor a wide range of opinions, even if the opinions are contrary to core beliefs.

▶ *Responsibility.* You are responsible for making choices that will provide you with the best education—choices that reflect fairness and honesty.

Violations of academic integrity include turning in previously submitted work, using unauthorized devices during an exam, providing unethical aid to another student, and downloading passages or whole papers from the Internet. When violations are found (often by computer programs designed for this purpose), consequences vary from school to school and include academic integrity seminars, grade reduction or course failure, suspension, and expulsion.

What does academic integrity have to do with a growth mindset? Well, first of all, being fair, honest, and responsible takes effort and choice. Second, and more important, academic integrity comes naturally to students who aim to grow and see struggle and failure as opportunities to learn. If you want to learn something, you know that cheating is likely to keep you from reaching your goal. In this sense, maintaining a growth mindset actually promotes academic integrity and makes the reasons for its worth that much more obvious (see Key 1.5).

Face your fears

Anything unknown—starting college, meeting new people—can be frightening. Facing fear with a growth mindset will allow you to proceed with courage as you reignite your motivation and learn. Following a step-by-step process can help you deal with otherwise overwhelming feelings.

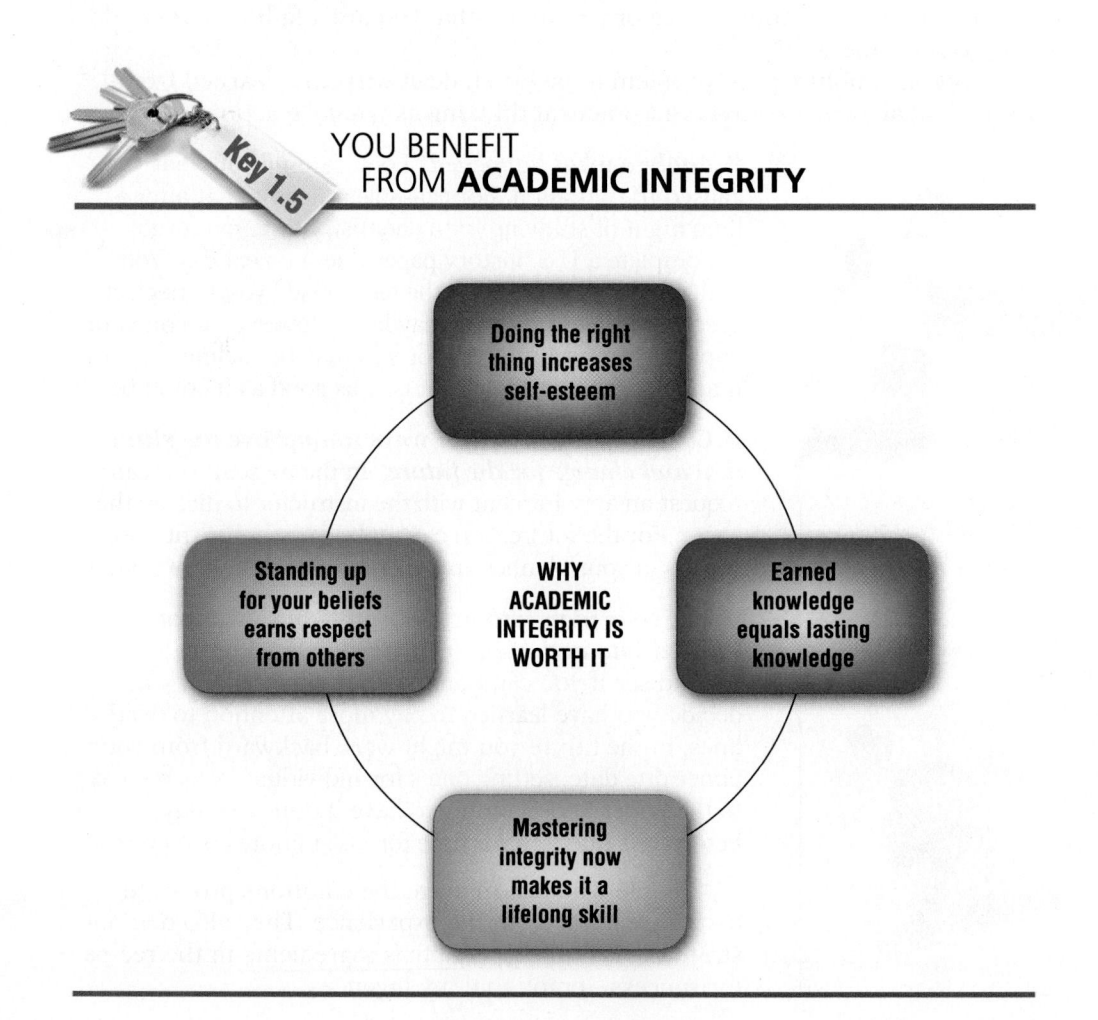

Key 1.5 YOU BENEFIT FROM **ACADEMIC INTEGRITY**

Doing the right thing increases self-esteem

Standing up for your beliefs earns respect from others

WHY ACADEMIC INTEGRITY IS WORTH IT

Earned knowledge equals lasting knowledge

Mastering integrity now makes it a lifelong skill

1. *Acknowledge fears.* Naming your fear can begin to release its hold on you. "I'm worried about understanding a Shakespeare play I have to read."
2. *Examine fears.* Determine what exactly is causing your fear. Sometimes deeper fears emerge. "I feel that if I don't understand the play, I won't do well on the test and it will affect my GPA. That could cause trouble with my financial aid or my major."
3. *Develop and implement a plan.* Come up with ways to manage your fear, choose how to move forward, and put the plan into action. "I will rent a film of the play and watch it after I read. I will talk to my instructor about my concerns."

When you've put your plan into action, you've done what a growth mindset gives you the power to do—take action and learn from the experience. Then perhaps next time you face a similar situation, your fear may not be as strong.

Learn from failure

Failure approached with a growth mindset can spark motivation, showing you what you can do better and driving you to improve. Increased effort in the face of failure is a hallmark of successful people—witness the fact that Michael Jordan got cut from his high school basketball team as a sophomore (and clearly took that as a cue to work harder).

However, for people with a fixed mindset, failure is evidence of low intelligence and ability and means that you should give up and try something else. "This mindset gives you no good recipe for overcoming it," says Dweck. "If failure means you lack competence or potential—that you are a failure—where do you go from there?"[18]

Approach failure as a "problem to be faced, dealt with, and learned from."[19] Employ analytical, creative, and practical thinking as you take action.

■ *Analyze what happened.* Look carefully at what caused the situation. For example, imagine that after a long night of studying for a chemistry test, you forgot to complete a U.S. history paper due the next day. You realize that your focus on the test caused you to neglect everything else. Now you may face a lower grade on your paper if you turn it in late, or you may be inclined to rush it and turn in a product that isn't as good as it could be.

■ *Come up with creative ways to improve the situation and change for the future.* In the present, you can request an appointment with the instructor to discuss the paper. For the future, you can make a commitment to set alarms in your planner and to check due dates more often.

■ *Put your plan into action now—and what you've learned into action in the future.* Talk with the instructor and see if you can hand in your paper late. If you decide you have learned to pay more attention to deadlines, in the future you might work backward from your paper due date, setting dates for individual tasks related to the paper and planning to have it done two days before it is due to have time for last-minute corrections.

People who can manage the emotions produced by failure learn from the experience. They also demonstrate the last of this chapter's ingredients in the recipe for success—emotional intelligence.

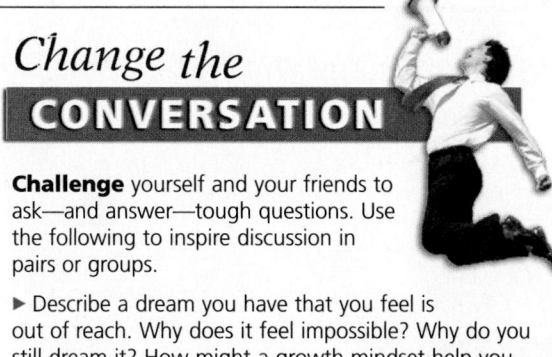

Change the
CONVERSATION

Challenge yourself and your friends to ask—and answer—tough questions. Use the following to inspire discussion in pairs or groups.

▶ Describe a dream you have that you feel is out of reach. Why does it feel impossible? Why do you still dream it? How might a growth mindset help you achieve it?

▶ How do you tend to respond to challenges—do they inspire you to take action, or do they make you want to give up and set your sights lower?

▶ **CONSIDER THE CASE:** If you had traveled with Jo Luck to Zimbabwe, would you have thought that Tererai Trent had any hope of achieving her dream? Tererai's first step was to raise money to travel to the United States. What would your first step be toward your dream?

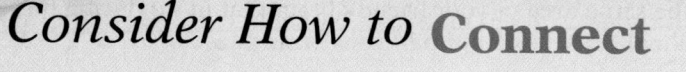

GET CREATIVE!

Consider How to Connect

Making connections with people and groups in your school early can benefit you later on. Brainstorm how you would like to spend whatever time you have available outside of your obligations (class time, work, family). On paper or on your computer, list your ideas. Try one or more of the following questions as a starting point:

If you had no fear, what horizon-broadening experience would you sign up for?

_____

_____

When you were in elementary school, what were your favorite activities? Which ones might translate into current interests and pursuits?

_____

_____

What kinds of organizations, activities, groups, experiences, or people make you think, "Wow, I want to do that"?

_____

_____

Think about the people that you feel bring out the best in you. What do you like to do with them? What kinds of activities are they involved with?

_____

_____

Why do you need emotional intelligence?

Success in a diverse world depends on relationships, and effective relationships demand emotional intelligence. Psychologists John Mayer, Peter Salovey, and David Caruso define *emotional intelligence* (EI) as the ability to understand "one's own and others' emotions and the ability to use this information as a guide to thinking and behavior."[20] Reading this definition carefully shows it isn't enough to just *understand* what you and others feel. An emotionally intelligent person uses that understanding to make choices about how to *think* and how to *act*.

In the past, and perhaps for some even today, the "head" (thought) was thought of as separate from, and perhaps more valuable than, the "heart" (emotion). However, modern science connects thought and emotion, and values both. "Emotions influence both what we think about and how we think," says Caruso. "We cannot check our emotions at the door because emotions and thought are linked—they cannot, and should not, be separated."[21]

Emotions also connect you to other people, as recent research has demonstrated. When a friend of yours is happy, sad, or fearful, you may experience similar feelings out of concern or friendship. Your brain and nervous system

The more able you are to work and communicate with others, the more you will learn as well as develop teamwork skills.
© Mary Kate Denny/PhotoEdit

have cells called *mirror neurons* that mimic an observed emotion, allowing you to "participate" in the feeling even though it comes from somewhere else. An MRI brain scan would show that the same area of your friend's brain that lit up during this emotional experience lit up in your brain as well.[22]

How emotional intelligence promotes success

Two short stories illustrate the power of emotional intelligence.

■ *Two applicants are competing for a job at your office.* The first has every skill the job requires, but doesn't respond well to your cues when you interview him. He answers questions indirectly and keeps going back to what he wants to say instead. The second isn't as skilled, but you feel during the interview as though you are talking with a friend. He listens carefully, picks up on your emotional cues, and indicates that he intends to make up for any lack of skill with a willingness to learn on the job. Whom would you hire?

■ *Two students are part of a group you are working with on a project.* One always gets her share of the job done but has no patience for anyone who misses a deadline. She is quick to criticize group members. The other is sometimes prepared, sometimes not, but always has a sense of what is going on with the group and responds to it. She works to make up for it when she hasn't gotten everything done, and when she is on top of her tasks she helps others. Which person would you want to work with again?

To be clear: Skills are crucial. The most emotionally tuned-in person in the world, for example, can't perform surgery without medical training. However, the role of emotional intelligence in communication and relationships makes it a strong predictor of success in work and life, as indicated by the following conclusions of research using an assessment measuring EI (MSCEIT).[23]

▶ Emotionally intelligent people are more competent in social situations and have higher quality relationships.
▶ Managers in the workplace with high EI have more productive working relationships and greater personal integrity.
▶ Employees scoring high in EI were more likely to receive positive ratings from peers and salary raises.
▶ Lower levels of EI are connected to higher amounts of drug, alcohol, and tobacco use, as well as aggression and conflict in teens.

The bottom line: More emotional intelligence means stronger relationships and more goal achievement.

The abilities of emotional intelligence

Emotional intelligence is a set of skills, or abilities, that can be described as *reasoning with emotion* (an idea illustrating how thought and emotion work together). Key 1.6 shows how you move through these skills when you reason with emotion.

TAKE AN **EMOTIONALLY INTELLIGENT** APPROACH

PERCEIVING EMOTIONS	**UNDERSTANDING EMOTIONS**	**MANAGING EMOTIONS**
Recognizing how you and others feel	Determining what the emotions involved in a situation tell you, seeing how they affect your thinking and mindset, and considering how you can adjust mindset or direct thinking in a productive way	Using what you learn from your emotions and those of others to choose behavior and actions that move you toward positive outcomes

Source: Adapted from John D. Mayer, Peter Salovey, and David R. Caruso, "Emotional Intelligence: New Ability or Eclectic Traits?" September 2008, *American Psychologist, 63*(6), pp. 505–507.

These skills allow you to create the best possible outcomes from your interactions. Given that you will interact with others in almost every aspect of school, work, and life, EI is a pretty important tool. You will see references to emotional intelligence throughout the text.

How might emotional intelligence fit into the rest of the skills discussed in this chapter? Think of it as *thinking skills applied to relationships.* Putting emotional intelligence to work means taking in and analyzing how you and others feel, shifting your thinking based on those feelings, and taking action in response—all with the purpose of achieving a goal.

How can this book prepare you to succeed?

Keys to Success is designed to help you build what you need for success in school and beyond, including thinking skills, attitudes, and emotional abilities that you can use to reach your goals.

Chapter content

Each chapter has several standard features:

▶ A chapter case showing how to think through and solve problems. Some cases are fact; some are fiction. All provoke thought and perhaps even conversation.
▶ An opening self-assessment so you can gauge your prior knowledge about chapter topics.
▶ In-chapter content and student profiles that illustrate growth mindset and thoughtful, emotionally intelligent choices.
▶ **Change the Conversation** questions that encourage you to revisit the case and investigate your thinking and emotions.
▶ A **Successful Intelligence Wrap-Up** that summarizes, in a visual format, the analytical, creative, and practical skills you have explored.

In-chapter activities

Within each chapter, three activities focus on building your thinking skills:

▶ **Get Analytical** gives you an opportunity to analyze a chapter topic.

GET PRACTICAL!

Use Emotional Intelligence to Get Involved

First, look in your student handbook at the resources and organizations your school offers. These may include some or all of the following:

Academic centers (reading, writing, etc.)

Academic organizations

Adult education center

Arts clubs (music, drama, dance, etc.)

Disabled student groups

Fraternities/sororities

International student groups

Minority student groups

On-campus work opportunities

Religious organizations

School publications

School TV/radio stations

Sports clubs

Student associations

Student government

Volunteer groups

As you read the list of possibilities, tune into your emotional intelligence and take note of how different organizations or activities make you feel. What do you want to try right away . . . what makes you turn the page . . . what scares you . . . and why? And is a positive outcome possible from trying something that scares you at first?

Taking this emotional intelligence feedback—as well as your analysis of yourself (Get Analytical, p. 10) and your creative ideas (Get Creative, p. 15)—into consideration, use the left-hand column on the grid that follows to list the three offices or organizations you plan to check out this term. Then use your school publications or online resources to fill in the next four columns of the grid. The last column requires action—fill it in when you have made contact with each office or organization. Finally, if you wish to become more involved after your initial contact, go for it.

OFFICE OR ORGANIZATION	LOCATION	HOURS, OR TIMES OF MEETINGS	WHAT IT OFFERS	PHONE NUMBER OR E-MAIL	INITIAL CONTACT— DATE AND WHAT HAPPENED

- ▶ **Get Creative** prompts you to think creatively about chapter material.
- ▶ **Get Practical** provides a chance to consider a practical application of a chapter idea.

End-of-chapter exercises

Here you apply what you have learned to important tasks:

- ▶ **Steps to Success** has you apply chapter skills at three levels of challenge, each building on the last.
- ▶ **Teamwork: Create Solutions Together** encourages you to apply different thinking abilities in a group setting.
- ▶ **Writing: Build Intrapersonal and Communication Skills** provides an "Emotional Intelligence Journal" question to respond to as well as a "Real-Life Writing" assignment that builds practical writing and communication skills.
- ▶ **Personal Portfolio: Prepare for Career Success** gets you ready for the workplace by helping you to build a portfolio of information useful in your academic and working life. As you complete portfolio items, you will also build a variety of 21st century skills.

Learning for life

The signs in Key 1.7 point to the need to be a *lifelong learner,* continuing to build knowledge and skills as your career and life demand. This book will help you fulfill that need.

Key 1.7

A **CHANGING WORLD** MEANS
LEARNING IS FOR LIFE

If you stop learning, your knowledge base will be inadequate to keep up with the changes in your career, thus affecting your marketability.

Knowledge in nearly every field is doubling every two to three years.

Technology is changing how you live and work.

The Internet and technology will shape communications and improve knowledge and productivity during the next twenty years—and will require continual learning.

The global economy is moving from a product and service base to a knowledge and talent base.

Workers are changing jobs and careers more frequently.

In the United States and abroad, jobs are being created that ask workers to think critically to come up with solutions.

Every time you decide to start a new career, you need new knowledge and skills.

This text gives you tools with which you can learn for life, meeting the changing demands of the modern world. Imagine: You are sitting in class with your *growth mindset,* open to learning. You are ready to use *analytical* and *creative* skills to examine the knowledge you take in and come up with new ideas. You are motivated to use your *practical* skills to move toward your goals. Your *emotional intelligence* has prepared you to adjust to and work with all kinds of people. The bar has been raised. **Get ready to use *Keys to Success* to fly over it and find out just how much you can grow.**

Case *Wrap-up*

What happened to Tererai? Feeling the pull of family obligation despite what she had been through, Trent worked to support her family while caring for her husband. Though her progress toward her master's degree slowed to part-time, she still completed it. After her husband's death, she began doctoral work on AIDS prevention in Africa. Tererai checked off the last of her goals on the worn piece of paper when she received her PhD. Now she has new goals, which include bringing others the opportunity to pursue their dreams. She works for Heifer as a program evaluator. She continues her quest to "work for the causes of women and girls in poverty" (as she wrote on the piece of paper that contained her original four goals).

What does this mean for you? You don't need to begin your life in poverty in another country, have five children by your early twenties, or suffer abuse to feel that you have a long road ahead to achieve your highest goals and most far-flung dreams. Let Tererai Trent's story inspire you to take your own dreams seriously. Think about the dream you have described in the Change the Conversation exercise. Start to make it a reality by mapping out a plan to achieve it—over a year, five years, or even ten years or more. List the steps you need to take toward your dream and when you think you can achieve each step.

What effects go beyond your world? Every dream realized can make the world a better place, step by step. Perhaps a goal that is meaningful to you can make a difference for someone else—or you can be inspired to create a new goal for yourself by learning about an area of need in the world. Go to www.heifer.org and click on "Our Work" and then on "Our Initiatives." There you will see seven areas in which Heifer International intends to make a difference. Choose one that you find important and read about what Heifer is doing. Then explore what you can do—either through Heifer (the "Get Involved" button) or through another organization or path. *Set one small goal that can make a difference for someone in the world.*

Successful Intelligence *Wrap-up*

HERE'S HOW YOU HAVE
BUILT SKILLS IN **CHAPTER 1**:

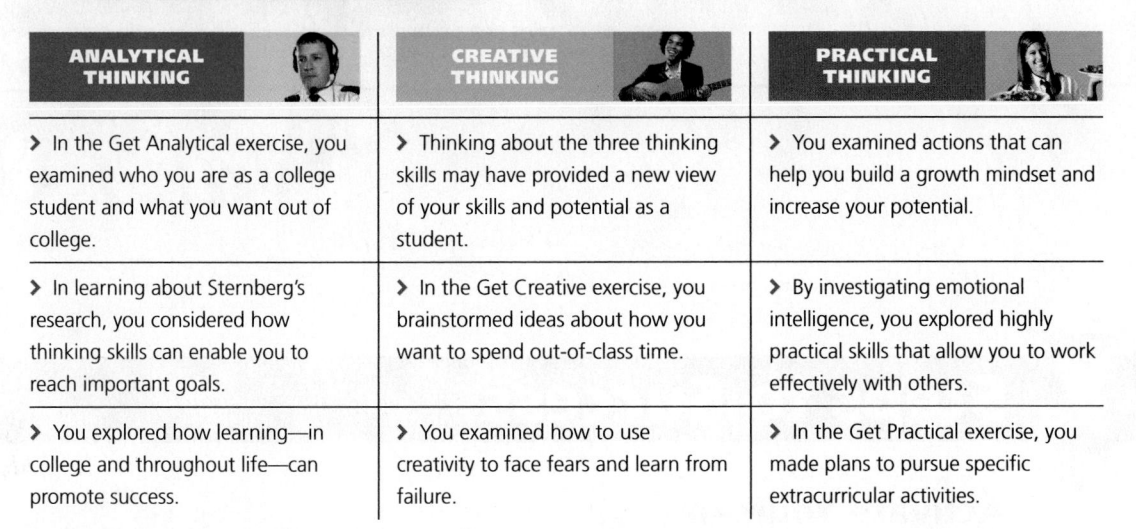

ANALYTICAL THINKING	CREATIVE THINKING	PRACTICAL THINKING
› In the Get Analytical exercise, you examined who you are as a college student and what you want out of college.	› Thinking about the three thinking skills may have provided a new view of your skills and potential as a student.	› You examined actions that can help you build a growth mindset and increase your potential.
› In learning about Sternberg's research, you considered how thinking skills can enable you to reach important goals.	› In the Get Creative exercise, you brainstormed ideas about how you want to spend out-of-class time.	› By investigating emotional intelligence, you explored highly practical skills that allow you to work effectively with others.
› You explored how learning—in college and throughout life—can promote success.	› You examined how to use creativity to face fears and learn from failure.	› In the Get Practical exercise, you made plans to pursue specific extracurricular activities.

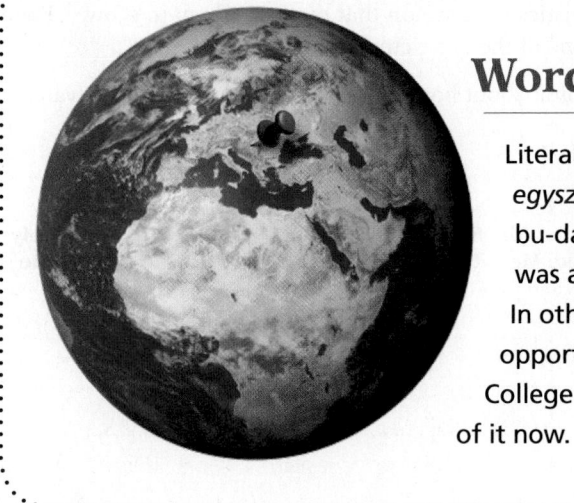

Word *for* Thought

Literally translated, the **Hungarian** phrase *egyszer volt budán kutyavásár* (edge-zehr volt bu-darn ku-tcho-vah-shahr) reads, "There was a dog-market in Buda only once."[24] In other words, it refers to a favorable opportunity that comes along one time only. College is that opportunity—make the most of it now.

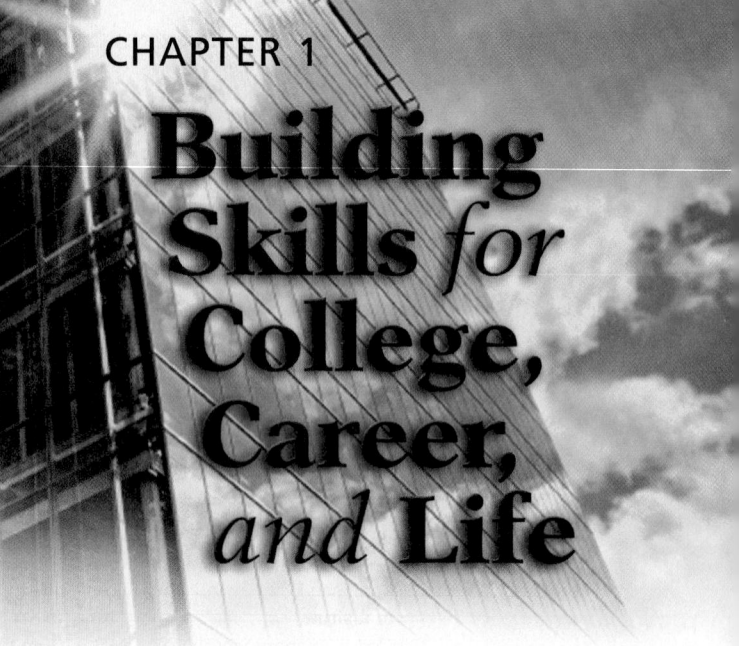

Building Skills *for* College, Career, *and* Life

Steps to Success

Activate Yourself

Robert Sternberg found that people who reach their goals successfully, despite differences in thinking and personal goals, have twenty particular characteristics in common that motivate them to grow.[25] Each of the "I" statements in the following list identifies one of the characteristics.

BUILD BASIC SKILLS. Use this self-assessment to think about how well you can get and stay motivated *right now*.

	1 Not at All Like Me	2 Somewhat Unlike Me	3 Not Sure	4 Somewhat Like Me	5 Definitely Like Me
Please circle the number that best represents your answer.					
1. I motivate myself well.	1	2	3	4	5
2. I can control my impulses.	1	2	3	4	5
3. I know when to persevere and when to change gears.	1	2	3	4	5
4. I make the most of what I do well.	1	2	3	4	5
5. I can successfully translate my ideas into action.	1	2	3	4	5
6. I can focus effectively on my goal.	1	2	3	4	5
7. I complete tasks and have good follow-through.	1	2	3	4	5
8. I initiate action—I move people and projects ahead.	1	2	3	4	5
9. I have the courage to risk failure.	1	2	3	4	5

	1 Not at All Like Me	2 Somewhat Unlike Me	3 Not Sure	4 Somewhat Like Me	5 Definitely Like Me
10. I avoid procrastination.	1	2	3	4	5
11. I accept responsibility when I make a mistake.	1	2	3	4	5
12. I don't waste time feeling sorry for myself.	1	2	3	4	5
13. I independently take responsibility for tasks.	1	2	3	4	5
14. I work hard to overcome personal difficulties.	1	2	3	4	5
15. I create an environment that helps me concentrate on my goals.	1	2	3	4	5
16. I don't take on too much work or too little.	1	2	3	4	5
17. I can delay gratification to receive the benefits.	1	2	3	4	5
18. I can see both the big picture and the details in a situation.	1	2	3	4	5
19. I am able to maintain confidence in myself.	1	2	3	4	5
20. I can balance analytical, creative, and practical thinking skills.	1	2	3	4	5

TAKE IT TO THE NEXT LEVEL. Choose five statements that focus on areas you most want to develop throughout the term. Circle or highlight them on the self-assessment. Then pretend to be an instructor recommending you for a scholarship or a job. Write a short e-mail about how strong you are in those five areas. Save the e-mail as a reminder of what you would like such a person to say about you.

MOVE TOWARD MASTERY. Select one of the five statements chosen in the previous section and take action in the following ways.

1. Find the section in the text that will help you develop this ability. If you wish to procrastinate less, for example, locate the time management information in Chapter 2.
2. Skim the text section and find one concept or strategy that catches your attention. Copy the concept or strategy onto a piece of paper or electronic file. Then, briefly describe how you plan to use it.
3. Take action in the next week based on your plan. You are on the road to growth.

In the last chapter, you will revisit this self-assessment and get more specific about actions you have taken, and plan to take, to promote personal growth.

Teamwork

Create Solutions Together

OVERCOME MOTIVATION BLOCKERS

Goal: To brainstorm ways around motivation blockers that interrupt your ability to succeed in school.

Time on task: 15 minutes as a group; 5 minutes on your own

Instructions: Gather in a group of three to five. In your group, brainstorm motivation blockers—situations, attitudes, types of people, things, or places that most often kill your motivation to succeed in school. When you have as many problems as you have group members, each person should choose one problem and write it at the top of a blank sheet of paper.

Look at the motivation blocker on your page. Under it, write one practical idea about how to overcome it. When everyone is finished, pass your page to the person on the left. Then, on your new page, write an idea about the new blocker below any other ideas already listed. If you can't think of anything, pass the page as is. Continue this way until your page comes back to you. Then discuss the ideas as a group, analyzing which might work better than others. Add other ideas if you think of them.

Finally, on your own but keeping in mind the group discussion, list three specific actions that you can take to keep motivation high when the going gets rough.

1. _____

2. _____

3. _____

Writing

Build Intrapersonal and Communication Skills

Record your thoughts on a separate piece of paper, in a journal, or electronically.

EMOTIONAL INTELLIGENCE JOURNAL

How you are feeling now. First, describe what you are feeling right now about college. Then discuss what those feelings tell you about how ready you are for the experience. Last, brainstorm some actions that will help you be as prepared as possible to benefit from the experience of college. (For example, if shyness prevents you from feeling ready to meet new people on campus, one action might be to join an organization or study group that will help you get to know people more easily.)

REAL-LIFE WRITING

Skills you have now. No matter what professional goals you ultimately pursue, the skills that the 21st century workplace demands will be useful in any career area. Look back at Key 1.3 to remind yourself of the four skill areas—and the individual skills within each category—defined as 21st century essentials for success. Identify three skills you have already built and can demonstrate. If you would like to read further, go to www.21stcenturyskills.org/route21 and click on any of the four areas to see details about specific skills.

For each skill, write a short paragraph that contains the following elements:

- A description of your abilities in this skill area
- Specific examples, from school or work, demonstrating these abilities
- Jobs or coursework in which you have built this skill

Keep this information on hand for building your resumé—or if you already have a resumé, use it to update your information and add detail that will keep your resumé current.

Personal Portfolio

Prepare for Career Success

ASSESS YOUR SUCCESSFUL INTELLIGENCE

This is the first of nine portfolio assignments you will complete, one for each chapter. By the end of the term, you will have compiled a portfolio of documents that can help you achieve career exploration and planning goals.

Type your work and save the documents electronically in one file folder. Use loose paper for assignments that ask you to draw or make collages, and make copies of assignments that ask you to write in the book. For safekeeping, scan and save loose or text pages to include in your portfolio file.

21st Century Learning Building Blocks

- Initiative and Self-Direction
- Critical Thinking and Problem Solving

As you begin this course, use this exercise to get a big picture look at how you perceive yourself as an analytical, creative, and practical thinker. For the statements in each of the three self-assessments, circle the number that best describes how it applies to you.

ASSESS YOUR ANALYTICAL THINKING SKILLS

For each statement, circle the number that feels right to you, from 1 for "not at all true for me" to 5 for "very true for me."

1. I recognize and define problems effectively.   1 2 3 4 5

2. I see myself as a "thinker," "analytical," "studious."   1 2 3 4 5

3. When working on a problem in a group setting, I like to break down the problem into its components and evaluate them.   1 2 3 4 5

4. I need to see convincing evidence before accepting information as fact.   1 2 3 4 5

5. I weigh the pros and cons of plans and ideas before taking action.   1 2 3 4 5

6. I tend to make connections among bits of information by categorizing them.   1 2 3 4 5

7. Impulsive, spontaneous decision making worries me.   1 2 3 4 5

8. I like to analyze causes and effects when making a decision.   1 2 3 4 5

9. I monitor my progress toward goals.   1 2 3 4 5

10. Once I reach a goal, I evaluate the process to see how effective it was.   1 2 3 4 5

Total your answers here: _____

ASSESS YOUR CREATIVE THINKING SKILLS

For each statement, circle the number that feels right to you, from 1 for "not at all true for me" to 5 for "very true for me."

1. I tend to question rules and regulations.   1 2 3 4 5

2. I see myself as "unique," "full of ideas," "innovative."   1 2 3 4 5

3. When working on a problem in a group setting, I generate a lot of ideas.   1 2 3 4 5

4. I am energized when I have a brand-new experience.   1 2 3 4 5

5. If you say something is too risky, I'm ready to give it a shot.   1 2 3 4 5

6. I often wonder if there is a different way to do or see something.   1 2 3 4 5

7. Too much routine in my work or schedule drains my energy.   1 2 3 4 5

8. I tend to see connections among ideas that others do not.   1 2 3 4 5

9. I feel comfortable allowing myself to make mistakes as I test out ideas.   1 2 3 4 5

10. I'm willing to champion an idea even when others disagree with me.   1 2 3 4 5

Total your answers here: _____

ASSESS YOUR PRACTICAL THINKING SKILLS

For each statement, circle the number that feels right to you, from 1 for "not at all true for me" to 5 for "very true for me."

1. I can find a way around any obstacle. 1 2 3 4 5

2. I see myself as a "doer," the "go-to" person; I "make things happen." 1 2 3 4 5

3. When working on a problem in a group setting, I like to figure out who will do what and when it should be done. 1 2 3 4 5

4. I apply what I learn from experience to improve my response to similar situations. 1 2 3 4 5

5. I finish what I start and don't leave loose ends hanging. 1 2 3 4 5

6. I note my emotions about academic and social situations and use what they tell me to move toward a goal. 1 2 3 4 5

7. I can sense how people feel and can use that knowledge to interact with others effectively. 1 2 3 4 5

8. I manage my time effectively. 1 2 3 4 5

9. I adjust to the teaching styles of my instructors and the communication styles of my peers. 1 2 3 4 5

10. When involved in a problem-solving process, I can shift gears as needed. 1 2 3 4 5

Total your answers here: _____

With your scores in hand, use the Wheel of Successful Intelligence to look at all the skills at once. In each of the three areas of the wheel, draw a curved line approximately at the level of your number score and fill in the wedge below that line. Look at what the wheel shows about the level of balance you perceive in your three aspects of successful intelligence. If it were a real wheel, would it roll?

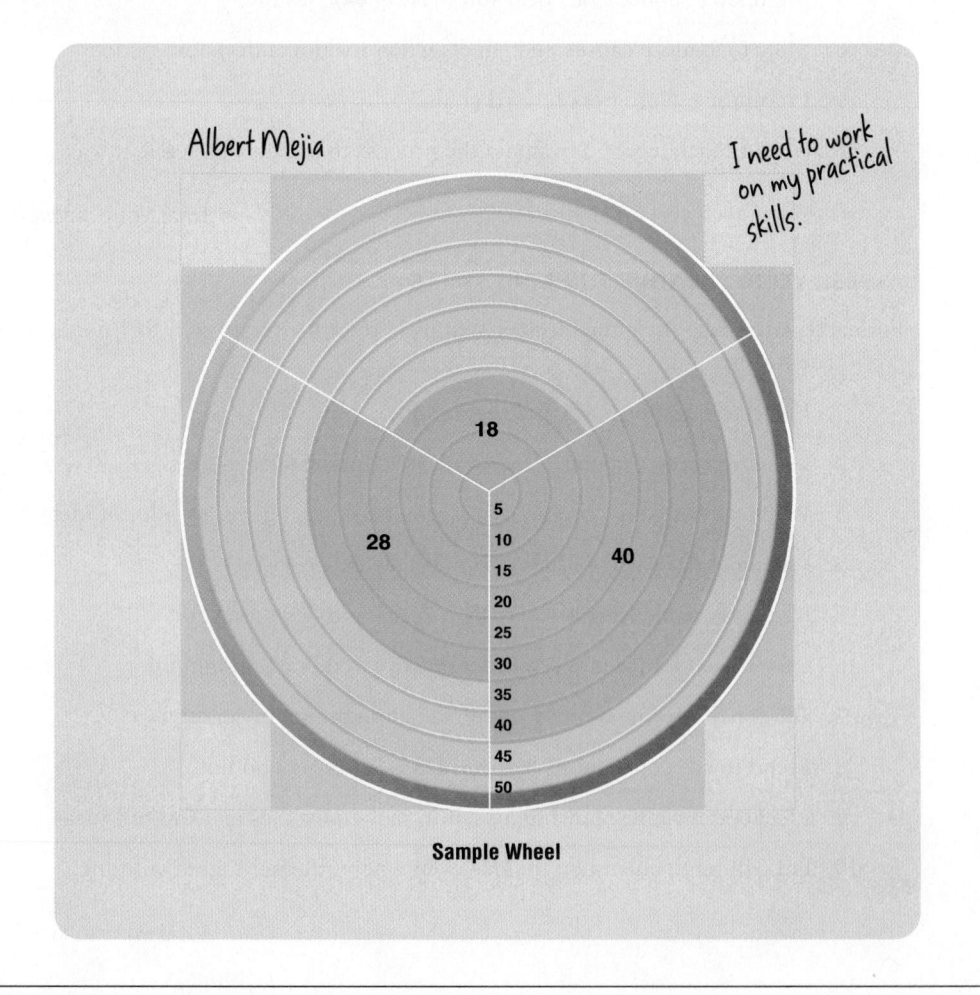

Sample Wheel

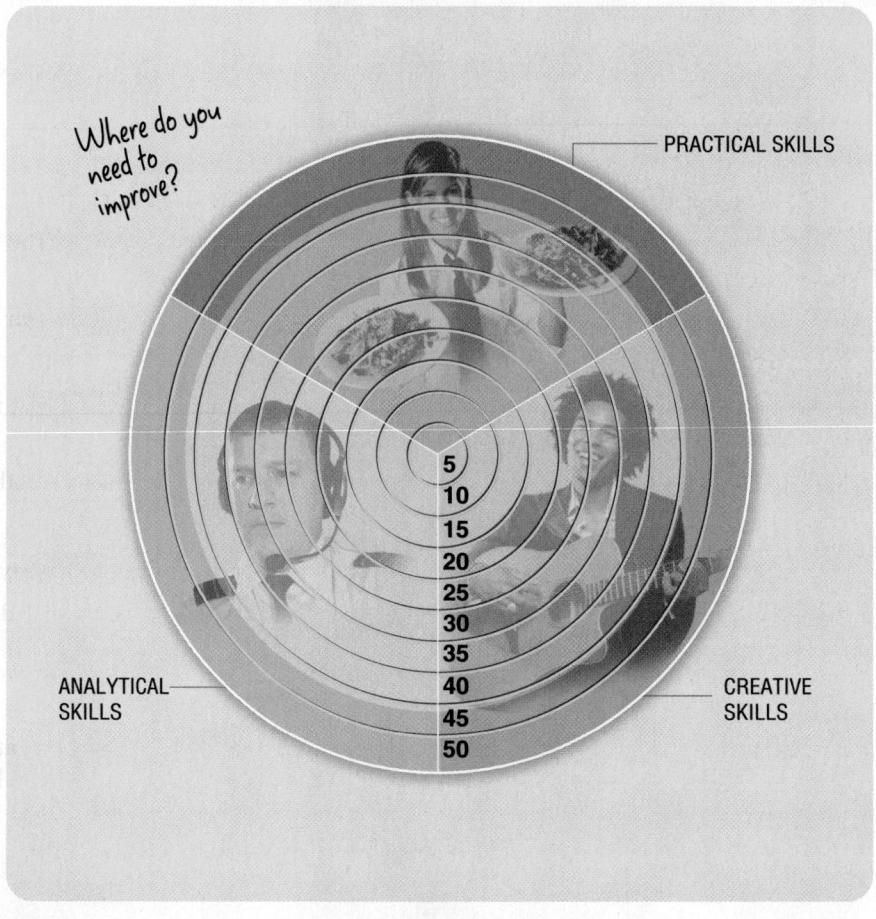

PRACTICAL SKILLS

Where do you need to improve?

5
10
15
20
25
30
35
40
45
50

ANALYTICAL SKILLS

CREATIVE SKILLS

Source: Based on "The Wheel of Life" model developed by the Coaches Training Institute. © Co-Active Space 2000.

Based on the appearance of the wheel, in which skill do you most need to build strength? Keep this goal in mind as you proceed through the text. In each chapter, pay special attention to the exercise that builds this thinking skill.

Social Networking

CONNECT TO THE WORKING WORLD

One of the most productive uses of online social networking is to help people market themselves and develop networks of professional contacts in the work world. At the end of each Personal Portfolio exercise, this segment will help you build a profile on one of the most widely used tools for this purpose—LinkedIn. The mission of LinkedIn is to help you connect to people you know and trust, and access wider networks of people through them, to become a more successful professional in the career of your choice.

Set up your account on LinkedIn to get started. Do the following:

- Go to www.linkedin.com and click on "What is LinkedIn?" to get an overview.
- Click on "Join Today" and follow the instructions to establish your account name and password.
- Be sure to read the User Agreement and Privacy Policy.

If you already have a LinkedIn account, sign on and make sure your basic information is up to date.

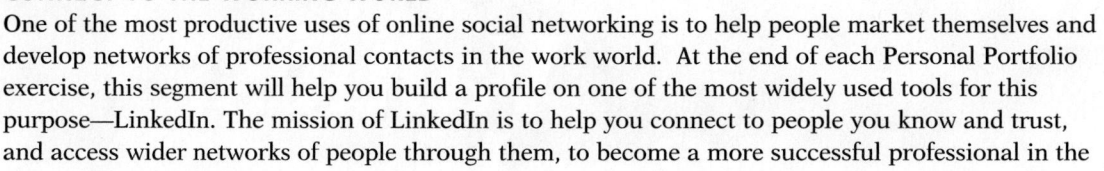

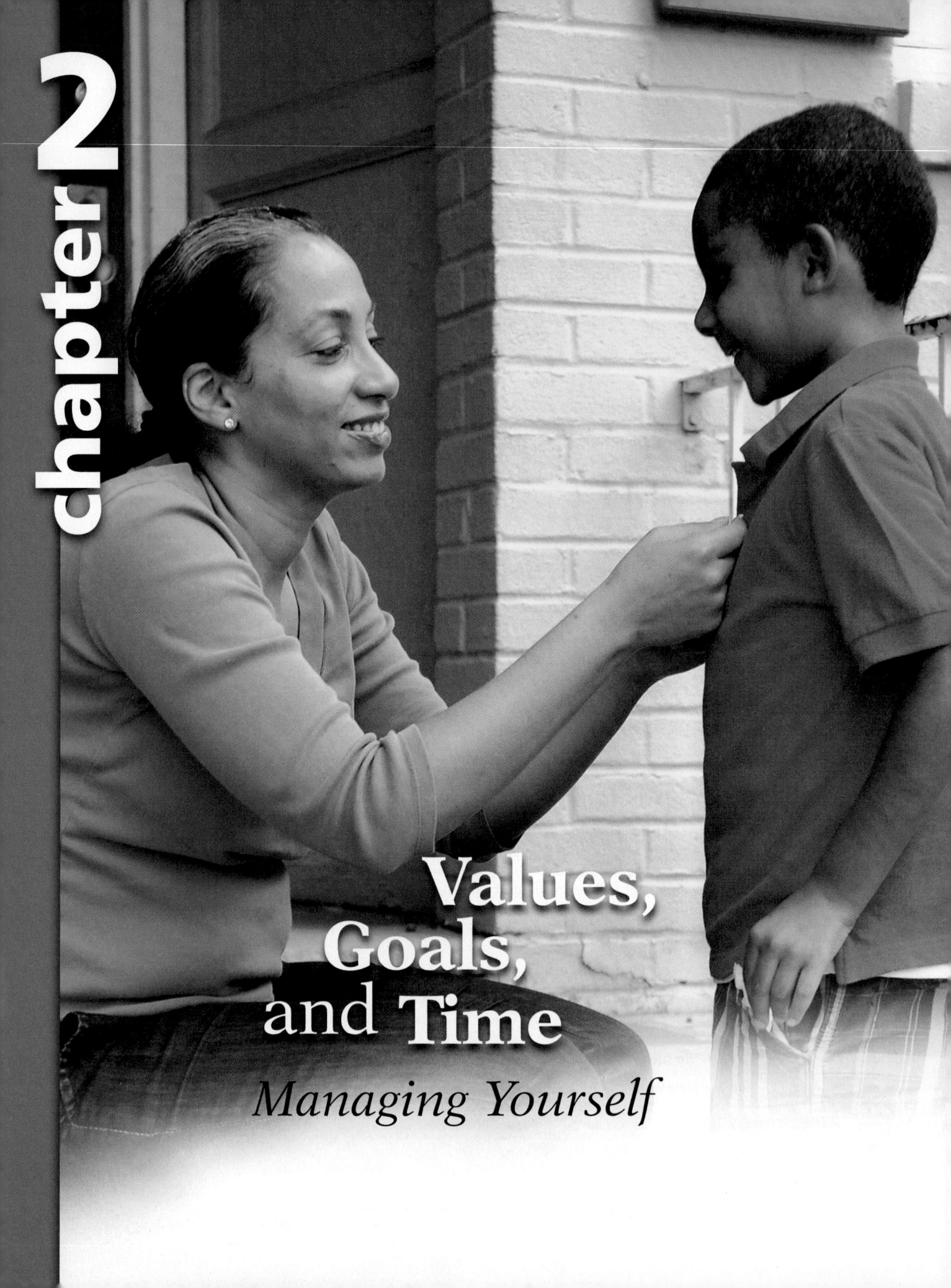

chapter 2

Values, Goals, and Time

Managing Yourself

A student 2 years away from college graduation who is pursuing this long-term goal might establish the following supporting set of 1-year long-term goals:

> Design courses for the year to make sure I am on track for pre-med course completion. Find medical practices in the area that could serve as a model for my business. Research medical schools.

To determine your long-term goals, think about the values that anchor your personal mission. For someone who values health and fitness, for example, possible long-term goals might involve working for an organic food company or training as a physical therapist. Basing your long-term goals on values increases your motivation to succeed. The stronger the link between your values and your long-term goals, the happier, more motivated, and more successful you are likely to be in setting and achieving those goals.

Set short-term goals

Lasting from an hour or less to as long as several months, *short-term goals* narrow your focus and encourage progress toward long-term goals. If you have a long-term goal of graduating with a degree in nursing, for example, you may set these short-term goals for the next 6 months:

▶ I will learn the name, location, and function of every human bone and muscle.
▶ I will work with a study group to understand the muscular-skeletal system.

These goals can be broken down into even smaller parts, such as the following 1-month goals:

▶ I will work with on-screen tutorials of the muscular-skeletal system until I understand and memorize the material.
▶ I will spend 3 hours a week with my study partners.

In addition to monthly goals, you may have short-term goals that extend for a week, a day, or even a couple of hours. To support your goal of regularly meeting with your study partners, you may set the following short-term goals:

▶ *By the end of today.* Text or e-mail study partners to ask them when they might be able to meet
▶ *1 week from now.* Schedule each of our weekly meetings this month
▶ *2 weeks from now.* Have our first meeting
▶ *3 weeks from now.* Type and distribute notes from first meeting; have second meeting

Set up a SMART goal-achievement plan

At any given time, you are working toward goals of varying importance. First, decide which goals matter most to you and are most deserving of your focus. Then draw

Find Ways to Get Unstuck

To start, think of a problem on which you tend to get stuck. It could be scheduling homework around extracurricular activities, finding time to hang out with friends, coming up with interesting career paths, or simply figuring out the theme of a literary work.

_____

_____

_____

Now come up with three reasonable ways to get unstuck. For example, if your issue is scheduling homework, one way to get unstuck might be to start your day earlier with a 1-hour work session.

1. _____

2. _____

3. _____

Now that you've determined the most logical solutions, use a visual organizer to think outside of the problem-solving box. First, write your problem in the center bubble. Then, begin filling in the surrounding bubbles with as many ideas as you can think of. Don't question their validity or whether or not they'll work; just keep writing until you've filled in every bubble with a possible solution.

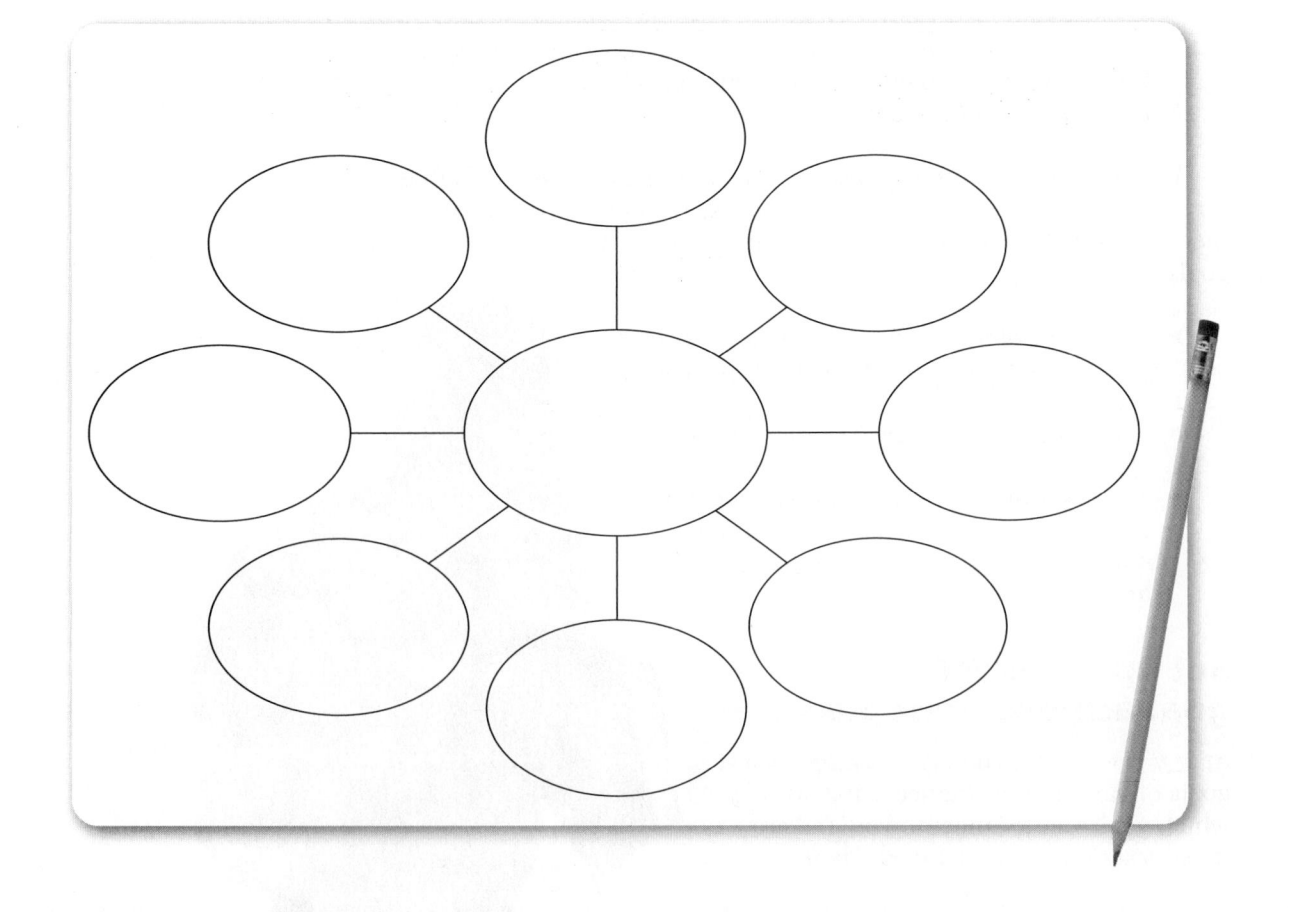

When you're finished, read through all of your creative solutions. Do any of them stick out to you? Find your two favorites and briefly describe how you might be able to use them next time you are faced with a similar situation.

_____

_____

_____

_____

_____

_____

_____

You just got yourself unstuck. Consider using this method when faced with a tough problem. Thinking creatively can be an extremely productive (not to mention fun) way to solve any problem you may encounter.

up a plan to achieve those goals, using the SMART system to make your goals Specific, Measurable, Achievable, Realistic, and linked to a Time Frame.

▶ *Step 1.* Define an Achievable, Realistic goal. *What do you want?* Is it **achievable**—do you have the skill, ability, and drive to get there? Is it **realistic**—will the external factors (time available, weather, money, other people, and so on) help or hinder you? To develop an achievable, realistic goal, consider your hopes, interests, and abilities. Then, reflect on how realistic it is, given your resources and circumstances. Write out a clear description of your goal.

▶ *Step 2.* Define a Specific path. *How will you get there?* Brainstorm different paths. Choose one; then map out its **specific** steps. Focus on behaviors and events that are under your control.

▶ *Step 3.* Link to a Time Frame. *When do you want to accomplish your goal?* Schedule steps within a realistic **time frame.** Create specific deadlines for each step you defined in Step 1. Charting your progress will help you stay on track.

▶ *Step 4.* Measure your progress. *What safeguards will keep you on track?* Will you record your progress in a weekly journal? Report to a friend? Use an alarm system on your smartphone to remind you to do something? Create a system to **measure** how well you are moving along.

▶ *Step 5.* Get unstuck: *What will you do if you hit a roadblock?* The path to a goal is often rocky and stressful. Anticipate problems and define **specific** ways to alter your plans if you run into trouble (stress management strategies are presented later in the chapter). Reach out to friends, family, and college personnel who can help you. Remind yourself of the benefits of your goal. Be ready to brainstorm other ideas if your plans don't work. The Get Creative activity will help you think your way past roadblocks.

▶ *Step 6.* Action time. Follow the steps in your plan until you achieve your goal.

GOAL: To decide on a major.

SMART KEY	MEANING	EXAMPLE
Specific	Name exactly how you will achieve your goal.	I will read the list of available majors, meet with my academic advisor, talk with instructors, and choose a major by the deadline.
Measurable	Find ways to measure your progress over time.	I will set alarms on my smartphone to remind me of when I should have accomplished steps. I will ask my mom to check in to make sure I'm getting somewhere.
Achievable	Set a goal that your abilities and drive can handle.	I'm driven to declare a major because I want to earn my degree, graduate, and gain work-ready skills.
Realistic	Define a goal that is workable given the resources (time and money) and other circumstances.	Because I'm starting early and already know how the process works, I should have time to think through this carefully.
Time Frame	Set up a time frame for achieving your goal and the steps toward it.	I have a year until the deadline. I will read the catalog in the next month; I will meet with my advisor by the end of the term; I will talk with instructors at the beginning of next term; I will declare a major by the end of next term.

MAJOR or
CONCENTRATION
An academic subject area chosen as a field of specialization, requiring a specific course of study.

See Key 2.2 for a way to apply this goal-setting plan to an important objective that nearly every college student will need to achieve—declaring a **major** or **concentration** (for the sake of simplicity, the term *major* will appear throughout the rest of the text).

Through the process of working toward your most important goals, you will often be thinking about how well you are using your time. In fact, being able to achieve any significant goal is directly linked to effective time management.

How can you effectively **manage your time?**

No matter how well you define the steps to your goals, you need to set those steps within a time frame to achieve them. Although the idea of "managing time" may seem impossible, time management can also be thought of as *behavioral management*—adjusting what you do so that you can meet your needs in the time you have available.

Everyone has only 24 hours in a day, and 8 or so of those hours involve sleeping (or should, if you want to remain healthy and alert enough to achieve your goals). You can't manage how time passes, but you *can* manage how you use it. Only by making active choices about your time can you hope to avoid that feeling of being swept along in time's swift tide that Devonne is experiencing. The first step in time management is to figure out your time profile and your preferences.

Identify your time profile and preferences

People have unique body rhythms and habits that affect how they deal with time. Some people are night owls who have lots of energy late at night. Others are early birds who do their best work early in the day. Some people are chronically late, whereas others get everything done with time to spare.

The more you're aware of your own time-related behaviors, the better able you'll be to create a schedule that maximizes your strengths and reduces stress. The following steps can help you get in touch with your own inner time clock:

■ **Create a personal time "profile."** Ask yourself these questions: At what time of day do I have the most energy? The least energy? Do I tend to be early, on time, or late? Do I focus well for long stretches or need regular breaks? Your answers will help you determine your profile.

■ **Evaluate the effects of your profile.** Which of your time-related habits and preferences will have a positive impact on your success at school? Which are likely to cause problems? Which can you make adjustments for, and which will just require you to cope?

■ **Establish schedule preferences.** Based on the time profile you have developed, list your preferences—or even map out an ideal schedule as a way of illustrating them. For example, one student's preference list might read, "Classes bunched together on Mondays, Wednesdays, and Fridays. Tuesdays and Thursdays free for studying and research. Study time primarily during the day."

Next, build a schedule that takes your profile and preferences into account wherever possible. You will have more control over some things than others. For example, a student who functions best late at night may have more luck scheduling study time than class meeting times (unless he attends one of several colleges that have begun to schedule late-night classes to handle an overload of students).

Build a schedule

Schedules help you gain control of your life in two ways: They provide segments of time for goal-related tasks and they remind you of tasks, events, due dates, responsibilities, and deadlines.

Use a planner

A planner is a tool for managing your time. Use it to keep track of events and commitments, schedule goal-related tasks, and rank tasks according to priority. Time management expert Paul Timm says that "rule number one in a thoughtful planning process is: Use some form of a planner where you can write things down."[2]

There are two major types of planners. One is a book or notebook, showing either a day or a week at a glance, in which to note commitments. Some planners contain sections for monthly and yearly goals. The other option is an electronic planner or smartphone such as an iPhone or iPod Touch, BlackBerry, or Sidekick. Basic functions allow you to schedule days and weeks, note due dates, make to-do lists, perform mathematical calculations, and create and store an address book. You can also transfer information to and from a computer.

Though electronic planners are handy and have a large data capacity, they cost more than the paper versions, and they can fail due to software or battery

Managing time effectively often means taking advantage of opportunities whenever they arise. This student, also a mother, fits schoolwork in during naptime.
© Michael Newman/PhotoEdit

Monday, March 14		
Time	Tasks	Priority
6:00 A.M.		
7:00		
8:00	Up at 8am — finish homewo	
9:00		
10:00	Business Administration	
11:00	Renew driver's license @ DM	
12:00 P.M.		
1:00	Lunch	
2:00	Writing Seminar (peer editi	
3:00	↓	
4:00	check on Ms.Schwartz's off	
5:00	5:30 work out	
6:00	└→6:30	
7:00	Dinner	
8:00	Read two chapters for	
9:00	Business Admin.	
10:00		
11:00		
12:00		

Monday, March 28			
8		Call: Mike Blair	1
9	BIO 212	Financial Aid Office	2
10			3
11	CHEM 203	EMS 262 *Paramedic	4
12		role-play*	5
Evening	6pm yoga class		

Tuesday, March 29			
8	Finish reading assignment!	Work @ library	1
9			2
10	ENG 112	(study for quiz)	3
11	↓		4
12		↓	5
Evening		until 7pm	

Wednesday, March 30			
8		Meet w/advisor	1
9	BIO 212		2
10		EMS 262	3
11	CHEM 203 *Quiz		4
12		Pick up photos	5
Evening	6pm Dinner w/study group		

problems. Analyze your preferences and options, and decide which tool you are most likely to use every day. A blank notebook, used conscientiously, may work as well for some people as a top-of-the-line smartphone. You might also consider online calendars, such as Google Calendar, which can "communicate" with your phone or other electronic planning device.

Keep track of events and commitments

Your planner is designed to help you schedule and remember events and commitments. A quick look at your notations will remind you when items are approaching. Your class syllabus is a crucial tool for keeping track of reading and homework assignments and test dates (see Key 2.3).

When you get your syllabi for the term, enter all relevant dates in your planner right away so you can prepare for crunch times. For example, if you see that you have three tests and a presentation coming up all in one week, you may have to rearrange your schedule during the preceding week to create extra study time.

Among the events and commitments worth noting in your planner are the following:

- Test and quiz dates; due dates for papers, projects, and presentations
- Details of your academic schedule, including term and holiday breaks
- Club and organizational meetings
- Personal items—medical appointments, due dates for bills, birthdays, social events
- Milestones toward a goal, such as due dates for sections of a project

It's important to include class prep time—reading and studying, writing, and working on assignments and projects—in the planner. As you read in Chapter 1, you should schedule at least 2 hours of preparation for every hour of class—that is, if you take twelve credits, you'll spend 24 hours or more a week on course-related activities in and out of class. It's tough to get that much studying in, especially if you are an athlete, a working student, or a parent. Situations like these demand creative time management and attention to your schedule.

Schedule tasks and activities that support your values and goals

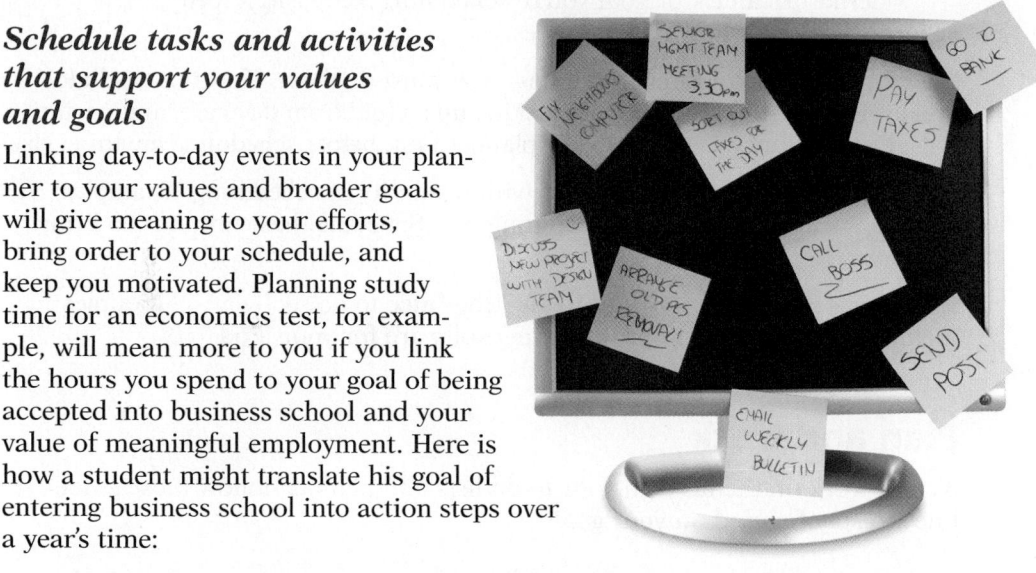

Linking day-to-day events in your planner to your values and broader goals will give meaning to your efforts, bring order to your schedule, and keep you motivated. Planning study time for an economics test, for example, will mean more to you if you link the hours you spend to your goal of being accepted into business school and your value of meaningful employment. Here is how a student might translate his goal of entering business school into action steps over a year's time:

- *This year.* Complete enough courses to meet curriculum requirements for business school and maintain class standing
- *This term.* Complete my economics class with a B average or higher
- *This month.* Set up economics study group schedule to coincide with quizzes and tests
- *This week.* Meet with study group; go over material for Friday's test
- *Today.* Go over Chapter 3 in econ text

The student can then arrange his time to move him in the direction of his goal. He schedules activities that support his short-term goal of doing well on the test and writes them in his planner. Achieving his overarching long-term goal of doing well in a course he needs for business school is the source of his motivation.

Before each week begins, remind yourself of your long-term goals and what you can accomplish over the next 7 days to move you closer to them. Additionally, every once in a while, take a hard look at your schedule to see whether you are spending time on what you most value. Key 2.3 shows parts of a daily schedule and a weekly schedule.

Make to-do lists and prioritize

Many people find it useful to create a daily or weekly *to-do list* and check off the items as they are completed. A to-do list can be useful on an especially busy day, during exam week, or at any other time that you anticipate being overloaded.

Making a list, however, is more than doing a "brain dump" of everything you have to do. You need to **prioritize** your list—code it, or organize it, according to how important each item is. Some people use numbers, some use letters (A, B, C), and some use different-colored pens or, for electronic planners, highlighting and font color tools. Prioritizing helps you focus the bulk of your energy and time on the most important tasks. Because many top-priority items (classes, work) occur at designated times, prioritizing helps you lock in these activities and schedule less urgent items around them.

Prioritizing isn't just for time management. You should also prioritize your long-term and short-term goals and the steps leading up to each. Keep these priorities alongside your daily lists so you can see how they influence one another. For instance, arriving at school a half hour early so you can meet with an advisor influences your long-term goal of deciding on a major.

Whether it's a task or goal you're scheduling, set basic priority levels according to the following guidelines.

- **Priority 1.** The most crucial items—you must do them. They may include attending class, working at a job, picking up a child from day care, and paying bills. Enter Priority 1 items in your planner first, before scheduling anything else.

- **Priority 2.** Important items but with flexibility in scheduling. Examples include library study time and working out. Schedule these around the Priority 1 items.

- **Priority 3.** Least important items—the "nice to do" activities. Examples include phoning a friend or upgrading software for your iPod.

Plan and track

As you work on the tasks in your to-do lists and planner, follow these guidelines to stay focused on your goals:

▶ *Plan regularly.* Set aside a regular time each day to plan your schedule (right before bed, with your morning coffee, on your commute to or from school, or whatever time and situation works best for you). This reduces stress and saves the hassle of forgetting something important.

▶ *Actively manage your schedule.* The most detailed planner won't do you a bit of good unless you look at it. Check your schedule at regular intervals throughout the day or week.

▶ *Use monthly and yearly calendars at home.* A standard monthly or yearly wall calendar is a great place to keep track of your major commitments. A wall calendar like the monthly calendar in Key 2.4 gives you the "big picture" overview you need.

▶ *Work to stay motivated.* If you can get a task done ahead of time, get it done; it will help you avoid pressure later. Focus on your growth mindset, reminding yourself that achievement requires persistent effort.

▶ *Avoid time traps.* Stay away from situations that eat up time. Learn to say no when you just can't fit in an extra responsibility. Reduce time spent with anything that distracts you, such as your cell phone, social networking sites, or Twitter account.

▶ *Schedule downtime.* It's easy to get so caught up in completing tasks that you forget to relax and breathe. Even a half hour of downtime a day will refresh you and improve your productivity when you get back on task.

PRIORITIZE
To arrange or deal with in order of importance.

MARCH

SUNDAY	MONDAY	TUESDAY	WEDNESDAY	THURSDAY	FRIDAY	SATURDAY
	1 WORK	2 Turn in English paper topic	3 Dentist 2 pm	4	5 WORK	6
7 Frank's birthday	8 Psych Test 9 am WORK	9	10 6:30 pm Meeting @ Acad Ctr	11 WORK	12	13 Dinner @ Ryan's
14	15 English paper due WORK	16 Western Civ paper	17	18 Library 6 pm WORK	19 Western Civ makeup class	20
21	22 WORK	23 2 pm meeting, psych group	24 Start running: 2 miles	25 WORK	26 Run 2 miles	27
28 Run 3 miles	29 WORK	30 Western Civ paper due	31 Run 2 miles			

Confront procrastination

It's human, and common for busy students, to leave difficult or undesirable tasks until later. If taken to the extreme, however, **procrastination** can develop into a habit that causes serious problems. For example, procrastinators who don't get things done in the workplace may prevent others from doing their work, possibly losing a promotion or even a job because of it.

This excerpt from the Study Skills Library at California Polytechnic State University at San Luis Obispo illustrates how procrastination can quickly turn into a destructive pattern.

> PROCRASTINATION
> The act of putting off a task until another time.

The procrastinator is often remarkably optimistic about his ability to complete a task on a tight deadline. . . . For example, he may estimate that a paper will take only five days to write; he has fifteen days; there is plenty of time, no need to start. Lulled by a false sense of security, time passes. At some point, he crosses over an imaginary starting time and suddenly realizes, "Oh no! I am not in control! There isn't enough time!"

At this point, considerable effort is directed toward completing the task, and work progresses. This sudden spurt of energy is the source of the erroneous feeling that "I work well only under pressure." Actually, at this point you are making progress only because you haven't any choice. . . . Progress is being made, but you have lost your freedom.

Conquer Your Time Traps

Different people get bogged down by different time traps. What are yours? They could be productive activities, like working out, or less productive activities, like checking your e-mail. Think of two common time traps that you encounter. For each, come up with two ways to say no graciously—to someone else, or even to yourself, as in the following example.

Time Trap: Text Messaging

Response 1: "I'll call you in an hour. I need to finish this paper."

Response 2: "I will respond to my text messages after I've read five pages."

Your turn:

Time Trap: _____

Response 1: _____

_____

Response 2: _____

_____

Time Trap:

Response 1: _____

_____

Response 2: _____

_____

Choose one of the situations you just named and use one or both of your responses the next time the trap threatens your time. Afterward, answer these questions:

How did the response affect your ability to take control of the situation? Did it help? Hurt? How?

_____

_____

_____

_____

What did the response teach you about your personal time traps? Do you find yourself needing to be stricter with your time? Why?

_____

_____

_____

_____

Barely completed in time, the paper may actually earn a fairly good grade; whereupon the student experiences mixed feelings: pride of accomplishment (sort of), scorn for the professor who cannot recognize substandard work, and guilt for getting an undeserved grade. But the net result is *reinforcement:* The procrastinator is rewarded positively for his poor behavior ("Look what a decent grade I got after all!"). As a result, the counterproductive behavior is repeated time and time again.[3]

People procrastinate for various reasons.

■ *Perfectionism.* According to Jane B. Burka and Lenora M. Yuen, authors of *Procrastination: Why You Do It and What to Do About It*, habitual procrastinators often gauge their self-worth solely by their ability to achieve. In other words, "an outstanding performance means an outstanding person; a mediocre performance means a mediocre person."[4] To the perfectionist procrastinator, not trying at all is better than an attempt that falls short of perfection.

■ *Fear of limitations.* Some people procrastinate in order to avoid the truth about what they can achieve. "As long as you procrastinate, you never have to confront the real limits of your ability, whatever those limits are," say Burka and Yuen.[5] A fixed mindset naturally leads to procrastination. "I can't do it," the person with the fixed mindset thinks, "so what's the point of trying?"

■ *Being unsure of the next step.* If you get stuck and don't know what to do, sometimes it seems easier to procrastinate than to make the leap to the next level of your goal.

■ *Facing an overwhelming task.* Some big projects create fear, as Devonne feels about her group project. If a person facing such a task fears failure, she may procrastinate in order to avoid confronting the fear. Get into your growth mindset and use the strategies from Chapter 1 to work through this or any other kind of fear, taking steps forward and knowing that you stand to learn something valuable.

Although it can bring relief in the short term, avoiding tasks almost always causes problems, such as a buildup of responsibilities and less time to complete them, work that is not up to par, the disappointment of others who depend on your work, and stress brought on by unfinished tasks. Particular strategies can help you avoid procrastination and its associated problems.

▶ *Analyze the effects.* What may happen if you continue to put off a task? Chances are you will benefit more in the long term facing the task head-on.

▶ *Set reasonable goals.* Unreasonable goals intimidate and immobilize you. If you concentrate on achieving one small step at a time, the task becomes less burdensome.

▶ *Get started whether you "feel like it" or not.* Take the first step. Once you start, you may find it easier to continue.

▶ *Ask for help.* Once you identify what's holding you up, find someone to help you face the task. Another person may come up with an innovative method to get you moving again.

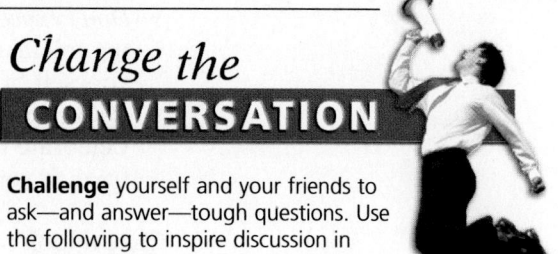

Change the CONVERSATION

Challenge yourself and your friends to ask—and answer—tough questions. Use the following to inspire discussion in pairs or groups.

▶ What time management issues do you see others face? How do they handle them?

▶ How do you handle similar situations? Do you think your approach is as good, better, or not as good? Why? What is the result?

▶ **CONSIDER THE CASE:** What do you think about Ms. Cordoza's suggestion that Devonne become more involved in the project in order to find personal meaning? If you were the instructor, what would you add to convince her?

> ▶ *Don't expect perfection.* People learn by starting at the beginning, making mistakes, and learning from them. If you avoid mistakes, you deprive yourself of learning and growth.
>
> ▶ *Reward yourself.* Boost your confidence when you accomplish a task. Celebrate progress with a reward—a break, a movie, whatever feels like a treat to you.

Take a look at Key 2.5 to explore five major reasons that people waste time and procrastinate—and how to take control of each.

Be flexible

Change is a part of life. No matter how well you think ahead and plan your time, sudden changes—ranging from a room change for a class to a medical emergency—can upend your plans. However, you have some control over how you handle circumstances. Your ability to evaluate situations, come up with creative options, and put practical plans to work will help you manage changes.

Small changes—the need to work an hour overtime at your after-school job, a meeting that runs late—can result in priority shifts that jumble your schedule. For changes that occur frequently, think through a backup plan ahead of time. For surprises, the best you can do is to keep an open mind about possibilities and rely on your internal and external resources.

TAKE CONTROL OF
TIME WASTERS

1. **Television**   It's easy to just keep flipping the channels when you know you've got something due.
   Take Control: Record favorite shows using a digital video recorder (DVR) or watch a movie instead. When your program of choice is over, turn the TV off.

2. **Commute**   Though not often something you can control, the time spent commuting from one place to another can be staggering.
   Take Control: Use your time on a bus or train to do homework, study, read assignments, or work on your monthly budget.

3. **Internet Browsing**   Currently, Internet misuse in the American workplace costs companies more than $178 billion per year in lost productivity.
   Take Control: If you use the Internet for research, consider subscribing to RSS feeds that can alert you when relevant information becomes available. When using the Internet for social or personal reasons, stick to a time limit.

4. **Fatigue**   Being tired can lead to below-quality work that may have to be redone and can make you feel ready to quit altogether.
   Take Control: Determine a stop time for yourself. When your stop time comes, put down the book, turn off the computer, and *go to bed*. During the day when you can, take naps to recharge your battery.

5. **Confusion**   When you don't fully understand an assignment or problem, you may spend unintended time trying to figure it out.
   Take Control: The number one way to fight confusion is to *ask*. As the saying goes, ask early and ask often. Students who seek help show that they want to learn.

When change involves serious problems—your car breaks down and you have no way to get to school, or you fail a class and have to consider summer school—use problem-solving skills to help you through (see Chapter 4). Resources available at your college can help you throughout this process. Your academic advisor, counselor, dean, financial aid advisor, and instructors may have ideas and assistance.

Manage stress by managing time

If you are feeling more **stress** in your everyday life as a student, you are not alone. Stress levels among college students have increased dramatically.[6] Stress factors for college students include adjusting to a new environment with increased work and difficult decisions as well as juggling school, work, and personal responsibilities.

> STRESS
> Physical or mental strain or tension produced in reaction to pressure.

Dealing with the stress of college life is, and will continue to be, one of your biggest challenges. But here's some good news: *Every time management strategy in this chapter contributes to your ability to cope with stress.* Remember that stress refers to how you react to pressure. When you create and follow a schedule that gets you places on time and helps you take care of tasks and responsibilities, you reduce pressure. Less pressure, less stress.

Analyze, and adjust if necessary, the relationship between stress and your time management habits. For example, if you're a night person with early classes and are consistently stressed about waking up in time, use strategies such as going to bed earlier a few nights a week, napping in the afternoon, exercising briefly before class to boost energy, or exploring how to schedule later classes next term. Reduce anxiety by thinking before you act.

The following practical strategies can help you cope with stress through time management. You will find more detail on stress in Chapter 9.

■ *Be realistic about time commitments.* For example, many students attempting to combine work and school find that they have to trim one or the other to reduce stress and promote success. Overloaded students often fall behind and experience high stress levels that can lead to dropping out. Determine what is reasonable for you; you may find that taking longer to graduate is a viable option if you need to work while in school.

■ *Put sleep into your schedule.* Sleep-deprived bodies and minds have a hard time functioning, and research reports that one-quarter of all college students are chronically sleep deprived.[7] Figure out how much sleep you need and do your best to get it. When you pull an all-nighter, make sure you play catch-up over the days that follow. With time for relaxation, your mind is better able to manage stress, and your schoolwork improves.

■ *Actively manage your schedule.* The most detailed datebook page can't help you unless you look at it. Get in the habit of checking at regular intervals throughout the day. Also, try not to put off tasks. If you can get it done ahead of time, get it done.

■ *Focus on one assignment at a time.* Stress is at its worst when you have five pressing assignments in five different classes all due in the next week. Focus on one at a time, completing it to the best of your ability as quickly as you can before moving to the next and the next until you're through.

■ ***Check things off.*** Each time you complete a task, check it off your to-do list, delete it from your electronic scheduler, or crumple up the sticky note. This physical action promotes the feeling of confidence that comes from getting something done.

Sometimes stress freezes you in place and blocks you from finding answers. At those times, remember that taking even a small step is a stress management strategy because it begins to move you ahead.

Case *Wrap-up*

What happened to Devonne? After agreeing to give the problems-of-the-world assignment a try, Devonne made it to the next meeting and listened to what her group had researched so far about the problem of worldwide water shortages. She realized that though her own problems felt overwhelming, the effects of the lack of water—food shortages, people in need who tap the resources of others, widespread pollution—could touch her life as well. She felt a little more committed to the project and to attending meetings. As a bonus, Devonne connected with a group member living nearby with her young son who also is home most mornings. She and Devonne discussed coming up with a schedule to trade off caring for the boys.

What does this mean for you? What is your take on the world's problems? Are you interested, or do you just pass right by that section of the news, perhaps because there is too much else on your mind? Explore the information about five large-scale issues at World's Biggest Problems (www.arlingtoninstitute.org/wbp/portal/home). Choose the one that interests you most and read the site's in-depth information about it. Write about your reaction: How do you think this problem touches—or could touch—your life directly? What can you do on a day-to-day scale that is manageable for you and might make a difference?

What effects go beyond your world? Project yourself 10 years into the future. You are using some of your best talents and passions working in a field that is somehow involved in improving this same world problem. What is your job, and what are you doing? What does this imaginary self and job tell you about the academic and personal goals you are pursuing now?

Successful Intelligence *Wrap-up*

HERE'S HOW YOU HAVE
BUILT SKILLS IN **CHAPTER 2** :

ANALYTICAL THINKING	CREATIVE THINKING	PRACTICAL THINKING
> As you read the section on goals, you broke down the goal-setting process into parts.	> You considered how to create a personal time profile.	> You explored the practical action of pursuing goals step by step.
> In the Get Analytical exercise, you explored your values and connected them to your educational goals.	> In the Get Creative exercise, you thought of innovative ideas to move past your toughest obstacles.	> In the Get Practical exercise, you identified your time traps and then thought of ways to say "no" in different situations.
> You thought about how who you are as a time manager affects your scheduling and procrastination habits.	> Exploring flexibility in time management showed you the role of creativity in the face of change.	> At the end of the chapter, you gathered practical techniques for managing stress.

Word *for* Thought

The **Spanish** word *paseo* (pah-say'-oh) refers to a relaxed late afternoon walk outdoors.[8] The relaxed pace of traditional life in many European countries holds a lesson for the overscheduled, harried student. Relaxation is crucial for stress management. Define your version of the paseo and make it a part of your life.

Building Skills *for* College, Career, *and* Life

Steps to Success

Discover How You Spend Your Time

BUILD BASIC SKILLS. Everyone has exactly 168 hours in a week. How do you spend yours? Start by making a guess, or estimate, about three particular activities. In a week, how much time do you spend on the following?

_____ hours   Studying

_____ hours   Sleeping

_____ hours   Interacting with media and technology (computer, online services, cell phone, texting, video games, television) for nonstudy purposes

Now, to find out the real story, record how you spend your time for 7 days. The chart on the next pages has blocks showing half hour increments. As you go through the week, write down what you do each hour, indicating starting and stopping times. Include sleep and leisure time. Record your *actual* activities instead of the activities you think you should be doing. There are no wrong answers.

After a week, add up how many hours you spent on each activity (round off to half hours—that is, mark 15 to 44 minutes of activity as a half hour and 45 to 75 minutes as one hour). Log the hours in the boxes of the table on page 53 using tally marks, with a full mark representing one hour and a half-size mark representing a half hour. In the third column, total the hours for each activity, and then add the totals in that column to make sure that your grand total is approximately 168 hours (if it isn't, go back and check your grid and calculations and fix any errors you find). Leave the "Ideal Time in Hours" column blank for now.

TAKE IT TO THE NEXT LEVEL. Take a look at your results, paying special attention to how your estimates of sleep, study, and technology time compare to your actual logged activity hours for the week. Use a separate sheet of paper or electronic file to answer the following questions:

- What surprises you about how you spend your time?
- Do you spend the most time on the activities representing your most important values—or not?
- Where do you waste the most time? What do you think that is costing you?
- On which activities do you think you should spend *more* time? On which should you spend *less* time?

TIME	MONDAY activity	TUESDAY activity	WEDNESDAY activity	THURSDAY activity
6:00 A.M.				
6:30 A.M.				
7:00 A.M.				
7:30 A.M.				
8:00 A.M.				
8:30 A.M.				
9:00 A.M.				
9:30 A.M.				
10:00 A.M.				
10:30 A.M.				
11:00 A.M.				
11:30 A.M.				
12:00 P.M.				
12:30 P.M.				
1:00 P.M.				
1:30 P.M.				
2:00 P.M.				
2:30 P.M.				
3:00 P.M.				
3:30 P.M.				
4:00 P.M.				
4:30 P.M.				
5:00 P.M.				
5:30 P.M.				
6:00 P.M.				
6:30 P.M.				
7:00 P.M.				
7:30 P.M.				
8:00 P.M.				
8:30 P.M.				
9:00 P.M.				
9:30 P.M.				
10:00 P.M.				
10:30 P.M.				
11:00 P.M.				
11:30 P.M.				
12:00 A.M.				
12:30 A.M.				
1:00 A.M.				
1:30 A.M.				
2:00 A.M.				

TIME	FRIDAY activity	SATURDAY activity	SUNDAY activity
6:00 A.M.			
6:30 A.M.			
7:00 A.M.			
7:30 A.M.			
8:00 A.M.			
8:30 A.M.			
9:00 A.M.			
9:30 A.M.			
10:00 A.M.			
10:30 A.M.			
11:00 A.M.			
11:30 A.M.			
12:00 P.M.			
12:30 P.M.			
1:00 P.M.			
1:30 P.M.			
2:00 P.M.			
2:30 P.M.			
3:00 P.M.			
3:30 P.M.			
4:00 P.M.			
4:30 P.M.			
5:00 P.M.			
5:30 P.M.			
6:00 P.M.			
6:30 P.M.			
7:00 P.M.			
7:30 P.M.			
8:00 P.M.			
8:30 P.M.			
9:00 P.M.			
9:30 P.M.			
10:00 P.M.			
10:30 P.M.			
11:00 P.M.			
11:30 P.M.			
12:00 A.M.			
12:30 A.M.			
1:00 A.M.			
1:30 A.M.			
2:00 A.M.			

Activity	Time Tallied Over One-Week Period	Total Time in Hours	Ideal Time in Hours
Example: Class	꒠꒠꒠ ꒠꒠꒠ ꒠꒠꒠ ⅼⅼ	16.5	
Class			
Work			
Studying			
Sleeping			
Eating			
Family time/child care			
Commuting/traveling			
Chores and personal business			
Friends and important relationships			
Telephone time			
Leisure/entertainment			
Spiritual life			
Other			

MOVE TOWARD MASTERY. Go back to the chart above and fill in the "Ideal Time in Hours" column. Consider the difference between actual hours and ideal hours. What changes are you willing to make to get closer to how you want to be spending your time? Write a short paragraph describing, in detail, two time management changes you plan to make this term so that you are focusing your time more effectively on your most important goals and values.

Teamwork

Create Solutions Together

SET A SMART GOAL

Goal: To utilize the SMART goal-setting system as a group.

Time on task: 20 minutes

Instructions: As a group, brainstorm important academic goals that can be accomplished within one year at school. Write your ideas on a piece of paper. From that list, pick out one goal to explore together.

Each group member takes 2 minutes alone to think about this goal in terms of the second goal achievement step on page 37—defining a *specific* strategy. In other words, answer the question: "How would I do it?" Each person writes down all of the paths they can think of.

The group then gathers for everyone to share strategies. The group evaluates strategies and chooses one that seems *achievable* and *realistic*. Finally, as a group, brainstorm the rest of the goal achievement process, based on the chosen strategy or path:

- *Set a timetable.* When do you plan to reach your goal? Discuss different *time frames* and how each might change the path.
- *Be accountable.* What safeguards will keep you on track? Talk about different ways to *measure* your progress.
- *Get unstuck.* What will you do if you hit a roadblock? Brainstorm the roadblocks that could get in the way of this particular goal. For each, come up with ways to overcome the obstacle.

At the end of the process, you should have a wealth of ideas for how to approach one particular academic goal—and an appreciation for how many paths you could take in order to get there.

Writing

Build Intrapersonal and Communication Skills

Record your thoughts on a separate piece of paper, in a journal, or electronically.

EMOTIONAL INTELLIGENCE JOURNAL

How you feel about your time management. Paying attention to your feelings about how you spend time can be a key step toward making time management choices that are more in line with your values. Think, and then write, about how your most time-demanding activities make you feel. What makes you happiest, most fulfilled, or most satisfied? What makes you most anxious, frustrated, or drained? What do these feelings tell you about your day-to-day choices? Describe how you could adjust your mindset, or make different choices, to feel better about how you spend your time.

REAL-LIFE WRITING

Examine two areas of academic specialty. Use your course catalog to identify two academic areas that look interesting. Write a short report comparing and contrasting the majors or concentrations in these areas, being sure to note GPA requirements, number of courses, relevance to career areas, campus locations, "feel" of the department offices, other requirements, and any other relevant characteristics. Conclude your report with observations about how this comparison and evaluation process has refined your thinking.

Personal Portfolio

Prepare for Career Success

EXPLORE CAREER GOALS THROUGH PERSONAL MISSION

21st Century Learning Building Blocks

- Initiative and Self-Direction
- Creativity and Innovation
- Productivity and Accountability

Complete the following in your electronic portfolio or separately on paper.

No matter what employment goals you ultimately pursue, a successful career will be grounded in your personal mission in one or more ways.

First, write a draft of your personal mission. Refer to the list on page 33 to remind yourself of the elements of a personal mission statement. Use these questions to get you thinking:

1. You are at your retirement dinner. You have had an esteemed career in your chosen field. Your best friend stands up and talks about the five aspects of your character that have taken you to the top. What do you think they are?
2. You are preparing for a late-in-life job change. Updating your resumé, you need to list your contributions and achievements. What would you like them to be?
3. You have been told that you have 1 year to live. With family or close friends, you talk about the values that mean the most to you. Based on that discussion, how do you want to spend your time in this last year? Which choices will reflect what is most important to you?

After you have a personal mission statement to provide vision and motivation, take some time to think more specifically about your working life. Spend 15 minutes brainstorming everything that you wish you could be, do, have, or experience in your career 10 years from now—the skills you want to have, money you want to earn, benefits, experiences, travel, anything you can think of. List your wishes, draw them, depict them using cutouts from magazines, or combine ideas—whatever you like best.

Now, group your wishes in order of priority. On paper or computer pages labeled Priority 1, Priority 2, and Priority 3, write each wish where it fits, with Priority 1 being the most important, Priority 2 the second most important, and Priority 3 the third.

Look at your priority lists. What do they tell you about what is most important to you? What fits into your personal mission, and what doesn't? Circle or highlight three high-priority wishes that mesh with your personal mission. For each, write down one action step you may have to take soon to make it come true.

You may want to look back at these materials at the end of the term to see what changes may have taken place in your priorities.

Social Networking

IDENTIFY YOURSELF

Sign in to your LinkedIn account and begin to build your profile. Click on "Edit My Profile" and then click on the Edit mark next to your name. Then fill in or edit this basic information:

- First and last name
- Display name (how you want it to appear to others viewing your profile)
- Professional "Headline"—how you identify yourself now (If you are not currently working, you may choose to identify yourself as a student and perhaps include your area of study.)
- Country and zip code
- Industry (if you are working)

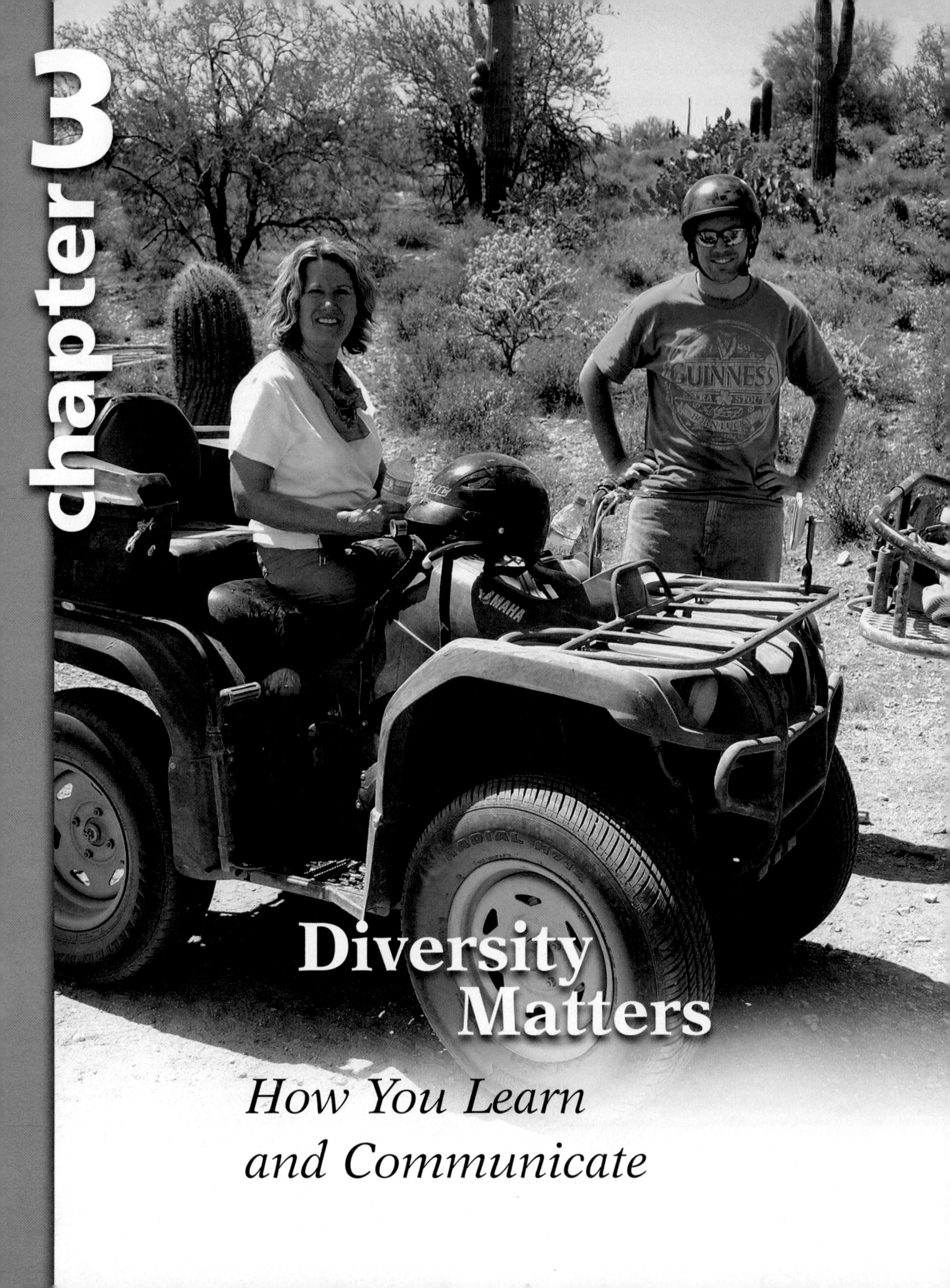

Diversity Matters

*How You Learn
and Communicate*

What Would You Do?

Think about this problem as you read, and consider how you would approach it. This chapter builds your awareness of diversity both visible and invisible. You will identify how you learn and how to use that information to make work and study choices, explore how to relate to others in a culturally competent way, and practice communication strategies that will help you build successful relationships in school and elsewhere.

*A*s a college student, author Joyce Bishop was confused by her spotty record—doing well in some classes but feeling totally lost in others, especially those that were lecture-based. She couldn't make sense of what she was hearing when she wasn't familiar with the information. If she read the material ahead of time, she could make visual pictures in her mind and look up concepts. This helped, but there wasn't often time for it.

Joyce also had trouble in small classes, because she heard voices around her as much as she heard the instructor. She would borrow classmates' notes in exchange for typing their term papers. The notes and the typing helped her to retain information. Ultimately, finding that science classes were somewhat less difficult than others, she majored in biology and managed to graduate.

Twelve years later, pursuing a master's in public health, Joyce was having trouble reading and her eye doctor was concerned about the stress it put on her eyes. He sent her to a center that usually tests small children for learning disabilities. The therapist who tested her determined that Joyce processed language on a fourth-grade level, a condition that had not changed in her adult life. Guessing that she had not made it past the tenth grade, the therapist

was shocked to hear that she was completing her master's degree. Joyce was beginning to understand what was behind so many years of mediocre grades and an intense struggle to learn. (To be continued . . .)

You don't have to have a learning disability to face learning challenges. For Joyce, doing adventure sports like riding ATVs is a way to grow from taking a risk just as she did when working through her disability. You'll learn more about Joyce, and revisit her situation, within the chapter.

In this chapter, you'll explore answers to these questions:

> What tools can help you assess how you learn and interact with others? p. 58

> How can you use your self-knowledge? p. 63

> How can you identify and manage learning disabilities? p. 72

> How can you develop cultural competence? p. 75

> How can you communicate effectively? p. 80

> How do you make the most of personal relationships? p. 84

ANALYTICAL   CREATIVE   PRACTICAL

STATUS *Check*

▶ **How aware are you of how you learn and interact with others?**

"Successfully intelligent people figure out their strengths and their weaknesses, and then find ways to capitalize on their strengths—make the most of what they do well—and to correct for or remedy their weaknesses—find ways around what they don't do well, or make themselves good enough to get by."

–Robert Sternberg

LEARNING STYLE
A particular way in which the mind receives and processes information.

What tools can help you assess how you learn and interact *with others?*

Every person is born with a unique **learning style** and particular levels of ability and potential in different areas. This combines with effort and environment to create a "recipe" for what you can achieve. Part of that recipe is the way you perceive your strengths and challenges, which come from many different sources and start in childhood.

Labels, from yourself and others, influence your ability to set and achieve goals. The danger in accepting a label as truth, as Sternberg did as a child, is that it can put you in a fixed mindset and limit your potential. However, you are not simply stuck with what you've been given. Picture a bag of rubber bands of different sizes. Some are thick, and some are thin; some are long, and some are short—*but all of them can stretch*. With effort and focus, you can grow whatever raw material you have at the start, perhaps beyond the natural gifts of someone who doesn't try. Joyce's story illustrates how far effort can stretch a person's natural abilities.

How assessments can help

The assessments you take in this chapter will help you both learn about yourself and make choices that maximize your ability to perform in school and beyond.

■ *Assessments help you learn about yourself.* With questions that get you thinking actively about your strengths, challenges, and learning preferences, assessments help you build self-knowledge and metacognition (the ability to think about how you think). As you search for answers, you are gathering important information about yourself that will help you define your rubber band and get ready to stretch it to its limit. (Learning disabilities—diagnosed, specific issues different from the learning challenges that all students face—are discussed later in the chapter.)

■ *Assessments help you make choices.* Self-knowledge gives you tools to choose how you respond to circumstances. With what you learn about yourself, you can more effectively analyze courses, study environments, and work group partners to come up with ideas and make practical choices about what, how, and where to study. The material after the assessments will help you make specific choices about what you do in class, during study time, and in the workplace.

Remember: An assessment is simply a snapshot of where you are at a given moment. There are no "right" answers, no "best" scores. Furthermore, as you gain experience, build skills, and learn more, your learning patterns are apt to change over time. You may want to take the assessments again in the future to see whether your results are different.

This chapter examines two assessments in depth. The first—Multiple Pathways to Learning—is a learning preferences assessment focusing on eight areas of potential, based on Howard Gardner's multiple intelligences (or MI) theory. The second—the Personality Spectrum—is a personality type assessment based on the Myers-Briggs Type Indicator that helps you evaluate how you react to people and situations. Following each assessment is information about the typical traits of each (intelligence) or personality spectrum dimension. As you will see from your scores, you have abilities in all areas, though some are more developed than others.

> INTELLIGENCE
> As defined by H. Gardner,
> an ability to solve problems
> or create products that are
> of value in a culture.

Assess your multiple intelligences with Pathways to Learning

In 1983, Howard Gardner changed the way people perceive intelligence and learning with his theory of multiple intelligences. Like Robert Sternberg, Gardner believes that the traditional view of intelligence—based on mathematical, logical, and verbal measurements comprising an "intelligence quotient" or IQ—does not comprehensively reflect the spectrum of human ability.

Gardner's research led him to believe that humans possess eight unique "intelligences," or areas of ability. These include the aptitudes traditionally associated with the term "intelligence"—logic and verbal skills—but go beyond, to encompass a wide range of (potentials) of the human brain.[1] These intelligences almost never function in isolation. You will almost always use several for any significant role or task.[2]

> POTENTIALS
> Abilities that may be
> developed.

Look at Key 3.1 for descriptions of each intelligence along with examples of people who have unusually high levels of ability in each intelligence. Different cultures value different abilities and therefore emphasize different intelligences. In Tibet, mountain dwellers prize the bodily-kinesthetic ability of a top-notch Himalayan guide. In Detroit, automakers appreciate the visual-spatial talents of

EACH INTELLIGENCE IS LINKED TO
SPECIFIC ABILITIES

INTELLIGENCE	DESCRIPTION	HIGH-ACHIEVING EXAMPLE
Verbal-Linguistic	Ability to communicate through language; listening, reading, writing, speaking	• Author J. K. Rowling • Orator and president Barack Obama
Logical-Mathematical	Ability to understand logical reasoning and problem solving; math, science, patterns, sequences	• Physicist Stephen Hawking • Mathematician Svetlana Jitomirskaya
Bodily-Kinesthetic	Ability to use the physical body skillfully and to take in knowledge through bodily sensation; coordination, working with hands	• Gymnast Nastia Liukin • Survivalist Bear Gryllis
Visual-Spatial	Ability to understand spatial relationships and to perceive and create images; visual art, graphic design, charts and maps	• Artist Walt Disney • Designer Stella McCartney
Interpersonal	Ability to relate to others, noticing their moods, motivations, and feelings; social activity, cooperative learning, teamwork	• Media personality Ellen DeGeneres • Former Secretary of State Colin Powell
Intrapersonal	Ability to understand one's own behavior and feelings; self-awareness, independence, time spent alone	• Animal researcher Jane Goodall • Philosopher Friedrich Nietzsche
Musical	Ability to comprehend and create meaningful sound; sensitivity to music and musical patterns	• Singer and musician Alicia Keys • Composer Andrew Lloyd Webber
Naturalist	Ability to identify, distinguish, categorize, and classify species or items, often incorporating high interest in elements of the natural environment	• Social activist Wanagri Maathai • Bird cataloger John James Audubon

a master car designer. Your goal is to identify what your levels are and to work your strongest intelligences to your advantage.

Gardner believes that all people possess some capacity in each intelligence and that every person has developed some intelligences more fully than others. When you find a task or subject easy, you are probably using a more fully developed intelligence. When you have trouble, you may be using a less developed intelligence.[3] Furthermore, Gardner believes your levels of development in the eight intelligences can grow or recede depending on efforts and experiences.

A related self-assessment that you may have heard of, or have already taken, is the VAK or VARK questionnaire. VAK/VARK assesses learning preferences in three (or four) areas: visual, auditory, (read/write), and kinesthetic. The multiple intelligences (MI) assessment is this book's choice because it incorporates and expands elements of VAK/VARK, giving you a more comprehensive picture of your abilities. For further information about VAK/VARK, go to www.vark-learn.com or search online using the keywords "VAK assessment."

Use the Multiple Pathways to Learning assessment to determine where you are right now in the eight intelligence areas. Then look at Key 3.2 immediately following the assessment to identify specific skills associated with each area. Finally, the Multiple Intelligence Strategies grids in Chapters 5 through 9 will help you apply your learning styles knowledge to key college success skills and to specific areas of study.

Assess your style of interaction with the Personality Spectrum

Personality assessments help you understand how you respond to the world around you, including people, work, and school. They also can help guide you as you explore majors and careers.

The concept of dividing human beings into four basic "personality types," as in the Personality Spectrum, goes as far back as Aristotle and Hippocrates, ancient Greek philosophers, and was further defined by psychologist Carl Jung early in the 20th century. Katharine Briggs and her daughter, Isabel Briggs Myers, developed an assessment based on Jung's typology, called the Myers-Briggs Type Inventory or MBTI (information is available online at www.myersbriggs.org). One of the most widely used personality inventories in the world, it creates sixteen possible types from the four dimensions. David Keirsey and Marilyn Bates later condensed the MBTI types into four temperaments, creating the Keirsey Sorter (found at www.keirsey.com).

When author Joyce Bishop developed the Personality Spectrum assessment in this chapter, she adapted and simplified the Keirsey Sorter and MBTI material into four personality types—Thinker, Organizer, Giver, and Adventurer. Like the assessments on which it is based, the Personality Spectrum helps you identify the kinds of interactions that are most, and least, comfortable for you. As with the multiple intelligences, these results may change over time as you experience new things, change, and continue to learn. Key 3.3, on page 67, shows skills characteristic of each personality type.

Students drawn to the sciences may find that they have strengths in logical-mathematical or naturalistic thinking.
© iStockPhoto

MULTIPLE PATHWAYS TO LEARNING ASSESSMENT

Each intelligence has a set of numbered statements. Consider each statement on its own. Then, on a scale from 1 (lowest) to 4 (highest), rate how closely it matches who you are right now and write that number on the line next to the statement. Finally, total each set of six questions.

1. rarely   2. sometimes   3. usually   4. always

1. ____ I enjoy physical activities.

2. ____ I am uncomfortable sitting still.

3. ____ I prefer to learn through doing.

4. ____ When sitting I move my legs or hands.

5. ____ I enjoy working with my hands.

6. ____ I like to pace when I'm thinking or studying.

____ **TOTAL for BODILY-KINESTHETIC**

1. ____ I use maps easily.

2. ____ I draw pictures/diagrams when explaining ideas.

3. ____ I can assemble items easily from diagrams.

4. ____ I enjoy drawing or photography.

5. ____ I do not like to read long paragraphs.

6. ____ I prefer a drawn map over written directions.

____ **TOTAL for VISUAL-SPATIAL**

1. ____ I listen to music.

2. ____ I move my fingers or feet when I hear music.

3. ____ I have good rhythm.

4. ____ I like to sing along with music.

5. ____ People have said I have musical talent.

6. ____ I like to express my ideas through music.

____ **TOTAL for MUSICAL**

1. ____ I like doing a project with other people.

2. ____ People come to me to help settle conflicts.

3. ____ I like to spend time with friends.

4. ____ I am good at understanding people.

5. ____ I am good at making people feel comfortable.

6. ____ I enjoy helping others.

____ **TOTAL for INTERPERSONAL**

1. ____ I enjoy telling stories.

2. ____ I like to write.

3. ____ I like to read.

4. ____ I express myself clearly.

5. ____ I am good at negotiating.

6. ____ I like to discuss topics that interest me.

____ **TOTAL for VERBAL-LINGUISTIC**

1. ____ I like math in school.

2. ____ I like science.

3. ____ I problem-solve well.

4. ____ I question how things work.

5. ____ I enjoy planning or designing something new.

6. ____ I am able to fix things.

____ **TOTAL for LOGICAL–MATHEMATICAL**

1. ____ I need quiet time to think.

2. ____ I think about issues before I want to talk.

3. ____ I am interested in self-improvement.

4. ____ I understand my thoughts and feelings.

5. ____ I know what I want out of life.

6. ____ I prefer to work on projects alone.

____ **TOTAL for INTRAPERSONAL**

1. ____ I like to think about how things, ideas, or people fit into categories.

2. ____ I enjoy studying plants, animals, or oceans.

3. ____ I tend to see how things relate to, or are distinct from, one another.

4. ____ I think about having a career in the natural sciences.

5. ____ As a child I often played with bugs and leaves.

6. ____ I like to investigate the natural world around me.

____ **TOTAL for NATURALISTIC**

Source: Developed by Joyce Bishop, PhD, Golden West College, Huntington Beach, CA. Based on Howard Gardner, *Frames of Mind: The Theory of Multiple Intelligences,* New York: Harper Collins, 1993.

MULTIPLE PATHWAYS TO LEARNING SCORING GRID

For each intelligence, shade the box in the row that corresponds with the range where your score falls. For example, if you scored 17 in Bodily-Kinesthetic intelligence, you would shade the middle box in that row; if you scored a 13 in visual-spatial, you would shade the last box in that row. When you have shaded one box for each row, you will see a "map" of your range of development at a glance.

A score of 20–24 indicates a high level of development in that particular type of intelligence, 14–19 a moderate level, and below 14 an underdeveloped intelligence.

	20–24 (HIGHLY DEVELOPED)	14–19 (MODERATELY DEVELOPED)	BELOW 14 (UNDERDEVELOPED)
Bodily-Kinesthetic			
Visual-Spatial			
Verbal-Linguistic			
Logical-Mathematical			
Musical			
Interpersonal			
Intrapersonal			
Naturalistic			

How can you use your self-knowledge?

As you complete the assessments, you are developing a clearer picture of who you are and how you interact with others. You can use this new picture to choose effective strategies for class, study time, the workplace, or technology.

Classroom Choices

Although you cannot always choose your courses or instructors, you *can* choose how you interact with your instructor and function in the classroom. It is impossible for instructors to tailor classroom presentation to 15, 40, or 300 unique learners. As a result, you may find yourself in a great learning situation with one teacher and in a complete mismatch with another. Sometimes, the way the class is structured can have more of an effect on your success than the subject matter; for example, a strong interpersonal learner who has trouble with writing may do well in a composition course that emphasizes group work.

After several class meetings, you should be able to assess each instructor's dominant teaching styles (see Key 3.4, p. 67) and figure out how to maximize your learning. As with learning styles, most instructors will demonstrate some combination of styles.

Although styles vary and instructors may combine styles, the word-focused lecture is still most common. For this reason, the

PARTICULAR **ABILITIES AND SKILLS** ARE ASSOCIATED WITH EACH INTELLIGENCE

Verbal-Linguistic		• Remembering terms easily • Mastering a foreign language • Using writing or speech to convince someone to do or believe something
Musical-Rhythmic	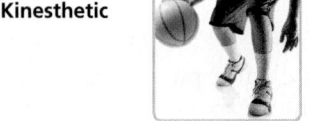	• Sensing tonal qualities • Being sensitive to sounds and rhythms in music and in spoken language • Using an understanding of musical patterns to hear music
Logical-Mathematical		• Recognizing abstract patterns • Using facts to support an idea and generating ideas based on evidence • Reasoning scientifically (formulating and testing a hypothesis)
Visual-Spatial		• Recognizing relationships between objects • Representing something graphically • Manipulating images
Bodily-Kinesthetic		• Strong mind–body connection • Controlling and coordinating body movement • Using the body to create products or express emotion
Intrapersonal		• Accessing one's internal emotions • Understanding feelings and using them to guide behavior • Understanding self in relation to others
Interpersonal		• Seeing things from others' perspectives • Noticing moods, intentions, and temperaments of others • Gauging the most effective way to work with individual group members
Naturalistic		• Ability to categorize something as a member of a group or species • Understanding of relationships among natural organisms • Deep comfort with, and respect for, the natural world

PERSONALITY SPECTRUM ASSESSMENT

STEP 1 Rank-order all four responses to each question from most like you (4) to least like you (1) so that for each question you use the numbers 1, 2, 3, and 4 one time each. Place numbers in the boxes next to the responses.

4. most like me   **3. more like me**   **2. less like me**   **1. least like me**

1. I like instructors who
   a. ___ tell me exactly what is expected of me.
   b. ___ make learning active and exciting.
   c. ___ maintain a safe and supportive classroom.
   d. ___ challenge me to think at higher levels.

2. I learn best when the material is
   a. ___ well organized.
   b. ___ something I can do hands-on.
   c. ___ about understanding and improving the human condition.
   d. ___ intellectually challenging.

3. A high priority in my life is to
   a. ___ keep my commitments.
   b. ___ experience as much of life as possible.
   c. ___ make a difference in the lives of others.
   d. ___ understand how things work.

4. Other people think of me as
   a. ___ dependable and loyal.
   b. ___ dynamic and creative.
   c. ___ caring and honest.
   d. ___ intelligent and inventive.

5. When I experience stress I would most likely
   a. ___ do something to help me feel more in control of my life.
   b. ___ do something physical and daring.
   c. ___ talk with a friend.
   d. ___ go off by myself and think about my situation.

6. I would probably not be close friends with someone who is
   a. ___ irresponsible.
   b. ___ unwilling to try new things.
   c. ___ selfish and unkind to others.
   d. ___ an illogical thinker.

7. My vacations could be described as
   a. ___ traditional.
   b. ___ adventuresome.
   c. ___ pleasing to others.
   d. ___ a new learning experience.

8. One word that best describes me is
   a. ___ sensible.
   b. ___ spontaneous.
   c. ___ giving.
   d. ___ analytical.

STEP 2 Add up the total points for each letter.

TOTAL FOR   a. ___ Organizer   b. ___ Adventurer   c. ___ Giver   d. ___ Thinker

STEP 3 Plot these numbers on the brain diagram on page 66.

---

traditional college classroom is generally a happy home for the verbal or logical learner and the Thinker and the Organizer. However, many students need to experience other modes in order to learn effectively. What can you do when your preferences don't match up with how your instructor teaches? Here are three suggestions:

▶ *Play to your strengths.* For example, a musical learner whose instructor delivers material in a random way might record lecture highlights digitally and listen to them on an MP3 player (be sure to see whether your instructor and school permit recording).

SCORING DIAGRAM FOR PERSONALITY SPECTRUM

Write your scores from page 65 in the four squares just outside the brain diagram—Thinker score at top left, Giver score at top right, Organizer score at bottom left, and Adventurer score at bottom right.

     Each square has a line of numbers that go from the square to the center of the diagram. For each of your four scores, place a dot on the appropriate number in the line near that square. For example, if you scored 15 in the Giver spectrum, you would place a dot between the 14 and 16 in the upper right-hand line of numbers. If you scored a 26 in the Organizer spectrum, you would place a dot on the 26 in the lower left-hand line of numbers.

THINKER

Technical
Scientific
Mathematical
Dispassionate
Rational
Analytical
Logical
Problem Solving
Theoretical
Intellectual
Objective
Quantitative
Explicit
Realistic
Literal
Precise
Formal

ORGANIZER

Tactical
Planning
Detailed
Practical
Confident
Predictable
Controlled
Dependable
Systematic
Sequential
Structured
Administrative
Procedural
Organized
Conservative
Safekeeping
Disciplined

Connect the four dots to make a four-sided shape. If you like, shade the four sections inside the shape using four different colors.

For the Personality Spectrum,
26–36 indicates a strong tendency in that dimension,
14–25 a moderate tendency,
and below 14 a minimal tendency.

Source for brain diagram: Understanding Psychology, 3rd ed., by Charles G. Morris, © 1996. Reproduced by permission of Pearson Education, Inc./Prentice Hall, Inc.

GIVER

Interpersonal
Emotional
Caring
Sociable
Giving
Spiritual
Musical
Romantic
Feeling
Peacemaker
Trusting
Adaptable
Passionate
Harmonious
Idealistic
Talkative
Honest

ADVENTURER

Active
Visual
Risking
Original
Artistic
Spatial
Skillful
Impulsive
Metaphoric
Experimental
Divergent
Fast-paced
Simultaneous
Competitive
Imaginative
Open-minded
Adventuresome

PARTICULAR **ABILITIES AND SKILLS** ARE ASSOCIATED WITH EACH PERSONALITY SPECTRUM DIMENSION

Thinker

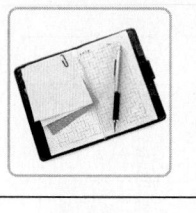

- Solving problems
- Developing models and systems
- Analytical and abstract thinking

Organizer

- Responsibility, reliability
- Neatness, organization, attention to detail
- Comprehensive follow-through on tasks

Giver

- Successful, close relationships
- Making a difference in the world
- Negotiation; promoting peace

Adventurer

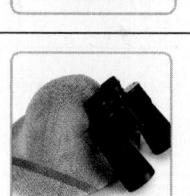

- Courage and daring
- Hands-on problem solving
- Active and spontaneous style

INSTRUCTORS OFTEN PREFER ONE OR MORE **TEACHING STYLES**

TEACHING STYLE	WHAT TO EXPECT IN CLASS
Lecture, verbal focus	Instructor speaks to the class for the entire period, with little class interaction. Lesson is taught primarily through words, either spoken or written on the board, on PowerPoints, handouts, or text.
Lecture with group discussion	Instructor presents material but encourages class discussion.
Small groups	Instructor presents material and then breaks class into small groups for discussion or project work.
Visual focus	Instructor uses visual elements such as PowerPoint slides, diagrams, photographs, drawings, transparencies, and videos.
Logical presentation	Instructor organizes material in a logical sequence, such as by steps, time, or importance.
Random presentation	Instructor tackles topics in no particular order and may jump around a lot or digress.
Conceptual presentation	Instructor spends the majority of time on the big picture, focusing on abstract concepts and umbrella ideas.
Detailed presentation	Instructor spends the majority of time, after introducing ideas, on the details and facts that underlie them.
Hands-on presentation	Instructor uses demonstrations, experiments, props, and class activities to show key points.

Maximize Your
Classroom Experience

Using what you know about yourself as a learner and about your instructors' teaching styles this term, decide which classroom situation is the most challenging for you. Use this exercise to come up with practical ideas about how to handle the situation.

Course: _____   Instructor style: _____

Describe the problem: _____

_____

Name three possible actions you can take to improve the situation:

1. _____

_____

2. _____

_____

3. _____

_____

Finally, choose one action and put it to practical use. Briefly note what happened: Were there improvements as a result?

_____

_____

_____

▶ *Work to strengthen weaker areas*. An Organizer, studying for a test from notes delivered by an instructor with a random presentation, could organize material using tables and timelines.

▶ *Ask your instructor for help*. If you are having trouble with coursework, communicate with your instructor or teaching assistant through e-mail or during office hours. This is especially important in large lectures where you are anonymous unless you speak up. A visual learner, for example, might ask the instructor to recommend graphs, figures, or videos that illustrate the lecture.

No instructor of a diverse group of learners can provide exactly what each one needs. However, adjusting to instructors' teaching styles builds flexibility that you need for career and life success. Just as you can't hand-pick your instructors, you will rarely, if ever, be able to choose your work colleagues or their ways of working or interacting with others.

Study Choices

Start now to use what you have learned about yourself to choose the best study techniques. For example, if you tend to learn successfully from a

student profile

Jad El-Adaimi
California Polytechnic State University, San Luis Obispo, California

About me:
I went to school in Lebanon. Then I came to Cupertino, California, where I went to De Anza College and attained my AS degree in biological sciences. After two years and a degree I transferred to Cal Poly in San Luis Obispo and graduated in June of 2010 with a B.S. in molecular and cellular biology. I started my master's program in September of 2010.

How I faced a challenge:
I grew up in Lebanon, where almost everyone was Lebanese. I was open and friendly with everyone, but had never lived with those from other cultures. When I came to college in the U.S. that all changed. I met people from around the world. I worked and studied with people from different backgrounds. In the beginning I felt disconnected and tried finding friends from my regional area. This did not help me adjust, but instead made me feel homesick. As soon as I started broadening my perspective of cultures and communicating with everyone, everything changed. We learn from everyone around us. I started being less secluded and more outgoing and close with people from all over the U.S. and the world, which included learning a few words from each language, eating their food, celebrating some of their holidays, and respecting their traditions. I think that broadening my communication allowed me to adjust to different cultures and people and helped me transfer successfully from De Anza to Cal Poly.

What will help me in the workplace:
We build our personality and experiences through the people around us. When you start a new job you will be meeting new people. Learn to adjust to everyone and accept them for who they are within your limits. This way you can do your work at the highest standard and still maintain a social aspect and enjoy your workplace. Accepting people or at least adjusting to them in some manner will help in any situation.

---

linear, logical presentation, you can look for order (for example, a *chronology*—information organized sequentially according to event dates—or a problem–solution structure) as you review notes. If you are strong in interpersonal intelligence, you can try to work in study groups whenever possible.

When faced with a task that challenges your weaknesses, use strategies that boost your ability. For example, if you are an Adventurer who does *not* respond well to linear information, you can apply your strengths to the material—for example, through a hands-on approach. Or you can focus on developing your area of weakness—try skills that work well for Thinker-dominant learners.

When you study with others, you and the entire group will be more successful if you understand the different learning styles in the group, as in the following examples.

▶ An Interpersonal learner could take the lead in teaching material to others.
▶ An Organizer could coordinate the group schedule.
▶ A Naturalistic learner might organize facts into categories that solidify concepts.

Look at Keys 3.5 and 3.6 for study strategies that suit each intelligence and Personality Spectrum dimension. Because you have some level of ability in each area and because there will be times that you need to boost your ability in a weaker area, you may find useful suggestions under any of the headings. Try different techniques. You may be surprised at what is useful, as Joyce was about how typing helped her retain information.

Technology choices

Technology is everywhere these days. You see it in social settings as people communicate using e-mail, text messaging, and social networking sites on the Internet. It also plays a significant role in academic settings, where you may encounter any of the following:

▶ Instructors who require students to communicate via e-mail
▶ Courses that have their own websites where you can access the syllabus and connect with resources and classmates
▶ Textbooks that have corresponding websites that you can, or are required to, use to complete assignments that you e-mail to your instructor

For some with extensive know-how, technology comes easily. For everyone else, knowing their strengths and challenges as learners can help them make decisions about how to approach technology. Are you strong in the logical-mathematical intelligence or Thinker dimension? Working with an online tutorial may be a good choice. Are you an interpersonal learner? Find a tech-savvy classmate to help you get the hang of it. An Adventurer may want to just dive in and try out the features of a book or course website in a random way. Know yourself and make choices that can best help you demystify technology and get you up to speed.

Workplace choices

Knowing how you learn and interact with others will help you work more effectively and make better career planning choices. How can an employee or job candidate benefit from self-awareness?

Better performance and teamwork

When you understand your strengths, you can find ways to use them on the job more readily. For tasks that take you out of your areas of strength, you will be more able to compensate and get help. In addition, you will be better able to work with others effectively. For example, a team leader might offer an intrapersonal team member the chance to take material home to think about before a meeting.

Add a new dimension to your experience of a course, and your learning, by talking to your instructor outside of class time.
© ThinkStock

CHOOSE STUDY TECHNIQUES TO
MAXIMIZE EACH INTELLIGENCE

Verbal-Linguistic		• Read text; highlight selectively • Use a computer to retype and summarize notes • Outline chapters • Recite information or write scripts/debates
Musical-Rhythmic		• Create rhythms out of words • Beat out rhythms with hand or stick while reciting concepts • Write songs/raps that help you learn concepts • Write out study material to fit into a wordless tune you have on a CD or MP3 player; chant or sing the material along with the tune as you listen
Logical-Mathematical		• Organize material logically; if it suits the topic, use a spreadsheet program • Explain material sequentially to someone • Develop systems and find patterns • Analyze and evaluate information
Visual-Spatial		• Develop graphic organizers for new material • Draw mind maps/think links • Use a computer to develop charts and tables • Use color in notes to organize
Bodily-Kinesthetic		• Move while you learn; pace and recite • Rewrite or retype notes to engage "muscle memory" • Design and play games to learn material • Act out scripts of material
Intrapersonal		• Reflect on personal meaning of information • Keep a journal • Study in quiet areas • Imagine essays or experiments before beginning
Interpersonal		• Study in a group • As you study, discuss information over the phone or send instant messages • Teach someone else the material • Make time to discuss assignments and tests with your instructor
Naturalistic		• Break down information into categories • Look for ways in which items fit or don't fit together • Look for relationships among ideas, events, facts • Study in a natural setting if it helps you to focus

CHOOSE STUDY TECHNIQUES TO
MAXIMIZE EACH PERSONALITY
SPECTRUM DIMENSION

Key 3.6

Thinker		• Convert material into logical charts, flow diagrams, and outlines • Reflect independently on new information • Learn through problem solving • Design new ways of approaching material or problems
Organizer	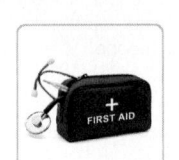	• Define tasks in concrete terms • Use a planner to schedule tasks and dates • Organize material by rewriting and summarizing class or text notes • Create, or look for, a well-structured study environment
Giver		• Study with others in person, on the phone, or using instant messages • Teach material to others • Seek out tasks, groups, and subjects that involve helping people • Connect with instructors, advisors, and tutors
Adventurer	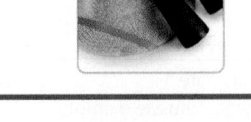	• Look for environments or courses that encourage nontraditional approaches • Find hands-on ways to learn • Use or develop games or puzzles to help memorize terms • Fight boredom by asking to do something extra or perform a task in a more active way

Better career planning

Exploring ways to use your strengths in school will help you make better choices about what jobs or careers will suit you. For most college students, **internships** and majors are more immediate steps on the road to a career. A strength in one or more intelligences might lead you to internships and majors that make sense for you.

Key 3.7 links majors and internships to the eight intelligences. This list is by no means complete; rather, it represents only a fraction of the available opportunities. Use what you see here to inspire thought and spur investigation.

Although all students have areas of strength and weakness, challenges diagnosed as learning disabilities are more significant. These merit specific attention. Focused assistance can help students with learning disabilities manage their conditions and excel in school.

INTERNSHIPS
Temporary work programs in which a student can gain supervised practical experience in a job and career area.

How can you **identify and manage** *learning disabilities?*

The information in this section will help you understand learning disabilities as well as the tools to manage their negative effects.

MULTIPLE INTELLIGENCES MAY OPEN DOORS TO **MAJORS AND INTERNSHIPS**

MULTIPLE INTELLIGENCE	CONSIDER MAJORING IN	THINK ABOUT AN INTERNSHIP AT A ...
Bodily-Kinesthetic	• Massage or physical therapy • Kinesiology • Construction engineering • Sports medicine • Dance or theater	• Sports physician's office • Physical or massage therapy center • Construction company • Dance studio or theater company • Athletic club
Intrapersonal	• Psychology • Finance • Computer science • Biology • Philosophy	• Accounting firm • Biology lab • Pharmaceutical company • Publishing house • Computer or Internet company
Interpersonal	• Education • Public relations • Nursing • Business • Hotel/restaurant management	• Hotel or restaurant • Social service agency • Public relations firm • Human resources department • Charter school
Naturalistic	• Geology • Zoology • Atmospheric sciences • Agriculture • Environmental law	• Museum • National park • Environmental law firm • Zoo • Geological research firm
Musical	• Music • Music theory • Voice • Composition • Performing arts	• Performance hall • Radio station • Record label or recording studio • Children's music camp • Orchestra or opera company
Logical-Mathematical	• Math • Physics • Economics • Banking/finance • Computer science	• Law firm • Consulting firm • Bank • Information technology company • Research lab
Verbal-Linguistic	• Communications • Marketing • English/literature • Journalism • Foreign languages	• Newspaper or magazine • PR/marketing firm • Ad agency • Publishing house • Network TV affiliate
Visual-Spatial	• Architecture • Visual arts • Multimedia designs • Photography • Art history	• Photo or art studio • Multimedia design firm • Architecture firm • Interior design firm • Art gallery

Identifying a learning disability

The National Center for Learning Disabilities (NCLD) defines learning disabilities as neurological disorders that interfere with one's ability to store, process, and produce information.[4] They do *not* include mental retardation, autism, behavioral disorders, impaired vision, hearing loss, or other physical disabilities. Nor do they include attention deficit disorder and attention deficit hyperactivity disorder, although these problems may accompany learning disabilities.[5] Often running in families, these are lifelong conditions; however, specific strategies can help manage and even overcome areas of weakness.

How can you determine whether you should be evaluated for a learning disability? According to the NCLD, persistent problems in areas such as reading, writing, understanding heard language, math calculations, or following a schedule may indicate a learning disability.[6] More details on specific learning disabilities appear in Key 3.8. For an evaluation, contact your school's learning center or student health center for a referral to a licensed professional. Note that a professional diagnosis is required in order for a person with learning disabilities to receive federally funded aid.

WHAT ARE **LEARNING DISABILITIES** AND HOW DO YOU RECOGNIZE THEM?

Key 3.8

DISABILITY OR CONDITION	WHAT ARE THE SIGNS
Dyslexia and related reading disorders	Problems with reading (spelling, word sequencing, comprehension, and processing (translating written language to thought or the revers)
Dyscalculia (developmental arithmetic disorders)	Difficulties in recognizing numbers and symbols, memorizing facts, understanding abstract math concepts, and applying math to life skills (time management, handling money)
Developmental writing disorders	Difficulties in composing sentences, organizing a writing assignment, or translating thoughts coherently to the page
Handwriting disorders (dysgraphia)	Disorder characterized by writing disabilities, including distorted or incorrect language, inappropriately sized and spaced letters, or wrong or misspelled words
Speech and language disorders	Problems with producing speech sounds, using spoken language to communicate, and/or understanding what others say
LD-related social issues	Problems in recognizing facial or vocal cues from others, controlling verbal and physical impulsivity, and respecting others' personal space
LD-related organizational issues	Difficulties in scheduling and in organizing personal, academic, and work-related materials

Source: LD Online: LD Basics, www.ncld.org/content/view/445/389/, © 2009.

Managing a learning disability

If you are diagnosed with a learning disability, valuable information is available that took Joyce until graduate school to obtain. Maximize your ability to learn by managing your disability.

▶ *Find information about your disability*. Search the library and the Internet—try NCLD at www.ncld.org or LD Online at www.ldonline.org—or call NCLD at 1-888-575-7373. If you have an Individualized Education Program (IEP)—a document describing your disability and recommended strategies—read it and make sure you understand the provisions.

▶ *Seek assistance from your school*. Speak with your advisor about getting a referral to the counselor who can help you get specific accommodations in your classes. Services mandated by law for students who are learning disabled include extended time on tests, note-taking assistance, and assistive technology devices (MP3 players, computers). Other services may be offered, such as tutoring, study skills assistance, and counseling.

▶ *Be a dedicated student*. Show up on time and pay attention in class. Read assignments before class. Sit where you can focus. Review notes soon after class. Spend extra time on assignments. Ask for help.

▶ *Build a positive attitude*. See your accomplishments in light of how far you have come. Rely on support from others, knowing that it will give you the best possible chance to succeed.

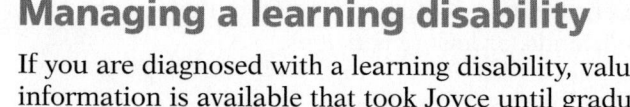

Change the CONVERSATION

Challenge yourself and your friends to ask—and answer—tough questions. Use the following to inspire discussion in pairs or groups.

▶ Do people perceive their own strengths accurately, or do you often see strengths in others that they don't believe they have?

▶ Has a point of difference—visible or invisible—ever kept you from connecting with someone? What made you hesitate? What might you gain from overcoming your hesitation?

▶ **CONSIDER THE CASE:** Not knowing about Joyce Bishop's learning disability, what would you have assumed as her instructor? What might an instructor assume about you that someone who knows you well—or even you yourself—may find inaccurate?

Being sensitive to your unique way of learning will benefit you in ways beyond your education and career. A better understanding of your learning strengths and preferences and personality traits will help you identify, appreciate, and adapt to the diversity among people.

How can you develop cultural competence?

The word *diversity* refers to differences *among* people (such as gender, skin color, ethnicity, physical characteristics, sexual orientation, beliefs and practices, and level of education) as well as differences *within* people (such as personality traits, learning style, and strengths and weaknesses—everything that makes an individual unique). In college, at work, and as you go about your daily life you are likely to meet people who reflect America's growing diversity, including the following:

▶ Bi- or multiracial individuals
▶ People from families with more than one religious tradition
▶ Nonnative English speakers who may have emigrated from outside the United States
▶ Students older than the "traditional" 18- to 22-year-old
▶ People living with various kinds of disabilities
▶ Gay, lesbian, bi, or transgender individuals

▶ People practicing different lifestyles—often expressed in the way they dress or their interests, friends, or leisure activities.

Interacting effectively with all kinds of people, which is crucial to your school and life success, is the goal of *cultural competence,* or the ability to understand and appreciate differences among people and adjust behavior in ways that enhance, rather than detract from, relationships and communication.[7] According to the National Center for Cultural Competence, developing cultural competence means taking the five specific actions that follow.[8]

Action 1: Value diversity

Valuing diversity means having a basic respect for the differences among people and an understanding of what is positive about those differences. No one likes everyone they meet, but if you value diversity, you treat people with tolerance and respect whether you like them or not, avoiding assumptions and granting them the right to think, feel, and believe without being judged. This attitude helps you to take emotionally intelligent actions as shown in Key 3.9.

It is important to note that valuing diversity is about more than just passive *tolerance* of the world around you (not causing conflict but not seeking harmony either). Moving further than that, toward *acceptance,* you value diversity by actively working toward teamwork and friendship, celebrating differences as an enriching part of life.

Key 3.9 APPROACH DIVERSITY WITH **EMOTIONAL INTELLIGENCE**

YOUR ROLE	SITUATION	CLOSED-MINDED RESPONSE	EMOTIONALLY INTELLIGENT RESPONSE
Fellow student	For an assignment, you are paired with a student old enough to be your mother.	You assume the student will be clueless about the modern world. You get ready to react against her preaching about how to do the assignment.	You acknowledge your feelings but try to get to know the student as an individual. You stay open to what you can learn from her experiences and realize you have things to offer as well.
Friend	You are invited to dinner at a friend's house. When he introduces you to his partner, you realize that he is gay.	Uncomfortable with the idea of two men in a relationship, you pretend you have a cell phone call and make an excuse to leave early. You avoid your friend after that.	You have dinner with the two men and make an effort to get to know more about them, individually and as a couple. You compare your immediate assumptions to what you learned about them at dinner.
Employee	Your new boss is of a different racial and cultural background than yours.	You assume that you and your new boss don't have much in common. Thinking he will be distant and uninterested in you, you already don't like him.	You acknowledge your stereotypes but work to set them aside so that you can build a relationship with your boss. You adapt to his style and make an effort to get to know him better.

Expand Your Perception of Diversity

The ability to respond to people as individuals requires that you become more aware of the diversity that is not always on the surface. Start by examining your own uniqueness. Brainstorm ten words or phrases that describe you. The challenge: Keep references to your ethnicity or appearance (brunette, Cuban American, wheelchair dependent, and so on) to a minimum, and fill the rest of the list with characteristics others can't see at a glance (laid-back, only child, 24 years old, drummer, marathoner, interpersonal learner, and so on).

1. _____
2. _____
3. _____
4. _____
5. _____

6. _____
7. _____
8. _____
9. _____
10. _____

Next, pair up with a classmate you do not know well. List on a separate sheet of paper any characteristics you know about him or her—chances are most of them will be visible. Then talk with the classmate, and both of you should round out your lists about each other with what you have discovered from your conversation. Finally, answer two questions.

What stands out to you about what you learned about your classmate, and why?

_____

_____

_____

What about your description of yourself would you like people to focus on more often, and why?

_____

_____

_____

Action 2: Identify and evaluate personal perceptions and attitudes

Bringing the first and second parts of emotional intelligence into play, you identify perceptions and attitudes by noticing your feelings about others and then you evaluate these attitudes by looking at the effect they have on you and on others. Many who value the *concept* of diversity experience negative feelings about the *reality* of diversity in their own lives. This disconnect often reveals prejudices and stereotypes.

Prejudice

Almost everyone has some level of **prejudice** that involves prejudging others, usually on the basis of characteristics such as gender, race, sexual orientation,

> PREJUDICE
> A preconceived judgment or opinion formed without just grounds or sufficient knowledge.

disability, and religion. People judge others without knowing anything about them because of factors like the following:

- *Influence of family and culture.* Children learn attitudes—including intolerance, superiority, and hate—from their parents, peers, and community.
- *Fear of differences.* It is human to fear and to make assumptions about the unfamiliar.
- *Experience.* One bad experience with a person of a particular race or religion may lead someone to condemn all people with the same background.

Stereotypes

STEREOTYPE ←
A standardized mental picture that represents an oversimplified opinion or uncritical judgment.

Prejudice is usually built on **stereotypes**—assumptions made, without proof or critical thinking, about the characteristics of a person or group of people, based on factors such as the following:

- *Desire for patterns and logic.* People often try to make sense of the world by using the labels, categories, and generalizations that stereotypes provide.
- *Media influences.* The more people see stereotypical images—the airhead beautiful blonde, the jolly fat man—the easier it is to believe that stereotypes are universal.
- *Laziness.* Labeling group members according to a characteristic they seem to have in common takes less work than asking questions about who each individual really is.

Stereotypes derail personal connections and block effective communication; pasting a label on a person makes it hard to see the real person underneath. Even stereotypes that seem "positive"—"Women are nurturing"; "Older people are wise"—may get in the way of perceiving uniqueness. To identify attitudes that hinder cultural competence, ask analytical questions about your own ideas and beliefs:

▶ How do I react to differences?
▶ What prejudices or stereotypes come to mind when I see people, in real life or the media, who are a different color than I am? From a different culture? Making different choices?
▶ Where do my prejudices and stereotypes come from?
▶ Are these prejudices fair? Are these stereotypes accurate?
▶ What harm can having these prejudices and believing these stereotypes cause?

With the knowledge you build as you answer these questions, move on to the next stage: looking carefully at what happens when people from different cultures interact.

Action 3: Be aware of what happens when cultures interact

Multicultural interaction among people can promote learning, build mutual respect, and broaden perspectives. However, as history has shown, such interaction can also produce problems caused by lack of understanding, prejudice, and stereotypes. At their mildest, these problems obstruct relationships and communication. At their worst, they result in discrimination and hate crimes.

Discrimination

Federal law says that you cannot be denied basic opportunities and rights because of your race, creed, color, age, gender, national or ethnic origin, religion, marital status, potential or actual pregnancy, or potential or actual illness or disability (unless the illness or disability prevents you from performing required tasks and unless accommodations are not possible). Despite these legal protections, **discrimination** is common and often appears on college campuses (a student or instructor, for example, may judge people according to their weight, accent, or body piercings).

> DISCRIMINATION Denying equal access to employment, educational, and housing opportunities or treating people as second-class citizens.

Hate crimes

When prejudice turns violent, it often manifests itself in hate crimes—actions motivated by a hatred of a specific characteristic thought to be possessed by the victim—usually based on race, ethnicity, or religious or sexual orientation. Because hate crime statistics include only reported incidents, they tell just a part of the story—many more crimes likely go unreported by victims fearful of what might happen if they contact authorities.

Focusing on the positive aspects of intercultural interaction starts with understanding the ideas and attitudes that lead to discrimination and hate crimes. With this awareness, you will be better prepared to push past negative possibilities and open your mind to positive outcomes. Dr. Martin Luther King Jr. believed that careful thinking could change attitudes.

> The tough-minded person always examines the facts before he reaches conclusions: in short, he postjudges. The tender-minded person reaches conclusions before he has examined the first fact; in short, he prejudges and is prejudiced. . . . There is little hope for us until we become tough minded enough to break loose from the shackles of prejudice, half-truths, and downright ignorance.[9]

Action 4: Build cultural knowledge

The successfully intelligent response to discrimination and hate, and the next step in your path toward cultural competence, is to gather knowledge about people who are different from you, including those you are likely to meet on campus. What are some practical ways to begin?

▶ *Read* newspapers, books, magazines, and websites that expose you to different perspectives.
▶ *Ask questions* of all kinds of people, about themselves and their traditions.
▶ *Observe* how people behave, what they eat and wear, how they interact with others.
▶ *Travel internationally* to unfamiliar places where you can experience different ways of living.
▶ *Travel locally* to equally unfamiliar but nearby places where you can learn something new.
▶ *Build friendships* with fellow students or co-workers you would not ordinarily approach.

Building knowledge also means exploring yourself. Talk with family, read, seek experiences that educate you about your own cultural heritage; then share what you know with others.

Action 5: Adapt to diverse cultures

Here's where you put cultural competence to work and bring in the final stage of emotional intelligence—taking action with the intent of bringing about a positive outcome. Choose actions that feel right to you, that cause no harm, and that make a difference, however small. Let the following suggestions inspire your own creative ideas about how you can relate to others.

▶ *Look past external characteristics.* If you meet a woman with a disability, get to know her. She may be an accounting major, a daughter, and a mother. She may love baseball, politics, and science fiction novels. These characteristics—not just her physical person—describe who she is.

▶ *Move beyond your feelings.* Engage your emotional intelligence to note what different people make you feel, and then examine the potential effect of those feelings. By working to move beyond feelings that could lead to harmful assumptions and negative outcomes, you will improve your chance for successful communication.

▶ *Put yourself in other people's shoes.* Ask questions about what other people feel, especially if there's a conflict. Offer friendship to someone new who is adjusting to your school community.

▶ *Adjust to cultural differences.* When you understand someone's way of being and put it into practice, you show respect and encourage communication. For example, if a study group member takes offense at a particular kind of language, avoid it when you meet.

▶ *Climb over language barriers.* When speaking with someone who is struggling with your language, choose words the person is likely to know, avoid slang expressions, be patient, and use body language to fill in what words can't say. Invite questions, and ask them yourself.

▶ *Help others.* There are countless ways to make a difference, from providing food or money to a neighbor in need to sending relief funds over the Internet to nations devastated by natural disasters. Every act, no matter how small, makes the world that much better.

▶ *Stand up against prejudice, discrimination, and hate.* When you hear a prejudiced remark, notice discrimination taking place, or suspect a hate crime, ask questions about how to encourage a move in the right direction. You may choose to make a comment or to get help by approaching an authority such as an instructor or dean. Support organizations that encourage tolerance.

▶ *Recognize that people everywhere have the same basic needs.* Everyone loves, thinks, hurts, hopes, fears, and plans. When you are trying to find common ground with diverse people, remember that you are united first through your essential humanity.

Just as there is diversity in skin color and ethnicity, there is also diversity in the way people communicate. Effective communication helps people of all cultures make connections.

How can you communicate effectively?

Spoken communication that is clear promotes success at school and work or in personal relationships. Thinking communicators analyze and adjust to communication styles, learn to give and receive criticism, analyze and make practical use of body language, and work through communication problems.

Adjust to communication styles

When you speak, your goal is for listeners to receive the message as you intended. Problems arise when one person has trouble "translating" a message coming from someone using a different communication style. Your knowledge of the Personality Spectrum will help you understand and analyze the ways diverse people communicate.

Identify your styles

Successful communication depends on understanding your personal style and becoming attuned to the styles of others. The following styles are associated with the four dimensions of the Personality Spectrum. No one style is better than another. As you read, keep in mind that these are generalizations—individuals will exhibit a range of variations within each style.

■ ***Thinkers communicate by focusing on facts and logic.*** As speakers, they tend to rely on logical analysis to communicate ideas and prefer quantitative concepts to conceptual or emotional approaches. As listeners, they often do best with logical messages. Thinkers may also need time to process what they have heard before responding. Written messages—on paper or via e-mail—are useful because creating them allows time to put ideas together logically.

■ ***Organizers communicate by focusing on structure and completeness.*** As speakers, they tend to deliver well-thought-out, structured messages that fit into an organized plan. As listeners, they often appreciate a well-organized message that defines practical tasks in concrete terms. As with Thinkers, a written format is often an effective form of communication to or from an Organizer.

■ ***Givers communicate by focusing on concern for others.*** As speakers, they tend to cultivate harmony, analyzing what will promote closeness in relationships. As listeners, they often appreciate messages that emphasize personal connection and address the emotional side of an issue. Whether speaking or listening, Givers often favor in-person talks over written messages.

■ ***Adventurers communicate by focusing on the present.*** As speakers, they focus on creative ideas, tending to convey a message as soon as the idea arises and then move on to the next activity. As listeners, they appreciate up-front, short, direct messages that don't get sidetracked. Like Givers, Adventurers tend to communicate and listen more effectively in person.

What is your style? Use this information as a jumping-off point for your self-exploration. Just as people tend to demonstrate characteristics from more than one Personality Spectrum dimension, communicators may demonstrate different styles.

Put your knowledge of communication style to use

Compare these communication styles to your own tendencies and also consider how others seem to respond to you. Your practical thinking skills can help you figure out what works well for you. However, you are only half of any communication picture. Your creative skills will help you shift your perspective to think about the other person's thoughts and feelings and what might work best interacting with that person's communication style.

■ *Speakers adjust to listeners.* Listeners may interpret messages in ways you never intended. Think about practical solutions to this kind of problem as you read the following interaction involving a Giver (instructor) and a Thinker (student):

> *Instructor:* "Your essay didn't communicate any sense of your personal voice."
>
> *Student:* "What do you mean? I spent hours writing it. I thought it was on the mark."

▶ *Without adjustment:* The instructor ignores the student's need for detail and continues to generalize. Comments like "You need to elaborate," "Try writing from the heart," or "You're not considering your audience" might confuse or discourage the student.

▶ *With adjustment:* Greater logic and detail will help. For example, the instructor might communicate better by saying "You've supported your central idea clearly, but you didn't move beyond the facts into your interpretation of what they mean. Your essay reads like a research paper. The language doesn't sound like it is coming directly from you."

■ *Listeners adjust to speakers.* As a listener, improve understanding by being aware of differences and translating messages so they make sense to you. The following example with an Adventurer (employee) and an Organizer (supervisor) shows how adjusting can pay off.

> *Employee:* "I'm upset about the e-mail you sent me. You never talked to me directly and you let the problem build into a crisis. I haven't had a chance to defend myself."

▶ *Without adjustment:* If the supervisor is annoyed by the employee's insistence on direct personal contact, he or she may become defensive: "I told you clearly what needs to be done. I don't know what else there is to discuss."

▶ *With adjustment:* In an effort to improve communication, the supervisor responds by encouraging the in-person exchange that is best for the employee. "Let's meet after lunch so you can explain to me how you believe we can improve the situation."

Although adjusting to communication styles helps you speak and listen more effectively, you also need to understand and learn how to effectively give and receive criticism.

Know how to give and take criticism

CONSTRUCTIVE CRITICISM
Criticism that promotes improvement or development.

Criticism can be either constructive or unconstructive. **Constructive criticism** is a practical problem-solving strategy, involving goodwill suggestions for improving a situation. In contrast, unconstructive criticism focuses on what went wrong, doesn't offer alternatives that might help solve the problem, and is often delivered negatively, creating bad feelings.

When offered constructively, criticism can help bring about important changes. Consider a case in which someone has continually been late to study

Give Constructive Criticism

Think of a situation that could be improved if you were able to offer constructive criticism to a friend or family member. Describe the situation and name the improvement you seek:

_____

_____

_____

_____

_____

_____

_____

Imagine that you have a chance to speak to this person. First describe the setting—time, place, atmosphere—where you think you would be most successful:

_____

_____

_____

_____

_____

_____

_____

_____

Now develop your "script." Analyze the situation and decide on the most constructive approach. Use a separate sheet of paper to free-write what you would say. Keep in mind the goal your communication seeks to achieve.

Finally, if you can, make your plan a reality. Will you do it?   Yes_____   No _____

If you have the conversation, was it worth it?   Yes _____   No _____

group sessions. Which comment from the group leader would better encourage a change in behavior?

▶ *Constructive.* The group leader talks privately with the student: "I've noticed that you've been late a lot. We count on you to contribute. Is there a problem that is keeping you from being on time? Can we help?"

▶ *Unconstructive.* The leader watches the student arrive late and says, in front of everyone, "If you can't start getting here on time, there's really no point in your coming."

At school, instructors criticize classwork, papers, and exams. On the job, criticism may come from supervisors, co-workers, or customers. No matter the source, constructive comments can help you grow. Be open to what you hear, and remember that most people want you to succeed.

■ *Offering constructive criticism.* Use the following strategies to increase your effectiveness:

▶ *Criticize the behavior, not the person.* Avoid personal attacks. "You've been late to five group meetings" is preferable to "You're lazy."
▶ *Define the specific problem.* Try to focus on the facts, backing them up with specific examples and minimizing emotions.
▶ *Suggest new approaches and offer help.* Talk about practical ways to handle the situation. Brainstorm creative options. Help the person feel supported.
▶ *Use a positive approach and hopeful language.* Express your belief that the person can turn the situation around.

■ *Receiving criticism.* When on criticism's receiving end, use the following techniques:

▶ *Analyze the comments.* Listen carefully and then evaluate what you hear. What does it mean? What is the intent? Try to let unconstructive comments go without responding.
▶ *Ask for suggestions on how to change your behavior.* Be open to what others say.
▶ *Summarize the criticism and your response.* The goal is for all to understand the situation.
▶ *Use a specific strategy.* Apply problem-solving skills to analyze the problem, brainstorm ways to change, choose a strategy, and take practical action to make it happen.

One of the primary goals of successful communication is to build and maintain good relationships with family, friends, and others you encounter in daily life. All of the communication and cultural competence strategies discussed in these pages will contribute to that goal. Read on for more ways to navigate your relationships successfully.

How do you make the most of personal relationships?

Personal relationships with friends, classmates, spouses and partners, and parents can be sources of great satisfaction and inner peace. Good relationships can motivate you to do your best in school and on the job. When conflict arises or relationships fall apart, however, it can affect your ability to function in all areas of your life. Relationships have enormous power.

The following straightforward approaches can help make your personal relationships as good as they can be while also showing how to manage problems when things move in the wrong direction.

Use positive relationship strategies

When you devote time and energy to education, work, and activities you enjoy, results are more likely to be positive. The same is true of human connections. Here are a few ways to nurture relationships:

▶ *Approach people and conversations with emotional intelligence.* The more you can notice feelings, understand what they mean, and handle them in ways that bring people closer to you instead of pushing them away, the better your relationships will be.

▶ *If you want a friend, be a friend.* If you treat others with the kind of loyalty and support that you appreciate, you are likely to receive the same in return.

▶ *Spend time with people you respect and admire.* Life is too short to hang out with people who bring you down or encourage you to ignore your values.

▶ *Work through tensions.* Negative feelings can fester when left unspoken. Get to the root of a problem by discussing it, compromising, forgiving, and moving on.

▶ *Take risks.* It can be frightening to reveal your deepest dreams and frustrations, to devote yourself to a friend, or to fall in love. However, if you open yourself up, you stand to gain the incredible benefits of companionship, which for most people outweigh the risks.

▶ *Find a dating pattern that suits you.* Some students date exclusively and commit early. Some students prefer to socialize in groups. Some students date casually. Be honest with yourself—and others—about what you want in a relationship.

▶ *If a relationship fails, find ways to cope.* When an important relationship becomes strained or breaks up, analyze the situation and choose practical strategies to move on. Some people need time alone; others want to be with friends and family. Some need a change of scene, whereas others let off steam with exercise or other activities. Whatever you do, believe that in time you will emerge stronger from the experience.

Plug into communication technology without losing touch

Modern technology has revolutionized the way people communicate. Today, you can call or text on a mobile phone; you can write a note via e-mail, instant message, or Twitter; you can communicate through blogs and chat rooms; and you can learn about one another on social networking sites such as Facebook. Younger students, who grew up with technology, tend to use it most. A recent Kaiser Family Foundation study found that 8- to 18-year-olds averaged 6½ hours a day in various media interactions, including texting, cell phones, and networking sites.[10]

Although communication technologies allow you to communicate faster, more frequently, and with more people than ever before, they also have drawbacks. Key 3.10 shows some positive and negative aspects of communication technology. Keep in mind that revealing too much about yourself on social networking sites may cause trouble, because many employers check these sites for information about prospective job candidates.[11] See the appendix for more information on social networking and media.

Notable among the problems with electronic communication is that it can hamper your ability to communicate in person and make friends. Real life demands the ability to interact effectively face-to-face. The ideal is to communicate electronically to enhance real-time interaction rather than replace it. Ultimately, you will develop your own "recipe" consisting of how—and how much—you want to communicate. How do you prefer to communicate with others? What forms of communication do you overuse, and what

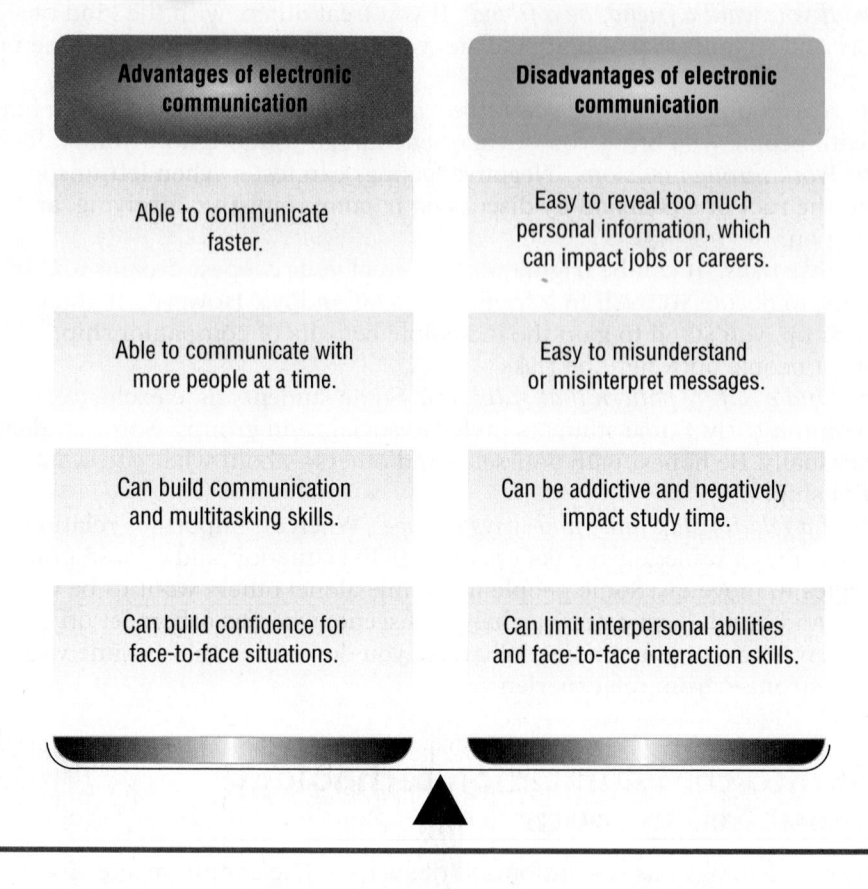

Advantages of electronic communication	Disadvantages of electronic communication
Able to communicate faster.	Easy to reveal too much personal information, which can impact jobs or careers.
Able to communicate with more people at a time.	Easy to misunderstand or misinterpret messages.
Can build communication and multitasking skills.	Can be addictive and negatively impact study time.
Can build confidence for face-to-face situations.	Can limit interpersonal abilities and face-to-face interaction skills.

effects result? Analyze situations, think creatively, and make practical decisions about how to move forward.

If you're concerned about the time you spend using forms of electronic communication, consider keeping a time journal. Any time you use an electronic device, log the time you start and stop. Review the log after a week, and think about any changes you need to make to bring your life back into balance.

Conflict occurs within nearly every relationship. With effort, you can manage it (and stay away from those who cannot).

Manage conflict

Conflicts, both large and small, arise when there is a clash of ideas or interests. You may have small conflicts with a housemate over a door left unlocked. You may have major conflicts with your partner about finances or with an instructor about a failing grade. Conflict, as unpleasant as it can be, is a natural element in the dynamic of getting along with others. Prevent it when you can—and when you can't, use problem-solving strategies to resolve it.

Conflict prevention strategies

Some strategies can help you to prevent conflict from starting in the first place.

ASSERTIVENESS FOSTERS
SUCCESSFUL COMMUNICATION

AGGRESSIVE	ASSERTIVE	PASSIVE
Blaming, name-calling, and verbal insults: "You created this mess!"	Expressing oneself and letting others do the same: "I have thoughts about this—first, what is your opinion?"	Feeling that one has no right to express anger: "No, I'm fine."
Escalating arguments: "You'll do it my way, no matter what it takes."	Using "I" statements to defuse arguments: "I am uncomfortable with that choice and want to discuss it."	Avoiding arguments: "Whatever you want to do is fine."
Being demanding: "Do this."	Asking and giving reasons: "Please consider doing it this way, and here's why . . . "	Being noncommittal: "I'm not sure what the best way to handle this is."

■ *Send "I" messages.* "I" messages communicate your needs rather than attacking someone else. Creating these messages involves some simple rephrasing: "You didn't lock the door!" becomes "I was worried when I came home and found the door unlocked." "I" statements soften the conflict by highlighting the effects that the other person's actions have on you, rather than focusing on the person or the actions themselves.

■ *Be assertive.* Most people tend to express themselves in one of three ways—aggressively, assertively, or passively. *Aggressive* communicators focus primarily on their own needs and can become impatient when needs are not satisfied. *Passive* communicators focus primarily on the needs of others and often deny themselves power, causing frustration. *Assertive* communicators are able to declare and affirm their opinions while respecting the rights of others to do the same. Assertive behavior strikes a balance between aggression and passivity and promotes the most productive communication. Key 3.11 contrasts these three communication styles.

What can aggressive and passive communicators do to move toward a more assertive style? Aggressive communicators might take time before speaking, use "I" statements, listen to others, and avoid giving orders. Passive communicators might acknowledge anger, express opinions, exercise the right to make requests, and know that their ideas and feelings are important.

Conflict resolution

All too often, people deal with conflict through *avoidance* (a passive tactic that shuts down communication) or *escalation* (an aggressive tactic that often leads to fighting). Conflict resolution demands calm communication, motivation, and careful thinking. Use analytical, creative, and practical thinking skills to apply the problem-solving plan that you will learn in Chapter 4 when discord occurs.

What happened to Joyce? Dr. Bishop now understands how her learning disability, *auditory processing disorder,* causes problems with understanding words she hears. Seeing how her strengths in visual-spatial, logical-mathematical, and bodily-kinesthetic intelligence served her well in science studies, she chose study strategies for those strengths and over time earned her master's and PhD degrees. Now a tenured psychology professor at Golden West College in California, Dr. Bishop has won Teacher of the Year twice at her school. She teaches both in-person and online courses and trains other teachers in online teaching strategies. She manages the challenges of her learning disability while pursuing her intention to learn throughout her life.

Case Wrap-up

What does this story mean for you? Getting perspective on strengths and weaknesses isn't just for those with diagnosed learning disabilities. Dr. Bishop got her wake-up call from an eye doctor and a therapist. Who can provide an outside perspective for you? Find someone who knows you well enough to have an opinion about you and who you believe will be honest and constructive. Tell this person ahead of time that you are looking for perspectives about what you do well and what challenges you. Prepare by making a short list of your three strongest and three weakest qualities. After receiving the outside perspective, compare it to your list. What matches up? What surprises you?

What effects go beyond your world? Broaden your knowledge of learning disabilities so you avoid inaccurate assumptions about people and support them in reaching their potential. Go to www.ldonline.org and read the article entitled "LD Basics." Then browse the articles at www.ldonline.org/indepth/adults to focus more closely on how adults with learning disabilities navigate school, work, and life. Finally, think about an assumption you may have made regarding someone with whom you live, work, or go to school. Combat your possibly false idea by approaching that person with an open mind from this point forward, looking for strengths as well as working reasonably with challenges (and maybe even helping the person to combat them). With every person who develops a more positive attitude and understanding perspective about those with learning disabilities or other challenges, the world becomes that much more of a supportive and productive place.

Successful Intelligence *Wrap-up*

HERE'S HOW YOU HAVE
BUILT SKILLS IN **CHAPTER 3** :

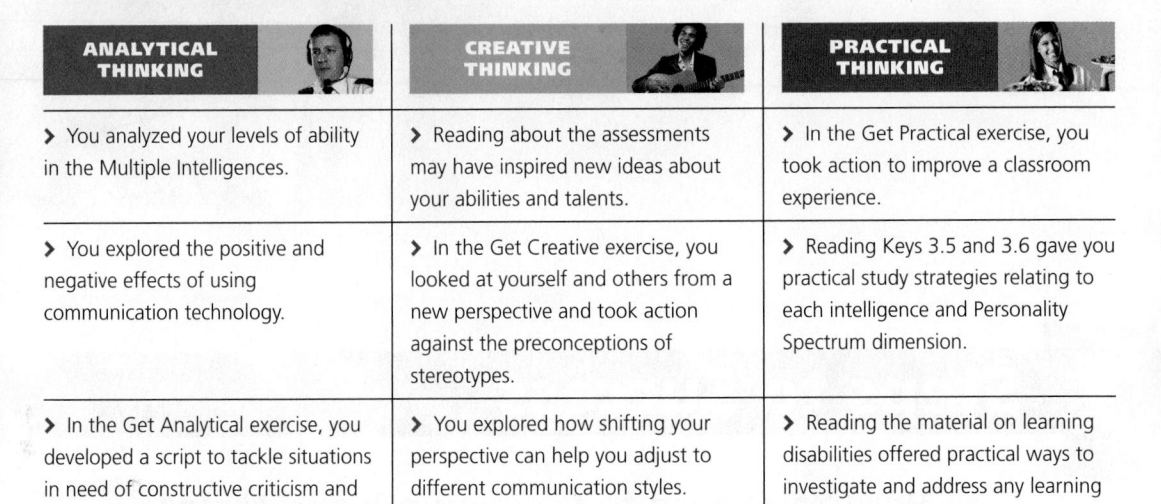ANALYTICAL THINKING	CREATIVE THINKING	PRACTICAL THINKING
> You analyzed your levels of ability in the Multiple Intelligences.	> Reading about the assessments may have inspired new ideas about your abilities and talents.	> In the Get Practical exercise, you took action to improve a classroom experience.
> You explored the positive and negative effects of using communication technology.	> In the Get Creative exercise, you looked at yourself and others from a new perspective and took action against the preconceptions of stereotypes.	> Reading Keys 3.5 and 3.6 gave you practical study strategies relating to each intelligence and Personality Spectrum dimension.
> In the Get Analytical exercise, you developed a script to tackle situations in need of constructive criticism and analyzed its effectiveness.	> You explored how shifting your perspective can help you adjust to different communication styles.	> Reading the material on learning disabilities offered practical ways to investigate and address any learning disability you may have.

Word *for* Thought

In the language of the **Yoruba**, an ethnic group living primarily in West Africa, *oruko lonro ni* (oh-roo'-ko lon'-ro nee) translates as "names affect behavior."[12] Think of this as you work to break through the confines of the names and labels that you give yourself or that others give you. Put learning styles information to work as tools to learn more, not boxes into which to fit yourself.

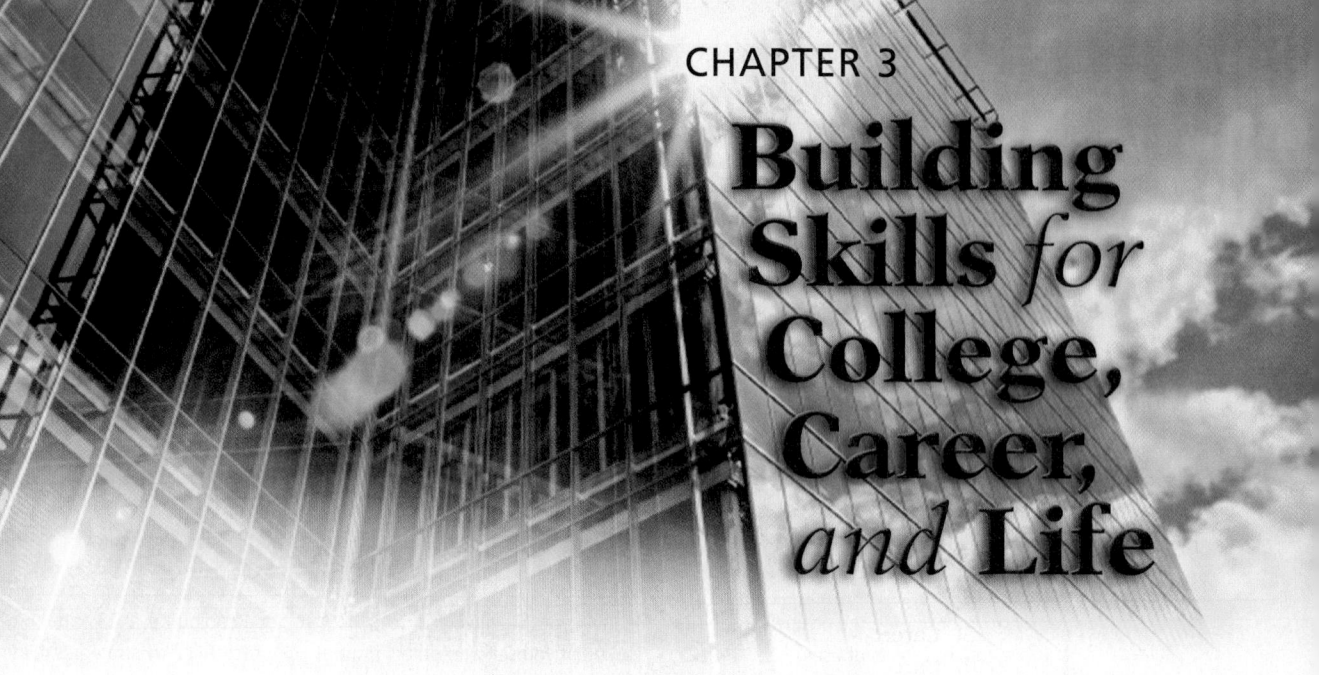

Building Skills *for* College, Career, *and* Life

Steps to Success

Link How You Learn to Coursework and Major

Apply what you know about yourself to some future academic planning.

BUILD BASIC SKILLS. On paper or on a computer, summarize yourself as a learner in a paragraph or two. Focus on what you have have learned about yourself from the chapter assessments.

Done? Check here. _____

TAKE IT TO THE NEXT LEVEL. Schedule a meeting with your academic advisor.

Name of advisor: _____

Office location/contact information: _____

Time/date of meeting: _____

Give the advisor an overview of your learning strengths and challenges, based on your summary. Ask for advice about courses that might interest you and majors that might suit you. Take notes. Based on your discussion, name two courses to consider in the next year:

1. _____

2. _____

MOVE TOWARD MASTERY. In your mind, project both of those courses ahead in time. What majors might each of them lead you toward? Based on those courses, name two majors to investigate:

1. _____

2. _____

Finally, create a separate to-do list of how you plan to explore one course offering and one major. Set a deadline for each task. And keep in mind that if you are having trouble choosing a major because of uncertainty about a career direction, see an advisor in the career center for guidance.

Teamwork

Create Solutions Together

IDEAS ABOUT PERSONALITY TYPES

Goal: To learn more about personality types—your own and others'

Time on Task: 25 minutes: 5 minutes to settle into groups, 10 minutes for group work, 10 minutes to share

Instructions: Divide into groups according to the four types of the Personality Spectrum—Thinkers in one group, Organizers in another, Givers in a third, and Adventurers in the fourth. Students whose scores point to more than one type can join whichever group is smaller. With your group, brainstorm about the following aspects of your type:

1. The strengths of this type
2. The struggles, or stressful aspects of this type
3. Career areas that tend to suit this type
4. Career areas that are a challenge for this type
5. Challenges for this type in relating to the other three Personality Spectrum types

If there is time, each group can present this information to the entire class to boost understanding and acceptance of diverse ways of relating to information and people.

Writing

Build Intrapersonal and Communication Skills

Record your thoughts on paper, in a journal, or electronically.

EMOTIONAL INTELLIGENCE JOURNAL

Emotional: Your experience with prejudice. Have you ever been discriminated against or experienced any other type of prejudice? Have you been on the other end and acted with prejudice yourself? Describe what happened and your feelings about the situation (if you have no personal experience, describe a situation you have seen or heard about). Outline an emotionally intelligent response that you feel would bring something positive or helpful out of the situation.

REAL-LIFE WRITING

Improve communication. Few students make use of the wealth of ideas and experience that academic advisors can offer. Think of a question you have—regarding a specific course, major, or academic situation—that your advisor might help you answer. Craft an e-mail in appropriate language to your advisor, and send it. Then, to stretch your communication skills, rewrite the same e-mail twice more: once in a format you would send to an instructor and once in a format appropriate for a friend. Send either or both of these if you think the response would be valuable to you.

Personal Portfolio

Self-Portrait

21st Century Learning Building Blocks

- Creativity and Innovation
- Initiative and Self-Direction

Complete the following on separate sheets of paper or electronically (if you can use a graphics program).

Because self-knowledge helps you to make the best choices about your future, a self-portrait can be an important tool in your career exploration. Use this exercise to synthesize everything you have been exploring about yourself into one comprehensive "self-portrait." Design your portrait in "think link" (mind map) style, using words and visual shapes to describe your dominant multiple intelligences, Personality Spectrum dimensions, values, abilities and interests, personal characteristics, and anything else that you have discovered through self-exploration.

A think link is a visual construction of related ideas, similar to a map or web, representing your thought process. Ideas are written inside geometric shapes, often boxes or circles, and related ideas and facts are attached to those ideas by lines that connect the shapes (see the note-taking section in Chapter 6 for more about think links).

If you want to use the style shown in Key 3.12, create a "wheel" of ideas coming off your central shape. Then, spreading out from each of those ideas (interests, values, and so forth), draw lines connecting the thoughts that go along with that idea. Connected to "Interests," for example, might be "singing," "stock market," and "history."

You don't have to use the wheel image, however. You might instead want to design a treelike think link, a line of boxes with connecting thoughts, or anything else you like. Let your design reflect who you are, just as your writing does. You may want to look back at it at the end of the term to see how you have changed and grown from the self-image you have today.

Social Networking

HELP OTHERS GET TO KNOW YOU

As you are building your self-knowledge, help viewers of your LinkedIn profile get to know you as well. Sign in to your LinkedIn account and click on "Edit My Profile." Look for "Summary" and click on the [Edit] mark next to it. Then, fill in the two areas there:

- Professional Experience & Goals (if you don't have any professional experience, you can fill in Goals only—remember, too, that you can include experience from internships, work study, apprenticeships, etc.)
- Specialties (in conjunction with talking about what you do well, you may want to consider including information related to learning styles—that you are highly visual, for example, or a strong organizer.)

In addition, scroll down to the "Personal Information" section and fill in any of the following that you choose to have visible on your profile:

- Phone
- Address
- IM
- Birthday
- Marital Status

Finally, post a photo—a respectable-looking one—if you choose to do so. Click on "Edit My Profile," then on "Add Photo" underneath the photo icon. It will then direct you to upload a photo.

Key 3.12

THIS IS ONE EXAMPLE OF
A SELF-PORTRAIT

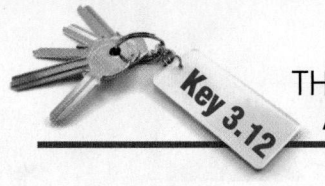

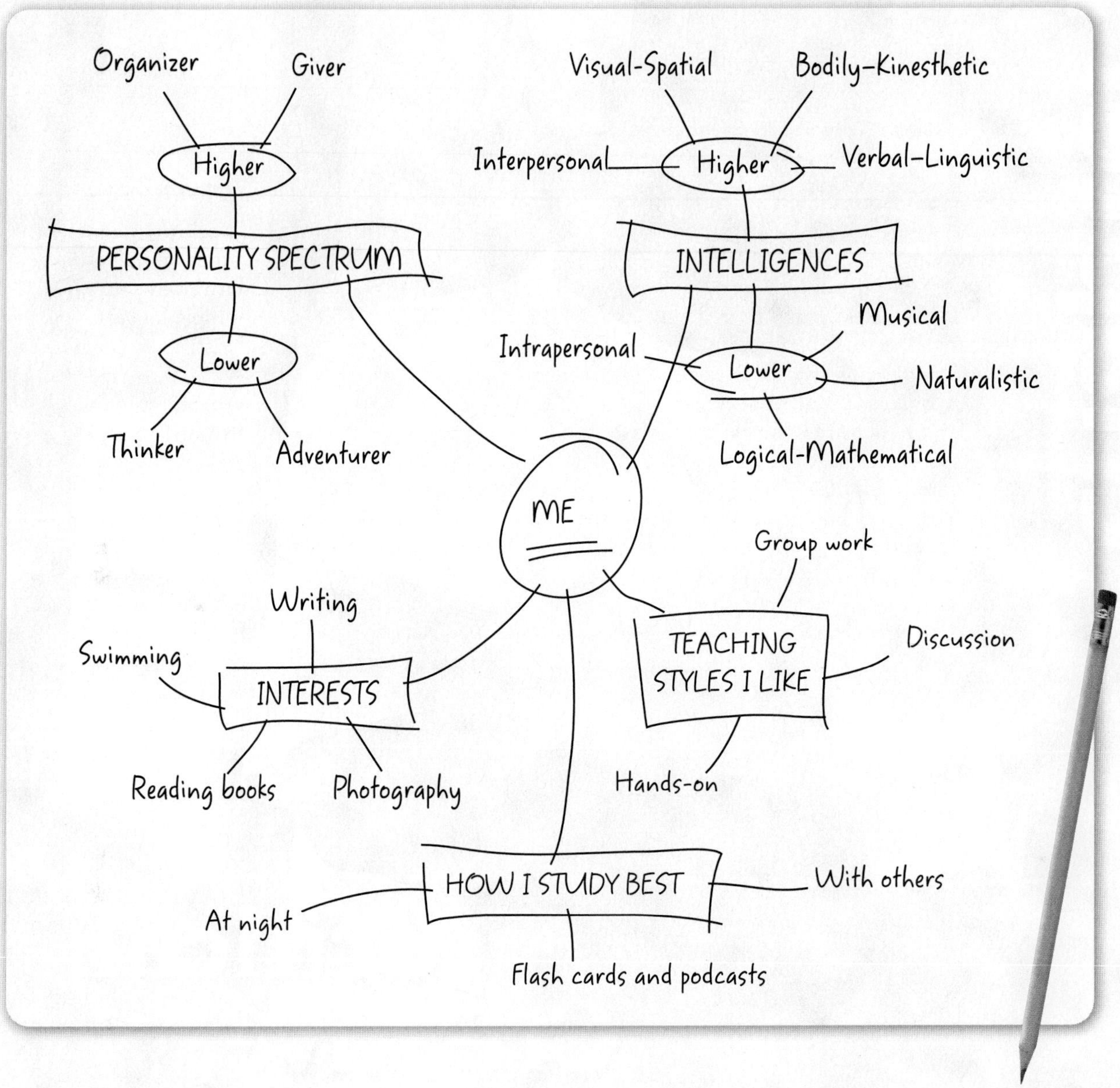
Organizer
Giver
Higher
PERSONALITY SPECTRUM
Lower
Thinker
Adventurer
Visual-Spatial
Bodily–Kinesthetic
Interpersonal
Higher
Verbal–Linguistic
INTELLIGENCES
Musical
Intrapersonal
Lower
Naturalistic
Logical-Mathematical
ME
Group work
TEACHING STYLES I LIKE
Discussion
Hands-on
Writing
Swimming
INTERESTS
Reading books
Photography
HOW I STUDY BEST
With others
At night
Flash cards and podcasts

Critical, Creative, and Practical Thinking

Solving Problems and Making Decisions

What Would You Do?

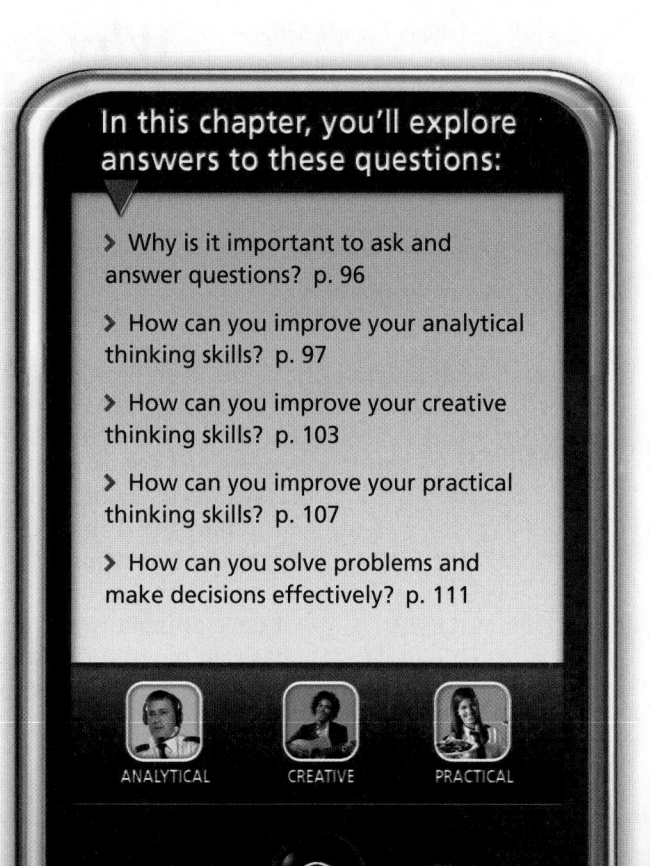

Think about this problem as you read, and consider how you would approach it. This chapter builds problem-solving and decision-making skills that will help you face challenges in college and beyond.

Ethan Gamal is carrying a twelve-credit load this term toward his major in computer programming. He has been working part-time at a local electronics store for his entire college career. It's hard to keep up with both work and school, but he can't afford the tuition without the income.

However, the chain that has employed him for the last 3 years is going into bankruptcy, and the consequences have hit home. He was notified that the store is closing in 2 weeks and all employees have been terminated. Trying to keep cash coming in, Ethan applied for local jobs and sent some resumés electronically to job websites, but hasn't yet gotten any bites.

Ethan's friend and co-worker Adam talked it over with him as they sat in the back room on a break. "Look at it this way: We'll both have more time to get schoolwork done. You know you've complained for weeks about being overloaded."

"What good is time to study if I can't pay tuition?" asked Ethan. "I was looking on the Bureau of Labor website for ideas, and it said demand for computer programmers is going to drop a lot in the next decade. Great. Why bother to stick with my degree if I won't even be able to find a job in a few years?"

"We're in the same boat," said Adam. "All of us need new jobs, and I've got to pay my own tuition just like you."

Ethan replied, "But you're headed toward an education major, and you're going to have job prospects. I don't know what to do, because there's nothing else I'm interested in. The truth is, I'm ready to quit." (To be continued . . .)

Problems can come up suddenly and throw you off balance. You'll learn more about Ethan, and revisit his situation, within the chapter.

In this chapter, you'll explore answers to these questions:

> Why is it important to ask and answer questions? p. 96

> How can you improve your analytical thinking skills? p. 97

> How can you improve your creative thinking skills? p. 103

> How can you improve your practical thinking skills? p. 107

> How can you solve problems and make decisions effectively? p. 111

ANALYTICAL   CREATIVE   PRACTICAL

For each statement, circle the number that feels right to you, from 1 for "not at all true for me" to 5 for "very true for me."

▶ I discover information, make decisions, and solve problems by asking and answering questions.	1 2 3 4 5
▶ I don't take everything I read or hear as fact; I question how useful, truthful, and logical it is before I decide whether I can use it.	1 2 3 4 5
▶ I look for biased perspectives when I read or listen because I am aware of how they can lead me in the wrong direction.	1 2 3 4 5
▶ Even if it seems like there is only one way to solve a problem, I brainstorm to think of other options.	1 2 3 4 5
▶ I try not to let the idea that things have *always* been done a certain way stop me from trying different approaches.	1 2 3 4 5
▶ When I work in a group, I try to manage my emotions and to notice how I affect others.	1 2 3 4 5
▶ I think about different solutions before I choose one and take action.	1 2 3 4 5
▶ I spend time researching different possibilities before making a decision.	1 2 3 4 5
▶ I avoid making decisions on the spur of the moment.	1 2 3 4 5
▶ When I make a decision, I consider how my choice will affect others.	1 2 3 4 5

Each of the topics in these statements is covered in this chapter. Note those statements for which you circled a 3 or lower. Skim the chapter to see where those topics appear, and pay special attention to them as you read, learn, and apply new strategies.

REMEMBER: *No matter how developed your thinking skills are, you can improve with effort and practice.*

"Successfully intelligent people define problems correctly and thereby solve those problems that really confront them, rather than extraneous ones. . . . [They] carefully formulate strategies for problem solving. In particular, they focus on long-range planning rather than rushing in and then later having to rethink their strategies."

—Robert Sternberg

Why is it important to **ask and answer questions?**

What is thinking? According to experts, it is what happens when you ask questions and move toward the answers.[1] "To think through or rethink anything," says Dr. Richard Paul, director of research at the Center for Critical Thinking and Moral Critique, "one must ask questions that stimulate our thought. Questions define tasks, express problems and delineate issues. . . . [O]nly students who have questions are really thinking and learning."[2]

As you answer questions, you turn information into material that you can use to achieve goals. A *Wall Street Journal* article entitled "The Best Innovations Are Those That Come from Smart Questions" relays the story of a cell biology student, William Hunter, whose professor told him that "the difference between good science and great science is the quality of the questions posed." Now a physician, Dr. Hunter asks questions about new ways to use drugs. His questions have helped his company reach the goal of developing a revolutionary product—a drug-coated mesh used to strengthen diseased blood vessels.[3]

How can you question effectively?

■ **Know why you question.** To ask useful questions, you need to know why you are questioning. Start by defining your purpose: What am I trying to accomplish, and why? For example, if Ethan's purpose for questioning were to find another part-time job, that would generate an entirely different set of questions than if his purpose were to find another major. As you continue your thought process, you will find more specific purposes that help you generate questions along the way.

■ **Want to question.** Knowing why you are questioning also helps you *want* to think. "Critical-thinking skills are different from critical-thinking dispositions, or a willingness to deploy these skills," says cognitive psychologist D. Alan Bensley of Frostburg State University in Maryland. In other words, having the skills isn't enough—you also need the desire to use them.[4] Having a clear understanding of your goal can help you be more willing to work to achieve it.

■ **Question in different ways.**

   ▶ Analyze (How bad is my money situation?)
   ▶ Come up with creative ideas (How can I earn more money?)
   ▶ Apply practical solutions (Who do I talk to about getting a job on campus?)

When you need to solve a problem or make a decision, combining all three thinking skills gives you the greatest chance of achieving your goal.[5] This chapter will explore analytical, creative, and practical thinking first individually and then will show how they work together to help you to solve problems and make decisions effectively. Asking questions opens the door to each thinking skill, and in each section you will find examples of the kinds of questions that drive that skill. Begin by exploring analytical thinking.

How can you improve your analytical thinking skills?

Analytical thinking is the process of gathering information, breaking it into parts, examining and evaluating those parts, and making connections for the purposes of gaining understanding, solving a problem, or making a decision.

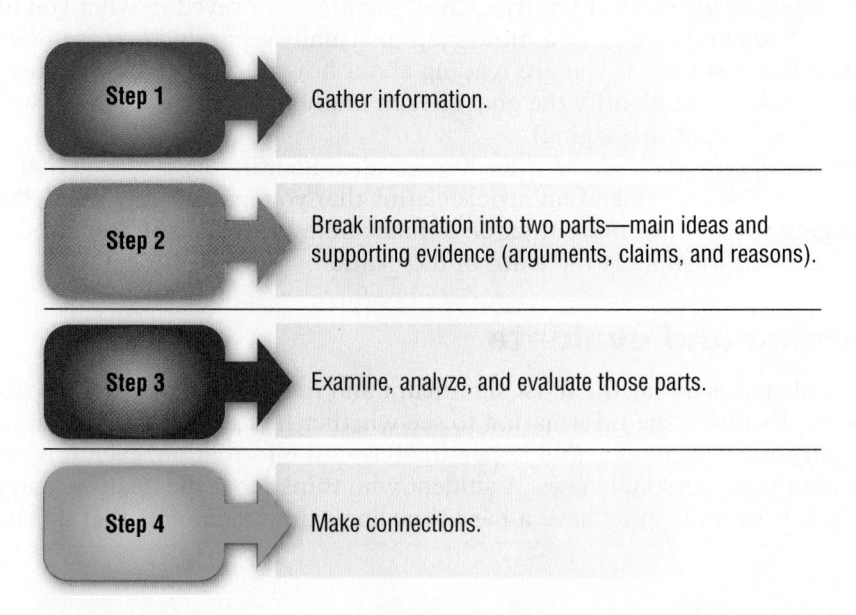

Step 1 Gather information.

Step 2 Break information into two parts—main ideas and supporting evidence (arguments, claims, and reasons).

Step 3 Examine, analyze, and evaluate those parts.

Step 4 Make connections.

Through the analytical process, you look for how pieces of information relate to one another, setting aside any pieces that are unclear, unrelated, unimportant, or biased. You may also form new questions that change your direction. Be open to them and to where they may lead you.

Gather information

Information is the raw material for thinking, so to start the thinking process you must first gather your raw materials. This requires analyzing how much information you need, how much time to spend gathering it, and whether it is relevant. Say, for instance, that you have to write a paper on one aspect of the media (TV, radio, Internet) and its influence on a particular group. Here's how analyzing can help you gather information for that paper:

Many types of work, such as the elevation drawings this engineering student is working on, involve analytical thinking.
© Shutterstock

> ▶ Reviewing the assignment terms, you note two important items: The paper should be approximately ten pages and describe at least three significant points of influence.
> ▶ At the library and online, you find thousands of articles in this topic area. Analyzing your reaction to them and how many articles concentrate on certain aspects of the topic, you decide to focus your paper on how the Internet influences young teens (ages 13–15).
> ▶ Examining the summaries of six comprehensive articles leads you to three in-depth sources.

In this way you achieve a subgoal—a selection of useful materials—on the way to your larger goal of writing a well-crafted paper.

Break information into parts

The next step is to search for the two most relevant parts of the information: the main idea or ideas (also called the **argument** or *viewpoint*) and the supporting evidence (also called *reasons* or *supporting details*).

> ▶ *Separate the ideas.* Identify each of the ideas conveyed in what you are reading. You can use lists or a mind map to visually separate ideas from one another. For instance, if you are reading about how teens ages 13 to 15 use the Internet, you could identify the goal of each method of access they use (websites, blogs, instant messaging).
> ▶ *Identify the evidence.* For each main idea, identify the evidence that supports it. For example, if an article claims that young teens rely on instant messaging three times more than on e-mails, note the facts, studies, or other evidence cited to support the truth of the claim.

ARGUMENT
A set of connected ideas, supported by examples, made by a writer to prove or disprove a point.

Examine and evaluate

The third step is by far the most significant and lies at the heart of analytical thinking. Examine the information to see whether it is going to be useful for your purposes. Keep your mind open to all useful information, even if it conflicts with your personal views. A student who thinks that the death penalty is wrong, for example, may have a hard time analyzing arguments that defend it or may focus his research on materials that support his perspective. Set aside personal prejudices when you analyze information.

The following four questions will help you examine and evaluate effectively.

Do examples support ideas?

When you encounter an idea or claim, examine how it is supported with examples or *evidence*—facts, expert opinion, research findings, personal experience, and so on (see Key 4.1 for an illustration). How useful an idea is to your work may depend on whether, or how well, it is backed up with solid evidence or made concrete with examples. Be critical of the information you gather; don't take it as truth without examining it.

For example, a blog written by a 12-year-old may make statements about what kids do on the Internet. The word of one person, who may or may not be telling the truth, is not adequate support. However, a study of youth technology use by the Department of Commerce under the provisions of the Children's Internet Protection Act may be more reliable.

Is the information factual and accurate, or is it opinion?

A *statement of fact* is information presented as objectively real and verifiable ("The Internet is a research tool"). In contrast, a *statement of opinion* is a belief, conclusion, or judgment that is inherently difficult, and sometimes impossible, to verify ("The Internet is always the best and most reliable research tool"). When you critically evaluate materials, one test of the evidence is whether it is fact or opinion. Key 4.2 defines important characteristics of fact and opinion.

Do causes and effects link logically?

Look at the reasons given for a situation or occurrence (causes) and the explanation of its consequences (effects, both positive and negative). For example, an article might detail what causes young teens to use the Internet after school and

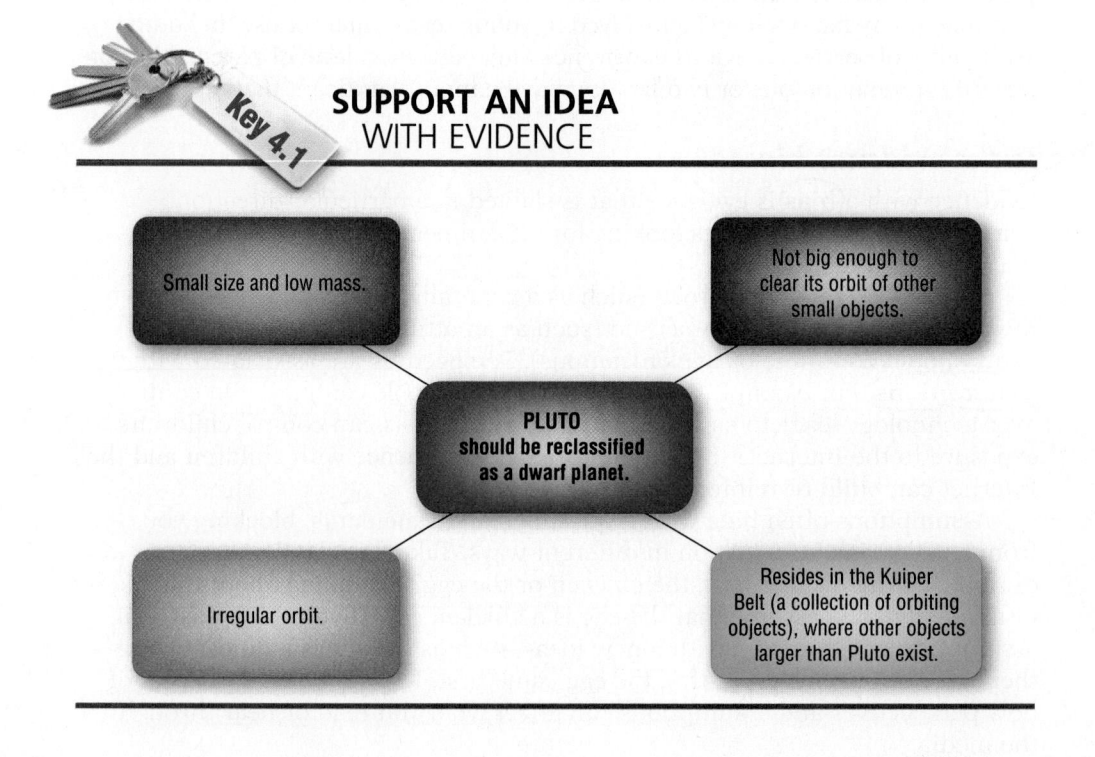

Key 4.1

SUPPORT AN IDEA
WITH EVIDENCE

Small size and low mass.

Not big enough to clear its orbit of other small objects.

PLUTO should be reclassified as a dwarf planet.

Irregular orbit.

Resides in the Kuiper Belt (a collection of orbiting objects), where other objects larger than Pluto exist.

EXAMINE HOW
FACT AND OPINION DIFFER

FACTS INCLUDE STATEMENTS THAT . . .	OPINIONS INCLUDE STATEMENTS THAT . . .
. . . deal with actual people, places, objects, or events. Example: "In 2002, the European Union introduced the physical coins and banknotes of a new currency—the euro—that was designed to be used by its member nations."	**. . . show evaluation.** Any statement of value indicates an opinion. Words such as *bad, good, pointless,* and *beneficial* indicate value judgments. Example: "The use of the euro has been beneficial to all the states of the European Union."
. . . use concrete words or measurable statistics. Example: "The charity event raised $50,862."	**. . . use abstract words.** Complicated words like *misery* or *success* usually indicate a personal opinion. Example: "The charity event was a smashing success."
. . . describe current events in exact terms. Example: "Mr. Barrett's course has 378 students enrolled this semester."	**. . . predict future events.** Statements about future occurrences are often opinions. Example: "Mr. Barrett's course is going to set a new enrollment record this year."
. . . avoid emotional words and focus on the verifiable. Example: "Citing dissatisfaction with the instruction, seven out of the twenty-five students in that class withdrew in September."	**. . . use emotional words.** Emotions are unverifiable. Words such as *delightful* or *miserable* express an opinion. Example: "That class is a miserable experience."
. . . avoid absolutes. Example: "Some students need to have a job while in school."	**. . . use absolutes.** Absolute qualifiers, such as *all, none, never,* and *always,* often express an opinion. Example: "All students need to have a job while in school."

Source: Adapted from Ben E. Johnson, *Stirring Up Thinking.* New York: Houghton Mifflin, 1998, pp. 268–270.

the effects that this has on their family life. The cause-and-effect chain should make sense to you. It is also important that you analyze carefully to seek out *key* or *"root" causes*—the most significant causes of a problem or situation. For example, many factors may be involved in young teens' Internet use, including availability of service, previous experience, and education level of parents, but on careful examination one or two factors may be more significant than others.

Is the evidence biased?

BIAS
A preference or inclination, especially one that prevents even-handed judgment.

Evidence with a **bias** is evidence that is slanted in a particular direction. Searching for a bias involves looking for hidden perspectives or assumptions that lie within the material.

PERSPECTIVE
A characteristic way of thinking about people, situations, events, and ideas.

A **perspective** can be broad (such as a generally optimistic or pessimistic view of life) or more focused (such as an attitude about whether students should commute or live on campus). Perspectives are associated with **assumptions.** For example, the perspective that people can maintain control over technology leads to assumptions such as "Parents can control children's exposure to the Internet." Having a particular experience with children and the Internet can build or reinforce such a perspective.

ASSUMPTION
A judgment, generalization, or bias influenced by experience and values.

Assumptions often hide within questions and statements, blocking you from considering information in different ways. Take this classic puzzler as an example: "Which came first, the chicken or the egg?" Thinking about this question, most people assume that the egg is a chicken egg. If you think past that assumption and come up with a new idea—such as the egg is a dinosaur egg—then the obvious answer is that the egg came first. Key 4.3 offers examples of how perspectives and assumptions can affect what you read or hear through the media.

DIFFERENT ARTICLES MAY PRESENT **DIFFERENT PERSPECTIVES** ON THE SAME TOPIC

Key 4.3

Topic: *How teens' grades are affected by Internet use*

STATEMENT BY A TEACHING ORGANIZATION	STATEMENT BY A PR AGENT FOR AN INTERNET SEARCH ENGINE	STATEMENT BY A PROFESSOR SPECIALIZING IN NEW MEDIA AND EDUCATION
"Too much Internet use equals failing grades and stolen papers."	"The Internet use allows students access to a plethora of information, which results in better grades."	"The effects of the Internet on young students are undeniable and impossible to overlook."

Examining perspectives and assumptions helps you judge whether material is *reliable*. The less bias you can identify, the more reliable the information.

After the questions: What information is most useful to you?

You've examined your information, looking at its evidence, validity, perspective, and any underlying assumptions. Now, based on that examination, you evaluate whether an idea or piece of information is important or unimportant, relevant or not, strong or weak, and why. You then set aside what is not useful and use the rest to form an opinion, possible solution, or decision.

In preparing your paper on young teens and the Internet, for example, you've analyzed a selection of information and materials to see how they apply to the goal of your paper. You then selected what you believe will be most useful in preparation for drafting.

Make connections

The last part of analytical thinking, after you have broken information apart, is to find new and logical ways to connect pieces together. This step is crucial for research papers and essays because it is where your original ideas are born—and it is also where your creative skills get involved (more on that in the next section). When you begin to write, you focus on your new ideas, supporting them effectively with information you've learned from your analysis. Use the following techniques to make connections.

■ ***Compare and contrast.*** Look at how ideas are similar to, or different from, each other. You might explore how different young teen subgroups (boys versus girls, for example) have different purposes for setting up pages on sites such as Facebook or MySpace.

When you think through something with others in a group, the variety of ideas gives you a better chance of finding a workable solution to a problem.
© iStockPhoto

■ *Look for themes, patterns, and categories.* Note connections that form as you look at how bits of information relate to one another. For example, you might see patterns of Internet use that link young teens from particular cultures or areas of the country together into categories.

Come to new information ready to hear and read new ideas, think about them, and make informed decisions about what you believe. The process will educate you, sharpen your thinking skills, and give you more information to work with as you encounter life's problems. See Key 4.4 for some questions you can ask to build and use analytical thinking skills.

ASK QUESTIONS LIKE
THESE TO **ANALYZE**

To gather information, ask:	• What kinds of information do I need to meet my goal? • What information is available? Where and when can I get to it? • Of the sources I found, which ones will best help me achieve my goal?
To analyze, ask:	• What are the parts of this information? • What is similar to this information? What is different? • What are the reasons for this? Why did this happen? • What ideas, themes, or conclusions emerge from this material? • How would you categorize this information?
To see whether evidence or examples support an idea, ask:	• Does the evidence make sense? • How do the examples support the idea/claim? • Are there examples that might disprove the idea/claim?
To distinguish fact from opinion, ask:	• Do the words in this information signal fact or opinion? • What is the source of this information? Is the source reliable? • If this is an opinion, is it supported by facts?
To examine perspectives and assumptions, ask:	• What perspectives might the author have, and what may be emphasized or deemphasized as a result? • What assumptions might lie behind this statement or material? • How could I prove—or disprove—an assumption? • How might my perspective affect the way I see this material?
To evaluate, ask:	• What information will support what I'm trying to prove or accomplish? • Is this information true or false, and why? • How important is this information?

Source: Adapted from www-ed.fnal.gov/trc/tutorial/taxonomy.html (Richard Paul, *Critical Thinking: How to Prepare Students for a Rapidly Changing World,* 1993) and from www.kcmetro.edu/longview/ctac/blooms.htm (Barbara Fowler, Longview Community College "Bloom's Taxonomy and Critical Thinking").

Pursuing your goals, in school and in the workplace, requires not just analyzing information but also thinking creatively about how to use what you've learned from your analysis.

How can you improve your creative thinking skills?

What is creativity?

▶ Some researchers define creativity as combining existing elements in an innovative way to create a new purpose or result (after doctors noticed that patients taking aspirin had fewer heart attacks, the drug was reinvented as a preventer of coronary disease).

▶ Others see creativity as the ability to generate new ideas from looking at how things are related (noting what ladybugs eat inspired organic farmers to bring them in to consume crop-destroying aphids).[6]

▶ Still others, including Sternberg, define it as the ability to make unusual connections—to view information in quirky ways that bring about unique results (using a weak adhesive to mark pages in a book, a 3M scientist created Post-it notes).

To think creatively is to generate new ideas that may bring change. Even though some people seem to have more or better ideas than others, creative thinking is a skill that can be developed. Creativity expert Roger von Oech highlights mental flexibility. "Like race-car drivers who shift in and out of different gears depending on where they are on the course," he says, you can enhance creativity by learning to "shift in and out of different types of thinking depending on the needs of the situation at hand."[7]

The following tips will help you make those shifts and build your ability to generate and capture the ideas that pop up. Get in the habit of writing them down as you think of them. Keep a pen and paper by your bed, your smartphone in your pocket, a notepad in your car, or a recorder in your backpack so that you can grab ideas before they fade.

Brainstorm

Brainstorming is also referred to as *divergent thinking:* You start with a question and then let your mind diverge—go in many different directions—in search of solutions. Brainstorming is *deliberate* creative thinking. When you brainstorm, you generate ideas without thinking about how useful they are, and evaluate their quality later. Brainstorming works well in groups because group members can become inspired by, and make creative use of, one another's ideas.[8]

One way to inspire ideas when brainstorming is to think of similar situations—in other words, to make *analogies* (comparisons based on a resemblance of things otherwise unlike). For example, Velcro is a product of analogy: After examining how burrs stuck to his dog's fur after a walk in the woods, the inventor imagined how a similar system of hooks and loops could make two pieces of fabric stick to each other.

When you are brainstorming ideas, don't get hooked on finding one right answer. Questions may have many "right answers"—answers that have degrees of usefulness. The more possibilities you generate, the better your chance of

> BRAINSTORMING
> Letting your mind wander to come up with different ideas or answers.

Analyze a Statement

Reread the case study that opens the chapter. Consider the statement below; then analyze it by answering the questions that follow.

> There's no point in pursuing a career area that you love
> if it isn't going to earn you a living.

Is this statement fact or opinion? Why?

_____
_____
_____
_____

What examples can you think of that support or negate this statement?

_____
_____
_____
_____
_____

What perspective(s) are guiding this statement?

_____
_____
_____
_____

What assumption(s) underlie the statement? What negative effects might result from accepting these assumptions without investigation?

_____
_____
_____
_____

As a result of your critical thinking, what is your evaluation of this statement?

_____
_____
_____
_____

finding the best one. Ethan might brainstorm things he likes to do and people he admires, for example, and from those lists he may come up with ideas of other majors that he wants to investigate.

Finally, don't stop the process when you think you have the best answer— keep going until you are out of steam. You never know what may come up in those last gasps of creative energy.[9]

Take a new and different look

If no one ever questioned established opinion, people would still think the sun revolved around the earth. Here are some ways to change how you look at a situation or problem:

■ *Challenge assumptions.* In the late 1960s, conventional wisdom said that school provided education and television provided entertainment. Jim Henson, a pioneer in children's television, asked, Why can't we use TV to educate young children? From that question, the characters of *Sesame Street,* and eventually many other educational programs, were born. Ethan might try to challenge his assumptions about what people with a computer programming major do in the workplace.

■ *Shift your perspective.* Try on new perspectives by asking others for their views, reading about new ways to approach situations, or deliberately going with the opposite of your first instinct.[10] Then use those perspectives to inspire creativity. For a political science course, for example, you might craft a position paper for a senatorial candidate that goes against your view of that particular issue. For a fun example of how looking at something in a new way can unearth a totally different idea, look at the perception puzzles in Key 4.5.

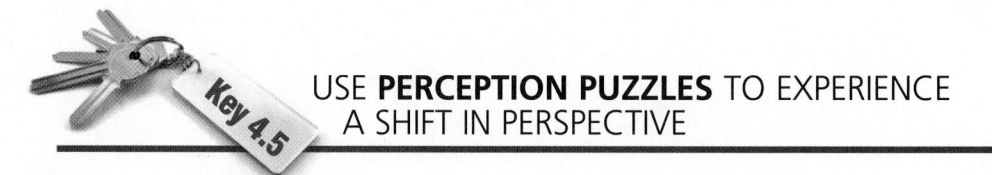

USE **PERCEPTION PUZZLES** TO EXPERIENCE A SHIFT IN PERSPECTIVE

There are two possibilities for each image. What do you see? (See page 123 for answers.)

Source of middle puzzle: "Sara Nadar" illustration from *Mind Sights* by Roger Shepard. Copyright © 1990 by Roger Shepard. Reprinted by permission of Henry Holt and Company, LLC.

GET CREATIVE!

Activate Your Creative Powers

First, think about the past month; then list three creative acts you performed.

1. To study, I _____

2. In my personal life, I _____

3. At work or in the classroom, I _____

Now think of a problem or situation that is on your mind. Brainstorm one new idea for how to deal with it.

_____

Write down a second idea—but focus on the risk-taking aspect of creativity. What would be a risky way to handle the situation? How do you hope it would pay off?

_____

_____

Finally, sit with the question—write down one more idea *only* after you have been away from this page for at least 24 hours.

_____

Keep these in mind. You may want to use one soon!

■ *Ask "what if" questions.* Set up imaginary environments in which new ideas can grow, such as, What if I had unlimited money or time? For example, the founders of Seeds of Peace, faced with long-term conflict in the Middle East, asked, What if Israeli and Palestinian teens met at a summer camp in Maine so that the next generation has greater understanding and respect? And what if follow-up programs and reunions strengthen friendships so that relationships change the politics of the Middle East? Based on the ideas that came up, they created an organization that helps teenagers from the Middle East develop leadership and communication skills.

Set the stage for creativity

Use these strategies to generate creative ideas.

■ *Choose, or create, environments that free your mind.* Find places that energize you. Play music that moves you. Seek out people who inspire you.[11]

■ *Be curious.* Try something new and different: Take a course outside of your major, listen to a new genre of music, read a book on an unfamiliar topic. Try something you don't think you will like to see if you have misjudged your reaction. Seeking out new experiences will broaden your knowledge, giving you more raw materials with which to build creative ideas.[12]

■ *Give yourself time to "sit" with a question.*
American society values speed, so much so that we
equate being "quick" with being smart.[13] In fact, creative ideas often come when you give your brain permission to "leave the job" for a while.[14] Take breaks
when figuring out a problem—get some exercise, nap,
talk with a friend, work on something else, do something fun. Even though he may not have the luxury of
too much time, Ethan may benefit from sitting with
the question of his major for as long as he can.

Take risks

Creative breakthroughs can come from sensible risk
taking.

■ *Go against established ideas.* The founders of
Etsy.com went against the idea that the American
consumer prefers cheap, conventional, mass-pro-
duced items. In 2005 they created an online company
that allows artisans to offer one-of-a-kind, handmade
products to the consumer. The site has also created a
community of artists and connects each artist personally to his or her customers.

■ *Let mistakes be okay.* Open yourself to the learning that comes from not
being afraid to mess up. When a pharmaceutical company failed to develop a
particular treatment for multiple sclerosis, the CEO said, "You have to cele-
brate the failures. If you send the message that the only road to career success
is experiments that work, people won't ask risky questions, or get any dramatically new answers."[15] If majoring in computer programming turns out not to
be the best choice for Ethan, for example, he may find that what he considers a
mistake was also a crucial voyage of self-discovery.

As with analytical thinking, asking questions powers creative thinking. See
Key 4.6 for examples of the kinds of questions you can ask to get your creative
juices flowing.

Creativity connects analytical and practical thinking. When you
generate ideas, solutions, or choices, you need to think analytically
to evaluate their quality. Then, you need to think practically about
how to make the best solution or choice happen.

How can you improve *your* practical thinking skills?

You've analyzed a situation. You've brainstormed ideas. Now,
with your practical skill, you make things happen.

Practical thinking—also called "common sense" or "street
smarts"—refers to how you adapt to your environment (both
people and circumstances), or shape or change your environment to adapt to you, to pursue important goals. Think again
about the successfully intelligent boy in the story in Chapter 1:

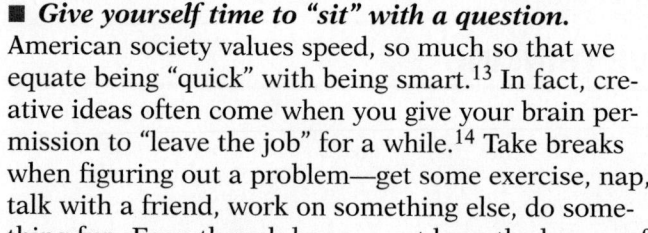

Change the CONVERSATION

Challenge yourself and your friends to ask—
and answer—tough questions. Use the following to inspire discussion in pairs or groups.

▶ What problem(s) do you see others avoid?
What happens as a result?

▶ What problem(s) do you avoid? How do you avoid
them, and what are the consequences?

▶ **CONSIDER THE CASE:**
What are the pros and cons
of each of Ethan's available
choices—to continue with his
chosen major or to branch
off into something new that
seems like a better financial
bet? What would you
recommend for him?

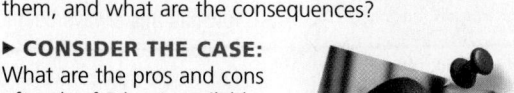

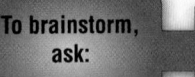
To brainstorm, ask:	• What do I want to accomplish? • What are the craziest ideas I can think of? • What are ten ways that I can reach my goal? • What ideas have worked before and how can I apply them?
To shift your perspective, ask:	• How has this always been done—and what would be a different way? • How can I approach this task or situation from a new angle? • How would someone else do this or view this? • What if . . . ?
To set the stage for creativity, ask:	• Where, and with whom, do I feel relaxed and inspired? • What music helps me think out of the box? • When in the day or night am I most likely to experience a flow of creative ideas? • What do I think would be new and interesting to try, to see, to read?
To take risks, ask:	• What is the conventional way of doing this? What would be a totally different way? • What would be a risky approach to this problem or question? • What is the worst that can happen if I take this risk? What is the best? • What have I learned from this mistake?

He quickly sized up his environment (bear and slower boy) and adapted (got ready to run) to pursue his goal (to escape becoming the bear's dinner).

Another example: Your goal is to pass freshman composition. You learn most successfully through visual presentations. To achieve your goal, you can use the instructor's PowerPoints or other visual media to enhance your learning (adapt to your environment) or enroll in a heavily visual Internet course (change your environment to adapt to you)—or both.

Why practical thinking is important

Real-world problems and decisions require you to add understanding of experiences and social interactions to your analytical abilities. Your success in a sociology class, for example, may depend almost as much on getting along with

your instructor as on your academic work. Similarly, the way you solve a personal money problem may have more impact on your life than how you work through a problem in an accounting course.

Keep in mind, too, that in the workplace you need to use practical skills to apply academic knowledge to problems and decisions. For example, although students majoring in elementary education may successfully quote child development facts on an exam, their career success depends on the ability to evaluate and address real children's needs in the classroom. Successfully solving real-world problems demands a practical approach.

Through experience, you build emotional intelligence

You gain much of your ability to think practically from personal experience, rather than from formal training.[16] What you learn from experience answers "how" questions—how to talk, how to behave, how to proceed.[17] For example, after completing several papers for a course, you may learn what your instructor expects—or, after a few arguments with a friend or partner, you may learn how to avoid topics that cause conflict. See Key 4.7 for ways in which this kind of knowledge can be shown in "if-then" statements.

As you learned in Chapter 1, emotional intelligence gives you steps you can take to promote success. For example, when Ethan was let go from his job, he was angry about it. With effort, his response involved these practical and emotionally and socially intelligent actions:

- ▶ After he received the letter, *recognizing* his feelings
- ▶ Working to *understand* what his feelings and mindset told him about what he wanted and how he perceived the situation
- ▶ *Adjusting* his thinking in order to gain something out of a bad situation

Key 4.7

HERE IS ONE WAY TO MAP OUT WHAT YOU **LEARN FROM EXPERIENCE**

Goal: You want to talk to the soccer coach about your status on the team.

IF the team has had a good practice and IF you've played well during the scrimmage and IF the coach isn't rushing off somewhere, THEN grab a moment with him right after practice ends.

IF the team is having a tough time and IF you've been sidelined and IF the coach is in a rush and stressed, THEN drop in during his office hours tomorrow.

> ► *Managing* his emotions by scheduling a meeting when he had calmed down, making his points at the meeting, keeping a productive goal in mind, and listening to what his supervisor said in response
> ► Politely requesting something related to his goal (such as a positive recommendation)

These emotionally intelligent actions make it more likely that Ethan's supervisor will be receptive and helpful and that there will be a positive outcome from the interaction.

If you know that social interactions are difficult for you, enlist someone to give you some informal coaching. Ask a friend to role-play the meeting with your instructor (your friend will act as if he is the instructor) and give you feedback on your words, tone, and body language. Or bring a friend with you to the actual meeting and talk later about how things went.

Practical thinking means action

Action is the logical result of practical thinking. Basic student success strategies that promote action—staying motivated, making the most of your strengths, learning from failure, managing time, seeking help from instructors and advisors, and believing in yourself—will keep you moving toward your goals.[18]

The key to making practical knowledge work is to use what you discover, assuring that you will not have to learn the same lessons over and over again. As Sternberg says, "What matters most is not how much experience you have had but rather how much you have profited from it—in other words, how well you apply what you have learned."[19]

See Key 4.8 for some questions you can ask in order to apply practical thinking to your problems and decisions.

ASK QUESTIONS LIKE THESE
TO ACTIVATE **PRACTICAL THINKING**

To learn from experience, ask:
- What worked well, or not so well, about my approach? My timing? My tone? My wording?
- What did others like or not like about what I did?
- What did I learn from that experience, conversation, event?
- How would I change things if I had to do it over again?
- What do I know I would do again?

To apply what you learn, ask
- What have I learned that would work here?
- What have I seen others do, or heard about from them, that would be helpful here?
- What does this situation have in common with past situations I've been involved in?
- What has worked in similar situations in the past?

To boost your ability to take action, ask:
- How can I get motivated and remove limitations?
- How can I, in this situation, make the most of what I do well?
- If I fail, what can I learn from it?
- What steps will get me to my goal, and what trade-offs are involved?
- How can I manage my time more effectively?

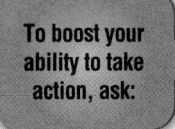

Take a Practical Approach to Building Successful Intelligence

Look back at your Wheel of Successful Intelligence in Chapter 1 on page 27. Write here the skill area in which you most need to build strength:

_____

Write down two practical actions you can take that will improve your skills in that area. For example, someone who wants to be more creative could take a course focused on creativity; someone who wants to be more practical could work on paying attention to social cues; someone who wants to be more analytical could decide to analyze one newspaper article every week.

1. _____

_____

2. _____

_____

How can you solve problems and make decisions **effectively?**

The best problem solvers and decision makers put their analytical, creative, and practical thinking skills together to solve problems and make decisions. Problem solving and decision making follow similar paths, both requiring you to identify and analyze a situation, generate possibilities, choose one, follow through on it, and evaluate its success. Key 4.9 gives an overview indicating the process at each step. Keys 4.11 and 4.12 show examples of how to map out problems and decisions effectively.

Understanding the differences between problem solving and decision making will help you know how to proceed. See Key 4.10 for more information. Remember, too, that whereas all problem solving involves decision making, not all decision making requires you to solve a problem.

Solve a problem

The following strategies will help you move through the problem-solving process outlined in Key 4.9.

■ *Use probing questions to define problems.* Ask, What is the problem? And what is causing the problem? Engage your emotional intelligence. If you determine that you are not motivated to do your work for a class, for example, you could ask questions like these:

▶ Do my feelings stem from how I interact with my instructor or classmates?
▶ Is the subject matter difficult? Uninteresting?

Chances are that how you answer one or more of these questions may help you define the problem—and ultimately solve it.

■ *Analyze carefully.* Gather information that will help you examine the problem. Consider how the problem is similar to, or different from, other problems. Clarify facts. Note your own perspective and look for others. Make sure your assumptions are not getting in the way.

■ *Generate possible solutions based on causes, not effects.* Addressing a cause provides a lasting solution, whereas "putting a Band-Aid on" an effect cannot. Say, for example, that your shoulder hurts when you type. Getting a massage is a helpful but temporary solution, because the pain returns whenever you go back to work. Changing your keyboard height is a lasting solution to the problem, because it eliminates the cause of your pain.

■ *Consider how possible solutions affect you and others.* What would suit you best? What takes other people's needs into consideration?

SOLVE PROBLEMS AND MAKE DECISIONS
USING SUCCESSFUL INTELLIGENCE

PROBLEM SOLVING	THINKING SKILL	DECISION MAKING
Define the problem—recognize that something needs to change, identify what's happening, look for true causes.	**STEP 1** **DEFINE**	**Define the decision**—identify your goal (your need) and then construct a decision that will help you get it.
Analyze the problem—gather information, break it down into pieces, verify facts, look at perspectives and assumptions, evaluate information.	**STEP 2** **ANALYZE**	**Examine needs and motives**—consider the layers of needs carefully, and be honest about what you really want.
Generate possible solutions—use creative strategies to think of ways you could address the causes of this problem.	**STEP 3** **CREATE**	**Name and/or generate different options**—use creative questions to come up with choices that would fulfill your needs.
Evaluate solutions—look carefully at potential pros and cons of each, and choose what seems best.	**STEP 4** **ANALYZE** **(EVALUATE)**	**Evaluate options**—look carefully at potential pros and cons of each, and choose what seems best.
Put the solution to work—persevere, focus on results, and believe in yourself as you go for your goal.	**STEP 5** **TAKE PRACTICAL ACTION**	**Act on your decision**—go down the path and use practical strategies to stay on target.
Evaluate how well the solution worked—look at the effects of what you did.	**STEP 6** **ANALYZE** **(REEVALUATE)**	**Evaluate the success of your decision**—look at whether it accomplished what you had hoped.
In the future, apply what you've learned—use this solution, or a better one, when a similar situation comes up again.	**STEP 7** **TAKE PRACTICAL ACTION**	**In the future, apply what you've learned**—make this choice, or a better one, when a similar decision comes up again.

EXAMINE HOW **PROBLEMS AND DECISIONS** DIFFER

SITUATION	YOU HAVE A PROBLEM IF . . .	YOU NEED TO MAKE A DECISION IF . . .
Planning summer activities	Your low GPA means you need to attend summer school—and you've already accepted a summer job.	You've been accepted into two summer abroad internship programs.
Declaring a major	It's time to declare, but you don't have all the prerequisites for the major you want.	There are three majors that appeal to you and you qualify for them all.
Handling communications with instructors	You are having trouble following the lecture style of a particular instructor.	Your psychology survey course has seven sections taught by different instructors; you have to choose one.

■ *Evaluate your solution and act on it in the future.* Once you choose a solution and put it into action, ask yourself, What worked that you would do again? What didn't work that you would avoid or change in the future?

What happens if you don't work through a problem comprehensively? Take, for example, a student having an issue with an instructor. He may get into an argument with the instructor, stop showing up to class, or take a quick-and-dirty approach to assignments. Any of these choices may have negative consequences. Now look at how the student might work through this problem using analytical, creative, and practical thinking skills. Key 4.11 shows how his effort can pay off.

Make a decision

As you use the steps in Key 4.9 to make a decision, remember these strategies.

■ *Look at the given options—then try to think of more.* Some decisions have a given set of options. For example, your school may allow you to major, double major, or major and minor. However, you may be able to brainstorm with an advisor to come up with more options such as an interdisciplinary major. Consider similar situations you've been in or heard about, what decisions were made, and what resulted from those decisions.

■ *Think about how your decision affects others.* What you choose might have an impact on friends, family, and others around you.

■ *Gather perspectives.* Talk with others who have made similar decisions. If you listen carefully, you may hear ideas you haven't thought about.

■ *Look at the long-term effects.* As with problem solving, it's key to examine what happens after you put the decision into action. For important decisions, do a short-term evaluation and another evaluation after a period of time. Consider whether your decision sent you in the right direction or whether you should rethink your choice.

WORK THROUGH A PROBLEM
RELATING TO AN INSTRUCTOR

Key 4.11

DEFINE PROBLEM HERE:	ANALYZE THE PROBLEM
I don't like my Sociology instructor	We have different styles and personality types—I am not comfortable working in groups and being vocal. I'm not interested in being there, and my grades are suffering from my lack of motivation.

Use boxes below to list possible solutions:

POTENTIAL POSITIVE EFFECTS	SOLUTION #1	POTENTIAL NEGATIVE EFFECTS
List for each solution: Don't have to deal with that instructor Less stress	Drop the course	List for each solution: Grade gets entered on my transcript I'll have to take the course eventually; it's required for my major
Getting credit for the course Feeling like I've honored a commitment	**SOLUTION #2** Put up with it until the end of the semester	Stress every time I'm there Lowered motivation Probably not such a good final grade
A chance to express myself Could get good advice An opportunity to ask direct questions of the instructor	**SOLUTION #3** Schedule meetings with advisor and instructor	Have to face instructor one-on-one Might just make things worse

Now choose the solution you think is best—circle it and make it happen.

ACTUAL POSITIVE EFFECTS	PRACTICAL ACTION	ACTUAL NEGATIVE EFFECTS
List for chosen solution: Got some helpful advice from advisor Talking in person with the instructor actually promoted a fairly honest discussion I won't have to take the course again	I scheduled and attended meetings with both advisor and instructor and opted to stick with the course.	List for chosen solution: Still have to put up with some group work I still don't know how much learning I'll retain from this course

FINAL EVALUATION: Was it a good or bad solution?

The solution has improved things. I'll finish the course, and I got the chance to fulfill some class responsibilities on my own or with one partner. I feel more understood and more willing to put my time into the course.

student profile

Brad Zak
Boston College, Chestnut Hill, Massachusetts

About me:

Always a sports enthusiast, I played basketball and football throughout high school in northern New Jersey, but decided not to pursue a sports career in college. I now attend BC's (Boston College's) Carroll School of Management.

What I focus on:

Early on, I developed a quiet, analytical way of weighing pros and cons before committing to a decision. Knowing I want a strong business background, I picked a major in finance even though I am not terribly interested in becoming an invest-

ment banker. When I arrived on campus, I decided it was crucial that I explore career options and build my resumé. I also realized that I missed being involved in sports, so I made my way over to the school newspaper and became a sports reporter.

Pretty quickly, I concluded that I want to pursue a career combining sports with business . . . but BC does not offer a sports management major. I needed some creative thinking to solve this problem! I declared communications as a second major and looked for more opportunities to develop skills in that field. In addition to writing for the BC newspaper, I've announced games on radio, written for ESPN Boston, worked as a campus rep for CBS College Sports,

competed in intramural sports . . . and became a Division I athlete. Well, not exactly—but I am a practice player for the women's basketball team.

What will help me in the workplace:

I believe I've used my problem-solving and decision-making skills to create the finance major's resumé for landing a job in the sports world. I certainly have some great experiences to talk about on job interviews!

Business world success is all about problem solving and decision making. My experiences will help me navigate the challenges ahead.

What happens when you make important decisions too quickly? Consider a student trying to decide whether to transfer schools. If she makes her decision based on a reason that ultimately is not the most important one for her (for example, close friends go to the other school), she may regret her choice.

Now look at how this student might make an effective decision. Key 4.12 shows how she worked through the analytical, creative, and practical parts of the process.

Keep your balance

No one has equal strengths in analytical, creative, and practical thinking. However, you think and work toward goals most effectively when you combine all three. Staying as balanced as possible requires that you analyze your levels

MAKE A DECISION ABOUT
WHETHER TO TRANSFER SCHOOLS

DEFINE PROBLEM HERE:	EXAMINE NEEDS AND MOTIVES
Whether or not to transfer schools	My father has changed jobs and can no longer afford my tuition. My goal is to become a physical therapist, so I need a school with a full physical therapy program. My family needs to cut costs. I need to transfer credits.

Use boxes below to list possible solutions:

POTENTIAL POSITIVE EFFECTS	SOLUTION #1	POTENTIAL NEGATIVE EFFECTS
List for each solution:	Continue at the current college	List for each solution:
No need to adjust to a new place or new people		Need to finance most of my tuition and costs on my own
Ability to continue course work as planned		Difficult to find time for a job
		Might not qualify for aid

POTENTIAL POSITIVE EFFECTS	SOLUTION #2	POTENTIAL NEGATIVE EFFECTS
Many physical therapy courses available	Transfer to the community college	No personal contacts there that I know of
School is close so I could live at home and save room costs		Less independence if I live at home
Reasonable tuition; credits will transfer		No bachelor's degree available

POTENTIAL POSITIVE EFFECTS	SOLUTION #3	POTENTIAL NEGATIVE EFFECTS
Opportunity to earn tuition money	Stop out for a year	Could forget so much that it's hard to go back
Could live at home		Could lose motivation
Status should be intact		A year might turn into more

Now choose the solution you think is best—circle it and make it happen.

ACTUAL POSITIVE EFFECTS	PRACTICAL ACTION	ACTUAL NEGATIVE EFFECTS
List for chosen solution:	Go to community college for two years; then transfer to a four-year school to get a B.A. and complete physical therapy course work.	List for chosen solution:
Money saved		Loss of some independence
Opportunity to spend time on studies rather than on working to earn tuition money		Less contact with friends
Availability of classes I need		

FINAL EVALUATION: Was it a good or bad solution?

I'm satisfied with the decision. It can be hard being at home at times, but my parents are adjusting to my independence and I'm trying to respect their concerns. With fewer social distractions, I'm really getting my work done. Plus the financial aspect of the decision is ideal.

of ability in the three thinking areas, come up with creative ideas about how to build areas where you need to develop, and put them to use with practical action. Above all, believe in your skills as a thinker.

"Successfully intelligent people," says Sternberg, "defy negative expectations, even when these expectations arise from low scores on IQ or similar tests. They do not let other people's assessments stop them from achieving their goals. They find their path and then pursue it, realizing that there will be obstacles along the way and that surmounting these obstacles is part of the challenge."[20] Let the obstacles come, as they will for everyone, in all aspects of life. You can face and overcome them with the power of your successfully intelligent thinking.

Case Wrap-up

What happened to Ethan? First of all, a savvy friend got him to look carefully at his short-term money situation. He realized that with his severance pay, even though it will only last a month, he can cover tuition expenses through the rest of the term. That will buy him time to think more carefully about what to do next. He also went back to the Bureau of Labor website to look at the thirty occupations anticipated to grow the most in the next 5 years. He noted that although programming is estimated to shrink, other related areas such as network systems and software engineering are looking good. He also reminded himself that a projection isn't necessarily going to come true. His mood began to turn more positive as he opened his mind up to other possibilities for how to use what he does well and has chosen to study.

What does this mean for you? Think about the areas of study that interest you at this point. Examine information at www.bls.gov to see if your interest(s) relate to any career areas projected to grow or recede in the next 10 years. Look up any other articles you can find on career projections. Then write about where you stand. How does what you've read change, or reinforce, your educational and career goals?

What effects go beyond your world? The volatile job market is affecting workers from the bottom of the ladder to the top. Imagine you are the president of your college, speaking at graduation. What would you say to your graduating students to prepare them to successfully enter—and thrive in—today's workplace?

Successful Intelligence *Wrap-up*

HERE'S HOW YOU HAVE
BUILT SKILLS IN **CHAPTER 4** :

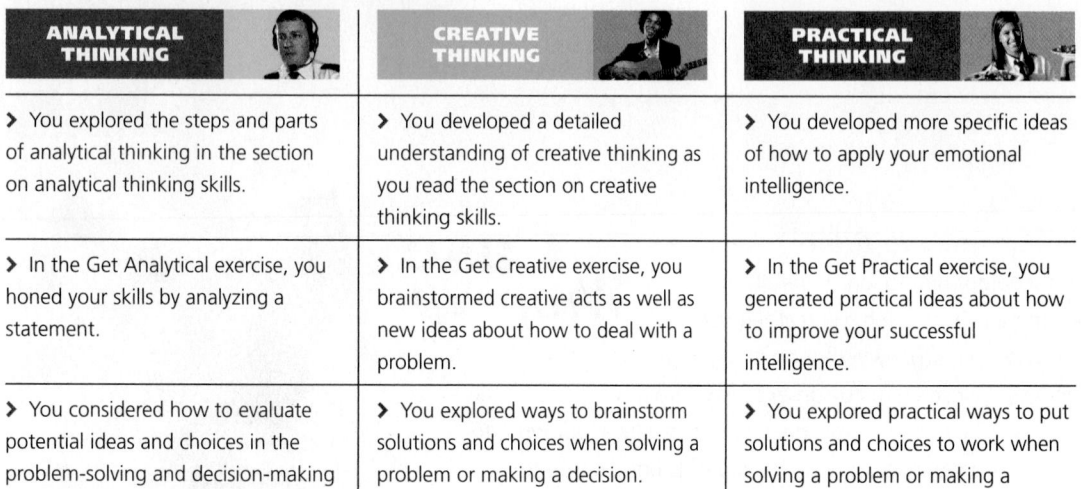

ANALYTICAL THINKING	CREATIVE THINKING	PRACTICAL THINKING
› You explored the steps and parts of analytical thinking in the section on analytical thinking skills.	› You developed a detailed understanding of creative thinking as you read the section on creative thinking skills.	› You developed more specific ideas of how to apply your emotional intelligence.
› In the Get Analytical exercise, you honed your skills by analyzing a statement.	› In the Get Creative exercise, you brainstormed creative acts as well as new ideas about how to deal with a problem.	› In the Get Practical exercise, you generated practical ideas about how to improve your successful intelligence.
› You considered how to evaluate potential ideas and choices in the problem-solving and decision-making processes.	› You explored ways to brainstorm solutions and choices when solving a problem or making a decision.	› You explored practical ways to put solutions and choices to work when solving a problem or making a decision.

Word *for* Thought

A recently coined **Norwegian** verb—*kunnskaping* (kun'-skahp-ping)—translates loosely as "knowledging," which can be read as developing knowledge and meaning that are useful in school and work (and more important than ever before in the global marketplace).[21] Work to develop the analytical, creative, and practical skills that can help you "knowledge" your way to success.

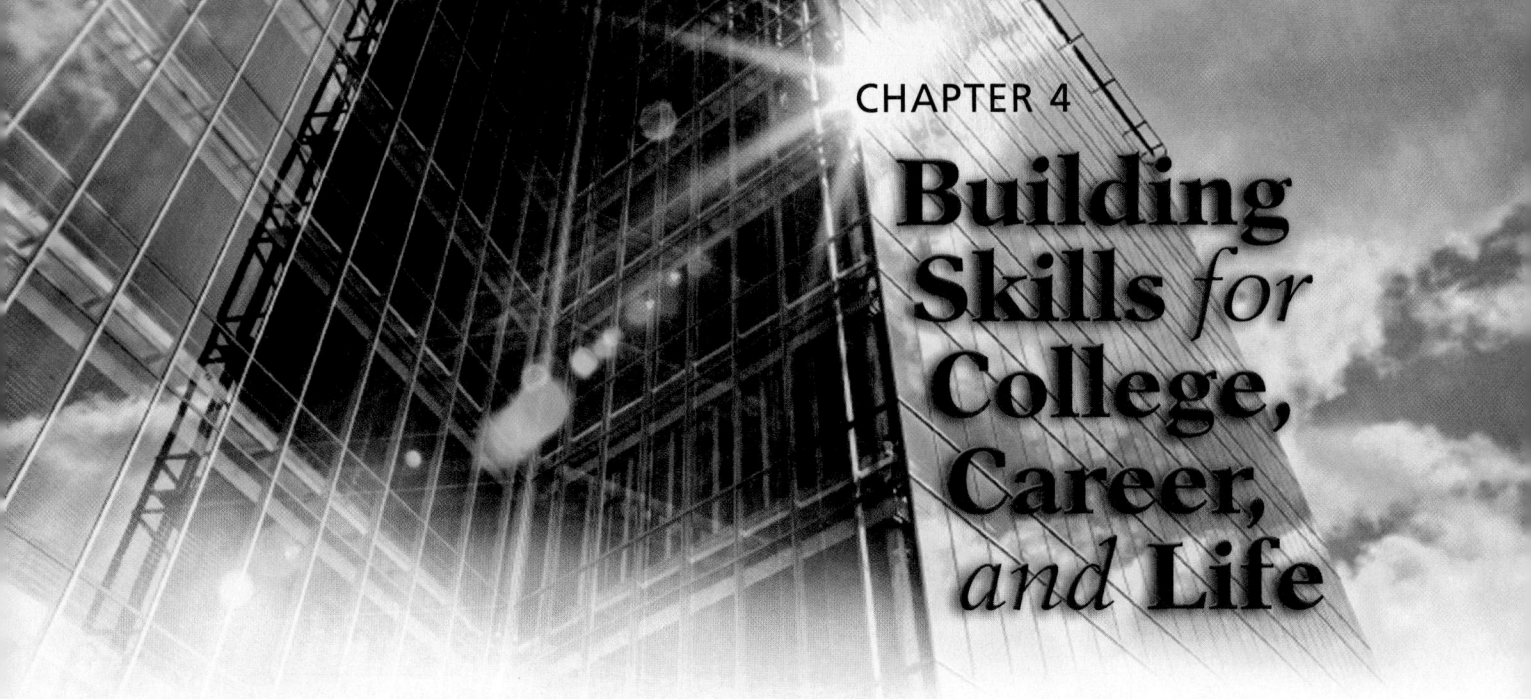

Building Skills *for* College, Career, *and* Life

Steps to Success

Make an Important Decision

BUILD BASIC SKILLS. List the steps of the decision-making process.

_____

_____

_____

_____

TAKE IT TO THE NEXT LEVEL. Think about how you would put the decision-making process to work on something that matters to you. Write an important long-term goal that you have, and define the decision that will help you fulfill it. Example: "My goal is to become a nurse. My decision: What to specialize in."

_____

_____

_____

_____

MOVE TOWARD MASTERY. Use a separate piece of paper to apply the decision-making process to your goal. Use the following steps to organize your thinking.

- *Examine needs and concerns.* What are your needs, and how do your values come into play? What is most needed in the health market, and how can you fulfill that need? What roadblocks might be involved? List everything you come up with. For example, the prospective nurse might list the following needs: "I need to feel that I'm helping people. I intend to help with the shortage of peri-natal or geriatric nurses. I need to make a good living."

- *Generate options.* Ask questions to imagine what's possible. Where might you work? What might be the schedule and pace? Who might work with you? What would you see, smell, and hear on your job? What would you do every day? List, too, all of the options you know of. The prospective nurse, for example, might list perinatal surgery, neonatal intensive care unit, geriatric nursing in a hospital or in a retirement community, and so on.

- *Evaluate options.* Think about how well your options will fulfill your needs. For two of your options, write potential positive and negative effects (pros and cons) of each.

Option 1: _____

Potential pros: _____

Potential cons: _____

Option 2: _____

Potential pros: _____

Potential cons: _____

- *Imagine acting on your decision.* Describe one practical course of action, based on your thinking so far, that you might follow. List the specific steps you would take. For example, the prospective nurse might list actions to help determine what type of nursing suits him best, such as interning, summer jobs, academic goals, and talking to working nurses.

An additional practical action is to go to an actual job site and talk to people. The prospective nurse might go to a hospital, a clinic, and a health center at a retirement community. Get a feel for what the job is like day-to-day so that can be part of your decision.

Teamwork

Create Solutions Together

POWERFUL GROUP PROBLEM SOLVING

Goal: To experience problem solving as a group and to generate useful and relevant solutions.

Time on task: 30 minutes

Instructions: On a 3 × 5 card or a plain sheet of paper, each student in the class writes a school-related problem—this could be a fear, a challenge, a sticky situation, or a roadblock. Students hand these in without names. The instructor writes the list up on the board.

Divide into groups of two to four. Each group chooses one problem to work on (try not to have two groups working on the same problem). Use the empty problem-solving flowchart (Key 4.13) to fill in your work.

Analyze: Define and examine the problem. As a group, look at the negative effects and state your problem specifically. Write down the causes and examine them to see what's happening. Gather information from all group members, verify facts, and go beyond assumptions.

Create: Generate possible solutions. From the most likely causes of the problem, derive possible solutions. Record all the ideas that group members offer. Each group member should choose one possible solution to evaluate independently.

Analyze: Evaluate each solution. In thinking independently through the assigned solution, each group member should (a) weigh the positive and negative effects, (b) consider similar problems, and (c) describe how the solution affects the causes of the problem. Will your solution work?

Get practical: Choose a solution. Group members then come together, share observations and recommendations, and then take a vote: Which solution is the best? You may have a tie or want to combine two different solutions. Try to find the solution that works for most of the group. Then together come up with a plan for putting your solution to work.

To wrap up, think and write. What did you learn about problem solving from doing it in a group setting? What was different, easier, harder, the same?

WORK THROUGH A PROBLEM
USING THIS **FLOWCHART**

DEFINE PROBLEM HERE:	ANALYZE THE PROBLEM

Use boxes below to list possible solutions:

POTENTIAL POSITIVE EFFECTS	SOLUTION #1	POTENTIAL NEGATIVE EFFECTS
List for each solution:		List for each solution:

	SOLUTION #2	

	SOLUTION #3	

Now choose the solution you think is best—circle it and make it happen.

ACTUAL POSITIVE EFFECTS	PRACTICAL ACTION	ACTUAL NEGATIVE EFFECTS
List for chosen solution:		List for chosen solution:

FINAL EVALUATION: Was it a good or bad solution?

Source: Based on heuristic created by Frank T. Lyman Jr. and George Eley, 1985.

Writing

Build Intrapersonal and Communication Skills

Record your thoughts on a separate piece of paper, in a journal, or electronically.

EMOTIONAL INTELLIGENCE JOURNAL

Make a wiser choice. Think about a decision you made that you wish you had handled differently. Describe the decision and what feelings resulted from it. Then, describe what you would do if you could approach the decision again, thinking about a mindset and actions that might produce more positive feelings and a better outcome.

REAL-LIFE WRITING

Address a problem. Think about a problem that you are currently experiencing in school—it could be difficulty with a course, a scheduling nightmare, or a conflict with a classmate. Write a letter—to an advisor, instructor, friend, medical professional, or anyone else who may help—that asks for help with your problem. Be specific about what you want and how the person to whom you are writing can help you. After you finish, consider sending your letter via mail or e-mail. Carefully assess the effect that it may have, and if you decide that it may help, send it. Be sure to have someone you trust review it for you before you send.

Personal Portfolio

Prepare for Career Success

GENERATE IDEAS FOR INTERNSHIPS

21st Century Learning Building Blocks

- Financial, Economic, Business, and Entrepreneurial Literacy
- Leadership and Responsibility
- Communication and Collaboration

Complete the following in your electronic portfolio or separately on paper.

Pursuing internships is a practical way to get experience, learn what you like and don't like, and make valuable connections. Even interning in a career area that you don't ultimately pursue can build skills that are useful in any career. The creative thinking skills you've built will help you generate ideas for where you might intern at some point during college.

First, use personal contacts to gather information about career fields. List two people here:

People whom I want to interview about their fields/professions, and why:

1. _____   Field: _____

   Because: _____

2. _____   Field: _____

   Because: _____

Talk to the people you have listed and take notes.

Next, look up each of these fields in the *Occupational Outlook Handbook* published by the U.S. Department of Labor (available at the library or online at http://stats.bls.gov/oco/home.htm). To get a better idea of whether you would want to intern in these fields, read OOH categories for each such as

Nature of the Work, Training, Working Conditions, Advancement, Job Outlook, Earnings, and so on. Take notes and compare the fields based on what you've learned.

Finally, consult someone in your school's career office about local companies that offer internships. Get specific information about internship job descriptions, timing (during the term, summer), and whether there is any financial compensation involved.

Analyze what you have learned from your reading, your interviews, and career office information. Write here the field or fields in which you would like to intern and why, and describe what practical action you plan to take to secure an internship within the next two years:

_____

_____

_____

_____

_____

_____

_____

_____

_____

_____

Social Networking

ESTABLISH YOUR HISTORY

Broaden your profile with information about any work history you have. Sign in to your LinkedIn account and click on "Edit My Profile." Then, fill in work information on the following (as applicable):

- Current (Click on "Current" and add information about your current employment: company name, job title, when you started working there, and description.)
- Past (Click on "Past" and add information about one or more past jobs: company name, job title, time period you worked, and description.)

If you have a lean or nonexistent work history, start thinking now about how to build that history while you are in school. Besides paid jobs in the workforce, other possibilities include internships, volunteering, and working on campus with faculty. Be sure to update your resumé and LinkedIn profile with work history as you build it.

■ *Answers to perception puzzles on p. 105:* First puzzle: A duck or a rabbit. Second puzzle: A face or a musician. Third puzzle: Lines or a letter.

chapter 5

Reading and Information Literacy

Learning from Print and Online Materials

What Would You Do?

Think about this problem as you read, and consider how you would approach it. This chapter focuses on reading in ways that help you take in information comprehensively, analyze it critically, and decide what to remember. It can help you with any reading struggle you need to address on your path to success.

Gary Montrose had no idea why he struggled in grade school, and neither did his family or teachers. He was the first to sit down during spelling bees and the last to turn in class exams, even though his hard work got him elected student body president at Palmdale High School. His guidance counselor told him that he "wasn't college material" and should consider going straight into a job at the local Lockheed assembly plant.

Determined to persevere, Gary enrolled at Antelope Valley College in Palmdale, California, and put his nose to the grindstone. After 2 years he was able to transfer to the University of California at Berkeley, but the confusing struggle remained, damaging his self-confidence and requiring survival strategies developed through experience. He avoided courses with in-class timed exams—an absolute terror—and looked for classes featuring papers he could write on his own time. He gave up 90 percent of a normal college student's social life and spent hours "unpacking" textbooks by reading the table of contents, chapter headings, tables, and charts. Knowing he was unlikely to complete any reading assignment without support, he needed to develop an idea of the scope of a book.

Despite graduating with high honors and a double major, Gary still lived with his "big secret," terrified about how slowly he read and wrote. Hoping for advice on what type of work he could suc-

cessfully pursue, he went to the career center while in graduate school, where a series of tests showed he was functioning at a seventh-grade reading level. From those results he learned that he had a reading disability called *dyslexia* that causes difficulty with recognizing and understanding words. He began to see why he needed to put in so much extra time and effort to appear normal to the outside world. (To be continued . . .)

Gary's ability to move out of his comfort zone has helped him turn learning into an adventure that he continues as a world-wide traveler. You'll learn more about Gary, and revisit his situation, within the chapter.

In this chapter, you'll explore answers to these questions:

> What sets you up for reading comprehension? p. 126

> How can SQ3R improve your reading? p. 129

> What strategies help with specific subjects and formats? p. 140

> How can you be an information literate reader and researcher? p. 146

> How can you respond critically to what you read? p. 149

ANALYTICAL   CREATIVE   PRACTICAL

For each statement, circle the number that feels right to you, from 1 for "not at all true for me" to 5 for "very true for me."

▶ I make choices in when and how I read that help me boost focus and comprehension.	1 2 3 4 5
▶ I preview a text before studying it by skimming and scanning front matter, chapter elements, and back matter for clues about content and organization.	1 2 3 4 5
▶ I develop questions to guide me before I begin to read.	1 2 3 4 5
▶ I practice reciting what I've learned from the reading by working with a study partner, taking notes, using flash cards, or some other study technique.	1 2 3 4 5
▶ I use text note taking and highlighting to turn my texts into study tools.	1 2 3 4 5
▶ I have a process for reading on-screen assignments and articles.	1 2 3 4 5
▶ I prioritize my reading assignments so that I focus on what is most important.	1 2 3 4 5
▶ When I get a research or writing assignment, I go first to general references for an overview.	1 2 3 4 5
▶ I don't just rely on the Internet for research—I also consult library materials.	1 2 3 4 5
▶ I evaluate every Internet source for signs of bias, validity, credibility, and reliability.	1 2 3 4 5

Each of the topics in these statements is covered in this chapter. Note those statements for which you circled a 3 or lower. Skim the chapter to see where those topics appear, and pay special attention to them as you read, learn, and apply new strategies.

REMEMBER: **No matter how developed your reading and information literacy skills are, you can improve with effort and practice.**

"Successful intelligence is most effective when it balances all three of its analytical, creative, and practical aspects. It is more important to know when and how to use these aspects of successful intelligence than just to have them."

—Robert Sternberg

What sets you up for reading comprehension?

College reading assignments—textbook chapters or other materials—are often challenging, requiring more focus and new strategies to understand the material fully. In exchange for your extra effort, though, you stand to receive a broad and deep range of information and knowledge. Working hard to understand material in introductory-level texts also provides a more solid foundation for your understanding in advanced courses. Finally, if you are open to it, the new worlds reading reveals can bring you great satisfaction and even joy.

On any given day, you may have a variety of reading assignments, such as the following:

▶ An eighteen-page text chapter on the history of South African apartheid (world history)
▶ An original research study on the relationship between sleep deprivation and the development of memory problems (psychology)
▶ The first three chapters in John Steinbeck's classic novel *The Grapes of Wrath* (American literature)

▶ A technical manual on the design of computer anti-virus programs (computer science—software design)

To face this challenge, it's helpful to use specific reading techniques. Before you open a book or log onto your computer, how can you get ready to make the most of your reading?

Define your reading purpose

The first step in improving your reading comprehension is to ask yourself *why* you are reading particular material. With a clear purpose you can decide how much time and effort to expend on your assignments. Key 5.1 shows four common reading purposes. Depending on what your instructor expects, you may have as many as three reading purposes for one assignment, such as understanding, critical evaluation, and practical application.

Use the class syllabus to help define your purpose for each assignment. For example, if the syllabus shows that inflation is the topic of your next economics class lecture, read the assigned chapter with that focus in mind: mastering the definition of inflation, evaluating historical economic events that caused inflation, and so on. And keep open the possibility that any reading assignment with purposes 1, 2, or 3 may also bring you purpose 4—enjoyment.

Take an active and positive approach

Many instructors spend little or no time reviewing reading in class because they expect you to complete it independently. How can you approach difficult material actively and positively?

If you look carefully at your schedule, you may find useful segments of time in between classes. Try using such time for reading assignments.
© Spencer Grant/Photo Researchers

Key 5.1 ESTABLISH WHY YOU ARE READING A GIVEN PIECE OF MATERIAL

WHAT'S MY PURPOSE?	EXPLANATION
1. To understand	Read to comprehend concepts and details. Details help explain or support general concepts, and concepts provide a framework for details.
2. To evaluate analytically	Read with an open mind as you examine causes and effects, evaluate ideas, and ask questions that test arguments and assumptions. Evaluation develops a level of understanding beyond basic information recall (see pages 97 to 102 for more on this topic).
3. For practical application	Read to find information to help reach a specific goal. For instance, when you read a lab manual for chemistry, your goal is to learn how to do the lab experiment.
4. For pleasure	Read for entertainment, such as *Sports Illustrated* magazine or a mystery or romance novel.

▶ *Start with a questioning attitude.* Consider questions such as, How can I connect the reading to what I already know? Look at the chapter headings and ask yourself questions about what the material means and why it is being presented in this way.

▶ *Look for order.* Use SQ3R and the critical reading strategies introduced later in this chapter to discover patterns, logic, and relationships. Text cues—how the material is organized, outlines, bold terms, and more—help you anticipate what's coming next.

▶ *Have an open mind.* Be careful not to prejudge assignments as impossible or boring or a waste of time before you begin.

▶ *Plan for multiple readings.* Don't expect to master challenging material on the first pass. Get an overview of key concepts on the first reading. Use later readings to build your understanding, relate information to what you know, and apply information elsewhere. Gary accepted multiple readings as necessary to his success.

▶ *Get help.* If material is tough to understand, consult resources—instructors, study group partners, tutors, related texts, and websites—for help. Build a library of texts in your major and minor areas of study and refer to them when needed.

Choose the right setting

Where, when, and with whom you study has a significant effect on your success.

▶ *Choose locations that work.* Know yourself and choose settings that distract you least—in your room at home, at a library, outdoors, in an empty classroom, anywhere that works. Your schedule may restrict your choices. For example, if you can only study late at night when the libraries are closed, you will probably have to work at home; if you spend a good deal of your day commuting, mass transit may be your best study spot. Evaluate how effectively you focus. If you spend too much time time being distracted at a particular location, try someplace different.

▶ *Choose times that work.* Pay attention to your body's natural rhythms, and try to read during times when you tend to be most alert and focused. For example, although night owls are productive when everyone else is sleeping, morning people may have a hard time reading late at night. The times you choose depend, of course, on what your schedule allows.

PRIMARY SOURCES Original documents, including academic journal articles and scientific studies.

SECONDARY SOURCES Other writers' interpretations of primary source documents.

Learn to concentrate

Even well-written college textbooks may require a lot of focus, especially when you encounter complex concepts and new terms. Even greater focus is often necessary when assignments are from **primary sources** rather than **secondary sources.**

When you focus your attention on one thing and only one thing, you are engaged in the act of *concentration.* The following active-learning methods can help maintain focus as you study. Many involve tapping into your emotional and social intelligence.

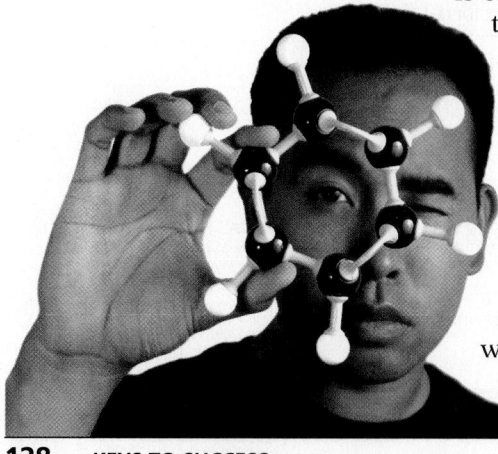

▶ *Deal with internal distractions.* When worries come up, such as to-do list items for other projects, write them down to deal with later. Sometimes you may want to take a break to deal with what's bothering you. Exercise may help, or music may relieve stress; a snack can reduce hunger.

▶ *Take control of technology.* Web surfing, e-mailing, instant messaging, or downloading songs onto your iPod are reading distractions. Wait for breaks or after you finish your work to spend time checking texts or downloading.

▶ *Structure your work session.* Set realistic goals and a specific plan for dividing your time. Tell yourself, "I'm going to read 30 pages and then go online for 30 minutes."

▶ *Manage family obligations.* Set up activities or child care if you have kids. Tell them, if they are old enough to understand, what your education will mean to them and to you.

▶ *Plan a reward.* Have something to look forward to. You deserve it!

The strongest motivation to concentrate comes from within. When you see the connection between what you study and your short- and long-term goals, you will be better able to focus, to remember, to learn, and to apply.

Expand your vocabulary

As reading materials become more complex, your vocabulary influences how much you comprehend—and how readily you do so. When reading a textbook, the first "dictionary" to search is the end-of-book glossary that explains technical words and concepts. The definitions there are usually limited to the meanings used in the text. Standard dictionaries provide broader information such as word origin, pronunciation, part of speech, synonyms, antonyms, and multiple meanings. Buy a standard dictionary and investigate websites like dictionary.com. The suggestions in Key 5.2 will help you make the most of your dictionary.

How can SQ3R improve **your reading?**

Reading may look like a one-way street in which you, the reader, take in words the author has written. However, it is intended as an interactive communication. The author communicates ideas to you and invites your response. How can you respond? One answer is provided in the SQ3R reading strategy, which stands for *Survey, Question, Read, Recite,* and *Review.*[1] This straightforward technique helps readers take in, understand, and remember what they read. It encourages you to fulfill your side of interactive communication by asking questions, marking key ideas, introducing your own connections, and more.

As you move through the stages of SQ3R, you will skim and scan your text. **Skimming** refers to the rapid reading of such chapter elements as section introductions and conclusions, boldface or italicized terms, pictures and charts, and summaries. The goal of skimming is a quick construction of the main ideas. In contrast, **scanning** involves a careful search for specific information. You might use scanning during the SQ3R review phase to locate particular facts.

Just like many strategies presented to you throughout your college career, SQ3R works best if you adapt it to your own needs. Explore techniques, evaluate what works, and then make the system your own. As you become familiar with the system, keep in mind that SQ3R works best with textbook-based courses like science, math, social sciences, and humanities. SQ3R is not recommended for literature courses.

SKIMMING
Rapid, superficial reading of material to determine central ideas and main elements.

SCANNING
Reading material in an investigative way to search for specific information.

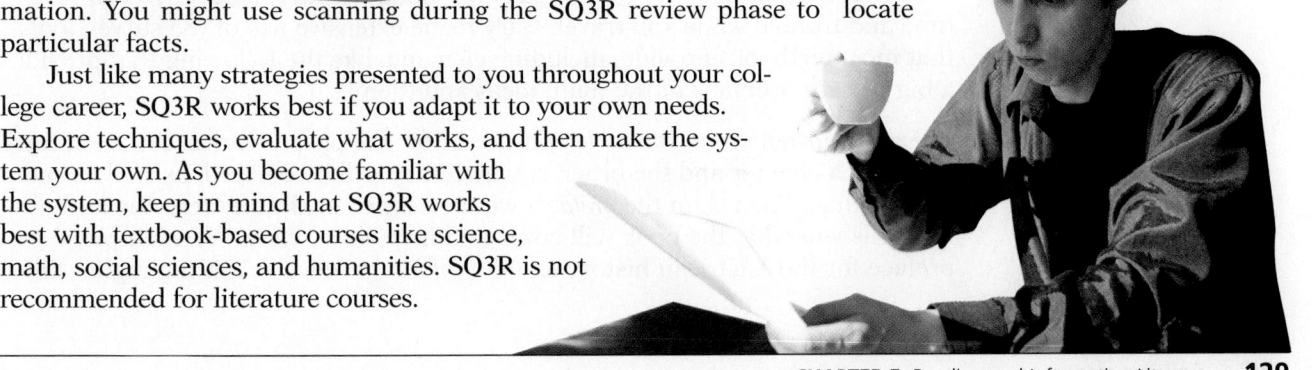

Use the word in the next 24 hours.

Not only does this demonstrate that you know how the word is used, but it also aids memorization.

Analyze word parts.

Many English words combine prefixes, roots, and suffixes. *Prefixes* are word parts added to the beginning of a root. *Suffixes* are added to the end of the root. The *root* is the central part or basis of a word around which prefixes and/or suffixes are added to produce different words. Recognizing these word parts can boost comprehesion.

Read beyond the first definition.

Then think critically about which meaning suits the context of the word in question and choose the one that makes the most sense.

dic-tio-nary

Pronunciation; \ˈdik-shə-ˌner-ē, -ˌne-rē\

Function: *noun*

Inflected Form(s): *plural* **dic·tio·nar·ies**

Etymology: Medieval Latin *dictionarium*, from Late Latin *diction-*, *dictio* word, from Latin, speaking

Date: 1526

1. A reference source in print or electronic form containing words usually alphabetically arranged along with information about their forms, pronunciations, functions, etymologies, meanings, and syntactical and idiomatic uses.

2. A book giving information on particular subjects or on a particular class of words, names, or facts, usually arranged alphabetically: *a biographical dictionary; a dictionary of mathematics.*

3. (*computing*) An associative array, a data structure where each value is referenced by a particular key, analogous to words and definitions in a physical dictionary.

Say and spell new words to boost recall.

Listen to the pronunciation on a hand-held electronic or online dictionary. Then practice writing the word to verify that you know the spelling.

Restate the definition in your own words.

When you can do this with ease, you know that you understand the meaning and are not merely parroting a dictionary definition.

Step 1: Survey

Surveying, the first stage in SQ3R, is the process of previewing, or prereading, a book before you study it. Compare it to looking at a map before starting a road trip; determining the route and stops along the way in advance will save time and trouble while you travel. Gary made extensive use of the survey tools that most textbooks provide, including elements like the following that provide a big picture overview of the main ideas and themes.

■ *Front matter.* Skim the *table of contents* for the chapter titles, the main topics in each chapter and the order in which they will be covered, as well as special features. Then skim the *preface,* which is a personal note from the author that tells you what the book will cover and its point of view. For example, the preface for the American history text *Out of Many* states that it highlights "the experiences of diverse communities of Americans in the unfolding story of our country."[2] This tells you that cultural diversity is a central theme.

■ **Chapter elements.** Text chapters use various devices to structure the material and highlight content.

▶ *Chapter titles* establish the topic and often the author's perspective.
▶ *Chapter introductions or outlines* generally list objectives or key topics.
▶ *Level headings* (first, second, third), including those in question form, break down material into bite-size chunks.
▶ *Margin materials* can include definitions, quotes, questions, and exercises.
▶ *Tables, charts, photographs, and captions* illustrate important concepts in a visual manner.
▶ *Sidebars or boxed features* are connected to text themes and introduce extra tidbits of information that supplement the text.
▶ *Different styles or arrangements of type* (**boldface,** *italics,* <u>underlining</u>, larger fonts, bullet points, boxed text) can flag vocabulary or important ideas.
▶ *End-of-chapter summaries* review chapter content and main ideas.
▶ *Review questions and exercises* help you understand and apply content in creative and practical ways.

In Key 5.3, a typical page from the college textbook *Psychology: An Introduction,* by Charles G. Morris and Albert A. Maisto, how many elements do you recognize? How do these elements help you grasp the subject even before reading it?

■ **Back matter.** Some texts include a *glossary* that defines text terms, an *index* to help you locate topics, and a *bibliography* that lists additional readings.

Step 2: Question

The next step is to ask questions about your assignment. Using the *questioning* process that follows leads you to discover knowledge on your own, making an investment in the material and in your own memory.

Ask yourself what you know

Before you begin reading, think about—and summarize in writing if you can—what you already know about the topic, if anything. This step prepares you to apply what you know to new material. Building on current knowledge is especially important in your major, where the concepts you learn from intro courses prepare you for the higher-level material in classes to come later on.

Write questions linked to chapter headings

Next, examine the chapter headings and, on a separate page or in the text margins, write questions linked to them. When you encounter an assignment without headings, divide the material into logical sections and then develop questions based on what you think is the main idea of each section. There are no "correct" questions. Given the same headings, two students could create two different sets of questions. Your goal in questioning is to begin to think critically about the material.

(186) **Chapter 5** • Learning

Classical (or Pavlovian) conditioning The type of learning in which a response naturally elicited by one stimulus comes to be elicited by a different, formerly neutral stimulus.

Unconditioned stimulus (US) A stimulus that invariably causes an organism to respond in a specific way.

Unconditioned response (UR) A response that takes place in an organism whenever an unconditioned stimulus occurs.

Conditioned stimulus (CS) An originally neutral stimulus that is paired with an unconditioned stimulus and eventually produces the desired response in an organism when presented alone.

Conditioned response (CR) After conditioning, the response an organism produces when only a conditioned stimulus is presented.

you are experiencing insight. When you imitate the steps of professional dancers you saw last night on television, you are demonstrating observational learning. Like conditioning, cognitive learning is one of our survival strategies. Through cognitive processes, we learn which events are safe and which are dangerous without having to experience those events directly. Cognitive learning also gives us access to the wisdom of people who lived hundreds of years ago, and it will give people living hundreds of years from now some insight into our experiences and way of life.

Our discussion begins with *classical conditioning*. This simple kind of learning serves as a convenient starting point for examining what learning is and how it can be observed.

Classical Conditioning

How did Pavlov's discovery of classical conditioning help to shed light on learning?

Ivan Pavlov (1849–1936), a Russian physiologist who was studying digestive processes, discovered classical conditioning almost by accident. Because animals salivate when food is placed in their mouths, Pavlov inserted tubes into the salivary glands of dogs to measure how much saliva they produced when they were given food. He noticed, however, that the dogs salivated before the food was in their mouths: The mere sight of food made them drool. In fact, they even drooled at the sound of the experimenter's footsteps. This aroused Pavlov's curiosity. What was making the dogs salivate even before they had the food in their mouths? How had they learned to salivate in response to the sound of the experimenter's approach?

To answer these questions, Pavlov set out to teach the dogs to salivate when food was not present. He devised an experiment in which he sounded a bell just before the food was brought into the room. A ringing bell does not usually make a dog's mouth water but, after hearing the bell many times just before getting fed, Pavlov's dogs began to salivate as soon as the bell rang. It was as if they had learned that the bell signaled the appearance of food, and their mouths watered on cue even if no food followed. The dogs had been conditioned to salivate in response to a new stimulus—the bell—that would not normally have prompted that response (Pavlov, 1927). Figure 5–1, shows one of Pavlov's procedures in which the bell has been replaced by a touch to the dog's leg just before food is given.

Elements of Classical Conditioning

Generally speaking, **classical (or Pavlovian) conditioning** involves pairing an *involuntary* response (for example, salivation) that is usually evoked by one stimulus with a different, formerly neutral stimulus (such as a bell or a touch on the leg). Pavlov's experiment illustrates the four basic elements of classical conditioning. The first is an **unconditioned stimulus (US)**, such as food, which invariably prompts a certain reaction—salivation, in this case. That reaction—the **unconditioned response (UR)**—is the second element and always results from the unconditioned stimulus: Whenever the dog is given food (US), its mouth waters (UR). The third element is the neutral stimulus—the ringing bell—which is called the **conditioned stimulus (CS)**. At first, the conditioned stimulus is said to be "neutral" with respect to the desired response (salivation), because dogs do not salivate at the sound of a bell unless they have been conditioned to react in this way by repeatedly presenting the CS and US together. Frequent pairing of the CS and US produces the fourth element in the classical conditioning process: the **conditioned response (CR)**. The conditioned response is the behavior that the animal has learned in response to the conditioned stimulus. Usually, the unconditioned response and the conditioned

Survey a Text

Practice will improve your surveying skills. Start now with this text or another you are currently using.

Skim the front matter, including the table of contents and preface. What does this material tell you about the theme? About the book's approach and point of view?

_____

_____

_____

Are there unexpected topics listed in the table of contents? Are there topics you expected to see that are missing?

_____

_____

Now look at a typical chapter. List the devices that organize the structure and content of the material.

_____

_____

After skimming the chapter, what do you know about the material? What elements helped you skim quickly?

_____

_____

Finally, skim the back matter. What elements can you identify?

_____

_____

How do you plan to use each of the elements you identified in your text survey when you begin studying?

_____

_____

Key 5.4 shows how this works. The column on the left contains primary and secondary headings from a section of *Out of Many*. The column on the right rephrases these headings in question form.

Use Bloom's Taxonomy to formulate questions

Questions can seek different types of answers and may require different levels of analytical thinking to solve. To help you understand and use different types of questions, consider the system educational psychologist Benjamin Bloom developed based on the idea that deeper learning occurs when the effort to understand is more rigorous.[3] Although some questions ask for a simple recall, said Bloom, others ask for higher thinking levels.

Key 5.5 shows the six levels of questions identified by Bloom: knowledge, understanding, application, analysis, synthesis, and evaluation. It also identifies

CREATE QUESTIONS
FROM HEADINGS

Key 5.4

HEADINGS	QUESTIONS
The Meaning of Freedom	What did freedom mean for both slaves and citizens in the United States?
Moving About	Where did African Americans go after they were freed from slavery?
The African American Family	How did freedom change the structure of the African American family?
African American Churches and Schools	What effect did freedom have on the formation of African American churches and schools?
Land and Labor After Slavery	How was land farmed and maintained after slaves were freed?
The Origins of African American Politics	How did the end of slavery bring about the beginning of African American political life?

USE BLOOM'S TAXONOMY TO
FORMULATE QUESTIONS
AT DIFFERENT COGNITIVE LEVELS

Key 5.5

Highest Level

Lowest Level

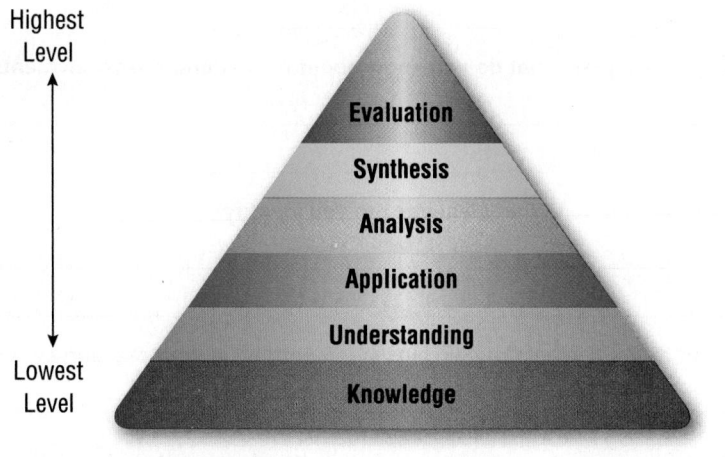

Evaluation
Synthesis
Analysis
Application
Understanding
Knowledge

Verbs That Indicate Each Level

1. **Knowledge:** average, define, duplicate, label, list, memorize, name, order, recognize, relate, recall, repeat, reproduce, state.

2. **Understanding:** classify, describe, discuss, explain, express, identify, indicate, locate, recognize, report, restate, review, select, translate.

3. **Application:** apply, choose, demonstrate, dramatize, employ, illustrate, interpret, operate, practice, schedule, sketch, solve, use, write.

4. **Analysis:** analyze, appraise, calculate, categorize, compare, contrast, criticize, differentiate, discriminate, distinguish, examine, experiment, question, test.

5. **Synthesis:** arrange, assemble, collect, compose, construct, create, design, develop, formulate, manage, organize, plan, prepare, propose, set up, write.

6. **Evaluation:** appraise, argue, assess, attach, choose, compare, defend, estimate, judge, predict, rate, score, select, support, value, evaluate.

verbs associated with each level. As you read, use these verbs to create specific questions that will help you learn. For instance, if you were to continue Key 5.4's process of creating questions based on the headings from *Out of Many,* the questions would change based on the level specified by Bloom's Taxonomy. See Key 5.6 for an example.

Step 3: Read

Your text survey and questions give you a starting point for *reading,* the first R in SQ3R. Retaining what you read requires an active approach.

▶ *Focus on the key points of your survey.* Pay special attention to points raised in headings, in boldface type, in the chapter objectives and summary, and in other emphasized text.
▶ *Focus on your Q-stage questions.* Read the material with the purpose of answering each question. Write down or highlight ideas and examples that relate to your questions.
▶ *Create text tabs.* Place plastic index tabs or adhesive notes at the start of each chapter so you can flip back and forth with ease.

Key 5.6 FOLLOW A QUESTION THROUGH THE STAGES OF BLOOM'S TAXONOMY

The Origins of African American Politics

Knowledge
• *List* three main characters of the early African American political scene.

Understanding
• *Explain* the struggles faced by African American politicians.

Application
• *Interpret* the impact of slavery on the early African American politicians.

Analysis
• *Compare* and *contrast* the Caucasian political environment of the time with the emerging African American politicians.

Synthesis
• *Arrange* the major events of the era as they corresponded with the emerging political movement.

Evaluation
• *Rate* the effectiveness of the first African American political campaign and note any changes since.

► *Mark up your text.* Write notes in the margins, circle main ideas, or underline supporting details to focus on what's important. For an e-book, use the "Insert comments" feature. These cues will boost memory and help you study for exams. Here are some tips for *annotating*—taking marginal notes on the pages of your text:

- Use pencil so you can erase comments or questions that are answered later.
- Write your Q questions in the margins next to text headings.
- Mark critical sections with marginal notations such as "Def." for definition, "e.g." for helpful example, "Concept" for an important concept, and so on.
- Write notes at the bottom of the page connecting the text to what you learned in class or in research. You can also attach adhesive notes with your comments.

► *Highlight your text.* *Highlighting* involves the use of special markers or regular pens or pencils to flag important passages. When working with e-books, make note of the highlighting function, which allows you to overlay a color on important text. When used correctly, highlighting is an essential learning technique. However, experts agree that you will not learn what to highlight unless you *interact* with the material through surveying, questioning, reciting, and reviewing. Use the following tips to make highlighting a true learning tool:

- *Develop a system and stick to it.* Decide whether you will use different colors to highlight different elements, brackets for long passages, or pencil underlining.
- *Consider using a regular pencil or pen instead of a highlighter pen.* The copy will be cleaner and may look less like a coloring book.
- *Mark text carefully if you are using a rented book or a book to be resold.* Use pencil as often as possible and erase your marks at the end of the class. Write on sticky notes that you can remove. Make copies of important chapters or sections for marking. If you are renting, check with the rental service to see what they permit.
- *Read an entire paragraph before you begin to highlight, and don't start until you have a sense of what is important.* Only then put pencil or highlighter to paper as you pick out the main idea, key terms, and crucial supporting details and examples.
- *Avoid overmarking.* Too much color can be overwhelming. Try enclosing long passages with brackets and avoid underlining entire sentences, when possible.

Key 5.7, from an introduction to business textbook describing the concepts of target marketing and market segmentation, shows how to underline and take marginal notes.

Find the main idea

Understanding what you read depends on your ability to recognize *main ideas* and link other ideas to them. The main idea may appear in a **topic sentence** at the beginning of the paragraph followed by supporting details, or at the end of the paragraph with supporting details leading up to it. Sometimes, though, it is harder to figure out. When the main idea of a passage is unclear, use a three-step approach to decide what it is:[4]

TOPIC SENTENCE
A one- to two-sentence statement describing the main idea of a paragraph.

1. *Search for the topic of the paragraph.* The topic of the paragraph is not the same as the main idea. Rather, it is the broad subject being discussed—for

Chapter 10: Understanding Marketing Processes and Consumer Behavior

297

How does target marketing and market segmentation help companies sell product?

■ TARGET MARKETING AND MARKET SEGMENTATION

Marketers have long known that products cannot be all things to all people. Buyers have different tastes, goals, lifestyles, and so on. The emergence of the marketing concept and the recognition of consumer needs and wants led marketers to think in terms of **target markets**—groups of people with similar wants and needs. Selecting target markets is usually the first step in the marketing strategy.

Target marketing requires **market segmentation**—dividing a market into categories of customer types or "segments." Once they have identified segments, companies may adopt a variety of strategies. Some firms market products to more than one segment. General Motors *(www.gm.com)*, for example, offers compact cars, vans, trucks, luxury cars, and sports cars with various features and at various price levels. GM's strategy is to provide an automobile for nearly every segment of the market.

In contrast, some businesses offer a narrower range of products, each aimed toward a specific segment. Note that segmentation is a strategy for analyzing consumers, not products. The process of fixing, adapting, and communicating the nature of the product itself is called *product positioning.*

Definitions

target market
Group of people that has similar wants and needs and that can be expected to show interest in the same products

← GM eg

market segmentation
Process of dividing a market into categories of customer types

GM makes cars for diff. market segments

How do companies identify market segments?

Identifying Market Segments

By definition, members of a market segment must share some common traits that affect their purchasing decisions. In identifying segments, researchers look at several different influences on consumer behavior. Three of the most important are *geographic, demographic,* and *psychographic variables.*

What effect does geography have on segmentation strategies?

Geographic Variables Many buying decisions are affected by the places people call home. The heavy rainfall in Washington State, for instance, means that people there buy more umbrellas than people in the Sun Belt. Urban residents don't need agricultural equipment, and sailboats sell better along the coasts than on the Great Plains. **Geographic variables** are the geographical units, from countries to neighborhoods, that may be considered in a segmentation strategy.

These patterns affect decisions about marketing mixes for a huge range of products. For example, consider a plan to market down-filled parkas in rural Minnesota. Demand will be high and price competition intense. Local newspaper ads may be

Buying decisions influenced by where people live

geographic variables
Geographical units that may be considered in developing a segmentation strategy

— good eg —
selling parkas in Minnesota

Thought
Geographical variables change with the seasons

example, Apple CEO Steve Jobs, hate crimes on campus, or binge drinking on campus.

2. *Identify the aspect of the topic that is the paragraph's focus.* If the general topic is Steve Jobs, the author may focus on any of thousands of aspects of that topic, such as his cofounding of Apple Computer in 1976; his role in Pixar, a computer animation company; or his involvement in the development of the iPod portable music player.

3. *Find what the author wants you to know about that specific aspect.* This is the main idea or topic sentence. Whereas the topic establishes the subject, a topic sentence narrows down the purpose of the paragraph into one or two focused statements. Thus, although the topic of the paragraph might be Apple CEO Steve Jobs, the main idea, or topic sentence, might be, "In his role as CEO of Apple, Steve Jobs oversaw the creation of the iPod portable music player, which changed the way the world listens to and purchases music."

Step 4: Recite

Once you finish reading a topic, stop and answer the questions you raised in the Q stage of SQ3R. Even if you have already done this during the reading phase, do it again now—with the purpose of learning and committing the material to memory by *reciting* the answers.

You can say each answer aloud, silently speak the answers to yourself, "teach" the answers to another person, or write your ideas and answers in note form. Whatever recitation method you choose, make sure you know how ideas connect to one another and to the general concept being discussed.

Writing is often the most effective way to learn new material. Write responses to your Q-stage questions and use your own words to explain new concepts; save your writing as a study tool for review. Writing gives you immediate feedback: When it agrees with the material you are studying, you know the information. When it doesn't, you still need work with the text or a study partner.

Keep your learning styles in mind while exploring different strategies (see Chapter 3). For example, an intrapersonal learner may prefer writing, whereas an interpersonal learner may choose to recite answers aloud to a classmate. A logical-mathematical learner may benefit from organizing material into detailed outlines or charts, as opposed to a musical learner, who might chant information aloud to a rhythm.

When do you stop to recite? Waiting for the end of a chapter is too late; stopping at the end of one paragraph is too soon. The best plan is to recite at the end of each text section, right before a new heading. Repeat the question–read–recite cycle until you complete the chapter. If you fumble for thoughts, reread the section until you are on solid ground.

Step 5: Review

Reviewing, both immediately and periodically in the days and weeks after you read, will help you memorize, understand, and learn material. If you close the book after reading it once, chances are that you will forget almost everything, which is why students who read material for the first time right before a test don't tend to do too well. *Reviewing is your key to learning.*

Reviewing the same material in several sessions over time will also help you identify knowledge gaps. It's

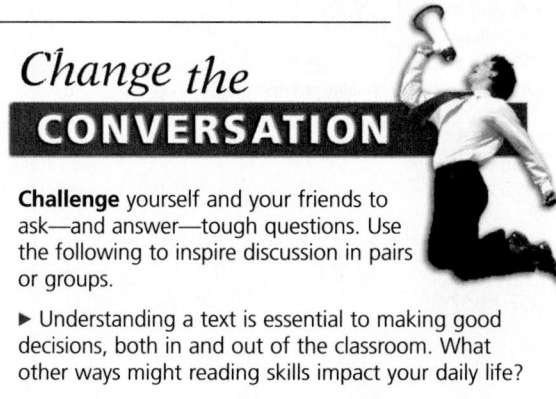

Change the
CONVERSATION

Challenge yourself and your friends to ask—and answer—tough questions. Use the following to inspire discussion in pairs or groups.

▶ Understanding a text is essential to making good decisions, both in and out of the classroom. What other ways might reading skills impact your daily life?

▶ What steps do you take to ensure that you understand texts? Have those strategies worked for you so far? Why or why not?

▶ **CONSIDER THE CASE:** What step (or steps) from SQ3R were most helpful to Gary in dealing with his particular challenge? What step or steps do you think will be most helpful to you, and why?

Mark Up a Page to Learn a Page

Below, the text material in Key 5.7 continues. Read it and mark it up, highlighting concepts and taking marginal notes. Compare your efforts to those of your classmates to see how each of you approached the task and what you can learn from their methods.

---

298   Part IV: Understanding Principles of Marketing

effective, and the best retail location may be one that is easily reached from several small towns.

Although the marketability of some products is geographically sensitive, others enjoy nearly universal acceptance. Coke, for example, gets more than 70 percent of its sales from international markets. It is the market leader in Great Britain, China, Germany, Japan, Brazil, and Spain. Pepsi's international sales are about 15 percent of Coke's. In fact, Coke's chief competitor in most countries is some local soft drink, not Pepsi, which earns 78 percent of its income at home.

demographic variables
Characteristics of populations that may be considered in developing a segmentation strategy

Demographic Variables Demographic variables describe populations by identifying such traits as age, income, gender, ethnic background, marital status, race, religion, and social class. For example, several general consumption characteristics can be attributed to certain age groups (18–25, 26–35, 36–45, and so on). A marketer can, thus, divide markets into age groups. Table 10.1 lists some possible demographic breakdowns. Depending on the marketer's purpose, a segment can be a single classification (*aged 20–34*) or a combination of categories (*aged 20–34, married with children, earning* $25,000–$34,999). Foreign competitors, for example, are gaining market share in U.S. auto sales by appealing to young buyers (under age 30) with limited incomes (under $30,000). Whereas companies such as Hyundai *(www.hyundai.net)*, Kia *(www.kia.com)*, and Daewoo *(www.daewoous.com)* are winning entry-level customers with high quality and generous warranties, Volkswagen *(www.vw.com)* targets under-35 buyers with its entertainment-styled VW Jetta.[4]

psychographic variables
Consumer characteristics, such as lifestyles, opinions, interests, and attitudes, that may be considered in developing a segmentation strategy

Psychographic Variables Markets can also be segmented according to such **psychographic variables** as lifestyles, interests, and attitudes. Take, for example, Burberry *(www.burberry.com)*, whose raincoats have been a symbol of British tradition since 1856. Burberry has repositioned itself as a global luxury brand, like Gucci *(www.gucci.com)* and Louis Vuitton *(www.vuitton.com)*. The strategy, which recently resulted in a 31-percent sales increase, calls for attracting a different type of customer—the top-of-the-line, fashion-conscious individual—who shops at such stores as Neiman Marcus and Bergdorf Goodman.[5]

Psychographics are particularly important to marketers because, unlike demographics and geographics, they can be changed by marketing efforts. For example, Polish companies have overcome consumer resistance by promoting the safety and desirability of using credit rather than depending solely on cash. One product of changing attitudes is a booming economy and the emergence of a robust middle class.

TABLE 10.1

Demographic Variables

Age	Under 5, 5–11, 12–19, 20–34, 35–49, 50–64, 65+
Education	Grade school or less, some high school, graduated high school, some college, college degree, advanced degree
Family life cycle	Young single, young married without children, young married with children, older married with children under 18, older married without children under 18, older single, other
Family size	1, 2–3, 4–5, 6+
Income	Under $9,000, $9,000–$14,999, $15,000–$24,999, $25,000–$34,999, $35,000–$45,000, over $45,000
Nationality	African, American, Asian, British, Eastern European, French, German, Irish, Italian, Latin American, Middle Eastern, Scandinavian
Race	Native American, Asian, Black, White
Religion	Buddhist, Catholic, Hindu, Jewish, Muslim, Protestant
Sex	Male, female

---

natural to forget material between study sessions, especially if it's complex. When you come back after a break, you can focus on where you need the most help.

Examine the following reviewing techniques (more on these in Chapter 7). Try them all, and use the ones that work best for you. Try using more than one strategy when you study—switching among several different strategies tends to strengthen learning and memory.

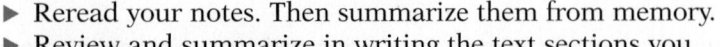

- ▶ Reread your notes. Then summarize them from memory.
- ▶ Review and summarize in writing the text sections you highlighted or bracketed.
- ▶ Rewrite key points and main concepts in your own words. Create written examples that will help solidify the content in your mind.
- ▶ Answer the end-of-chapter review, discussion, and application questions.
- ▶ Reread the preface, headings, tables, and summary.
- ▶ Recite important concepts to yourself, or record and play them back on a tape player.
- ▶ Listen to MP3 audio recordings of your text and other reading materials on your iPod.
- ▶ Make flash cards with a word or concept on one side and a definition, examples, or other related information on the other. Test yourself.
- ▶ Quiz yourself, using the questions you raised in the Q stage.
- ▶ Discuss the concepts with a classmate or in a study group. Answer one another's Q-stage questions.
- ▶ Ask your instructor for help with difficult material.

Refreshing your knowledge is easier and faster than learning it the first time. Make a weekly review schedule and stick to it until you're sure you know everything.

What strategies help with specific subjects and formats?

> **GENERAL EDUCATION REQUIREMENTS** Courses required for graduation in a variety of academic fields, including the humanities, social sciences, math, and science.

If your college has **general education requirements,** you may have to take a wide variety of courses to graduate. Knowing how to approach reading materials in different academic areas will help you learn.

Math and science

Math and science courses relate closely to one another, and almost all science courses require a base of math knowledge. Mathematical and scientific strategies help you develop thinking and problem-solving skills. In a world that is being transformed by new discoveries and technologies, a strong math and science background prepares you for tomorrow's jobs and can also help you create monthly budgets, choose auto insurance, understand illnesses, and more.

Math and science textbooks move *sequentially*. That is, your understanding of later material depends on how well you learned material in earlier chapters. Try the following strategies to get the most from your textbooks, and get extra help right away when you are confused.

■ *Interact with math material actively through writing.* Math textbooks are made up of problems and solutions. As you read, highlight important information and take notes on examples. Work out any missing problem steps on your pad or in the book. Draw sketches to help visualize the material. Try not to

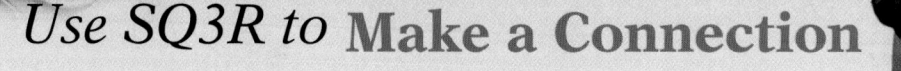

GET CREATIVE!

Use SQ3R to Make a Connection

For this exercise, partner up with someone in your class. To begin, each of you will write a mini-biography—approximately three to five paragraphs—answering the following questions:

▶ Where are you from?

▶ How would you describe your family?

▶ How have they influenced the student you are today?

▶ What three facts or ideas about yourself would you like someone else to know?

Include a title that reflects your biography as a whole. Also, for each paragraph in the middle (not the first or last), provide a title "header" that tells the reader what to expect in the paragraph (for example, "My Childhood in Malaysia," "Daytime Student, Nighttime Employee," and so on).

Once you're finished, read over what you've written for spelling, punctuation, and clarity. Switch papers with your partner and read his or her biography. Using SQ3R:

1. *Survey:* Scan your partner's paper for any words that stand out or phrases that seem important. Circle or highlight anything you notice right away.

2. *Question:* Thinking about what you learned from your survey, write questions in the margins. Your questions should reflect what you expect to learn as you read.

3. *Read:* Read through the biography. Make notes in the margins when you find answers to your Q-stage questions. Use your pen to circle or underline main ideas.

4. *Recite:* Discuss what you learned from the paper with your partner. How accurate was your comprehension of the biography? Were there any areas that were not clear or that you misunderstood? If so, what might help in those cases?

5. *Review:* Summarize the biography of your partner in writing for yourself. Be sure to note any important information that relates to getting to know your partner. If there is time, solidify your review by reciting the summary aloud in front of the class. Introduce your partner to the class as if he or she had just joined, focusing on the most interesting and unique information from the biography.

Finally, discuss the impact of using SQ3R with your partner. How did it affect your comprehension of the biography? What might you try differently next time?

---

move on until you understand example problems and how they relate to the central ideas. Write down questions for your instructor or fellow students.

■ *Pay attention to formulas.* Math and science texts are filled with formulas. Focus on learning the main ideas behind each formula, and do problems to make sure your understanding sticks.

> FORMULAS
> General facts, rules, or principles usually expressed in mathematical symbols.

■ *Use memory strategies to learn science.* Science textbooks are packed with vocabulary specific to the field (for example, an environmental science text may refer to the *greenhouse effect, integrated waste management,* and the *law of limiting factors*). To remember what you read, use mnemonic devices, test yourself with flash cards, and rehearse aloud or silently (see Chapter 6).

student profile

Aneela Gonzales

Golden West College, Huntington Beach, California

About me:

I was born into a bicultural family: Hispanic American and Pakistani. My dad left the family when I was 3 months old and my mother became ill with cancer when I was 6. She passed away when I was 11, and the next few years were very difficult. I had to move to a new state to live with my aunt and uncle.

What I focus on:

Since I was a child I had dreamed of being a nurse. However, once I finally got to college to study nursing, remembering what I read was a problem and I was struggling to pass exams. I had to come up with specific techniques to help. One that worked for me is using different colored highlighters while I read (pink for somewhat important and yellow for very important), and then typing out all the very important points and reviewing that sheet several times. To figure out what to highlight I would pay close attention to what the instructor lectures about and I would reread those topics in the text.

Something else that I learned was important for me was to read in a quiet environment with few distractions. I read much better in the library with my phone off. When I didn't understand something I was reading I would go to the Tutoring Center. I also found it useful to talk about the reading one-on-one with another person. Finally, I realized that outside stresses, such as having to work to support myself through school, had an effect on my reading skills. Learning to manage my stress enabled me to better remember what I had read.

What will help me in the workplace:

I have just graduated college and started work as a nurse. I have much to read at work so it helps to apply some of the techniques I learned in college. First, I find it is important to find a quiet place to read. In addition, I first skim the material to find out if it is relevant for me; then I can slow down and read only those portions that I need. I find this saves me a lot of time.

Social sciences and humanities

Courses in the social sciences and humanities prepare you to be a well-rounded person, able and ready to fulfill your responsibilities to yourself, your family, and a free democracy. They also prepare you for 21st century jobs by focusing on critical thinking, civic and historic knowledge, and ethical reasoning. As you study these disciplines, look for themes with critical thinking as the foundation for your work. Build knowledge by using what you know to learn new material.

Themes

The National Council for the Social Studies (www.socialstudies.org) organizes the study of the social sciences and humanities under ten themes, providing "umbrellas" under which you can group ideas that you encounter in different classes and reading materials:

- ► Culture
- ► Time, continuity, and change
- ► People, places, and environment
- ► Individual development and identity
- ► Individuals, groups, and institutions
- ► Power, authority, and governance
- ► Production, distribution, and consumption
- ► Science, technology, and society
- ► Global connections
- ► Ideals and practices of citizenship

Look for these themes as you read, even if they are not spelled out. For example, as you read a chapter in a political science text on presidential politics, you might think of the history of presidential elections or how the Internet is changing electoral politics.

Think critically

Courses in the social sciences ask hard questions about ethics, human rights and freedoms, personal and community responsibility, looking at these topics over time and in different cultures. Critical thinking will help you maximize learning and understanding as you ask questions about what you read, think of material in terms of problems and solutions, look for evidence in arguments, consider possible bias of the writers, and examine big picture statements for solid cause-and-effect logic.

Literature

Even if you're not an English major, you will probably take one or more literature courses, exposing you to books that allow you to experience other times and cultures and understand how others react to the problems of daily life. Additionally, the thoughts and emotions you experience in reaction to what you read give you the opportunity to learn more about yourself.

Literature courses ask you to look at different literary elements to find meaning on various levels. As you read, use critical reading skills to consider the various aspects.

- ► *Character.* How do characters reveal who they are? How are the main characters similar or different? How do a character's actions change the course of the story?
- ► *Plot.* How would you evaluate the power of the story? Did it hold your interest?
- ► *Setting.* How does the setting relate to the actions of the major and minor characters?
- ► *Point of view.* How are the author's views expressed through characters' actions?
- ► *Style.* How would you describe the writing style?
- ► *Imagery.* How does the author use imagery as part of the theme?
- ► *Theme.* What is the goal of the work? What is it trying to communicate?

Visual aids

Many textbooks use tables, charts, drawings, maps, and photographs—all types of visual aids—to show, clarify, or summarize

MULTIPLE INTELLIGENCE STRATEGIES
for Reading

Apply Different Intelligences to Concepts in Sociology

INTELLIGENCE	USE MI STRATEGIES TO BECOME A BETTER READER	APPLY MI READING STRATEGIES TO LEARN ABOUT SOCIAL GROUPS FOR YOUR INTRODUCTION TO SOCIOLOGY COURSE
Verbal-Linguistic	• Use the steps in SQ3R, focusing especially on writing Q-stage questions, summaries, and so on. • Make marginal text notes as you read.	• Summarize in writing the technical differences among social groups, categories, and crowds.*
Logical-Mathematical	• Logically connect what you are reading with what you already know. Consider similarities, differences, and cause-and-effect relationships. • Draw charts showing relationships and analyze trends.	• Create a table comparing and contrasting the characteristics of primary and secondary social groups.
Bodily-Kinesthetic	• Use text highlighting to take a hands-on approach to reading. • Take a hands-on approach to learning experiments by trying to recreate them yourself.	• Create an experiment that might turn a crowd of strangers into a social group joined together by a common problem.
Visual-Spatial	• Make charts, diagrams, or think links illustrating difficult ideas you encounter as you read. • Take note of photos, tables, and other visual aids in the text.	• Create a visual aid showing four primary mechanisms through which people with shared experiences, loyalties, and interests meet—for example, through school and business—and how initial contacts may lead to deep social group relationships.
Interpersonal	• Discuss reading material and clarify concepts in a study group. • Talk to people who know about the topic you are studying.	• Interview people who shared a difficult experience with a crowd of strangers—for example, people stuck in an elevator or train for an extended period—about how relationships changed as focus turned to a common problem.
Intrapersonal	• Apply concepts to your own life; think about how you would manage. • Try to understand your personal strengths and weaknesses to lead a study group on the reading material.	• After reading about the nature of primary groups, think about the nature of your personal family relationships and the degree to which family members are your key support system.
Musical	• Recite text concepts to rhythms or write a song to depict them. • Explore relevant musical links to the material.	• Listen to a rock concert that was performed in front of a live crowd. Then listen to the same music recorded in a studio. Think about performance differences that might link to the presence or absence of a crowd.
Naturalistic	• Tap into your ability to notice similarities and differences in objects and concepts by organizing reading materials into relevant groupings.	• Over the next few weeks, ask some close friends if you can have dinner with them and their families. After the visits, try to identify characteristics that all the families share. Create a chart to report your findings.

*For information on social groups, see John J. Macionis, *Sociology,* 11th ed., Upper Saddle River, NJ: Prentice Hall, 2007.

information in a form that is easy to read and understand. Pay attention to these elements as you are reading—often they contain important information not found elsewhere. Visual learners especially may benefit from information delivered in a format other than chapter text.

Certain types of visual aids—word and data tables as well as charts/graphs (pie, bar, or line)—are designed to compare information and statistics that show the following types of information:

- ▶ *Trends over time*. For example, the number of computers with Internet connections per household in 2010 compared to 2002
- ▶ *Relative rankings*. For example, the sizes of the advertising budgets of four major companies
- ▶ *Distributions*. For example, student performance on standardized tests by geographic area
- ▶ *Cycles*. For example, the regular upward and downward movement of the nation's economy as defined by periods of prosperity and recession

Online materials

Almost any student's success in college depends on being able to read both printed and on-screen material effectively. For some "digital natives" who have grown up with technology and the Internet, screen reading comes naturally and may even be preferable. Others may prefer printed materials they can hold in their hands and write on. For either group, the goal is to get the most out of what you must read online.

Screen readers tend to focus on heads and subheads, bullet points, and visuals, scanning material for the important points instead of staying focused through long paragraphs or articles.[5] They may also develop what Web researcher Jakob Nielsen calls *F-pattern reading*—reading across the line at the beginning of a document, then reading less and less of the full width of the line as you move down the page, and only seeing the left-hand text by the time you reach the bottom of the document.[6]

Nielsen suggests making the most of screen reading using a step-by-step process, which includes aspects of SQ3R:

1. *Skim through the article.* See whether it contains important ideas.
2. *Before reading in depth, save the article on your computer.* This gives you the ability to highlight and add notes, just as you would on a printed page.
3. *Survey the article.* Read the title, subtitle, headings, figures, charts, and tables.
4. *Come up with questions to guide your reading.* Ask yourself what general and specific information you want to learn from the article.
5. *Read the article in depth.* You have already judged that the material is important, so take it much slower than you would normally.
6. *Highlight and take notes.* Use the program's highlighter function and comment boxes.
7. *Print out articles you would rather study on paper.* Make sure the printouts include your highlighting and notes.
8. *Review your notes.* Combine them with your class notes and those on your printed text.

Finally, your awareness that screen reading skills are different from those needed to read printed textbooks will help you shift gears when picking up a book. Textbooks require close, slow reading that may seem like walking through mud after spending time on the Internet.

How can you be an
information literate reader and researcher?

Although many students' first instinct is to power up the computer and start jumping around on Google, there is a wealth of research resources at your fingertips. Many of the materials you'll find in a library have been evaluated by librarians and researchers and are likely to be reliable—a definite time-saver when compared to the myriad of both credible and less-than-credible sources available online.

Map out the possibilities

To select the most helpful information for your research, you need to first know what is available to you. Sign up for a library orientation session. Familiarize yourself with the library resources shown in Key 5.8.

For a key advantage in any search for information, get to know a librarian. These professionals can assist you in locating unfamiliar or hard-to-find sources, navigating catalogs and databases, uncovering research shortcuts, and dealing with pesky equipment. Know what you want to accomplish before asking a question. At many schools, you can query a librarian via cell phone, e-mail, or instant messaging.

GET TO KNOW **WHERE THINGS ARE** IN THE LIBRARY

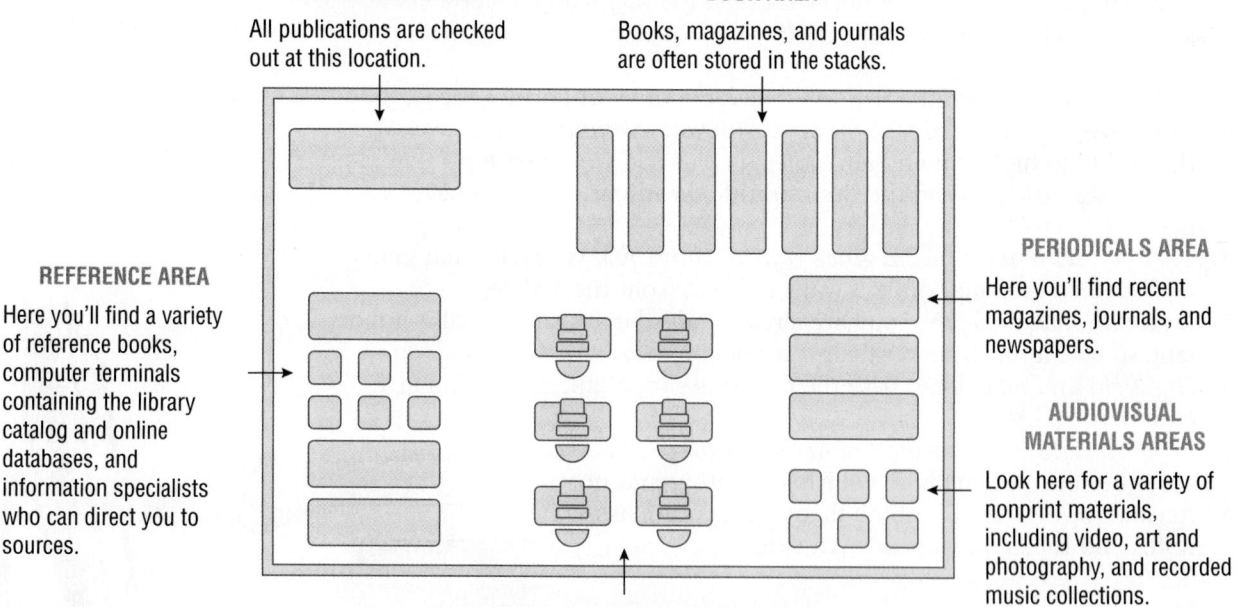

CIRCULATION DESK

All publications are checked out at this location.

BOOK AREA

Books, magazines, and journals are often stored in the stacks.

REFERENCE AREA

Here you'll find a variety of reference books, computer terminals containing the library catalog and online databases, and information specialists who can direct you to sources.

PERIODICALS AREA

Here you'll find recent magazines, journals, and newspapers.

AUDIOVISUAL MATERIALS AREAS

Look here for a variety of nonprint materials, including video, art and photography, and recorded music collections.

ELECTRONIC LIBRARY RESOURCES

Network systems allow access to online materials via computers. If your school has a wireless wi-fi system, you can conduct research anywhere on campus.

Conduct an information search

To avoid becoming buried in the sheer magnitude of resources available, use a practical, step-by-step search method. Key 5.9 shows how you start wide and then move in for a closer look at specific sources.

When using virtual or online catalogues, you will need to adjust your research methods. Searching library databases requires that you use a *keyword search*—an exploration that uses a topic-related natural language word or phrase as a point of reference to locate other information. To narrow your topic and reduce the number of "hits" (resources pulled up by your search), add more keywords. For example, instead of searching through the broad category "art," focus on "French art" or, more specifically, "19th century French art." Key 5.10 shows how to use the keyword system to narrow searches with what is called *Boolean logic*.

Be a critical Internet searcher

The *Internet*, a worldwide computer network, can connect you to billions of information sources. Unlike your college library collection or databases, Internet resources may not be evaluated by anyone who vouches for their quality. As a result, your research depends on critical thinking.

Much, although not all, research can be done using online databases. Get to know the databases and other resources that your school provides for you.
© Sarah Lyman Kravits

USE A STEP-BY-STEP
SEARCH METHOD

Start with General Reference Works
Examples include encyclopedias, almanacs, dictionaries, and biographical references.

Move to Specialized Reference Works
Examples include encyclopedias and dictionaries that focus on a narrow field.

Use the Electronic Catalog to Locate Materials
Search the library catalog by author, title, or subject to learn where to locate specific books, periodicals, and journals. Most library catalogs are virtual and can be accessed by computers throughout the library. Ask a librarian for assistance, if needed.

Browse through Relevant Books and Articles
Using your results from the catalog search, dive in deeper by finding and accessing helpful information in books and articles related to your topic.

IF YOU ARE SEARCHING FOR...	DO THIS	EXAMPLE
A word	Type the word normally.	Aid
A phrase	Type the phase in its normal word order (use regular word spacing) or surround the phrase with quotation marks.	financial aid, "financial aid"
Two or more keywords without regard to order	Type the words in any order, surrounding the words with quotation marks. Use *and* to separate the words.	"financial aid" and "scholarships"
Topic A or topic B	Type the words in any order, surrounding the words with quotation marks. Use *or* to separate the words.	"financial aid" or "scholarships"
Topic A but not topic B	Type topic A first within quotation marks, and then topic B within quotation marks. Use *not* to separate the words.	"financial aid" not "scholarships"

Start with search engines

Among the most popular and effective search engines are Google (www.google .com) and Yahoo! (www.yahoo.com). Search engines aimed at academic audiences include the Librarian's Index to the Internet (www.lii.org) and INFO-MINE (www.infomine.com). At these academic directories, someone has screened the sites and listed only those sources that have been determined to be reputable and regularly updated.

Additionally, your school may include access to certain nonpublic academic search engines in the cost of your tuition. Sites like LexusNexus, InfoTrac, GaleGroup, and OneFile are known for their credibility in the academic world as well as their vast amounts of information. Check with your school's library to see how to access these sites.

Use a search strategy

The World Wide Web has been called "the world's greatest library, with all its books on the floor." With no librarian in sight, you need to master a practical Internet search strategy.

1. *Use natural language phrases or keywords to identify what you are looking for.* University of Michigan professor Eliot Soloway recommends phrasing your search in the form of a question—for example, What vaccines are given to children before age 5? Then he advises identifying the important words in the question (vaccines, children, before age 5) as well as related words (polio, shot, pediatrics, and so on). This will give you a collection of terms to use in different combinations as you search.[7]

2. *Use a search engine to isolate valuable sites.* Enter your questions, phrases, and keywords in various combinations to generate lists of "hits." Vary word order to see what you can generate. If you get too many hits, try using fewer or more specific keywords.

3. *Skim sites to evaluate what seems most useful.* Check the synopsis of the site's contents, the content providers, and the purpose of the site. Does the site seem relevant, reputable, or biased in favor of a particular point of view? A site owned by a company will want to promote its new product rather than provide unbiased consumer information. Consider the purpose—a blog is apt to focus on opinion in contrast to an article

in a scholarly journal, which is likely to focus on facts and research findings.

4. *Save, or bookmark, the sites you want to focus on.* Make sure you can access them again. You may want to copy URLs and paste them into a separate document.

5. *When you think you are done, start over.* Choose another search engine and search again. Different systems access different sites.

The limitations of Internet-only research make it smart to combine Internet and library research. Search engines can't find everything, in part because not all sources are in digital format. The Internet also prioritizes current information. Furthermore, some digital sources that are not part of your library's subscription offerings cost money. Finally, Internet searches require electricity or battery power and an online connection. Consider printing out Internet materials that you know you will need to reference over and over again.

Your need to be an effective researcher doesn't stop at graduation—especially in a workplace dominated by information and media. The skills you develop as you do research for school projects will serve you well in any kind of job that requires you to use the Internet and other resources to find and evaluate information.

How can you respond critically to **what you read?**

With anything you read—trade books, journal and newspaper articles, Internet documents, primary sources, and even textbooks that are supposed to be as accurate as possible—it is crucial to be a questioning reader who does not simply accept material as truth. Critical reading involves questioning, analysis, and evaluation. Think of the reading process as an archaeological dig. First, you excavate a site and uncover the artifacts. Then you separate out what you've found, make connections among ideas, and evaluate what is important. This process allows you to focus on the most important materials.

Different purposes engage different parts of critical reading. When you are reading to learn and retain information or to master a skill, you *focus on important information* (analyzing and evaluating how the ideas are structured, how they connect, and what is most crucial to remember). When you are reading to search for truth, you *ask questions to evaluate arguments* (analyzing and evaluating the author's point of view as well as the credibility, accuracy, reliability, and relevancy of the material).

Focus on important information

Before determining how to respond to something you've read, ask yourself what is important and what you have to remember. According to Adam Robinson, co-founder of the *Princeton Review*, "The only way you can effectively absorb the relevant information is to ignore the irrelevant information."[8] The following tips will help you determine what is most important to focus on as you study. Check to see whether the information does the following:

▶ Contains headings, charts, tables, captions, key terms and definitions, or an introduction or summary (for a textbook, check mid-chapter or end-of-chapter exercises)

▶ Offers definitions, crucial concepts, examples, an explanation of a variety or type, critical relationships or comparisons

- Sparks questions and reactions as you read
- Surprises or confuses you
- Mirrors what your instructor emphasizes in class or in assignments

When trying to figure out what to study and what to skim, ask yourself whether your instructor would expect you to know the material. If you are unsure and the topic is not on your syllabus, e-mail your instructor and ask for clarification.

Ask questions to evaluate arguments

An *argument* refers to a persuasive case—a set of connected ideas supported by examples—that a writer makes to prove or disprove a point. Many scholarly books and articles, in print form or on the Internet, are organized around particular arguments (look for *claims*—arguments that appear to be factual but don't have adequate evidence to support them). Critical readers evaluate arguments and claims to determine whether they are accurate and logical. When quality evidence combines with sound logic, the argument is solid.

It's easy—and common—to accept or reject an argument according to whether it fits with your point of view. If you ask questions, however, you can determine the argument's validity and understand it in greater depth (see Key 5.11). Evaluating an argument involves looking at several factors:

EVIDENCE
Facts, statistics, and other materials that are presented in support of an argument.

- The quality of the **evidence** (facts, statistics, and other materials supporting an argument)
- Whether the evidence fits the idea concept
- The logical connections

Approach every argument with healthy skepticism. Have an open mind to assess whether you are convinced or have serious questions.

Evaluate every source

Evidence examination is important for all reading materials, but especially when you research on the Internet, because online resources vary widely in reliability. In fact, your Internet research is only as strong as your critical

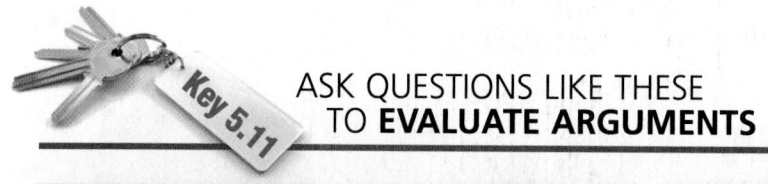

ASK QUESTIONS LIKE THESE TO **EVALUATE ARGUMENTS**

Key 5.11

EVALUATE THE VALIDITY OF THE EVIDENCE	DETERMINE WHETHER THE EVIDENCE SUPPORTS THE CONCEPT
Is the source reliable and free of bias?	Is there enough evidence?
Who wrote this and with what intent?	Do examples and ideas logically connect?
What assumptions underlie this material?	Is the evidence convincing?
Is this argument based on opinion?	Do the examples build a strong case?
How does this evidence compare with evidence from other sources?	What different and perhaps opposing arguments seem equally valid?

USE THE CARS TEST TO DETERMINE
INFORMATION QUALITY ON THE INTERNET

CREDIBILITY	ACCURACY	REASONABLENESS	SUPPORT
Examine whether a source is believable and trustworthy.	*Examine whether information is correct— i.e., factual, comprehensive, detailed, and up to date (if necessary).*	*Examine whether material is fair, objective, moderate, and consistent.*	*Examine whether a source is adequately supported with citations.*
What are the author's credentials? Look for education and experience, title or position of employment, membership in any known and respected organization, reliable contact information, biographical information, and reputation.	*Is it up to date, and is that important?* If you are searching for a work of literature, such as Shakespeare's play *Macbeth,* there is no "updated" version. However, you may want reviews of its latest productions. For most scientific research, you will need to rely on the most updated information you can find.	*Does the source seem fair?* Look for a balanced argument, accurate claims, and a reasoned tone that does not appeal primarily to your emotions.	*Where does the information come from?* Look at the site, the sources used by the person or group who compiled the information, and the contact information. Make sure that the cited sources seem reliable and that statistics are documented.
Is there quality control? Look for ways in which the source may have been screened. For example, materials on an organization's website have most likely been approved by several members; information coming from an academic journal has to be screened by several people before it is published.	*Is it comprehensive?* Does the material leave out any important facts or information? Does it neglect to consider alternative views or crucial consequences? Although no one source can contain all of the available information on a topic, it should still be as comprehensive as is possible within its scope.	*Does the source seem objective?* While there is a range of objectivity in writing, you want to favor authors and organizations who can control their bias. An author with a strong political or religious agenda or an intent to sell a product may not be a source of the most truthful material.	*Is the information corroborated?* Test information by looking for other sources that confirm the facts in this information—or, if the information is opinion, sources that share that opinion and back it up with their own citations. One good strategy is to find at least three sources that corroborate each other.
Is there any posted summary or evaluation of the source? You may find abstracts of sources (summary) or a recommendation, rating, or review from a person or organization (evaluation). Either of these—or, ideally, both—can give you an idea of credibility before you decide to examine a source in depth.	*For whom is the source written, and for what purpose?* Looking at what the author wants to accomplish will help you assess whether it has a bias. Sometimes biased information will not be useful for your purpose; sometimes your research will require that you note and evaluate bias (such as if you were to compare Civil War diaries from Union soldiers with those from Confederate soldiers).	*Does the source seem moderate?* Do claims seem possible, or does the information seem hard to believe? Does what you read make sense when compared to what you already know? While wild claims may turn out to be truthful, you are safest to check everything out.	*Is the source externally consistent?* Most material is a mix of both current and old information. External consistency refers to whether the old information agrees with what you already know. If a source contradicts something you know to be true, chances are higher that the information new to you may be inconsistent as well.
Signals of a potential lack of credibility: Anonymous materials, negative evaluations, little or no evidence of quality control, bad grammar or misspelled words	*Signals of a potential lack of accuracy:* Lack of date or old date, generalizations, one-sided views that do not acknowledge opposing arguments	*Signals of a potential lack of reasonableness:* Extreme or emotional language, sweeping statements, conflict of interest, inconsistencies or contradictions	*Signals of a potential lack of support:* Statistics without sources, lack of documentation, lack of corroboration using other reliable sources

Source: Robert Harris, "Evaluating Internet Research Sources," November 17, 1997, VirtualSalt (www.virtualsalt.com/evalu8it.htm).

thinking. Robert Harris, professor and Web expert, has developed an easy-to-remember system for evaluating Internet information called the CARS test for information quality (Credibility, Accuracy, Reasonableness, Support). Use the information in Key 5.12 to question any source you find as you conduct research. You can also use it to test the reliability of non-Internet sources.

Reading is the tool you will use over and over again to acquire information in school, on the job, and in life (to understand your 401(k) retirement plan, to learn about local and world news, to understand the fine print in a cell phone contract). Develop the ability to read with focus, purpose, and follow-through, and you will never stop enjoying the benefits.

Case *Wrap-up*

What happened to Gary? With perseverance and support, Gary has become a health care management and strategic planning consultant whose clients include state Medicaid directors and Fortune 500 insurance companies. However, he lives every day with the challenge of dyslexia. Because of the time and effort he needs to read, he has spent most of his adult life working in small private offices or a home office. He can't read directions fast enough to avoid wrong turns on highways and often makes spelling mistakes. The support of his wife, Lynne, a gifted writer and public speaker, has proven essential in his struggle to persevere. Armed with today's knowledge about learning differences, Gary and Lynne tested their children early and often and were able to provide their son with an academic environment that addressed his reading challenges. With their support, he has developed a soaring sense of self-confidence—the kind that Gary still strives for.

What does this story mean for you? Learning to be a productive member of society, with the gifts you are born with or can develop, is the name of the game. It also helps to have an understanding support system. Nearly everyone has a "big secret"—or perhaps a "small secret"—that causes challenges in school or on the job. Whether a learning disability like dyslexia, a negative attitude about a task like reading or math, or some other obstacle, it gets in the way as you strive for success. Think about one secret that you have, and put it in writing. Then write the name of a person whom you trust to support you. Finally, talk with this person and begin to come up with ideas of how you will address and manage your secret.

What effects go beyond your world? Reading is the essential success skill for the 21st century information-focused workplace. The more the world's citizens know how to read, the more they will be able to lead productive and successful lives. To start exploring what is happening in the promotion of literacy, go to www.roomtoread.org and explore what this organization is doing to build schools, stock libraries, and support education. Click on their "Get Involved" tab to see how to support their initiatives. Perhaps you will want to get involved yourself—or, if not, look into ways you can support literacy in your community, at your college, or even within your own family. Be a part of the solution.

Successful Intelligence *Wrap-up*

HERE'S HOW YOU HAVE
BUILT SKILLS IN **CHAPTER 5** :

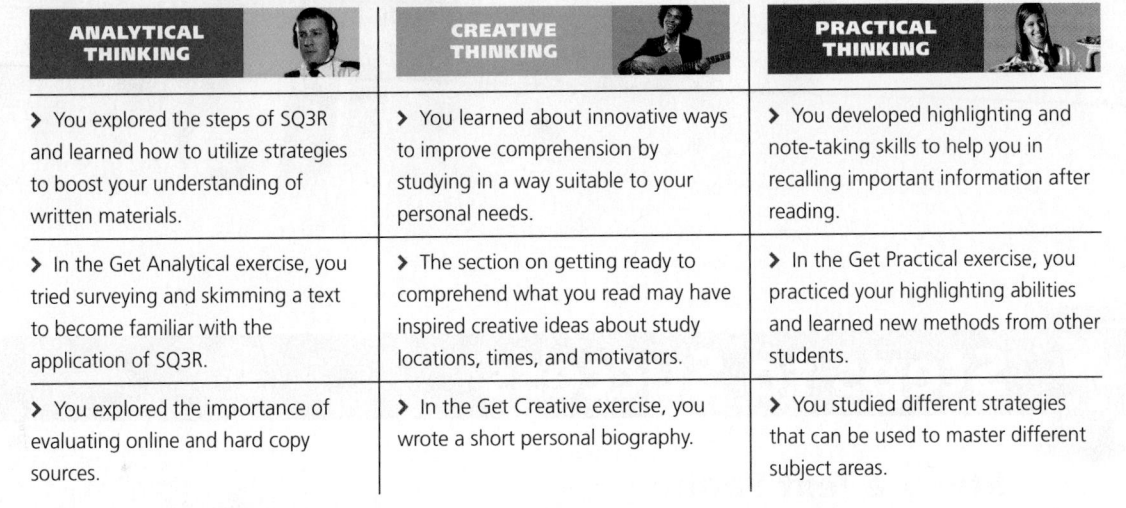

ANALYTICAL THINKING	CREATIVE THINKING	PRACTICAL THINKING
› You explored the steps of SQ3R and learned how to utilize strategies to boost your understanding of written materials.	› You learned about innovative ways to improve comprehension by studying in a way suitable to your personal needs.	› You developed highlighting and note-taking skills to help you in recalling important information after reading.
› In the Get Analytical exercise, you tried surveying and skimming a text to become familiar with the application of SQ3R.	› The section on getting ready to comprehend what you read may have inspired creative ideas about study locations, times, and motivators.	› In the Get Practical exercise, you practiced your highlighting abilities and learned new methods from other students.
› You explored the importance of evaluating online and hard copy sources.	› In the Get Creative exercise, you wrote a short personal biography.	› You studied different strategies that can be used to master different subject areas.

Word *for* Thought

Reading college textbooks may feel at times like the disorientation implied by the **Japanese** word *yokomeshi* (yo-ko-meh'-shee), which literally means "eating a meal sideways."[9] The word describes the Japanese learner's difficulty with a foreign language written horizontally, unlike Japanese script, which reads from top to bottom. You are not alone in trying to figure out what things mean. Keep your sense of humor and commit to the task, and it is likely to feel more comfortable over time.

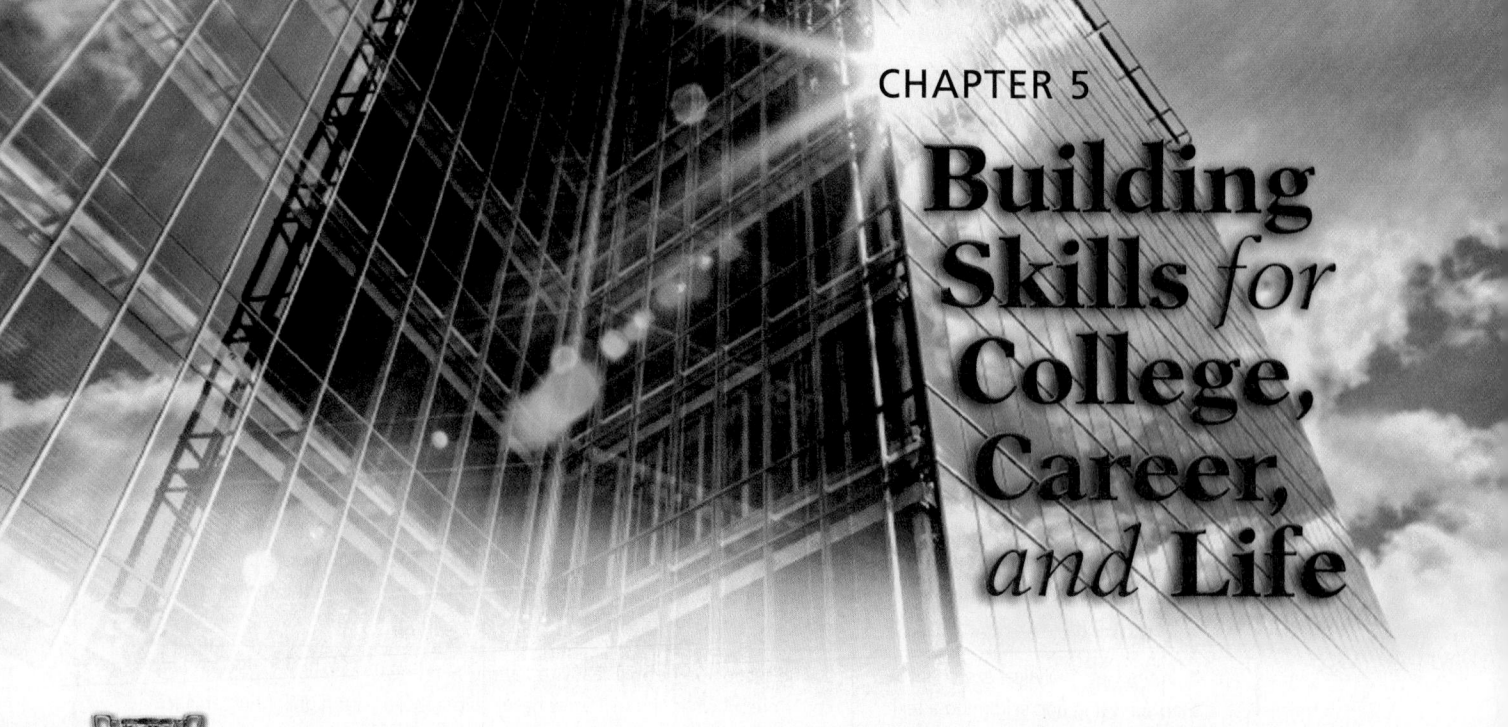

CHAPTER 5

Building Skills *for* College, Career, *and* Life

Steps to Success

Study a Text Page

BUILD BASIC SKILLS. The facing page is from the chapter "Groups and Organizations" in the sixth edition of John J. Macionis's *Sociology*.[10] Skim the excerpt. Identify the headings on the page and the relationships among them. Mark primary-level headings with a numeral 1, secondary headings with a 2, and tertiary (third-level) headings with a 3.

TAKE IT TO THE NEXT LEVEL. Analyze the headings and text.

Which heading serves as an umbrella for the rest?

_____

What do the headings tell you about the content of the page?

_____

_____

_____

_____

Name three concepts that seem important to remember.

1. _____

2. _____

3. _____

Based on the three concepts you pulled out, write three study questions that you can review with an instructor, a teaching assistant, or a fellow student.

1. _____

2. _____

3. _____

SOCIAL GROUPS

Virtually everyone moves through life with a sense of belonging; this is the experience of group life. A social group refers to *two or more people who identify and interact with one another.* Human beings continually come together to form couples, families, circles of friends, neighborhoods, churches, businesses, clubs, and numerous large organizations. Whatever the form, groups encompass people with shared experiences, loyalties, and interests. In short, while maintaining their individuality, the members of social groups also think of themselves as a special "we."

Groups, Categories, and Crowds

People often use the term "group" imprecisely. We now distinguish the group from the similar concepts of category and crowd.

■ *Category.* A *category* refers to people who have some status in common. Women, single fathers, military recruits, homeowners, and Roman Catholics are all examples of categories.

Why are categories not considered groups? Simply because, while the individuals involved are aware that they are not the only ones to hold that particular status, the vast majority are strangers to one another.

■ *Crowd.* A *crowd* refers to a temporary cluster of individuals who may or may not interact at all. Students sitting in a lecture hall do engage one another and share some common identity as college classmates; thus, such a crowd might be called a loosely formed group. By contrast, riders hurtling along on a subway train or bathers enjoying a summer day at the beach pay little attention to one another and amount to an anonymous aggregate of people. In general, then, crowds are too transitory and impersonal to qualify as social groups.

The right circumstances, however, could turn a crowd into a group. People riding in a subway train that crashes under the city streets generally become keenly aware of their common plight and begin to help one another. Sometimes such extraordinary experiences become the basis for lasting relationships.

Primary and Secondary Groups

Acquaintances commonly greet one another with a smile and the simple phrase, "Hi! How are you?" The response is usually a well scripted, "Just fine, thanks, how about you?" This answer, of course, is often more formal than truthful. In most cases, providing a detailed account of how you are *really* doing would prompt the other person to beat a hasty and awkward exit.

Sociologists classify social groups by measuring them against two ideal types based on members' genuine level of personal concern. This variation is the key to distinguishing *primary* from *secondary* groups.

According to Charles Horton Cooley (1864–1929), a **primary group** is a *small social group whose members share personal and enduring relationships.* Bound together by primary relationships, individuals in primary groups typically spend a great deal of time together, engage in a wide range of common activities, and feel that they know one another well. Although not without periodic conflict, members of primary groups display sincere concern for each other's welfare. The family is every society's most important primary group.

Cooley characterized these personal and tightly integrated groups as *primary* because they are among the first groups we experience in life. In addition, the family and early play groups also hold primary importance in the socialization process, shaping attitudes, behavior, and social identity.

Source: John J. Macionis, *Sociology,* 6th ed., p. 145, © 1997 Prentice-Hall, Inc. Reproduced by permission of Pearson Education, Inc., Upper Saddle River, NJ.

MOVE TOWARD MASTERY. Read the excerpt, putting SQ3R to work. Using a marker pen, highlight key phrases and sentences. Write short marginal notes to help you review the material later. After reading this page thoroughly, write a short summary paragraph.

_____

_____

_____

_____

Teamwork

Create Solutions Together

FORM A STUDY GROUP

Goal: To organize a study group with the intent of preparing for an upcoming event.

Time on task: 30 minutes; ongoing

Instructions: Get together with three or four members of your class with whom you would like to form a group. These are your study group members. Do the following at the group's first meeting:

- *Set a specific goal.* Create a weekly schedule for reaching your goal—to prepare for an upcoming test, for example. Write everything down and give everyone a copy.
- *Talk about the specific ways you will work together.* Discuss which of the following methods you want to try in the group: pooling your notes; teaching each other difficult concepts; making up, administering, and grading quizzes for each other; creating study flash cards; using SQ3R to review required readings. Set specific guidelines for how group members will be held accountable.

As an initial group exercise, try the following:

- *Review the study questions that you wrote for the* Sociology *excerpt in the previous exercise.* Each person should select one question to focus on while reading (no two people should have the same question). Group members should then reread the excerpt individually, thinking about their questions as they read and answering them in writing.
- *When you finish reading critically, gather as a group.* Each person should take a turn presenting the question, the response or answer that was derived through critical reading, and other thoughts. Other members may then add to the discussion. Continue until everyone presents a concept.

Over several weeks, evaluate the different methods as a group, singling out those that were most helpful. Then incorporate them into your ongoing study sessions.

Writing

Build Intrapersonal and Communication Skills

Record your thoughts on a separate piece of paper, in a journal, or electronically.

EMOTIONAL INTELLIGENCE JOURNAL

Reading challenges. Which current course presents your most difficult reading challenge? Describe what makes the reading tough—type of material, length of assignments, level of difficulty, or something else. What feelings come up for you when you read, and what effect do they have on your reading? Describe techniques you learned in this chapter that can help you get into a growth mindset to read productively.

REAL-LIFE WRITING

Ask for help. Self-help plans often involve reaching out to others. Draft an e-mail to your instructor describing the difficulties in your challenging course as well as the specific help you need to move to the next step. Make sure that your message is clear and accurate, your grammar, spelling, and punctuation correct, and your tone appropriate. (See Quick Start for guidelines on communicating with instructors.) *Whether you send the e-mail or not is up to you.* In either case, writing it will help you move forward in your reading improvement plan.

Prepare for Career Success

READING SKILLS ON THE JOB

21st Century Learning Building Blocks

- Information Literacy
- Media Literacy
- ICT Literacy

Complete the following in your electronic portfolio or separately on paper.

Excellent reading skills are a requirement for almost every 21st century job. Employers expect that you will read independently to master new skills and keep up with change. Whether in print or electronic form, on-the-job reading will challenge you as does college reading. For example, sociology courses may involve reading textbooks, journals, and case studies, but actually working in the field requires that you keep on top of case reports, government regulations, court documents, and an unending stream of work-related e-mails.

Prepare yourself by honestly assessing your practical skills *right now*. Use the following list to rate your ability on a scale of 1 to 10, with 10 being the highest:

- Ability to concentrate, no matter the distractions
- Ability to use emotional triggers to learn and remember material
- Ability to define your reading purpose and use it to guide your focus and pace
- Ability to use specific vocabulary-building techniques to improve comprehension
- Ability to use every aspect of SQ3R to master content
- Ability to skim and scan
- Ability to use analytical thinking skills when reading
- Ability to use highlighting and notes to help you master content

For the two skill areas in which you rated yourself lowest, think about how you can improve. Make a problem-solving plan for each (you may want to use a flowchart like the one on page 121). Check your progress in one month and at the end of the term. Finally, write down how you anticipate using the reading skills you learned in this chapter in your chosen career.

Social Networking

INCLUDE YOUR EDUCATION

Information about your education is often important when networking for jobs. Sign in to your LinkedIn account and click on "Edit My Profile." Then, click on "Education" and fill in the following:

- Country
- State
- Degree (either attained or working toward)
- Field(s) of study
- Dates attended (Current students enter their graduation year.)
- Activities and societies
- Additional notes (Give any other information about your education that you think would be valuable to a contact or potential employer—awards, honors, details about your major, study abroad, and so on.)

If you have a previously earned degree at another institution, don't forget to fill in a separate Education field about that as well.

Listening and Note Taking

Taking In and Recording Information

What Would You Do?

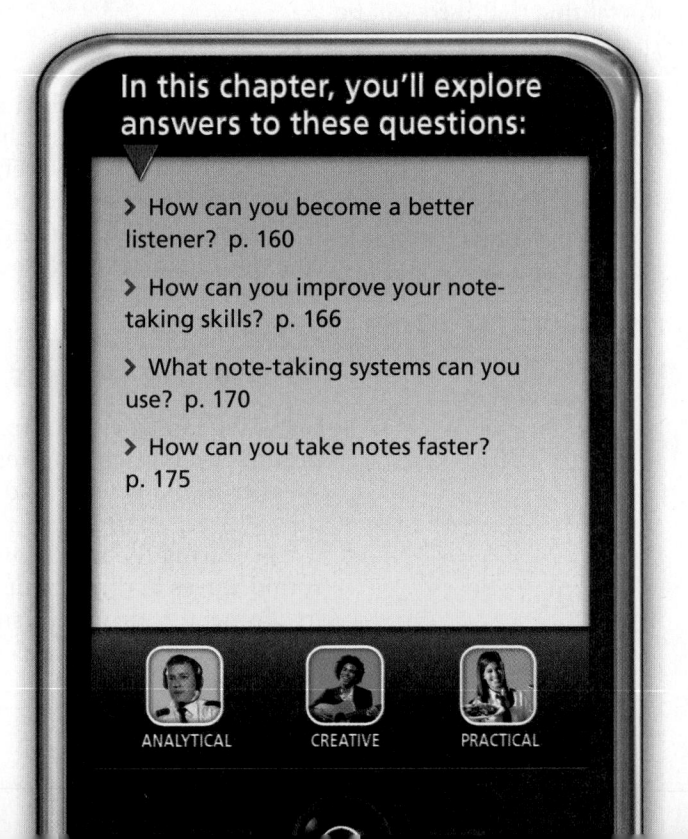

Think about this problem as you read, and consider how you would approach it. This chapter introduces you to listening and note-taking skills that will help you successfully take in, and write down, knowledge that you can use.

Halfway through her first term in college, Maya Leanza is not feeling the connection she expected—neither to her coursework nor her school. She is working her way through a full load of core requirements, none of which really interests her. In fact, although she is not sure what her academic focus or major will be, after only half a term she is sure that it won't be in any of the departments of the courses she is taking now.

She and her study partner Ross have a once-a-week session on Tuesdays for their contemporary civilization class. When they met to prepare for the midterm, they exchanged sets of notes as planned. Looking at hers, Ross said, "Maya, did you miss some of class? You have about half as many pages as I do, and I'm having trouble following your notes." Maya responded, "No, I was there the whole time. Honestly, Ross, I'm trying to listen but nothing sticks. I'm just done, and we still have seven weeks to go." "Well, is it okay if we study from my notes? The midterm is Friday and I'm a little stressed," said Ross. Maya agreed, and they worked through Ross's notes and their textbook chapters for an hour.

When they were packing up, Ross said, "Maya, it's hard to get anywhere with this stuff unless you somehow believe it is important. Does it mean anything to you?" "I'm not sure," Maya said. "I feel like, what's the point?" "Well, try just thinking about why you are here," replied Ross. "Find some reason that will keep you going, even if it's just 'A degree will help me get a better job.'" Maya thought for a minute. "I'm not sure that's enough," she said. "I don't know what is enough, but I guess I'm wasting my time and money if I don't figure it out." (To be continued . . .)

Many students, at some point during college, feel disconnected from their coursework. You'll learn more about Maya, and revisit her situation, within the chapter.

In this chapter, you'll explore answers to these questions:

> How can you become a better listener? p. 160

> How can you improve your note-taking skills? p. 166

> What note-taking systems can you use? p. 170

> How can you take notes faster? p. 175

ANALYTICAL   CREATIVE   PRACTICAL

STATUS *Check*

For each statement, circle the number that feels right to you, from 1 for "not at all true for me" to 5 for "very true for me."

▶ I know and understand the stages of listening.	1 2 3 4 5
▶ I arrive early for class prepared to absorb information by having read the required text ahead of time.	1 2 3 4 5
▶ I ask questions during lectures and listen for verbal clues to understand important information.	1 2 3 4 5
▶ I understand the differences between internal and external distractions and work to control my learning environment whenever possible.	1 2 3 4 5
▶ I use different note-taking systems depending on my instructor's teaching styles and the material being taught.	1 2 3 4 5
▶ I know how to use visuals in my notes to clarify tough concepts discussed in class.	1 2 3 4 5
▶ I believe that good preparation is a necessary first step toward taking comprehensive notes.	1 2 3 4 5
▶ I use strategies to make sense of and record large class discussions.	1 2 3 4 5
▶ I review notes within 24 hours of taking them.	1 2 3 4 5
▶ I use shorthand to take notes faster.	1 2 3 4 5

Each of the topics in these statements is covered in this chapter. Note those statements for which you circled a 3 or lower. Skim the chapter to see where those topics appear, and pay special attention to them as you read, learn, and apply new strategies.

REMEMBER: *No matter how developed your listening and note-taking skills are, you can improve with effort and practice.*

"Successfully intelligent people find their path and then pursue it, realizing that there will be obstacles along the way and that surmounting these obstacles is part of their challenge."

—Robert Sternberg

LISTENING
A process that involves sensing, interpreting, evaluating, and reacting to spoken messages.

How can you become a better listener?

The act of *hearing* is not the same as the act of **listening.** *Hearing* refers to sensing spoken messages and sounds from their source. You can hear all kinds of things and not understand or remember any of them. Listening, however, is a communication process that starts with hearing but also includes focused thinking about what you hear. Listening is a learnable skill that engages your analytical, creative, and practical thinking abilities and extends far beyond the classroom, enhancing your ability to relate with work and school colleagues, friends, and family.

Know the stages of listening

Listening is made up of four stages that build on one another: sensing, interpreting, evaluating, and reacting. These stages take the message from the speaker to the listener and back to the speaker (see Key 6.1).

▶ During the *sensation* stage (also known as *hearing*) your ears pick up sound waves and transmit them to the brain. For example, you are sitting in class and hear your instructor say, "The only opportunity to make up last week's test is Tuesday at 5:00 P.M."

THE **LISTENING PROCESS** MOVES MESSAGES ALONG A LISTENING LOOP

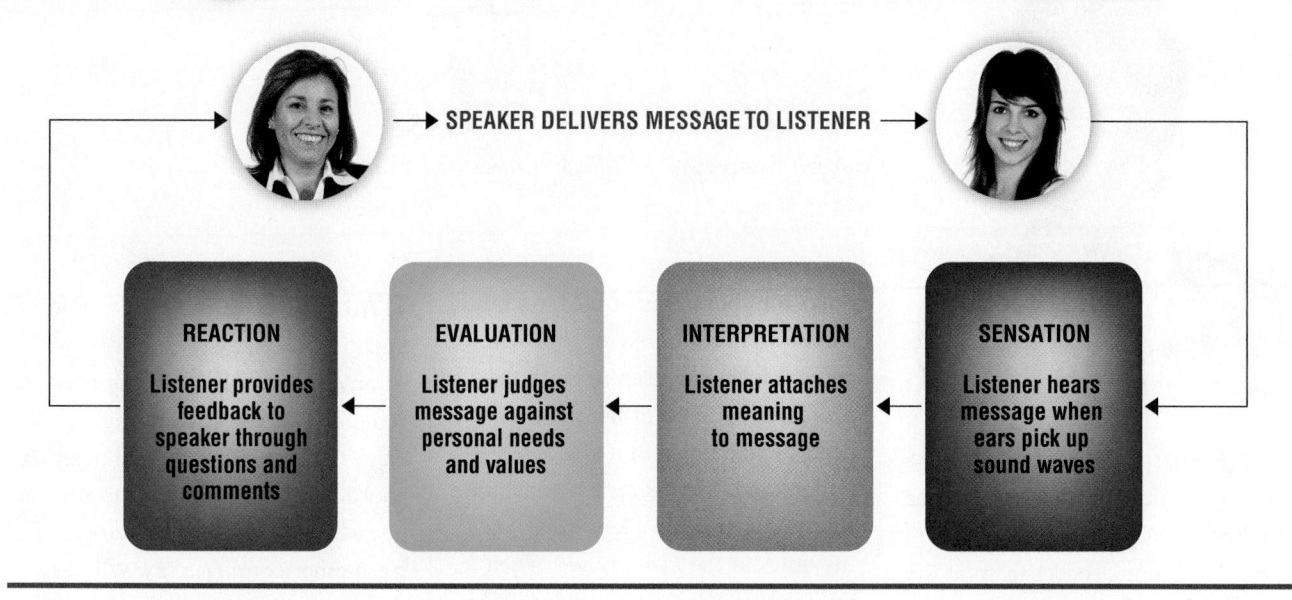

SPEAKER DELIVERS MESSAGE TO LISTENER

REACTION

Listener provides feedback to speaker through questions and comments

EVALUATION

Listener judges message against personal needs and values

INTERPRETATION

Listener attaches meaning to message

SENSATION

Listener hears message when ears pick up sound waves

▶ In the *interpretation* stage, you attach meaning to a message. You understand what is said and link it to what you already know. You relate this message to your knowledge of the test, whether you need to make it up, and what you are doing on Tuesday at 5:00.

▶ In the *evaluation* stage, you evaluate the message as it relates to your needs and values. If the message goes against your values or does not fulfill your needs, you may reject it, stop listening, or argue in your mind with the speaker. In this example, if you need to make up the test but have to work Tuesday at 5:00, you may evaluate the message in an unfavorable way.

▶ The final stage of listening is a *reaction* to the message in the form of direct feedback. In a classroom, direct feedback often comes in the form of questions and comments. Your reaction, in this case, may be to ask the instructor if she can schedule another test time.

You will become a better listener by learning to recognize and manage listening challenges and becoming actively involved with the material.

Become an active listener

On the surface, listening seems like a passive activity. You sit back as someone else speaks. In reality, effective listening is an active process that involves the following factors.

■ *Be there.* Being an active listener requires that you show up on time—preferably a few minutes before class begins. Instructors often make important announcements in the first few minutes and may also summarize the last lecture.

Listening to other students can be as important as listening to instructors. These students may learn something useful from their fellow student's presentation.
© iStockPhoto

Tomohito Kondo
De Anza Community College, Cupertino, California

About me:

I came here in spring 2009 right after I graduated from my high school in Japan. I am on the soccer team at the college and I'm majoring in political science. I plan on transferring to a four-year university next fall.

What I focus on:

In college, most professors move from topic to topic when they want to, no matter where students may be in their note taking. To take good notes for yourself is important, but it can be so hard to take notes when you are trying to keep up with the professor. The point here is that you need to take notes that you can understand. I focus on listening and I write down several key words on my notes at the same time. When I read it over later, my keywords help me remember what the teacher was talking about. Even if your handwriting is really awful, it doesn't matter as long as you can read it. I think my note-taking skills help me not only to be successful in my classes, but also to save me time so I can enjoy the fun side of college life.

What will help me in the workplace:

At any time of your life, you need to remember key points. In my case, I want to be an international meeting coordinator, so I will have to remember whatever the representatives from other countries say. Whatever your job will be, the skill of taking notes helps you to remember the information, and it will help you to get into a better position. You want to move on to the next stage, right? Good listening and note-taking skills will give you a boost.

■ *Set purposes for listening.* Before every class, use your analytical intelligence to establish what you want to achieve, such as understanding a particular concept. Many instructors start a lecture with a statement of purpose, so listen carefully and write the purpose at the top of your notes to help you focus. If you read assignments and review previous notes before class, you may be able to follow along more easily. Come to class with ideas about how what you hear will help you achieve your goals (this would help Maya make her purpose for listening more personal).

■ *Focus on understanding.* Rather than taking notes on everything, record information only when you can say to yourself, "I get it!" If you miss important material, leave holes in your notes and return later. Your instructor may repeat the point you missed, or another comment may help you piece it together.

■ *Ask questions.* Active listeners ask analytical questions to clarify their understanding and to associate new ideas with what they already know. Questions like "What is this part of?" or "How is it similar to yesterday's topic?" signal active involvement. Get into the habit of jotting down your questions and coming back to them during a discussion period so they don't interfere with listening.

Manage listening challenges

Sitting in your classes, you probably have noticed a variety of not-so-academic activities that interfere with listening. Some people may be texting or surfing the Internet, some may be talking or sleeping, and some might just be daydreaming. In all of these cases the students are probably not absorbing much—or any—information from the instructor, and they may be distracting you from listening as well. Read on to see how to address these issues, and others, on your path to becoming a better listener.

Issue 1: Distractions that divide your attention

The common distractions that interfere with listening can be divided into *internal distractions* (worry, illness, fatigue, hunger, feeling too hot or too cold) and *external distractions* (chatting, computer use, any kind of movement or noise). Distractions like these nip away at you while you're trying to pay attention.

Fix 1: Focus, focus, focus

First of all, tell yourself you're in the class to learn and that you *really need* to know the material. You may even want to remind yourself of what you're paying to sit in this class. Find practical ways to minimize distractions.

- ▶ Sit near the front of the room.
- ▶ Move away from talkative classmates.
- ▶ Turn off your cell phone or put it on silent mode when in class.
- ▶ Get enough sleep to stay alert.
- ▶ Eat enough so you're not hungry—or bring small snacks if allowed.
- ▶ Try to put your worries aside during class.

The often overwhelming pace of modern life leads students to multitask (do several things at once), under the impression that multitasking can help them accomplish goals effectively in less time. Although you may think you can handle distractions because you are used to multitasking, recent research shows that multitasking actually *decreases* both memory power and performance. In a study at Stanford, low multitaskers actually outperformed high multitaskers on all tasks.[1] Try to keep your focus on one thing at a time.

Issue 2: Listening lapses

Even the most fantastic instructor can't make you listen. You and you alone can do that. If you decide that a subject is too difficult or uninteresting, you may tune out and miss what comes next, as Maya found out. You may also focus on certain points and shut out everything else. Either way, you run the risk of not being prepared and not making the most of your time.

Fix 2: An I-can-do-it attitude

- ▶ *Start with a productive mindset.* If the class is hard, that's all the more reason to pay attention. Instructors are generally more sympathetic to, and eager to help, students who've obviously been trying even when it's tough.
- ▶ *Concentrate.* Work to take in the whole message so you will be able to read over your notes later,

combine your class and text notes, and think critically about what is important. Making connections between ideas can alleviate the difficulty of the material in some cases and boredom if you're familiar with the concepts.

▶ *Refocus.* If you experience a listening lapse, try to get back into the lecture quickly instead of worrying about what you missed. After class, look at a classmate's notes to fill in the gaps.

▶ *Be aware.* Pay attention to **verbal signposts** to help organize information, connect ideas, and indicate what is important and what is not. See Key 6.2 for examples.

VERBAL SIGNPOSTS
Spoken words or phrases that call attention to information that follows.

Issue 3: Rushing to judgment

It's common to stop listening when you hear something you don't like or don't agree with. You react, and then your emotions take focus. Unfortunately, you can spend valuable class time thinking of all the reasons your instructor is wrong and miss everything else. The situation might not seem particularly bad that day, but when the test comes around, you may feel differently about having missed material.

Judgments also involve reactions to speakers themselves. If you do not like your instructors or have preconceived notions about their race, ethnicity, gender, physical characteristics, or disability, you may dismiss their ideas—and miss out on your opportunity to learn.

Fix 3: Recognize and correct your patterns

Although it can be human nature to stop listening when you react to a speaker or message, it can make listening a lot harder. College is about broadening your horizons and looking for what different people can teach you, even though they and their beliefs may differ from you and yours. So what do you do?

Key 6.2   PAY ATTENTION TO **VERBAL SIGNPOSTS**

SIGNALS POINTING TO KEY CONCEPTS	SIGNALS OF SUPPORT
A key point to remember . . .	A perfect example, . . .
Point 1, point 2, etc. . . .	Specifically, . . .
The impact of this was . . .	For instance, . . .
The critical stages in the process are . . .	Similarly, . . .

SIGNALS POINTING TO DIFFERENCES	SIGNALS THAT SUMMARIZE
On the contrary, . . .	From this you have learned, . . .
On the other hand, . . .	In conclusion, . . .
In contrast, . . .	As a result, . . .
However, . . .	Finally, . . .

▶ Recognize your pattern so you can change it. When you feel yourself reacting to something said in a lecture, stop and take a moment to breathe. Count to ten. Take one more breath and see how you feel.

▶ Know that you can't hear—and therefore can't learn anything from—others if you are filled with preconceived notions about them and their ideas. Put yourself in their shoes; would you want them to stop listening to you if they disagreed, or would you want to be heard completely?

▶ Stop it. It's as simple as that. Listen with an open mind even when you disagree or have a negative reaction to an instructor. Being open to the new and different, even when it makes you a bit uncomfortable, is part of what education is about.

Issue 4: Partial hearing loss and learning disabilities

If you have a hearing loss or a learning disability, listening effectively in class may prove challenging. As discussed in Chapter 3, learning disabilities can come in a variety of forms affecting different parts of cognition.

Fix 4: Get help

If you have a hearing loss, find out about available equipment. For example, listening to a taped lecture at a higher-than-normal volume can help you hear things you missed. Ask instructors if digitalized recordings are available for download to a computer or iPod. Meeting with your instructor outside of class to clarify your notes may also help, as will sitting near the front of the room.

If you have (or think you have) a learning disability, learn what services are available. Talk to your advisor and instructor about your problem, seek out a tutor, visit academic centers that can help (such as the writing center if you have a writing issue), scan the college website, or connect to the office for students with disabilities. Know that you can succeed and that people are there to help you.

Issue 5: Comprehension difficulties for speakers of other languages

If English isn't your first language, listening and understanding material in the classroom can be challenging, requiring concentration, dedication, and patience. Specialized vocabulary, informal language, and the rate of speech can add to the challenge.

Fix 5: Take a proactive approach to understanding

Talk to your instructor as soon as possible about your situation. Recognizing a need early and meeting to discuss it keeps your instructor informed and shows your dedication. In some cases, your professor will give you a list of key terms to review before class. During class, keep a list of unfamiliar words and phrases to look up later, but whenever possible, don't let these terms prevent you from understanding the main ideas. Focus on the main points of the lecture and plan to meet with classmates after class to fill gaps in your understanding. If, after several weeks, you're still having difficulties, consider enrolling in an English refresher course, getting a tutor, or visiting the campus advising center for more assistance. Be proactive about your education.

Listening isn't always easy and it isn't always comfortable. As poet Robert Frost once said, "Education is the

Discover Yourself as a Listener

Complete the following as you focus on your personal listening habits:

Analyze how present you are as a listener. Are you easily distracted, or can you focus well? Do you prefer to listen, or do you tend to talk?

_____

_____

When you are listening, what tends to distract you?

_____

_____

What happens to your listening skills when you become confused?

_____

_____

How do you react when you strongly disagree with something your instructor says—when you are convinced that you are right and your instructor is wrong?

_____

_____

Thinking about your answers, list two strategies from the chapter that will help you improve listening skills.

1. _____

2. _____

ability to listen to almost anything without losing your temper or your self-confidence." Keeping an open, engaged mind takes practice, but when excellent listening becomes second nature, you'll thank yourself for the work it took. Effective listening skills are the basis for effective note taking—an essential and powerful study tool.

How can you improve your note-taking skills?

Taking notes makes you an active class participant—even when you don't say a word—and provides you with study materials. What's on the line is nothing short of your academic success.

Class notes have two primary purposes: to serve as a record of what happened in class and to use for studying, alone and in combination with your text notes. Because it is virtually impossible to take notes on everything you hear, note taking encourages you to use your analytical intelligence to critically evaluate what is worth remembering. Exploring the strategies outlined next can help you prepare and take notes in class, review notes, and take notes on reading materials.

Prepare

Showing up for class on time is just the start. Here's more about preparing to take notes:

■ *Preview your reading material.* More than anything else you can do, reading assigned materials before class will give you the background to take effective notes. Check your class syllabi daily for assignment due dates and plan your reading time with these deadlines in mind.

■ *Review what you know.* Taking 15 minutes before class to review your notes from the previous class and your reading assignment notes for that day will enable you to follow the lecture from the start.

■ *Set up your environment.* Find a comfortable seat, away from friends if sitting with them distracts you. Use a separate notebook for each course, and start a new page for each class. If you use a laptop, open the file containing your class notes right away. Be ready to write (or type) as soon as the instructor begins speaking.

■ *Gather support.* In each class, set up a support system with one or two students so you can look at their notes after an absence. Find students whose work you respect, as Maya did with Ross.

■ *Choose the best note-taking system.* Take these factors into account to select a system that works best in each class:

> ▶ *The instructor's style* (which will be clear after a few classes). In the same term, you may have an instructor who is organized and speaks slowly, another who jumps around and talks rapidly, and a third who goes off topic in response to questions. Be flexible as you adapt.
> ▶ *The course material.* You may decide that an informal outline works best for a highly structured lecture and that a think link (discussed later in the chapter) is right for a looser presentation. Try one note-taking system for several classes and then adjust if necessary.
> ▶ *Your learning style.* Choose strategies that make the most of your strengths and compensate for your weaknesses.

Examples of various note-taking systems, and a more thorough discussion, appear later in the chapter.

Good listening powers note taking. When taking notes in class, stop to listen to the information before deciding what to write down.
© iStockPhoto

Record information effectively during class

The following practical suggestions will help you record what is important in a format that you can review later:

> ▶ *Start a new page or section for each new topic,* especially if your instructor jumps from topic to topic during a single class.
> ▶ *Record whatever your instructor emphasizes* by paying attention to verbal and nonverbal cues.
> ▶ *Write down all key terms and definitions* so that you can refer back to them easily.

GET PRACTICAL!

Face a Note-Taking Challenge

Get set to take in and record information in your most difficult class.

Course name and date of class:

_____

Consult your syllabus, and then list what you have to read (text sections and/or other materials) before your next class:

_____

_____

Where will you sit in class to focus your attention and minimize distractions?

_____

Which note-taking system is best suited for the class and why?

_____

_____

Write the phone numbers and e-mail addresses of two classmates whose notes you can borrow if you miss a class or are confused about material:

_____

_____

▶ *Note relevant examples, applications, and links to other material* when you encounter difficult concepts.

▶ *Ask questions.* If your instructor allows questions during class, ask them. Chances are several other students have similar queries. If your instructor prefers to answer questions at the end of class, keep a separate sheet of paper to jot down questions as you think of them.

▶ *Write down every question your instructor raises,* because these questions may be on a test.

▶ *Be organized, but not fussy.* Remember that you can always improve your notes later.

▶ *Leave blank spaces between points* to make it easy see where one topic ends and another begins. (This suggestion does not apply if you are using a think link.)

▶ *Draw pictures and diagrams* to illustrate ideas.

▶ *Be consistent.* Use the same system to show importance—such as indenting, spacing, or underlining—on each page.

▶ *Record as much as you can if you have trouble understanding a concept.* Then leave space for an explanation and flag the margin with a large question mark. After class, try to clarify your questions by reading the text or ask a classmate or your instructor for help.

▶ *Consider that your class notes are only part of the picture.* You will learn best when you combine your text and class notes.

► *Go beyond the PowerPoint.* Increasingly, instructors are using computer software to present lectures in the classroom. Although it may be tempting to simply copy down what's written on the slide, realize that instructors usually show the main points, not the details that may be tested later. Take notes on what your instructor says about each main idea highlighted on a PowerPoint slide.

Finally, don't stop taking notes when your class engages in a discussion. Even though it isn't part of the instructor's planned presentation, it often includes important information. Key 6.3 has suggestions for how to make the most of discussions.

Review and revise

By their very nature, class notes require revision. They may be incomplete in some places, confusing in others, and illegible in still others. That is why it is critical to review and revise your notes as soon as possible after class. This will enable you to fill in gaps while the material is fresh, to clarify sloppy handwriting, or to raise questions.

If you can review your notes within 24 hours of taking them down in class, you are likely to reactivate and strengthen the new neural pathways you created when you learned the material. Waiting longer than 24 hours can result in losing the information you worked so hard to record. Reviewing and revising your class notes prepares you for the vital step of combining class and text notes.

IMPROVE YOUR NOTES
DURING CLASS DISCUSSION

- Listen to everyone; you never know when something important will be said.

- Listen for threads that weave through comments. They may signal an important point.

- Listen for ideas the instructor likes and for encouraging comments, such as "You make a great point" or "I like your idea."

- Take notes when the instructor rephrases and clarifies a point.

Taking notes from a text

Taking notes while reading a text follows the same basic principles as taking notes in class, but with a bit of an SQ3R twist. Although you won't be asking as many probing questions of the material, you'll need your skills in observation, as well as in recording and reviewing, to make it a success.

You might take notes from a text when the book is a library copy or borrowed from a classmate—or when you don't have enough room to take notes in the margin. In that case, it's best to start by identifying what you want to get from the notes. Are you looking for the basic topics from a chapter? An in-depth understanding of a particular concept? Once you've decided on the need, then you can identify the method.

Revisit the note-taking methods listed earlier in the chapter. Different note-taking approaches work best for different situations. For instance, mind maps work well to understand broad connections, overall relationships, or how your text works in relation to your instructor's lecture. On the other hand, formal outlines can make sense of complicated information in a structured way that can provide clarity. Try different approaches to see which ones work for you.

What note-taking systems can you use?

Now that you have gathered some useful note-taking strategies, take a look at different approaches to note taking. As you read, keep some questions in mind:

▶ What class or type of instruction would this system be best suited for? Why?
▶ How could I make use of this system?
▶ Which system seems most comfortable to me?
▶ What system might be most compatible with my learning style strengths? Why?

Outlines

Outlines use a standard structure to show how ideas interrelate. *Formal outlines* indicate idea dominance and subordination with Roman numerals, uppercase and lowercase letters, and numbers. In contrast, *informal outlines* show the same associations but replace the formality with a system of consistent indenting and dashes.

When a lecture seems well organized, an informal outline can show how ideas and supporting details relate while also indicating levels of importance. Key 6.4 shows how the structure of an informal outline helps a student take notes on the topic of tropical rain forests. The multiple intelligences table in this chapter (see page 172) is designed to help harness different learning approaches for an earth science course. Specifically, the table will suggest different note-taking strategies you can use to study the topic of tropical rain forests.

AN **INFORMAL OUTLINE** IS USEFUL FOR TAKING NOTES IN CLASS

Tropical Rain Forests

What are tropical rain forests?

—Areas in South America and Africa, along the equator

—Average temperatures between 25° and 30° C (77°–86° F)

—Average annual rainfalls range between 250 to 400 centimeters (100 to 160 inches)

—Conditions combine to create the Earth's richest, most biodiverse ecosystem.

  –A biodiverse ecosystem has a great number of organisms coexisting within a defined area.

  –Examples of rain forest biodiversity

   –2½ acres in the Amazon rain forest has 283 species of trees

   –a 3-square-mile section of a Peruvian rain forest has more than 1,300 butterfly species and 600 bird species.

   –Compare this biodiversity to what is found in the entire U.S.—only 400 butterfly species and 700 bird species

How are humans changing the rain forest?

—Humans have already destroyed about 40% of all rain forests.

  –They are cutting down trees for lumber or clearing the land for ranching or agriculture.

—Biologist Edwin O. Wilson estimates that this destruction may lead to the extinction of 27,000 species.

—Rain forest removal is also linked to the increase in atmospheric carbon dioxide, which worsens the greenhouse effect.

  –The greenhouse effect refers to process in which gases such as carbon dioxide trap the sun's energy in the Earth's atmosphere as heat resulting in global warning.

—Recognition of the crisis is growing as are conservation efforts.

Source: Teresa Audesirk, Gerald Audesirk, and Bruce E. Byers. *Life on Earth,* 2nd ed. Upper Saddle River, NJ: Prentice Hall, 2000, pp. 660–662.

When an instructor's presentation is disorganized, it may be difficult to use an outline. Focus instead on taking down whatever information you can as you try to connect key topics. The Cornell system and other note-taking methods discussed next can be beneficial in such situations.

From time to time, an instructor may give you a guide, usually in outline form, to help you take notes in class. This outline, known as *guided notes,* may be on the board, projected onto a screen, or in a handout that you receive at the beginning of class. Because guided notes are usually general and sketchy, they require that you fill in the details.

Cornell T-note system

The *Cornell note-taking system,* also known as the *T-note system,* consists of three sections on ordinary notepaper.[2]

▶ *Notes,* the largest section, is on the right. Record your notes here in whatever form you choose. Skip lines between topics so you can clearly see where a section begins and ends.

▶ The *cue column* goes to the left of your notes. Leave it blank while you read or listen, and then fill it in later as you review. You might insert keywords or comments that highlight ideas, clarify meaning, add examples, link ideas, or draw diagrams. Many students use this column to raise questions, which they answer when they study.

▶ The *summary* goes at the bottom of the page. Here you reduce your notes to critical points, a process that will help you learn the material. Use this section to provide an overview of what the notes say.

Apply Different Intelligences to Concepts to Taking Notes in Earth Science

INTELLIGENCE	USE MI STRATEGIES TO IMPROVE YOUR NOTES	APPLY MI NOTE-TAKING STRATEGIES TO THE TOPIC OF TROPICAL RAIN FORESTS FOR AN EARTH SCIENCE COURSE
Verbal-Linguistic	• Rewrite your class notes in an alternate note-taking style to see connections more clearly. • Combine class and text notes to get a complete picture.	• Rewrite and summarize your reading and lecture notes to understand the characteristics of tropical rain forests.*
Logical-Mathematical	• When reviewing or rewriting notes, put information into a logical sequence. • Create tables that show relationships.	• Create a table comparing and contrasting the different species found in a typical rain forest.
Bodily-Kinesthetic	• Think of your notes as a crafts project that enables you to see "knowledge layers." Use colored pens to texture your notes. • Study with your notes spread in sequence around you so that you can see knowledge building from left to right.	• Fill a tube with 160 inches of water (that's 13⅓ feet!) to give you a physical sense of the annual rainfall in a rain forest. Or fill a bathtub with 10 inches of water and multiply by 16 to imagine rainfall totals. How would you react to living with so much rain? Take notes on your reaction.
Visual-Spatial	• Take notes using colored markers or pens. • Rewrite lecture notes in think link format, focusing on the most important points.	• As part of your notes, create a chart that covers the types of vegetation that grow in a rain forest. Use a different colored marker for each plant species.
Interpersonal	• Try to schedule a study group right after a lecture to discuss class notes. • Review class notes with a study buddy. Compare notes to see what the other missed.	• Interview someone you know who has visited a rain forest about what she saw, or interview a natural scientist at a museum about this environment. Use a different note-taking system for each person.
Intrapersonal	• Schedule some quiet time soon after a lecture to review and think about your notes. • As you review your notes, decide whether you grasp the material or need help.	• Think about the conflict between economic modernization and the preservation of rain forests in underdeveloped areas. Include your thoughts in your notes.
Musical	• To improve recall, recite concepts in your notes to rhythms. • Write a song that includes material from your class and text notes. Use the refrain to emphasize what is important.	• Use the Internet to find songs about the biodiversity of rain forests written by indigenous peoples who live in or near them. Then, use the song to remember key concepts. Take notes on what you find.
Naturalistic	• Notice similarities and differences in concepts by organizing material into natural groupings.	• If possible, visit a museum of natural history with exhibits of rain forests. Try to see common characteristics that make vegetation and species thrive in this environment. Take notes on your observations.

*For information on tropical rain forests, see Frederick Lutgens, Edward Tarbuck, and Dennis Tasa, *Foundations of Earth Science,* 5th ed., Upper Saddle River, NJ: Prentice Hall, 2008.

Create this note-taking structure before class begins. Picture an upside-down letter *T* as you follow these directions:

▶ Start with a sheet of 8½-by-11-inch lined paper. Label it with the date and lecture title.

▶ To create the cue column, draw a vertical line about 2½ inches from the left side of the paper. End the line about two inches from the bottom of the sheet.

▶ To create the summary area, start at the point where the vertical line ends (about two inches from the bottom of the page) and draw a horizontal line that spans the entire paper.

Key 6.5 shows how the Cornell system is used in a business course.

Key 6.5

THE **CORNELL SYSTEM** HAS SPACE FOR NOTES, COMMENTS, AND A SUMMARY

October 3, 2010, p. 1

Label a sheet of paper with the date and title of the lecture.

Understanding Employee Motivation

Why do some workers have a better attitude toward their work than others?

Purpose of motivational theories
— To explain role of human relations in motivating employee performance
— Theories translate into how managers actually treat workers

Some managers view workers as lazy; others view them as motivated and productive.

2 specific theories
— Human resources model, developed by Douglas McGregor, shows that managers have radically different beliefs about motivation.
— Theory X holds that people are naturally irresponsible and uncooperative
— Theory Y holds that people are naturally responsible and self-motivated

Create the cue column by drawing a vertical line about 2½ inches from the left side of the paper. End the line about 2 inches from the bottom of the sheet.

Maslow's Hierarchy

self-actualization needs (challenging job)
esteem needs (job title)
social needs (friends at work)
security needs (health plan)
physiological needs (pay)

— Maslow's Hierarchy of Needs says that people have needs in 5 different areas, which they attempt to satisfy in their work.
— Physiological need: need for survival, including food and shelter
— Security need: need for stability and protection
— Social need: need for friendship and companionship
— Esteem need: need for status and recognition
— Self-actualization need: need for self-fulfillment
Needs at lower levels must be met before a person tries to satisfy needs at higher levels.
— Developed by psychologist Abraham Maslow

Create the summary area by starting where the vertical line ends (about 2 inches from the bottom of the page) and drawing a horizontal line across the paper.

Two motivational theories try to explain worker motivation. The human resources model includes Theory X and Theory Y. Maslow's Hierarchy of Needs suggests that people have needs in 5 different areas: physiological, security, social, esteem, and self-actualization.

Think links

A *think link,* also known as a *mind map* or *word web,* is a visual form of note taking that encourages flexible thinking. When you draw a think link, you use shapes and lines to link ideas with supporting details and examples. The visual design makes the connections easy to see, and shapes and pictures extend the material beyond words.

To create a think link, start by circling or boxing your topic in the middle of the paper. Next, draw a line from the topic and write the name of one major idea at the end of the line. Circle that idea. Then jot down specific facts related to the idea, linking them to the idea with lines. Continue the process, connecting thoughts to one another with circles, lines, and words. Key 6.6, a think link on the sociological concept "stratification," follows this structure.

Examples of think link designs include stair steps showing connected ideas that build toward a conclusion and a tree with trunk and roots as central concepts and branches as examples. Key 8.5 on page 231 shows another type of think link called a "jellyfish."

A think link may be difficult to construct in class, especially if your instructor talks quickly. If this is the case, transform your notes into think link format later when you review.

Key 6.6

USE A **THINK LINK** TO CONNECT IDEAS VISUALLY

Definition: a system in which society ranks categories of people in a hierarchy

Caste System
- Birth alone determines social destiny
- Examples: India and South Africa

SOCIAL STRATIFICATION

Functions

Davis-Moore thesis asserts that stratification benefits society

People hold different jobs of varying importance

The greater the importance of a position, the greater the rewards given to the people doing it

Example: a surgeon earns more than an auto mechanic

Class System
- Individual achievement determines social destiny
- Schooling and skills increase social mobility

This implies a meritocracy— a system of social stratification based on personal merit

Charting method

Sometimes instructors deliver information in such quantities and at such speeds that taking detailed notes becomes nearly impossible. In such situations, when a lot of material is coming at you very quickly, the charting method might prove quite useful. It is also excellent for classes presented chronologically or sequentially.

To create charting notes, look ahead in your syllabus to determine the topics of the day's lecture. Then separate your paper into distinct columns, such as definitions, important phrases, and key themes. As you listen to the lecture, this will eliminate excessive writing, help you track dialogues that can be easy to lose, and provide quick memorization tools by splitting material into relevant categories. Shown is a partial set of charting notes for a history class:

Time Period	Important People	Events	Importance
1969–1974	Richard Nixon	Watergate, Vietnam War	Ended Vietnam War, Opened relations with China, First president to resign

Other visual strategies

Other strategies that help organize information are especially useful to visual learners, although they may be too involved to complete during class. Use them when taking text notes or combining class and text notes for review.

▶ *Pictures and diagrams.* Copy any and all diagrams from the board and feel free to adapt your own. Make complex concepts into images or cartoons. The act of converting material into a visual display will activate both your bodily-kinesthetic attributes as well as your visual intelligence.

▶ *Timelines.* Use a timeline to organize information into chronological order. Draw a vertical or horizontal line on the page and connect each item to the line, in order, noting the dates and basic event descriptions.

▶ *Tables.* Use the columns and rows of a table to organize information as you condense and summarize your class and text notes.

▶ *Hierarchy charts.* Charts showing an information hierarchy can help you visualize how pieces fit together. For example, you can use a hierarchy chart to show ranks within a government bureaucracy or levels of scientific classification of animals and plants.

How can you take notes faster?

SHORTHAND
A system of rapid handwriting that employs symbols, abbreviations, and shortened words to represent words and phrases.

Personal shorthand is a practical intelligence strategy that enables you to write faster. Because you are the only intended reader, you can misspell and abbreviate words in ways that only you understand. A risk of using shorthand is that you might forget what your writing means. To avoid this problem, review your notes shortly after class and spell out words that are confusing.

Another risk is forgetting to remove shorthand from work you hand in. This can happen when you use the same system for class notes as you do when talking to friends online. For example, when students take notes in text message shorthand they may be so accustomed to omitting capitalization and punctuation, using acronyms, and replacing long words with creative contractions that they may forget to correct their final work.

The suggestions that follow will help you master shorthand. Many will be familiar and, in fact, you may already use many of them to speed up your e-mail and text messaging.

1. Use standard abbreviations in place of complete words.

w/, w/o	with, without	Cf	compare, in comparison to
ur	you are	Ff	following
→	means; resulting in	Q	question
←	as a result of	gr8	great
↑	increasing	Pov	point of view
↓	decreasing	<	less than
∴	therefore	>	more than
b/c	because	=	equals
≈	approximately	b&f	back and forth
+ or &	and	Δ	change
Y	why	2	to; two; too
no. or #	number	Afap	as far as possible
i.e.	that is,	e.g.	for example
cos	change of subject	c/o	care of
Ng	no good	lb	pound
POTUS	President of the United States	hx	history

2. Shorten words by removing middle vowels.

prps = purpose
lwyr = lawyer
cmptr = computer

3. Substitute word beginnings for entire words.

assoc = associate; association
info = information
subj = subject

4. Form plurals by adding *s* to shortened words.

prblms = problems
envlps = envelopes
prntrs = printers

5. Make up your own symbols and use them consistently.

b/4   = before
4tn   = fortune
2thake = toothache

6. Use standard or informal abbreviations for proper nouns such as places, people, companies, scientific substances, events, and so on.

DC   = Washington, D.C.
H_2O = water
Moz. = Wolfgang Amadeus Mozart

7. If you know that a word or phrase will be repeated, write it once and then establish an abbreviation for the rest of your notes. For example, the first time your political science instructor mentions the Iraq Study Group,

Craft Your Own Shorthand

Now that you've read through some suggestions for shorthand, it's time to customize it to your needs.

Identify a class in which you take a lot of notes or one in which you would like to begin taking better notes.

_____

Next, write ten terms that are used often in this class. For instance, if you were creating a list for your psychology class, you might include terms like *Sigmund Freud, child development,* or *neuropsychology.*

_____

_____

_____

_____

_____

Finally, create a list of shorthand terms for the items you chose. Be creative but remember that they should be easy for you to remember and use. Thus, your shorthand should not be longer or more complex than the word itself. Use numbers, symbols, or even small images (like a heart or smiley face). For the list of psychology terms, the shorthand might look like the following:

Sigmund Freud	=	**SigFrd**
Child development	=	**ChDev**
Neuropsychology	=	**nro-psych**

the 2006 bipartisan commission that issued recommendations to the president on the Iraq War, write the name in full. After that, use the initials ISG.

8. Write only what is essential. Include only the information nuggets you want to remember, even if your instructor says much more. Do this by paring down your writing. Say, for example, your instructor had the following to say on the subject of hate crimes.[3]

After the terrorist attacks on September 11, 2001, law enforcement officials noted a dramatic shift in the nature of hate crimes. For the first time, replacing crimes motivated by race as the leading type of hate crime were crimes that targeted religious and ethnic groups and particularly Muslims.

Your shorthand notes might look something like this:

—After 9/11 HCs ▲ focus & targeted religious and ethnic groups, esp. Muslims.
—Reduction of HC based on race.

Case Wrap-up

What happened to Maya? With Ross's help, Maya passed the midterm. Afterward, she found herself once again "there but not there" in her contemporary civ class as well as others. Trying to find meaning in the coursework, she talked with her parents. Her mother commented that she was building incredible skills for life, because not having much interest in the material meant that she needed extra motivation, commitment, and responsibility to get through it successfully. This awakened a sense of pride in Maya. Determined to improve during the remaining weeks, she concentrated on finding a note-taking system that made sense to her and deliberately used it in her classes. She found that the structure actually helped her pay more attention, and her increased focus helped her notice some ideas that interested her more than she had expected.

What does this mean for you? Nearly every student has to fulfill core requirements as part of a degree program. Chances are that some—or even many—of the core courses you have to take will not be on your list of favorites. In many ways this is a useful exercise for life, in which you will rarely be able to choose your favorite job, most desired co-workers, ideal neighbors, or perfect day-to-day schedule. Sure, sometimes you may find a way to enjoy a particular course, even if the material doesn't inspire you. You may make friends in the class, develop a good relationship with the instructor, or get motivated by the simple fact that passing the course moves you toward your goal of graduation. However, just getting through it with your GPA intact can teach you a useful skill—how to take something valuable away from any experience.

What effects go beyond your world? Searching for meaning in your coursework or your working life can mean more than just fulfillment for you. The more interested, committed, and fulfilled you are, the more the benefits radiate out from you and affect others. Read the article "Meaningful Work" located at www.psychologytoday.com/blog/the-meaning-in-life/200905/work-youre-meant-do-or-just-paid-do. Reflect on what kind of job might fulfill the three criteria for meaningful work (it must make sense to you, have a point or goal, and serve the greater good in some way). Brainstorm ideas for work that you believe would have positive effects on others, going beyond your needs for a steady paycheck and personal fulfillment.

Successful Intelligence *Wrap-up*

HERE'S HOW YOU HAVE
BUILT SKILLS IN **CHAPTER 6** :

ANALYTICAL THINKING	CREATIVE THINKING	PRACTICAL THINKING
❯ You examined common challenges you face when listening.	❯ You developed new systems for note taking and how to apply them to your courses.	❯ You compiled practical tools for managing listening challenges.
❯ In the Get Analytical exercise, you analyzed your own listening skills to better understand your personal needs.	❯ In the Get Creative exercise, you brainstormed personal shorthand terms to speed up note taking.	❯ In the Get Practical exercise, you explored how to use note-taking systems in difficult situations.
❯ You explored note-taking systems and considered which would work best for you given certain locations and classes.	❯ You may have been inspired to think about new ways in which you might listen and receive information in classes.	❯ You learned shorthand techniques to add to your understanding of note-taking strategies.

Word *for* Thought

In **Swedish,** the word *lagom* (lagh'-ohm) refers to the place between extremes, the spot that is neither too much nor too little, but just right.[4] Think of the quest for lagom as you work to improve listening and note-taking skills. You can never hope to take in and record every word your instructor says—and that's okay. You are aiming for "just right."

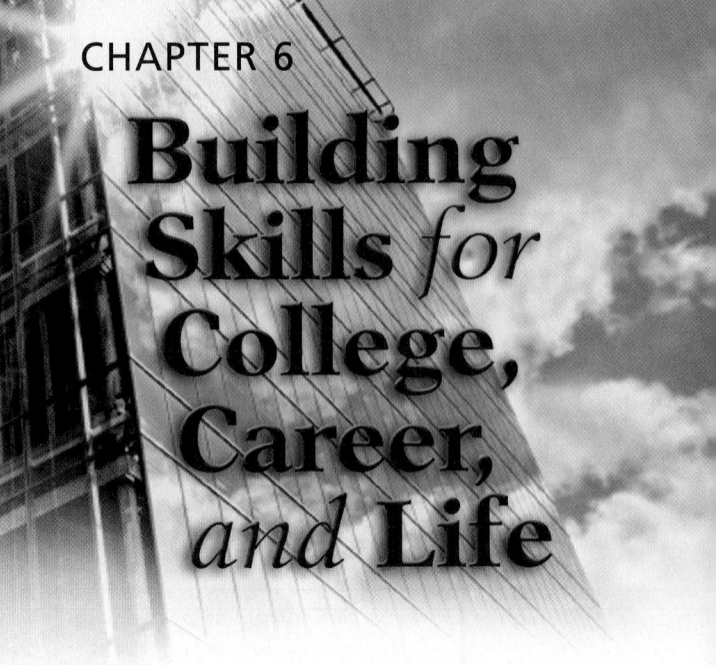

Building Skills *for* College, Career, *and* Life

Steps to Success

Your Best Listening and Note-Taking Conditions

BUILD BASIC SKILLS. Think of a recent class in which you were *able to listen and take notes effectively.*

Describe the environment (course title, classroom setting, and so on):

_____

_____

_____

_____

Describe the instructor's style (lecture, group discussion, Q and A):

_____

_____

_____

Describe your level of preparation and attitude toward the class:

_____

_____

_____

_____

Describe the note-taking style you generally use in the class and how effective it is for you:

_____

_____

_____

_____

Describe any barriers to effective listening that were present:

_____

_____

_____

_____

Now think of a recent class in which you found it *hard to listen and take notes.*

Describe the environment (course title, classroom setting, and so on):

_____

_____

_____

_____

Describe the instructor's style (lecture, group discussion, Q and A):

_____

_____

_____

_____

Describe your level of preparation and attitude toward the class:

_____

_____

_____

_____

Describe the note-taking style you generally use in the class and how effective it is for you:

_____

_____

_____

_____

Describe any barriers to effective listening that were present:

_____

_____

_____

_____

TAKE IT TO THE NEXT LEVEL. Examine the two situations. From what you notice, identify three conditions that seem, for you, to be crucial for effective listening and note taking:

1. _____

2. _____

3. _____

MOVE TOWARD MASTERY. Think about the more difficult listening and note-taking situation. For each of the three conditions you named, describe either how you can make sure that condition occurs or how you can compensate for it if it is out of your control.

1. _____
_____

2. _____
_____

3. _____
_____

Teamwork

Create Solutions Together

TEAM UP TO TAKE NOTES

Goal: To create a note-taking team.

Time on task: One week; 30 minutes of review

Instructions: In your most demanding course, form a study group with two classmates. Ask everyone to gather together a week's worth of class notes so that you can review and compare the different versions. Focus on the following:

- Legibility (Can everyone read what is written?)
- Completeness (Did you all record the same information? If not, why not?)
- Organizational effectiveness (Does everyone get an idea of how ideas flow?)
- Value of the notes as a study aid (Will this help everyone remember the material?)

What did you learn? Use your insights to improve personal note-taking skills. As a bonus, exchange contact information with the two students. Contact them to swap notes in the future or form a study group.

Writing

Build Intrapersonal and Communication Skills

Record your thoughts on a separate piece of paper, in a journal, or electronically.

EMOTIONAL INTELLIGENCE JOURNAL

Understanding your needs and making changes. Think about a situation when you've had trouble taking effective notes. Was it the teacher's pace? The subject matter of the class? How did you feel about the situation, and what did you do? After you describe the situation, find and write three note-taking strategies discussed in this chapter that could help you in the future. How might they help you create a more positive outcome?

REAL-LIFE WRITING

Determining the best method for you. Over the next week, commit to trying at least two different types of note-taking systems in your classes. If possible, choose a different method for each subject. Prepare for your method before entering the class by readying your notebook with the correct formatting. Try to complete your classes using the new method. When the week is over, reflect on which style worked best for you and which would be the most beneficial going forward.

Personal Portfolio

Prepare for Career Success

LEARN MORE ABOUT CAREER SUCCESS

21st Century Learning Building Blocks

- Financial, Economic, Business, and Entrepreneurial Literacy
- Information Literacy
- Media Literacy

Complete the following in your electronic portfolio or on separate paper.

Put your listening and note-taking skills to work as you investigate what brings success in the workplace. Write down a few potential career areas that interest you.

1. _____

2. _____

3. _____

Next, visit an Internet website that hosts user-loaded videos like YouTube.com. Perform a search for a career interview of your choice. You might try search terms like "marketing interview," "what's it like to be a dental technician?" or "what does a movie producer do?" When you've found a usable video (keep in mind that you're looking for credible, realistic information), practice one of the note-taking techniques discussed in this chapter.

Watch the video once all the way through, concentrating on main points and overall themes. Then, watch it again focusing on filling in gaps, understanding key terms and concepts, and gathering interesting extras. Remember to use shorthand when necessary.

After you've watched the video twice and taken thorough notes, write a one-page summary of the career for your portfolio. Include important information discussed in the video, such as the training required, salary expectations, daily duties, and so on. Keep the summary in your portfolio for future career searches.

Social Networking

BUILD CONTACTS

Begin to build, or continue to build, your network on LinkedIn. Sign in to your account and click on "Add Connections." Find and contact 10 people in one of the following ways:

- Enter the name of someone you know in the "People" field at the top of the screen to see whether that person has a LinkedIn account. If they do, click on "Add to network" to invite them to join your network.
- Use the "See Who You Already Know on LinkedIn" feature to search your e-mail contacts for people who have LinkedIn accounts.
- In the "Enter E-mail Addresses" box, enter the e-mail addresses of people you want to invite to your network. Each will receive an invitation, regardless of whether they are already LinkedIn members.

Think carefully about who you want as part of your network. Consider family, friends, and coworkers. Choose people who you believe will help you move forward toward your goals, and who you think may have interesting and useful networks themselves.

Memory and Studying

Retaining What You Learn

What Would You Do?

Think about this problem as you read, and consider how you would approach it. This chapter shows how memory works and then helps you use it effectively as you study. Although it's easier to remember what you want to know, the strategies you learn will help you study materials no matter how you feel about them.

orton Ewart struggled from fourth grade through high school. Overwhelmed by the work and the level of independence, he did the least amount of work possible and earned a C average. He enrolled in the liberal arts program at Mohawk Valley Community College in Utica, New York, out of a desire to please his parents. Uninterested in the coursework and not ready for the independence of college life, Norton hitchhiked home each weekend to work as a housepainter and left school 10 weeks later. He then moved to his aunt's house in Colorado, where he skied black diamond runs, worked as a ski technician, and tried to figure out who he was and what he wanted.

After two years, Norton decided he wanted to return to college and moved back home. Thinking he might follow the family path of engineering, as had three generations before him, he decided to pursue an associate's degree in math and science at Hudson Valley Community College in Troy, New York. Despite his newfound confidence and the fun of a state-of-the-art calculator his father had given him, he could not move on right away from his inconsistent study habits. He received Cs and Ds in calculus and physics courses during his first year.

Norton was behind, but for the first time he was determined to excel. He found himself enjoying the creativity and beauty of math and how the mind interacts with it. On the advice of an academic advisor, he spent a year in a civil technology program while retaking every calculus and physics course. Aware that he was more motivated when working with others, he put together a study group. His group of fellow engineering students called themselves the "Engineering Defense League" and met daily to work through problems, drill one another on formulas and problem-solving steps, and experience the struggle together. (To be continued . . .)

Skiing and working in Colorado gave Norton a sense of ownership of his success as well as a desire—and a reason—to get back to college. You'll learn more about Norton, and revisit his situation, within the chapter.

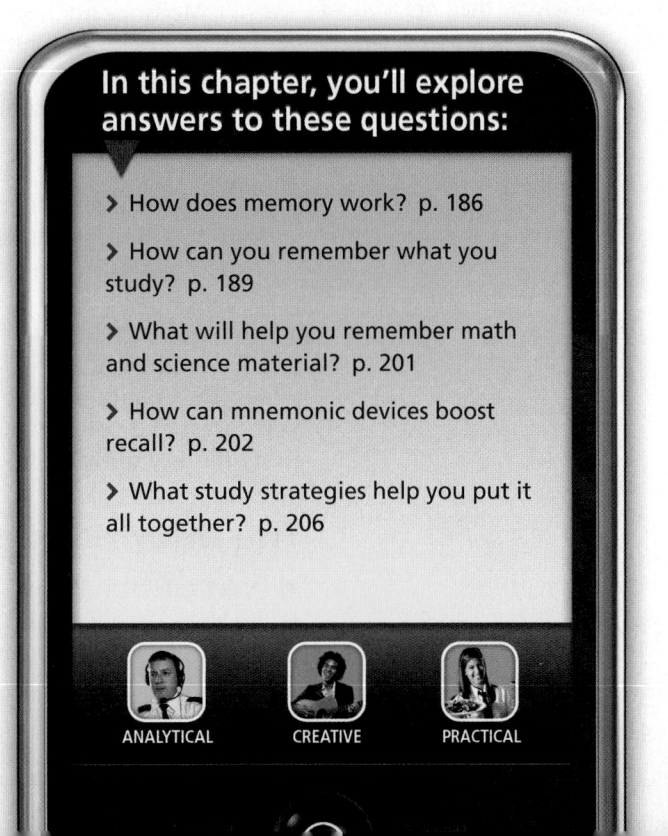

In this chapter, you'll explore answers to these questions:

> How does memory work? p. 186

> How can you remember what you study? p. 189

> What will help you remember math and science material? p. 201

> How can mnemonic devices boost recall? p. 202

> What study strategies help you put it all together? p. 206

ANALYTICAL   CREATIVE   PRACTICAL

STATUS *Check*

▶ *How developed are your memory and studying skills?*

For each statement, circle the number that feels right to you, from 1 for "not at all true for me" to 5 for "very true for me."

▶ I know that not everything that I hear and read will necessarily stay in my memory for long—or at all.	1 2 3 4 5
▶ When I am studying, I try to choose what is most important to remember.	1 2 3 4 5
▶ Through trial and error, I have figured out study locations and times that work best for me.	1 2 3 4 5
▶ After a test or presentation is over, I retain much of what I had to know.	1 2 3 4 5
▶ I write, rewrite, and summarize information to remember it.	1 2 3 4 5
▶ I use flash cards and other active memory strategies to remember what I study.	1 2 3 4 5
▶ I create mnemonic devices with images and associations as memory hooks.	1 2 3 4 5
▶ I try to review material in several sessions over time rather than cram the night before a test.	1 2 3 4 5
▶ If I find myself looking up something over and over again, I make an effort to memorize it.	1 2 3 4 5
▶ I know how to study class and text notes effectively to prepare for tests.	1 2 3 4 5

Each of the topics in these statements is covered in this chapter. Note those statements for which you circled a 3 or lower. Skim the chapter to see where those topics appear, and pay special attention to them as you read, learn, and apply new strategies.

REMEMBER: *No matter how developed your memory and studying skills are, you can improve with effort and practice.*

> "Successfully intelligent people are aware of the circumstances under which they are able to function at their best. They create those circumstances and then use them to their maximum advantage."
>
> —Robert Sternberg

How does memory work?

Memory anchors all learning and performance—on tests as well as at work. The information you remember—concepts, facts, processes, formulas, and more—is the raw material with which you think, write, create, build, and perform day-to-day in school and out. Tasks ranging from high-level chemistry experiments to running a load of laundry through the washing machine all require you to retain and use information in your memory.

Memorization also gives you the tools to tackle higher-level thinking, such as in Chapter 5's discussion of Bloom's taxonomy (see pp. 133–135). You need to recall and understand information before you can apply, analyze, synthesize, or evaluate it.

Through studying, you build your memory and use it to move toward your goals. This chapter provides a host of memory improvement techniques that you can make your own with a positive attitude and active involvement. The first step is exploring how memory works.

The information processing model of memory

Memory refers to the way the brain stores and recalls information or experiences that are acquired through the five senses. Although you take in thousands of pieces of information every second—everything from the shape and

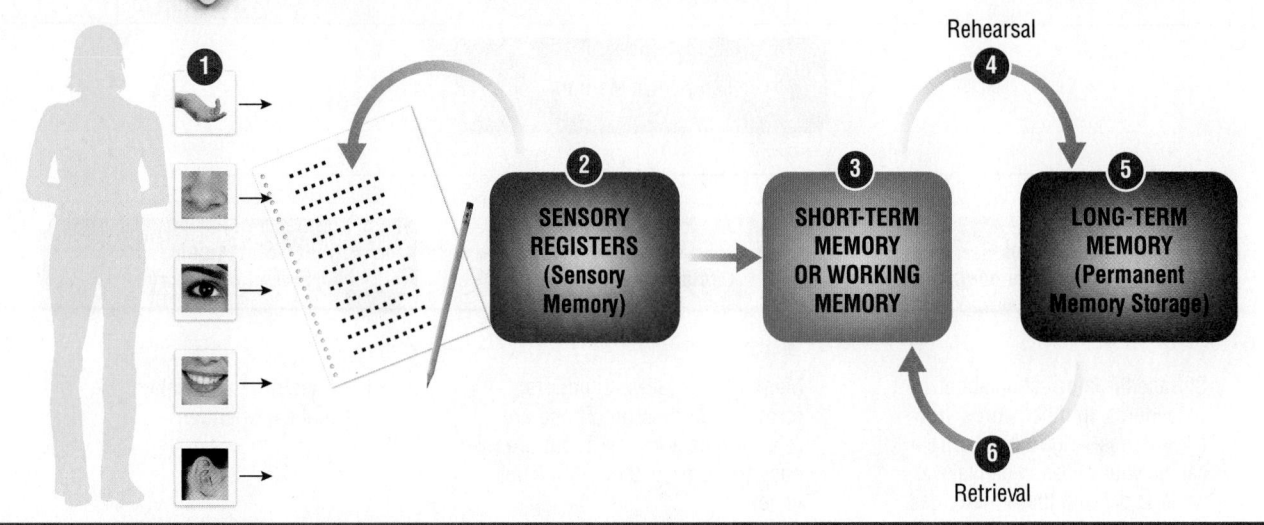

color of your chair to how your history text describes Abraham Lincoln's presidency—you remember few. Unconsciously, your brain sorts through stimuli and stores only what it considers important.

Key 7.1 illustrates how the brain forms lasting memories.

1. Raw information, gathered through the five senses, reaches the brain (for example, the tune of a song you're learning in your jazz ensemble class).

2. This information enters **sensory registers**, where it stays for only seconds. (As you play the notes for the first time, the sounds stop first in your auditory register.)

3. You then choose whether to pay attention to information in the sensory register. When you selectively look, listen, smell, taste, or feel the information, you move it into **short-term memory**, also known as *working memory*, which contains what you are thinking at any moment and from where information can be made available for further processing. (The part of the song that is your responsibility, for example, the clarinet solo, will likely take up residence in your working memory.) You can temporarily keep information in short-term memory through *rote rehearsal*—the process of repeating information to yourself or even out loud.

4. Information moves to **long-term memory** through focused, active rehearsal repeated over time. (As you practice the song in class and at home, your brain stores the tone, rhythm, and pace in your long-term memory, where you will be able to draw on it again.) Long-term memory stores everything you know from Civil War battle dates to the location of your grade school. As shown in Key 7.2, long-term memory has three separate storage houses. There are no limits to how much information long-term memory can hold or how long it is held, but most people retain memories of personal experiences and procedures longer than concepts, facts, formulas, and dates.

When you need a piece of information from long-term memory, the brain retrieves it and places it in short-term memory. On test day, this enables you to choose the right answer on a multiple-choice question or lay out a fact-based argument for an essay question.

> SENSORY REGISTER
> Brain filters through which sensory information enters the brain and is sent to short-term memory.

> SHORT-TERM MEMORY
> The brain's temporary information storehouse, in which information remains for a limited time (from a few seconds to half a minute).

> LONG-TERM MEMORY
> The brain's permanent information storehouse, from which information can be retrieved.

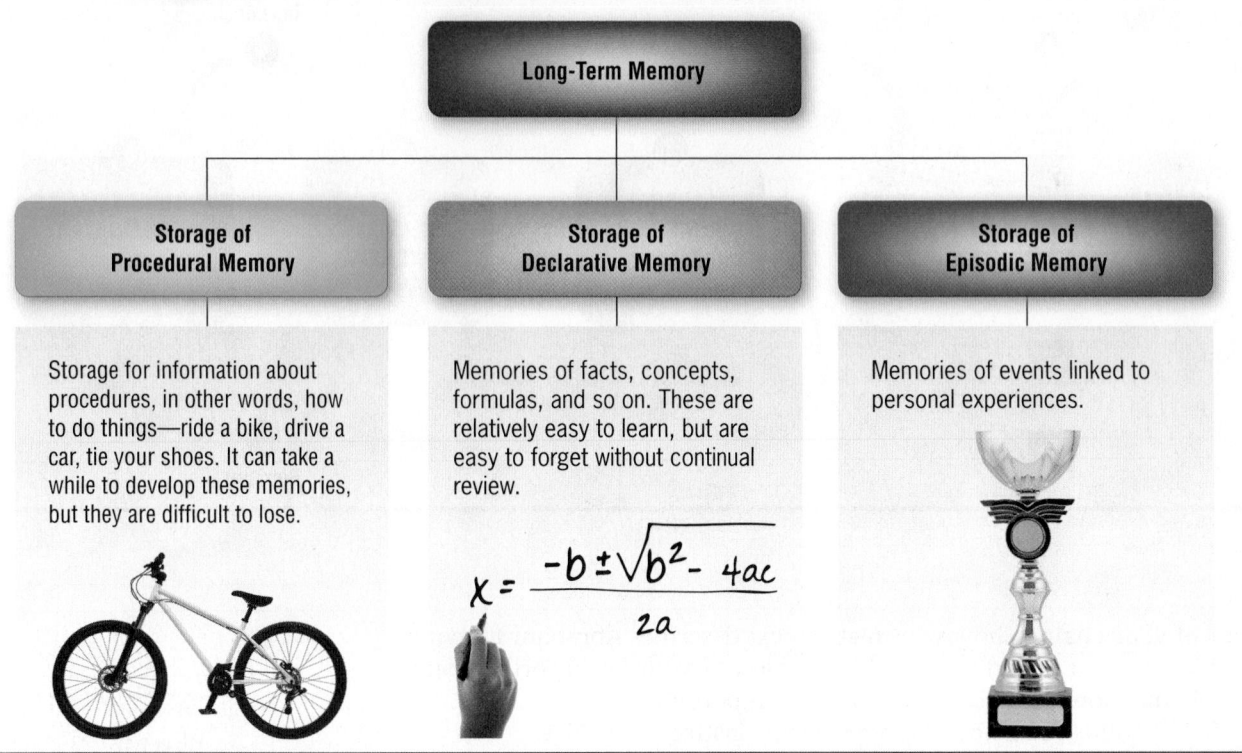

Long-Term Memory

Storage of Procedural Memory

Storage for information about procedures, in other words, how to do things—ride a bike, drive a car, tie your shoes. It can take a while to develop these memories, but they are difficult to lose.

Storage of Declarative Memory

Memories of facts, concepts, formulas, and so on. These are relatively easy to learn, but are easy to forget without continual review.

$$x = \frac{-b \pm \sqrt{b^2 - 4ac}}{2a}$$

Storage of Episodic Memory

Memories of events linked to personal experiences.

The movement of information in your brain, from short-term to long-term memory and then back again, strengthens the connections among neurons (brain cells). As you read in Chapter 1, learning happens and memories are built when neurons grow new dendrites and form new synapses. When you learn an algebra formula, for example, your brain creates new connections. Every time you review it, the connections get stronger.

Why you forget

Health issues and poor nutrition can cause memory problems. Stress is also a factor; research shows that even short-term stress can interfere with cell communication in the learning and memory regions of the brain.[1] However, *the most common reason that information fails to stay in long-term memory is ineffective studying*—not doing what you should to retain what you learn.

As Key 7.3 shows, retaining information requires continual review. You are still learning information 10 minutes after you hear it the first time. If you review the material over time—after 24 hours, a week, a month, 6 months, and more—you will retain the knowledge. If you do not review, the neural connections will weaken, and eventually you will forget. For Norton, a combination of unfocused listening and reading and a lack of consistent studying made it tough for him to retain important information.

In a classic study conducted in 1885, researcher Herman Ebbinghaus memorized a list of meaningless three-letter words such as CEF and LAZ. He then examined how quickly he forgot them. Within 1 hour, he had forgotten more than 50 percent of

Key 7.3

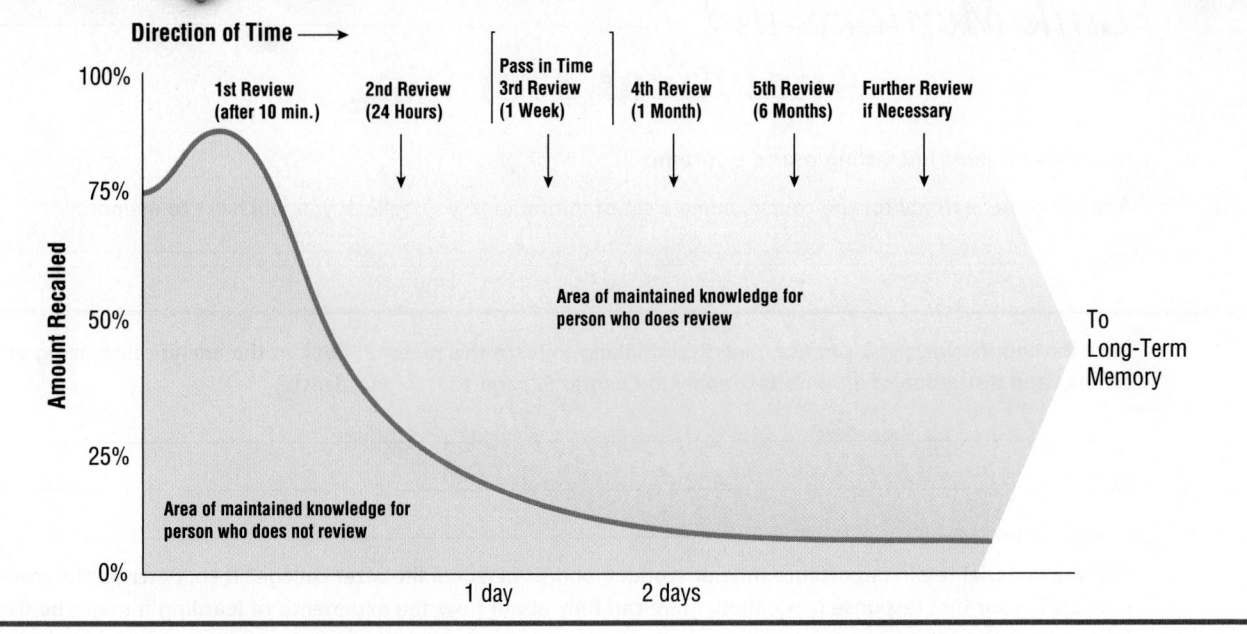

Direction of Time ⟶

1st Review (after 10 min.)	2nd Review (24 Hours)	Pass in Time 3rd Review (1 Week)	4th Review (1 Month)	5th Review (6 Months)	Further Review if Necessary

(Amount Recalled — vertical axis: 0%, 25%, 50%, 75%, 100%)

Area of maintained knowledge for person who does review

To Long-Term Memory

Area of maintained knowledge for person who does not review

1 day   2 days

Source: From Tony Buzan, Use Both Sides of Your Brain, copyright © 1974, 1983, 1991 by Tony Buzan. Used by permission of Dutton, a division of Penguin Group (USA) Inc., and by kind permission of Tony Buzan, www.thinkbuzan.com.

what he had learned; after 2 days, he knew fewer than 30 percent of the memorized words. Although Ebbinghaus's recall of the nonsense syllables remained fairly stable after that, his experiment shows how fragile memory can be—even when you take the time and expend the energy to memorize information.[2]

Now that you know more about how memory works, get down to the business of how to retain the information you think is important—and provide that information when you need it.

How can you remember what you study?

Whatever you study—textbooks, course materials, notes, primary sources—your goal is to anchor important information in long-term memory so that you can use it, for both short-term goals like tests and long-term goals like being an information technology specialist. To remember what you study, you need to carefully figure out and use what works best for you. One great way to do this is with *journalists' questions*—the six questions journalists need to answer to write an effective newspaper story.

1. **When, Where, Who**—determine the times, places, and company (or none) that suit you.
2. **What, Why**—choose what is important to study, and set the rest aside.
3. **How**—find the specific tips and techniques that work best for you.

Link Memory and Analytical Thinking

Identify your most interesting course this term.

Analyzing the material for the course, name a set of information you believe you will have to memorize:

_____

_____

Describe specific ways you can use analytical thinking to learn this material (look at the analytical thinking procedures and discussion of Bloom's taxonomy in Chapter 5, page 133, to get ideas):

_____

_____

_____

Will the material retain importance in your working and/or personal life after college? If so, describe the connection. If your first response is no, think more carefully about how the experience of learning it might be useful to you in the future.

_____

_____

When, where, and who: Choosing your best setting

Figuring out the when, where, and who of studying is all about self-management. You analyze what works best for you, create ideas about how to put that self-knowledge to work, and use practical thinking to implement those ideas as you study.

When

The first part of *When* is "How Much." Having the right amount of time for the job is crucial. One formula for success is the simple calculation you have read about earlier in this book: *For every hour you spend in the classroom each week, spend at least 2 to 3 hours preparing for the class.* For example, if you are carrying a course load of fifteen credit hours, you should spend 30 hours a week studying outside of class. Check your syllabus for the dates reading assignments are due, and give yourself enough time to complete them.

The second part of *When* is "What Time." If two students go over their biology notes from 8 to 9 A.M., but one is a morning person who went to bed at 11 P.M. and the other is a night owl who hit the sack around 2 A.M., you can guess who has a greater chance of remembering the information. First, determine the time available to you in between classes, work, and other commitments. Then, thinking about when you function best, choose your study times carefully. You may not always have the luxury of being free during your peak energy times—but do the best you can.

The third part of *When* is "How Close to Original Learning." Because most forgetting happens right after learning, as you saw in Key 7.3, the review that helps you retain information most effectively happens close to when you first learn the material. If you can, review notes the same day you took them in class, make an organizer of important information from a text chapter shortly after you read it, or write a summary of a group study session within 24 hours of the meeting.

The final part of *When* is "When to Stop." Take a break, or go to sleep, when your body is no longer responding. Forcing yourself to study when you're not focused doesn't work.

Where

Where you study matters. As with time, consider your restrictions first—there may be only so many places available to you, within a reasonable travel distance, and open when you have study time free. Also, analyze previous study sessions. If you spent over 20 percent of your time blocking out distractions at a particular location, try someplace different.

Who

Some students prefer to study alone, and some in pairs or groups. Many mix it up, doing some kinds of studying—first reading, close reading, creating note sets—alone, and others—test review, problem sets—with one or more people. Some find that they prefer to study certain subjects alone and others with a group. For Norton, knowing he was going to work with others motivated him to be prepared, and sharing the work helped him learn.

Even students who study primarily alone can benefit by working with others from time to time. Besides the obvious benefit of greater communication and teamwork skills, group study enhances your ability to remember information in several ways:[3]

- ▶ Gets you to say what you know out loud, which solidifies your understanding
- ▶ Exposes you to the ideas of others and gets you thinking in different ways
- ▶ Increases the chance that all of the important information will be covered
- ▶ Motivates you to study in preparation for a group meeting
- ▶ Subjects you to questions about your knowledge, and maybe even some challenges, that make you clarify and build on your thinking

Instructors sometimes initiate student study groups, commonly for math or science courses, as peer-assisted study sessions or supplemental instruction. However, don't wait for your instructor—or for exam crunch time—to benefit from studying with others. As you begin to get to know students in your classes, start now to exchange phone numbers and e-mails, form groups, and schedule meetings. Here are some strategies for study group success:

- ▶ *Limit group size.* Groups of five or less tend to experience the most success.

The study location that works for you depends on your individual needs. This student has found he can concentrate best on his physical geology material if he reads it at a table in the library.
© Davis Barber/PhotoEdit

Answer Your
Journalists' Questions

Think about a past study session that did not prepare you well for a test, and recall which strategies—if any—you used.

Now, plan a study session that will take place within the next 7 days—one that will help you learn something important to know for one of your current courses. Answer the following questions to create your session:

When will you study, and for how long?

_____

Where will you study?

_____

Who will you study with, if anyone?

_____

What will you study?

_____

Why is this material important to know?

_____

How will you study it—what strategy (or strategies) do you plan to use?

_____

_____

How do you think the journalists' questions in this structure would have helped you get more from your previous study session?

_____

_____

The final step is putting this plan to work. Date you will use it: _____

▶ *Set long-term and short-term goals.* At your first meeting, determine what the group wants to accomplish, and set mini-goals at the start of the first meeting.

▶ *Determine a regular schedule and leadership rotation.* Determine what your group needs and what the members' schedules can handle. Try to meet weekly or, at the least, every other week. Rotate leadership among members willing to lead.

▶ *Create study materials for one another.* Give each person a task of finding a piece of information to compile and share with the group. Teach material to one another.

▶ *Share the workload and pool note-taking resources.* The most important factor is a willingness to work, not knowledge level. Compare notes with group members and fill in information you don't have.

▶ *Know how to be an effective leader.* The leader needs to define projects, assign work, set schedules and meeting goals, and keep people focused, motivated, and moving ahead.

▶ *Know how to be an effective participant.* Participants are "part owners" of the team process with a responsibility for, and a stake in, the outcome. Participants need to be organized, fulfill the tasks they promise to do, and stay open to discussion.

One final part of *Who* is dealing with "Who Might Be Distracting." You may have friends who want you to go out. You may have young children or other family members who need you. Think carefully about your choices. Do you want to head out with a group of friends you can see anytime, even if it compromises your ability to do well in an important course? Can you schedule your study time when your kids are occupied for an hour or so?

Tell your friends why studying is important to you. Friends who truly care about you are likely to support your goals. Tell your kids (if they are old enough to understand) what your education and eventual degree will mean to you—and to them. Children may be more able to cope if they see what lies at the end of the road. Key 7.4 shows some ways that parents or others caring for children can maximize their efforts.

What and why: Evaluating study materials

Even if you had hours of study time and boundless energy, you would be likely to go on overload if you studied every word and bit of information.

Key 7.4

MANAGE CHILDREN
WHILE STUDYING

STUDYING WITH CHILDREN	STUDYING WITH INFANTS

STUDYING WITH CHILDREN

- **Keep them up-to-date on your schedule.** Kids appreciate being involved, even though they may not understand entirely. Let them know when you have a big test or project due and what they can expect of you.

- **Find help.** Know your schedule and arrange for child care if necessary. Consider offering to help another parent in exchange for babysitting, hiring a sitter, or using a day care center.

- **Utilize techonology.** You may be able to have a study session over the phone, through instant messaging, by e-mail, or over social networking sites. Additionally, some sites offer tools that allow multiple users to work on a document or project remotely.

- **Be prepared and keep them active.** Consider keeping some toys, activities, or books that only come out during study time. This will make the time special for children.

- **Plan for family time.** Offset your time away from your children with plans to do something together such as a movie or ice cream. Children may be more apt to let you study when they have something to look forward to.

STUDYING WITH INFANTS

- **Utilize your baby's sleeping schedule.** Study at night if your baby goes to sleep early or in the morning if your baby sleeps late.

- **Make time in the middle.** Study during nap times if you aren't too tired yourself.

- **Talk to your baby.** Recite your notes to the baby. The baby will appreciate the attention, and you will get work done.

- **Keep them close.** Put your baby in a safe and fun place while you study, such as a playpen, motorized swing, or jumping seat.

Before you get ready to dive into your books and materials, engage your analytical thinking skills for a critical task: Decide *what* to study by examining *why* you need to know it. Here's how to accomplish this:

▶ *Choose materials to study.* Put away materials or notes you know you do not need to review. Then examine what's left. Within textbooks or other materials, which chapters or sections are important to know for your immediate goal (for example, to study for an upcoming test) and why? Thinking about the *Why* highlights your purpose and can increase your focus.

▶ *Prioritize materials.* First of all, there's no point in spending the bulk of your study time reviewing material you already know well. Determine what you need the most work on, and study that first. Almost every student has more steam at the beginning of a study session than at the end; plus, fatigue or an interruption may prevent you from covering everything.

▶ *Set specific goals.* Looking at what you need to cover and the time available, decide what you will accomplish—for example, reading a specific section in a certain textbook, reviewing three sets of class notes, and creating a study sheet from both the book and your notes. Make a list for reference and check things off as you go.

▶ *Within the sections you study, separate main points from unimportant details.* Ask yourself, "What is the most important information?" Highlight only the key points in your texts, and write notes in the margins about main ideas.

How: Using study strategies

After figuring out the *When, Where, Who, What,* and *Why* of studying, focus on the *How*—the strategies that will anchor the information you need in your brain (Key 7.5). You may already use several of them. Try as many as you can, and keep what works.

Have purpose, intention, and emotional connection

If you can remember the lyrics to dozens of popular songs but not the functions of the pancreas, perhaps emotion is involved. When you care about something, your brain responds differently, and you learn and remember more easily.

To achieve the same results in school, try to create a purpose and will to remember by a kind of emotional involvement with what you study. For example, an accounting student might think of a friend who is running a small business and needs to keep his records in order—to pay bills on time, to record income, to meet tax payments. Putting himself in the position of his friend's accountant, the student connects learning accounting principles with making a difference in a friend's life.

Put your notes to work

It is common to let notes sit in a notebook unread until just before midterms or finals. Even the most comprehensive, brilliant notes won't do you any good if you don't refer back to them. Regularly reread your notes in batches (for example, every one or two weeks) to build your recall of information. As you reread, do the following:

THE "HOW" OF **STUDY SUCCESS**

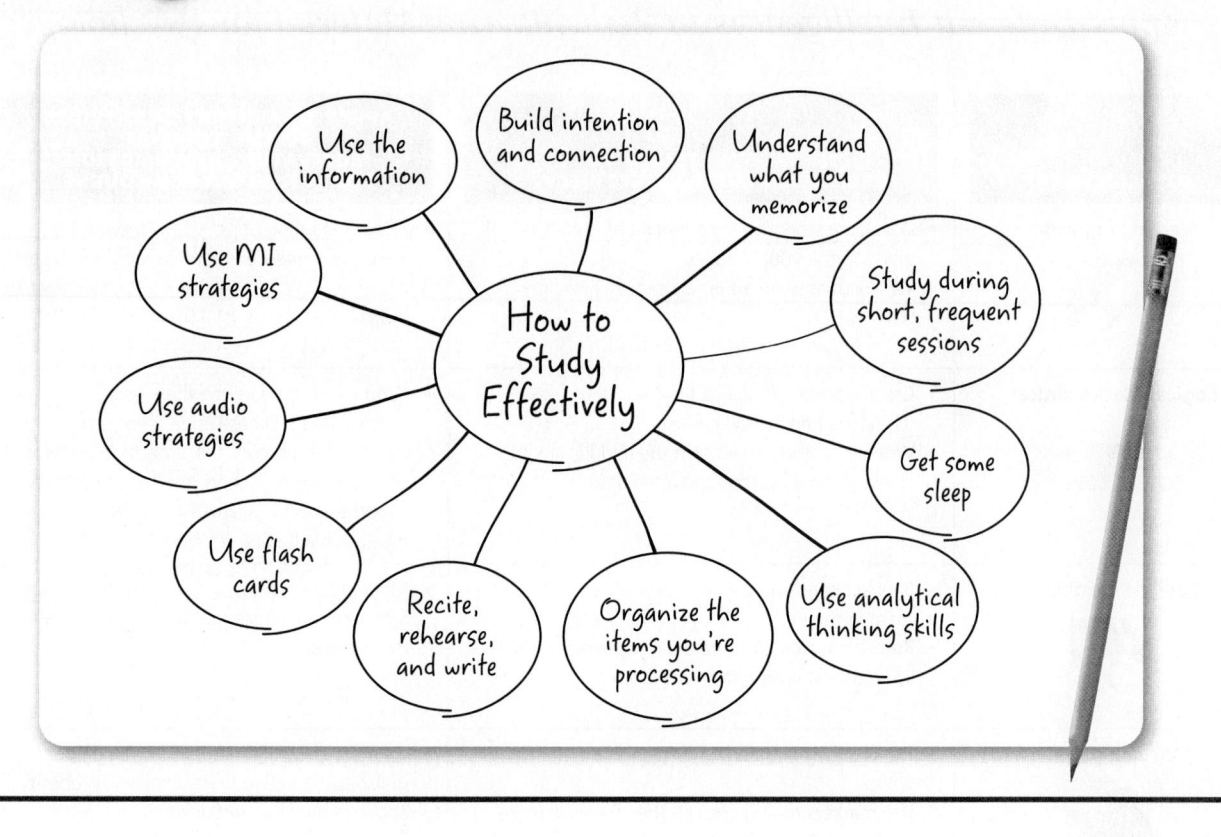

- ▶ Fill in any gaps or get help with trouble spots.
- ▶ Mark up your notes by highlighting main ideas and key supporting points.
- ▶ Add recall or practice test questions in the margins.
- ▶ Add relevant points from homework, text, and labwork into your notes.

Understand what you memorize

It sounds kind of obvious—but something that has meaning is easier to recall than something that makes little sense. This basic principle applies to everything you study. Figure out logical connections, and use these connections to help you learn. For example, in a plant biology course, memorize plants in family groups; in a history course, link events in a cause-and-effect chain.

When you are have trouble remembering something new, think about how the new idea fits into what you already know. A simple example: If you can't remember what a word means, look at the word's root, prefix, or suffix. Knowing that the root *bellum* means "war" and the prefix *ante* means "before" will help you recognize that *antebellum* means "before the war."

Study during short, frequent sessions

You can improve your chances of remembering material by learning it more than once. A pattern of short sessions—say, three 20-minute study sessions—followed by brief periods of rest is more effective than continual studying with little or no rest. Try studying on your own or with a classmate during breaks in

Apply Different Intelligences to Remembering Material for Psychology

INTELLIGENCE	USE MI STRATEGIES TO REMEMBER MORE EFFECTIVELY	APPLY MI MEMORY STRATEGIES TO THE TOPIC OF MOTIVATION AND EMOTION FOR A PSYCHOLOGY COURSE
Verbal-Linguistic	• Develop a story line for a mnemonic first; then work on the visual images. • Write out answers to practice essay questions.	• Answer learning objectives as though they were essay questions: "What are three types of needs?" "What are instinct approaches to motivation?"*
Logical-Mathematical	• Create logical groupings that help you memorize knowledge chunks. • When you study material in the middle, link it to what comes before and after.	• Group and compare the theories of emotion—the James-Lange theory, the Cannon-Bard theory, the Schachter-Singer and cognitive arousal theory, the facial feedback hypothesis, and Lazarus's cognitive-mediational theory.
Bodily-Kinesthetic	• Reenact concepts physically if you can to solidify them in memory. • Record information onto a digital recorder and listen as you walk between classes.	• Model facial expressions with another student and take turns guessing the emotion behind the expression.
Visual-Spatial	• Focus on visual mnemonics such as mental walks. • Use markers to add color to the images you use in your mnemonics.	• Create a colorful mnemonic to remember maladaptive eating problems such as obesity, anorexia nervosa, and bulimia.
Interpersonal	• Do flash card drills with a study partner. • Recite important material to a study partner.	• Working with a study partner, recite and explain Maslow's hierarchy of needs to each other.
Intrapersonal	• Listen to an audio podcast that reviews test material. • Create vocabulary cartoons and test yourself on the material.	• Understand incentive approaches by considering what kind of external stimuli create incentive for you.
Musical	• Play music while you brainstorm ideas. • Create a mnemonic in the form of a musical rhyme.	• Write a rap that lists and explains the different approaches to understanding motivation.
Naturalistic	• Organize what you have to learn so you see how everything fits together. • Sit outside and go through your flash cards.	• Make a chart organizing explanatory details of the three elements of emotion—physiology, behavior, and subjective experience.

*For information on motivation and emotion, see Saundra K. Ciccarelli and Glenn E. Meyer, *Psychology*. Upper Saddle River, NJ: Prentice Hall, 2006.

your schedule. Although studying between classes isn't for everyone, you may find that it can help you remember more.

In addition, scheduling regular, frequent review sessions over time will help you retain information more effectively. If you have 2 weeks before a test, set up study sessions three times per week instead of putting the final 2 days aside for hours-long study marathons.[4]

Get your body ready

Even though sleep may take a back seat with all you have to do in crunch times, research indicates that shortchanging your sleep during the week impairs your ability to remember and learn, even if you try to make up for it by sleeping all weekend.[5] Sleep improves your ability to remember what you studied before you went to bed. So does having a good breakfast. Even if you're running late, grab enough food to fill your stomach.

When you study for a test with a classmate, you can help each other understand difficult concepts as well as fill in the holes in each other's notes.
© Shutterstock

Use analytical thinking skills

Analytical, or critical, thinking encourages you to associate new information with what you already know. Imagine you have to remember information about the signing of the Treaty of Versailles, which ended World War I. How can critical thinking help?

▶ Recall everything that you know about the topic.
▶ Think about how this event is similar to other events in history.
▶ Consider what is different and unique about this treaty in comparison to other treaties.
▶ Explore the causes that led up to this event, and look at the event's effects.
▶ Evaluate how successful you think the treaty was.

This critical exploration makes it easier to remember the material you are studying.

Organize the items you are processing

▶ *Divide material into manageable sections.* Master each section, put all the sections together, and then test your memory of all the material.

▶ *Use the chunking strategy.* **Chunking** increases the capacity of short-term and long-term memory. For example, though it is hard to remember these ten digits—4808371557—it is easier to remember them in three chunks—480 837 1557. In general, try to limit groups to ten items or fewer. The 8-day study plan in Key 7.6 relies on chunking.

→ CHUNKING
Placing disconnected information into smaller units that are easier to remember.

▶ *Use organizational tools.* Rely on an outline, a think link, or another organizational tool to record material with logical connections among the elements (see Chapter 6 for more on note taking).

▶ *Be mindful when studying more than one subject.* When studying for several tests at once, avoid studying two similar subjects back-to-back. Your memory may be more accurate when you study history after biology rather than chemistry after biology.

▶ *Notice what ends up in the middle—and practice it.* When studying, you tend to remember what you study first and last. The weak link is likely

STUDY PLAN SUCCESS
DEPENDS ON A GOOD MEMORY

Key 7.6

DAY 8 (IN EIGHT DAYS, YOU'LL BE TAKING A TEST)

PLANNING DAY
- List everything that may be on the exam. (Check your syllabus and class notes; talk with your instructor.)
- Divide the material into four learning chunks.
- Decide on a study schedule for the next 7 days—when you will study, with whom you will study, the materials you need, and so on.

DAY 7 (COUNTDOWN: SEVEN DAYS TO GO)
- Use the techniques described in Chapters 7 and 8 to study chunk A.
- Memorize key concepts, facts, formulas, and so on that may be on the test.
- Take an active approach to learning: take practice tests, summarize what you read in your own words, use critical thinking to connect ideas.

DAY 6 (COUNTDOWN: SIX DAYS TO GO)
- Use the same techniques to study chunk B.

DAY 5 (COUNTDOWN: FIVE DAYS TO GO)
- Use the same techniques to study chunk C.

DAY 4 (COUNTDOWN: FOUR DAYS TO GO)
- Use the same techniques to study chunk D.

DAY 3 (COUNTDOWN: THREE DAYS TO GO)
- Combine and review chunks A and B.

DAY 2 (COUNTDOWN: TWO DAYS TO GO)
- Combine and review chunks C and D.

DAY 1 (COUNTDOWN: ONE DAY TO GO)

PUT IT ALL TOGETHER: REVIEW CHUNKS A, B, C, AND D
- Take an active approach to review all four chunks.
- Make sure you have committed every concept, fact, formula, process, and so on to memory.
- Take a timed practice test. Write out complete answers so that concepts and words stick in your memory.
- Create a sheet with important information to memorize (again) on test day.

TEST DAY—DO YOUR BEST WORK
- Look at your last-minute study sheet right before you enter the test room so that difficult information sticks.
- As soon as you get your test, write down critical facts on the back of the paper.

Source: Adapted from the University of Arizona. "The Eight-Day Study Plan." (http://ulc.arizona.edu/documents/8day_074.pdf)

to be what you study midway. Knowing this, try to give this material special attention.

Recite, rehearse, and write

Repetition is a helpful memory tool. The more you can repeat, and the more ways you can repeat, the more likely you are to remember. Reciting, rehearsing, and writing help you diversify your repetition and maximize memory.

When you *recite* material, you repeat key concepts aloud, summarizing them in your own words, to aid memorization. *Rehearsing* is similar to reciting but is done silently. *Writing* is reciting on paper. The following steps represent one way to benefit from these strategies:

▶ Focus as you read on *main ideas,* which are usually found in the topic sentences of paragraphs (see Chapter 5). Then recite, rehearse, or write the ideas down.

▶ Convert each main idea into a keyword, phrase, or visual image—something easy to recall that will set off a chain of memories bringing you back to the original material. Write each keyword or phrase on an index card.

▶ One by one, look at the keywords on your cards and recite, rehearse, or write all the associated information you can recall. Check your recall against the original material.

These steps are part of the process of consolidating and summarizing lecture and text notes as you study—a key study strategy explored later in this chapter.

Reciting, rehearsing, and writing involve more than rereading material and then parroting words out loud, in your head, or on paper. Because rereading does not necessarily require involvement, you can reread without learning. However, you cannot help but think and learn when you convert text concepts into key points, rewrite main ideas as keywords and phrases, and assess what you know and what you still need to learn.

Use flash cards

Flash cards give you short, repeated review sessions that provide immediate feedback. Either find an online site on which you can create electronic flash cards or use the front of a 3-by-5-inch index card to write a word, idea, or phrase you want to remember. Use the back for a definition, explanation, example, or other key facts. Key 7.7 shows two flash cards used to study for a psychology exam.

Key 7.7

FLASH CARDS HELP YOU MEMORIZE IMPORTANT FACTS

Theory
- Definition: Explanation for a phenomenon based on careful and precise observations
- Part of the scientific method
- Leads to hypotheses

Hypothesis
- Prediction about future behavior that is derived from observations and theories
- Methods for testing hypotheses: case studies, naturalistic observations, and experiments

The following suggestions can help you make the most of your flash cards:

▶ *Use the cards as a self-test.* As you go through them, create two piles—the material you know and the material you are learning.
▶ *Carry the cards with you and review frequently.* You'll learn the most if you start using cards early in the course, well ahead of exam time.
▶ *Shuffle the cards and learn the information in various orders.* This will help you avoid putting too much focus on some items and not enough on others.
▶ *Test yourself in both directions.* First, look at the terms and provide the definitions or explanations. Then turn the cards over and reverse the process.
▶ *Reduce the stack as you learn.* Eliminate cards when you know them well. As the pile shrinks, your motivation may grow. Do a final review of all the cards before the test.

Use audio strategies

Although audio strategies can benefit all students, they are especially useful if you learn best through hearing.

▶ *Create audio flash cards.* Record short-answer study questions by leaving 10 to 15 seconds blank after questions, so you can answer out loud. Record the correct answer after the pause to give yourself immediate feedback. For example, part of a recording for a writing class might say, "Three elements that require analysis before writing are . . . [10–15 second pause] . . . topic, audience, and purpose."
▶ *Use podcasts.* An increasing amount of information is presented in podcasts—knowledge segments that are downloadable to your computer or MP3 player. Ask your instructors if they intend to make any lectures available in podcast format.

Use learning styles strategies

Look back to your MI and Personality Spectrum assessments in Chapter 3. Identify your strongest areas and locate study techniques applicable for each. For example, if you scored high in bodily-kinesthetic, try reciting material aloud while standing or walking. Be open to trying something new—even if it sounds a little odd to begin with. Effective studying is about finding what works, often by any means necessary.

Use the information

In the days after you learn something new, try to use the information in every way you can. Apply it to new situations and link it to problems. Explain the material to a classmate. Test your knowledge to make sure the material is in long-term memory. "Don't confuse recognizing information with being able to recall it," says learning expert Adam Robinson. "Be sure you can recall the information without looking at your notes for clues. And don't move on until you have created some sort of sense-memory hook for calling it back up when you need it."[6]

What will help you remember math and science material?

The strategies you've just explored apply to all sorts of academic areas. However, recalling what you learn in math and science courses can demand particular attention and some specific techniques, as Norton really found out the second time around.

■ *Review processes and procedures.* Much of math and science work involves knowing how to work through each step of a proof, a problem-solving process, or a lab experiment. Review your class notes as soon as possible after each class. Look at your notes with the textbook alongside and compare the lecture information to the book. Fill in missing steps in the instructor's examples before you forget them. You may want to write the instructor's examples in the book next to the corresponding topics.

■ *Do problems, problems, and more problems.* Working through problems provides examples that will help you understand concepts and formulas. Plus, becoming familiar with a group of problems and related formulas will help you apply what you know to similar problems on other assignments and tests.

■ *Fight frustration with action.* If you are stuck on a problem, go on to another one. If you repeatedly get a wrong answer, look at the steps you've taken and see whether anything doesn't make sense. If you hit a wall, take a break to clear your head. If you have done the assigned homework but still don't feel secure, do additional problems or ask for help.

■ *Work with others.* Working with one or more classmates can be particularly helpful when trying to figure out math and science problems. Do as much homework as you can on your own, and then meet to discuss it and work through additional problems. Be open to other perspectives, and ask others how they arrived at answers, especially if they used different approaches. When the work is really tough, try to meet daily, as Norton's study group did.

■ *Focus on learning styles.* Use strategies that activate your strengths. A visual learner might draw pictures to illustrate problems, and an interpersonal learner might organize a study group. Musical learners might create songs describing math concepts. Barbara Aaker wrote 40 songs for her students at the Community College of Denver to help musical learners retain difficult concepts. Key 7.8 presents one of her algebra songs.

■ *Strive for accuracy.* Complete a step of an algebra problem or biology lab project inaccurately, and your answer will be incorrect. In class, the consequences of inaccuracy are reflected in low grades. In life, the consequences could show in a patient's health or in the strength of a bridge. Check over the details of your work and always try to get it exactly right.

Because many math and science courses require you to memorize sets and lists of information, one key tool

Change the CONVERSATION

Challenge yourself and your friends to ask—and answer—tough questions. Use the following to inspire discussion in pairs or groups.

▶ All students experience the frustration of working hard to remember something that seems unimportant and irrelevant to their lives. How do you handle this? How *should* you handle it?

▶ What memorization techniques do you resist trying? Is it because they seem too unrelated to the information—or too goofy? What would you be willing to try out just to see whether it works?

▶ **CONSIDER THE CASE:** How do you respond when, like Norton, you have no interest in what you are studying? Do you attempt to find meaning, do the minimum, give up? How do the people in your life advise you to proceed—and what do you think of the advice?

"HOW MUCH IS THAT *X* IN THE EQUATION?"

(to the tune of "How Much Is That Doggie in the Window?")

How much is that *x* in the equation?
What value will make it be true?
To find the *x* and get the solution
The numbers attached we **undo.**

The **connector** is plus or minus seven,
To find *x* we have to **undo.**
Just write below both sides—make it even.
We **undo** to find the *x* value.

If multiply or divide is showing,
The **connector** tells what has been done.
To **undo** is where we still are going—
We're trying to get *x* alone.

Source: Reprinted with permission. Barbara Aaker, *Mathematics: The Musical,* Denver: Crazy Broad Publishing, 1999.

is the *mnemonic device.* As you will see next, mnemonic devices create sense-memory hooks that are difficult to forget.

How can mnemonic devices **boost recall?**

MNEMONIC DEVICES
Memory techniques that
use vivid associations and
acronyms to link new
information to what
you already know.

Certain performers entertain audiences by remembering the names of 100 strangers or flawlessly repeating 30 ten-digit numbers. Although these performers probably have superior memories, they also rely on memory techniques, known as **mnemonic devices** (pronounced neh-MAHN-ick), for assistance. Mnemonics include visual images and associations and acronyms.

Mnemonics depend on vivid associations (relating new information to other information) that engage your emotions. Instead of learning new facts by *rote* (repetitive practice), associations give you a "hook" on which to hang these facts and retrieve them later. Mnemonics make information unforgettable through unusual mental associations and visual pictures.

Mnemonics take time and effort to create, and you'll have to be motivated to remember them. Because of this, use them only when necessary—for instance, to distinguish confusing concepts that consistently trip you up. Also know that no matter how clever they are and how easy they are to remember, mnemonics usually do not contribute to understanding. Their objective is to help you memorize.

Craft Your Own Mnemonic

Create a mnemonic to help you remember some facts.

Identify a group of facts that you have to memorize—for example, the names of all the world's major religions or a series of elements in the periodic table.

_____

_____

Now create your own mnemonic to remember the grouping, using any of the devices in this chapter. Write the mnemonic here (or, if you need more space, use separate paper).

_____

_____

_____

Describe your mnemonic. Is it focused on images or sounds—or both? Is it humorous, ridiculous, or colorful?

_____

_____

Considering your learning style preferences, describe why you think this particular device will help you retain the information.

_____

_____

_____

_____

Create visual images and associations

Turning information into mental pictures helps improve memory, especially for visual learners. To remember that the Spanish artist Picasso painted _The Three Women_, you might imagine the women in a circle dancing to a Spanish song with a pig and a donkey (_pig-asso_). The best images involve bright colors, three dimensions, action scenes, inanimate objects with human traits, and humor.

As another example, say you are trying to learn some Spanish vocabulary, including the words _carta_, _libro_, and _dinero_. Instead of relying on rote learning, you might come up with mental images such as those in Key 7.9.

Use visual images to remember items in a list

With the _mental walk_ strategy, you imagine storing new ideas in familiar locations. Say, for example, that on your next biology test you have to remember the body's major endocrine glands. To do this, think of your route to the library.

SPANISH WORD	DEFINITION	MENTAL IMAGE
carta	letter	A person pushing a shopping cart filled with letters into a post office.
dinero	money	A man eating lasagna at a diner. The lasagna is made of layers of money.
libro	book	A pile of books on a table at a library.

You pass the college theater, the science center, the bookstore, the cafeteria, the athletic center, and the social science building before reaching the library. At each spot along the way, you "place" a concept you want to learn. You then link the concept with a similar-sounding word that brings to mind a vivid image (see Key 7.10):

▶ At the campus theater, you imagine bumping into the actor Brad *Pitt* (pituitary gland).
▶ At the science center, you visualize a body builder with bulging *thighs* (thyroid gland).
▶ At the campus bookstore, you envision a second body builder with his *thighs* covered in *mus*tard (thymus gland).
▶ In the cafeteria, you bump into *Dean Al* (adrenal gland).
▶ At the athletic center, you think of the school team, the Panthers—nicknamed the Pans—and remember the sound of the cheer *"Pans-R-Us"* (pancreas).
▶ At the social science building, you imagine receiving a standing *ova*tion (ovaries).
▶ And at the library, you visualize sitting at a table taking a *test* that is *easy* (testes).

Make acronyms

Another helpful association method involves **acronyms.** In history class, you can remember the Allies during World War II—Britain, America, and Russia—with the acronym BAR. This is an example of a *word acronym,* because the first letters of the items you want to remember spell a word. The word (or words) spelled don't necessarily have to be real words. See Key 7.11 for an acronym—the name Roy G. Biv—that will help you remember the colors of the spectrum.

ACRONYM
A word formed from the first letters of a series of words created to help you remember the series.

Other acronyms take the form of an entire sentence, in which the first letters of the words in the sentence stand for the first letters of the memorized terms. This is called a *list order acronym.* When astronomy students want to remember the list of planets in order of distance from the sun (Mercury, Venus, Earth, Mars, Jupiter, Saturn, Uranus, and Neptune), they might learn the sentence *My very elegant mother just served us nectarines.*

Suppose you want to remember the names of the first six U.S. presidents. You notice that the first letters of their last names—Washington, Adams, Jefferson, Madison, Monroe, and Adams—together read W A J M M A. To remember

Key 7.10

A **MENTAL WALK** HELPS YOU REMEMBER ITEMS IN A LIST

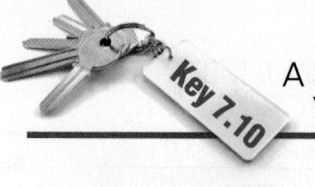

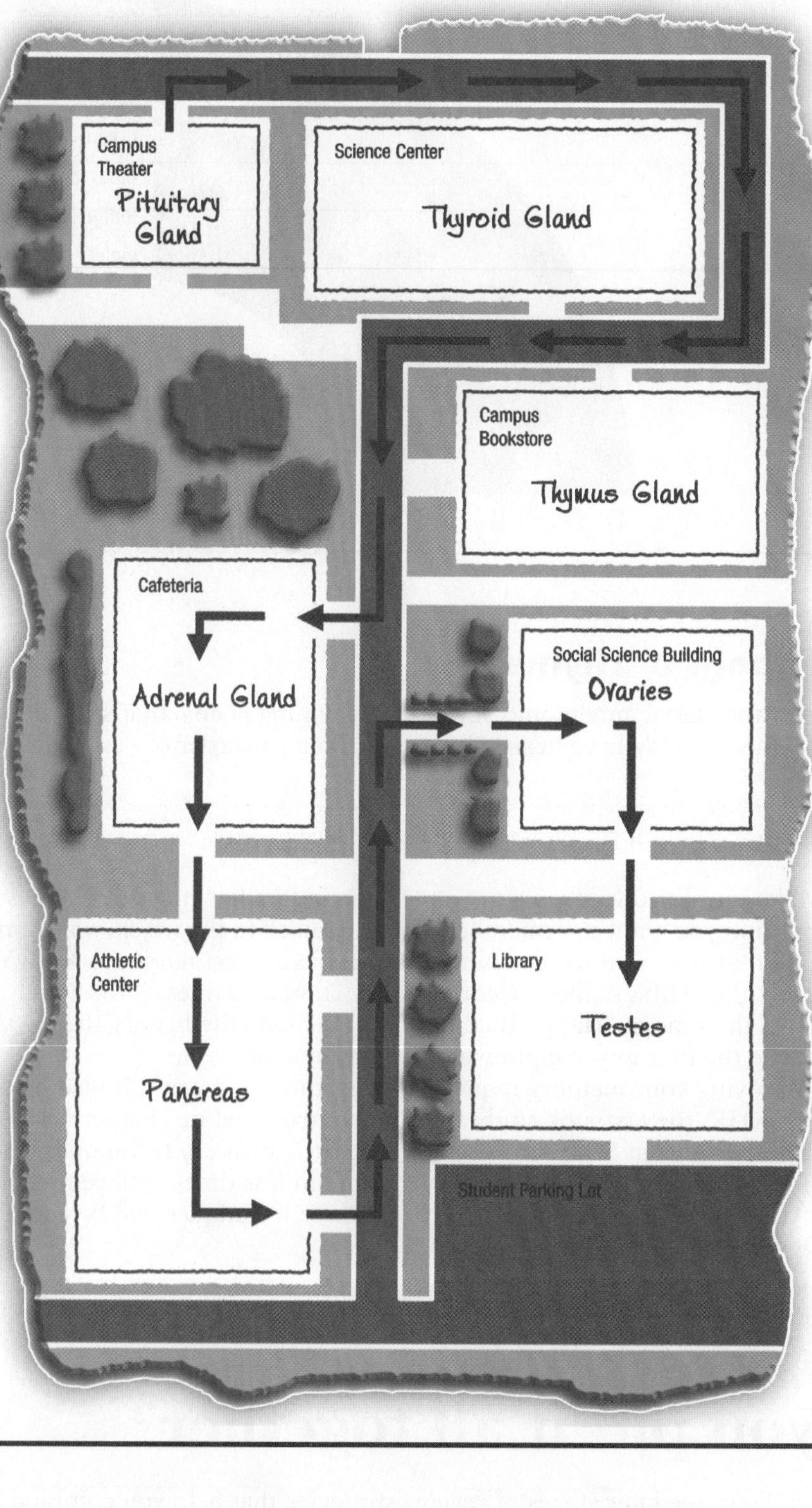
Campus Theater
Pituitary Gland
Science Center
Thyroid Gland
Campus Bookstore
Thymus Gland
Cafeteria
Adrenal Gland
Social Science Building
Ovaries
Athletic Center
Pancreas
Library
Testes
Student Parking Lot

them, first you might insert an *e* after the *j* and create a short nonsense word—*wajemma*. Then to make sure you don't forget the nonsense word, visualize the six presidents sitting in a row and wearing pajamas.

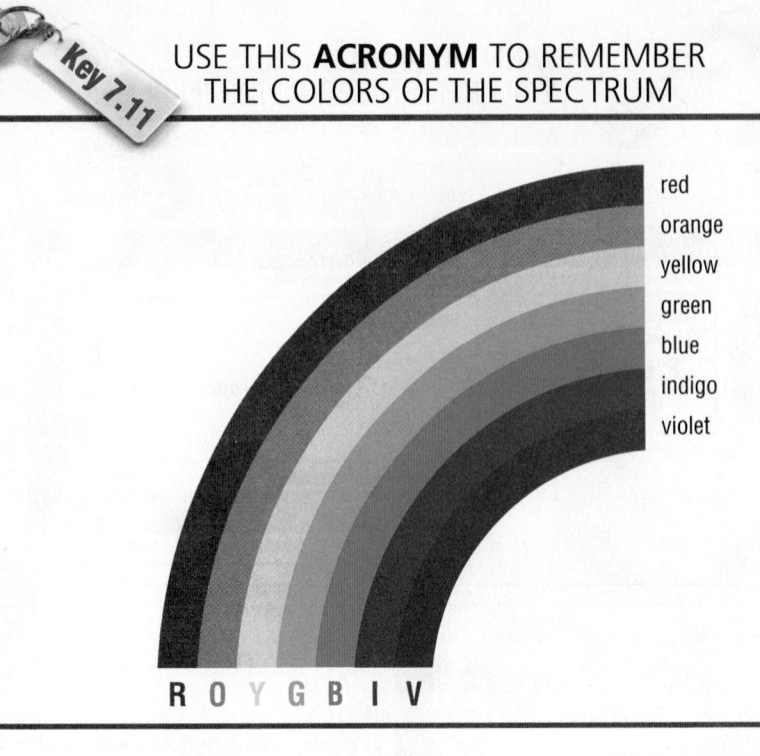

USE THIS **ACRONYM** TO REMEMBER
THE COLORS OF THE SPECTRUM

red
orange
yellow
green
blue
indigo
violet

R O Y G B I V

Use songs or rhymes

Some of the classic mnemonic devices are rhyming poems that stick in your mind. One you may have heard is the rule about the order of *i* and *e* in spelling:

> Spell *i* before *e*, except after *c*, or when sounded like *a* as in *neighbor* and *weigh*. Four exceptions if you please: *either, neither, seizure, seize*.

Make up your own poems or songs, linking familiar tunes or rhymes with information you want to remember. Thinking back to the *wajemma* example, imagine that you want to remember the presidents' first names as well. You might set those first names—George, John, Thomas, James, James, and John—to the tune of "Happy Birthday." Or to extend the history theme, you might use the first musical phrase of the national anthem.

Improving your memory requires energy, time, and work. It also helps to master SQ3R, the textbook study technique introduced in Chapter 5. By going through the steps in SQ3R and using the specific memory techniques described in this chapter, you will be able to learn more in less time—and remember what you learn long after exams are over. These techniques will be equally valuable when you start a career.

What study strategies help you put it all together?

Especially in the later stages of review, strategies that help you combine and condense information are crucial. Such strategies help you relate information to what you know, connect information in new ways, and boost your ability to use it to think analytically and creatively—especially important for essay exams.

student profile

Alexis Zendejas
Brigham Young University, Provo, Utah

About me:

I am a Native American woman from Omaha, Nebraska, and am excited to be attending BYU (Brigham Young University) this fall. I am the seventh of eight children. Growing up in a big family was a lot of fun as well as challenging; my personal goal was to keep up with my older brothers and sisters educationally and mentally. I know that I can count on my family to help me achieve my aspirations. I plan to major in business marketing with a minor in American history. After completing my undergraduate degree I hope to earn a joint juris doctorate (law degree) and master's of business administration (MBA).

What I focus on:

When I first started high school, I didn't have to work that hard to do well in class. That all changed junior year when I took three advanced placement classes and three honors classes. Studying got tougher. I actually had to apply myself after school, not just finish my assigned homework and be done with school until 7:45 the next morning.

Here is how I approach studying. If my brain is fried after a day of classes, I give myself a short break, setting a time to return to my studies. When I go back, I start by reading my notes from my classes for about 15 minutes or sometimes a bit longer, depending on the class and my ability to understand what was learned. My extra workload requires this extra effort. I work hard to focus and not let myself get distracted during my study time. I do take breaks, however—just short 10-minute breaks to get a drink of water, listen to a song, or move around. I also make and use a lot of flash cards (flash cards are my studying salvation!) for subjects where repetitive learning is required to grasp the words and their meanings. However, it's important to apply what you've learned after memorizing from the flash cards. For example, I would make flash cards for Spanish, then speak the vocabulary words in my day-to-day speech (you may think this approach odd at first but it will pay off).

What will help me in the workplace:

One of my sisters works in a law firm and I see that she has to do a lot of research. It's easy to imagine that all a lawyer does is work in a courtroom pleading the case to a judge or showcase evidence to persuade a grand jury, but I see her spending more time gathering information she needs. I know that the study skills I practice will come in handy during my intended career whenever I need to learn and focus.

Create a summary of reading material

When you summarize main ideas in your own words, you engage analytical thinking, considering what is important to include as well as how to organize and link it together. To construct a summary, focus on the main ideas and examples that support them. Don't include your own ideas or evaluations at this point. Your summary should simply condense the material, making it easier to focus on concepts and interrelationships when you review.

Use the following suggestions for creating effective summaries:

▶ Organize your summary by subject or topic—a textbook chapter, for example, or an article.
▶ Before you summarize, identify the main ideas and key supporting details by highlighting or annotating the material.
▶ Wherever possible, use your own words. When studying a technical subject with precise definitions, you may have little choice but to use text wording.
▶ Try to make your writing simple, clear, and brief. Eliminate less important details.
▶ Consider creating an outline of your notes or the portion of the text so you can see how ideas relate to one another.
▶ Include information from tables, charts, photographs, and captions in your summary; these visual presentations may contain important information not written in the text.
▶ Combine word-based and visual note-taking forms that effectively condense the information, such as a concept map, timeline, chart, or outline.
▶ Use visual strategies such as a color-coding system to indicate different ideas or different-colored pens to indicate levels of importance for information.

Combine class and reading notes into a master set

Studying from either text or class notes alone is not enough; your instructor may present material in class that is not in your text or may gloss over topics that your text covers in depth. The process of combining class and text notes enables you to see patterns and relationships among ideas, find examples for difficult concepts, and much more. It takes time, but pays off enormously because it strengthens memory and offers a more cohesive and connected study tool.

Some students may prefer to act quickly, combining class and reading notes as close to that class meeting as possible so the material is fresh. Others may prefer to use this strategy nearer to midterm or finals time.

Follow these steps to combine your class and text notes into a **master note set:**

MASTER NOTE SET
A complete, integrated note set that contains both class and text notes.

■ *Step 1: Focus on what's important by condensing to the essence.* Reduce your combined notes so they contain only main ideas and key supporting details, such as terms, dates, formulas, and examples. (Eliminating the repetition you are likely to find in your notes will also help reduce the material.) Tightening and summarizing forces you to critically evaluate which ideas are most important and to rewrite your notes with only this material. As you begin to study, move back and forth between the full set and the reduced set. Key 7.12 shows a comprehensive outline and a reduced key-term outline of the same material.

■ *Step 2: Recite what you know.* As you approach exam time, use the terms in your bare-bones notes as cues for reciting what you know about a topic. Many students assume that they know concepts simply because they understand what they read. This type of passive understanding doesn't necessarily mean that they can recreate the material on an exam or apply it to problems. Make the process more active by reciting out loud during study sessions, writing your responses on paper, making flash cards, or working with a partner.

REDUCE YOUR FULL NOTES INTO KEY-TERM
NOTES TO HELP YOU **MASTER CONTENT**

Different Views of Freedom and Equality in the American Democracy

I.   U.S. democracy based on 5 core values: freedom and equality, order and stability, majority rule, protection of minority rights, and participation.

   A. U.S. would be a "perfect democracy" if it always upheld these values.

   B. U.S. is less than perfect, so it is called an "approaching democracy."

II. Freedom and Equality

   A. Historian Isaiah Berlin defines freedom as either positive or negative.

      1. Positive freedoms allow us to exercise rights under the Constitution, including right to vote.

      2. Negative freedoms safeguard us from government actions that restrict certain rights, such as the right to assemble. The 1st Amendment restricts government action by declaring that "Congress shall make no law . . ."

   B. The value of equality suggests that all people be treated equally, regardless of circumstance. Different views on what equality means and the implications for society.

      1. Equality of opportunity implies that everyone has the same chance to develop inborn talents.

         a. But life's circumstances—affected by factors like race and income—differ. This means that people start at different points and have different results. E.g., a poor, inner-city student will be less prepared for college than an affluent, suburban student.

         b. It is impossible to equalize opportunity for all Americans.

      2. Equality of result seeks to eliminate all forms of inequality, including economic differences, through wealth redistribution.

   C. Freedom and equality are in conflict, say text authors Berman and Murphy: "If your view of freedom is freedom from government intervention, then equality of any kind will be difficult to achieve. If government stays out of all citizen affairs, some people will become extremely wealthy, others will fall through the cracks, and economic inequality will multiply. On the other hand, if you wish to promote equality of result, then you will have to restrict some people's freedoms—the freedom to earn and retain an unlimited amount of money, for example."*

KEY-TERM OUTLINE OF THE SAME MATERIAL

Different Views of Freedom and Equality in the American Democracy

I.   America's 5 core values: freedom and equality, order and stability, majority rule, protection of minority rights, and participation.

   A. "Perfect democracy"

   B. "Approaching democracy"

II. Value #1—Freedom and equality

   A. Positive freedoms and negative freedoms

   B. Different views of equality: equality of opportunity versus equality of result

   C. Conflict between freedom and equality centers on differing views of government's role

*Larry Berman and Bruce Allen Murphy, *Approaching Democracy: Portfolio Edition,* Upper Saddle River, NJ: Prentice Hall, 2005, pp. 6–8.

■ **Step 3: Use critical thinking.** Now reflect on ideas in the following ways as you review your combined notes:

> ▶ Brainstorm examples from other sources that illustrate central ideas. Write down new ideas or questions that come up as you review.
> ▶ Think of ideas from your readings or from class that support or clarify your notes.
> ▶ Consider how your class notes differ from your reading notes and why.
> ▶ Apply concepts to questions at the ends of text chapters, to problems posed in class, or to real-world situations.

■ **Step 4: Create study sheets.** Putting your master notes in their shortest, most manageable (and portable) form, a study sheet is a one-page synthesis of all key points on one theme, topic, or process. Use critical thinking skills to organize information into themes or topics that you will need to know on an exam. On an individual study sheet, include the related lecture and text page references, a quick summary, possible questions on the topic, key terms, formulas, dates, people, examples, and so on.

■ **Step 4: Review and review again.** To ensure learning and prepare for exams, review your condensed notes, study sheets, and critical thinking questions until you know every topic cold.

Try to vary your review methods, focusing on active involvement. Recite the material to yourself, have a Q and A session with a study partner, or create and take a practice test. Another helpful technique is to summarize your notes in writing from memory after reviewing them. This will tell you whether or not you'll be able to recall the information on a test.

What happened to Norton? With increased effort and help from his study group, Norton did well in his courses the second time around and returned to the pre-engineering program, later transferring to Union College where he graduated with a bachelor's in electrical engineering. He was hired by Hewlett-Packard after college and worked his way up to management over 20 years. One of several jobs there took him to Boeblingen, Germany, on international assignment for 3 years. His current work in the area of product management, defining high-tech products to address what the market wants and needs, combines his passion for engineering, business, and new technologies. He is still an expert skier and has learned to become just as successful in his personal life and career as he is when playing outdoors.

Case Wrap-up

What does this mean for you? No student can spend every second of class time taking courses that are meaningful and inspiring. You will always experience different levels of motivation and interest for different courses. Your challenge is to find a way to do the work well when your interest doesn't provide the energy. Choose the course you are taking right now that interests you the least. Make three lists with the following headers: "Study Strategies That Can Help," "How I Will Use What I Learn in This Course," and "How I Will Reward Myself If I Persist in This Course." Then fill each list with as many items as you can. Refer to the lists whenever your focus or motivation begin to slip over the course of the term.

What effects go beyond your world? Anywhere you turn, from your immediate neighborhood to a country halfway around the world, you can find organizations looking for support. The demands of your everyday life may be so pressing that you cannot see how you will have the time to help out. Think about a person, place, thing, idea, or situation that has grabbed your attention and sparked your interest and emotion—your version of Norton's H-P calculator. Find an organization that relates to it and investigate to see how you can help in some small way. One action now, no matter how small, can help. Who knows? Maybe you can make time for more action in the future.

Successful Intelligence *Wrap-up*

HERE'S HOW YOU HAVE BUILT SKILLS IN **CHAPTER 7** :

ANALYTICAL THINKING 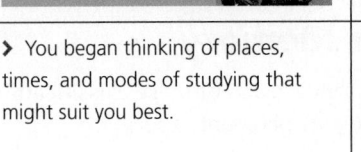	**CREATIVE THINKING**	**PRACTICAL THINKING**
❯ You analyzed why memory strategies work—and why people forget.	❯ You began thinking of places, times, and modes of studying that might suit you best.	❯ You explored strategies you can put to work to remember what you study, including specific strategies for math and science.
❯ You learned how analyzing your personal tendencies can help you design the most effective study plan.	❯ You considered different ways to use mnemonic devices to boost recall.	❯ You learned about how to create summaries of notes and text readings as well as helpful study sheets.
❯ In the Get Analytical exercise, you explored how analytical thinking will help you retain information for one of your courses.	❯ In the Get Creative exercise, you came up with your own mnemonic device for some information you need to remember.	❯ In the Get Practical exercise, you developed a study plan based on journalists' questions.

Word *for* Thought

Research shows that sleep helps solidify information in memory. In the Dyak language, spoken in **Borneo,** a figure called a *ngarong* (nn-ga'-rawng) or "dream-helper" comes to sleepers and helps clarify ideas. Let your ngarong have a chance to do his or her good work—get some sleep.[7]

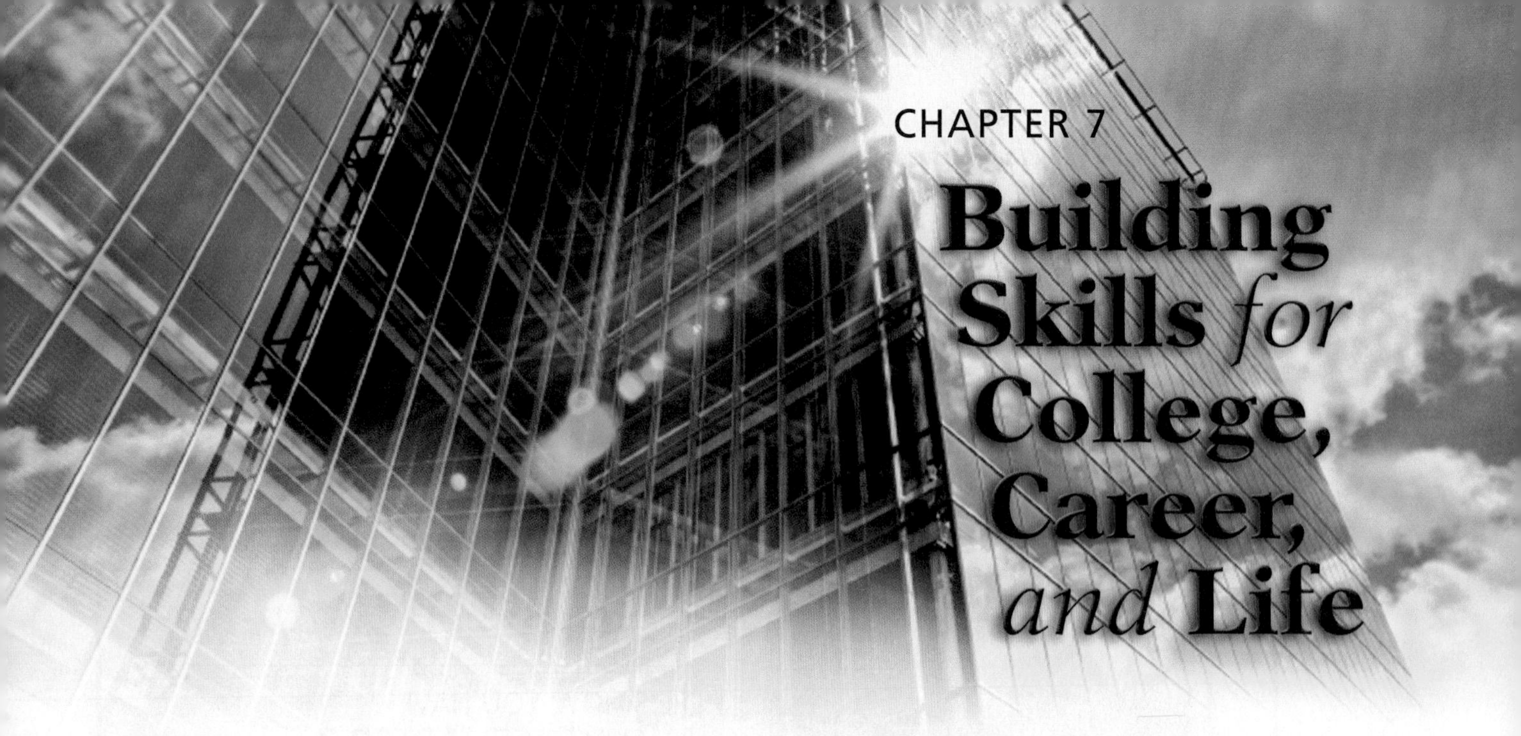

Building Skills *for* College, Career, *and* Life

Steps to Success

Evaluate Your Memory

BUILD BASIC SKILLS. Under each of these classifications of information in long-term memory, write down an example from your personal experience:

Episodic memory (events). Example: I remember the first time I conducted an experiment in chemistry class.

_____

_____

Declarative memory (facts). Example: I know that the electoral college must vote before a new U.S. president is officially elected.

_____

_____

Procedural memory (motion). Example: I know how to type without looking at the keyboard.

_____

_____

TAKE IT TO THE NEXT LEVEL.

Which type of information (events, facts, motion) is easiest for you to remember? Why?

_____

_____

_____

Which type of information is hardest for you to remember? Why?

_____

_____

MOVE TOWARD MASTERY. Address the type of information you find *most difficult* to remember.

Name an example from your life of some information in this category that you need to be able to recall and use.

_____

_____

_____

Name two approaches from the chapter that you believe will help you strengthen it.

1. _____

2. _____

Now give both a try. Circle the one that worked best.

Teamwork

Create Solutions Together

ASSESS AND BUILD YOUR MEMORY POWER

Goal: To improve your ability to remember.

Time on Task: 15 minutes

Instructions: Gather as a class if there are fewer than twenty people, or divide into two groups if there are more. Proceed according to the following steps (you'll need a timer or a cell phone that can act as one):

- Each person in your group should place at least one item on a table (try to avoid repeats). Try to reach a total of fifteen items—from your backpack or bag, study area, home, or classroom— anything small enough to easily fit on the table. Find something that will cover them all—a jacket or newspaper, for example—and place it over the items. Let them stay covered for at least 10 minutes before beginning the activity. Alternatively, the instructor can gather fifteen items ahead of time.
- Allow 1 minute for everyone to look at the items, using the watch or cell phone timer.
- When the time is up, cover the items. Each person should list as many as possible on a sheet of paper.

Compare your lists to the actual items. Talk as a group about the results and about what you did and didn't remember. Describe your observations here.

_____

_____

_____

_____

_____

Now repeat the exercise using a mnemonic device in the following steps:

- Talk as a group about ways to remember more items, considering different mnemonic devices or strategies. Together, choose a device or strategy to try.
- Create a new group of fifteen items (if you can't swap out all of them, exchange as many as you can) and cover them.
- Uncover and allow 1 minute of observation as before, but focus on the mnemonic device as you look at the items.
- When time is up, cover again and make a new list.
- Think and talk about the difference between the two experiences. Write your findings here.

_____

_____

_____

_____

_____

_____

_____

_____

_____

_____

_____

_____

_____

_____

_____

Writing

Build Intrapersonal and Communication Skills

Record your thoughts on a separate piece of paper, in a journal, or electronically.

EMOTIONAL INTELLIGENCE JOURNAL

How feelings connect study success. Think about how you were feeling when you were most able to recall and use information in a high-stress situation—a test, a workplace challenge, a group presentation. What thought, action, or situation put you in this productive mindset that helped you succeed? Did you go for a run? talk to your best friend? take 30 minutes for yourself? Create a list of thoughts or actions you can call on when you will be faced with a challenge to your memory and want the best possible outcome.

REAL-LIFE WRITING

Combining class and text notes. Choose a course for which you have a test coming up in the next 4 weeks. Create a master set of notes for that course combining one week's classes and reading assignments (make sure it is material you need to know for your test). Your goal is to summarize and connect all the important information covered during the period.

Personal Portfolio

Prepare for Career Success

MEMORY AND NETWORKING

21st Century Learning Building Blocks

- Communication and Collaboration
- Social and Cross-Cultural Skills

Complete the following in your electronic portfolio or separately on paper.

Your ability to remember people you meet or interact with in the workplace—their names, what they do, other relevant information about them—is an enormous factor in your career success.

Consider this scenario: You are introduced to your supervisor's new boss, someone who is in a position to help you advance in the company, and you both exchange small talk for a few minutes. A week later you run into him outside the building. If you greet him by name and ask whether his son is over the case of the flu he had, you have made a good impression that is likely to help you in the future. If you call him by the wrong name, realize your mistake, and slink off to work, you may have set up a bit of a hurdle for yourself as you try to get ahead.

Using what you know about memory strategies and what works for you, set up a system to record and retain information about people you meet whom you want to remember. For your system, decide on a tool (address book, set of notecards, electronic organizer, computer file), what to record (name, phone, e-mail, title, how you met, important details), and how you will update. Choose a tool that you are most likely to use and that will be easy for you to refer to and update.

Tool of choice: _____

Information to record:

_____

When to record and how often to check or update:

_____

Get started by putting in information for all the people you consider to be important networking contacts at this point—family, friends, instructors and advisors, or work colleagues and supervisors. Make this the start of a database that will serve you throughout your career.

 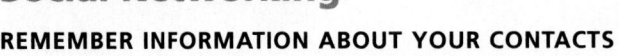 ## Social Networking

REMEMBER INFORMATION ABOUT YOUR CONTACTS

Use LinkedIn to connect with the list of important contacts you just developed—sign in to your account and invite them to join your network using any of the methods from the Chapter 6 exercise.

When at least three of these contacts have responded by joining your network, use the LinkedIn "My Connections" area to fill in helpful information about them that you want to remember.

- Click on "My Connections."
- Choose a name from your connections list and click on "view and edit details" beneath that person's name.
- Fill in any relevant information—phone, address, website, birthday, and notes about your contact with this person.

Test Taking

Showing What You Know

What Would You Do?

Think about this problem as you read, and consider how you would approach it. This chapter helps you use preparation, persistence, and strategy to conquer test anxiety fears, show what you know, and learn from test mistakes.

Teo Velez is working toward an associate's degree in nursing. Although hoping to finish in 2 years, he struggled in two particular required courses and has to repeat them during a fifth term. His advisor called him in for a meeting.

Sitting down in Mr. Sorrenti's office, Teo spoke first: "I know why I'm here. I have to repeat Nursing II and Pharmacology. I just couldn't make it happen; the tests killed me." "I talked to your professors," said Mr. Sorrenti. "Both of them said you were on your game in class time and with projects. But your test scores brought everything down too far in both cases. Do you have problems memorizing that kind of material?"

"No, actually . . . it's just . . . I have terrible text anxiety," replied Teo. "Always have. It's worst when it comes to lists, terms, sets of things that I should be able to memorize straight up. All the stuff for the two courses I failed, really." Mr. Sorrenti thought for a moment. "Well, Teo, the fact that you can pinpoint the issue is a huge step in the right direction. What do you think causes the anxiety?"

"Oh, I'm not really sure, but if a test is coming up that I think will be a problem, I get so freaked out that I can't even study for it. Then the night before I go crazy cramming all this information into my head, and I show up exhausted for the test, and my brain goes blank, and I get shaky and my palms sweat, and I screw up the test, and then I just tell myself it was because I didn't prepare properly, and I try to forget it ever happened."

"You know, you are setting yourself up for failure," said Mr. Sorrenti. "It's a vicious cycle. You are nervous, you don't study, and then you don't succeed in part because you don't have the knowledge. If you gave yourself a chance by preparing well, you might find ways to settle down at test time and see what you are really capable of."

Teo looked at him. "Sounds great, but easier said than done," he replied. (To be continued . . .)

Tests are a reality that all students have to deal with. You'll learn more about Teo, and revisit his situation, within the chapter.

In this chapter, you'll explore answers to these questions:

> How can preparation improve test performance? p. 218

> How can you work through test anxiety? p. 224

> What general strategies can help you succeed on tests? p. 226

> How can you master different types of test questions? p. 232

> What can you learn from test mistakes? p. 238

ANALYTICAL   CREATIVE   PRACTICAL

STATUS *Check*

▶ *How prepared are you for taking tests?*

For each statement, circle the number that feels right to you, from 1 for "not at all true for me" to 5 for "very true for me."

▶ I use strategies to help me predict what will be on tests.	1 2 3 4 5
▶ I actively prepare and review before taking exams.	1 2 3 4 5
▶ I do anything to avoid cramming.	1 2 3 4 5
▶ When I recognize signs of test anxiety, I use relaxation methods to calm down.	1 2 3 4 5
▶ I read test directions before beginning.	1 2 3 4 5
▶ I use certain strategies to answer questions I'm unsure of.	1 2 3 4 5
▶ I don't think cheating is worth the price.	1 2 3 4 5
▶ I know the difference between objective and subjective questions and how to answer each.	1 2 3 4 5
▶ I look for action verbs when answering essay questions.	1 2 3 4 5
▶ I learn from my testing mistakes and actively grow from them.	1 2 3 4 5

Each of the topics in these statements is covered in this chapter. Note those statements for which you circled a 3 or lower. Skim the chapter to see where those topics appear, and pay special attention to them as you read, learn, and apply new strategies.

REMEMBER: *No matter how prepared you are for taking tests, you can improve with effort and practice.*

"Successfully intelligent people seek to perform in ways that not only are competent but distinguish them from ordinary performers. They realize that the gap between competence and excellence may be small but the greatest rewards, both internal and external, are for excellence."

—Robert Sternberg

How can preparation improve **test performance?**

Although you may dread taking tests and exams, consider this: *The goal of a test is to see what you have learned.* Every day that you are learning—by attending class, staying on top of assignments, completing readings and projects, and participating in class discussions—you are preparing for tests. The following strategies, specific to tests, put your analytical, creative, and practical thinking skills into action to help you be as prepared as possible.

Identify test type and what you will be expected to know

Before you begin studying, take practical steps to find out as much as you can about the test, including the following:

▶ *Topics that will be covered.* Will the test cover everything since the term began or will it be more limited?

▶ *Material you will be tested on.* Will the test cover only what you learned in class and in the text or will it also include outside readings?

▶ *Types of questions.* Will the questions be objective (multiple choice with only one correct answer, multiple choice with more than one correct answer, true/false, sentence completion), subjective (essay), or a combination?

▶ *Supplemental information you may be able to have.* Is the test open book (meaning you can use your class text)? Open note (meaning you can use any notes you've taken)? Both? Or neither? Are you able to work with a partner on any part of it? Is it a take-home exam? Will you be expected to complete part or all of it online?

Part of successful test preparation is knowing when to stop. To avoid overload, study in shorter segments over a period of time, and get the sleep you need before test day.
© Alvis Upitis/Image Bank/Getty Images

Instructors routinely answer questions like these. If you are unsure, ask for clarification. Chances are, some other students are wondering the same thing.

As you begin thinking about the test, remember that not all tests are created equal—a quiz is not as important as a midterm or final, although accumulated grades on small quizzes add up and can make a difference in your final grade. Plan and prioritize your study time and energy according to the value of the quiz or test. Consult your syllabus for test and quiz dates and times.

Here are other practical strategies for predicting what may be on a test.

▶ *Use your textbook.* Check features such as summaries, vocabulary terms, and study questions for clues about what's important to remember.

▶ *Listen at review sessions.* Many instructors offer review sessions before midterms and finals. Bring your questions to these sessions and listen to the questions others ask.

▶ *Make an appointment to see your instructor.* Spending a few minutes talking about the test one-on-one may clarify misunderstandings and help you focus on what to study.

▶ *Get information from people who already took the course.* Try to get a sense of test difficulty, whether tests focus primarily on assigned readings or class notes, what materials are usually covered, and the types of questions that are asked.

▶ *Examine old tests, if the instructor makes them available.* You may find old tests in class, online, or on reserve in the library. Old tests will help you answer questions like the following:

- Do tests focus on examples and details, general ideas and themes, or a combination?
- Are the questions straightforward or confusing and sometimes tricky?
- Will you be asked to apply principles to new situations and problems?

After taking the first exam in a course, you will have a better idea of what to expect.

Determine where and how the test will be given

Where you take a test can affect your performance. For instance, a take-home exam may sound like an easy A, but distractions like children and TV can threaten your focus. Similarly, if you miss a test date and need to make it up, you may find yourself taking an exam in a testing center. Being prepared for the stresses of your environment will help you manage test time.

student profile

Kevin Ix
Bergen Community College, Paramus, New Jersey

About me:

After high school, I attended college for three semesters studying to become an electrician. Later, with the way the housing market has been plummeting and the direction the economy is heading, I decided a business major made a lot more sense. I am now working toward a degree in business. I keep myself busy during the summer months with one full-time and one part-time job.

How I faced a challenge:

Taking the time to read directions has never been a strong point of mine. Whether it's setting up a new television or taking a final exam, my initial reaction is to jump right into the task without paying attention to the instructions. On one particular occasion I remember being given a test and started answering the questions without even glancing at the directions. At the end of the test, the teacher began collecting the exams and occasionally gave out a laugh as she made her way around the room. As it turned out, the directions on the top of the test clearly read, "If you're reading these directions, please do not fill in the answer sheet." Certainly this test was more focused on testing our ability to follow directions than on the curriculum. Needless to say, while I wasn't the only one to make this foolish mistake, I did not fare too well on that particular test! I work to combat my tendencies by paying careful attention to directions.

What will help me in the workplace:

The expression "measure twice, cut once" was commonly instilled into our minds while I was enrolled at my former technical college. If you didn't pay particular attention to measurements and directions, your mistake could become extremely expensive in material costs. This simple saying reminds me to focus on directions because, as I have learned over time, simply glancing at directions can lead to various forms of costly mistakes.

Online tests, like open book tests, may seem easier than tests in the classroom. In reality, due to the wide amount of information available at your fingertips, online tests are generally more challenging and require strong critical thinking skills. You may be able to Google factual information about a topic, but test questions will probably ask you to analyze and evaluate situations related to that information.

Create a study schedule and checklist

If you establish a plan ahead of time and write it down, you are more likely to follow it. Use journalists' questions to map out a study plan.

▶ Ask *what* and *why* to decide what you will study. Go through your notes, texts, related primary sources, and handouts, and set aside materials you don't need. Then prioritize the remaining materials to focus on the information most likely to be on the exam.

▶ Ask *when, where,* and *who*—and use the time management and goal-setting skills from Chapter 2—to prepare a schedule. Consider all of the relevant factors—your study materials, who you will study with, the number of days until the test, and the time and place you can study each day. Note study sessions in your planner ahead of time.

▶ Ask *how* to figure out what strategies you will use.

A comprehensive *checklist* will help you organize and stay on track as you prepare. Use the checklist to assign specific tasks to particular study times and sessions. Try out the checklist in Key 8.1 or create your own.

Use reading and studying strategies

Put what you have learned about thinking, reading, memory, and studying in Chapters 4, 5, and 7 into action to give yourself the best shot at remembering material.

▶ *Think analytically.* College exams often ask you to analyze and apply material in more depth than you experienced in high school. For example, your history instructor may ask you to place a primary source in its historical context. Prepare for these challenges as you study by continually asking analytical thinking questions (see Chapter 4) and using the higher levels of Bloom's taxonomy (see Chapter 5).

▶ *Use SQ3R.* This reading method provides an excellent structure for reviewing your reading materials (see Chapter 5).

▶ *Employ strategies from* how *questions.* Use flash cards, audio strategies, chunking, or anything else that suits you and the material you are studying (see pages 194–200).

▶ *Create mnemonic devices.* Memory strategies help make what you review stick.

▶ *Actively review your combined class and text notes.* Summaries and master sets of combined text and class notes provide comprehensive study tools.

Make and take a pretest

Use end-of-chapter text questions to create your own pretest. If your course doesn't have an assigned text, develop questions from notes and assigned readings. Old homework problems will also help target areas that need work. Some texts also provide a website with online activities and pretests designed to help you review material. Keep in mind that the same test-preparation skills you learn in college will help you do well on standardized tests for graduate school.

Answer your questions under test-like conditions—in a quiet place where you can see a clock to tell you when to quit, with no books or notes (unless the exam is open book). This type of low-pressure test experience may help people like Teo calm test-taking fears.

Prepare for final exams

Studying for final exams, which usually take place the last week of the term, is a major commitment that requires careful time management. Your college may schedule study days (also called a *reading period*) between the end of classes

PREPARE FOR A TEST

Complete the following checklist for each exam to define your study goals, get organized, and stay on track:

Course: _____ Instructor: _____

Date, time, and place of test: _____

Type of test (Is it a midterm or a minor quiz?): _____

What instructor said about the test, including types of test questions, test length, and how much the test counts toward your final grade:

_____

_____

Topics to be covered on the test, in order of importance (information should also come from your instructor):

1. _____

2. _____

3. _____

4. _____

5. _____

Study schedule, including materials you plan to study (texts, class notes, homework problems, and so forth) and dates you plan to complete each:

Material   **Completion Date**

1. _____   _____

2. _____   _____

3. _____   _____

4. _____   _____

5. _____   _____

Materials you are expected to bring to the test (textbook, sourcebook, calculator, etc.):

_____

_____

_____

Special study arrangements (such as planning study group meeting, asking the instructor for special help, getting outside tutoring):

_____

_____

_____

Life-management issues (such as rearranging work hours):

_____

_____

_____

Source: Adapted from Ron Fry, *"Ace" Any Test,* 3rd ed., Franklin Lakes, NJ: Career Press, 1996, pp. 123–124.

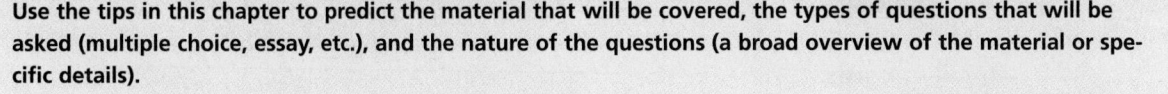

GET CREATIVE!

Write Your Own Test

Use the tips in this chapter to predict the material that will be covered, the types of questions that will be asked (multiple choice, essay, etc.), and the nature of the questions (a broad overview of the material or specific details).

Then be creative. Your goal is to write questions that your instructor is likely to ask—interesting questions that tap what you have learned and make you think about the material in different ways. Go through the following steps:

1. Write the questions you come up with on a separate sheet of paper.

2. Use what you have created as a pretest. Set up test-like conditions—a quiet, timed environment—and see how you do.

3. Evaluate your pretest answers against your notes and the text. How did you do?

_____

_____

4. Finally, after you take the actual exam, evaluate whether you think this exercise improved your performance. Would you use this technique again? Why or why not?

_____

_____

and the beginning of finals. Lasting from a day or two to several weeks, this period gives you time to prepare for exams and finish papers.

End-of-year studying requires flexibility. Libraries are often packed, and students may need to find alternative locations. Consider outdoor settings (if weather permits), smaller libraries (many departments have their own libraries), and empty classrooms. Set up times and places that will provide the atmosphere you need.[1]

Prepare physically

Most tests ask you to work at your best under pressure, so try to get a good night's sleep before the exam. Sleep improves your ability to remember what you studied before you went to bed.

Eating a light, well-balanced meal including protein (eggs, milk, yogurt, meat and fish, nuts, or peanut butter) will keep you full longer than carbohydrates alone (breads, candy, or pastries). When time is short, don't skip breakfast—grab a quick meal such as a few tablespoons of peanut butter, a banana, or a high-protein granola bar.

Make the most of last-minute cramming

Cramming—studying intensively and around the clock right before an exam—often results in information going into your head and popping right back out when the exam is over. *If learning is your goal, cramming will not help you reach it.* The reality, however, is that you are likely to cram for tests, especially midterms and finals, from time to time in your college career. You may also cram if, like Teo, anxiety leads you to avoid studying. Use these hints to make the most of this study time:

▶ *Focus on crucial concepts.* Summarize the most important points and try to resist reviewing notes or texts page by page.
▶ *Create a last-minute study sheet to review right before the test.* Write down key facts, definitions, and formulas on a single sheet of paper or on flash cards.
▶ *Arrive early.* Review your study aids until you are asked to clear your desk.

After the exam, evaluate how cramming affected your performance. Did it help, or did it load your mind with disconnected details? Did it increase or decrease anxiety at test time? Then evaluate how cramming affected your recall. Within a few days, you will probably remember very little—a reality that will work against you in advanced courses that build on the knowledge being tested and in careers that require it. Think ahead about how you can start studying earlier next time.

How can you work through test anxiety?

A certain amount of stress can be a good thing. You are alert, ready to act, and geared up to do your best. Some students, however, experience incapacitating stress before and during exams, especially midterms and finals. Test anxiety can cause sweating, nausea, dizziness, headaches, and fatigue. It can reduce concentration and cause you to forget everything you learned. Sufferers may get lower grades because their performance does not reflect what they know or because, as in Teo's case, their fear has affected their ability to prepare effectively.

Prepare well and have a positive attitude

Being prepared—both by reviewing material and following a detailed study plan—is the most essential way to ready yourself for an academic showdown. Only by knowing the material as best you can will you have reason to believe in your ability to pass the test. The other key tool is a positive attitude that says, "I know this material and I'm ready to show it."

Anxiety is defined as an emotional disturbance, meaning that it tends to be based on an imagined risk rather than an actual one, and often leads you away from your goals rather than toward them.[2] With this in mind, think metacognitively about your anxiety over a test:

▶ Look at the risk you *think* you are facing—and compare it with the *actual* risk. Consider the possibility that you may be more prepared than you realize.

▶ Look at your goal for this test. Identify the physical and mental responses caused by your anxiety, and note how they are affecting your ability to reach that goal.

Use the strategies in Key 8.2 to be both prepared and positive.

Math anxiety

For some students, math exams cause more anxiety than other academic challenges. A form of test anxiety, *math anxiety* is often based on common misconceptions about math, such as the notion that an ability to think quantitatively is an inborn talent some people have and others don't or that men are better at math than women. Students who feel that they can't do math may give up without asking for help. At exam time, they may experience test anxiety symptoms that reduce their ability to concentrate and leave them feeling defeated.

The test anxiety strategies just discussed will also help combat math anxiety. In addition, math anxiety sufferers should focus heavily on problem-solving

Change the CONVERSATION

Challenge yourself and your friends to ask—and answer—tough questions. Use the following to inspire discussion in pairs or groups.

▶ What did you learn about yourself from the questionnaire on page 227? If you experience test anxiety, what effect do you think it will have on your future?

▶ Which suggestions for reducing test anxiety are you likely to use? How do you think they will help you feel more comfortable at test time? What other ways can you think of for improving your performance?

▶ **CONSIDER THE CASE:** If you were Teo's advisor, what would you tell him to do first in order to get ready to handle tests next term? If he claimed he was doomed to freeze up on tests no matter what, how would you try to help him shake off that attitude?

Key 8.2 USE STRATEGIES TO **BUILD A POSITIVE ATTITUDE** AND GET PREPARED

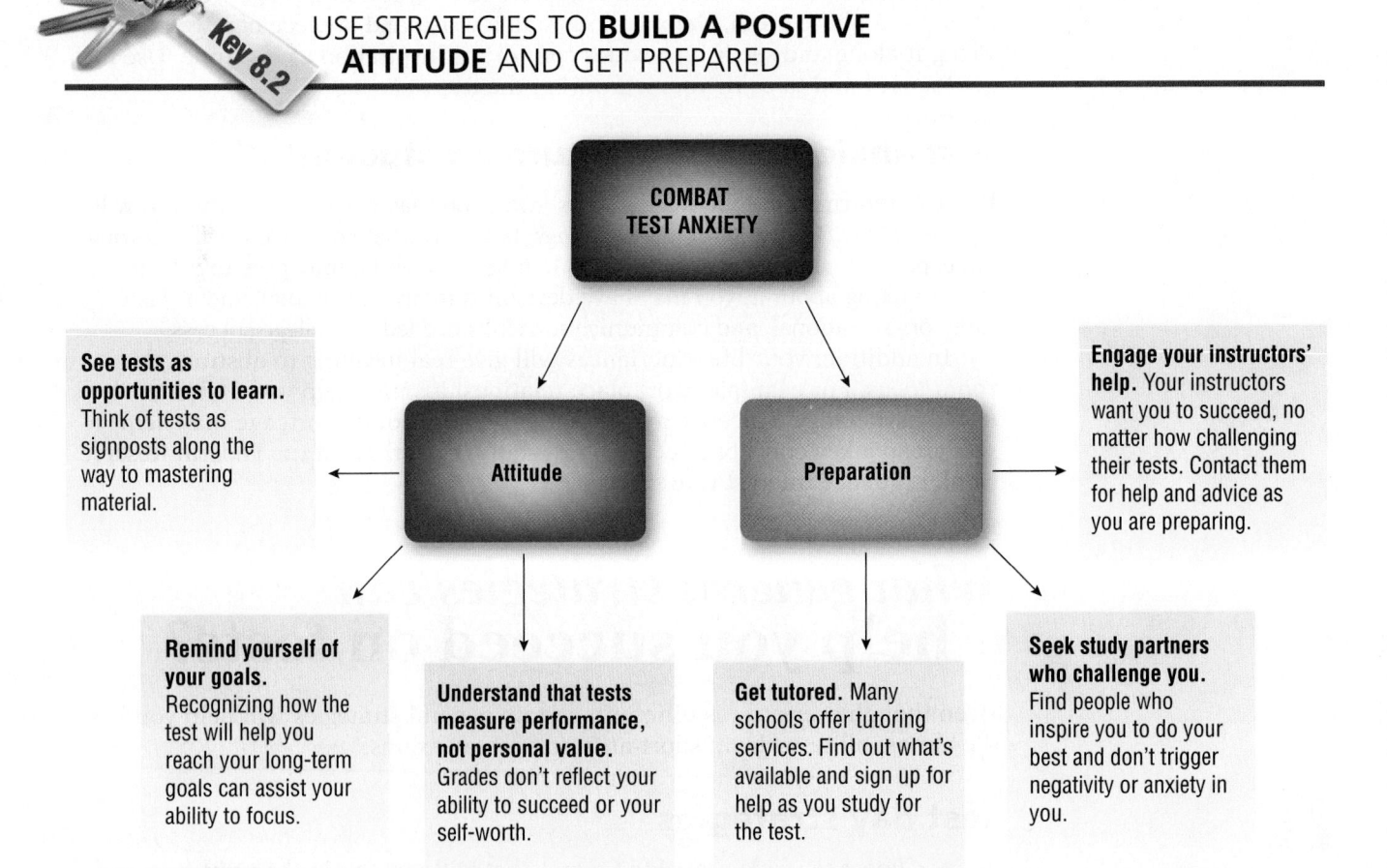

COMBAT TEST ANXIETY

Attitude

See tests as opportunities to learn. Think of tests as signposts along the way to mastering material.

Remind yourself of your goals. Recognizing how the test will help you reach your long-term goals can assist your ability to focus.

Understand that tests measure performance, not personal value. Grades don't reflect your ability to succeed or your self-worth.

Preparation

Engage your instructors' help. Your instructors want you to succeed, no matter how challenging their tests. Contact them for help and advice as you are preparing.

Get tutored. Many schools offer tutoring services. Find out what's available and sign up for help as you study for the test.

Seek study partners who challenge you. Find people who inspire you to do your best and don't trigger negativity or anxiety in you.

techniques, as in the math and science study strategies on page 201, and should also seek help from instructors and tutors early and often.

Test time strategies

When test time comes, several strategies may help you manage and calm test anxiety.

▶ *Manage your environment.* Make a conscious effort to sit away from students who might distract you. If it helps, listen to relaxing music on an MP3 player while waiting for class to begin.

▶ *Use positive self-talk.* Tell yourself that you can do well and that it is normal to feel anxious, particularly before an important exam.

▶ *Practice relaxation.* Close your eyes, breathe deeply and slowly, and visualize positive mental images like getting a good grade. Or try a more physical tensing-and-relaxing method:[3]

1. Put your feet flat on the floor.
2. With your hands, grab underneath the chair.
3. Push down with your feet and pull up on your chair at the same time for about 5 seconds.
4. Relax for 5 to 10 seconds.
5. Repeat the procedure two or three times.
6. Relax all your muscles except those actually used to take the test.

▶ *Bring a special object.* You may have an object that has special meaning for you—a photograph, a stone or crystal, a wristband, a piece of jewelry, a hat. Bring it along and see if it provides comfort or inspiration at test time. Use it to get focused and to calm yourself during the test.

Test anxiety and the returning student

If you're returning to school after years away, you may wonder how well you will handle exams. To deal with these feelings, focus on what you have learned through life experience, including the ability to handle work and family pressures. Without even thinking about it, you may have developed many time management, planning, organizational, and communication skills needed for college success.

In addition, your life experiences will give real meaning to abstract classroom ideas. For example, workplace relationships may help you understand social psychology concepts, and refinancing your home mortgage may help you grasp a key concept in economics—how the actions of the Federal Reserve Bank influence interest rate swings.

What general strategies can help you succeed on tests?

Even though every test is different, certain general strategies will help you handle almost all tests, from short-answer to essay exams.

Test day strategies

▶ *Choose the right seat.* Find a seat that will put you in the right frame of mind and minimize distractions. Choose a place near a window, next to a wall,

GET PRACTICAL!

Assess Test Anxiety with the Westside Test Anxiety Scale

The first step toward becoming a fearless test taker is understanding your personal level of test anxiety. Answer the questions below as honestly as possible.

Rate how true each of the following is of you, from "Always true" to "Never true." Use the following 5 point scale. Circle your answers.

5 = Always true; 4 = Usually true; 3 = Sometimes true; 2 = Seldom true; 1 = Never true

1. The closer I am to a major exam, the harder it is for me to concentrate on the material.	5 4 3 2 1
2. When I study for my exams, I worry that I will not remember the material on the exam.	5 4 3 2 1
3. During important exams, I think that I am doing awful or that I may fail.	5 4 3 2 1
4. I lose focus on important exams, and I cannot remember material that I knew before the exam.	5 4 3 2 1
5. I remember answers to exam questions only after the exam is already over.	5 4 3 2 1
6. I worry so much before a major exam that I am too worn out to do my best on the exam.	5 4 3 2 1
7. I feel out of sorts or not really myself when I take important exams.	5 4 3 2 1
8. I find that my mind sometimes wanders when I am taking important exams.	5 4 3 2 1
9. After an exam, I worry about whether I did well enough.	5 4 3 2 1
10. I struggle with written assignments, or avoid doing them, because I want them to be perfect.	5 4 3 2 1

Sum of the 10 questions: _____

Now divide the sum by 10. Write it here. _____ This is your test anxiety score.

Compare your score against the following scale. How does your level of test anxiety rate? In general, students that score a 3.0 or higher on the scale tend to have more test anxiety than normal and may benefit from seeking additional assistance.

1.0–1.9   Comfortably low test anxiety

2.0–2.4   Normal or average test anxiety

2.5–2.9   High normal test anxiety

3.0–3.4   Moderately high (some items rated 4—high)

3.5–3.9   High test anxiety (half or more of the items rated 4—high)

4.0–5.0   Extremely high anxiety (items rated 4—high and 5—extreme)

Reflect on your results. Do they show a high level of test anxiety? A normal level? Based on what you've learned about yourself, select anxiety-reducing strategies that you will use when studying for or taking your next test. Record your plan on a sheet of paper or computer file.

Source: Used by permission of Richard Driscoll.

Apply Different Intelligences to Preparing for a Geometry Exam

INTELLIGENCE	USE MI STRATEGIES TO IMPROVE TEST PREPARATION	APPLY MI TEST-PREP STRATEGIES TO STUDY FOR A TEST ON GEOMETRIC SHAPES AND MEASUREMENT*
Verbal-Linguistic	• Write test questions your instructor might ask. Answer the questions and then try rewriting them in a different format (essay, true/false, and so on). • Underline important words in review or practice questions.	• Underline important vocabulary words in the chapter. Then make a set of flash cards, with the word on one side and the definition on the other. Test yourself.
Logical-Mathematical	• Logically connect what you are studying with what you know. Consider similarities, differences, and cause-and-effect relationships. • Draw charts that show relationships and analyze trends.	• Create a table that highlights the similarities and differences among polygons, circles, and three-dimensional shapes. Use columns to note qualities such as number of sides, number of angles, measurement of angles, formulas that apply consistently, and special features (for example, in a rectangle, all angles are right angles).
Bodily-Kinesthetic	• Use text highlighting to take a hands-on approach to studying. • Create a sculpture, model, or skit to depict a tough concept that will be on the test.	• Use pencils, Popsicle sticks, pipe cleaners, containers, or other materials to create the shapes on which you will be tested.
Visual-Spatial	• Make charts, diagrams, or think links illustrating concepts. • Make drawings related to possible test topics.	• Draw illustrations that represent all of the postulates (statements assumed to be true) in the chapter.
Interpersonal	• Form a study group to prepare for your test. • In your group, come up with possible test questions. Then use the questions to test each other's knowledge.	• With a study partner, work through the exercise set on polygons and circles. Try either working through problems together or having partners "teach" problems to each other.
Intrapersonal	• Apply concepts to your own life; think about how you would manage. • Brainstorm test questions and then take the sample "test" you developed.	• Reread the "Geometry Around Us" material in your text to reinforce your understanding of how geometry functions in the real world. Write two additional ideas about how geometry relates to your world.
Musical	• Recite text concepts to rhythms or write a song to depict them. • Explore relevant musical links to reading material.	• Write a song that helps you remember the types of triangles and their definitions.
Naturalistic	• Try to notice similarities and differences in objects and concepts by organizing your study materials into relevant groupings.	• Create a table or visual organizer that arranges all of the types of two- and three-dimensional shapes into logical groupings.

*For information on geometric shapes and measurement, see Gary L. Musser, Lynn E. Trimpe, and Vikki R. Maurer, *College Geometry: A Problem-Solving Approach with Applications,* 2nd ed., Upper Saddle River, NJ: Pearson/Prentice Hall, 2008.

or in the front row so you can look into the distance. Know yourself: For many students, it's smart to avoid sitting near friends.

▶ *Write down key facts.* Before you even look at the test, write down key information, including formulas, rules, and definitions, that you don't want to forget. (Use the back of the question sheet so your instructor knows that you made these notes after the test began.)

▶ *Start with the big picture.* Spend a few minutes at the start gathering information about the questions—how many of which types are in each section, along with their point values. Use this information to schedule your time. Take level of difficulty into account as you parcel out your time. For example, if you think you can do the short-answer questions in 45 minutes and sense that the writing section will take longer, you can budget 1 hour and 15 minutes for the essay.

▶ *Directions count, so read them.* Reading test directions carefully can save you trouble. For example, you may be required to answer only one of three essay questions, or you may be penalized for incorrect responses to short-answer questions.

▶ *Mark up the questions.* Mark up instructions and keywords to avoid careless errors. Circle qualifiers such as *always, never, all, none, sometimes,* and *every;* verbs that communicate specific instructions; and concepts that are tricky or need special attention.

> QUALIFIERS
> Words and phrases that can alter the meaning of a test question and thus require careful attention.

▶ *Be precise when taking a machine-scored test.* Use the right pencil (usually a no. 2) on machine-scored tests, and mark your answer in the correct space, filling it completely. Periodically check answer numbers against question numbers to make sure they match.

▶ *Work from easy to hard.* Begin with the easiest questions and answer them quickly without sacrificing accuracy. This will boost your confidence and leave more time for harder questions. Mark tough questions as you reach them, and return to them after answering the questions you know.

▶ *Watch the clock.* If you are worried about time, you may rush through the test and have time left over. When this happens, check over your work instead of leaving early. If, on the other hand, you are falling behind, be flexible about the best use of the remaining time.

▶ *Take a strategic approach to questions you cannot answer.* Key 8.3 has ideas to consider when you face questions that stump you.

▶ *Use special techniques for math tests.* Use the general test-taking strategies presented in this chapter as well as the techniques in Key 8.4 to achieve better results on math exams.

Maintain academic integrity

You're starting on a test when your cell phone vibrates. Your friend, who has this same class the day before, has sent you a text with answers to the multiple-choice sections. Although cheating has the immediate gain of possibly passing a test or getting a few free answers, its long-term consequences aren't so beneficial. If you cheat, you run the risk of being caught and subsequently disciplined (which can include expulsion), not to mention that you probably will not actually learn the material. Cheating that goes on your record can also damage your ability to get a job.

In recent years, cheating has become high-tech, with students using their cell phones, iPods, personal digital assistants (PDAs), graphing calculators, and Internet-connected laptops to share information through text messaging or to search the Internet. Because this type of cheating can be difficult to discover when exams are administered in large lecture halls, some instructors ban all electronic devices from the room.

Valid concerns can put students under great pressure: "I have to do well on the final. I am in a constant time crunch. I need a good grade to qualify for the next course in my major. I can't risk failing because I'm

UNDERSTAND **WHAT TO DO** IF YOU DON'T KNOW THE ANSWER

Ask for clarification. ➔ Sometimes a simple rewording will make you realize that you do know the material.

Skip the question and come back to it later. ➔ Letting your subconscious mind work on the question sometimes can make a difference.

Build logical connections. ➔ Take a calculated risk by using what you already know about the topic.

Bring up a "mental map" of your notes. ➔ Remembering where material was covered in your notes and text may jog your memory about content.

Just start writing. ➔ The act of writing about related material may help you recall the targeted information. You may want to do this kind of writing on a spare scrap of paper, think about what you've written, and then write your final answer on the test paper or booklet.

TRY THESE TECHNIQUES TO SUCCEED ON **MATH EXAMS**

Read through the exam first. When you receive an exam, read through every problem quickly and make notes on how you might attempt to solve the problems.

Analyze problems carefully. Categorize problems according to type. Take the "givens" into account, and write down any formulas, theorems, or definitions that apply. Focus on what you want to find or prove.

Estimate to come up with a "ballpark" solution. Then work the problem and check the solution against your estimate. The two answers should be close. If they're not, recheck your calculations.

Break the calculation into the smallest possible pieces. Go step-by-step and don't move on to the next step until you are clear about what you've done so far.

Recall how you solved similar problems. Past experience can provide valuable clues.

Draw a picture to help you see the problem. Visual images such as a diagram, chart, probability tree, or geometric figure may help clarify your thinking.

Be neat. Sloppy numbers can mean the difference between a right and a wrong answer. A 4 that looks like a 9 will be marked wrong.

Use the opposite operation to check your work. Work backward from your answer to see if you are right.

Look back at the question to be sure you did everything. Did you answer every part of the question? Did you show all required work?

already in debt and I have to graduate and get a job." Compounded, these worries can often drive students to thoughts of academic dishonesty. In the end, the choice is yours. Remember that there is often more than one solution to the problem and that every possible solution has potential positive and negative effects. Key 8.5 shows you some choices and potential consequences of cheating on a final exam.

Your decisions will have lasting impacts on your future and your life. The next time you are tempted to break the rules of academic integrity, remember: *You are responsible for your own choices and the consequences of your actions.*

Key 8.5 THINK THROUGH THE **CONSEQUENCES** OF CHEATING

Choice 1

Use every way I can think of to cheat on the exam to get the highest possible grade.

Potential Positive Effects

I will get the grade I need to move ahead.

Cheating will save me a lot of time that I can use to earn money.

Potential Negative Effects

If I get caught, I will get in academic trouble. The incident will go on my transcript, and I will fail the course.

I won't learn the material, and I need to know this stuff for the higher-level course I take next semester.

Choice 2

Cheat in small ways—nothing major. Do only what is absolutely necessary to raise my grade without getting in trouble.

Potential Positive Effects

I will be "perfecting" the cheating skills I need in the workforce.

Potential Negative Effects

Even "minor" cheating undermines learning and reflects poorly on my character.

Cheating is cheating. My instructor may throw the book at me if I'm caught.

Choice 3

Play it straight—no cheating allowed.

Potential Positive Effects

I hunker down and actually learn the material so that I come into the test fully prepared.

I will have the knowledge I need for courses and for the workplace.

Potential Negative Effects

I risk getting a lower grade than I would if I cheated.

I will be spending a lot more time studying and won't be able to work as many hours on my job.

**FROM CHAPTER 29, "THE END OF IMPERIALISM,"
IN WESTERN CIVILIZATION: A SOCIAL AND CULTURAL HISTORY, 2ND EDITION**

- **MULTIPLE-CHOICE QUESTION**

India's first leader after independence was:

A. Gandhi   B. Bose   C. Nehru   D. Sukharno

(answer: C)

- **FILL-IN-THE-BLANK QUESTION**

East Pakistan became the country of _____ in 1971.

A. Burma   B. East India   C. Sukharno   D. Bangladesh

(answer: D)

- **TRUE/FALSE QUESTION**

The United States initially supported Vietnamese independence.

T   F

(answer: false)

- **ESSAY QUESTION**

Answer one of the following:

1. What led to Irish independence? What conflicts continued to exist after independence?

2. How did Gandhi work to rid India of British control? What methods did he use?

**FROM CHAPTER 6, "UNEMPLOYMENT AND INFLATION,"
IN MACROECONOMICS: PRINCIPLES AND TOOLS, 3RD EDITION**

- **MULTIPLE-CHOICE QUESTION**

If the labor force is 250,000 and the total population 16 years of age or older is 300,000, the labor-force participation rate is

A. 79.5%   B. 83.3%   C. 75.6%   D. 80.9%

(answer: B)

- **FILL-IN-THE-BLANK QUESTION**

Mike has just graduated from college and is now looking for a job, but has not yet found one. This causes the employment rate to _____ and the labor-force participation rate to _____.

A. increase; decrease   C. stay the same; stay the same
B. increase; increase   D. increase; stay the same

(answer: C)

- **TRUE/FALSE QUESTION**

The Consumer Price Index somewhat overstates changes in the cost of living because it does not allow for substitutions that consumers might make in response to price changes.   T   F   *(answer: true)*

- **ESSAY QUESTION**

During a press conference, the Secretary of Employment notes that the unemployment rate is 7.0%. As a political opponent, how might you criticize this figure as an underestimate? In rebuttal, how might the secretary argue that the reported rate is an overestimate of unemployment?

(Possible answer: The unemployment rate given by the secretary might be considered an underestimate because discouraged workers, who have given up the job search in frustration, are not counted as unemployed. In addition, full-time workers may have been forced to work part-time. In rebuttal, the secretary might note that a portion of the unemployed have voluntarily left their jobs. Most workers are unemployed only briefly and leave the ranks of the unemployed by gaining better jobs than they had previously held.)

How can you master different types of test questions?

Every type of test question is a different way of finding out how much you know. Questions fall into two general categories.

■ *Objective questions.* You generally choose or write a short answer, often selecting from a limited number of choices, for objective questions. They can include multiple-choice, fill-in-the-blank, matching, and true/false questions.

- **MATCHING QUESTION**

You are learning new words and your teacher asks you to think of an object similar to or related to the words he says. His words are listed below. Next to each word, write a related word from the list below.

el reloj   el cuaderno   el pupitre   una computadora

el televisor   la tiza   el lápiz   la mochila

1. el escritorio   _____   4. la pizarra _____

2. el bolígrafo   _____   5. el libro   _____

3. la videocasetera   _____

(answers: 1. el pupitre; 2. el lápiz; 3. el televisor; 4. la tiza; 5. el cuaderno)

- **ESSAY QUESTION**

Your mother always worries about you and wants to know what you are doing with your time in Granada. Write a short letter to her describing your experience in Spain. In your letter, you should address the following points:

1. What classes you take

2. When and where you study

3. How long you study every day

4. What you do with your time (mention three activities)

5. Where you go during your free time (mention two places)

- **MULTIPLE-CHOICE QUESTION**

What units are bonded together to make a strand of DNA?

A. chromatids   B. cells   C. enzymes   D. nucleotides
E. proteins   *(answer: D)*

- **FILL-IN-THE-BLANK QUESTION**

In a normal DNA molecule, adenine always pairs with _____ and cytosine always pairs with _____.

(answers: thymine, guanine)

- **TRUE/FALSE QUESTION**

Errors never occur in DNA replication, because the DNA polymerases edit out mistakes.   T   F

(answer: false)

- **MATCHING QUESTIONS**

Match the scientists and the approximate time frames (decades of their work) with their achievements.

Column 1	Column 2
_____ 1. Modeled the molecular structure of DNA	_____ A. George Beadle and Edward Tatum, 1930s and 1940s
_____ 2. Generated X-ray crystallography images of DNA	_____ B. James Watson and Francis Crick, 1950s
_____ 3. Correlated the production of one enzyme with one gene	_____ C. Rosalind Franklin and Maurice Wilkins, 1950s

(answers 1–B; 2–C; 3–A)

Sources: [*Western Civilization* test items] Margaret L. King, *Western Civilization: A Social and Cultural History,* 2nd ed., Upper Saddle River, NJ: Pearson Education, Inc., 2003. Questions from *Instructor's Manual and Test Item File* by Dolores Davison Peterson. Used with permission. [*Macroeconomics* test items] Arthur O'Sullivan and Steven M. Sheffrin, *Macroeconomics: Principles and Tools,* 3rd ed., Upper Saddle River, NJ: Pearson Education, Inc., 2003. Questions from *Test Item File 2* by Linda Ghent. Used with permission. [*Mosaicos* test items] Matilde Olivella de Castells, Elizabeth Guzmán, Paloma Lupuerta, and Carmen García, *Mosaicos: Spanish as a World Language,* 3rd ed., Upper Saddle River, NJ: Pearson Education, Inc., 2002. Questions from *Testing Program* by Mark Harpring. Used with permission. [*Biology* test items] David Krogh, *Biology: A Guide to the Natural World,* 2nd ed., Upper Saddle River, NJ: Pearson Education, Inc., 2002. Questions from *Test Item File* edited by Dan Wivagg. Used with permission.

■ *Subjective questions.* Demanding the same information recall as objective responses, subjective questions also require you to plan, organize, draft, and refine a response. All essay questions are subjective.

Key 8.6 shows samples of real test questions from Western civilization, macroeconomics, Spanish, and biology college texts published by Pearson Education. Included are exercises and multiple-choice, true/false, fill-in-the-blank, matching, and essay questions. Analyzing the types, formats, and complexities of these questions will help you gauge what to expect when you take your exams.

Look also at the Multiple Intelligence Strategies for Test Preparation on page 228. Harness the strategies that fit your learning strengths to prepare for geometry exams.

Note that some suggestions are repeated in the following sections, in order to reinforce the importance of these suggestions and their application to different types of test questions.

Multiple-choice questions

Multiple-choice questions are the most popular type of question on standardized tests. The following analytical and practical strategies will help you answer them:

▶ *Read the directions carefully and try to think of the answer before looking at the choices.* Then read the choices and make your selection.

▶ *Underline keywords and significant phrases.* If the question is complicated, try to break it down into small sections that are easy to understand.

▶ *Make sure you read every word of every answer.* Focus especially on qualifying words such as *always, never, tend to, most, often,* and *frequently.* Look also for negatives in a question ("Which of the following is *not . . .*").

▶ *When questions are linked to a reading passage, read the questions first.* This will help you focus on the information you need to answer the questions.

The following examples show the kinds of multiple-choice questions you might encounter in an introductory psychology course (the correct answer follows each question):

1. Arnold is at the company party and has had too much to drink. He releases all of his pent-up aggression by yelling at his boss, who promptly fires him. Arnold normally would not have yelled at his boss, but after drinking heavily he yelled because

   a. parties are places where employees are supposed to be able to "loosen up"

   b. alcohol is a stimulant

   c. alcohol makes people less concerned with the negative consequences of their behavior

   d. alcohol inhibits brain centers that control the perception of loudness   *(answer: C)*

2. Which of the following has not been shown to be a probable cause of or influence in the development of alcoholism in our society?

   a. intelligence

   b. culture

   c. personality

   d. genetic vulnerability   *(answer: A)*

3. Geraldine is a heavy coffee drinker who has become addicted to caffeine. If she completely ceases her intake of caffeine over the next few days, she is likely to experience each of the following *except:*

   a. depression

   b. lethargy

   c. insomnia

   d. headaches   *(answer: C)*

Source: Gary W. Piggrem and Charles G. Morris, *Test Item File for Understanding Psychology,* 3rd ed., © 1996 Prentice-Hall, Inc. Reprinted by permission of Pearson Education, Inc., Upper Saddle River, NJ.

True/false questions

Read true/false questions carefully to evaluate what they are asking. Look for absolute qualifiers (such as *all, only,* or *always,* which often make an otherwise true statement false) and conservative qualifiers (*generally, often, usually,* or *sometimes,* which often make an otherwise false statement true). For example, "The grammar rule '*i* before *e* except after *c*' is *always* true" is false, whereas "The grammar rule '*i* before *e* except after *c*' is *usually* true" is true.

Be sure to read *every* word of a true/false question to avoid jumping to an incorrect conclusion. Common problems in reading too quickly include missing negatives (*not, no*) that would change your response and deciding on an answer before reading the complete statement.

The following examples show the kinds of true/false questions you might encounter in an introductory psychology course (the correct answer follows each question):

Are the following questions true or false?

1. Alcohol use is clearly related to increases in hostility, aggression, violence, and abusive behavior.   *(true)*

2. Marijuana is harmless.   *(false)*

3. Simply expecting a drug to produce an effect is often enough to produce the effect.   *(true)*

4. Alcohol is a stimulant.   *(false)*

Source: Gary W. Piggrem and Charles G. Morris, *Test Item File for Understanding Psychology,* 3rd ed., © 1996 Prentice-Hall, Inc. Reprinted by permission of Pearson Education, Inc., Upper Saddle River, NJ.

Matching questions

Matching questions ask you to match the terms in one list with the entries in another list. For example, the directions may tell you to match a communicable disease with the microorganism that usually causes it. The following strategies will help you handle these questions.

▶ *Make sure you understand the directions.* The directions tell you whether each answer can be used only once (common practice) or more than once.

▶ *Work from the column with the longest entries.* The column on the left usually contains terms to be defined or questions to be answered, with the column on the right for definitions or answers. As a result, entries on the right are usually longer than those on the left. Reading those items only once will save time.

▶ *Start with the matches you know.* On your first run-through, pencil in these matches. When you can use an answer only once, you may have to adjust if you rethink a choice.

▶ *Finally, tackle the matches you're not sure of.* Think back to your class lectures, text notes, and study sessions as you try to visualize the correct response. If one or more phrases seem to have no correct answer and you can use answers only once, consider the possibility that one of your sure-thing answers is wrong.

Fill-in-the-blank questions

Fill-in-the-blank questions, also known as *sentence completion questions,* ask you to supply one or more words or phrases to complete the sentence. These strategies will help you make successful choices.

▶ *Be logical.* Insert your answer; then reread the *sentence from begin-ning* to end to be sure it makes sense and is factually and grammatically correct.

▶ *Note the lengths and number of the blanks.* If two blanks appear right after one another, the instructor is probably looking for a two-word answer. If a blank is longer than usual, the correct response may require additional space.

▶ *If there is more than one blank and the blanks are widely separated, treat each one separately.* Answering each as if it were a separate sentence-completion question increases the likelihood that you will get at least one answer correct.

▶ *If you are uncertain, guess.* Have faith that after hours of studying, the correct answer is somewhere in your subconscious mind and that your guess is not completely random.

The following examples show fill-in-the-blank questions you might encounter in an introductory astronomy course (correct answers follow questions):

1. A _____ is a collection of hundreds of billions of stars.   *(galaxy)*

2. Rotation is the term used to describe the motion of a body around some _____.   *(axis)*

3. The solar day is measured relative to the sun; the sidereal day is measured relative to the _____.   *(stars)*

4. On December 21, known as the _____ _____, the sun is at its _____ _____.   *(winter solstice; southernmost point)*

Source: Eric Chaisson and Steve McMillan, *Astronomy Today,* 3rd ed., 1999. Reprinted by permission of Pearson Education, Inc., Upper Saddle River, NJ.

Essay questions

Essay questions ask you to express your knowledge and views in a less structured way than short-answer questions. With freedom of thought and expression comes the challenge to organize your ideas and write well under time pressure. The following steps—basically a shortened version of the writing process—will help you plan, draft, revise, and edit your responses.

1. *Read every question.* Decide which to tackle (if there's a choice). Use critical thinking to identify exactly what the question is asking.

2. *Map out your time.* Schedule how long to allot for each answer, remem-bering that things don't always go as planned. Above all, be flexible.

3. *Focus on action verbs.* Key 8.7 shows verbs that tell you what to do to answer the question. Underline action verbs and use them to guide your writing.

4. *Plan.* Think about what the question is asking and what you know. On scrap paper, outline or map your ideas and supporting evidence. Then develop a thesis statement that defines your content and point of view. Don't skimp on planning. Not only does planning result in a better essay, but it also reduces stress because it helps you get in control.

5. *Draft.* Note the test directions before drafting your answer. Your essay may need to be of a certain length, for example, or may need to take a certain format. Use the following guidelines as you work:

- State your thesis, and then get right to the evidence that backs it up.
- Structure your essay so that each paragraph presents an idea that supports the thesis.

FOCUS ON **ACTION VERBS**
IN ESSAY TESTS

ANALYZE—Break into parts and discuss each part separately.

COMPARE—Explain similarities and differences.

CONTRAST—Distinguish between items being compared by focusing on differences.

CRITICIZE—Evaluate the issue, focusing on its problems or deficiencies.

DEFINE—State the essential quality or meaning.

DESCRIBE—Paint a complete picture; provide the details of a story or the main characteristics of a situation.

DIAGRAM—Present a drawing, chart, or other visual.

DISCUSS—Examine completely, using evidence and often presenting both sides of an issue.

ELABORATE ON—Start with information presented in the question, and then add new material.

ENUMERATE/LIST/IDENTIFY—Specify items in the form of a list.

EVALUATE—Give your opinion about the value or worth of a topic and justify your conclusion.

EXPLAIN—Make meaning clear, often by discussing causes and consequences.

ILLUSTRATE—Supply examples.

INTERPRET—Explain your personal views and judgments.

JUSTIFY—Discuss the reasons for your conclusions or for the question's premise.

OUTLINE—Organize and present main and subordinate points.

PROVE—Use evidence and logic to show that a statement is true.

REFUTE—Use evidence and logic to show that a statement is not true or tell how you disagree with it.

RELATE—Connect items mentioned in the question, showing, for example, how one item influenced another.

REVIEW—Provide an overview of ideas and establish their merits and features.

STATE—Explain clearly, simply, and concisely.

SUMMARIZE—Give the important ideas in brief, without comments.

TRACE—Present a history of a situation's development, often by showing cause and effect.

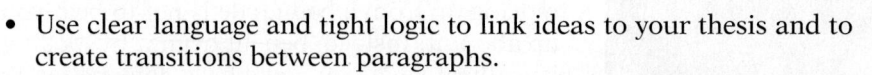

- Use clear language and tight logic to link ideas to your thesis and to create transitions between paragraphs.
- Look back at your planning notes periodically to make sure you cover everything.
- Wrap it up with a short, to-the-point conclusion.

6. *Revise.* Although you may not have the time to rewrite your entire answer, you can improve it with minor changes. Check word choice, paragraph structure, and style. If you notice anything missing, use editing marks to neatly insert it into the text. When you're done, make sure your response is the best possible representation of your ideas.

As you check over your essay, ask yourself questions about it:

- Have I answered the question?
- Does my essay begin with a clear thesis statement, and does each paragraph start with a strong topic sentence that supports the thesis?
- Have I provided the support necessary in the form of examples, statistics, and relevant facts to prove my argument, organized with tight logic?
- Have I covered all the points in my original outline or map?
- Is my conclusion an effective wrap-up?

7. *Edit.* Check for mistakes in grammar, spelling, punctuation, and usage. Correct language—and neat, legible handwriting—leaves a positive impression and helps your grade.

Key 8.8 shows a student's completed response to an essay question on body language, including the word changes and inserts she made while revising the draft.

To answer an essay question for a communications test, one student created the planning outline shown in Key 8.9 (p. 231). Notice how abbreviations and shorthand help the student write quickly.

Neatness is crucial. No matter how good your ideas are, if your instructor can't read them, your grade will suffer. If your handwriting is a problem, try printing or skipping every other line, and be sure to write on only one side of the page. Students with illegible handwriting might ask to take the test on a computer.

The purpose of a test is to see how much you know, not merely to get a grade. Embrace this attitude to learn from your mistakes.

What can you learn from test mistakes?

Evaluating their test results will help these students understand their performance as well as learn from their mistakes.
© Sarah Lyman Kravits

Congratulations! You've finished the exam, handed it in, and gone home to a well-deserved night of sleep. At the next class meeting you've returned refreshed, rejuvenated, and ready to accept a high score. As you receive the test back from your instructor, you look wide-eyed at your grade. *How could that be?*

No one aces every test. And no one understands every piece of the material perfectly. Making mistakes on tests and learning from them is as much a part of your academic experience as studying, taking notes, working with others, and yes, even getting good grades. After all, if you never made any mistakes, what would you have to learn from?

The most important idea to remember when moving on from a bad grade is not to beat yourself up about it. Instead, benefit from it by looking realistically at what you could have done better. With exam in hand, consider the following areas to identify what you can correct—and perhaps change the way you study for, or take, your next exam.

RESPONSE TO AN ESSAY QUESTION
WITH **REVISION MARKS**

QUESTION: Describe three ways that body language affects interpersonal communication.

Body language plays an important role in interpersonal communication and helps shape the impression you make. *, especially when you meet someone for the first time* Two of the most important functions of body language are to contradict and reinforce verbal statements. When body language contradicts verbal language, the message ~~conveyed~~ *delivered* by the body is dominant. For example, if a friend tells you that she is feeling "fine," but her posture is slumped, *her eye contact minimal,* and her facial expression troubled, you have every reason to wonder whether she is telling the truth. If the same friend tells you that she is feeling fine and is smiling, walking with a bounce in her step, and has direct eye contact, her body language is ~~telling the truth.~~ *accurately reflecting and reinforcing her words.*

The nonverbal cues that make up body language also have the power to add shades of meaning. Consider this statement: "This is the best idea I've heard all day." If you were to say this three different ways—in a loud voice while standing up; quietly while sitting with arms and legs crossed and looking away; and while ~~maintening~~ *maintaining* eye contact and taking the receiver's hand—you might send three different messages.

Finally, the impact of nonverbal cues can be greatest when you meet someone for the first time. When you meet someone, you tend to make assumptions based on nonverbal behavior such as posture, eye contact, gestures, and speed and style of movement.

In summary, nonverbal communication plays a ~~crusial~~ *crucial* role in interpersonal relationships. It has the power to send an accurate message that may ~~destroy~~ *belie* the speaker's words, offer shades of meaning, and set the tone of a first meeting.

Although first impressions emerge ~~from a combination of nonverbal cues, tone of voice, and choice of words,~~ nonverbal elements (cues and tone) ~~usually come~~ across first and strongest.

■ *Ask yourself global questions that may help you identify correctable patterns.*
Honest answers can help you change the way you study for the next exam.

▶ What were your biggest problems? Did you get nervous, misread the question, fail to study enough, study incorrectly, or focus on memorizing material instead of on understanding and applying it?

GET ANALYTICAL!

Write to the Verb

Focusing on the action verbs in essay test instructions can mean the difference between giving instructors what they want and answering off the mark. Start by getting to know action verbs a little better.

Choose five verbs from Key 8.7 that you've seen used in essay questions. In the spaces below, write out what the verb inspires you to do *without reusing the verb.*

Verb 1: _____ makes me _____.

Verb 2: _____ makes me _____.

Verb 3: _____ makes me _____.

Verb 4: _____ makes me _____.

Verb 5: _____ makes me _____.

Now that you have a few favorites, put them to work.

Start by writing down a topic you have learned about in this text—for example, the concept of successful intelligence or different barriers to listening.

_____

_____

_____

Put yourself in the role of instructor. Write an essay question on this topic, using one of the action verbs in Key 8.7 to frame the question. For example, "List the three aspects of successful intelligence" or "Analyze the classroom-based challenges associated with internal barriers to listening."

_____

_____

_____

_____

Now choose three other action verbs from Key 8.7. Use each one to rewrite your original question.

1. _____

2. _____

3. _____

Finally, analyze how each new verb changes the focus of the essay.

1. _____

_____

2. _____

_____

3. _____

_____

- Did your instructor's comments clarify where you slipped up? Did your answer lack specificity? Did you fail to support your thesis well? Was your analysis weak?
- Were you surprised by the questions? For example, did you expect them all to be from the lecture notes and text instead of from your notes and supplemental readings?
- Did you make careless errors? Did you misread the question or directions, blacken the wrong box on the answer sheet, skip a question, or write illegibly?
- Did you make conceptual or factual errors? Did you misunderstand a concept? Did you fail to master facts or concepts?

■ *Rework the questions you got wrong.* Based on instructor feedback, try to rewrite an essay, recalculate a math problem from the original question, or redo questions following a reading selection. If you discover a pattern of careless errors, redouble your efforts to be more careful, and save time to double-check your work.

■ *After reviewing your mistakes, fill in your knowledge gaps.* If you made mistakes because you didn't understand important concepts, develop a plan to learn the material.

■ *Talk to your instructor.* Focus on specific mistakes on objective questions or a weak essay. The fact that you care enough to review your errors will make a good impression. If you are not sure why you were marked down on an essay, ask what you could have done better. If you feel that an essay was unfairly graded, ask for a rereading. When you use your social intelligence and approach your instructor in a nondefensive way, as Teo did, you are likely to receive help.

■ *Rethink the way you studied.* Make changes to avoid repeating your errors. Use the varied techniques in *Keys to Success* to study more effectively so that you can show yourself and your instructors what you are capable of doing. The

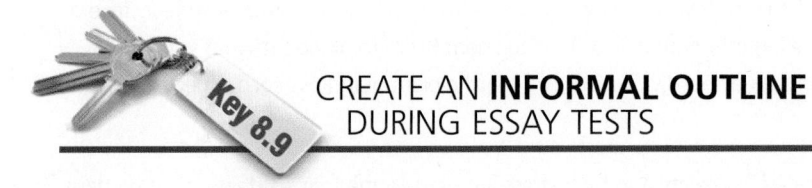

CREATE AN **INFORMAL OUTLINE** DURING ESSAY TESTS

Key 8.9

Essay question: Describe three ways in which body language affects interpersonal communication.

Roles of BL in IC

1. To contradict or reinforce words
   —e.g., friend says "I'm fine"
2. To add shades of meaning
   —saying the same sentence in 3 diff. ways
3. To make lasting 1st impression
   —impact of nv cues and voice tone greater than words
   —we assume things abt person based on posture, eye contact, etc.

earlier in the term you make positive adjustments the better, so make a special effort to analyze and learn from early test mistakes.

■ *If you fail a test, don't throw it away.* Use it to review troublesome material, especially if you will be tested on it again. You might also want to keep it as a reminder that you can improve. When you compare a failure to later successes, you'll see how far you've come.

Case Wrap-up

What happened to Teo? Mr. Sorrenti went through the aspects of test anxiety with Teo—how it creates an unrealistic view of risk, puts him off his goal path, and creates problematic physical effects and behaviors. He helped him combat each aspect with an action. To ease risk as well as see it more realistically, Teo set up a regular study schedule. To focus on his goal, he created a written set of goals for this term and beyond. Finally, Mr. Sorrenti gave him some ideas for how to combat test-time jitters. At this point halfway through the term, Teo is doing better at studying regularly. For his first exam last week he got seven hours of sleep beforehand, arrived early to stretch and breathe, and kept a picture of his girlfriend on the desk as a reminder of his plan for a successful life. He is waiting for his test grade, feeling hopeful.

What does this mean for you? What creates anxiety for you? Even if you don't experience test anxiety, you likely have some idea, situation, or issue to which you react with more than a healthy and productive fear. Take a look at the article on anxiety at www.counseling.mtu.edu/anxiety_management.html. Think about what you would like to be able to handle productively rather than anxiously. Write out a specific plan to address each aspect of anxiety for your particular situation.

What effects go beyond your world? Anxiety and high stress are unwelcome but real features of modern society in many countries. In fact, modern science has discovered that high stress is related to aging. The body's cells have small pieces of DNA called *telomeres* that become shorter each time the cell divides, ultimately getting so short that they prevent the cell from dividing anymore. Do a little research on people, societies, or groups who find ways to alleviate stress. What can you learn from them that will help you keep your telomeres as long as they can be? What about your life's goals will allow you to help others face and overcome anxiety?

Successful Intelligence *Wrap-up*

HERE'S HOW YOU HAVE BUILT SKILLS IN **CHAPTER 8** :

ANALYTICAL THINKING 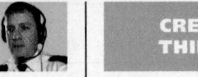	**CREATIVE THINKING**	**PRACTICAL THINKING**
❯ You examined test-preparation techniques with an eye toward what works best for you.	❯ In reading about test anxiety, you encountered a different perspective of tests as opportunities to learn rather than contests that you win or lose.	❯ You gathered specific test-preparation techniques. You learned specific ways to calm test anxiety and attack objective test questions.
❯ In the Get Analytical exercise, you wrote a series of original essay questions, analyzing the effect that different action verbs had on what the questions were asking.	❯ With the Get Creative exercise, you produced your own pretest that will help you assess if you have mastered crucial material.	❯ In the Get Practical exercise, you used a test anxiety instrument to gauge your level of testing stress and plan for productive solutions in the future.
❯ You investigated specific ways to maximize your chances of answering objective and subjective test questions correctly.	❯ The scheduling and study techniques may have inspired you to create a personal study schedule and regimen that help you make the most of your time.	❯ You expanded your knowledge of how to use planning tools, such as a keyword outline, to help you write test essays.

Word *for* Thought

In **Polish,** *hart ducha* (hahrt doo'-cha) means "strength of will" to overcome life's challenges.[4] In college, instructors challenge you on tests to demonstrate what you know and what you can do. Both before and during each test, call on your hart ducha to help you work hard and reach your academic potential.

Building Skills *for* College, Career, *and* Life

Steps to Success

Prepare Effectively for Tests

Take a careful look at your performance on and preparation for a recent test.

BUILD BASIC SKILLS. Think about how you did on the test.

Were you pleased or disappointed with your performance and grade? Why?

_____

_____

Circle any of the listed problems that you experienced on this exam. If you experienced one or more problems not listed here, write them in the blank spaces provided.

- Incomplete preparation
- Fatigue
- Feeling rushed during the test
- Shaky understanding of concepts
- Poor guessing techniques
- Feeling confused about directions
- Test anxiety
- Poor essay organization or writing

_____

_____

_____

Now for each problem you identified, think about why you made mistakes.

TAKE IT TO THE NEXT LEVEL. Be creative about test-preparation strategies.

If you had all the time and materials you needed, how would you have prepared for this test? Describe briefly what your plan would be and how it would address your problem(s).

Now think back to your actual test preparation—the techniques you used and the amount of time you spent. Describe the difference between your ideal study plan and what you actually did.

_____

_____

_____

MOVE TOWARD MASTERY. Improve your chances for success on the next exam by coming up with specific changes in your preparation.

What I did this time but do not intend to do next time:

_____

_____

What I did not do this time but intend to do next time:

_____

_____

Teamwork

Create Solutions Together

PREPARE FOR A TEST

Goal: To discover preparation strategies as a group and explore their effectiveness.

Time on task: 20 minutes in the group (after individual preparation)

Instructions: Form a study group with two or three other students. When your instructor announces the next exam, ask study group members to record everything they do to prepare for the exam, including the following:

- Learning what to expect on the test (topics and material that will be covered, types of questions that will be asked)
- Examining old tests
- Creating and following a study schedule and checklist
- Using SQ3R to review material
- Taking a pretest
- Getting a good night's sleep
- Doing last-minute cramming
- Mastering general test-taking strategies
- Mastering strategies for handling specific types of test questions

After the exam, come together to compare preparation strategies. What important differences can you identify in the routines followed by group members? How did learning styles play a role in those differences? How do you suspect that different routines affected test performance and outcome? On a separate piece of paper or on a computer file, for your own reference, write down what you learned from the test-preparation habits of your study mates that may help you as you prepare for upcoming exams.

Writing

Build Intrapersonal and Communication Skills

Record your thoughts on paper, in a journal, or electronically.

EMOTIONAL INTELLIGENCE JOURNAL

Test types. What type of test do you feel most comfortable with, and what type brings up more negative feelings? Thinking of a particular situation involving the test type that challenges you, describe how it made you feel and how that feeling affected your performance. Discuss ways in which you might be able to shift your mindset in order to feel more confident about this type of test.

REAL-LIFE WRITING

Ask your instructor for feedback on a test. Nearly every student has been in the position of believing that a response on an essay exam was graded unfairly. The next time this happens to you—when you have no idea why you lost points or disagree with the instructor's assessment of your work—draft a respectful e-mail to your instructor explaining your position and asking for a meeting to discuss the essay. (See the e-mail etiquette guidelines in the Quick Start.) Use clear logic to defend your work and refer back to what you learned in class and in the text. It is important to address specifically any comments or criticisms the instructor made on the test paper. Before sending the e-mail, analyze your argument: Did you make your case effectively or was the instructor correct? When you have the meeting, the work you did on the e-mail will prepare you to defend your position.

Personal Portfolio

Prepare for Career Success

ON-THE-JOB TESTING

21st Century Learning Building Blocks

- Information Literacy
- Initiative and Self-Direction
- Productivity and Accountability

Complete the following in your electronic portfolio or separately on paper.

You will probably encounter different tests throughout your career. For example, if you are studying to be a nurse you are tested on subjects like anatomy and pharmacology. After you graduate you will be required to take certification and recertification exams that gauge your mastery of the latest information in different aspects of nursing.

Some postgraduate tests are for entry into the field; some test proficiency on particular equipment; some move you to the next level of employment. Choose one career you are thinking about and investigate what tests are involved as you advance through different career stages.

Use the accompanying grid to organize what you find. You'll be searching for the following information:

- The name of the test
- When the test is taken and if it needs to be retaken
- What it covers
- How you can prepare
- Web resources like pretests, websites, or review materials

TEST NAME	WHEN TAKEN	WHAT IT COVERS	PREPARATION	WEB RESOURCES

 ## Social Networking

ESTABLISH YOUR PRIVACY

Informed users of technology take advantage of tools that help them control it. You are in charge of what you allow people to view and send you on LinkedIn. Sign in to your account, click on "Settings" at the top of the screen, and look over the categories under "Privacy Settings." Establish the settings you prefer by clicking on each of the subheads and following the instructions:

- Research Surveys
- Connections Browse
- Profile Views
- Viewing Profile Photos

- Profile and Status Updates
- Service Provider Directory
- Partner Advertising
- Authorized Applications

Consider your privacy settings carefully. Find the balance that will keep your information as private as you want it to be, but also allow you to benefit from what LinkedIn can do for you when it shares your information.

Social networking refers to interacting with a community of people through an online network such as Facebook, MySpace, forums (message boards), or chat rooms. *Social media* are the types of media people use to share information online (examples include Web logs or "blogs," podcasts, websites, videos, and news feeds). Social media allow participation through comments and ratings. The people who provide social media content range from experts to amateurs, which means the content will not always be accurate or trustworthy.

In general, social networking and media make three things possible:

1. Communicating information about yourself to others
2. Connecting with people who have similar interests
3. Networking with others to accomplish goals

Social networking has grown rapidly worldwide through sites like the following:

▶ **Facebook** enables users to set up personal profiles and communicate with other users through profile updates, public or private messages, games, and photos
▶ **Twitter** enables users to send or receive short text updates, or "tweets," to other users signed up on their accounts
▶ **Skype** enables users to make calls over the Internet

How they can help
you in college

Use social networking and media to:

▶ *Connect with peers to achieve academic goals.* Students might create groups that correspond to courses, study together on an Internet call, or post course-related questions and comments on a message board or chat room used by the class. (Try: Facebook, Skype)
▶ *Manage coursework and projects.* Particular sites can help you search for information, study, and ask questions. When doing a group project, social networking can help you collaborate in an online format. (Try: Evernote, Google Docs, EtherPad, Wikidot)
▶ *Network with students who have shared interests.* A student might start a blog on an academic topic and hope to attract interested readers, or look for groups or Internet forums. (Try: Facebook, MySpace, forums on specific topics)
▶ *Adjust to college.* Ask other students at your school about local issues (bus schedules, library hours), or ask students anywhere in the world about more general concerns (test anxiety). You can even use social media to stay organized. (Try: Twitter, Facebook, GradeMate, Backpack)
▶ *Focus on career development.* Put your qualifications and career goals out there for others to peruse, and build a network that may lead you to job opportunities. (Try: LinkedIn, Zumeo)
▶ *Stay connected to loved ones.* Students might tweet or blog happenings to family and old friends, post updates, or make free phone calls. A budgeting bonus: Most social networking tools cost nothing to use as long as you have Internet access. (Try: Twitter, Facebook, Skype)

▶ *Share your opinion.* Blogs allow you to communicate to an audience on a regular basis, and creating a blog is usually free. Another tool, the forum or message board, encourages individuals to come together and discuss a common knowledge or experience. (Try: Blogger, MySpace)

Ten strategies for success

Follow these guidelines to get the most from your time and energy on social networks and with social media.

1. *Control your personal information.* Read the privacy policy of any network you join. Adjust security settings, indicating what information, photos, and so on you want to be visible or invisible. Know what will always be visible to users.
2. *Control your time.* One quick check of your e-mail can lead to hours spent online that you should have spent getting something else done. To stay focused and in control:

   - Create a separate e-mail for alerts from your social networking sites.
   - Set your status to "offline" or "do not disturb" when you are studying.
   - Set up goals and rewards. Try doing a defined portion of your homework and then rewarding yourself with ten minutes on your favorite social networking site.

3. *Be an information literate critical thinker.* Evaluate what you read on social networking sites or social media with a critical eye. Use the CARS test (p. 151) to check Credibility, Accuracy, Reasonableness, and Support of any source or statement.
4. *Keep career goals in mind.* With anything you write, think: How will this look to others who may evaluate me in the future? Also, choose and post photographs carefully, because some employers use social networking sites for background checks.
5. *Use caution with forums and chat rooms.* There is no way to know who is posting on a forum or in a chat room. Consider using a name that differs from your legal name or regular e-mail address. Remember, too, that everything you write can be copied and saved.
6. *Watch your temper.* Wait, and think, before you post on emotional topics. Forums can turn into hostile environments. Snarky tweets and updates can come back to haunt you if they are viewed by potential employers, instructors, or others who may judge you by them.
7. *Separate the personal and the academic/professional.* You probably don't want an employer seeing that crass video your cousin posted on your page. Consider having two profiles on a network if you want to use one to communicate with students or advance your career.
8. *Show restraint.* Although it's easy to get carried away, keep your purpose in mind. For example, if one goal is to keep up with friends using Facebook, you are defeating your purpose if you have so many friends that you can't possibly stay up-to-date with them.
9. *Understand what a blog or website requires.* Blogs need updating at least weekly if not more often, and require time and motivation. Websites can be even more labor-intensive.
10. *Network with integrity.* Treat others with respect. Search for, and use, information legitimately. Cite sources honestly.

ENDNOTES

QUICK START

1. Alexander W. Astin, *Preventing Students from Dropping Out,* San Francisco: Jossey-Bass, 1976.

2. Robert J. Sternberg, *Successful Intelligence: How Practical and Creative Intelligence Determine Success in Life,* New York: Plume, 1997, p. 24.

CHAPTER 1

1. Adapted from "Hope in a Box," *The Oprah Winfrey Show,* October 1, 2009, www.oprah.com/world/Tererai-Trents-Inspiring-Education.

2. Thomas Friedman, *The World Is Flat,* New York: Farrar, Straus & Giroux, 2006, p. 8.

3. Daniel Pink, "Revenge of the Right Brain," *Wired Magazine,* February 2005, www.wired.com/wired/archive/13.02/brain.html?pg=1&topic=brain&topic_set=.

4. Robert J. Sternberg, *Successful Intelligence: How Practical and Creative Intelligence Determine Success in Life,* New York: Plume, 1997, pp. 85–90; Carol S. Dweck, *Mindset: The New Psychology of Success,* New York: Random House, 2006, p. 5; and Susanne Jaeggi, Martin Buschkuehl, John Jonides, and Walter J. Perrig, "Improving Fluid Intelligence with Training on Working Memory," 2008, *Proceedings of the National Academy of Sciences USA,* 105, pp. 6829–6833.

5. Sternberg, *Successful Intelligence,* p. 11.

6. Dweck, *Mindset,* pp. 3–4.

7. The Society for Neuroscience, *Brain Facts: A Primer on the Brain and Neurosystem,* Washington, DC: The Society for Neuroscience, 2008, pp. 34–35.

8. Sternberg, *Successful Intelligence,* p. 12.

9. Ibid., p. 127.

10. Ibid., p. 11.

11. Ibid., pp. 127–128.

12. Carol Dweck, "The Mindsets," 2006, www.mindsetonline.com/whatisit/themindsets/index.html.

13. Dweck, *Mindset,* p. 16.

14. Ibid.

15. Rick Pitino, *Success Is a Choice,* New York: Broadway Books, 1997, p. 40.

16. Dweck, *Mindset,* p. 51.

17. Center for Academic Integrity, Kenan Institute for Ethics, Duke University, "The Fundamental Values of Academic Integrity," October 1999, www.academicintegrity.org/fundamental_values_project/pdf/FVProject.pdf.

18. Dweck, *Mindset,* p. 35.

19. Ibid., p. 33.

20. John D. Mayer, Peter Salovey, and David R. Caruso, "Emotional Intelligence: New Ability or Eclectic Traits?," September 2008, *American Psychologist,* 63, no. 6, p. 503.

21. David R. Caruso, "Zero In on Knowledge: A Practical Guide to the MSCEIT," Multi-Health Systems, 2008, p. 3.

22. Sandra Blakeslee, "Cells That Read Minds," January 10, 2006, *New York Times,* www.nytimes.com/2006/01/10/science/10mirr.html.

23. Mayer, Salovey, and Caruso, pp. 510–512.

24. Christopher J. Moore, *In Other Words: A Language Lover's Guide to the Most Intriguing Words Around the World,* New York: Walker & Company, 2004, p. 43.

25. List and descriptions based on Sternberg, *Successful Intelligence,* pp. 251–268.

CHAPTER 2

1. Stephen Covey, *The Seven Habits of Highly Effective People,* New York: Simon & Schuster, 1989, pp. 70–144, 309–318.

2. Paul Timm, *Successful Self-Management: A Psychologically Sound Approach to Personal Effectiveness,* Los Altos, CA: Crisp Publications, 1987, pp. 22–41.

3. William E. Sydnor, "Procrastination," from the California Polytechnic State University Study Skills Library, www.sas.calpoly.edu/asc/ssl/procrastination.html. Based on *Overcoming Procrastination* by Albert Ellis. Used with permission.

4. Jane B. Burka and Lenora M. Yuen, *Procrastination: Why You Do It, What to Do About It,* Reading, MA: Perseus Books, 1983, pp. 21–22.

5. Ibid.

6. mtvU and Associated Press College Stress and Mental Health Poll Executive Summary, Spring 2008, www.halfofus.com/_media/_pr/mtvU_AP_College_Stress_and_Mental_Health_Poll_Executive_Summary.pdf.

7. Jane E. Brody, "At Every Age, Feeling the Effects of Too Little Sleep," *New York Times*, October 23, 2007, www.nytimes.com/2007/10/23/health/23brod.html.

8. Christopher J. Moore, *In Other Words: A Language Lover's Guide to the Most Intriguing Words Around the World*, New York: Walker & Company, 2004, pp. 36–37.

CHAPTER 3

1. Howard Gardner, *Multiple Intelligences: The Theory in Practice*, New York: HarperCollins, 1993, pp. 5–49.

2. Howard Gardner, *Multiple Intelligences: New Horizons*. New York: Basic Books, 2006, p. 8.

3. Gardner, *Multiple Intelligences: The Theory in Practice*, p. 7.

4. National Center for Learning Disabilities. "LD at a Glance" [on-line]. Available: www.ncld.org/LDInfo Zone/InfoZone_FactSheet_LD.cfm (May 2003).

5. National Center for Learning Disabilities. "Adult Learning Disabilities: A Learning Disability Isn't Something You Outgrow. It's Something You Learn to Master" (pamphlet). New York: National Center for Learning Disabilities.

6. LD Advocates Guide, n.d., National Center for Learning Disabilities, www.ncld.org/index.php?option=content&task=view&id=291.

7. "Conceptual Frameworks/Models, Guiding Values and Principles," National Center for Cultural Competence, 2002, http://gucchd.georgetown.edu//nccc/framework.html.

8. Information in the sections on the five stages of building competency is based on Mark A. King, Anthony Sims, and David Osher, "How Is Cultural Competence Integrated in Education?" Cultural Competence, www.air.org/cecp/cultural/Q_integrated.htm#def.

9. Martin Luther King Jr., from his sermon "A Tough Mind and a Tender Heart," *Strength in Love*, Philadelphia: Fortress Press, 1986, p. 14.

10. Betsy Israel, "The Overconnecteds," *New York Times* Education Life, November 5, 2006, p. 20.

11. Ibid.

12. Christopher J. Moore, *In Other Words: A Language Lover's Guide to the Most Intriguing Words Around the World*, New York: Walker, 2004, p. 78.

CHAPTER 4

1. Vincent Ruggiero, *The Art of Thinking*, 2001, quoted in "Critical Thinking," http://success.oregonstate.edu/criticalthinking.html.

2. Richard Paul, "The Role of Questions in Thinking, Teaching, and Learning," 1995, www.criticalthinking.org/resources/articles/the-role-of-questions.shtml.

3. "The Best Innovations Are Those That Come from Smart Questions," *Wall Street Journal*, April 12, 2004, p. B1.

4. Sharon Begley, "Critical Thinking: Part Skill, Part Mindset and Totally Up to You," *Wall Street Journal*, October 20, 2006, p. B1.

5. Matt Thomas, "What Is Higher-Order Thinking and Critical/Creative/Constructive Thinking?" n.d., Center for Studies in Higher-Order Literacy, http://a-s.clayton.edu/tparks/What%20is%20Higher%20Order%20Thinking.doc.

6. Charles Cave, "Definitions of Creativity," August 1999, http://members.optusnet.com.au/~charles57/Creative/Basics/definitions.htm.

7. Roger von Oech, *A Kick in the Seat of the Pants*, New York: Harper & Row, 1986, pp. 5–21.

8. Dennis Coon, *Introduction to Psychology: Exploration and Application*, 6th ed., St. Paul, MN: West, 1992, p. 295.

9. Roger von Oech, *A Whack on the Side of the Head*, New York: Warner Books, 1990, pp. 11–168.

10. J. R. Hayes, *Cognitive Psychology: Thinking and Creating*, Homewood, IL: Dorsey, 1978.

11. Robert Sternberg, *Successful Intelligence*, New York: Plume, 1996, p. 219.

12. Adapted from T. Z. Tardif and R. J. Sternberg, "What Do We Know About Creativity?" in *The Nature of Creativity*, ed. R. J. Sternberg, London: Cambridge University Press, 1988.

13. Sternberg, p. 212.

14. Hayes, *Cognitive Psychology*.

15. "The Best Innovations Are Those That Come from Smart Questions," p. B1.

16. Sternberg, p. 236.

17. Robert J. Sternberg and Elena L. Grigorenko, "Practical Intelligence and the Principal," Yale University: Publication Series No. 2, 2001, p. 5.

18. Sternberg, pp. 251–269.

19. Ibid., p. 241.

20. Ibid., p. 128.

21. Christopher J. Moore, *In Other Words: A Language Lover's Guide to the Most Intriguing Words Around the World*, New York: Walker, 2004, p. 61.

CHAPTER 5

1. Francis P. Robinson, *Effective Behavior*, New York: Harper & Row, 1941.

2. John Mack Faragher, Mari Jo Buhle, Daniel Czitrom, and Susan H. Armitage, *Out of Many: A History of the American People*, 5th ed., Upper Saddle River, NJ: Prentice Hall, 2005, p. xxxvii.

3. Benjamin S. Bloom, *Taxonomy of Educational Objectives, Handbook I: The Cognitive Domain*, New York: McKay, 1956.

4. Ophelia H. Hancock, *Reading Skills for College Students*, 5th ed., Upper Saddle River, NJ: Prentice Hall, 2001, pp. 54–59.

5. Mark Bauerlein, "Online Literacy Is a Lesser Kind," *The Chronicle of Higher Education*, September 19, 2008, http://chronicle.com/article/Online-Literacy-Is-a-Lesser/28307.

6. Ibid.

7. Lori Leibovich, "Choosing Quick Hits over the Card Catalog," *New York Times*, August 10, 2001, p. 1.

8. Adam Robinson, *What Smart Students Know*, New York: Three Rivers Press, 1993, p. 82.

9. Christopher J. Moore, *In Other Words: A Language Lover's Guide to the Most Intriguing Words Around the World*, New York: Walker, 2004, p. 87.

10. John J. Macionis, *Sociology*, 6th ed., Upper Saddle River, NJ: Prentice Hall, 1997, p. 174.

CHAPTER 6

1. Alina Tugend, "Multitasking Can Make You Lose . . . Um . . . Focus," *New York Times*, October 25, 2008, p. B7.

2. System developed by Cornell professor Walter Pauk. See Walter Pauk, *How to Study in College*, 10th ed. Boston: Houghton Mifflin, 2011, pp. 236–241.

3. Information from Frank Schmalleger, *Criminal Justice Today*, 8th ed., Upper Saddle River, NJ: 2005, p. 71.

4. Christopher J. Moore, *In Other Words: A Language Lover's Guide to the Most Intriguing Words Around the World*, New York: Walker, 2004, p. 45.

CHAPTER 7

1. University of California–Irvine, "Short-Term Stress Can Affect Learning and Memory," *ScienceDaily*, March 13, 2008, www.sciencedaily.com/releases/2008/03/080311182434.htm.

2. Herman Ebbinghaus, *Memory: A Contribution to Experimental Psychology*, trans. H. A. Ruger and C. E. Bussenius, New York: Teachers College, Columbia University, 1885.

3. Bulletpoints from Kenneth C. Petress, "The Benefits of Group Study," 2004, *Education*, 124, www.questia.com/googleScholar.qst;jsessionid=L4TDXZJvQmb4whQFL7v1mjGfBgp4YGzjJyg0mL3g1SJKyjvXK4hN!-747430471!743789914?docId=5006987606.

4. Dartmouth College Academic Skills Center, "How to Avoid Cramming for Tests," 2001, www.dartmouth.edu/~acskills/handouts.html.

5. "Study Shows How Sleep Improves Memory," *Science Daily*, June 29, 2005, www.sciencedaily.com/releases/2005/06/050629070337.htm.

6. Adam Robinson, *What Smart Students Know: Maximum Grades, Optimum Learning, Minimum Time*, New York: Three Rivers Press, 1993, p. 118.

7. Christopher J. Moore, *In Other Words: A Language Lover's Guide to the Most Intriguing Words Around the World*, New York: Walker, 2004, p. 45.

CHAPTER 8

1. Ben Gose, "Notes from Academe: Living It Up on the Dead Days," *The Chronicle of Higher Education*, June 8, 2002, http://chronicle.com/article/Living-It-Up-on-the-Dead-Days/8983.

2. "Anxiety Management," Michigan Technological University, www.counseling.mtu.edu/anxiety_management.html.

3. From Paul D. Nolting, *Math Study Skills Workbook, Your Guide to Reducing Test Anxiety and Improving Study Strategies*, Boston: Houghton

Mifflin, 2000. Cited in "Test Anxiety," West Virginia University at Parkersburg, www.wvup .edu/Academics/more_test_anxiety_tips.htm.

4. Christopher J. Moore, *In Other Words: A Language Lover's Guide to the Most Intriguing Words Around the World,* New York: Walker, 2004, p. 45.

Index

Note: A bold page number indicates the page on which the term is defined in the margin.

Note taking (continued)
  purposes of, 166
  questions/questioning strategies for, 168
  review/revision of, 169, 194–195, 221
  strategies for, 167–169, 172, 175–177
  by study groups, 182, 192
  systems for, 167, 170–175
  and teaching style, 167
  from textbooks, 170, 208–210
  and time management, 167
  visual strategies for, 168, 175

Obesity, 252, 253
Objective questions, in tests, 232. See also
    Tests/Test taking, types/formats of
Online materials. See also Internet
  evaluation of, 148–149, 151–152
  vs. library materials, 149
  reading of, 145
  researching of, 146–149
Online services, and job search, 276
Opinions vs. facts, 99, 100
Outlines
  for essay tests, 236, 237, 241
  for note taking/studying, 167, 170–171,
    197, 208, 209

Paragraphs, structure of, 136–138
Partnership for 21st Century Skills, 5.
    See also Framework for 21st Century
    Learning
Personality
  assessment of, 61. See also Personality
    Spectrum
  and career building, 271–273
  and communication styles, 81
  development of, 61
  and study strategies, 72
  types of, 61, 66, 67
Personality Spectrum, 59, 61, 65, 66, 67,
    81, 271–273. See also Personality
Personal mission statement, 32–33, 54–55,
    286
Personal relationships, 84–87
  and communication, 58
  skills needed for, 17. See also Emotional
    intelligence
  strategies for, 84–85
  and technology use, 85–86
Personal time profile/preferences, 38–39.
    See also Time management
Perspectives, in evidence/opinions, 100,
    101, 105
Placement/Career planning office, of
    college, 276
Planners/Schedules, use of, 39–41
Podcasts, of classes/lectures, 200, 291
Postgraduate tests, 246–247
Potentials, of individuals, 59
Practical thinking, 107–110
  application of, 9, 14, 108, 110
  assessment of, 26, 289
  definition of, 9, 107
  development of, 109–110
  and emotional intelligence, 109–110
  and questions/questioning strategies, 110
  and successful intelligence, 111

Prejudice, 77–78, 80. See also Cultural
    diversity
Pretests, for test preparation, 221. See also
    Tests/Test taking, preparation for
Primary vs. secondary sources, 128
Prioritization
  in studying, 194
  in time management/goal setting, 42
Problem solving, 111–113
  activity for, 120, 121
  vs. decision making, 111, 113. See also
    Decision making
  process for, 111–113, 114, 120, 121
  and thinking skills, 111
Procrastination, 43–46. See also Time
    management

Qualifiers, in test questions, 229, 235
Question, as step in SQ3R, 129, 131–135
Questions/Questioning strategies
  for critical reading, 150
  for listening, 162–163
  for note taking, 168
  and problem solving, 111–112
  and reading textbooks, 131–135, 138
  and test taking, 221. See also Tests/Test
    taking, types/formats of
  and thinking skills, 96–97, 100, 108, 110

Reaction, stage of listening, 161
Read, as step in SQ3R, 135–138
Reading, 126–140
  assessing skills in, 126
  concentration for, 128–129
  critical approach to, 149–152
  and difficulty of college materials, 126–
    127, 128, 129, 156
  environment for, 128. See also Studying,
    environment for
  and multiple intelligences, 144
  and note taking, 170, 208–210. See also
    Note taking
  of online materials, 145. See also Online
    materials
  purposes of, 127
  subject-specific strategies for, 140–143
  strategies for, 127–129, 138–143, 144.
    See also SQ3R
  and test taking, 221
  and time management, 128, 129
  and vocabulary. See Vocabulary
Recite
  as step in SQ3R, 138
  as study strategy, 198–199
Recordings, use in studying, 65, 140, 165,
    200
Registration, for college, xxiii
Rehearse, as study strategy, 198–199
Relationships. See Personal relationships
Resumés, 276–277, 286–287
Returning students, test anxiety of, 226
Review
  and memory, 188, 189, 191, 210
  as step in SQ3R, 138–140
Revising, of essay tests, 238, 239
Rhymes/Songs, use as study strategy, 206
Robinson, Adam, 149, 200

Scanning vs. skimming, 129
Schedules/Planners, use of, 39–41. See also
    Time management, tools for
Scholarships, 268. See also Financial aid
Science
  reading strategies for, 140–141
  study strategies for, 201–202
Screen reading, 145. See also Online
    materials
Search engines, 148. See also Internet,
    researching materials on
Second-language learners, listening by,
    165
Secondary vs. primary sources, 128
Self-esteem, 11–12. See also Growth
    mindset
Self-knowledge, 63–72
  application of, 59, 61, 63
  assessment of, 58, 59
  and career building, 70–72
  and study strategies, 68–70
  and teaching strategies, 63–68
  and technology, 70
Self-management skills, assessment of, 30
Self-portrait activity, 92, 93
Sensation, stage of listening, 160, 161
Sensory registers, and memory, 187
Seven Habits of Highly Effective People, The
    (Covey), 32
Sex/Sexuality, 261–263
Sexually transmitted diseases/infections
    (STDs/STIs), 261–263
Shorthand, for note taking, 175–177
Short-term goals, vs. long-term goals,
    31–32, 34–35. See also Goal setting
Short-term memory, 187. See also Memory
Skillset, and employers' expectations, 275
Skimming vs. scanning, 129
Skype, 291
Sleep, 254
  deprivation of, 254
  and memory, 197, 223
  strategies for improving, 254
  and test taking, 223
SMART goals, 35–38, 53–54. See also Goal
    setting
Smartphones, 37, 39, 40, 103, 277, 280
Social media, 291. See also Social
    networking, effective use of
Social networking, effective use of,
    291–292. See also Facebook; LinkedIn;
    MySpace; Twitter
Social sciences, reading strategies for,
    142–143, 144
Songs/Rhymes, use as study strategy, 206
SQ3R, 129–139
  activity for, 141
  application of, 129
  definition of, 129
  steps in, 129, 130–139. See also specific
    steps
  use in note taking, 170
  use in studying, 170
  use in test taking, 221
  use with online materials, 145
STDs/STIs. See Sexually transmitted
    diseases/infections

Credits

Unit 1

Whole Number Review

Mathematics is a key skill of health care workers. As a health care worker, you know that accuracy is important. Being competent in whole number concepts and addition, subtraction, multiplication, and division will form the basis for successful computations on the job. These basic skills form the foundation for the other daily math functions you will use in the workplace.

> Approach math matter-of-factly; math is a job skill and a life skill.

The number line is a line labeled with the integers in increasing order from left to right. The number line extends in both directions:

$$-10\ -9\ -8\ -7\ -6\ -5\ -4\ -3\ -2\ -1\quad 0\quad 1\quad 2\quad 3\quad 4\quad 5\quad 6\quad 7\quad 8\quad 9\quad 10$$

Remember that any integer on the right is always greater than the integer on the left.

Symbols and Number Statements

Symbols may be used to show the relationship among numbers.

Symbol	Meaning	Example
=	is equal to	$1 + 7 = 8$
>	is greater than	$19 > 6$
<	is less than	$5 < 12$
≤	is equal to or less than	age ≤ 5
≥	is equal to or greater than	weight ≥ 110 pounds

A number statement or simple equation shows the relationship between numbers, operations and/or symbols.

Practice 1: Use the symbols ($=$, $>$, and $<$, $\leq$, $\geq$) to complete the number statement.

1. 14 _____ 34

2. −5 _____ 0

3. 12 _____ 7

4. 12 P.M. _____ noon

5. Seven less than 4 _____ the numbers −5, −4, −3

6. $2.00 _____ 2 hundred pennies

7. 235 _____ 187

8. 2 nickels _____ a quarter

9. 245 _____ 78 + 34 + 3

10. One dollar + 2 quarters _____ $1.35

11. The numbers 0, 1, 2, are _____ the number 2

12. 3 _____ 4 ÷ 2

Practice 2: Write five number statements:

1. _____

2. _____

3. _____

4. _____

5. _____

Addition

Review

To add, line up the numbers in a vertical column and add to find the total. In addition problems, the total, or answer, is called the *sum*.

Practice Find the sum of each problem.

1. $1 + 4 + 5 + 9 =$

2. $51 + 23 =$

3. $297 + 90 + 102 + 3 =$

4. $216 + 897 =$

5. $1,773 + 233 + 57 =$

6. $9 + 245 + 32 =$

7. $11 + 357 + 86 + 34 =$

8. $24,578 + 9,075 =$

9. $443 + 2,087 + 134 =$

10. $910 + 3 + 125 =$

Applications Inventory is an important clerical function in the health care industry. Sometimes this work is done by supply technicians, clerks, nursing assistants, or other staff. Keeping accurate inventory reduces overstocking and helps avoid the problem of under stocking medical supplies.

1. Inventory is done monthly at the Golden Years Care Center. Find the sum for each category.

Category	Sum
a. Examination gloves: $31 + 88 + 47$ + two boxes of 50	_____
b. Thermometer covers: $281 + 304 + 17 + 109$	_____
c. Medicine cups: $313 + 245 + 106 + 500 + 12$	_____
d. Boxes of disposable syringes (50 per box): $2 + 6 + 9 + 3$	_____

2. Intake and output totals require addition skills. Unlike household measurements in cups, health care patient intake and output units are measured in cubic centimeters (cc). Intake includes oral ingestion of fluids and semi-liquid food, intravenous feedings, and tubal feedings.
   Find the intake totals.

Type of Intake	Cubic Centimeters (cc)	Sum
a. Oral	120, 210, 150, 240	_____
b. Intravenous	250, 500	_____
c. Blood	500	_____
d.	Total Intake	_____

The intake sums would be charted in the patient's medical record.

3. Measuring output is important because it helps the health care worker ensure a patient's health and hydration. Output is measured in cubic

centimeters. Output includes liquid bowel movements or diarrhea, urine, emesis (vomiting), and gastric drainage. Find the output totals.

Type of Output	Cubic Centimeters (cc)	Sum
a. Diarrhea	100, 200	_____
b. Urine	330, 225, 105, 60	_____
c. Gastric Drainage	40, 35	_____
d. Blood/Emesis	110	_____
e.	Total Output	_____

4. Assuming that the patient is the same as in problems 2 and 3, has this patient had a greater intake or a greater output? _____

Subtraction

Review

To subtract, line up the numbers according to place value. Place value shows the ones, tens, hundreds, etc. columns. Start with the right side of the math problem and work your way toward the left side, subtracting each column.

> Fewer errors occur if the subtraction problem is set up vertically. Rewrite the problems.

Example

$$89 - 31 = \underline{\hspace{1cm}} \qquad 475 - 34 = \underline{\hspace{1cm}}$$

$$\begin{array}{r} 89 \\ -31 \\ \hline 58 \end{array} \qquad \begin{array}{r} 475 \\ -34 \\ \hline 441 \end{array}$$

If a number cannot be subtracted from the number directly above it, then increase the value of the smaller number by borrowing 1 from the column to its immediate left.

> Keep track of borrowing by marking through the column borrowed from and reducing the numbers involved by 1.

Example

$$\begin{array}{r} 3^7 \cancel{8}^1 1 \\ -\ 65 \\ \hline 316 \end{array}$$

Practice   1. $475 - 81 =$

2. $176 - 37 =$

3. $289 - 54 =$

4. $4{,}547 - 2{,}289 =$

5. $1{,}236 - 799 =$

6. $1{,}575 - 896 =$

7. $2{,}001 - 128 =$

8. $10{,}300 - 497 =$

9. $4{,}301 - 89 =$

10. $4{,}547 - 2{,}289 =$

Applications   Subtraction is used in inventory as well. Some applications are given below.

1. At the beginning of the month, a dental office started with 2,258 latex examination gloves. On the last working day of the month, 784 remained. How many gloves were used during the month?

2. Inventory of dental file labels is to be kept at 2,000. Paula's inventory indicates 579 on hand. How many labels does she need to order?

3. Labels come in boxes of 500. Use the answer from problem 2 to determine how many boxes of labels Paula should order to obtain the required 2,000 minimum inventory. Draw a sketch to help visualize this problem.

4. Patients see the dentist most during the summer months. Dr. Brown has a total of 13,576 patient files. If he sees 8,768 of these patients during the summer, how many remain to be contacted for an appointment?

Multiplication

Memorizing the multiplication tables is essential to sound mental math. If you have been calculator dependent or have forgotten some of the tables, practice memorizing the multiplication tables using the chart shown in Table 1.1.

Table 1.1   Multiplication Table

X	1	2	3	4	5	6	7	8	9	10	11	12
1												
2												
3												
4												
5												
6												
7												
8												
9												
10												
11												
12												

Review

To multiply, line up the numbers according to place value. By putting the largest number on top of the problem, you will avoid careless errors.

Avoid These Common Errors

Remember, you are multiplying, not adding.

Remember to move the numbers from the second and succeeding lines over one column to the left—use a zero (0) to indicate these movements.

$$2 \times 14 = \underline{} \qquad \rightarrow \begin{array}{r} 14 \\ \times\ 2 \\ \hline 28 \end{array}$$

$$\begin{array}{r} 178 \\ \times\ \ 23 \\ \hline 534 \\ 3560 \\ \hline 4{,}094 \end{array}$$

Move the second line of numbers one place to the left. Adding a zero keeps your numbers aligned.

Practice

1. $\begin{array}{r} 12 \\ \times\ 8 \\ \hline \end{array}$

4. $\begin{array}{r} 70 \\ \times\ 9 \\ \hline \end{array}$

7. $\begin{array}{r} 512 \\ \times\ 24 \\ \hline \end{array}$

10. $\begin{array}{r} 803 \\ \times\ 17 \\ \hline \end{array}$

2. $\begin{array}{r} 82 \\ \times\ 13 \\ \hline \end{array}$

5. $\begin{array}{r} 1,020 \\ \times\ 98 \\ \hline \end{array}$

8. $\begin{array}{r} 927 \\ \times\ 35 \\ \hline \end{array}$

11. $\begin{array}{r} 346 \\ \times\ 12 \\ \hline \end{array}$

3. $\begin{array}{r} 1,306 \\ \times\ 18 \\ \hline \end{array}$

6. $\begin{array}{r} 189 \\ \times\ 27 \\ \hline \end{array}$

9. $\begin{array}{r} 5,791 \\ \times\ 16 \\ \hline \end{array}$

12. $\begin{array}{r} 9,004 \\ \times\ 73 \\ \hline \end{array}$

Applications

1. Last month a nurse worked fourteen 10-hour shifts and two 12-hour shifts. At $21 per hour, what was the nurse's total hourly income before deductions?

2. Health-care facilities monitor all medications taken by their patients. Assume that the same dosage is given each time the medication is dispensed. What is the total daily dosage of each medication received?

    Total medication received is as follows:

    a. Patient Bao   50 milligrams   4 times a day   _____ milligrams

    b. Patient Mary   25 milligrams   2 times a day   _____ milligrams

    c. Patient Luke   125 micrograms   3 times a day   _____ micrograms

    d. Patient Vang   375 micrograms   2 times a day   _____ micrograms

3. The radiology lab ordered 15 jackets for its staff. The jackets cost approximately $35 each. What is the estimated cost of this order?

Prime Factorization

Sometimes in a math class, students are asked to use factor trees to illustrate prime factors of a number. A factor is a number which divides exactly into another number. When two or more factors are multiplied, they form a product. A prime factor is a number that can only be the product of 1 and itself.

For example: 4 (factor) $\times$ 12 (factor) =
    48 (product)

The prime factors of 48 are 2 and 3.
    ($2 \times 2 \times 2 \times 3 = 24$)

$$
\begin{array}{c}
48 \\
\wedge \\
4 \quad\quad 12 \\
\wedge \quad\quad \wedge \\
2\ 2 \quad 4\ 3 \\
\wedge \\
2\ 2 \\
2 \times 2 \times 2 \times 2 \times 3 = 48 \\
\text{or}\ \ 2^4 \bullet 3 = 48 \\
\text{or}\ \ (2^4)(3) = 48
\end{array}
$$

Note that $16 \times 3 = 48$.

The prime factors are still the same:

$2 \times 2 \times 2 \times 2 \times 3$.

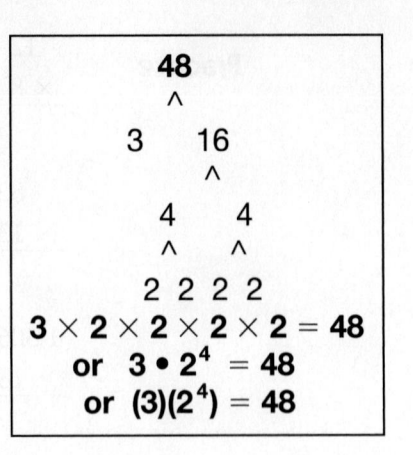

The prime factors are always the same for any number.

Practice   Draw the factor trees for the following numbers and write the prime factors on the lines below.

124	75	92

1. _____   2. _____   3. _____

Division

Review

To divide whole numbers determine (a) what number is being divided into smaller portions; and (b) the size of the portions.

Division can appear in three formats:

a. $27 \div 3 =$

b. Twenty-seven divided by three

c. $3\overline{)27}$

Setting up the problem correctly will help ensure the correct answer.

Example $\underset{\underset{\text{dividend}}{\uparrow}}{81} \div \underset{\underset{\text{divisor}}{\uparrow}}{3} = \underline{\hspace{1cm}}$ means eighty-one divided by three
or how many 3s are in 81.
The answer is the quotient.

$$27 \leftarrow \text{quotient}$$
$$\text{divisor} \rightarrow 3\overline{)81} \leftarrow \text{dividend}$$
$$\underline{6}$$
$$21$$
$$\underline{21}$$
$$0$$

Practice the correct setup, but do not work the problems.

1. Divide 145 by 76

2. 1,209 ÷ 563

3. Forty-nine divided by seventeen is what number?

4. What is 8,794 ÷ 42?

5. A person works a total of 2,044 hours a year. How many days does the person work if he works 8 hours a day?

Follow the steps below to complete all of your whole number division problems:

Step 1: Underline the number of places that the divisor can go into, then write the number of times the divisor can go into the dividend on the quotient line. Place it directly above the underlined portion of the number. This keeps track of your process. Multiply the number by the divisor and place it below the underlined portion of the dividend. Then subtract the numbers.

Example

$$1$$
$$34\overline{)5492}$$
$$\underline{-34}$$
$$20$$

Step 2: Bring down the next number of the dividend. Use an arrow to keep alignment and track of which numbers you have worked with. Then repeat step 1.

$$161$$
$$34\overline{)5492}$$
$$\underline{-34}\downarrow$$
$$20$$

$$161 \text{ R } 18$$
$$34\overline{)5492}$$
$$\underline{-34}\downarrow$$
$$209$$
$$\underline{204}\downarrow$$
$$52$$
$$\underline{34}$$
$$18$$

Repeat steps 1 and 2 until all the numbers of the dividend have been used. The number remaining is called the remainder. Place it next to an *R* to the right of the quotient. In fractions, the remainder becomes a fraction; in whole numbers, it remains a whole number.

After bringing a number down from the dividend, a number must be placed in the quotient. Zeros may be used as place holders. Follow the division steps as shown above to solve the practice problems.

$$
\begin{array}{r}
106 \text{ R } 41 \\
75\overline{)7991} \\
-75\downarrow \\
\hline
49 \\
-0\downarrow \\
\hline
491 \\
-450 \\
\hline
41
\end{array}
$$

Practice

1. $6\overline{)564}$

2. $3\overline{)5736}$

3. $4\overline{)12345}$

4. $956 \div 66 =$

5. $4\overline{)1244}$

6. $53\overline{)5088}$

7. $15\overline{)23648}$

8. $1{,}254 \div 29 =$

9. $2\overline{)46882}$

10. $18\overline{)12564}$

11. $7\overline{)87543}$

12. $74{,}943 \div 271 =$

Applications

1. Room rates vary by the services provided. At the local hospital, intensive care unit (ICU) rooms are $784 a day. Bob's overall room charge was $10,192. How many days was Bob in ICU?

2. Carbohydrates have 4 calories per gram. If a serving of soup has 248 calories of carbohydrates, how many grams of carbohydrates are in that serving?

3. A medical assistant subscribes to 14 magazines for the office. If the total subscription bill is $294, what is the average cost of each magazine subscription?

4. A pharmacy technician receives a shipment of 302 boxes of acetaminophen. This shipment needs to be returned to the supplier because the expiration date on the medicine did not allow sufficient time to sell the medicine. If each case holds 36 individual boxes, how many cases must the pharmacy technician use to pack the medicine?

5. A surgical technologist made $39,744 last year. He is paid twice a month. What is the gross or total amount of each of his paychecks?

6. A licensed practical nurse gives 1,800 milligrams of a penicillin-type drug over a 36-hour time period. If the dosage occurs every 6 hours, how many milligrams are in each dose if each dose is the same amount?

7. Each gram of fat contains 9 calories. How many grams of fat are in 81 calories of fat in a piece of steak?

Solving for the Unknown Number with Basic Mathematics

Sometimes number statements in math class ask for the unknown number. Looking for an unknown number is an aspect of algebra. Solving for these requires that one understand the relationship between the numbers.

For example, _____ + 12 = 75

To find the unknown number, you must subtract 12 from 75. The answer, or unknown number, is 63.

Practice 1: Use addition to solve for the unknown number.

1. 13 + _____ = 87

2. _____ + 12 + 2 = 145

3. 45 + _____ = 98

4. _____ = 98 + 17

5. _____ + 987 = 1,000

Practice 2: Use subtraction to solve for the unknown number.

1. $98 - 12 =$ _____

2. $237 -$ _____ $= 67$

3. _____ $- 17 = 543$

4. $45 - 19 =$ _____

5. $12 =$ _____ $- 23$

Practice 3: Use multiplication to solve for the unknown number.

1. $13 \times 3 =$ _____

2. _____ $\times 11 = 99$

3. _____ $\times 23 = 92$

4. $125 \times$ _____ $= 500$

5. _____ $= 15 \times 5$

Practice 4: Use division to solve for the unknown number.

1. $396 \div 3 =$ _____

2. _____ $\div 12 = 4$

3. $51 \div$ _____ $= 17$

4. $125 =$ _____ $\div 5$

5. $108 \div 6 =$ _____

Rounding

Review

Whole numbers have place values. The number 3,195 has four specific place values: $\dfrac{3,\quad 1\quad 9\quad 5}{\uparrow\quad\uparrow\quad\uparrow\quad\uparrow}$ (three thousand one hundred ninety-five)

thousand hundreds tens ones

By using the place values in a number, we can round the number to a particular and specific place unit. Rounding is valuable because it helps to estimate supplies, inventory, and countable items to the nearest unit.

> Rounding is used when an exact number is not necessary, as in taking inventory and ordering: Round up to make a full case of a product when you are placing an order. If a full case has 36 boxes and you need to order 32 boxes, you will order 1 case or 36 boxes, so you have rounded up to the nearest case.

Rounding is accomplished in three steps.

Example   Round 7,872 to the nearest hundred.

Step 1: Locate the hundreds place and underline it.

$$7,8\underline{8}72$$

Step 2: Circle the number to the right of the underlined number.

$$7,8⑦2$$

Step 3: If the circled number is 5 or greater, add 1 to the underlined number and change the number(s) to the right of the underlined number to zero(s).

$$7,\underline{8}\;⑦\;2$$
$$\downarrow\;\downarrow$$
$$7,9\;0\;0$$

Rounding is used a great deal in health care. Rounding of whole numbers exists in inventory and packaging of supplies as well as in daily activities.

Practice   1. Round to the nearest 10:
   a. 3,918 __3,920__   c. 6,952 __6,950__   e. 15,932 __15,930__
   b. 139 __140__   d. 1,925 __1,930__   f. 99 __100__

2. Round to the nearest 100:
   a. 3,918 __3,900__   c. 8,975 __9,000__   e. 35,292 __35,300__
   b. 3,784 __3,800__   d. 17,854 __17,900__   f. 1,925 __1,900__

3. Round to the nearest 1,000:
   a. 3,190 _____   c. 6,950 _____   e. 432,500 _____
   b. 87,987 _____   d. 12,932 _____   f. 2,987 _____

Additional rounding practice will be presented in Unit 3: Decimals.

Estimation

Estimation is a method of coming up with a math answer that is general, not specific. When we estimate, we rely on rounding to help us get to this general answer. For example, with money rounding is done to the nearest dollar. If an amount has 50 cents or more, *round* to the nearest dollar and drop the cent amount. If an amount is under 50 cents, *retain* the dollar amount and drop the cent amount.

Example   Estimate Bob's expenses for his co-payment of his dental expenses for his two six-month checkups.

	Actual Expense	**Estimated Expense**
March	$65.85	$66
October	$59.10	$59

Add the estimated expenses of $66 + $59 = _____
The estimated annual total is $125.
So estimation is a skill that uses rounding to reach a general rather than a specific answer.

Practice   1. Find the sum using estimation to the nearest dollar:

   a. $56.90 + $12.45 + $124.78

   b. $127.46 + $13.98 + $21.20

   c. $23.45 + $32.29 + $56.65

   d. $2,900.87 + $12.89

2. Find the sum using estimation to the nearest hour:

   a. 1 hour 25 minutes + 2 hours 14 minutes + 5 hours 37 minutes

   b. 7 hours 8 minutes + 10 hours 34 minutes + 15 hours 45 minutes

   c. 3 hours 35 minutes + 22 hours 16 minutes + 9 hours 59 minutes

   d. 6 hours 39 minutes + 13 hours 18 minutes + 5 hours 2 minutes

Basics of Statistical Analysis

The basics of statistical analysis includes the topics of *mean* (average), *mode*, *median*, and *range*. Each of these topics deals with groups or subsets of numbers and their relationships to each other and the set as a whole.

Arithmetic Mean or Average

Review   The arithmetic *mean* is also called the average. An average is a number that represents a group of the same unit of measure. It provides a general number that represents this group of numbers if all the numbers were the same units. Averages are useful in health occupations because they provide general trends and information. Averages are computed using addition and division skills.

To compute a mean or average, follow these two steps:

Step 1:   Add the individual units of measure.

Step 2:   Divide the sum of the units of measure by the number of individual units.

Example   Mary Ann wanted to know the average score of her anatomy and physiology tests. Her scores were 92%, 79%, 100%, 89%, and 95%.

Step 1: $92 + 79 + 100 + 89 + 95 = 455$

$$\begin{array}{r} 91 \\ 5\overline{)455} \\ \underline{45}\!\downarrow \\ 5 \\ \underline{5} \\ 0 \end{array}$$

Step 2: There were a total of 5 grades.

Mary Ann's average score was 91%.

Practice   1. Deb needed to purchase new calendars for the examination rooms. Find
the average if the calendars cost $11, $7, $10, $5, $10, $12, $8, and $9.

2. Certified nursing assistants work a varied number of hours every week
at Village Nursing Home. The weekly hours are 32, 38, 40, 35, 40, 16, and
30. What is the average number of hours each assistant works?

3. The staff phone use during morning break is increasing. The director is
considering adding additional phones and is researching the usage in
minutes. Using the following data, compute the average length of each
call: 7, 4, 3, 1, 2, 4, 5, 7, and 12.

4. A diabetic patient is counting calories. The patient adds up calories from
portions of fruit: 90, 80, 60, 15, 40. What is the average caloric intake
from each portion?

5. Beth was working hard to increase the fruit and vegetables in her diet.
She kept a log of servings: Monday, 8; Tuesday, 7; Wednesday, 6; Thurs-
day, 5; Friday, 8; Saturday, 6; Sunday, 9. What is the mean daily intake of
fruits and vegetables for Beth?

Median

The *median* is the middle number in a list of numbers. To determine the
median, follow these steps:

Step 1: Sort the list of numbers from smallest to largest.

Step 2: Cross off one number from each end of the line of numbers until
one number is reached in the middle.

Example   Find the median of this set of numbers: 23, 54, 76, 34, 12.

Step 1: Sort from smallest to largest   12, 23, 34, 54, 76

Step 2: Cross a number off from each end   ~~12~~, 23, 34, 54, ~~76~~
until the middle number is reached.   ~~12~~, ~~23~~, 34, ~~54~~, ~~76~~

34 is the median

If there is an even set of numbers, the final two numbers are added and then divided by 2 to get the median. For example, consider the following set of numbers: 23, 54, 76, 34, 12, 36.

Step 1: Sort from smallest to largest   12, 23, 34, 36, 54, 76

Step 2: Cross a number off from each end   ~~12~~, 23, 34, 36, 54, ~~76~~
until the last pair is reached.   ~~12~~, ~~23~~, 34, 36, ~~54~~, ~~76~~

Step 3: Add the two remaining numbers $34 + 36 = 70$

Step 4: Divide the answer by 2 to get the $70 \div 2 = 35$
median.

35 is the median.

Note: The median may include a partial number such as $1/2$ or 0.5.

Practice   1. Bah's temperature fluctuated all day. Her temperature readings were 98, 99, 97, 101, and 100. What is her median temperature?

2. The young patients played a game. The scores for five games were 365, 251, 105, 280, and 198. What is the median of this set of scores?

3. The medical assistant was working on inventory. She wanted to figure out the median of the number of cases of protective sheeting that were used for the first six months of the year in the large medical practice.

Month	Number of cases
January	26
February	22
March	31
April	28
May	26
June	19

What is the median for this set of data?

4. Azeb is an excellent student. She is curious about the median of her test scores in biology class. Her scores are 99, 100, 98, 97, 100. Her median is _____.

5. The students were measuring tardiness to class by incidence each week. Look at the data set: 7, 8, 10, 10, 15, 12, 8, 7. What is the mean of this data set?

Mode

The mode is the "most popular" value or the most frequently occurring item in a set of numbers to locate the mode in a series or listing of numbers, locate the number, which occurs the most.

For example, look at the calories of Bob's snack food intake for a two-day period:

Bob's caloric intake of snacks by day

Saturday: 120, 120, 50, 78, 134, 187

Sunday: 220, 125, 90, 85, 120, 120

What is the mode of the calorie intake of Bob's snack intake over this two-day period?

The answer is 120. It occurs four times.

Practice

1. Look at the pH values of the following data set: 8, 11, 23, 14, 8, 12. What is the mode for this data set?

2. Look at the prices of toothbrushes: $2.00; $4.00, $3.00; $3.00, $1.00; $3.00. What is the mode of these toothbrush prices?

3. The color combinations preferred by new dental offices include: paint sample #24, paint sample #154, paint sample #654, paint sample #24, paint sample #154, paint sample #24, and paint sample #63. What is the mode?

4. Designer eyeglass frames cost a lot. This season's top selling frame prices are from $330, $199, $230, $400, $497, and $330. What is the mode of these eyeglass frame prices?

5. The Healthville Residence is having a problem with absenteeism during the summer months.

The administrator wants to find out who is missing work the most. First add the days absent for each employee, and write the number in the "Total days absent" column. Compare the total days absent from work; what is the mode for the number of days absent for the summer months?

Employee	Days absent in June	Days absent in July	Days absent in August	Total days absent
Verna	3	2	2	_____
Xuyen	4	4	3	_____
Cam	3	2	1	_____
Debbie	3	3	3	_____
Ed	2	2	2	_____
Vasily	1	3	4	_____
Ted	3	2	2	_____

Range

The range of a set of numbers is the largest value in the set minus the smallest value in the set. Note that the range is a single number, not many numbers. The range is the difference between the largest and the smallest numbers.

For example, the hospital delivered six babies today. The weight in pounds of these newborns was 6, 9, 10, 8, 7, 5.

Step 1: Locate the smallest number and the largest number   5 and 10

Step 2: Subtract the smallest number from the largest number. $10 - 5 = 5$

The range is 5.

Practice: 1. The age of patients in the hospital fluctuates. Look at the data and calculate the range of patients' ages: 68, 94, 23, 45, 98, 100, 69 18, 25, 75, 87.

2. The workforce at the Village care Center is diverse in age. Look at the data and calculate the range of workers' ages: 19, 21, 24, 23, 45, 34, 28, 25, 31, 56, 64, 71, 49, 52.

3. The breakfast meals served in the cafeteria vary in calories. Look at the data and calculate the range of calories in the meals: 120, 220, 280, 340, 440, 480.

4. The public health nurse has a rural route to drive each week. What is the range that the daily miles, 7, 14, 23, 24, 16, 12, record?

5. The bandages sold in a local drug store have a wide price range. Each bandage costs as follows: 50 cents, 35 cents, 78 cents, 89 cents, 99 cents, 12 cents, and 25 cents. What is the range in individual bandage costs?

Roman Numerals

In our daily lives, we use Arabic numerals 0 to 9 and combinations of these digits to do most of our mathematical activities. In the health care field, Roman numerals are sometimes used along with Arabic numerals. Roman numerals are often found in prescriptions and in medical records and charts. Roman numerals consist of lower- and uppercase letters that represent numbers. For medical applications, Roman numerals will be written in lowercase letters for the numbers 1 to 10. Use uppercase when smaller numbers are part of a number over 30 such as 60: LX not lx. Do not use commas in Roman numerals.

Roman Numerals

Roman numerals are formed by combining the numbers.	1 = i or I	6 = vi or VI	$\frac{1}{2}$ = ss
	2 = ii or II	7 = vii or VII	50 = L
	3 = iii or III	8 = viii or VIII	100 = C
	4 = iv or IV	9 = ix or IX	500 = D
	5 = v or V	10 = x or X	1,000 = M

Mnemonic Device Note the pattern: 50-100-500-1000

L = 50	Lovely
C = 100	Cats
D = 500	Don't
M = 1000	Meow!

This will help you to remember the order and value of each Roman numeral.

Use the following basic Roman numeral concepts to accurately read and write Roman numerals.

Concept 1

Add Roman numerals of the same or decreasing value when they are placed next to each other. Read these from left to right.

Examples   vii = 5 + 2 = 7   xxi = 10 + 10 + 1 = 21

Practice   Write the numerals in Arabic or Roman numerals.

1. xiii   6. 17

2. xv   7. 31

3. xxxi   8. 120

4. LV   9. $1\frac{1}{2}$

5. MI   10. 11

Concept 2

Subtract a numeral of decreasing or lesser value from the numeral to its right.

Examples   iv = 5 − 1 = 4   XC = 100 − 10 = 90

          IM = 1000 − 1 = 999   xix = 10 + 10 − 1 = 19

Practice   Write the numerals in Arabic or Roman numerals:

1. ixss   6. 19

2. XL   7. 39

3. CD   8. $24\frac{1}{4}$

4. LM   9. 240

5. XCIX   10. 499

Concept 3

When converting long Roman numerals to Arabic numerals, it is helpful to separate the Roman numerals into groups and work from both ends.

Example   CDLXXIV → CD L XX IV

1. Start with the IV = 5 − 1 = 4   4
2. Next, X + X = 20   20
3. C − D = 500 − 100 = 400   400
4. L = 50   +50
5. Then add the elements   474

Practice   1. CXIV   6. XLss

2. LVIII   7. CDIV

3. DXIV   8. MCML

4. MDCIXss   9. DXCIIss

5. LXXXIX   10. CMLXXIVss

This method of separating the elements and working from both ends also works well for converting from Arabic to Roman numerals.

Example   Convert 637 to Roman numerals

600   DC
30   XXX
7   VII

Then rewrite the Roman numeral from the largest number on the left to the smallest numbers on the right. → DCXXXVII

Practice   1. $14\frac{1}{2}$ 6. 789

2. 33   7. 450

3. 146   8. 76

4. 329   9. 17

5. 999   10. 1294

Mixed Practice   Convert between Roman numerals and Arabic numerals:

1. DCCL   3. XVIII

2. XXIVss   4. 23

5. 19   13. 362

6. 1,495   14. 16

7. 607   15. 999

8. CCLIVss   16. XXXIXss

9. 66   17. LXXVIII

10. MVII   18. $309\frac{1}{2}$

11. CMVIII   19. 2,515

12. MCDLIV   20. What should you do to convert a number
                                  with decimal 0.5 in it to a Roman numeral?

Time in Allied Health

Universal (military) time is used in many health-care facilities. The Universal time system avoids the confusion over A.M. and P.M. Universal time is based on the 24-hour clock, which begins at 0001, which is one minute after midnight.

Colons are not used between these numbers. Compare the two clocks below:

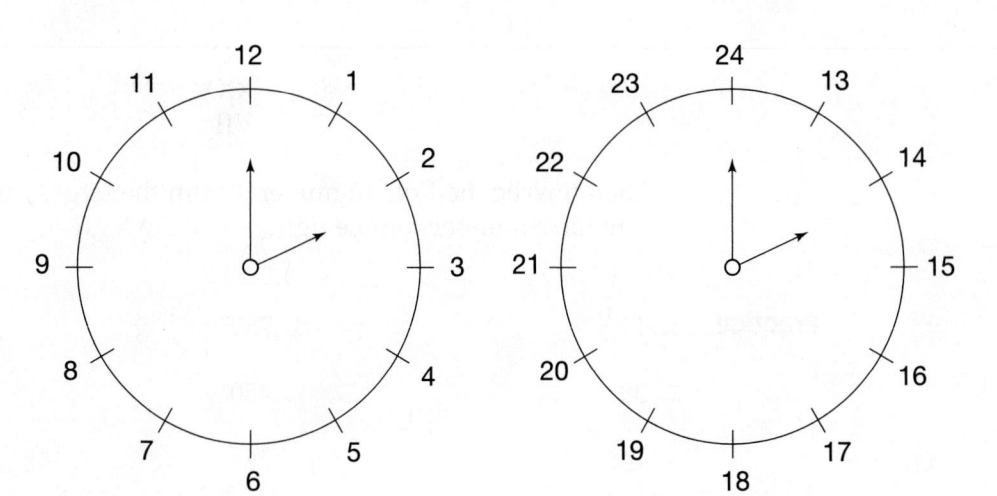

How to Convert to Universal Time:

The hours have four digits: 1 A.M. or 1:00 A.M. = 0100
                                      10 A.M. or 10:00 A.M. = 1000

Add 1200 to any time after noon   2 P.M. or 2:00 P.M. = 1400
                                      2 + 1200 = 1400 in Universal
                                      time
                                      5:36 P.M. or 5:36 P.M. = 1736
                                      in Universal time

Practice 1:   Complete the chart.

Standard Time	Universal or Military Time
12:05 A.M.	_____
3:15 P.M.	_____
7:39 A.M.	_____
7:39 P.M.	_____
12:45 P.M.	_____
8:17 A.M.	_____
5:57 P.M.	_____
1:23 A.M.	_____
9:25 P.M.	_____
11:03 P.M.	_____

Practice 2:   Complete the chart.

Universal or Military Time	Standard Time
1256	_____
0136	_____
0009	_____
1236	_____
0048	_____
2400	_____
1524	_____
2006	_____
0912	_____
1630	_____

WHOLE NUMBER SELF-TEST

1. Complete this number statement. 329 + _____ + 217 = 1,621

2. An activity director in a long-term care facility is purchasing recreational supplies. Find the sum of the purchases: 3 Bingo games at $13

each, 10 puzzles at $9 each, 24 jars of paint at $3 each, and 2 rolls of paper for $31 each.

3. Using the information from problem 2 above, determine the mean (average) cost of these supplies. Round to the nearest dollar.

4. A medical assistant student needs 250 hours of practical work experience to complete the college's course. If the student has completed 184 hours, how many hours remain to fulfill the requirement?

5. Three certified nursing assistants assist 16 rooms of patients on the Saturday morning shift. If each room has 3 patients, how many patients does each assistant care for if they are equally divided up among the staff?

6. Uniform jackets are required at Valley Pharmacy. Each pharmacy technician is asked to purchased two jackets at $21 per jacket and one name badge for $8. What is the cost of these items for each pharmacy technician?

7. The medical clerk is asked to inventory the digital thermometers. In the six examination rooms, the clerk finds the following number of digital thermometers: 2, 4, 5, 2, 1, and 3. The total inventory is _____.

8. The dental assistants in a new office are setting up their free patient sample display. They order the following:

	Quantity	Unit	Item	Per Unit Cost (in dollars)	Total Cost
a.	1,500	each	toothbrush	1	_____
b.	100	each	floss (smooth)	2	_____
c.	75	each	floss (glide)	2	_____
d.	1,000	per 100	information booklet	10	_____
e.	25	each	poster	15	_____
f.				Subtotal	_____

9. After a mild heart attack, Mary spent 3 days in a coronary care unit. Her room bill was $2,898. What was her daily room rate?

10. White blood cell (WBC) count can indicate illness or health. The WBC count of patient B is checked. Before surgery, the WBC count of patient B was 12,674; post-surgery, he had a count of 6,894. What is the difference in patient B's count before and after surgery?

11. The cook has a variety of meals to prepare for Villa Center's residents. She averages 16 vegetarian meals every day of the week. Round the number of weekly meals to the nearest 10.

12. The newest staff member at the hospital is a surgery technologist. Her pay is approximately $14 an hour. If she is scheduled to work 36 hours a week, what is her weekly pay before deductions?

13. Read the number: 9\underline{5}6,123.
    The place value of the underlined digit is _____.

Unit 2

Fractions

Part-to-Whole Relationships

A fraction is a number that has two parts: a part and a whole. A minute is 1 part of 60 minutes in a whole hour. This relationship of part to whole can be shown in a fraction:

$$\frac{1}{60} \begin{array}{l} \leftarrow \text{numerator (the part)} \\ \leftarrow \text{denominator (the whole)} \end{array}$$

The 1 is called the *numerator*, and it represents the part of the whole. The 60 is the *denominator*, and it represents the whole or sum of the parts. Take another common part-to-whole relationship. Many people sleep an average of 8 hours a night. The relationship of sleeping hours to total hours in a day is 8 to 24, or $\frac{8}{24}$, or a reduced fraction of $\frac{1}{3}$.

Fractions are important to know because you will come across them many times in health care occupations. Fractions appear in medication dosages, measurements, sizes of instruments, work assignments, and time units. Practice writing out the numerator (part) to denominator (whole) relationships:

Example

$$\frac{1}{12} = \text{one part to twelve total parts}$$

36

1. $\dfrac{3}{4}$ = _____

2. $\dfrac{5}{6}$ = _____

3. $\dfrac{7}{8}$ = _____

4. $\dfrac{16}{21}$ = _____

Proper or common fractions are fractions with a numerator less than the number of the denominator: $^3/_7$, $^{24}/_{47}$, $^9/_{11}$. The value of any proper or common fraction will be less than 1.

Mixed numbers are fractions that include both a whole number and a proper fraction: $3^3/_4$, $12^9/_{11}$, $101^{13}/_{22}$.

An *improper fraction* has a numerator equal to or larger than the denominator: $^{17}/_{12}$, $^{33}/_{11}$, $^9/_9$. Improper fractions are equal to 1 or larger. Improper fractions are used in the multiplication and division of fractions. Answers that appear as improper fractions need to be reduced so that the answer is a mixed number.

Equivalent Fractions

Understanding *equivalent fractions* is important in making measurement decisions. Equivalent fractions represent the same relationship of part to whole, but there are more pieces or parts involved. The fractions involved, however, are equal. The size of the pieces or parts is what varies.

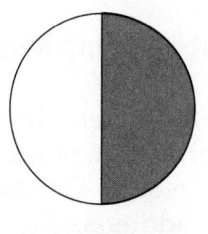

2 large pieces
$^1/_2$ is shaded

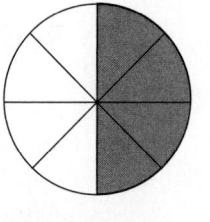

8 smaller pieces
$^4/_8$ are shaded

The shaded areas are the same size; the number of parts varies. Making fractions equal is easy using multiplication. Look at the fractions: $^1/_6$ and $^?/_{18}$. The denominators are 6 and 18. Ask: 6 times what = 18? The answer is 3, so multiply the numerator by 3, and you will have formed an equivalent fraction. Thus, $^1/_6 = ^3/_{18}$.

The key to getting the correct answer is in remembering that the number the denominator is multiplied by must also be used to multiply the numerator. If this method is difficult for you, then divide the smaller denominator into the larger one; your answer will then be multiplied by the first numerator to get the second numerator.

$$\frac{1}{6} = \frac{?}{18} \quad 6\overline{)18,} \quad \text{then } 3 \times 1 = 3$$

Another way to work this problem is:

$$\frac{1(\times 3)}{6(\times 3)} = \frac{3}{18}$$

Thus, $\frac{1}{6} = \frac{3}{18}$.

Practice

1. $\frac{1}{2} = \frac{?}{12}$

2. $\frac{1}{4} = \frac{?}{16}$

3. $\frac{1}{5} = \frac{?}{40}$

4. $\frac{2}{14} = \frac{?}{28}$

5. $\frac{5}{9} = \frac{?}{27}$

6. $\frac{1}{13} = \frac{?}{39}$

7. $\frac{4}{8} = \frac{?}{72}$

8. $\frac{1}{5} = \frac{?}{100}$

9. $\frac{7}{9} = \frac{42}{?}$

10. $\frac{1}{3} = \frac{8}{?}$

The skill of making equivalent fractions will be used in adding, subtracting, and comparing fractions.

Reducing to Lowest or Simplest Terms

As in making fractions equivalent, reducing fractions to their lowest or simplest terms is another important fraction skill. Most tests and practical applications of fractions require that the answers be in the lowest terms. After each calculation of addition, subtraction, multiplication, or division, you will need to reduce the answer to its lowest terms. Two methods will help you get to the lowest terms:

Multiplication Method

To use the multiplication method, look at the numbers in the fraction. Find a number that divides into both the numerator and denominator evenly. Such numbers are called *factors* of the numbers. Write out the multiplication for the numerator and denominator. Cross out the two identical numbers in the multiplication problems. What is left will be the reduced fraction.

$$\frac{2}{16} = \frac{2 \times 1}{2 \times 8} \rightarrow \frac{\cancel{2} \times 1}{\cancel{2} \times 8}$$

So, $\frac{2}{6} = \frac{1}{8}$. Depending on the multiple you choose, you may need to do this more than once.

$$\frac{8}{24} = \frac{4 \times 2}{4 \times 6} = \frac{2}{6} \rightarrow \frac{1}{3}$$

or

$$\frac{8}{24} = \frac{8 \times 1}{8 \times 3} = \frac{1}{3}$$

Sometimes students only partially reduce a fraction, so try to find the largest possible factor of the numbers when you are reducing.

> Choose the largest possible multiple to avoid having to repeat the steps in reduction.

Division Method

Look at the numbers of the numerator and the denominator. Choose a number that divides into both the numerator and the denominator. Next, divide the numerator and denominator by that number. Check to ensure that the resulting fraction is in its lowest form.

$$\frac{2}{16} = \frac{2 \div 2}{16 \div 2} = \frac{1}{8}$$

$$\frac{8}{24} = \frac{8 \div 4}{24 \div 4} = \frac{2}{6}$$

This fraction is not reduced, so it must be reduced again.

$$\frac{2}{6} = \frac{2 \div 2}{6 \div 2} = \frac{1}{3}$$

This fraction is reduced to its lowest form.

How do you decide on the best method to use?

Choose your strongest skill—multiplication or division—and use it to reduce fractions.

You will make fewer errors if you select one method and use it consistently.

Practice

1. $\frac{2}{14} = \frac{1}{7}$

2. $\frac{3}{27} \div 3 = \frac{1}{9}$

3. $\frac{4}{8} \div 4 = \frac{1}{2}$

4. $\frac{13}{39} \div 13 = \frac{1}{3}$

5. $\frac{25}{100} \div 25 = \frac{1}{4}$

6. $\frac{64}{72} \div 8 = \frac{8}{9}$

7. $\dfrac{24}{48}$ 9. $\dfrac{15}{45}$

8. $\dfrac{63}{90}$ 10. $\dfrac{5}{255}$

When working with a mixed number, set aside the whole number. Handle the fraction portion of the number and then place it beside the whole number.

$$14\dfrac{3}{9} \to 14 \text{ and } \dfrac{3}{9} \to \dfrac{3}{9} = \dfrac{1 \times 3}{3 \times 3} = \dfrac{1}{3} \to 14\dfrac{1}{3}$$

> Set aside the whole number, reduce the fraction, then replace the whole number next to the reduced fraction.

Practice   1. $13\dfrac{2}{8}$

2. $7\dfrac{12}{16}$

3. $1\dfrac{33}{66}$

4. $2\dfrac{2}{20}$

5. $3\dfrac{3}{12}$

6. $5\dfrac{14}{64}$

7. $2\dfrac{11}{99}$

8. $10\dfrac{30}{80}$

9. $6\dfrac{45}{90}$

10. $4\dfrac{22}{30}$

Fractional parts or relationships are common in health care.

Example   In a class of 30 people, 13 students are male and 17 are female. To write the relationship of the number of males to the total number of students, we place the part (13) over the whole (30) or total number of students.

$$\dfrac{13}{30}$$

Practice   Write the fractional part that represents the relationships of the part to the whole. Then reduce all your answers to the lowest form.

1. 50 of the 125 patients see the physical therapist each week.

2. The dietitian uses 35 six-ounce glasses and 50 eight-ounce glasses at breakfast. Represent in fraction form the relationship of six-ounce glasses to eight-ounce glasses used at breakfast.

3. 30 out of 90 patients at the short-term care facility are women. What is the fractional part of women to total patients?

4. 14 female babies and 16 male babies were born on Saturday. Express the female babies to male babies as a fraction.

5. About 500 medicine cups are used daily at a long-term care facility. The nurse claims that approximately 4,000 medicine cups are used a week. What is the day-to-week use rate of medicine cups?

Improper Fractions

Working with improper fractions also requires reducing fractions. An improper fraction is a fraction that has a larger numerator than a denominator.

$$\frac{16}{8} = \frac{8 \times 2 = 2}{8 \times 1 = 1} \rightarrow 2$$

If the numerator and the denominator do not have a common number by which the numbers can be multiplied, simply divide the denominator into the numerator.

$$\frac{11}{8} \qquad 8{\overline{)11}} \; \begin{array}{r} 1\frac{3}{8} \\ \underline{8} \\ 3 \end{array}$$

The remainder 3 is a whole number. Place it on top of the divisor to form a fraction.

Improper fractions are either whole numbers or mixed numbers.
Improper fractions are used for dividing mixed numbers.

Practice

1. $\dfrac{15}{2}$

2. $\dfrac{18}{4}$

3. $\dfrac{39}{2}$

4. $\dfrac{27}{5}$

5. $\dfrac{66}{7}$

6. $\dfrac{7}{3}$

7. $\dfrac{19}{8}$

8. $\dfrac{16}{2}$

9. $\dfrac{100}{100}$

10. $\dfrac{23}{18}$

Adding Fractions with Like Denominators

Addition of fractions with the same denominator is straightforward. Follow the two steps below:

Step 1: Line up the fractions vertically, add the numerators, and place the answer over the common, or like, denominator.

Step 2: Reduce, if necessary. Check your work to ensure accuracy.

$$\begin{array}{r} \dfrac{3}{6} \\[4pt] +\dfrac{2}{6} \\[4pt] \hline \dfrac{5}{6} \end{array} \qquad \begin{array}{r} \dfrac{4}{8} \\[4pt] +\dfrac{5}{8} \\[4pt] \hline \dfrac{9}{8} \end{array} \quad \text{Reduce by } 9 \div 8 = 1\dfrac{1}{8}$$

When reducing the answer, you find that the result is a whole number with a 1 for its denominator. In this case, use the numerator, a whole number alone. Do not use the 1 since the answer is actually a whole number rather than a fraction.

Step 1: $\begin{array}{r} \dfrac{12}{15} \\[4pt] +\dfrac{18}{15} \\[4pt] \hline \dfrac{30}{15} \end{array}$ **Step 2:** $\dfrac{30}{15} = \dfrac{\cancel{15} \times 2}{\cancel{15} \times 1} \qquad \dfrac{2}{1} = 2$

If a whole number exists with the fractions, simply add it separately and place the fraction next to the answer. The whole number will be affected only if the fraction answer is larger than 1—then the whole number resulting from the fraction addition is added to the whole number answer.

Example

$$14\frac{2}{8}$$
$$+7\frac{1}{8}$$
$$\overline{21\frac{3}{8}}$$

Add the fractions: $\frac{2}{8} + \frac{1}{8} = \frac{3}{8}$

Add the whole numbers: $14 + 7 = 21$

Write the answer. No reduction is necessary.

Example

$$10\frac{2}{4}$$
$$+4\frac{3}{4}$$
$$\overline{14\frac{5}{4}}$$

example. ⊖

$$\frac{3}{4} \cancel{-} \frac{1}{6} = \frac{18-4}{24} \quad \frac{14 \div 2 = 7}{24 \quad 12}$$

Add the fractions: $\frac{2}{4} + \frac{3}{4} = \frac{5}{4}$

Add $10 + 4 = 14$

$^5/_4$ must be reduced. It is an improper fraction.

Divide 5 by 4 = $1^1/_4$. The whole number 1 is added to 14 ($14 + 1 = 15$) and the fraction $^1/_4$ is placed next to the whole so that the answer is $15^1/_4$.

Practice   Add the following fractions. Reduce as necessary:

1. $\frac{1}{6} + \frac{5}{6}$

2. $\frac{2}{8} + \frac{4}{8}$

3. $\frac{9}{10} + \frac{11}{10}$

4. $\frac{1}{13} + \frac{4}{13}$

5. $\frac{3}{12} + \frac{4}{12}$

6. $\frac{2}{5} + \frac{3}{5}$

7. $\frac{3}{13} + \frac{4}{13}$

8. $13\frac{8}{12} + 2\frac{2}{12}$

9. $10\frac{1}{6} + 12\frac{4}{6}$

example. ⊕

$$\frac{2}{3} \cancel{-} \frac{4}{5} = \frac{10+12}{15} = \frac{22^{-15}}{15} \quad 1\frac{7}{15}$$

$$\xrightarrow{\quad} \quad \underset{2^{nd}}{\nwarrow} \quad \underset{3^{rd}}{\nearrow}$$
$$\underset{1^{st}}{}$$

10. $11\frac{1}{4} + \frac{3}{4}$

11. $\frac{3}{5} + \frac{1}{5}$

12. $\frac{2}{7} + \frac{3}{7} + \frac{4}{7}$

13. $\frac{3}{8} + \frac{4}{8} + \frac{1}{8}$

14. $2\frac{1}{12} + 3\frac{5}{12} + 6\frac{4}{12}$

15. $101\frac{3}{4} + 33\frac{1}{4} + 5\frac{1}{4}$

example.

$add \rightarrow 1\frac{+1}{2}^{+1}_{\times 2} + 2\frac{+2}{\times 3}^{+2}$

$mul. \rightarrow \frac{3}{2} \times \frac{0}{3} \rightarrow = \frac{9+16}{6} = \frac{25}{6} = 4\frac{1}{6}$

Finding the Common Denominator

Adding and subtracting fractions requires that the denominator be of the same number, also referred to as a *common denominator*. The lowest common denominator is the smallest number or multiple that both of the denominators of the fractions can go into.

By using multiplication, find a smallest number or multiple that the numbers can go into.

Step 1:

$$\frac{2}{3} \quad \frac{}{3 \times 2 = 6} = ?$$

$$+\frac{1}{6} \rightarrow \quad \frac{1}{6}$$

In the above problem, 3 and 6 are the denominators. $3 \times 2 = 6$, so 6 is the common denominator.

Step 2: Once you have the common denominator in place, multiply the numerator by the same number with which you multiplied the denominator. The result will be equivalent fractions, so the number relationships remain the same.

$$\frac{2}{3} \quad \frac{2 \times 2 = 4}{3 \times 2 = 6}$$

$$+\frac{1}{6} \rightarrow \quad +\frac{1}{6}$$

$$\frac{5}{6}$$

Practice Find the common denominator in the following pairs of numbers. Set the problems up vertically and think about their multiples to find the common denominators.

> Fewer errors occur if the setup is vertical. You can see the numbers and their relationships easier.

1. $\dfrac{2}{4}$ and $\dfrac{1}{5}$

2. $\dfrac{3}{8}$ and $\dfrac{1}{16}$

3. $\dfrac{22}{44}$ and $\dfrac{1}{11}$

4. $\dfrac{1}{9}$ and $\dfrac{5}{45}$

5. $\dfrac{2}{5}$ and $\dfrac{3}{25}$

6. $\dfrac{3}{7}$ and $\dfrac{9}{49}$

7. $\dfrac{1}{200}$ and $\dfrac{5}{20}$

8. $\dfrac{4}{50}$ and $\dfrac{10}{150}$

9. $\dfrac{3}{9}$ and $\dfrac{4}{27}$

10. $\dfrac{1}{6}$ and $\dfrac{4}{18}$

Practice   Add the following fractions with unlike denominators:

1. $\dfrac{3}{5} + \dfrac{1}{4}$

2. $\dfrac{1}{2} + \dfrac{4}{6}$

3. $\dfrac{4}{9} + \dfrac{2}{3}$

4. $\dfrac{7}{10} + \dfrac{3}{5}$

5. $\dfrac{11}{30} + \dfrac{2}{15}$

6. $\dfrac{5}{25} + \dfrac{1}{5}$

7. $\dfrac{4}{7} + \dfrac{1}{21}$

8. $\dfrac{2}{5} + \dfrac{1}{10} + \dfrac{3}{10}$

9. $\dfrac{3}{5} + \dfrac{1}{3} + \dfrac{2}{15}$

10. $\dfrac{2}{3} + \dfrac{1}{12} + \dfrac{2}{4}$

11. $\dfrac{1}{10} + \dfrac{1}{2} + \dfrac{4}{5}$

12. $12\dfrac{1}{6} + \dfrac{3}{4}$

13. $55\dfrac{1}{3} + 51\dfrac{5}{9}$

14. $5\dfrac{1}{2} + 2\dfrac{4}{5} + 5\dfrac{3}{10}$

15. $4\dfrac{3}{4} + 1\dfrac{1}{16} + 3\dfrac{2}{32}$

Sometimes one must consider a wider range of possible numbers for common denominators. For example, you may have a pair of fractions in which one of the denominators cannot be multiplied by a number to get the other denominator. In this case, it is often easiest to simply multiply the two denominators with each other. The result will be a common denominator.

Example

$$\dfrac{3}{13} \text{ and } \dfrac{1}{4}$$

What is the common denominator? If you multiply 13×4, your answer is 52. Use that number as the common denominator.

> To find the more difficult common denominators, multiply the denominators with each other.

$$\dfrac{3}{13} \rightarrow 13 \times 4 = 52$$

$$\dfrac{1}{4} \rightarrow 4 \times 13 = 52$$

Then multiply each numerator by the same number that you multiplied its denominator by. Do this for each fraction and the result will be a common denominator.

$$\dfrac{3}{13} \rightarrow \dfrac{3 \times 4 = 12}{13 \times 4 = 52}$$

$$\dfrac{1}{4} \rightarrow \dfrac{1 \times 13 = 13}{4 \times 13 = 52}$$

By finding the common denominator, you have also created equivalent fractions.

Practice Find the common denominator for each of the following sets of fractions:

1. $\dfrac{3}{4}$ and $\dfrac{2}{5}$

2. $\dfrac{7}{8}$ and $\dfrac{1}{3}$

3. $\dfrac{24}{32}$ and $\dfrac{1}{6}$

4. $\dfrac{1}{7}$ and $\dfrac{4}{8}$

5. $\dfrac{3}{5}$ and $\dfrac{7}{9}$

6. $\dfrac{2}{26}$ and $\dfrac{1}{3}$

7. $\dfrac{3}{9}$ and $\dfrac{1}{4}$

8. $\dfrac{2}{5}$ and $\dfrac{6}{9}$

9. $\dfrac{3}{10}$ and $\dfrac{2}{3}$

10. $\dfrac{1}{9}$ and $\dfrac{7}{8}$

Practice   Add the following mixed fractions:

1. $3\dfrac{2}{3} + 6\dfrac{1}{4}$

2. $10\dfrac{1}{2} + 13\dfrac{5}{22}$

3. $9\dfrac{1}{6} + 4\dfrac{3}{9}$

4. $11\dfrac{7}{8} + 2\dfrac{1}{7}$

5. $\dfrac{1}{2} + 4\dfrac{1}{7} + 2\dfrac{1}{14}$

6. $12\dfrac{3}{5} + 22\dfrac{1}{30}$

7. $10\dfrac{4}{5} + 8\dfrac{1}{6}$

8. $3\dfrac{4}{9} + 1\dfrac{2}{3} + 5\dfrac{2}{9}$

9. $11\dfrac{2}{5} + 7\dfrac{1}{2}$

10. $7\dfrac{11}{16} + 3\dfrac{4}{8} + \dfrac{1}{2}$

11. $2\dfrac{2}{9} + 6\dfrac{1}{3} + 8\dfrac{2}{27}$

12. $6\dfrac{2}{3} + 8\dfrac{4}{5} + 3\dfrac{6}{10}$

13. $6\dfrac{1}{4} + 13\dfrac{2}{3} + 19\dfrac{1}{2}$

14. $6\dfrac{7}{16} + \dfrac{3}{24} + 2\dfrac{1}{48}$

15. $\dfrac{3}{5} + \dfrac{6}{30} + 12\dfrac{2}{3}$

16. $8\dfrac{9}{11} + 3\dfrac{1}{33} + \dfrac{2}{66}$

17. $3\dfrac{5}{16} + \dfrac{5}{8} + \dfrac{2}{4}$

18. $\dfrac{5}{6} + 3\dfrac{3}{9} + 7\dfrac{2}{3}$

19. $4\dfrac{5}{6} + \dfrac{2}{5} + \dfrac{4}{15}$

20. $55\dfrac{4}{17} + 101\dfrac{3}{51}$

Applications

1. The certified nurse assistants weigh patients each month. Mrs. Smith weighed 120 pounds last month. Over the last two months, she gained $1\frac{1}{2}$ and $\frac{1}{4}$ pounds. What is Mrs. Smith's current weight?

2. The lab technician uses a cleaning solution daily. The technician used $4\frac{1}{2}$ ounces, $1\frac{1}{3}$ ounces, and 5 ounces of the cleaning solutions. What is the total amount of solution used?

3. A new baby grew $\frac{3}{4}$ of an inch in June and $\frac{7}{16}$ of an inch in July. How many total inches did the baby grow during these two months?

4. A sick child drinks $\frac{1}{2}$ cup of juice and an hour later $\frac{3}{4}$ cup of water. At dinner, the child drinks $1\frac{1}{4}$ cups more of water. What is the child's total fluid intake?

5. The nurse gives a patient $1\frac{1}{2}$ grains of medication followed by $2\frac{1}{3}$ grains. What is the total dosage the nurse has dispensed to the patient?

Ordering Fractions

Comparing fractions in health-care fields appears when sizes of medical items or pieces of equipment are being computed. It is useful to be able to determine the size relationships of instruments and place them in order for a surgeon before a surgery. This is accomplished by using the common denominator method.

Know these symbols: <, =, >

3 is less than 4 is represented by 3 < 4

7 is greater than 5 is represented by 7 > 5

$\frac{2}{2}$ equals 1 is represented by $\frac{2}{2}$ = 1

Example   Which is larger $\frac{1}{4}$ or $\frac{3}{8}$?

Step 1: Convert the fractions to give each a common denominator.

$$\frac{1}{4} \qquad \frac{1 \times 2 = 2}{4 \times 2 = 8}$$

$$\frac{3}{8} \rightarrow \qquad \frac{3}{8}$$

Step 2: Order by the numerators now that the fractions have the same denominator. 3 is larger than 2, so $\frac{3}{8} > \frac{2}{8}$ or $\frac{1}{4}$.

Practice   Order the following fractions from largest to smallest.

1. $\frac{1}{4}, \frac{2}{9}, \frac{4}{12}$

2. $\frac{9}{22}, \frac{5}{11}, \frac{8}{11}$

3. $\frac{6}{25}, \frac{20}{50}, \frac{33}{100}$

4. $\frac{7}{8}, \frac{2}{16}, \frac{3}{4}, \frac{1}{2}$

Subtraction of Fractions

Subtraction of fractions follows the same basic principles as addition of fractions. The fractions must have common denominators before any subtraction can be done.

Example   **Step 1:** Make a common denominator if necessary.

$$\frac{7}{8} - \frac{5}{8} = \underline{\quad} \text{ (8 is the common denominator.)}$$

Step 2: Subtract the numerators and then reduce if necessary.

$$\frac{7}{8} - \frac{5}{8} = \frac{2}{8}, \text{ which is reduced to } \frac{1}{4}.$$

Practice

1. $\dfrac{3}{9} - \dfrac{2}{9}$

2. $\dfrac{5}{8} - \dfrac{2}{8}$

3. $\dfrac{3}{11} - \dfrac{1}{11}$

4. $\dfrac{22}{44} - \dfrac{11}{44}$

5. $10\dfrac{5}{12} - 8\dfrac{3}{12}$

6. $25\dfrac{3}{4} - 20\dfrac{1}{4}$

7. $101\dfrac{13}{24} - 56\dfrac{10}{24}$

8. $6\dfrac{6}{7} - \dfrac{3}{5}$

9. $\dfrac{15}{16} - \dfrac{7}{16}$

10. $20\dfrac{5}{6} - 12\dfrac{2}{6}$

11. $\dfrac{3}{4} - \dfrac{1}{2}$

12. $\dfrac{6}{8} - \dfrac{1}{4}$

13. $12\dfrac{1}{2} - \dfrac{3}{10}$

14. $20\dfrac{6}{14} - 2\dfrac{3}{7}$

15. $39\dfrac{11}{18} - 8\dfrac{3}{6}$

16. $25\dfrac{1}{3} - 20\dfrac{1}{8}$

17. $124\dfrac{11}{12} - \dfrac{5}{6}$

18. $18\dfrac{3}{4} - 12\dfrac{2}{3}$

19. $200\dfrac{9}{11} - 188\dfrac{2}{3}$

20. $500\dfrac{4}{5} - 150\dfrac{2}{9}$

Borrowing in Subtraction of Fractions

Two specific situations require that a number be borrowed in the subtraction of fractions: (1) subtraction of a fraction from a whole number, and (2) after a common denominator is established and the top fraction of the problem is less or smaller than the fraction that is being subtracted from it.

Recall that the borrowing in whole numbers is accomplished as shown below. Set the problem up vertically.

$$124 - 8 = \underline{\hspace{2cm}}$$

Step 1: Borrow 1 from the tens column. Add it to the ones column.

Step 2: Subtract.

$$\begin{array}{r} 1^{1}2^{1}4 \\ -8 \\ \hline 116 \end{array}$$

In fractions, the same borrowing concept is used; the format varies only slightly. The difference is that the borrowed number must be put into a fractional form.

> Any whole number over itself equals 1. So $^{101}/_{101} = 1$, $^{3}/_{3} = 1$, and $^{12}/_{12} = 1$.

Example

$$17\frac{3}{8}$$
$$-14\frac{4}{8}$$

In the example above, the numerator 4 in the second fraction cannot be subtracted from the first fraction's numerator 3. Thus, borrowing is required in the first fraction.

$$1^{6}\cancel{7}\frac{3}{8} + \frac{8}{8}$$
$$-14\frac{4}{8}$$

Step 1: Borrow 1 from the whole number. Convert the 1 into an improper fraction having the same common denominator as the first fraction. Then add the two fractions.

Step 2: Rewrite the problem so it incorporates the changes, then subtract the numerator only. Place it over the denominator. Reduce as necessary.

$$16\frac{11}{8}$$
$$-14\frac{4}{8}$$
$$\overline{2\frac{7}{8}}$$

> **Borrowing in Subtraction Rules**
> 1. Must have a common denominator.
> 2. To borrow from the whole number, make it a fractional part.
> 3. Add fractional parts.
> 4. Subtract; reduce if necessary.

Practice

1. $11 - \dfrac{5}{6}$

2. $9 - \dfrac{3}{5}$

3. $10 - \dfrac{2}{8}$

4. $13 - \dfrac{5}{9}$

5. $15 - \dfrac{7}{13}$

6. $30 - \dfrac{4}{11}$

7. $8\dfrac{2}{7} - 2\dfrac{3}{7}$

8. $14\dfrac{3}{12} - 10\dfrac{10}{12}$

9. $15\dfrac{1}{5} - 4\dfrac{4}{5}$

10. $9\dfrac{2}{4} - 5\dfrac{3}{4}$

Remember that when you are subtracting, the first rule is that you must have a common denominator. Once the common denominator is in place, borrow if necessary. Then subtract, placing the answer over the denominator; reduce as necessary.

Practice

1. $14\dfrac{2}{5} - 6\dfrac{3}{4}$

2. $34\dfrac{1}{4} - 10\dfrac{4}{5}$

3. $36\dfrac{1}{6} - 16\dfrac{3}{5}$

4. $13\dfrac{3}{4} - 7\dfrac{7}{8}$

5. $16\frac{3}{11} - 10\frac{1}{2}$

6. $19\frac{1}{2} - 15\frac{7}{12}$

7. $112\frac{1}{2} - \frac{11}{15}$

8. $18\frac{3}{7} - 2\frac{7}{14}$

9. $45\frac{3}{8} - 13\frac{3}{4}$

10. $125\frac{2}{12} - 28\frac{5}{6}$

11. $29\frac{1}{4} - 12\frac{5}{12}$

12. $12\frac{1}{6} - 1\frac{4}{5}$

13. $90\frac{4}{9} - 13\frac{3}{4}$

14. $28\frac{1}{7} - 4\frac{6}{7}$

15. $13\frac{2}{20} - 6\frac{6}{10}$

Additional Practice

1. $12\frac{1}{2} - 4\frac{7}{8}$

2. $14 - \frac{3}{7}$

3. $12\frac{1}{16} - 2\frac{5}{16}$

4. $20\frac{2}{3} - 10\frac{7}{9}$

5. $54\frac{1}{2} - 42\frac{3}{4}$

6. $22\frac{3}{5} - 17\frac{5}{6}$

7. $87 - 14\frac{2}{7}$

8. $225\frac{1}{4} - 34\frac{3}{8}$

9. $90\frac{1}{3} - 6\frac{3}{4}$

10. $45 - \frac{15}{16}$

Application 1. A patient is on a low sodium, low fat diet. Three months ago the patient weighed $210\frac{1}{4}$ pounds. Now the patient weighs $198\frac{3}{4}$ pounds. How many pounds did the patient lose?

2. The school nurse encourages all students to drink at least 4 pints of water daily. Most students drink at least $1\frac{1}{2}$ pints. How much additional water should the students consume?

3. The pharmacy technician helps with annual inventory. If there were 125 boxes of computer labels at the beginning of the inventory period, and $25\frac{3}{4}$ remain, how many boxes of labels were used throughout the year?

4. The dietitian had a 100 pound bag of unbleached flour at the beginning of the month. If she used $73\frac{1}{2}$ pounds, how much flour does she have left?

5. The recreation center is helping residents make placemats for the holidays. Each resident is given 45 inches of decorative edging per placemat. If each placemat uses $41\frac{1}{2}$ inches of decorative edging, how much edging is left over from each placemat?

Multiplication of Fractions

To facilitate multiplication and division of fractions, set up the problems horizontally.

One of the simplest computations in fractions is to multiply a common fraction. No common denominator is needed.

Example **Step 1:** Set up the problem horizontally and multiply the fraction straight across.

$$\frac{7 \times 1}{8 \times 4} \begin{array}{l} \rightarrow \\ \rightarrow \end{array} \begin{array}{l} = \\ = \end{array} \frac{7}{32}$$

Step 2: Reduce to the lowest terms, if necessary. $\frac{7}{32}$ does not need to be reduced.

Then multiply the changed numerals straight across.

$$\frac{1}{5} \times \frac{3}{2} = \frac{3}{10}$$

The answer is $^3/_{10}$. If the problem was done without canceling, the answer after multiplication would be $^6/_{20}$, which needs to be reduced to $^3/_{10}$. Reducing first saves time by allowing you to work with smaller numbers. For more complicated problems, it may be easier to cancel by writing out the number involved.

Example   **Step 1:** Write out the multiples of each number to find numbers that each can go into evenly.

$$\begin{array}{cc} (10 \times 1) & (3 \times 1) \\ \dfrac{10}{15} \quad \times & \dfrac{3}{100} \\ (3 \times 5) & (10 \times 10) \end{array}$$

Step 2: Then, begin by crossing out the matching numbers, working from top to bottom and crossing out like numbers. Cross out the matching numbers.

$$\begin{array}{cc} (\cancel{10} \times 1) & (3 \times 1) \\ \dfrac{10}{15} \quad \times & \dfrac{3}{100} \\ (\cancel{3} \times 5) & (\cancel{10} \times 10) \end{array}$$

Step 3: Then multiply the remaining numbers straight across.

$$\left.\begin{array}{ccl} (\cancel{10} \times 1) & (\cancel{3} \times 1) & \rightarrow 1 \times 1 = \underline{1} \\ \dfrac{10}{15} \quad \times & \dfrac{3}{100} & \\ (\cancel{3} \times 5) & (\cancel{10} \times 10) & \rightarrow 5 \times 10 = 50 \end{array}\right\} \dfrac{1}{50}$$

When there are more than two fractions, reducing of fractions can occur anywhere within the fraction as long as the reducing is done by the top and bottom numbers. There can be multiple reductions of fractions as well.
    For example:

$$\frac{11}{16} \times \frac{3}{12} \times \frac{8}{66} \quad \rightarrow \quad \text{Set the problem up using the factors for each number.}$$

$$\begin{array}{ccc} (11 \times 1) & (3 \times 1) & (2 \times 4) \\ \dfrac{11}{16} \quad \times & \dfrac{3}{12} \quad \times & \dfrac{8}{66} \\ (2 \times 8) & (4 \times 3) & (6 \times 11) \end{array}$$

$$\left.\begin{array}{ccc}(\cancel{11} \times 1) & (\cancel{3} \times 1) & (\cancel{2} \times \cancel{4}) \\ \dfrac{11}{16} \times & \dfrac{3}{12} \times & \dfrac{8}{66} \\ (\cancel{2} \times 8) & (\cancel{4} \times \cancel{3}) & (6 \times \cancel{11})\end{array}\right\} \quad \text{After reducing, multiply to get } \dfrac{1}{48}$$

Practice

1. $\dfrac{4}{5} \times \dfrac{15}{7}$

2. $\dfrac{12}{20} \times \dfrac{4}{24}$

3. $\dfrac{3}{7} \times \dfrac{21}{36}$

4. $\dfrac{5}{6} \times \dfrac{3}{30}$

5. $\dfrac{11}{15} \times \dfrac{3}{44}$

6. $\dfrac{3}{7} \times \dfrac{7}{11}$

7. $\dfrac{14}{20} \times \dfrac{10}{28}$

8. $\dfrac{1}{3} \times \dfrac{3}{6} \times \dfrac{2}{4}$

9. $\dfrac{11}{16} \times \dfrac{4}{12} \times \dfrac{22}{44}$

10. $\dfrac{9}{10} \times \dfrac{1}{3} \times \dfrac{8}{13}$

11. $\dfrac{8}{14} \times \dfrac{25}{48} \times \dfrac{7}{50}$

12. $\dfrac{5}{12} \times \dfrac{33}{34} \times \dfrac{17}{20} \times \dfrac{60}{66}$

Multiplication of Mixed Numbers

Mixed numbers are whole numbers with fractions. Multiplication involving mixed numbers requires that the mixed number be changed to an improper fraction.

Example   Change $1\frac{3}{4}$ into an improper fraction.

Step 1: Multiply the whole number times the denominator, then add the numerator.

$$1\frac{3}{4} \rightarrow \ 1 \times 4 + 3 = 7$$

Step 2: Place the answer from step 1 over the denominator.

$$1\frac{3}{4} \rightarrow \ 1 \times 4 + 3 = 7 \ \rightarrow \ \frac{7}{4}$$

$$\frac{7}{4} \quad \text{So } 1\frac{3}{4} = \frac{7}{4}$$

This improper fraction is not further reduced or changed. It may now be multiplied by another fraction.

Practice Change these mixed numbers into improper fractions.

1. $8\frac{1}{4}$

2. $5\frac{2}{3}$

3. $17\frac{3}{5}$

4. $24\frac{4}{7}$

5. $2\frac{3}{12}$

6. $4\frac{3}{8}$

7. $3\frac{5}{9}$

8. $12\frac{1}{4}$

9. $4\frac{5}{12}$

10. $10\frac{1}{3}$

After converting mixed numbers to improper fractions, continue by following the same rules as for multiplying common fractions.

Example $$\frac{1}{3} \times 5\frac{1}{4}$$

Step 1: Change the mixed number into an improper fraction.

$$5\frac{1}{4} \rightarrow 5 \times 4 = 20 + 1 = \frac{21}{4}$$

Step 2: Reduce, if possible.

$$(3 \times 7)$$

$$\frac{1}{3} \quad \times \quad \frac{21}{4}$$

$$(3 \times 1)$$

Step 3: Multiply straight across.

$$1 \times 7 = 7$$
$$\overline{1 \times 4 = 4}$$

Step 4: Change the improper fraction to a mixed fraction.

$$\frac{7}{4} \rightarrow 7 \div 4 = 1\frac{3}{4}$$

Example

$$3\frac{1}{4} \times 5\frac{2}{5}$$

Step 1: Change to improper fractions.

$$3\frac{1}{4} \rightarrow 3 \times 4 = 12 + 1 = \frac{13}{4} \quad \text{and}$$

$$5\frac{2}{5} \rightarrow 5 \times 5 = 25 + 2 = \frac{27}{5}$$

Step 2: Reduce, if possible.

$$\frac{13}{4} \times \frac{27}{5} \quad \text{— not possible}$$

Step 3: Multiply straight across.

$$\frac{13}{4} \times \frac{27}{5} = \frac{351}{20}$$

Step 4: Reduce — Divide 351 by 20. Write it as a mixed fraction.

$$\begin{array}{r} 17\frac{11}{20} \\ 20\overline{)351} \\ \underline{20\downarrow} \\ 151 \\ \underline{140} \\ 11 \end{array}$$ Answer: $17\frac{11}{20}$

Practice

1. $2\dfrac{5}{12} \times \dfrac{1}{7}$

2. $4\dfrac{2}{3} \times \dfrac{4}{5}$

3. $\dfrac{3}{10} \times 1\dfrac{3}{4}$

4. $2\dfrac{1}{8} \times \dfrac{6}{11}$

5. $\dfrac{4}{9} \times 1\dfrac{2}{3}$

6. $3\dfrac{5}{7} \times 2\dfrac{5}{14}$

7. $17\dfrac{1}{4} \times 2\dfrac{1}{3}$

8. $1\dfrac{1}{4} \times 2\dfrac{1}{5}$

9. $2\dfrac{1}{5} \times 1\dfrac{3}{4}$

10. $3\dfrac{1}{6} \times 3\dfrac{1}{4}$

Applications

1. A bottle of medicine contains 30 doses. How many doses are in $2\frac{1}{3}$ bottles?

2. The nurse worked a total of $2\frac{1}{4}$ hours overtime. She is paid \$32 an hour for overtime work. What are her overtime earnings?

3. One tablet contains 250 milligrams of pain medication. How many milligrams are in $3\frac{1}{2}$ tablets?

4. One cup holds 8 ounces of liquid. If a cup is $\frac{2}{3}$ full, how many ounces are in the cup?

5. The dietitian is working in a long-term care residence. Each day she prepares a high protein drink for 25 residents. If each drink measures $^3/_4$ cup, how many total cups of the drink will she prepare a day?

Division of Fractions

To divide fractions, two steps are required to compute the answer.

Example Solve: $\dfrac{1}{8} \div \dfrac{1}{4} =$ _____

Step 1: Change the sign to a × sign.

$$\frac{1}{8} \div \frac{1}{4} \rightarrow \frac{1}{8} \times \frac{1}{4}$$

Step 2: Invert the fraction to the right of the ÷ sign.

$$\frac{1}{8} \div \frac{1}{4} \rightarrow \frac{1}{8} \times \frac{4}{1}$$

This inversion causes the fraction to change from $^1/_4$ to $^4/_1$, which is called the reciprocal of $^1/_4$.

> The reciprocal of any fraction is its inverse:
>
> $$\frac{2}{3} \rightarrow \frac{3}{2} \qquad \frac{12}{35} \rightarrow \frac{35}{12} \quad \text{and} \quad \frac{9}{11} \rightarrow \frac{11}{9}$$

Step 3: Follow the steps of multiplication of fractions: Reduce if possible; then multiply straight across and reduce as necessary.

$$\text{Reduce} \quad \begin{array}{c} (4 \times 1) \\ \dfrac{1}{8} \times \dfrac{4}{1} = \\ (4 \times 2) \end{array} \quad \dfrac{1}{2}$$

Example Solve: $\dfrac{4}{9} \div \dfrac{1}{3} =$ _____

Step 1: Change the ÷ sign to an × sign.

$$\frac{4}{9} \times \frac{1}{3}$$

Step 2: Invert the fraction after the ÷ sign.

$$\frac{4}{9} \times \frac{3}{1}$$

Step 3: Multiply straight across.

Reduce

$$\frac{4}{9} \times \frac{3}{1} = \frac{12}{9}$$

$$\begin{array}{r} 1\frac{3}{9} \\ 9)\overline{12} \\ \underline{-9} \end{array}$$

The answer is $1\frac{3}{9}$. Note $\frac{3}{9}$ reduces to $\frac{1}{3}$, so the answer is $1\frac{1}{3}$.

Practice

1. $\frac{3}{7} \div \frac{3}{5}$

2. $\frac{5}{35} \div \frac{11}{21}$

3. $\frac{3}{12} \div \frac{6}{7}$

4. $\frac{7}{9} \div \frac{4}{5}$

5. $\frac{8}{9} \div \frac{1}{9}$

6. $33 \div \frac{11}{12}$

7. $\frac{1}{3} \div 15$

8. $6 \div \frac{1}{3}$

9. $\frac{7}{28} \div 30$

10. $8\frac{6}{10} \div 1\frac{4}{5}$

11. $4\frac{3}{8} \div 1\frac{2}{16}$

12. $7\frac{1}{2} \div 3\frac{1}{5}$

13. $12\frac{4}{8} \div 4\frac{1}{2}$

14. $12\frac{4}{10} \div 3\frac{1}{3}$

15. $5\frac{1}{2} \div 1\frac{1}{8}$

16. $3\dfrac{5}{8} \div 2\dfrac{1}{2}$

17. $2\dfrac{3}{14} \div 9\dfrac{2}{7}$

18. $1\dfrac{7}{9} \div \dfrac{8}{11}$

19. $10\dfrac{6}{7} \div 7\dfrac{1}{2}$

20. $1\dfrac{9}{12} \div \dfrac{1}{12}$

Applications

1. A lab technician worked $45\,^3\!/_4$ hours in 5 days. He worked the same number of hours each day. How many hours a day did he work?

2. How many $^1\!/_4$ gram doses can be obtained from a $7\,^1\!/_2$ gram vial of medication?

3. The pharmacy technician's paycheck was for $1,123.85. If the technician worked $84\,^1\!/_2$ hours, what is the hourly rate of pay?

4. The nurse must give a patient 9 milligrams of a medication. If the tablets are 2 milligrams each, how many tablets are needed?

5. The pharmacy has 5 gram vials of medication. How many $^1\!/_2$ gram doses are available?

Fraction Formula

Follow these two setups:

To convert Celsius to Fahrenheit: $\left(°C \times \dfrac{9}{5}\right) + 32 = °F$

To convert Fahrenheit to Celsius: $(°F - 32) \times \dfrac{5}{9} = °C$

The decimal unit (Unit 3) will include the formula for handling temperature conversions using decimals.

Follow these steps to change a Fahrenheit temperature to a Celsius temperature:

Example $5°C = \underline{\hspace{1cm}} °F$

Step 1: Solve within the parentheses first, and then work left to right.

$$\left(°C \times \dfrac{9}{5}\right) + 32 = °F$$

$$°C \times \frac{9}{5} \rightarrow \quad 5 \times \frac{9}{5} = \frac{45}{5} \quad 5\overline{)45}^{\,9} = 9$$
$$\underline{45}$$

Step 2: Add 32 to the step 1 answer to get the °C.

$$9 + 32 = 41 \text{ °F}$$

Fractions are used to convert between Celsius and Fahrenheit temperatures. Fractions are more accurate than decimals because there is no change in the numbers as a result of the rounding of decimals.

Practice

1. 20°C = _____ °F

2. 35°C = _____ °F

3. 25°C = _____ °F

4. 60°C = _____ °F

5. 40°C = _____ °F

6. 45°C = _____ °F

7. 80°C = _____ °F

8. 15°C = _____ °F

Follow these steps to change a Fahrenheit temperature to a Celsius temperature:

Example

$$122°F = \text{\_\_\_\_\_} °C$$

Step 1: Solve within the parenthesis first. $(°F - 32) \times \frac{5}{9} = °C$

$$
\begin{array}{ll}
°F - 32 = \text{\_\_\_\_\_} & \text{Subtract 32 from the} \\
122°F & \text{Fahrenheit temperature.} \\
\underline{-32} & \\
90 &
\end{array}
$$

Step 2: Multiply step 1 answer by $5/_9$ to get the °C.

$$90 \times \frac{5}{9} = \frac{450}{9} \quad \text{Divide 450 by 9.}$$

$$\begin{array}{r} 50 \\ 9\overline{)450} \\ 45\downarrow \\ \hline 00 \end{array}$$

So, 122°F is 50°C.

Practice   1. 104°F = _____ °C

2. 32°F = _____ °C

3. 50°F = _____ °C

4. 113°F = _____ °C

5. 59°F = _____ °C

6. 131°F = _____ °C

7. 86°F = _____ °C

8. 122°F = _____ °C

Some temperatures will require working with decimals. Additional practice will be provided in Unit 3: Decimals.

Complex Fractions

Complex fractions are used to help nurses and pharmacy technicians compute exact dosages. Complex fractions may also more efficiently solve difficult problems. A complex fraction is a fraction within a fraction.

Example

$$\dfrac{\frac{1}{4}}{6}\nwarrow \qquad \dfrac{\frac{3}{4}}{\frac{1}{100}}\nwarrow$$

These fraction lines should be viewed as a division sign.

Complex fractions are solved by using the rules of division. These examples become:

$$\frac{1}{4} \div 6 \to \frac{1}{4} \div \frac{6}{1} \to \frac{1}{4} \times \frac{1}{6} = \frac{1}{24}$$

$$\frac{3}{4} \div \frac{1}{100} \to \frac{3}{4} \div \frac{1}{100} \to \frac{3}{4} \times \frac{100}{1} = \frac{300}{4} \quad \text{Reduce to } \frac{75}{1} = 75$$

> Whole numbers require placing a 1 as a denominator prior to any division or multiplication of their digits.

Practice   Solve these complex fractions. Reduce to the lowest terms.

1. $\dfrac{\dfrac{3}{8}}{4}$

6. $\dfrac{\dfrac{3}{4}}{\dfrac{2}{3}}$

2. $\dfrac{\dfrac{1}{8}}{100}$

7. $\dfrac{\dfrac{1}{125}}{\dfrac{2}{200}}$

3. $\dfrac{\dfrac{1}{300}}{50}$

8. $\dfrac{\dfrac{1}{2}}{\dfrac{1}{4}}$

4. $\dfrac{40}{\dfrac{1}{25}}$

9. $\dfrac{\dfrac{1}{80}}{\dfrac{1}{75}}$

5. $\dfrac{\dfrac{1}{50}}{\dfrac{1}{60}}$

10. $\dfrac{\dfrac{1}{10}}{\dfrac{1}{100}}$

Dosage problems will also combine complex fractions with whole numbers and decimal numbers to compute the correct dosage. This work will be further covered in Unit 11: Dosage Calculations.

$$\dfrac{\dfrac{1}{300}}{\dfrac{1}{100}} \times 200$$

Example   These types of problems appear more difficult than they actually are. Group the work into sections so that it is manageable, and you can track your progress.

Step 1: Solve the complex fraction first by dividing it.

$$\frac{1}{300} \div \frac{1}{100} \rightarrow \frac{1}{300} \times \frac{100}{1} = \frac{100}{300} \rightarrow \text{Reduce to } \frac{1}{3}$$

Step 2: Next, rewrite the entire problem.

$$\frac{1}{3} \times 200 \qquad \text{Then work this portion of the problem.}$$

$$\frac{1}{3} \times \frac{200}{1} = \frac{200}{3} \quad \text{Reduce by dividing 200 by 3.}$$

The answer is $66\frac{2}{3}$. If the problem has a fraction it in, the answer may have a fraction in it. Do not convert this fraction to a decimal number.

Practice   Solve these problems.

1. $\dfrac{\frac{5}{8}}{\frac{1}{4}} \times 2$

4. $\dfrac{\frac{1}{125}}{\frac{1}{500}} \times 25$

2. $\dfrac{\frac{1}{200}}{\frac{1}{100}} \times 80$

5. $\dfrac{\frac{1}{3}}{\frac{1}{2}} \times 1\frac{1}{2}$

3. $\dfrac{\frac{15}{500}}{\frac{1}{100}} \times 4$

6. $\dfrac{\frac{1}{100}}{\frac{2}{25}} \times 10\frac{1}{4}$

FRACTION SELF-TEST

Reduce all answers to lowest terms.

1. A day has 24 hours. Six hours is what fractional part of the 24 hours?

2. Write two equivalent fractions for $\frac{1}{6}$.

3. Reduce $\frac{122}{11}$

4. $8\dfrac{1}{6} + 3\dfrac{3}{4}$

5. $52 - 12\dfrac{1}{5}$

6. $14\dfrac{1}{2} \times 2\dfrac{1}{8}$

7. $5\dfrac{2}{6} \div 12$

8. $77° \, \text{F} = \underline{\hspace{3em}} °\,\text{C}$

9. Order from smallest to largest: $\dfrac{3}{8}, \dfrac{1}{3}, \dfrac{1}{4}, \dfrac{2}{12}$

10. Solve: $\dfrac{\frac{1}{4}}{\frac{1}{8}} \times 25$

11. The doctor orders grain $\frac{1}{8}$ of a medicine. The nurse has grain $\frac{1}{6}$ on hand in the medicine cabinet. Will the nurse give more or less of the dose on hand? $\underline{\hspace{3em}}$

12. The physical therapist asks Mr. Smith to walk 20 minutes in one hour to improve his ambulation. What fractional part of an hour is Mr. Smith to exercise? $\underline{\hspace{3em}}$

13. Among the fractions $\frac{1}{3}, \frac{1}{5}, \frac{5}{8}$, which one is equivalent to $\frac{15}{24}$? $\underline{\hspace{3em}}$

14. On the dietitian's beverage tray, there are 16 filled six-ounce glasses. Four glasses contain prune juice and two glasses contain red wine. What fractional part of the glasses contains some beverage other than prune juice or red wine? Express the answer as a fraction. $\underline{\hspace{3em}}$

15. Sally works in a nursery. Her job includes recording an accurate weight for each baby. One baby weighs $7\frac{1}{3}$ pounds, two babies weigh $6\frac{1}{2}$ pounds, and a fourth baby weighs $5\frac{7}{8}$ pounds. What is the current total weight of the babies? $\underline{\hspace{3em}}$

Unit 3

Decimals

Decimals are used every day in health care settings. Understanding the application of decimals provides a strong foundation for measurement conversions, the metric system, medication dosages, and general charting work. Most medication orders are written using the metric system, which relies on decimals.

A decimal represents a part or fraction of a whole number. Decimal numbers are parts of 10s, 100s, 1000s, and so on. In other words, decimals are multiples of ten. The decimal point (•) represents the boundary between whole numbers and decimal numbers.

Decimal Place Values								
whole numbers					**decimal numbers**			
thousands	hundreds	tens	ones	and	tenths	hundredths	thousandths	ten-thousandths	hundred-thousandths
	1	0	4	•	9	9			

Consider $104.99. We understand this number to be one hundred four dollars and ninety-nine cents. The decimal point is the *and* if we write the number in words.

Any number to the left of the decimal point is always a whole number and any number to the right of the decimal point is a decimal number. Without a whole number, a decimal number is always less than 1. So we understand that 0.89 and 0.123 are less than 1.

Health care workers include a zero to the left of the decimal point for any decimal that does not include a whole number. This signals the reader that the dose, measurement, or amount is less than 1. The zero also helps avoid errors caused by misreading a decimal number. This does not change the value of the number.

Examples   0.89 and 0.123

Decimal Place Values

whole numbers				and	decimal numbers				
thousands	hundreds	tens	ones	and	tenths	hundredths	thousandths	ten-thousandths	hundred-thousandths
		4	2	•	1	2	5		

Reading decimal numbers is simple if you follow these tips: To read decimal numbers, say the numbers from left to right as if they were whole numbers, then add the decimal place value.

42.125 → read as forty-two and one hundred twenty-five thousandths.

> Identify decimal numbers by looking for the words that end in "th" or "ths."

Write the decimals in words using this method:

1. 0.7

2. 0.89

3. 0.05

4. 4.3

5. 150.075

6. 34.009

7. 125.023

8. 47.9

9. 18.08

10. 0.126

Write the following words in decimal numbers:

1. two tenths

2. thirteen thousandths

3. three hundred and two thousandths

4. sixteen hundredths

5. six and three hundredths

To double-check your work, the final or last number should be placed in the place value spot of the words used to describe it. If it is hundredths, then the second decimal place must have a number in it.

Example

fifty-six thousandths

0.056

↑ thousandths place

Rounding Decimals

Decimals are rounded in health care to create manageable numbers. We may have a difficult time visualizing a number such as 14.39757. However, we can easily understand the number 14.4 or 14.40. Rounding to a specific decimal place is accomplished in the same way that whole numbers are rounded. In general, health care workers round decimal numbers to the nearest tenth or the nearest hundredth.

Example Round 1.75 to the nearest tenth.

Step 1: Underline the place to which you are rounding

1.7̲5

Step 2: Circle one number to the right of the underlined number. If the circled number is 5 or greater, add 1 to the underlined number, and drop all the numbers to the right of the changed number.

1.7̲5̄   → 1.8

If the circled number is less than 5, do not change the underlined number, and drop all the numbers to the right of that number.

Sometimes a health care worker will round to the tenths place value and the whole number will be affected.

Example   Round 4.97 to the nearest tenth.

Step 1:   4.97

Step 2:   4.9⬚   4.9(Add 1 to 9) = 5.0 or 5

Practice   Round to the nearest tenth:

1. 6.74 $= 6.7$ 6. 704.95 $= 705.0$

2. 249.86 $= 249.9$ 7. 0.0943 $= 0.1$

3. 0.78 $= 0.8$ 8. 349.37 $= 349.4$

4. 3.612 $= 3.6$ 9. 9.89 $= 9.9$

5. 25.02 $= 25.0$ 10. 0.087 $= 0.1$

Round to the nearest hundredth:

1. 17.327 $= 17.33$ 6. $2,104.399 $= $2,104.40$

2. 0.975 $= 0.98$ 7. 32.651 $= 32.65$

3. 4.8166 $= 4.82$ 8. 9.27194 $= 9.27$

4. 0.0650 $= 0.07$ 9. 46.085 $= 46.09$

5. 0.0074 $= 0.01$ 10. 4.719 $= 4.72$

When and which place value to round to is a frequently asked question. General guidelines for rounding will be provided in Unit 11: Dosage Calculations.

Comparing Decimals

Comparing decimals is valuable in health occupations because many different pieces of equipment are used that may be in metric measurements. Decimals are part of the metric system, thus understanding them is necessary to determine which instrument or measurement is larger or smaller. Comparing decimals is a skill that is also useful in sorting and ordering inventory items by size.

To compare decimals, you will rely on your eyes rather than any specific math computation.

Example   Which is larger: 0.081 or 0.28?

Step 1: Line the decimals up like buttons on a shirt. This will help make the decimal numbers appear to have the same number of decimal places.

$$0.081$$
$$0.28$$

Step 2: Add zeros to fill in the empty place values so that the numbers have the same number of places or digits.

$$0.081$$
$$0.280$$

Step 3: Disregard the decimal point for a moment and read the numbers as they are written from left to right, including the added zero place values.

$$0.081 \rightarrow \text{eighty-one}$$
$$0.280 \rightarrow \text{two hundred eighty}$$

So, 0.28 is larger than 0.081.

Practice   Which decimal number is smaller?

1. 0.9 or 0.89

2. 0.025 or 0.5

3. 2.12 or 2.012

4. 0.4 or 0.04

5. 0.0033 or 0.03

Which is larger?

1. 0.0785 or 0.0195

2. 0.345 or 0.35

3. 0.5 or 0.055

4. 100.75 or 100.07

5. 0.0679 or 0.675

Using the same method, arrange the sets of numbers from largest to smallest:

1. 0.75, 7.5, 0.7, 7.075, 0.07

2. 0.01, 1.01, 10.01, 1.001

3. 0.5, 5.15, 5.55, 5.05, 0.05

4. 0.04, 0.004, 0.4, 0.044

Addition of Decimals

To add decimals, first line up the decimal points, then add. This might mean that the problem presented in a horizontal pattern may need to be rewritten in a vertical pattern.

A whole number always has a decimal point to the right side of the final number: 56 = 56.

$$2.32 + 0.14 = ? \rightarrow \quad \begin{array}{r} 2.32 \\ +0.14 \\ \hline 2.46 \end{array}$$

$$48 + 1.75 = \underline{} \rightarrow \quad \begin{array}{r} 48.00 \\ + 1.75 \\ \hline 49.75 \end{array} \leftarrow \text{Place a decimal point and fill the empty spaces with zeros.}$$

Lining up the decimals is the first step in ensuring the correct answer for the addition of decimals.

$$2.46 + 0.005 + 1.3 = \underline{} \rightarrow \quad \begin{array}{r} 2.460 \\ 0.005 \\ + 1.300 \\ \hline 3.765 \end{array} \quad \text{Fill the empty spaces with zeros.}$$

Step 1: Line up the decimals. The order of the numbers to be added is unimportant.

Step 2: Add the numbers and bring the decimal point straight down.

Practice

1. 0.9 + 36 + 1.25

2. 15.2 + 17.071 + 0.74

3. 0.11 + 86 + 0.125

4. 10.79 + 0.99 + 0.25

5. 0.0096 + 50.24 + 39

6. 0.849 + 1.6 + 56.3

7. 14.28 + 16.24 + 97

8. 0.75 + 23.87 + 124.07

9. $13.75 + 0.001 + 200.53$

10. $35.01 + 76.02 + 0.0998$

Applications

1. A 25-year-old patient receives the following medication dosages daily: 1.5 milligrams, 2.25 milligrams, and 0.75 milligrams. What is his total dosage?

2. A child weighs 15.9 kilograms. The child has gained 0.9 and 1.5 kilograms during the past two months. What is the child's current weight?

3. Patient Smith receives 4 tablets of medication dosages daily: One tablet is 225 milligrams, two tablets are 0.125 milligrams each, and one tablet is 0.75 milligrams. What is the patient's total daily dosage of medication in milligrams?

4. One tablet is labeled 124 milligrams and another is labeled 0.5 milligrams. What is the total dosage of these two tablets?

5. A child measured 122 centimeters in a semiannual checkup with the doctor. What would be the child's height at the next office visit if the child grew by 2.54 centimeter?

Subtraction of Decimals

To subtract decimals, two steps are followed:

$$95.5 - 0.76 = \underline{\hspace{1cm}}$$

Step 1: Set the problem up vertically. Put the larger number or the number from which the second number is to be subtracted above, then line up the decimals.

$$\begin{array}{r} 95.50 \\ -\,0.76 \\ \hline \end{array}$$ ← Fill in the empty places with zeros.

Step 2: Subtract and then bring the decimal straight down.

$$9^45.^{14}5^10$$
$$-\ 0.\ \ 7\ \ 6$$
$$\overline{94.\ \ 7\ \ 4}$$

Practice

1. $3.4 - 2.68 =$

2. $69.4 - 5.04 =$

3. $15 - 0.935 =$

4. $0.48 - 0.3925 =$

5. $3.7 - 0.1987 =$

6. $12 - 1.932 =$

7. $0.2 - 0.025 =$

8. $14.47 - 0.3108 =$

9. $87.56 - 0.124 =$

10. $0.07 - 0.007 =$

Applications

1. A patient started with a 1 liter bag of IV solution. When the doctor checked in on the patient, the bag contained 0.35 liters of solution. How much solution was infused into the patient?

2. A bottle of medicine contains 30 milliliters. After withdrawing 2.25 milliliters for an injection, how many milliliters of medicine remain in the bottle?

3. A patient is to receive 4.25 milligrams of a drug daily. The patient has already received 2.75 milligrams. What is his remaining dosage in milligrams?

4. Patient B is on a low fat diet. He weighed 89.9 kilograms last month. This month he weighs 88.45 kilograms. How many kilograms has he lost?

5. A patient had a temperature of 101.4°F. If after medication, the patient's temperature is 99.6°F, what is the decrease in temperature?

Multiplication of Decimals

To multiply decimals, use the same process as in whole number multiplication. Do not line up the decimals. The decimal places are counted, not aligned in decimal multiplication.

Example $4.75 \times .4$

Step 1: Write the problem vertically.

$$\begin{array}{r} 4.75 \\ \times\ \ .4 \\ \hline \end{array}$$

Step 2: Multiply the numbers.

$$\begin{array}{r} 4.75 \\ \times\ \ \ .4 \\ \hline 1900 \end{array}$$

Step 3: Count the total number of decimal places in the two numbers multiplied together. Count these places from the right in to the left. Then begin at the right of the answer and count over the same number of places and place the decimal point.

4.75
⌣⌣ 2 places
0.4
⌣ 1 place
1.900
⌣⌣⌣

Place the decimal point three places from the right. The extra zeros are dropped unless they serve a particular purpose, such as place holders for money in dollar figures.

$$\begin{array}{ll} 17.750 & \rightarrow 17.75 \\ 205.12600 & \rightarrow 205.126 \\ \$12.00 & \rightarrow \$12.00 \end{array}$$

Practice Set up multiplication problems vertically:

1. 4.2×3

2. 9.3×7

3. 21×1.6

4. 465×0.3

5. 9.17×14

6. 0.985×50

7. 6.74×0.12

8. 3.190×0.56

9. 0.278×1.7

10. 4.79×2.2

11. 0.08×0.03

12. 5.6×0.39

13. 5.175×29.2

14. $3,764 \times 13.75$

15. 9.708×0.17

16. 114.6×22.6

17. 190.8×0.04

18. 827.9×1.9

19. 574×12.095

20. 0.135×73.7

21. 53.9×24.9

22. 204.7×13.87

23. 0.347×28.95

24. 94.13×32.09

Applications   1. Village Center health care workers' earnings start at $10.52 an hour. If the employees work 40 hours per week, what is the minimum amount that each worker could earn in a week?

2. One mile has 1.6 kilometers. How many kilometers are in 35.5 miles?

3. Sheila earns $13.05 an hour. If she works 124 hours in August, what are her gross earnings for the month?

4. One kilogram equals 2.2 pounds. If patient A weighs 79.5 kilograms, what is his weight in pounds?

5. The recreation department is making placemats. The cost of materials for each placemat is $1.28. The activity director is estimating the cost of materials for 100 placemats. What is the estimated budget needed for this project?

Division of Decimals

To divide decimals, one needs to place the decimal point first, then divide the numbers. Once the decimal point is placed, it is not moved. Students have a tendency to want to move the decimal point once the division process is underway; the result is an error in decimal placement.

Follow the steps below to divide a number that has a decimal in the dividend:

Step 1: Move the decimal point straight up to the same place in the quotient. Place the decimal point and then divide the numbers.

$$6 \overline{)2.58}$$

Step 2: Divide, adding a zero in front of all decimal numbers that do not include a whole number.

$$
\begin{array}{r}
0.43 \\
6 \overline{)2.58} \\
\underline{2\,4} \\
18 \\
\underline{18} \\
0
\end{array}
$$

Practice   1. $19\overline{)11.97}$

2. $5\overline{)67.75}$

3. $2\overline{)0.464}$

4. $21\overline{)9.03}$

5. $12\overline{)1.44}$

6. $4\overline{)68.4}$

7. $32\overline{)1676.8}$

8. $17\overline{)51.17}$

9. $25\overline{)75.50}$

10. $34\overline{)2603.72}$

Zeros as Placeholders in Decimal Division

Health care students may need some practice in dividing decimals that involve zeros in the quotient. This is one area where errors are commonly made. To avoid this situation, recall that after a number has been brought down from the dividend, the divisor must be applied to that number. Place the decimal point and then divide the number. If the divisor does not go into the dividend, then a zero must be placed in the quotient. Use a zero to hold a space.

Example

$$
\begin{array}{r}
2.405 \\
14\overline{)33.67} \\
28\downarrow \\
\overline{56} \\
56\downarrow \\
\overline{07} \\
0\downarrow \\
\overline{70} \\
70 \\
\overline{0}
\end{array}
$$

Because 14 cannot go into 7, place a zero in the quotient.

Setup Tip

Remember in division problem setup

$475 \div 4.5 =$

$\longrightarrow$ *$4.5\overline{)475}$

*The last number in the problem divides into the first number.

To divide a decimal number by a decimal number, change the divisor to a whole number by moving the decimal point to the right. Then move the decimal point in the dividend the same number of places. Use zeros as placeholders if needed. Then place the decimal point and divide.

For example, $0.42\overline{)0.6216}$

Step 1: Move the decimal $0.42\overline{)0.6216}$ Rewrite → $42\overline{)62.16}$
                                  ∪∪ ∪∪

Step 2: Divide $42\overline{)62.16}$

Practice

1. 530 ÷ 0.5

2. 0.081 ÷ 9

3. 66.56 ÷ 32

4. 0.022 ÷ 11

5. 3.297 ÷ 3

6. 0.6250 ÷ 5

7. 183.96 ÷ 6

8. 6.030 ÷ 3

9. 0.18891 ÷ 0.9

10. 12.24 ÷ 4

Additional Practice

1. $0.5\overline{)2.65}$

2. $0.04\overline{)6.48}$

3. $2.6\overline{)0.104}$

4. $0.55\overline{)141.35}$

5. $3.8\overline{)5.282}$

6. $0.7\overline{)78.75}$

7. $0.02\overline{)8.078}$

8. $0.3\overline{)4.608}$

Simplified Multiplication and Division of Decimals

Using the shortcuts of simplified multiplication and division can save time in working with decimals. In health-care fields, this shortcut is important to your work in metrics and in efficiently working longer problems.

This shortcut only works with multiples of ten: 10, 100, 1,000, etc. The process is straightforward. To multiply, move the decimal point to the right. To divide, move the decimal point to the left. The number of spaces depends on which multiple you are working with. Look at the number of zeros included in the multiple, then move the decimal in either direction depending on the operation: multiplication or division, the same number of spaces and the number of zeros.

Simplified Multiplication

To multiply by 10, locate the decimal point and move it to the right by one place.

To multiply by 100, locate the decimal point and move it to the right by two places.

To multiply by 1,000, locate the decimal point and move it to the right by three places.

Whole numbers have their decimal places to the far right of the last digit: $9 = 9., 75 = 75., 125 = 125.$

Example
$$4.5 \times 10 = 45 \qquad 4.5$$
$$4.5 = 45 \qquad \underline{\times\ 10}$$
$$\cup \qquad\qquad 45.0 \qquad \text{(The Zero is dropped.)}$$

Note that the answer is the same if the problem is worked the long way. Sometimes zeros must be added as placeholders.

In simplified multiplication locate the decimal point, count the zeros in the divisor and move the decimal point the same number of places to the right.

Example Zeros must fill the spaces if needed.

$$34.7 \times 1000 = \underline{\quad\quad}$$
$$34.7\,0\,0 =$$
$$\cup\cup\cup \rightarrow 34{,}700$$

Practice
1. 13.5×10

2. 4.56×100

3. 125.75×10

4. $1{,}000 \times 45.3$

5. 0.06×100

6. 0.234×10

7. $12.67 \times 1,000$

8. 0.975×100

9. $0.476 \times 1,000$

10. 87×10

11. 1.345×10

12. $98.345 \times 1,000$

13. 1.009×10

14. 32.901×100

15. $23.850 \times 1,000$

Simplified Division

To divide by 10, locate the decimal point and move it to the left by one place.

To divide by 100, locate the decimal point and move it to the left by two places.

To divide by 1,000, locate the decimal point and move it to the left by three places.

In simplified division, locate the decimal point, count the zeros in the divisor and move the decimal point the same number of places to the left.

Example $9.5 \div 10 =$ _____ $0.75 \div 100 =$ _____
              9.5   0 0 0.75 → 0.0075   Zeros must be used to fill
              U → 0.95   UU   in places if needed.

Practice   1. $12.9 \div 10$

2. $45.56 \div 100$

3. $125 \div 10$

4. $98.762 \div 1,000$

5. $0.25 \div 10$

6. $176.5 \div 100$

7. 15.8 ÷ 100

8. 3,234 ÷ 10

9. 32.50 ÷ 100

10. 0.09 ÷ 10

11. 10,010 ÷ 1,000

12. 9,765 ÷ 1,000

13. 3.076 ÷ 100

14. 429.6 ÷ 1,000

15. 10.275 ÷ 100

Applications

1. A nursing student spends $379.50 for textbooks. If the student purchases six textbooks, what is the average cost of each book?

2. A patient's goal is to lose 24.6 pounds. The doctor wants the patient to lose these pounds slowly, over a twelve-month period. How many pounds should the patient attempt to lose each month?

3. Doctor Brown prescribed a medication dosage of 4.5 grams. How many 1.5 grams tablets need to be administered?

4. The dietitian serves a protein dish at three meals. If the total daily grams of protein are 225.9 grams, assuming that the grams are equally divided for the three meals a day, what is the average meal's grams of protein?

5. Bob made $131.20 in 5 hours. What is his hourly wage?

Changing Decimals to Fractions

It is important to be able to convert between number systems so that you are comfortable with comparing sizes of items or quantities of supplies. Changing decimals to fractions requires the use of decimal places and placing the numbers in fractions that represent the very same numbers.

Example   Convert 0.457 to a fraction.

Step 1: To convert a decimal to a fraction, count the number of decimal places in the decimal number.

$$0.\underline{4}\,\underline{5}\,\underline{7}$$ Three decimal places means thousandths in decimal numbers.

Step 2: Write the number 457 as the numerator and 1,000 as the denominator.

$$\frac{457}{1,000}$$

Step 3: Reduce if necessary $\frac{457}{1,000}$ cannot be reduced. The answer is $\frac{457}{1,000}$.

Example   Convert 2.75 to a fraction.

Step 1: Place 2 as the whole number. Your answer is going to be a mixed number because there is a whole number. Count the decimal places in $.\underline{7}\,\underline{5}$ = two places.

$$2 \underline{\hspace{2cm}}$$

Step 2: Write 75 as the numerator and 100 as the denominator.

$$2\frac{75}{100}$$

Step 3: Reduce the fraction to $2^{3}/_{4}$ because

$$\frac{75}{100} = \frac{\cancel{25} \times 3}{\cancel{25} \times 4} \rightarrow \frac{3}{4}$$

The answer is $2\frac{3}{4}$.

Practice   Convert the decimals to fractions:

1. 0.04

2. 0.025

3. 6.25

4. 1.78

5. 225.05

6. 10.5

7. 7.75

8. 0.08

9. 9.3

10. 100.46

Changing Fractions to Decimals

To change fractions to decimals, divide the denominator into the numerator. Critical to the success of this division is the placement of the decimal point. Once it is placed, do not move it.

Example Change $\frac{3}{4}$ to a decimal. Divide the denominator into the numerator. Place a decimal point after 3 and also in the quotient. Then add a zero after 3 and divide. Add zeros as needed to continue the division process.

$$
\begin{array}{r}
.75 \\
4\overline{)3.0} \\
28\downarrow \\
\hline
20 \\
20 \\
\hline
0
\end{array}
$$

Example Change $\frac{1}{3}$ into a decimal. Divide 3 into 1. Place the decimal point. Add zeros as needed to continue division. The division may not come out evenly but rather begin to repeat itself. After two places, make the remainder into a fraction by putting the remaining number over the divisor.

$$
\begin{array}{r}
.33\frac{1}{3} \\
3\overline{)1.0} \\
9\downarrow \\
\hline
10 \\
9 \\
\hline
1
\end{array}
$$

When the decimal answer is a number like 0.50, drop the final zero so that the answer is 0.5.

Practice   1. $\dfrac{1}{2}$

2. $\dfrac{3}{5}$

3. $\dfrac{7}{8}$

4. $\dfrac{1}{6}$

5. $\dfrac{6}{25}$

6. $\dfrac{5}{12}$

7. $\dfrac{3}{15}$

8. $\dfrac{7}{10}$

9. $\dfrac{5}{6}$

10. $\dfrac{3}{18}$

Temperature Conversions with Decimals

The following temperature conversions include decimals. Round the decimal numbers in temperatures to the nearest tenth place. The temperature conversion used in Unit 2: Fractions, relied on fractions. The same fraction method can be converted into a decimal method. In deciding which method to use, select the method of fractions or decimals based on your strongest skill. Then consistently use that conversion formula.

Decimal Conversion Formula

To convert Celsius to Fahrenheit, ($^\circ$C $\times$ 1.8) + 32 = $^\circ$F

To convert Fahrenheit to Celsius, ($^\circ$F − 32) ÷ 1.8 = $^\circ$C

Example   To convert from Celsius to Fahrenheit

$$41^\circ\text{C} = \underline{\hspace{1cm}} \,^\circ\text{F}$$

Step 1: Solve the parentheses first, and then work left to right. Multiply the Celsius temperature by 1.8. The number 1.8 is the decimal form of $\frac{9}{5}$.

$$
\begin{array}{r}
41 \\
\times\ 1.8 \\
\hline
328 \\
41 \\
\hline
73.8
\end{array}
$$

Step 2: Add 32 to the step 1 answer.

$$
\begin{array}{r}
73.8 \\
+\ 32 \\
\hline
105.8
\end{array}
$$

The answer is 105.8°F.

To convert from Fahrenheit to Celsius

Step 1: Subtract the 32 from the Fahrenheit temperature.

$$
\begin{array}{r}
107.6 \\
-\ 32 \\
\hline
75.6
\end{array}
$$

Step 2: Divide the step 1 answer by 1.8.

$$
\rightarrow 1.8 \overline{)75.6} \rightarrow
\begin{array}{r}
42. \\
18\overline{)756.} \\
72 \\
\hline
36 \\
36 \\
\hline
0
\end{array}
$$

The answer is 42°C.

Practice

1. 34°C = _____ °F

2. 46.6°F = _____ °C

3. 107°C = _____ °F

4. 101.5°F = _____ °C

5. 42°C = _____ °F

6. 40°F = _____ °C

7. 100.4°F = _____ °C

8. 69°C = _____ °F

9. 12°C = _____ °F

10. 105.8°F = _____ °C

Solving Mixed Fraction and Decimal Problems

Sometimes problems will include both fractions and decimals. The very same processes of solving the problems are still needed; however, the order of handling the parts of the problem may vary. Group the math computations inside the problem to best manage the separate operations.

> If the problem has a complex fraction multiplied by a decimal number, work the complex fraction first. Then complete the decimal multiplication.

Example

$$\dfrac{\frac{1}{2}}{\frac{1}{5}} \times 2.2 =$$

Step 1:
$$\frac{1}{2} \div \frac{1}{5} \rightarrow \frac{1}{2} \times \frac{5}{1} = \frac{5}{2}$$

Reduce to $2\frac{1}{2}$. Make the $\frac{1}{2}$ into .5 so that the multiplication is easy. So by first working the complex fraction, the answer is 2.5.

Step 2: Multiply 2.5 × 2.2.

$$
\begin{array}{r}
2.5 \\
\times\ 2.2 \\
\hline
50 \\
50 \\
\hline
5.50
\end{array}
$$

The answer to this mixed problem is 5.5.

> If the problem includes a decimal number, solve the decimals by first multiplying straight across, then complete the process by dividing that answer by the denominator. This allows for the division of decimals only once, and it saves time.

Example

$$\frac{0.25}{0.5} \times 1.5$$

Step 1: Multiply 0.25×1.5.

$$
\begin{array}{r}
0.25 \\
\times\ 1.5 \\
\hline
125 \\
25 \\
\hline
0.375
\end{array}
$$

Step 2: Divide 0.375 by 0.5.

$$0.5\overline{)0.375}$$

$$
\begin{array}{r}
0.75 \\
0.5\overline{)0.375} \\
0.35 \\
\hline
0025 \\
0025 \\
\hline
0
\end{array}
$$

The answer is 0.75.

Practice

1. $\dfrac{\frac{1}{200}}{\frac{1}{100}} \times 4.4$

2. $\dfrac{0.8}{0.64} \times 4.5$

3. $\dfrac{\frac{3}{4}}{\frac{1}{4}} \times 2.5$

4. $\dfrac{0.75}{0.15} \times 1.5$

5. $\dfrac{0.002}{0.125} \times 10.5$

6. $\dfrac{\frac{1}{12}}{\frac{1}{6}} \times 3.6$

7. $\dfrac{0.005}{0.01} \times 15.35$

8. $\dfrac{7\frac{1}{2}}{1\frac{1}{2}} \times 5.4$

DECIMAL SELF-TEST

1. Write in words: 0.045

2. What is the sum of 1.7, 19, 0.25, and 0.8?

3. $17 - 0.075$

4. 4.5×1.009

5. $18.04 \div 0.2$

6. Round to the nearest hundredth: 978.735

7. Order these decimals from largest to smallest: 0.81, 0.080, 0.018, 8.018.

8. 10.009×100

9. A child receives 0.5 milligrams of a drug 4 times a day. How many milligrams is the child's daily dose?

10. A patient receives 2.25 grams of a medication daily. Tablets come in 0.75 gram dosages. How many tablets does the patient take daily?

11. Convert this decimal to a fraction: 0.125

12. Convert this fraction to a decimal: $\dfrac{13}{50}$

13. Convert this fraction to a decimal: $3\dfrac{5}{8}$

14. Convert 103° Fahrenheit to °Celsius.

15. Solve:

$$\dfrac{0.136}{0.2} \times 2.5$$

Unit 4

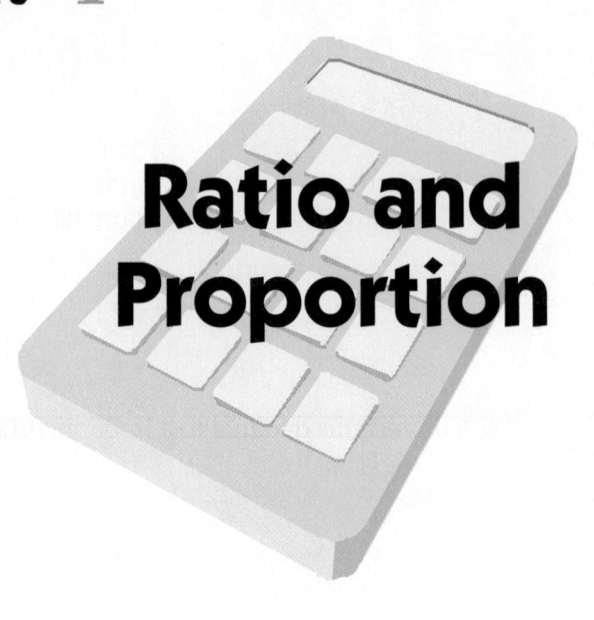

Ratio and Proportion

Ratio

A ratio is used to show a relationship between two numbers. These numbers are separated by a colon (:) as in 3 : 4. Ratios may be presented in three formats that provide the setup for solving proportions.

    a. 3 : 4

    b. $\dfrac{3}{4}$

    c. 3 is to 4

The relationship can represent something as simple as the 1 : 3 ratio commonly used to mix frozen juices. We use 1 can of frozen juice concentrate to 3 cans of water. Ratios are fractions that represent a part-to-whole relationship. Ratios are always reduced to their lowest form. For example, 8 hours of sleep to 24 hours in a day

$$8 : 24 \rightarrow \frac{8}{24} \quad \frac{8 \times 1}{8 \times 3} = \frac{1}{3}, \quad \text{so the ratio is } 1 : 3.$$

Write the following relationships as ratios using a colon. Reduce to the lowest terms, if necessary.

1. 5 days out of 7 days

2. eight teeth out of thirty-two teeth

3. 3 students out of 15 students

4. 16 scalpels to 45 syringes

5. 7 inlays to 14 crowns

Simplifying ratios is an important skill. To simplify a ratio, divide the first number by the second.

For example, simplify the following ratio: $4\frac{1}{2} : 6$

$$4\frac{1}{2} \div 6 \rightarrow \frac{9}{2} \div \frac{6}{1} \rightarrow \frac{9}{2} \times \frac{1}{6} = \frac{9}{12} \rightarrow \frac{3 \times 3}{3 \times 4} = \frac{3}{4}$$ which becomes $3 : 4$ as a simplified ratio.

The answer is $3 : 4$.

For example, simplify the following ratio: $11\frac{1}{4}$

Convert the mixed number into an improper fraction, then reduce if necessary.

$$11\frac{1}{4} \rightarrow 11 \times 4 + 1 = 45 \rightarrow \frac{45}{4} = 45 : 4$$

The answer is $45 : 4$.

Simplify the following ratios. Write each answer as a ratio.

1. $45 : 1\frac{2}{3}$ = _____

2. $\frac{120}{100} : 12$ = _____

3. $15 : \frac{3}{4}$ = _____

4. $\frac{1}{3} : 45$ = _____

5. $0.8 : \frac{2}{5}$ = _____

6. $\frac{1}{2} : \frac{1}{8}$ = _____

7. $4\frac{1}{3} : 7$ = _____

8. $0.875 : \frac{1}{4}$ = _____

9. $2\frac{1}{2}$ = _____

10. $\frac{2}{3} : 0.33$ = _____

Proportion

Proportions can be applied to almost every health care profession in one way or another. In addition to on-the-job applications, proportions provide a simple and quick method for solving many everyday math problems such as measurement conversions, recipe conversions for increasing or decreasing the amounts of ingredients, and map mileage.

Proportions are *two or more equivalent ratios or fractions*. The terms of the first ratio/fraction have the same relationship of part to whole as the second ratio/fraction.

Example

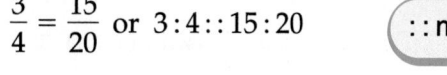

$$\frac{3}{4} = \frac{15}{20} \text{ or } 3:4::15:20 \qquad \boxed{::\text{ means }=}$$

Test the two ratios/fractions to see whether they are equivalent by multiplying diagonally (cross multiply).

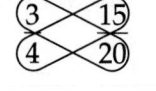 $4 \times 15 = 60$ and $3 \times 20 = 60$. This is a proportion.

If the two numbers that are diagonal result in the same answer when they are multiplied, you are working with a proportion.

Proportions are powerful tools in health care. You can rely on them for solving a majority of your math conversions and problems. Check to see if the following ratios are proportions:

Are these ratios proportions?

1. $5:2 = 4:1$ _____ Yes _____ No

2. $16:15 = 8:7$ _____ Yes _____ No

3. $40:30 = 4:3$ _____ Yes _____ No

4. $10:16 = 5:8$ _____ Yes _____ No

5. $100:1 = 50:2$ _____ Yes _____ No

Solving for *x*

The ratio and proportion method of solving for *x* is done in two steps.

Step 1: Set the problems up like fractions. If units of measure such as inches and feet are given, place inches across from inches and feet across from feet. Then cross multiply (diagonally) the two numbers. Set the ratios up like fractions using a vertical line.

$$\frac{3}{4} = \frac{?}{16} \qquad 3 \times 16 = 48$$

Step 2: Divide the answer from step 1 by the remaining number.

$$
\begin{array}{r}
12 \\
4\overline{)48} \\
\underline{4\downarrow} \\
8 \\
\underline{8}
\end{array}
$$

The quotient 12 is the answer to ? or x. This method is an easy way to find the answers for measurement conversions, dosage conversions, and math questions that provide part but not all of the information.

Practice Solve for x or ?

1. $20 : 40 = x : 15$

2. $x : 1 = 5 : 10$

3. $4 : 8 = 8 : x$

4. $7 : x = 21 : 24$

5. $3 : 9 = ? : 81$

6. $13 : 39 = 1 : ?$

7. $2 : 11 = ? : 77$

8. $x : 125 = 5 : 25$

9. $2 : 26 = 4 : ?$

10. $1 : x = 5 : 200$

Using ratios is often the simplest method of solving other health care math problems, such as dosage calculations and measurement problems.

Example Zoe weighs 35 pounds. The doctor ordered a drug that relies on milligrams of medication to kilograms of body weight. The pharmacy technician will need to convert pounds to kilograms. By using the ratio of 1 kilogram to 2.2 pounds, the answer is quickly computed.

known	*unknown*
1 kilogram	?
2.2 pounds	35 pounds

Step 1: Multiply the numbers diagonally.

$$1 \times 35 = 35$$

Step 2: Divide 35 by 2.2. The answer is 15.9 kilograms.

So 35 pounds equals 15.9 kilograms.

Example How many pounds are in 24 ounces?

Set the problem up by placing what you know on the left side of the equation and what you do not know on the right. If you set up all your problems with the known on the left and the unknown on the right, you will have less information for the brain to process because the pattern will be familiar to you.

$$\frac{known}{} \qquad \frac{unknown}{}$$

$$\frac{1 \text{ pound}}{16 \text{ ounces}} \qquad \frac{? \text{ pounds}}{24 \text{ ounces}}$$

Step 1: $1 \times 24 = 24$

Step 2: $24 \div 16 = 1.5$

The answer is $1\frac{1}{2}$ pounds or 1.5 pounds.
An answer for a ratio may have a decimal or a fraction in it.

Example Bob is 176 centimeters (cm) tall. How tall is he in inches? Round the answer to the nearest tenth.

$$\frac{known}{} \qquad \frac{unknown}{}$$

$$\frac{1 \text{ inch}}{2.54 \text{ cm}} \qquad \frac{? \text{ inches}}{176 \text{ cm}}$$

Step 1: $1 \times 176 = 176$

Step 2: $176 \div 2.54 = 69.29$

Rounded to the nearest tenth.
The answer is 69.3 inches.

$$
\begin{array}{r}
69.29 \\
254\overline{)17600} \\
1524\!\downarrow \\
\hline
2360 \\
2286\!\downarrow \\
\hline
740 \\
508\!\downarrow \\
\hline
2320 \\
2286 \\
\hline
34
\end{array}
$$

Some basic guidelines need to be followed for formatting answers in measurement conversions:

If the answer is in feet, yards, cups, pints, quarts, gallons, teaspoons, tablespoons, or pounds, use fractions if there is a remainder.

If the answer is in kilograms, milliliters, or money amounts, use decimals. The correct format ensures correct answers.

Approximate Equivalents

1 inch	= 2.54 centimeters	1 cup	= 8 ounces
1 foot	= 12 inches	1 pint	= 500 milliliters
1 yard	= 3 feet	1 quart	= 32 ounces
1 pound	= 16 ounces	1 quart	= 1,000 milliliters
1 kilogram	= 2.2 pounds		
1 tablespoon	= 3 teaspoons	1 fluid ounce	= 30 milliliters
1 quart	= 2 pints	1 teaspoon	= 5 milliliters
1 gallon	= 4 quarts	1 fluid ounce	= 2 tablespoons

Notice that the conversions are set up so that the unit (1) elements are all on the left and that these will be placed on the top of the known part of the ratio and proportion equation. This simplifies the learning process, expedites learning, and helps recall of these conversions.

Practice Because inches are rounded to the nearest tenth, go to the hundredth place and then stop multiplying. At that point, you will have enough information to round to the nearest tenth.

Using this ratio and proportion setup, solve the following conversions.

$$\frac{known}{\rule{2cm}{0.4pt}} = \frac{unknown}{\rule{2cm}{0.4pt}}$$

Set up these conversions using ratios and proportions.

1. 23 feet = _____ yards → $\dfrac{1 \text{ yd}}{3 \text{ ft}} = \dfrac{?}{23 \text{ ft}}$

2. 12 quarts = _____ gallons

3. 4 quarts = _____ pints

4. 4 pints = _____ cups

5. 3 tablespoons = _____ teaspoons

6. $2\frac{1}{2}$ quarts = _____ milliliters

7. $\frac{1}{2}$ cup = _____ ounces

8. 1 injection at \$29.50 = 3 injections at _____

9. $3\frac{1}{2}$ pounds = _____ ounces

10. 3 medicine cups = _____ milliliters

    (One medicine cup equals 1 fluid ounce)

11. 12.5 mL = _____ teaspoons

12. 5 fluid ounces = _____ tablespoons

13. _____ tablespoons = 15 teaspoons

14. 64 ounces = _____ cups

15. 750 milliliters = _____ pints

16. 48 inches = _____ feet

17. 5 pounds = _____ ounces

18. _____ quarts = 5,000 milliliters

29. _____ kilograms = 11 pounds

20. $3\frac{1}{2}$ cups = _____ ounces

More practice with conversions of measurements between systems and with multiple steps in conversions will be given in Unit 6: Combined Applications.

Word Problems Using Proportions

When solving word problems involving proportions, follow these two basic steps:

Step 1: Set the problem up so that the same type of elements are directly across from one another.

Example If 12 eggs cost \$1.49, how much do 18 eggs cost?

$$\frac{\text{Eggs}}{\text{Cost}} = \frac{\text{Eggs}}{\text{Cost}} \rightarrow \frac{12\,\text{eggs}}{\$1.49} = \frac{18\,\text{eggs}}{\$?}$$

Step 2: Ensure that the story problem is understood, then place the known information on the left side of the proportion and the unknown on the right. By doing so, you will not switch the ratio relationships, but rather rely on the known part to whole relationships.

1. A caplet contains 325 milligrams of medication. How many caplets contain 975 milligrams of medication?

2. If a dose of 100 milligrams is contained in 4 cubic centimeters, how many cubic centimeters are in 40 milligrams?

3. If 35 grams of pure drug are contained in 150 milliliters, how many grams are contained in 75 milliliters?

4. Two tablets of ulcer medication contain 350 milligrams of medication. How many milligrams are in twelve tablets?

5. If 1 kilogram equals 2.2 pounds, how many kilograms are in 61.6 pounds?

Solving for *X* in More Complex Problems Using Proportion

Decimals and fractions may appear in your proportion problems. Although the numbers may be visually distracting, the *very* same principles apply.

Example　　　　　　　$0.25 \text{ mg} : 0.8 \text{ mL} = 0.125 \text{ mg} : x \text{ mL}$

Step 1: Place mg across from mg and mL across from mL. Place the known information on the left side of the equation and the unknown on the right.

$$\frac{\overset{known}{0.25 \text{ mg}}}{0.8 \text{ mL}} \quad \frac{\overset{unknown}{0.125 \text{ mg}}}{x \text{ mL}}$$

Cross multiply $0.8 \times 0.125 \text{ mg} = 0.1$.

Step 2: $0.1 \div 0.25 = 0.4 \text{ mL}$

Example

$$\frac{1}{8} : \frac{1}{2} :: 1 : x$$

Step 1: Set up and cross multiply. Multiply $\frac{1}{2} \times 1 = \frac{1}{2}$.

$$\frac{1/8}{1/2} = \frac{1}{x}$$

Step 2: Divide $\frac{1}{2}$ by $\frac{1}{8}$.

$$\frac{1}{2} \div \frac{1}{8} \rightarrow \frac{1}{2} \times \frac{8}{1} = \frac{8}{2}, \quad \text{which is reduced to 4.}$$

Sometimes you will find that medical dosages have both fractions and decimals in the problems. Analyze the situation and convert the numbers into the same system. As a general rule, fractions are always more accurate for calculating than decimals because some decimal numbers have repeating digits, which create variable answers.

Example

$$\frac{1}{16} : 1.6 :: \frac{1}{8} x$$

Step 1: Convert 1.6 into a fraction. So $1.6 = 1\frac{6}{10}$. Then multiply $1\frac{6}{10} \times \frac{1}{8} = \frac{2}{10}$

$$\frac{1/16}{1\frac{6}{10}} = \frac{1/8}{x} \qquad 1\frac{6}{10} \times \frac{1}{8} = \frac{16}{10} \times \frac{1}{8} = \frac{16}{80} \text{ or } \frac{2}{10}$$

Step 2: Divide $\frac{2}{10}$ by $\frac{1}{16}$.

$$\frac{2}{10} \div \frac{1}{16} \rightarrow \frac{2}{10} \times \frac{16}{1} = \frac{32}{10} \quad \text{Reduced to } 3\frac{2}{10} \rightarrow 3\frac{1}{5}.$$

Practice Include a unit of measure in your answer. Round any partial unit to the nearest tenth.

> Tablets can be divided if they are scored; use $\frac{1}{2}$ not 0.5

1. $1.5 \text{ mg} : 2 \text{ caps} = 4.5 \text{ mg} : x \text{ caps}$

2. $8 \text{ mg} : 2.5 \text{ mL} = 4 \text{ mg} : x \text{ mL}$

3. $12.5 \text{ mg} : 5 \text{ mL} = 24 \text{ mg} : x \text{ mL}$

4. $0.3 \text{ mg} : 1 \text{ tab} = 6 \text{ mg} : x \text{ tabs}$

5. grains $\frac{1}{4} : 15 \text{ mg} = $ grains $? : 60 \text{ mg}$

6. $x \text{ mg} : \frac{1}{2} \text{ tab} = 6 \text{ mg} : 4 \text{ tabs}$

7. grains $\frac{1}{100} : 2 \text{ mL} = $ grains $\frac{1}{15c} : x \text{ mL}$

8. $600 \text{ mg} : 1 \text{ cap} = x \text{ mg} : 2 \text{ caps}$

9. $1000 \text{ units} : 1 \text{ mL} = 2400 \text{ units} : x \text{ mL}$

10. $1 \text{ tab} : 0.1 \text{ mg} = x \text{ tabs} : 0.15 \text{ mg}$

11. A drug comes in 100 milligram tablets. If the doctor orders 150 milligrams daily, how many tablets should the patient receive daily?

12. A medical chart states that the patient weighs 78.4 kilograms. What is the patient's weight in pounds? Round to the nearest tenth.

Nutritional Application of Proportions

Carbohydrates, fats, and protein provide fuel factors for our bodies. The factors are easily applied by using proportions to solve for the unknown.

> Carbohydrates → 4 calories per 1 gram
>
> Fats   → 9 calories per 1 gram
>
> Proteins   → 4 calories per 1 gram

Example   400 carbohydrate calories = _____ grams

$$\underset{\text{known}}{\frac{1 \text{ gram}}{4 \text{ calories}}} \qquad \underset{\text{unknown}}{\frac{? \text{ grams}}{400 \text{ calories}}}$$

Step 1: Multiply diagonally.

$$1 \times 400 = 400$$

Step 2: Divide answer from step 1 (400) by the remaining number in the equation (4).

$$\begin{array}{r} 100 \\ 4\overline{)400} \\ \underline{4} \\ 00 \end{array}$$

So 400 carbohydrate calories are available in 100 grams of carbohydrates.

Use proportion to solve the following problems:

1. 81 calories of fat = _____ grams

2. 120 calories of protein = _____ grams

3. 36 calories of carbohydrate = _____ grams

4. 145 calories of carbohydrate = _____ grams

5. _____ calories in 12 grams of protein

6. _____ calories in 99 grams of fat

7. _____ calories in 328 grams of carbohydrate

8. _____ calories in 2450 grams of protein

Proportion is also useful in solving measurement problems that have to do with amounts of sodium, calories, fat, and protein in food or an amount in a drug dosage. The proportion will use the information in a scenario to solve for the unknown quantities in a specific amount.

Example   If one glass of milk contains 280 milligrams of calcium, how much calcium is in $1\frac{1}{2}$ glasses of milk?

$$\frac{1 \text{ glass}}{280 \text{ milligrams}} = \frac{1\frac{1}{2} \text{ glasses}}{? \text{ milligrams}}$$

$$280 \times 1\frac{1}{2} = 420 \text{ mg of calcium}$$

1. One-half cup of baked beans contains 430 milligrams of sodium. How many milligrams of sodium are there in $\frac{3}{4}$ cup of baked beans?

2. Baked beans contain 33 grams of carbohydrates in a $\frac{1}{2}$ cup serving. How many milligrams of carbohydrates are in three $\frac{1}{2}$ cup servings?

3. A $\frac{1}{2}$ cup serving of fruit cocktail contains 55 milligrams of potassium. How many milligrams of potassium are in 2 cups of fruit cocktail?

4. If $\frac{1}{2}$ cup of fruit cocktail contains 13 grams of sugar, then $1\frac{1}{4}$ cup of fruit cocktail contains how many grams of sugar?

5. Old-fashioned oatmeal contains 27 grams of carbohydrates per $\frac{1}{2}$ cup of dry oats. How many grams of carbohydrates are available in $2\frac{1}{4}$ cups of the dry oats?

Practice with Food Labels

Carefully read the label and then use the information from the label to solve each question.

Albert's Tomato Soup

Nutrition facts	Amount/serving %DV*		Amount/serving %DV*	
Serving size ½ cup (120 ml)	Total fat 0 g	0%	Total carbohydrates 20 g	7%
Condensed soup	Saturated fat 0 g	0%	Fiber 1 g	4%
Servings about 2.5	Cholesterol 0 mg	0%	Sugars 15 g	
Calories 90	Sodium 710 mg	30%	Protein 2 g	
Fat calories 0	Vitamin A 12% · Vitamin C 12% · Calcium 0% · Iron 0%			

*Percent daily values (%DV) are based on a 2,000 calorie diet.

1. If $\frac{1}{2}$ cup of soup equals 120 milliliters, then how many milliliters (mL) are in $3\frac{1}{2}$ cups of soup?

2. If a can has 2.5 servings, how many cans are needed to serve 10 people?

3. One serving contains 90 calories, how many calories are in $4\frac{1}{2}$ servings?

4. One gram of fiber constitutes 4% of a daily dietary value. How many grams of fiber would be present in 25% of the daily value?

5. How many grams of carbohydrates are present if the portion meets 15% of the daily value of carbohydrates? Round to the nearest tenth.

Use the information from the label to complete these proportions.

Big Al's Organic Sweet and Juicy Dried Plums

Nutrition facts Serving size 1½ oz (40 g in about 5 dried plums) Servings per container about 30		Amount per serving Calories 100 Calories from fat 0	
	%DV*		%DV*
Total fat 0 g	0%	Potassium 290 mg	8%
Saturated fat 0 g	0%	Total carbohydrates 24 g	8%
Cholesterol 0 mg	0%	Dietary fiber 3 g	11%
Sodium 5 mg	0%	Soluble fiber 1 g	
Vitamin A 10% (100% as beta carotene)		Insoluble fiber 1 g	
Vitamin C 0%	·	Sugars 12 g	
Calcium 2%		Protein 1 g	
Iron 2%		**Big Al's Organic Sweet and Juicy Dried Plums/Prunes**	

*Percent daily values (%DV) are based on a 2,000 calorie diet. Your daily values may be higher or lower depending on your calorie needs.

6. How many total grams (g) of weight are present in 34 prunes?

7. If 100 calories are consumed with 5 prunes, how many calories are consumed with 12 prunes?

8. If 5 prunes have 290 milligrams (mg) of potassium and that accounts for 8% of percent daily value, how many prunes are needed to equal 15% of the percent daily value? Round to the nearest whole number.

9. If 5 prunes equals 10% of the Vitamin A needed daily, what percent of the daily % of Vitamin A is present in 20 prunes?

10. If a serving size is $1\frac{1}{2}$ ounces (oz), how many ounces are five servings?

Use the information from the label to complete these proportions.

Jade's Soy Milk

Nutrition facts	Amount/serving %DV*		Amount/serving %DV*	
Serving size 1 cup (240 ml)	Total fat 4 g	6%	Total Carbohydrates 4 g	1%
Servings about 8 per 1.89 L	Saturated fat 0.5 g	3%	Fiber 1 g	4%
Calories 80	Trans fat 0 g		Cholesterol 0 mg	0%
Fat calories 35	Polyunsaturated fat 2.5 g		Sugars 12 g	
	Monounsaturated fat 1 g		Protein 7 g	
	Sodium 85 mg 4%		Potassium 300 mg 8%	
	Vitamin A 10% · Vitamin C 0% · Calcium 30% · Iron 6%			
	Vitamin D 10% · Folate 6% · Magnesium 10% · Selenium 8%			

*Percent daily values (%DV) are based on a 2,000 calorie diet.

11. If 1 cup of soup contains 4 grams (g) total fat, then how many grams of total fat are in $2\frac{3}{4}$ cups of Jade's Soy Milk?

12. If a cup of soy milk contains 85 milligrams of sodium, and an individual consumes $2\frac{2}{3}$ cups of soy milk per day, what is the sodium intake from soy milk? Round to the nearest whole number.

13. If one serving of Jade's Soy Milk provides 1% of the daily carbohydrates. How many milliliters make 5% of the daily carbohydrate intake?

14. One serving contains 80 calories, how many calories are in $3\frac{1}{4}$ servings?

15. If 1 cup of Jade's Soy Milk provides 1 gram of fiber and 4% of the recommended daily fiber intake, how many cups of this soy milk are needed to make 25% of the dietary fiber?

RATIO AND PROPORTION SELF-TEST

Show all your work.

1. Write a definition for proportion. Provide one health profession application or example.

2. $30 : 120 = ? : 12$

3. 1 glass contains 8 ounces. How many full glasses are in 78 ounces?

4. $\dfrac{1}{2} : 4 = \dfrac{1}{3} : x$

5. $x : 625 = 1 : 5$

6. If 10 milligrams are contained in 2 milliliters, how many milligrams are contained in 28 milliliters?

7. A tablet contains 30 milligrams of medication. How many tablets will be needed to provide Ms Smith with 240 milligrams of medication?

8. 100 micrograms of a drug are contained in 2 cubic centimeters. How many cubic centimeters are contained in 15 micrograms?

9. $\dfrac{1}{100} : 6 = \; ? : 8$

10. $0.04 : 0.5 = 0.12 : \; ?$

11. How many minutes are in 130 seconds? Your answer will have both minutes and seconds. Show your setup.

12. Four out of every six dental patients request fluoride treatment after their dental cleaning treatments. If 120 patients have dental cleanings this week, how many will choose to have fluoride treatments as well?

13. If the doctor's office uses 128 disposal thermometer covers each day, how many covers will be used in a five-day workweek?

14. Solve: $\dfrac{1}{125} : 3 :: \underline{\hspace{1cm}} : 12$

15. If the doctor ordered six ounces of cranberry juice four times a day for four days, how many total ounces would be served the patient?

Unit 5

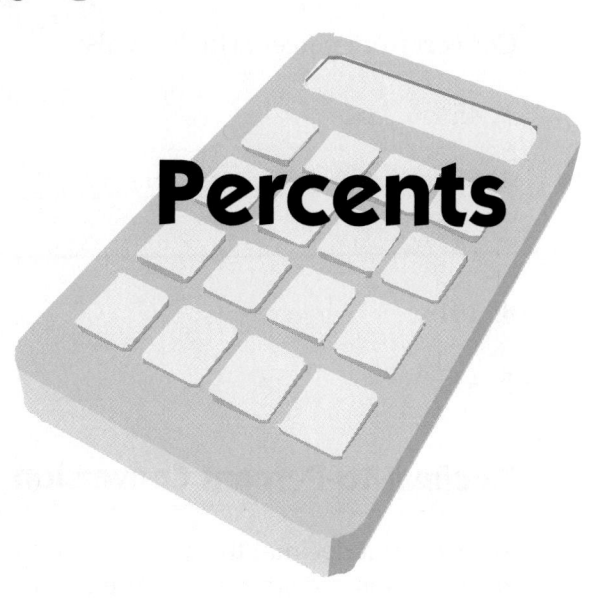

Percents

Percents are another example of a part-to-whole relationship in math. Percents are *parts of one hundred* and are represented by the % sign. Percents can be written as fractions: 35 parts of 100 or $^{35}/_{100}$.

Knowledge of percents in health care will help you understand the strength in percent of solutions for patient medications, interest on loans and taxes, and discounts and markups in pharmacies and retail stores. In general, percent applications are seen less frequently than fractions and decimals by general health care professionals.

Percent-to-Decimal Conversion

To convert a percent to a decimal, shift the decimal point two places to the *left*. The process of doing this quick division replaces having to divide the number by 100. This is the same method of simplified division as shown in Unit 3: Decimals.

> A whole number has its decimal to the far right of the final digit or number.
>
> $$125\% = 125.\% \qquad 76\% = 76.\%$$

Example
$$75\% \rightarrow 7\ 5.\% \rightarrow 0.75$$
$$\cup\ \cup$$

If a percent has a fractional part, the decimal occurs between the whole number and the fractional part.

111

Example

$$33\frac{1}{3}\% \to 33.\frac{1}{3}\% \to 0.33\frac{1}{3}$$

Practice   Convert from percents to decimals:

1. 45%

2. 57%

3. $78\frac{1}{5}\%$

4. 101%

5. $44\frac{1}{2}\%$

Decimal-to-Percent Conversion

To convert a decimal to a percent, shift the decimal point two places to the *right*. This is the simplified multiplication method as practiced in Unit 3: Decimals.

    If a number has a decimal in it and you are converting from a decimal to a percent, use the existing decimal point as the starting point for the conversion. It is possible to have percents greater than 100.

> Begin counting from wherever the decimal is placed.
>
> $$0.023 \to 02.3\% \quad 2.56 \to 256\%$$
>
> Handle a mixed fraction by placing the decimal point between whole number and the fraction, then convert the fraction to a whole number by dividing the numerator by the denominator. Then move the decimal two places right and add a % sign.
>
> $$14\frac{3}{4} \to 14 \cdot \frac{3}{4} \to 14 \cdot 7\,5 \to 1475\%$$
> $$\qquad\qquad\qquad\qquad \cup\cup$$

Examples

$$0.25 \to 0.2\,5\% = 25\%$$
$$\qquad \cup\cup$$

$$13 \to 13. \to 13.0\,0 = 1300\%$$
$$\qquad\qquad\qquad \cup\cup$$

Practice   Convert from decimals to percents:

1. 0.625

2. 55.75

3. 8.6

4. 12.5

5. 0.076

Mixed Practice
Convert

1. 76.89% to a decimal

2. 0.05% to a decimal

3. 86% to a decimal

4. 6.25 to a percent

5. 0.078 to a percent

6. $9\frac{3}{4}$ to a percent

7. $1.25\frac{1}{4}$ to a percent

8. $78\frac{1}{9}\%$ to a decimal

9. 1.5% to a decimal

10. $0.67\frac{1}{4}$ to a percent

Using Proportion to Solve Percent Problems

Proportions are also very useful in solving percent problems. To accomplish this, use the formula

$$\frac{\%}{100} = \frac{\text{is (the part)}}{\text{whole (the total)}}$$

To solve any percent problem, take the information from the problem and put it into the formula. There are three possible places that the information can go.

$$\frac{?}{100} = \frac{?}{?}$$

The 100 never changes because that indicates that every percent is part of 100. It is important to set up the problem correctly. The following questions ask for different information. Therefore, the setup of the problems will be different.

Problem	Setup
What is 25% of 75?	$\frac{25}{100} = \frac{?}{75}$
What % of 75 is 18.75?	$\frac{?}{100} = \frac{18.75}{75}$
18.75 is 25% of what?	$\frac{25}{100} = \frac{18.75}{?}$

Note that the ? is in a different place each time. When the problem is worked, each of the above answers will be different.

Practice   Set up the problems, but do not solve.

1. What is 25% of 200?

2. 75 is what % of 125?

3. Find 8.5% of 224.

4. 40 percent of what number is 350?

5. 18 is what percent of 150?

6. What is $1\frac{1}{2}$% of 400?

7. 75 of 90 is what percent?

8. Out of 200, 140 is what percent?

9. 50% of what number is 75?

10. $8\frac{1}{3}$% of 144 is what?

To solve percent problems in health care, one needs to be aware that the problem may include whole numbers, fractions, and decimals. The skills used in percents draw on the foundation you have in these areas of math computation. It is important to remember and apply the fraction concepts learned when dealing with fractions in percents because a fraction is more accurate and exact than a decimal number that has a repeating final digit.

To solve percent problems, use the proportion method studied in Unit 4: Ratio and Proportion.

Example   Fifteen is what percent of 300?

$$\frac{x\%}{100} = \frac{15}{300}$$

Step 1: Cross multiply the two numbers.

$$(100 \times 15 = 1500)$$

Step 2: Divide the step 1 answer by the remaining number—the number diagonal from the x or ?

$$1{,}500 \div 300 = 5$$

The answer is 5%. So we know that 15 is 5% of 300.

Practice   1. 15% of 120 is _____.

2. 33 is what % of 44?

3. 62 is what percent of 248?

4. 40% of 120 is what?

5. What is 35% of 16.8?

6. Find 9% of 3,090.

7. 45 is what percent of 200?

8. 74 is what percent of 74?

9. What is 44% of 40?

10. 121 is what % of 220?

More complex percents include fractions, and the most efficient way of handling these is as complex fractions. By setting up the problem in proportion format, the work is put into manageable steps. A common error is that students multiply the first two numbers and consider their work done; however, there is always a final division step that must be performed.

Example   What is $8\frac{1}{3}$% of 150?

$$\frac{8\frac{1}{3}}{100} = \frac{x}{150}$$

Step 1: Multiply $8\frac{1}{3}$ and 150. Deal with the fraction; do not change it to a decimal because if you do, your answer will not be as exact. Convert the mixed fraction into an improper fraction. Multiply the whole number by the denominator and add the numerator. Place this number over the denominator. Then multiply this improper fraction by the number 150.

$$8\frac{1}{3} = \frac{25}{3} \times 150 = \frac{3,750}{3} = 1250$$

Step 2: Divide the step 1 answer of 1,250 by 100. Use simplified division. Simplified division moves the decimal 2 places to the left to divide by 100.

$$1,250 : 1,2\underset{\cup}{5}\underset{\cup}{0} = 12.5 \text{ or } 12\frac{1}{2} \quad 0.5 \text{ equals } \frac{1}{2}.$$

Practice   1. What is $33\frac{1}{3}$% of 125? Round to the nearest hundredth.

2. $1\frac{1}{2}$% of 400 is what?

3. $66\frac{2}{3}$% of 90 is what?

4. $35\frac{1}{4}$% is what part of 150? Round to the nearest hundredth.

5. $12\frac{1}{2}$% of 125 is what? Round to the nearest hundredth.

6. 50 is $83\frac{1}{3}$% of what number?

7. 160 is $12\frac{1}{2}$% of what number?

8. 45 is $15\frac{1}{3}$% of what number? Round to the nearest hundredth.

9. 200 is $37\frac{1}{2}$% of what number? Round to the nearest hundredth.

10. $87\frac{1}{2}$% of 120 is what?

Two other applications of percents are important for the health care student: the percent strength of a solution and the single trade discount.

Percent Strength of Solutions

The strength of solutions is an important application of percents. A solution is a liquid that has had medication, minerals, or other products dissolved in it. Percent strength refers to how much of a substance has been dissolved in a specific amount of liquid.

Key to percent strength is your knowledge of part-to-whole relationships: A percent is x parts to 100 total parts. Solution refers to a two-part substance: a solute that is the drug, mineral, or product and a solvent or liquid that can be a variety depending on the medical application. Solutes will occur either as a dry drug measured in grams or as a liquid measured in milliliters. The total volume of the liquid is always in milliliters.

Example   A 15% drug solution has 15 parts of drug to 100 parts of solution. There are 15 grams of drug to 100 milliliters of solution. As a ratio, this would be shown in the reduced form as 3 : 20.

Sometimes the solution will be given as a ratio rather than a percent. To express the solution strength as a percent, set up the problem as a proportion with 100 ml of the total solution. Recall that percent is always part of 100.

Practice   Percent strength: What is the ratio of pure drug to solution? Simplify, if necessary.

1. 4% solution   _____

2. 10% solution   _____

3. $1\frac{1}{2}$% solution   _____

4. 7.5% solution   _____

5. 5% solution   _____

Knowledge of proportion is useful in converting to smaller or larger amounts of solution. In health care, professionals may not always require 100 mL of a solution. It is important to maintain the correct ratio of pure drug to solution to ensure that the patient is getting the medication or solution the doctor intended. Note that the ratio of pure drug remains consistent no matter how much solution is to be prepared.

Example   Percent strength 8% means that there are 8 g of drug to 100 mL of solution. If the doctor orders 25 mL of an 8% strength solution, then a proportion may be used to ensure that the ratio of pure drug to solution represents 8%.

$$\underbrace{\frac{8\text{ g of drugs}}{100\text{ mL solution}}}_{known} = \underbrace{\frac{?\text{ g of drug}}{25\text{ mL solution}}}_{unknown}$$

Step 1: $8 \times 25 = 200$

Step 2: $200 \div 100 = 2$

So to make 25 mL of an 8% solution using this ratio of pure drug to solution, 2 g of pure drug to 25 mL of solution are required. This keeps the percent strength of the medication consistent with the doctor's order for an 8% strength solution. Note that the amount of mixed solution changes, not the percent strength itself.

Example   Ten grams of drug in 25 mL of solution. What is the percent strength of this medication?

To convert this ratio into a percent, write it as a proportion. Then solve for x which will become the percent.

$$\overset{known}{\frac{10 \text{ g}}{25 \text{ mL}}} = \overset{unknown}{\frac{x \text{ g}}{100 \text{ mL}}}$$

Follow proportion steps to solve. Cross multiply $10 \times 100 = 1000$. Divide 1000 by $25 = 40$, so the answer is 40% strength.

Practice   1. The doctor has ordered a 5% saline solution to be prepared. How many grams of pure drug will be needed to make each of these amounts of solution at the 5% strength?

    a. 25 mL of solution

    b. 35 mL of solution

    c. 65 mL of solution

    d. 125 mL of solution

2. Nine milliliters of pure drug are in 100 mL of solution.

    a. What is the percent strength of the solution?

    b. How many milliliters of drug are in 75 mL of that solution?

3. Fifteen grams of pure drug are in 50 mL.

    a. What is the percent strength of the solution?

    b. How many grams of pure drug are in 200 mL of the solution?

Additional Practice with Solution Strength

1. A $12\frac{3}{4}$% strength solution has been prepared.

    a. How many grams of medication is in the $12\frac{3}{4}$% strength solution?

    b. How many milliliters of solution are in this $12\frac{3}{4}$% strength solution?

    c. Express this solution as a simplified ratio.

    d. How much pure drug is needed to create 35.5 mL of this solution? Round to the nearest tenth. Your answer will be in grams.

    e. How much pure drug is needed to create 80 mL of this solution? Your answer will be in grams.

    f. If you have 60 mL of solution, how many grams of pure drug will you have in order to keep the $12\frac{3}{4}$%? Round to the nearest tenth. Your answer will be in grams.

2. A 0.09% strength solution has been prepared.

    a. How many grams of medication is in the 0.09% strength solution?

    b. How many milliliters of solution are in this 0.09% strength solution?

    c. Express this solution as a simplified ratio.

    d. How much pure drug is needed to create 54 mL of this solution? Round to the nearest hundredth. Your answer will be in grams.

    e. How much pure drug is needed to create 24 mL of this solution? Round to the nearest hundredth. Your answer will be in grams.

    f. If you have 50 mL of solution, how many grams of pure drug will you have in order to keep the 0.09% solution. Round to the nearest hundredth. Your answer will be in grams.

3. A 78% strength solution has been prepared.

   a. How many grams of medication is in the 78% strength solution?

   b. How many milliliters of solution are in this 78% strength solution?

   c. Express this solution as a simplified ratio.

   d. How much pure drug is needed to create 65.5 mL of this solution? Round to the nearest tenth. Your answer will be in grams.

   e. How much pure drug is needed to create 90 mL of this solution? Round to the nearest tenth. Your answer will be in grams.

   f. If you have 450 mL of solution, how many grams of pure drug will you have in order to keep the 78%? Your answer will be in grams.

Single Trade Discount

Single trade discounts are useful to individuals who handle products or inventory that must be marked up. The single trade discount provides the net price of items when a single discount has been given. Some health care organizations that use certain name brands receive these discounts from manufacturers of the products they use or sell most often.

Example   What is the net price of a surgical instrument listed at $189.90 with a trade discount of 40%?

Step 1:   The percentage is first made into a decimal by moving the decimal point two places to the left. Then, multiply the list price by the trade discount.

> You may need to round your decimal number to the nearest cent.

$$\begin{array}{r} \$189.90 \\ \times \quad .40 \\ \hline 00000 \\ 75960 \\ \hline \$75.96 \end{array}$$

Step 2:   Subtract the amount of the discount (the answer from step 1) from the list price to get the net price.

$$\begin{array}{r} \$189.90 \\ -75.96 \\ \hline \$113.94 \end{array}$$

The net price of this instrument is $113.94.

Practice   Find the net price by using the single trade discount method. If necessary, round to the nearest penny. Show your work.

	List price	Trade discount	Amount of discount	Net price
1.	$475.50	15%	_____	_____
2.	$179.85	20%	_____	_____
3.	$125.55	12.5%	_____	_____
4.	$455.86	30%	_____	_____
5.	$352.90	25%	_____	_____
6.	$72.35	10%	_____	_____
7.	$250.40	45%	_____	_____
8.	$862.75	35%	_____	_____
9.	$158.00	40%	_____	_____
10.	$73.85	10%	_____	_____

PERCENT SELF-TEST

1. Write the definition of a percent. Provide one example.

2. Convert the following into percents:

   a. $0.87\frac{1}{4}$

   b. $\frac{5}{6}$

3. 75% of 325 is what number?

4. 8 is what % of 40?

5. 28 is 14% of what number?

6. What does $5\frac{1}{2}$% solution mean?

7. The doctor has ordered 25 mL of 9% saline solution. How much pure drug is needed to make this order?

8. The list price for a case of medicine is $129.50. Your pharmacy will receive a 12% trade discount.

   a. What is the amount of the discount? _____

   b. What is the net cost of a case of medicine? _____

9. What percent is 3 tablets of a prescription written for 36 tablets?

10. If a pharmacy gave a 15% discount on walkers, what would be the discount for a total bill of $326.00 for a six-month rental?

11. If a ratio of 3 : 25 is given for a solution, what percent strength is this solution?

12. What is $\frac{1}{2}$% of 500?

13. Express 8 : 125 as a percent.

14. What is $\frac{3}{4}$% of 20?

15. 35 is 0.05% of what?

Unit 6

Combined Applications

Health care workers rely on a variety of math systems to achieve their daily tasks. Knowledge of ways to convert efficiently between systems will benefit you on the job as your expertise grows and your circle of responsibility increases. It is important to have the ability to convert between fractions, decimals, ratios, and percents. Although these skills have been separately reviewed, they are brought together here to develop some strategies for doing these conversions in the most efficient way.

Conversions among Fractions, Decimals, Ratios, and Percent

Review the basics of conversion:

Conversion	Method/Formula
Fraction to decimal	Divide the denominator into the numerator.

$$\frac{3}{4} = \begin{array}{r} 0.75 \\ 4\overline{)3.0} \\ 28\downarrow \\ \overline{20} \\ 20 \\ \overline{0} \end{array}$$

124

Decimal to fraction	Count the decimal places, place the number over 1 with zeros to match the same number of decimal places.

$$0.0\underline{2} \text{ (2 places)} \rightarrow \frac{2}{10\,\underline{0}} \text{ (2 zeros)}$$

Reduce to $^1/_{50}$.

Proper fraction to ratio, ratio to proper fraction	Ratios are shown with : instead of /. Fractions and ratios are interchangeable simply by changing the symbol.

$$\frac{1}{8} \rightarrow 1:8 \text{ and } 4:31 \rightarrow \frac{4}{31}$$

The first ratio number is always the numerator and the second ratio number is always the denominator. All fractions and ratios must be in lowest terms.

Mixed number to ratio, ratio to mixed number	If the fraction is a mixed number, the mixed number first must be made into an improper fraction before setting up the ratio.

$$1\frac{3}{4} \rightarrow 1 \times 4 + 3 = \frac{7}{4} \rightarrow 7:4$$

If the ratio is an improper fraction when the conversion is made, make it a mixed number.

$$\frac{11}{4} \rightarrow 11 \div 4 = 2\frac{3}{4}$$

Decimal to percent	Move the decimal point two places to the right. Add the percent sign.

$$0.25 \rightarrow 25\% \quad 1.456 \rightarrow 145.6\%$$

Percent to decimal	Move the decimal point two places to the left. Add zeros if needed as placeholders.

$$90\% \rightarrow 0.9 \text{ and } 5\% \rightarrow 0.05$$

$$57\frac{1}{2}\% \rightarrow 0.57\frac{1}{2} \text{ or } 0.575$$

Fraction to percent	Convert fraction to decimal, then to percent.
Decimal to ratio	Convert decimal to fraction, then change sign to ratio.

Convert the following numbers to the other number systems. Using the review sheet of conversion methods, try to compute only one math problem per line by carefully selecting the order of the conversions to be done. By carefully selecting the order of conversions, you will minimize extra work.

Example

Fraction	Decimal	Ratio	Percent
_____	0.05	_____	_____

Figuring out the order takes a little practice. When 0.05 is changed to a percent first, no math calculation needs to be done: Simply move the decimal.

Fraction	Decimal	Ratio	Percent
_____	0.05	_____	5%

Next convert the decimal to a fraction. Count the number of decimal places and then place the 5 over a 1 with the same number of zeros as the decimal places. Reduce the fraction to lowest terms.

Fraction	Decimal	Ratio	Percent
$\frac{5}{100} \to \frac{1}{20}$	0.05	_____	5%

Take the reduced fraction and write it in ratio form.

Fraction	Decimal	Ratio	Percent
$\frac{5}{100} \to \frac{1}{20}$	0.05	$1:20$	5%

Example

Fraction	Decimal	Ratio	Percent
$7\frac{3}{5}$	_____	_____	_____

This mixed number must be made into an improper fraction before it can become a ratio.

$$\left(7 \times 5 + 3 = 38 \to \frac{38}{5} \right)$$

Change the signs from / to : to make the ratio.

Fraction	Decimal	Ratio	Percent
$7\frac{3}{5}$	_____	$38:5$	_____

Next change to a decimal. Handle the whole number 7 separately. Place it on the line as a whole number, then divide the denominator into the numerator.

$$3 \div 5 = 0.6$$

Add this to the whole number to make 7.6.

Fraction	Decimal	Ratio	Percent
$7\frac{3}{5}$	7.6	38 : 5	_____

Finally, move the decimal point from the decimal number two places to the right. Add the percent sign.

Fraction	Decimal	Ratio	Percent
$7\frac{3}{5}$	7.6	38 : 5	760%

Suggested Order of Operations

If starting with percent, move from → decimal → fraction → ratio.

If starting with ratio, move from → fraction → decimal → percent.

If starting with fraction, move from → ratio → decimal → percent.

If starting with decimal, move from → percent → fraction → ratio.

Some conversions can be memorized easily:

$\frac{1}{2} \rightarrow 0.5 \rightarrow 50\%$

$\frac{1}{4} \rightarrow 0.25 \rightarrow 25\%$

$\frac{3}{4} \rightarrow 0.75 \rightarrow 75\%$

$\frac{1}{3} \rightarrow 0.33\frac{1}{3} \rightarrow 33\frac{1}{3}\%$

$\frac{2}{3} \rightarrow 0.66\frac{2}{3} \rightarrow 66\frac{2}{3}\%$

Provide the following measures. Reduce to lowest terms as necessary. Round to the nearest hundredth, if necessary.

	Fraction	Decimal	Ratio	Percent
1.	$\frac{3}{4}$	_____	_____	_____
2.	_____	_____	1 : 20	_____

	Fraction	Decimal	Ratio	Percent
3.	_____	_____	_____	50%
4.	_____	0.625	_____	_____
5.	_____	_____	1 : 250	_____
6.	$\dfrac{7}{8}$	_____	_____	_____
7.	_____	0.06	_____	_____
8.	_____	_____	_____	12.5%
9.	$\dfrac{1}{10}$	_____	_____	_____
10.	_____	_____	_____	$33\dfrac{1}{3}\%$
11.	_____	1.36	_____	_____
12.	$12\dfrac{1}{2}$	_____	_____	_____
13.	_____	_____	2 : 5	_____
14.	_____	$0.66\dfrac{2}{3}$	_____	_____
15.	_____	_____	16 : 25	_____
16.	_____	0.004	_____	_____
17.	$\dfrac{5}{6}$	_____	_____	_____
18.	_____	_____	_____	$7\dfrac{1}{4}\%$
19.	_____	0.01	_____	_____
20.	_____	_____	7 : 3	_____

Using Combined Applications in Measurement Conversion

In health care, a solid working knowledge of weights and measures is essential. Three systems of measure will be used in your work: household or standard measurement, metric measurement, covered in this unit, and apothecary measurement, covered in Unit 11: Dosage Calculations. Critical to your success in measurement conversion is your ability to remember a few key conversions and the proportion method for solving conversions. Metric-to-metric conversions use a different conversion method, which is also covered in Unit 11.

Household or standard measurements are used by all of us in our daily activities. Household measures tend to be less accurate than either metric or apothecary measures because of their nature and our methods of using them. So household measures are used in the less critical measurements in health care. Abbreviations of units of measure are used and some new abbreviations are introduced below:

Drop = gtt

Teaspoon = t (tsp)

Tablespoon = T (tbsp)

Practice   Write the word for each abbreviation.

Flashcards

1. ft. = _feet_   6. t = _teaspoon_   kg = kilogram
2. yd. = _yard_   7. qt. = _quart_   mg = milligram
3. oz. = _ounce_   8. pt. = _pint_   mL = milliliter
4. T = _Tablespoon_   9. gtt = _drop_
5. lb. = _pound_   10. gal. = _gallon_

Standard Units of Measure

The basics of standard measure conversion were covered in Unit 4: Ratio and Proportion. To refresh yourself on the application of proportion to measurement conversions, complete the review exercises.

Time		Approximate Equivalents	
1 minute = 60 seconds		grain i	= 60 milligrams
1 day	= 24 hours	1 teaspoon	= 5 milliliters
1 week	= 7 days	1 tablespoon	= 3 teaspoons
1 year	= 12 months	fluid dram 1	= 4 milliliters
		fluid ounce 1	= fluid drams 8
Weight		fluid ounce 1	= 2 tablespoons
1 kilogram	= 2.2 pounds	fluid ounce 1	= 30 milliliters
1 pound	= 16 ounces	1 cup	= 250 milliliters
			= fluid ounces 8
Linear Measure		1 pint	= 500 milliliters
1 foot	= 12 inches		= 2 cups or fluid ounces 16
1 yard	= 3 feet		
1 meter	= 39.4 inches	1 quart	= fluid ounces 32
1 inch	= 2.5 or 2.54 centimeters		= 1 liter or 1000 milliliters
Liquid Measure		1 cubic	
1 tablespoon = 3 teaspoons		centimeter	= 1 milliliter
1 cup	= 8 ounces	1 kilogram	= 2.2 pounds
1 pint	= 2 cups	fluid ounce 1	= 2 tablespoons
1 quart	= 2 pints		
1 gallon	= 4 quarts		

Review   Use the provided tables to assist you in proportion conversions.

  1. 1250 milliliters = _____ pints

  2. 15 kilograms = _____ pounds

  3. 12.5 inches = _____ centimeters

  4. _____ milliliters = 13 teaspoons

  5. _____ ounces = 90 milliliters

  6. 38.1 centimeters = _____ inches

  7. _____ ounces = $1\frac{1}{2}$ pints

  8. _____ quarts = 15 liters

  9. _____ teaspoons = 12.5 milliliters

  10. _____ cubic centimeters = 15 teaspoons

More Combined Applications

Sometimes measurement conversions require more than one conversion to get to the answer.

Example   Two conversions are required to convert from ounces to teaspoons.

Step 1: Convert the ounces to milliliters:

$$\overset{known}{\frac{1\ ounce}{20\ mL}} = \overset{unknown}{\frac{8\ ounces}{?\ mL}} \rightarrow 160\ milliliters$$

Step 2: Convert milliliters to teaspoons.

$$\frac{1\ teaspoon}{5\ mL} = \frac{?\ teaspoons}{160\ mL} \rightarrow 32\ teaspoons$$

These problems cannot be solved by making a straight conversion from what is known to what is unknown. A path must be developed so that you can establish how to get the answer. Think about what conversions most closely match the problem itself, then set up the problem.

> Do not rush through the two-step conversions. These require some forethought about how to get from what is known to what is unknown.

Plastic medicine cups are used in the health care industry to measure liquid dosages. A medicine cup is typically marked off in milliliters. Often one medicine cup is 1 fluid ounce, which is 30 mL.

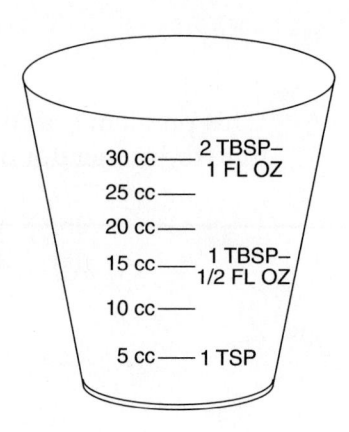

Practice   1. 1 medicine cup = _____ teaspoons

2. 3 teaspoons = _____ (drops)

3. $2\frac{1}{4}$ pints = _____ ounces

4. 1 cup = _____ teaspoons

5. 1 pint = _____ tablespoons

6. 15 tablespoons = _____ cubic centimeters

7. 68,000 grams = _____ pounds

8. 28 inches = _____ millimeters

9. _____ ounces = 24 teaspoons

10. $1\frac{1}{2}$ ounces = _____ teaspoons

Sometimes math problems require multiple setups. To solve these, group the work into the most logical format.

Example $\dfrac{25\%}{\dfrac{1}{4}}$

Step 1: Look at the problem and decide what to do to make the units similar. Convert 25% into a fraction.

$$\rightarrow \frac{25}{100}$$

Step 2: Review the problem to see what operation should be completed.

$$\frac{\dfrac{25}{100}}{\dfrac{1}{4}}$$

This problem is a complex fraction. Divide the denominator of $\frac{1}{4}$ into the numerator of $\frac{25}{100}$.

$$\frac{25}{100} \div \frac{1}{4} \rightarrow \frac{25}{100} \times \frac{4}{1} = \frac{100}{100} = 1$$

Mixed Review Practice

1. $\dfrac{50\%}{\dfrac{1}{4}}$

2. $\dfrac{1:150}{1:300} \times 2$

3. $12\dfrac{1}{2}\% \times \dfrac{\dfrac{1}{2}}{\dfrac{3}{4}}$

4. $\dfrac{\dfrac{1}{2}\%}{4} \times 1000$

5. $5\% \times \dfrac{1:2}{3:4}$

Converting among Systems Worksheet

Provide the following measures. Reduce to lowest terms as necessary.

	Fraction	Decimal	Ratio	Percent
1.	$\dfrac{7}{8}$	_____	_____	_____
2.	_____	_____	1 : 30	_____
3.	_____	_____	_____	75%
4.	$\dfrac{1}{17}$	_____	_____	_____
5.	_____	_____	2 : 5	_____
6.	$\dfrac{5}{6}$	_____	_____	_____
7.	_____	0.08	_____	_____
8.	_____	_____	_____	10.25%

	Fraction	Decimal	Ratio	Percent
9.	$\frac{3}{5}$	_____	_____	_____
10.	_____	_____	1 : 200	_____
11.	_____	1.625	_____	_____
12.	$\frac{1}{8}$	_____	_____	_____
13.	_____	_____	11 : 50	_____
14.	_____	0.15	_____	_____
15.	_____	_____	3 : 25	_____
16.	_____	0.008	_____	_____
17.	$\frac{1}{6}$	_____	_____	_____
18.	_____	_____	_____	$15\frac{1}{4}\%$
19.	_____	0.04	_____	_____
20.	_____	_____	9 : 10,000	_____

COMBINED APPLICATIONS SELF-TEST

Show all your work.

1. Convert $\frac{3}{75}$ to a decimal.

2. Convert $\frac{1}{2}\%$ to a ratio.

3. Convert 1.05 to a fraction.

4. Convert $4\frac{1}{8}$ to a ratio.

5. Convert $27\frac{1}{4}$ to a decimal.

6. Convert 12 : 200 to a percent.

7. Convert 14.25% to a ratio.

8. $3\frac{1}{4}$ cups = _____ ounces

9. 12 fluid ounces = _____ tablespoons

10. $3\frac{1}{2}$ feet = _____ centimeters

11. 18 hours = _____ minutes

12. 1 gallon = _____ cups

13. If a teaspoon has approximately 60 drops, how many drops are in $2\frac{1}{3}$ tablespoons?

14. $12\% \times 0.67$

15. $\dfrac{15\%}{\frac{1}{2}}$

Unit 8

The Metric System

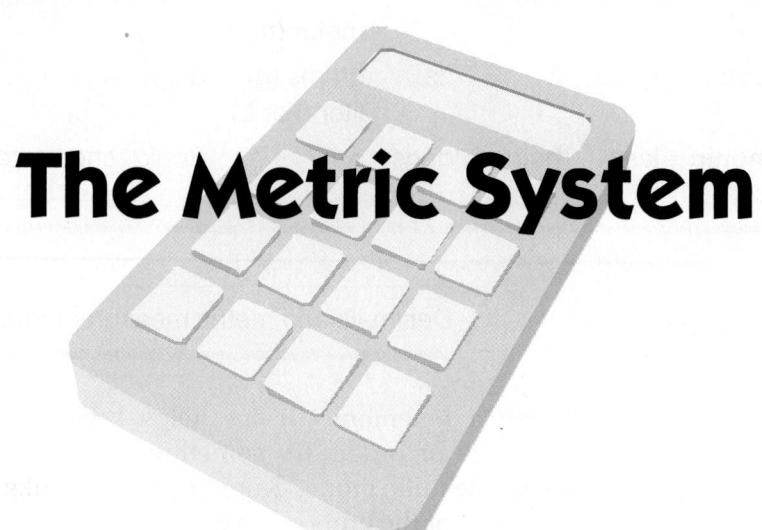

Metric measurements are used for many types of measurements in the health care professions. Some uses include the following:

- weight calculations

- dosage calculations

- food intake (in grams) measurements

- height and length measurements

- liquid and medication measurements

Metric units come in base units. These units measure different types of materials.

Base unit	Measurement type	Examples
Liter	volume	liquids, blood, urine
Gram	weight	an item's weight
		an amount of medicine
Meter	length	height, length, instruments

The metric system uses units based on multiples of ten. For this reason, metric numbers are written in whole numbers or decimal numbers, never fractions. Metric conversion problems can be solved by moving the decimal either to the left or to the right. This chart resembles the decimal place value chart on page 160. Review the similarities.

Unit:	kilo-	hecto-	deka	base	deci	centi-	milli-	x	x	micro
Value:	1,000	100	10	1 meter (m)	0.1	0.01	0.001			0.000001
Symbol:	k	h	da	grams (g) liter (I or L)	d	c	m			mc or μ
Mnemonic Device:	kiss	hairy	dogs	but	drink	chocolate	milk,	m	o	m

> Decimals and metric measurements are based on units of ten.

Using a mnemonic device helps keep the metric units in the correct sequence or order. Try something silly like "kiss hairy dogs but drink chocolate milk, mom." Knowing a device like this will help you remember the order of the units on an exam.

Note that the *mo* are placeholders. This helps one remember to count the spaces in the mnemonic device.

Using the Metric Symbols

The metric system uses the unit of measure, a prefix, and a base element to form the metric units. To form *millimeter*, take *m* from *milli* and *m* from meter and form *mm*, which represents the *millimeter*.

The metric system combines prefixes that give the unit and root words that indicate the type of measurement, as in volume, weight, or length. The prefixes are the key to deciphering what number of units you have.

Prefix	Meaning	Symbol
kilo-	thousand	k
hecto-	hundred	h
deka-	ten	da
base	one	m, g, L
deci-	tenth	d
centi-	hundredth	c
milli-	thousandth	m
micro-	millionth	mc or μ

Root	Use	Symbol
gram	weight	g
meter	length	m
liter	volume	L or l

Every metric prefix may be combined with every root. The application of these terms depends on the measurement being completed. Thus, liquids are measured in liters, and dry medication uses grams because this type of drug is measured by weight.

Supply the words or abbreviations:

1. kilogram
2. mL
3. gram
4. mg
5. centimeter
6. mm
7. kilometer
8. mcg
9. L
10. kg
11. km
12. meter
13. microgram
14. kL
15. cm

> k h d b d c m m o m

You can use the first letters of the metric units to recall their order by writing them on a piece of scratch paper or an answer sheet on examination days.

Changing Unit Measures

To change units within the metric system, review the number's place value and then consider where you are converting to. Count the number of spaces from the number you are starting with and the place you are converting to.

$$45.5 \text{ grams} = \underline{\hspace{1cm}} \text{ milligrams}$$

> k   h   d   b   d   c   m   m   o   m
> ← 3 spaces → ← 3 spaces → ← 3 spaces →

Note that the *mo* are placeholders. This helps one remember to count the spaces in the mnemonic device. Also, most conversions in health care are between the units of kilo (k), gram, meter, liter (b) and milli (m) and micro (m). There are three spaces to move between each of these to make the conversions.

From gram to milligram, there are three spaces. Note the direction from gram to milligram is to the right. Move the decimal three places to the right. Thus,

$$45.5 \text{ grams} = 45\,5\,0\,0 \text{ milligrams}$$
$$\text{ᴗᴗᴗ}$$

Note that most of the health care conversions are done between kilogram and gram, gram and milligram, milligram and microgram, meter and centimeter, and liter and milliliter. Once these are practiced, converting between units will feel natural. Practice making the conversion by moving the decimal from one unit to another. Use a pencil to draw the ∪ as you count the spaces. Start at the existing decimal and move to the right of each metric unit. Remember that "b" stands for the base units of meters, liters, or grams.

In other fields, a cubic centimeter (cc) is viewed as a ⬚, but in health care professions a cubic centimeter is the same as milliliter. The logic for this is that a syringe has a tube and measures volume in cc or ml. Thus, cubic centimeter equals milliliter.

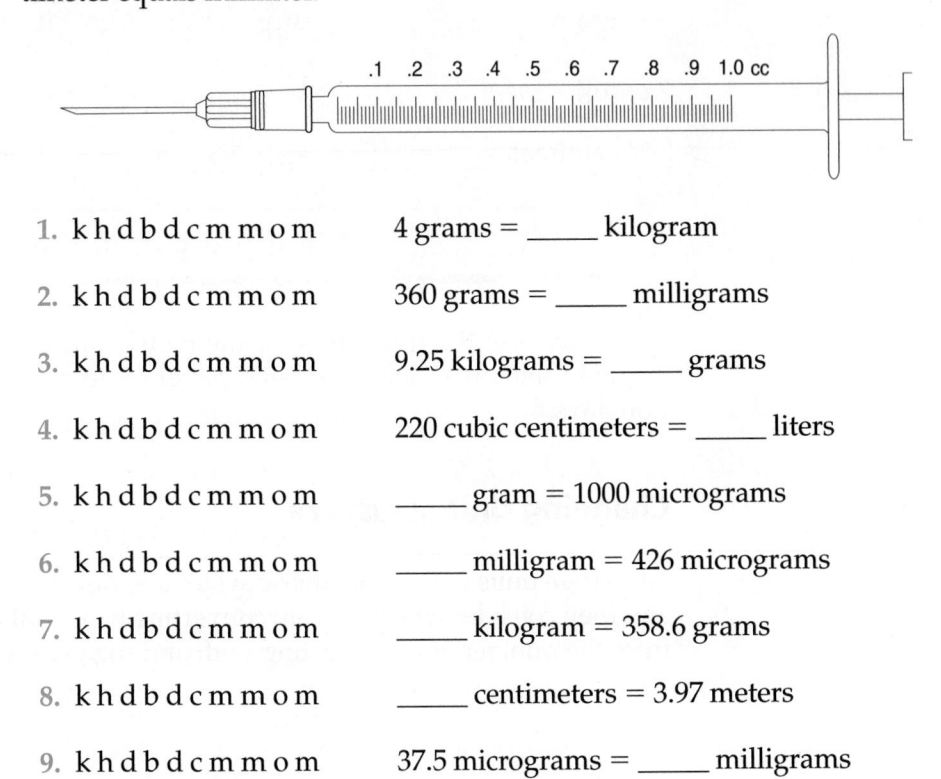

1. k h d b d c m m o m   4 grams = _____ kilogram

2. k h d b d c m m o m   360 grams = _____ milligrams

3. k h d b d c m m o m   9.25 kilograms = _____ grams

4. k h d b d c m m o m   220 cubic centimeters = _____ liters

5. k h d b d c m m o m   _____ gram = 1000 micrograms

6. k h d b d c m m o m   _____ milligram = 426 micrograms

7. k h d b d c m m o m   _____ kilogram = 358.6 grams

8. k h d b d c m m o m   _____ centimeters = 3.97 meters

9. k h d b d c m m o m   37.5 micrograms = _____ milligrams

10. k h d b d c m m o m   _____ centimeter = 6.75 millimeters

Use these letters and the mnemonic device as a quick memory tool for test recall or assignments.

Example   Use as work space with the mnemonic device.

50 milliliters = _____ liter   k h d b d c m m o m

0.0 5 0
∪∪∪ = 0.05 liter

Practice   1. 1 cubic centimeter = _____ milliliter

2. 0.5 liter = _____ milliliter

3. _____ milligram = 26 micrograms

4. 0.75 gram = _____ milligrams

5. 19.5 kilograms = _____ grams

6. 15 milligrams = _____ gram

7. _____ grams = 0.3 kilogram

8. 8.5 liter = _____ milliliters

9. 0.07 milligram = _____ micrograms

10. 4 kilograms = _____ milligrams

11. 14 centimeters = _____ meter

12. 0.001 kilogram = _____ gram

13. _____ liter = 250 cubic centimeters

14. 3.8 milligrams = _____ gram

15. _____ milligrams = 0.6 gram

16. 56.75 milliliters = _____ liter

17. _____ milligram = 36 grams

18. _____ gram = 10 milligrams

19. 7500 milliliters = _____ liters

20. _____ millimeters = 50 centimeters

Additional Practice

Unit:	kilo-	hecto-	deka	base	deci	centi-	milli-	x	x	micro
Value:	1,000	100	10	1 meter (m)	0.1	0.01	0.001			0.000001
Symbol:	k	h	da	grams (g) liter (L)	d	c	m			mc or μ
Mnemonic Device:	kiss	hairy	dogs	but	drink	chocolate	milk,	m	o	m

21. 12.5 milligrams = _____ micrograms

22. 5.78 grams = _____ kilogram

23. 24 decimeters = _____ centimeters

24. 250 micrograms = _____ milligram

25. 12.76 kilograms = _____ grams

26. 45 meters = _____ millimeters

27. 23.5 centimeters = _____ millimeters

28. 750 micrograms = _____ milligram

29. 800 centimeters = _____ meters

30. 0.0975 milligram = _____ micrograms

31. 1000 milliliters = _____ liter

32. 3 kilograms = _____ grams

33. 12500 centimeters = _____ meters

34. 75.5 milligrams = _____ micrograms

35. 0.125 gram = _____ milligrams

36. 0.150 milligram = _____ microgram

37. 45250 milligram = _____ gram

38. 9500 grams = _____ kilograms

39. 1000 micrograms = _____ gram

40. 25 microgram = _____ milligram

41. 5524 grams = _____ kilograms

42. 45 milliliters = _____ liter

43. 1.25 meters = _____ centimeters

44. 550 micrograms = _____ milligram

45. 0.09 liter = _____ milliliters

46. 24.5 centimeters = _____ meter

47. 0.1 gram = _____ milligrams

48. 0.25 liter = _____ milliliters

49. 8500 micrograms = _____ milligrams

50. 0.625 gram = _____ micrograms

Practice with Word Problems

1. The medical assistant was asked to measure the infant. The infant measured 0.4453 meters or _____ centimeters.

2. The client in the cardiac unit was asked to exercise on the treadmill. The physical assistant recorded 0.5 kilometers for the first day of physical therapy. The next day the client walked 0.68 kilometers. How many more meters did the client walk on the second day? _____

3. The nutritional aide noted that a plastic container of cranberry juice contained 1.89 liters. How many milliliters are in the bottle? _____ If the nutritional aide was asked to pour 180 milliliters servings from this container, how many full servings could be poured? _____

4. The medical assistant asked the client's family to ensure adequate fluid intake. She recommended at least 2.2 liters of fluids. How many milliliters would that be? _____ How many full 240 milliliters (8 ounce glasses) portions should the client drink a day? _____

5. The certified nurses aide measures the patient's output of urine to be 3100 milliliters. The patient is on a liquid diet and IV. In total, the patient has received 2.5 liters of dextrose water and drank a total of 1850 cubic centimeters of juice, water, tea, and broth. What is the difference in patient's intake from output in cubic centimeters? _____

6. A drug label notes that the client's medicine has 250 milligrams in 5 milliliters of syrup. How many milliliters would deliver 125 milligrams of medicine? _____

7. A child claims to have grown 3.5 centimeters since his last check up. His previous height was 1.2 meters. The medical assistant measures the child and discovers that he has grown 3.56 centimeters. What is the child's new recorded height in centimeters for his medical record? _____ What is the child's new recorded height in meters? _____

8. A can of pear halves weighs 425 grams. How many kilograms does the can weigh?

9. The pharmacy technician reads a prescription. The physician has ordered 0.03 grams of cevimeline hydrochloride for a client. The pharmacy has on hand 30 milligrams capsules. Is the physician's order consistent with the supply on hand in the pharmacy? _____ How do you know this? _____

_____.

10. Look at the following drug label.

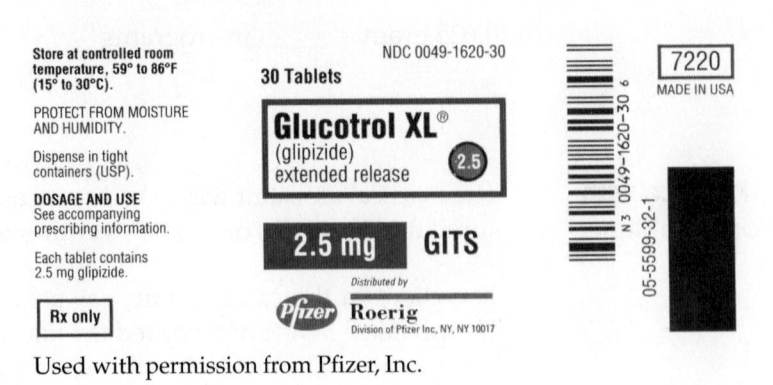

Used with permission from Pfizer, Inc.

How many micrograms are given in each tablet? _____

METRIC SYSTEM SELF-TEST

1. Look at the drug label. How many micrograms are in 5 milliliters of Neurontin? _____

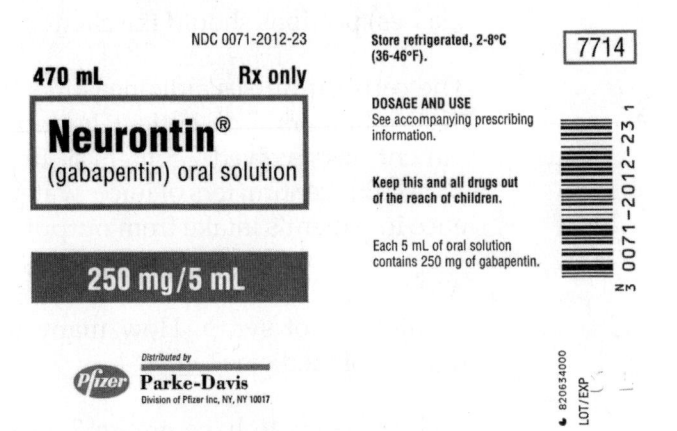

Used with permission from Pfizer, Inc.

2. _____ milligrams = 75 micrograms

3. _____ kilogram = 54.6 grams

4. 8.3 liters = _____ cubic centimeters

5. 0.014 gram = _____ micrograms

6. 1.2 milliliters = _____ liter

7. 10 micrograms = _____ gram

8. _____ liter = 250 cubic centimeter

9. _____ milligrams = 0.015 gram

10. _____ micrograms = 30 milligrams

11. 0.008 microgram = _____ milligram

12. The medical assistant was asked to measure the infant. The infant measured 0.345 meters or _____ centimeters.

13. A drug label notes that the client's medicine has 250 milligrams in 5 milliliters of syrup. How many milliliters would deliver 375 milligrams of medicine? _____

14. The pharmacy technician aide noted that a plastic container of medication contained 0.24 liter. How many milliliters are in the bottle? _____

15. 0.75 gram = _____ milligrams

Math for Health Care Professionals Post-Test

Whole Number Skills

1. Find the mean of the set of numbers: 16, 4, 25, 9, 10, 9, 3, 20
   _____

2. $345 +$ _____ $+ 37 = 658$

3. $1846 - 979 =$ _____

4. $324 \times 87 =$ _____

5. $27\overline{)654} =$ _____

6. The heights of the members of Michele's family are 66 inches, 81 inches, 69 inches, 70 inches, and 64 inches. Find the range in height of the members of Michele's family. _____

7. Convert from 8:15 P.M. standard time to universal time. _____

Fraction Skills

8. Order the fractions from smallest to largest: $\dfrac{2}{3}, \dfrac{6}{7}, \dfrac{6}{21}, \dfrac{13}{21}$ _____

9. $20\dfrac{3}{5} + 6 + 3\dfrac{5}{6} =$ _____

10. $56\dfrac{1}{3} - 17\dfrac{11}{12} =$ _____

11. $2\dfrac{4}{5} \times \dfrac{2}{7} \times 5 =$ _____

12. $4\dfrac{1}{6} \div \dfrac{3}{8} =$ _____

13. Solve: $\dfrac{\frac{1}{10}}{\frac{1}{200}} =$ _____

Decimal Skills

14. Express as a fraction: 4.06 _____

15. Express as a decimal: $12\dfrac{5}{8}$ _____

16. $10.6 + 6 + 2.09 =$ _____

17. $65.7 - 12.68 =$ _____

18. $0.9 \times 41.2 =$ _____

19. $248.06 \div 0.8 =$ _____

Ratio and Proportion Skills

20. A container holds 34 milliliters of medication. How many *full* 1.25 milliliter doses can be administered from this container? _____

21. Solve: $12 : 75 :: 2.5 : x$ Round to the nearest hundredth.

    $x =$ _____

22. Solve: $8 : x :: 42 : 50$

    $x =$ _____ Answer should be in mixed number.

23. Solve: $\dfrac{1}{2} : 8 :: x : 32$ $x =$ _____

24. Solve: $\dfrac{1}{50} : 10 :: \dfrac{10}{250} : x$ $x =$ _____

25. Simplify the ratio to the lowest terms: $9\dfrac{3}{8} : 5$ _____

Percent Skills

26. What is $3\frac{2}{3}\%$ of 125? Write the answer as a mixed number. _____

27. What percent is 22 of 144? _____ Round to the nearest hundredth.

28. 24% of 250 is what number? _____

29. The original price minus a $45 discount is the sale price of a new desk. The sale price is $350. What was the original price? _____ _____

30. There are 8 grams of pure drug in 75 milliliters of solution. What is the percent strength of solution? Round to the nearest hundredth. _____

Combined Application

31. $5\dfrac{1}{4}$ feet = _____ inches

32. _____ quarts = $7\dfrac{1}{2}$ pints

33. 36 pounds = _____ kilograms

34. _____ teaspoons = 62 milliliters

35. Convert 0.7% to a fraction = _____

36. Convert $4\dfrac{1}{2}$ to a percent = _____

37. Convert 9 to a percent = _____

38. Write 0.002 as a fraction = _____

39. Write 0.03% as a decimal = _____

Pre-Algebra

40. $75 + (-8) =$ _____

41. $-15 - 22 =$ _____

42. $-72 \div 9 =$ _____

43. $-124 \times (-3) =$ _____

44. $21 + \sqrt{169} =$ _____

45. $(100 - 40) \div 4 =$ _____

Drug Labels

46. Complete the table for this drug label. If the information is not provided, write *Not shown.*

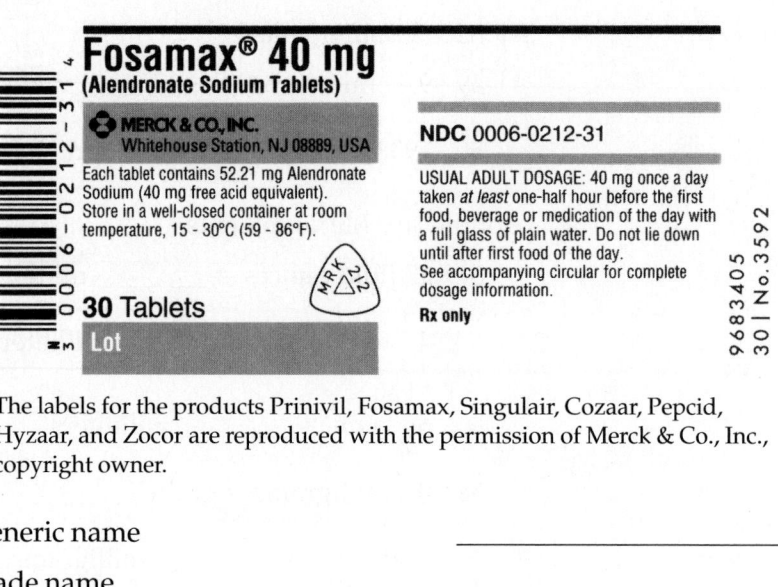

The labels for the products Prinivil, Fosamax, Singulair, Cozaar, Pepcid, Hyzaar, and Zocor are reproduced with the permission of Merck & Co., Inc., copyright owner.

Generic name   _____

Trade name   _____

Manufacturer   _____

National Drug Code (NDC) number   _____

Lot number (control number)   _____

Drug form   _____

Dosage strength   _____

Usual adult dose   _____

Total amount in vial, packet, box   _____

Prescription warning   _____

Expiration date   _____

47. The medical assistant was asked to dispense 23 milliliters of a liquid medication. Shade the medicine cup to indicate this dosage.

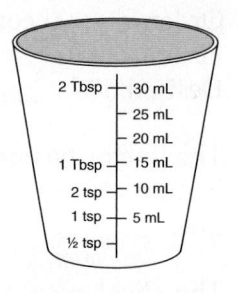

48. The physician has ordered an IM injection of 0.6 milliliters. Shade the syringe to indicate this volume of medication.

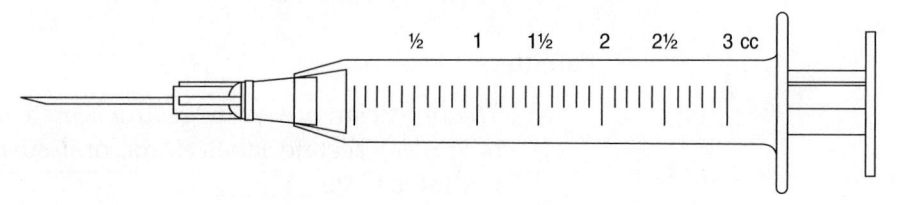

Metric Measurements

49. 9.43 micrograms = _____ milligrams

50. 193 grams = _____ kilogram. Round to the nearest tenth.

Apothecary Measurements

51. 12 fluid ounces = _____ milliliters

52. $4\frac{1}{4}$ teaspoons = _____ milliliters

53. $6\frac{1}{2}$ pints = _____ milliliters

54. 0.2 milligrams = grain _____

55. grain $\frac{1}{100}$ = _____ milligrams

56. 45 grams = grain _____

57. $4\frac{3}{4}$ teaspoons = _____ milliliters

Oral Medications

58. Desired: Aspirin 0.5 grams every 4 hours
    Available: Aspirin 500 milligrams scored tablets
    Give: _____

59. The patient is ordered Vistaril 12 milligrams orally every 6 hours for nausea relief. You have on hand Vistaril oral suspension 5 milligrams per 2.5 milliliters.
    You adminster _____.

Dosage Calculations

60. Ordered: Zocor 50 milligrams
    Have: Zocor 12.5 milligrams per tablet
    Desired dose: _____.

61. The doctor has ordered Zyloprim 0.5 gram orally twice a day. On hand is Zyloprim 100 milligrams scored tablets. The nurse should give _____.

62. The client receives an order for Augmentin 250 milligrams. The Augmentin is labeled 100 milligrams in 5 milliliters. The client will be given _____.

Parenteral Dosages

63. The physician orders megestrol acetate 600 milligrams per day. The megestrol acetate label reads, oral suspension 40 milligrams per milliliter. Give _____.

64. Give Dilaudid 0.5 milligrams IM from a vial that is labeled 5 milligrams per milliliter.
Give _____.

65. Ordered: Atropine sulfate 0.5 milligrams IM
Have: Atropine sulfate 0.25 milligrams per milliliter
Give _____

66. The doctor prescribes heparin 4000 units sub-Q four times a day. You have heparin 1500 units per milliliter. You give_____.

67. Ordered: Quinidine 0.4 gram orally every 4 hours. Quinidine is supplied in 100 milligrams tablets. How many tablets will you give?_____.

Calculating IV dosages

68. The patient with oliguria has an order for 125 milliliters of 0.9% NS over 2 hours. The drop factor is 15 drops per milliliter. How many drops per minute should be given?_____

69. The nurse receives an order that reads: 1200 milliliters D_5W IV at 60 milliliter per hour. Infuse for _____.

70. The nurse will administer an IV solution at 125 milliliter per hour for 6 hours. What is the total volume infused? _____

Basic Dosages by Body Weight

Perform the calculations to determine whether the following is a therapeutic dosage for this child:

 Ordered medication XZY 5 milligrams orally every 12 hours for a child weighing 14 pounds. You have medication XYZ 10 milligrams per milliliter. The recommended daily oral dosage for a child is 1.5 milligrams per kilogram per day in divided doses every 8 hours.

Medication XYZ
Oral Solution
10 mg/mL

---

71. This child's weight is _____ kilograms.

72. What is the recommended dosage for this child?_____ milligrams per day

Weight: 24 pounds 4 ounces
Ordered dose: 1.6 milligrams per kilogram per day
Recommended dosage from drug label: 3 milligrams every 8 hours

73. What is the daily dose? _____

74. What is the individual dose? _____

75. Does the dose ordered match the recommended dosage? _____

Answers for the Post-Test

1. 12
2. 276
3. 867
4. 28,188
5. 24.22, or 24 R 6, or $24\frac{2}{9}$
6. 17
7. 0815
8. $\frac{6}{21}, \frac{13}{21}, \frac{2}{3}, \frac{6}{7}$
9. $30\frac{13}{30}$
10. $38\frac{5}{12}$
11. 4
12. $11\frac{1}{9}$
13. 20
14. $4\frac{3}{50}$
15. 12.625
16. 18.69
17. 53.02
18. 37.08
19. 310.075
20. 27 doses
21. 21.29
22. $9\frac{11}{24}$

23. 2
24. 20
25. 15 : 8
26. $4\frac{7}{12}$
27. 15.28
28. 60
29. $395.00
30. 10.67
31. 63
32. 15
33. 16.4
34. 14
35. 70
36. 450%
37. 900%
38. $\frac{1}{500}$
39. $\frac{3}{10,000}$
40. 67
41. −37
42. −8
43. 372
44. 34
45. 15

46.
Generic name	Alendronate sodium
Trade name	Fosamax
Manufacturer	Merck & Co., Inc.
National Drug Code (NDC) number	0006-0212-31
Lot number (control number)	Not shown
Drug form	Tablet
Dosage strength	40 milligrams
Usual adult dose	40 milligrams Once a day taken at least one-half hour before the food, beverage, or medication of the day
Total amount in vial, packet, box	30 Tablets
Prescription warning	Rx only
Expiration date	Not shown

47. 23 milliliters

48. 0.6 milliliter

49. 0.00943 milligram

50. 0.2 kilogram

51. 360 milliliters

52. 21.25 milliliters

53. 3250 milliliters

54. grain $\dfrac{1}{300}$

55. 0.6 milligram

56. grain $7\dfrac{1}{2}$ or grain viiss

57. 23.75 milliliters

58. 1 tab

59. 6 milliliters

60. 4 tablets

61. 5 tablets

62. 12.5 milliliter

63. 15 milliliters

64. 0.1 milliliter

65. 2 milliliters

66. 2.67 milliliters

67. 4 tabs

68. 16 drops per minute

69. 20 hours

70. 750 milliliters

71. 6.36 kilograms

72. 9.54 milligrams per day

73. 18.37 milligrams per day

74. 6.12 milligrams

75. No, contact the physician for clarification.

Appendix of Practice Tests Units 1–6, 8

Unit 1 Practice Exam   **Name** _____

Solve each problem below. Place your answer on the blank line.

1. $968 + 45 + 19 =$ _____

2. $529 + 3,456 =$ _____

3. The heights of the people in Michele's family are 68 inches, 65 inches, 73 inches, 74 inches, and 84 inches. Find the range of the people in Michele's family. _____

4. $709 +$ _____ $+ 49 = 1670$

5. $2,852 - 1,418 =$ _____

6. $2,003 -$ _____ $= 907$

7. _____ $- 95 = 896$

8. $1,455 - 509 =$ _____

9. Write 1322 in standard time. _____

10. The dental office ordered 8 jackets for its staff. The jackets cost $37.00 each. What is the total cost for the 8 jackets? Write a number statement to solve this problem. Include the answer. _____

11. The heights of the members of Michele's family are 69 inches, 75 inches, 70 inches, 85 inches, and 73 inches. Find the median height of the members of Michele's family. _____

12. $14 \times 3 \times 12 =$ _____

13. $45 \times 138 =$ _____

14. Divide 932 by 8 = _____

15. 5,860 ÷ 14 = _____

16. $12\overline{)907}$ = _____

17. Heather's math tests had the following scores: 98, 75, 92, 98, 76, 87, 75, and 80. What is the mode of her scores? _____

18. Each gram of fat contains 9 calories. How many grams of fat are in 144 calories of fat in a piece of steak? _____

19. Bette was working hard to get a good grade. Her test scores were: 68%, 79%, 100%, 85%, and 88%. What is the mean or average of her grades? _____

20. Round 12,885 to the nearest ten. _____

21. Use one of the symbols (=, >, <, ≤, ≥) to complete the number statement: 285 + 17 _____ 51 × 6

22. Write the Roman numeral xixss as an Arabic numeral. _____

23. After a heart attack, Bob spent two days in the coronary care unit. His bill was $4,596.00. What was his daily room rate? Write a number statement that represents this problem. _____

24. Write a number statement using the symbol (>) _____

25. Find the prime factorization for 80. _____

Unit 2 Practice Exam   Name _____

Solve each problem. Put your answer on the blank line. Correct format is necessary.

1. Make into an equivalent fraction: $\dfrac{1}{4} = \dfrac{}{36}$ _____

2. Reduce to the lowest/simplest terms: $\dfrac{3}{129} =$ _____

3. Write as an improper fraction: $12\dfrac{3}{4} =$ _____

4. Write as a mixed number: $\dfrac{235}{9} =$ _____

5. $\dfrac{4}{5} + \dfrac{3}{8} =$ _____

6. $14\dfrac{3}{4} + \dfrac{5}{6} + 2\dfrac{7}{12} =$ _____

7. $22\dfrac{1}{5} + 1\dfrac{7}{9} =$ _____

8. $48\dfrac{2}{7} - 21\dfrac{5}{21} =$ _____

9. $676 - \dfrac{3}{11} =$ _____

10. $42\dfrac{5}{12} - 17\dfrac{5}{6} =$ _____

11. $\dfrac{3}{8} \times \dfrac{5}{7} =$ _____

12. $\dfrac{7}{12} \times 8 =$ _____

13. $7\dfrac{3}{4} \times 2\dfrac{1}{3} =$ _____

14. A bottle of medicine contains 12 doses of medication. How many full doses are in $4\dfrac{1}{4}$ bottles? _____

15. $\dfrac{3}{14} \div \dfrac{1}{5} =$ _____

16. $7\dfrac{1}{8} \div 10 =$ _____

17. How many full grain $^3/_4$ doses can be obtained from a grain $9^1/_2$ vial? _____

18. $35°C =$ _____ $°F$

19. $68°F = $ _____ °C

20. $\dfrac{\frac{2}{5}}{\frac{1}{7}} = $ _____

21. $\dfrac{\frac{1}{200}}{\frac{1}{6}} = $ _____

22. Order the following the following fractions by writing them in order from smallest to largest—do not just put the number of the order on top of the fraction. $\frac{1}{2}\ \frac{3}{4}\ \frac{4}{9}\ \frac{17}{36}$ _____

23. One cup holds 8 ounces. If a cup is $\frac{2}{5}$ full, how many ounces are in the cup? _____

24. The nurse gave the patient a tablet of grains $\frac{1}{20}$ of medicine followed by a second tablet of grains $\frac{5}{80}$. How many total grains of the medication did the patient receive? _____

25. The physical therapist suggested that Bob begin a series of stretches. He told Bob to work out for $\frac{1}{3}$ of an hour. How many minutes is $\frac{1}{3}$ of an hour? _____ minutes.

Unit 3 Practice Exam   Name _____

1. Write the words in decimal numbers: seven-hundredths. _____

2. Write the decimal number of 17.005 in words. _____

3. Round 25.075 to the nearest hundredth: _____

4. Which is larger: 10.07 or 10.7 = _____

5. $0.4 + 12 + 0.11 =$ _____

6. $36.05 + 1.7 + 0.009 =$ _____

7. One medication is labeled 48.5 milliliters and another is 0.5 milliliters. What is the total dosage in milliliters given of this medication? _____

8. $8.008 - 0.98 =$ _____

9. $0.9 - 0.007 =$ _____

10. Patient Smith was on a diet. He weighed 122.6 kilograms. After one month he weighed 112.8 kilograms. What was his total weight loss in one month? _____

11. $0.596 \times 2.3 =$ _____

12. $405 \times 3.02 =$ _____

13. $16\overline{)42.98}$ Round to the nearest tenth = _____

14. $1.9\overline{)28.09}$ Round to the nearest hundredth = _____

15. Change 2.85 to a fraction. Reduce if necessary. _____

16. Write $\dfrac{7}{8}$ as a decimal. _____

17. $98.5°F =$ _____ °C

18. $14°C =$ _____ °F

19. $\dfrac{12.50}{0.50} \times 4.5 =$ _____

20. Something was wrong with Tu. He felt sick, and he had a fever. At 3:00 P.M. his temperature was 101.8°F. By 5:00 P.M. it was 102.3°F. How many degrees had his temperature gone up by? _____

21. Valley Vista used a 45.6 ounce can of kidney beans in a chili casserole recipe. If each portion gets an equal amount of the beans and the recipe serves 9 people, how many ounces will each serving contain? Round to the nearest whole number. _____

22. I had an interview at the dental clinic for a dental assistant post. I had to stop to get gas. I put 7 gallons of gas in my car. Each gallon cost me $2.86. How much did I spend on gas? _____

23. The farm raises its own produce and meat. Will has a cow that produces milk. She gives 2.3 gallons of milk a day. How many gallons does she give in a month that has 30 days? _____

24. Bradley Benjamin heard that the nursing staff at Sky View earns $13.93 per hour. He is currently earning $12.46 per hour. How much more could he earn a week at Sky View than his current job if he calculated the rate for a 40 hour week? _____

25. Sally is trying to increase her dietary fiber intake. She eats 20.8 grams of fiber a day. If her goal is to eat 32 grams of dietary fiber, how many more grams of fiber does she need to eat? _____

Unit 4 Practice Exam   Name _____

Solve the ratio and proportion problems. Remember that ratios are reduced to their simplest form.

1. Write 8 days out of 15 as a ratio: _____

2. Is this an example of a proportion? Check the answer box.

   $2 : 3 :: 20 : 15$ ☐ Yes ☐ No

3. $5 : 30 = 12 : ?$ $? = $ _____

4. $\frac{1}{4} : 5 = ? : 70$ $? = $ _____

5. $82 : ? = \frac{1}{2} : 18$ $? = $ _____

6. $\frac{2}{4} = \frac{?}{98}$ $? = $ _____

7. $\frac{\frac{1}{2}}{\frac{1}{4}} = \frac{90}{?}$ $? = $ _____

8. $\frac{1}{12} : 28 = ? : 84$ $? = $ _____

9. If eggs cost $2.10 a dozen, how much do 16 eggs cost? _____

10. If Jerry makes $13.10 an hour, what is her pay for 15 hours? _____

11. A mouthwash cost $4.36 for 32 ounces. How much is paid per ounce? _____

12. Each calendar for the nursing home fund raiser costs $8.75. What is the cost for 25 calendars? _____

13. Simplify the following ratio $12\frac{1}{4} : 8$ _____

14. Simplify the following ratio $15 : \frac{1}{3}$ _____

15. Solve $^{1.7}/_{x} = {}^{8.2}/_{0.8}$ Round to the nearest tenth. _____

16. A set of three surgical masks cost $1.39. How many complete sets of masks can you buy with a budget of ten dollars. Do not worry about tax or shipping _____

17. 17 teaspoons = _____ tablespoons

18. 1 inch = 2.5 centimeters so 17.8 inches = _____ centimeters. Round to the nearest tenth.

19. 1 kilogram = 2.2 pounds so 49 kilograms = _____ pounds

20. $\dfrac{5}{7\frac{2}{4}} = \dfrac{?}{12\frac{1}{2}}$? = _____

Thresa's Roasted Red Tomato Soup

Nutrition facts	Amount/serving	%DV*	Amount/serving	%DV*
Serving size ½ cup (120 milliliters) Condensed soup Servings about 2.5 Calories 90 Fat calories 0	Total fat 0 gram	0%	Total carbohydrates 20 grams	7%
	Saturated fat 0 gram	0%	Fiber 1 gram	4%
	Cholestrol 0 milligram	0%	Sugars 15 grams	
	Sodium 610 milligrams	30%	Protein 2 grams	
	Vitamin A 10% · Vitamin C 10% · Calcium 0% · Iron %			

*Percent daily values (%DV) are based on a 2,000 calories diet.

21. If ½ cup of soup equals 120 milliliters, then how many milliliters are in 3¼ cups of soup? _____

22. If a can has 2.5 servings, how many cans are needed to serve 12 people? _____

23. One serving contains 90 calories, how many calories are in 4½ servings? _____

24. 1 gram of fiber constitutes 4% of a daily dietary value. How many grams of fiber would be present in 25% of the daily value? _____

25. How many grams of carbohydrates are present if the portion meets 30% of the daily value of carbohydrates? Round to the nearest tenth if necessary. _____

Unit 5 Practice Exam   Name _____

1. Convert $3\frac{1}{4}$ to a percent. _____

2. Convert 0.625 to a percent _____

3. Convert 453 to a percent _____

4. Convert $\frac{2}{5}$ to a percent _____

5. Convert $4\frac{1}{5}$ to a percent _____

6. Convert $\dfrac{\frac{2}{5}}{75}$ to a percent _____

7. Convert 45% to a decimal _____

8. Convert $5\frac{1}{4}\%$ to a decimal _____

9. Convert $\frac{3}{4}\%$ to a fraction _____

10. What is 12% of 233? _____

11. Find 56% of 250 _____

12. What is $22\frac{1}{2}\%$ of 400? _____

13. What percent of 80 is 14? _____

14. Find 32% of 360. _____

15. What is $12\frac{2}{3}\%$ of 120? _____

16. $15\frac{1}{4}\%$ of what number is 45.75? _____

17. What is 0.9% of 34? _____

18. Write the ratio of pure drug to solution: 16% _____

19. Write the ratio of pure drug to solution: 1.08% _____

20. Write the ratio of pure drug to solution: $2\frac{2}{5}\%$ _____

21. There are 3 grams of pure drug are in 45 milliliters of solution. What is the percent strength of solution? _____

22. There are 35 milliliters of pure drug in 100 milliliters of solution. How many milliliters of pure drug are needed to make 85 milliliters of this solution. _____

23. Take a 8% discount from a final sales price of $120.00. The final sales price would now be _____.

24. Write as a simplified ratio of the pure drug form: $6\frac{1}{4}$% solution _____

25. Write as a simplified ratio of the pure drug form: 9% solution_____

Unit 6 Practice Exam   Name _____

1–15. Complete the table below:

Fraction	Decimal	Ratio	Percent
$\dfrac{1}{100}$	_____	_____	_____
_____	0.08	_____	_____
_____	_____	2 : 5	_____
_____	_____	_____	$5\dfrac{1}{4}\%$
_____	0.1	_____	_____

16. If 1 tablespoon is equivalent to 3 teaspoons, how many tablespoons are in 13 teaspoons? _____

17. One inch equals approximately 2.54 centimeters. If an infant is measured at 48 centimeters, how long is the infant in inches? Round to the nearest tenth. _____

18. One cup has 8 ounces. So $14\dfrac{1}{4}$ cups equals _____ ounces.

19. One teaspoon contains 5 milliliters. Nine and one-half teaspoons contains _____ milliliters.

20. If one pound contains 16 ounces, how many ounces are in 24 pounds? _____

21. If 1 kilogram equals 2.2 pounds, how many kilograms are in 70 pounds? _____

22. $3\dfrac{1}{4}$ feet = _____ inches

23. _____ quarts = 12 pints

24. 15 pounds = _____ kilograms

25. _____ teaspoons = 30 milliliters

Unit 8 Practice Test   Name _____

1. The numerical value for centi- is _____.

2. The numerical value for micro- is _____.

3. The numerical value for milli- is _____.

4. Gram and milligram are metric measures for measuring _____.

5. Liter and milliliter are metric measures for measuring _____.

Circle the correct metric notation for each:

6. Twelve and one-half kilograms

   a. $12\frac{1}{2}$ kg   b. 12.5 KG   c. 12.5 kg   d. $12\frac{1}{2}$ KG

7. One hundred five micrograms

   a. 105 mg   b. 0.105 mcg   c. 105 mcg   d. 100.5 mcg

8. Write the correct metric notation for six hundredth of a milliliter. _____

9. Write the correct metric notation for two tenths of a milligram. _____

10. Write the correct metric notation for ninety-three milligram. _____ _____

11. Write the correct metric notation for twelve hundredths of a kilogram. _____

12. 2.76 milligrams = _____ micrograms

13. 25 centimeters = _____ millimeters

14. 120.8 grams = _____ kilogram

15. _____ milligram = 4.7 micrograms

16. _____ liter = 95 milliliters

17. 12 grams = _____ milligrams

18. 9.05 milliliters = _____ liter

19. _____ gram = 10000 micrograms

20. _____ centimeters = 54 millimeters

21. 0.5 gram = _____ micrograms

22. 1200 milliliters = _____ liters

23. _____ kilogram = 23.8 grams

24. 33.7 meters = _____ millimeters

25. A newborn weighs 3090 grams. How many kilograms does it weigh?
_____

Complete Answer Key for Student Work Text

Unit 1: Whole Number Review

Symbols and Number Statements
Practice 1: p. 12

1. <
3. >
5. ≥
7. >
9. >
11. ≤

Practice 2: p. 12

Answers will vary

Addition Practice: p. 13

1. 19
3. 492
5. 2,063
7. 488
9. 2,664

Addition Applications: pp. 13–14

1. a. 266
   b. 711
   c. 1,176
   d. 20 boxes
3. a. 300
   b. 720
   c. 75

d. 110
e. 1,205

Subtraction Practice: p. 15

1. 394
3. 235
5. 437
7. 1,873
9. 4,212

Subtraction Applications: p. 15

1. 1,474
3. 3 boxes

Multiplication Practice: p. 17

1. 96
3. 23,508
5. 99,960
7. 12,288
9. 92,656
11. 4,152

Multiplication Applications: p. 17

1. $3,444.00
3. $525.00

Prime Factorization: p. 18

1. $2^2 \cdot 31$
3. $2^2 \cdot 23$

Division Setup Practice: p. 19

1. $76\overline{)145}$
3. $17\overline{)49}$
5. $8\overline{)2044}$

Division Practice: p. 20

1. 94
3. 3,086 R 1
5. 311
7. 1,576 R 8
9. 23,441
11. 12,506 R 1

Division Applications: pp. 20–21

1. 13 days
3. $21
5. $1,656.00
7. 9 grams

Solving for the Unknown Number with Basic Mathematics: p. 21

Practice 1: p .21

1. 74
3. 53
5. 13

Practice 2: p. 22

1. 86
3. 560
5. 35

Practice 3: p. 22

1. 39
3. 4
5. 75

Practice 4: p. 22

1. 132
3. 3
5. 18

Rounding Practice: p. 23

1. a. 3,920
    b. 140
    c. 6,950
    d. 1,930
    e. 15,930
    f. 100
3. a. 3,000
    b. 88,000
    c. 7,000
    d. 13,000
    e. 433,000
    f. 3,000

Estimation Practice: p. 24

1. a. $194
    b. $162
    c. $112
    d. $2,914

Basics of Statistical Analysis: p. 24

Mean/Average: p. 25

1. $9
3. 5
5. 7

Median: p. 26

1. 99
3. 26
5. 9

Mode: pp. 27–28

1. 8
3. #24
5. 6 & 7

Range: pp. 28–29

1. 82
3. 360
5. 87

Roman Numerals: Concept 1 Practice: p. 30

1. 13
3. 31
5. 1001
7. xxxi
9. iss

Concept 2 Practice: p. 30

1. $9\frac{1}{2}$
3. 400
5. 99
7. xxxix
9. CCXL

Concept 3 Practice: p. 31

1. 114
3. 514
5. 89
7. 404
9. $592\frac{1}{2}$

Practice: p. 31

1. xivss
3. CXLVI
5. IM
7. CDL
9. xvii

Mixed Practice: pp. 31–32

1. 750
3. 18
5. xix
7. DCVII
9. LXVI
11. 908
13. CCCLXII
15. IM

17. 78
19. MMDXV

Time in Allied Health: p. 32

Practice Convert to Universal Time: p. 33

1. 0005
3. 0739
5. 1245
7. 1757
9. 2125

Practice in Standard Time: p. 33

1. 12:56 P.M.
3. 12:09 A.M.
5. 12:48 A.M.
7. 3:24 P.M.
9. 9:12 P.M.

Whole Number Self-Test: pp. 33–35

1. 1,075
2. 263 dollars or $263.00
3. 7 dollars
4. 66
5. 16
6. 50
7. 17
8. a. $1,500
   b. $200
   c. $150
   d. $100
   e. $375
   f. $2,325.00
9. $966.00
10. 5,780
11. 110
12. $504
13. ten thousands
14. >
15. $19\frac{1}{2}$

Unit 2: Fractions

Part to Whole Relationships: p.37

1. Three parts to four total parts
3. Seven parts to eight total parts

Equivalent Fractions Practice: p. 38

1. 6
3. 8
5. 15
7. 36
9. 54

Reducing Fractions Practice: pp. 39–40

1. $\frac{1}{7}$
3. $\frac{1}{2}$
5. $\frac{1}{4}$
7. $\frac{1}{2}$
9. $\frac{1}{3}$

Reducing Mixed Numbers Practice: p. 40

1. $13\frac{1}{4}$
3. $1\frac{1}{2}$
5. $3\frac{1}{4}$
7. $2\frac{1}{9}$
9. $6\frac{1}{2}$

Fractional Parts from Words Practice: p. 41

1. $\frac{2}{5}$
3. $\frac{1}{3}$
5. $\frac{1}{8}$

Improper Fractions to Mixed Numbers Practice: pp. 41–42

1. $7\frac{1}{2}$
3. $19\frac{1}{2}$
5. $9\frac{3}{7}$
7. $2\frac{3}{8}$
9. 1

Adding Like Denominators Practice: pp. 43–44

1. 1
3. 2
5. $\frac{7}{12}$
7. $\frac{7}{13}$
9. $22\frac{5}{6}$
11. $\frac{4}{5}$
13. 1
15. $140\frac{1}{4}$

Finding Common Denominator Practice: pp. 44–45

1. 20
3. 44
5. 25
7. 200
9. 27

Adding Unlike Fractions Practice: pp. 45–46

1. $\frac{17}{20}$

3. $1\frac{1}{9}$

5. $\frac{1}{2}$

7. $\frac{13}{21}$

9. $1\frac{1}{15}$

11. $1\frac{2}{5}$

13. $106\frac{8}{9}$

15. $8\frac{7}{8}$

Finding the Common Denominator Practice: pp. 46–47

1. 20

3. 192

5. 45

7. 36

9. 30

Adding Fractions Practice: pp. 47–48

1. $9\frac{11}{12}$

3. $13\frac{1}{2}$

5. $6\frac{5}{7}$

7. $18\frac{29}{30}$

9. $18\frac{9}{10}$

11. $16\frac{17}{27}$

13. $39\frac{5}{12}$

15. $13\frac{7}{15}$

17. $4\frac{7}{16}$

19. $5\frac{1}{2}$

Addition Applications: p. 48

1. $121\frac{3}{4}$

3. $1\frac{3}{16}$

5. $3\frac{5}{6}$

Ordering Fractions Practice: p. 49

1. $\frac{4}{12}, \frac{1}{4}, \frac{2}{9}$

3. $\frac{20}{50}, \frac{33}{100}, \frac{6}{25}$

Subtracting Like Fractions Practice: p. 50

1. $\frac{1}{9}$

3. $\frac{2}{11}$

5. $2\frac{1}{6}$

7. $45\frac{1}{8}$

9. $\frac{1}{2}$

11. $\frac{1}{4}$

13. $12\frac{1}{5}$

15. $31\frac{1}{9}$

17. $124\frac{1}{12}$

19. $12\frac{5}{33}$

Subtracting Mixed Numbers from Whole Numbers Practice: p. 52

1. $10\frac{1}{6}$

3. $9\frac{3}{4}$

5. $14\frac{6}{13}$

7. $5\frac{6}{7}$

9. $10\frac{2}{5}$

Subtracting Fractions Practice: pp. 52–53

1. $7\frac{13}{20}$

3. $19\frac{17}{30}$

5. $5\frac{17}{22}$

7. $111\frac{23}{30}$

9. $31\frac{5}{8}$

11. $16\frac{5}{6}$

13. $76\frac{25}{36}$

15. $6\frac{1}{2}$

Additional Practice in Subtraction with Borrowing: pp. 53–54

1. $8\frac{5}{8}$

3. $9\frac{3}{4}$

5. $11\frac{3}{4}$

7. $72\frac{5}{7}$

9. $83\frac{7}{12}$

Subtraction Application: p. 54

1. $11\frac{1}{2}$

3. $99\frac{1}{4}$

5. $3\frac{1}{2}$

Multiplication Practice: p. 55

1. $\frac{1}{16}$

3. $\frac{28}{45}$

5. $\frac{3}{35}$

7. $\frac{4}{9}$

9. $\frac{13}{66}$

Multiplication: Fractions and Whole Numbers Practice: p. 56

1. $1\frac{1}{2}$

3. $16\frac{1}{3}$

5. $5\frac{3}{5}$

7. $11\frac{2}{3}$

9. 4

Multiplication Practice: p. 58

1. $1\frac{5}{7}$

3. $\frac{1}{4}$

5. $\frac{1}{20}$

7. $\frac{1}{4}$

9. $\frac{11}{96}$

11. $\frac{1}{24}$

Making Improper Fractions Practice: p. 59

1. $\frac{33}{4}$

3. $\frac{88}{5}$

5. $\frac{27}{12}$

7. $\frac{32}{9}$

9. $\frac{53}{12}$

Multiplying Fractions: p. 61

1. $\frac{29}{84}$

3. $\frac{21}{40}$

5. $\frac{20}{27}$

7. $40\frac{1}{4}$

9. $3\frac{17}{20}$

Multiplication Application: pp. 61–62

1. 70 doses

3. 875 milligrams

5. $18\frac{3}{4}$ cups

Dividing Fractions Practice: pp. 63–64

1. $\frac{5}{7}$

3. $\frac{7}{24}$

5. 8

7. $\frac{1}{45}$

9. $\frac{1}{120}$

11. $3\frac{8}{9}$

13. $2\frac{7}{9}$

15. $4\frac{8}{9}$

17. $\frac{31}{130}$

19. $1\frac{47}{105}$

Division Applications: p. 64

1. $9\frac{3}{20}$

3. $13.30

5. 10

Celsius to Fahrenheit Temperature Conversions Practice: p. 65

1. 68

3. 77

5. 104

7. 176

Fahrenheit to Celsius Temperature Conversions Practice: p. 66

1. 40

3. 10

5. 15

7. 30

Complex Fractions Practice: p. 67

1. $\frac{3}{32}$

3. $\dfrac{1}{15,000}$

5. $1\dfrac{1}{5}$

7. $\dfrac{4}{5}$

9. $\dfrac{15}{16}$

Mixed Complex Fraction Problems Practice: p. 68

1. 5
3. 12
5. 1

Fraction Self-Test: pp. 68–69

1. $\dfrac{1}{4}$
2. Answers will vary: $\dfrac{2}{12}, \dfrac{3}{18}, \dfrac{4}{24}$, etc.
3. $11\dfrac{1}{11}$
4. $11\dfrac{11}{12}$
5. $39\dfrac{4}{5}$
6. $30\dfrac{13}{16}$
7. $\dfrac{4}{9}$
8. 25
9. $\dfrac{2}{12}, \dfrac{1}{4}, \dfrac{1}{3}, \dfrac{3}{8}$
10. 50
11. more
12. $\dfrac{1}{3}$
13. $\dfrac{5}{8}$
14. $\dfrac{3}{8}$
15. $26\dfrac{5}{24}$

Unit 3: Decimals

Decimals in Words: pp. 71–72

1. Seven tenths
3. Five hundredths
5. One hundred fifty and seventy-five thousands
7. One hundred nine and twenty-three thousands
9. Eighteen and eight hundredths

Words to Decimals: p. 72

1. 0.2
3. 300.002
5. 6.03

Rounding to the Nearest Tenth Practice: p. 73

1. 6.7
3. 0.8
5. 25.0 or 25
7. 0.1
9. 9.9

Rounding to the Nearest Hundredth Practice: p. 73

1. 17.33
3. 4.82
5. 0.01
7. 32.65
9. 46.09

Smaller Decimals Practice: p. 74

1. 0.89
3. 2.012
5. 0.0033

Larger Decimals Practice: p. 74

1. 0.0785
3. 0.5
5. 0.675

Ordering from Largest to Smallest Practice: pp. 74–75

1. 7.5, 7.075, 0.75, 0.7, 0.07
3. 5.55, 5.15, 5.05, 0.5, 0.05

Adding Decimals Practice: pp. 75–76

1. 38.15
3. 86.235
5. 89.2496
7. 127.52
9. 214.281

Addition Applications: p. 76

1. 4.5 milligrams
3. 226 milligrams
5. 124.54 centimeters

Subtracting Decimals Practice: p. 77

1. 0.72
3. 14.065
5. 3.5013
7. 0.175
9. 87.436

Subtraction Applications: pp. 77–78

1. 0.65 liters
3. 1.5 milligrams
5. 1.8°F

Multiplying Decimals Practice: p. 79

1. 12.6
3. 33.6
5. 128.38
7. 0.8088
9. 0.4726
11. 0.0024
13. 151.11
15. 1.65036
17. 7.632
19. 6,942.53

21. 1,342.11
23. 10.04565

Multiplication Applications: p. 80

1. $420.80
3. $1,618.20
5. $128.00

Dividing Decimals Practice: p. 81

1. 0.63
3. 0.232
5. 0.12
7. 52.4
9. 3.02

Dividing with Zeros as Placeholders Practice: p. 82

1. 1,060
3. 2.08
5. 1.099
7. 30.66
9. 0.2099

Additional Practice: p. 82

1. 5.3
3. 0.04
5. 1.39
7. 403.9

Simplified Multiplication Practice: pp. 83–84

1. 135
3. 1,257.5
5. 6
7. 12,670
9. 476
11. 13.45
13. 10.09
15. 23,850

Simplified Division Practice: pp. 84–85

1. 1.29
3. 12.5
5. 0.025
7. 0.158
9. 0.325
11. 10.01
13. 0.03076
15. 0.10275

Division Applications: p. 85

1. $63.25
3. 3 tablets
5. $26.24

Decimal to Fraction Conversion Practice: pp. 86–87

1. $\frac{1}{25}$

3. $6\frac{1}{4}$

5. $225\frac{1}{20}$

7. $7\frac{3}{4}$

9. $9\frac{3}{10}$

Fraction to Decimal Conversion Practice: p. 88

1. 0.5
3. 0.875
5. 0.24
7. 0.2
9. $0.83\frac{1}{3}$ or 0.083

Temperature Conversions with Decimals Practice: pp. 89–90

1. 93.2
3. 224.6
5. 107.6

7. 38
9. 53.6

Mixed Fraction and Decimal Problems Practice: p. 91

1. 2.2
3. 7.5
5. 0.168
7. 7.675

Decimal Self-Test: pp. 92–93

1. Forty-five thousandths
2. 21.75
3. 16.925
4. 4.5405
5. 90.2
6. 978.74
7. 8.018, 0.81, 0.08, 0.018
8. 1,000.9
9. 2 milligrams
10. 3 tablets
11. $\frac{1}{8}$
12. 0.26
13. 3.625
14. 39.4°C
15. 1.7

Unit 4: Ratio and Proportion

Ratios: pp. 94–95

1. 5 : 7
3. 1 : 5
5. 1 : 2

Simplifying Ratio: pp. 95–96

1. 27 : 1
3. 20 : 1
5. 2 : 1
7. 13 : 21
9. 5 : 2

Proportions: p. 96

1. No
3. Yes
5. No

Solving with Proportions Practice: p. 97

1. 7.5
3. 16
5. 27
7. 14
9. 52

Measurement Conversions Using Proportions Practice: pp. 99–100

1. $7\frac{2}{3}$
3. 8
5. 9
7. 4
9. 56
11. $2\frac{1}{2}$
13. 5
15. $1\frac{1}{2}$
17. 80
19. 5

Word Problems Using Proportions Practice: p. 101

1. 3 caplets
3. 17.5 grams
5. 28 kilograms

Solving for x in Complex Problems Practice: pp. 102–103

1. 6
3. 9.6
5. 1
7. $1\frac{1}{3}$

9. 2.4
11. 1.5

Nutrition Applications: p. 104

1. 9
3. 9
5. 48
7. 1312

pp. 104–105

1. 645
3. 220
5. 121.5

Practice with Food Labels: pp. 105–108

1. 840 milliliters
3. 405 calories
5. 42.9 grams
7. 240 calories
9. 40%
11. 11 grams
13. 1200 milliliters
15. $6\frac{1}{4}$ cups

Ratio and Proportion Self-Test: pp. 108–110

1. Answers vary.
2. 3
3. 9
4. $2\frac{2}{3}$
5. 125
6. 140 milligrams
7. 8 tablets
8. 0.3 cubic centimeters
9. $\frac{1}{75}$
10. 1.5
11. 2 minutes 10 seconds
12. 80 patients
13. 640

14. $\frac{4}{125}$

15. 96 ounces

Unit 5: Percents

Percent-to-Decimal Practice: p. 112

1. 0.45

3. $0.78\frac{1}{5}$ or 0.782

5. $0.44\frac{1}{2}$ or 0.445

Decimal-to-Percent Practice: pp. 112–113

1. 62.5%

3. 860%

5. 7.6%

Mixed Practice: p. 113

1. 0.7689

3. 0.86

5. 7.8%

7. $125\frac{1}{4}$% or 125.25%

9. 0.015

Set Up of Percents Practice: p. 114

1. $\frac{25}{100} = \frac{x}{200}$

3. $\frac{8.5}{100} = \frac{x}{224}$

5. $\frac{x}{100} = \frac{18}{150}$

7. $\frac{x}{100} = \frac{75}{90}$

9. $\frac{50}{100} = \frac{75}{x}$

Percents Practice: p. 115

1. 18

3. 25%

5. 5.88

7. 22.5%

9. 17.60

More Complex Percents Practice: p. 116

1. 41.67

3. 60

5. 15.63

7. 1280

9. 533.33

Percent Strength Practice: p. 117

1. 1 gram of pure drug to 25 milliliters of solution

3. 1.5 grams of pure drug to 100 milliliters of solution

5. 1 gram of pure drug to 20 milliliters of solution

Percent Equivalents in Solutions Practice: pp. 118–119

1. a. 1.25 grams
   b. 1.75 grams
   c. 3.25 grams
   d. 6.25 grams

3. a. 30%
   b. 60 grams

Additional Practice with Solution Strength: pp. 119–120

1. a. 12.75 grams
   b. 100 milliliters
   c. 51 : 400
   d. 4.5 grams
   e. 10.2 grams
   f. 7.7 grams

3. a. 78 grams
   b. 100 milliliters
   c. 39 : 50
   d. 51.1 grams
   e. 70.2 grams
   f. 351 grams

Single Trade Discounts Practice: p. 121

1. $71.33 $404.17
3. $15.69 $109.86
5. $88.23 $264.67
7. $112.68 $137.72
9. $63.20 $94.80

Percent Self-Test: pp. 121–123

1. Answers vary. A percent is a number which is part of a whole. 75% is 75 parts of 100.

2. a. $87\frac{1}{4}\%$ or 87.25%

   b. $83\frac{1}{3}\%$

3. 243.75
4. 20
5. 200
6. There are 5.5 grams of pure drug in 100 milliliters of solution.
7. 2.25 grams of pure drug
8. a. $15.54
   b. $113.96
9. 8.3% or $8\frac{1}{3}\%$
10. $48.90
11. 12%
12. 2.5
13. 6.4%
14. 0.15
15. 70000

Unit 6: Combined Applications

Conversions: pp. 127–128

Fraction	Decimal	Ratio	Percent
1. $\frac{3}{4}$	0.75	3 : 4	75%
3. $\frac{1}{2}$	0.5	1 : 2	50%
5. $\frac{1}{250}$	0.004	1 : 250	0.4%
7. $\frac{3}{50}$	0.06	3 : 50	6%
9. $\frac{1}{10}$	0.1	1 : 10	10%
11. $1\frac{9}{25}$	1.36	34 : 25	136%
13. $\frac{2}{5}$	0.4	2 : 5	40%
15. $\frac{16}{25}$	0.64	16 : 25	64%
17. $\frac{5}{6}$	$0.83\frac{1}{3}$	5 : 6	$83\frac{1}{3}\%$
19. $\frac{1}{100}$	0.01	1 : 100	1%

Using Combined Application in Measurement Convertions Abbreviations: p. 129

1. Foot
3. Ounce
5. Pound
7. Quart
9. Drop

Standard Units of Measurement Conversion Review: p. 130

1. $2\frac{1}{2}$
3. 31.25 or 31.75
5. 3
7. 24
9. $2\frac{1}{2}$

More Combined Applications Practice: p. 131

1. 6
3. 36
5. 32
7. 149.6
9. 4

Mixed Review Practice: p. 132

1. 2

3. $\frac{1}{12}$

5. $\frac{1}{30}$

Converting among Systems: pp. 132–133

Fraction	Decimal	Ratio	Percent
1. $\frac{7}{8}$	0.875	7 : 8	$87\frac{1}{2}\%$
3. $\frac{3}{4}$	0.75	3 : 4	75%
5. $\frac{2}{5}$	0.40	2 : 5	40%
7. $\frac{2}{25}$	0.08	2 : 25	8%
9. $\frac{3}{5}$	0.6	3 : 5	60%
11. $1\frac{5}{8}$	1.625	13 : 8	162.5%
13. $\frac{11}{50}$	0.22	11 : 50	22%
15. $\frac{3}{25}$	0.12	3 : 25	12%
17. $\frac{1}{6}$	$0.16\frac{2}{3}$	1 : 6	$16\frac{2}{3}\%$
19. $\frac{1}{25}$	0.04	1 : 25	4%

Combined Application Self-Test: pp. 133–134

1. 0.04

2. 1 : 200

3. $1\frac{1}{20}$

4. 33 : 8

5. 27.25

6. 6%

7. 57 : 400

8. 26

9. 24

10. 105 or 106.68

11. 1,080

12. 16

13. 420

14. 0.0804

15. 0.3

Unit 8: The Metric System

Metric System: Units Practice: p. 161

1. kg
3. g
5. cm
7. km
9. liter
11. kilometer
13. mcg or µg
15. centimeter

Metric Conversions: p. 162

1. 0.004
3. 9250
5. 0.001
7. 0.3586
9. 0.0375

Conversion Practice: pp. 162–165

1. 1
3. 0.026
5. 19500
7. 300
9. 70
11. 0.14
13. 0.25
15. 600

17. 36000
19. 7.5
21. 12500
23. 240
25. 12760
27. 235
29. 0.8
31. 1
33. 125
35. 125
37. 45.25
39. 0.001
41. 5.524
43. 125
45. 90
47. 100
49. 8.5

Practice with Word Problems: pp. 165–166

1. 44.53 centimeters
3. 1890 liters, 10 servings

5. 1250 cubic centimeters
7. 123.56 centimeters, 1.2356 meters
9. Yes, 0.03 grams converts to 30 milligrams

Metric Self-Test: pp. 166–167

1. 250000
2. 0.075
3. 0.0546
4. 8300
5. 14000
6. 0.0012
7. 0.00001
8. 0.25
9. 15
10. 30000
11. 0.000008 milligrams
12. 34.5 centimeters
13. 7.5 milliliters
14. 240 milliliters
15. 750 milligrams

Practice Exam Answer Key

Unit 1: pp. 240–241

1. 1,032
2. 3,985
3. 16
4. 912
5. 2,346
6. 1,096
7. 991
8. 946
9. 1:22 P.M.
10. $8 \times \$37.00 = \$296.00$—May vary in format.
11. 73 inches
12. 504
13. 6,210
14. 7,456
15. 418 R 8
16. 75 R 7
17. 75 & 98
18. 16 grams
19. 84%
20. 12,890
21. $<$
22. $19\frac{1}{2}$
23. $\$4,596 \div 2 = \$2,298$
24. Answers will vary. $7 > 4$
25. $2^4 \times 5$

Unit 2: pp. 242–243

1. $\frac{9}{36}$
2. $\frac{1}{43}$
3. $\frac{51}{4}$
4. $26\frac{1}{9}$

5. $1\frac{7}{40}$
6. $18\frac{1}{6}$
7. $23\frac{44}{45}$
8. $27\frac{1}{21}$
9. $675\frac{8}{11}$
10. $24\frac{7}{12}$
11. $\frac{15}{56}$
12. $4\frac{2}{3}$
13. $18\frac{1}{12}$
14. 51 doses
15. $1\frac{1}{14}$
16. $\frac{57}{80}$
17. 12 doses
18. 95°F
19. 20°C
20. $2\frac{4}{5}$
21. $\frac{3}{100}$
22. $\frac{4}{8}, \frac{17}{36}, \frac{1}{2}, \frac{3}{4}$
23. $3\frac{1}{5}$
24. $\frac{9}{80}$
25. 20 minutes

Unit 3: pp. 244–245

1. 0.07
2. Seventeen and five thousandths
3. 25.08
4. 10.7 should be circled
5. 12.51
6. 37.759
7. 49 milliliters
8. 7.028
9. 0.893
10. 9.8
11. 1.3708
12. 1223.10
13. 2.7
14. 14.78
15. $2\frac{17}{20}$
16. 0.875
17. 36.8
18. 57.2
19. 112.5
20. 0.5°F
21. 5 ounces
22. $20.02
23. 69 gallons
24. $58.80
25. 11.2 grams

Unit 4: pp. 246–247

1. 8 : 15
2. No
3. 72
4. 3.5
5. 2952
6. 49
7. 45
8. $\frac{1}{4}$ or 0.25

9. $2.80
10. $196.50
11. $0.14 or 14¢
12. $218.75
13. 49 : 32
14. 45 : 1
15. 0.2
16. 7 sets
17. $5\frac{2}{3}$
18. 7.12
19. 107.8 or $107\frac{4}{5}$
20. $8\frac{1}{3}$
21. 780 milliliters
22. $4\frac{4}{5}$ cans
23. 405 calories
24. 6.25 grams
25. 85.7 grams

Unit 5: pp. 248–249

1. 325%
2. $62\frac{1}{2}$% or 62.5%
3. 45300%
4. 40%
5. 420%
6. 3.2%
7. 0.45
8. 0.0525
9. $\frac{3}{400}$
10. 27.96
11. 140
12. 90
13. 17.5%
14. 115.20

15. 15.20
16. 300
17. 0.306
18. 4 : 25
19. 27 : 2500
20. 3 : 125
21. $6\frac{2}{3}$% or 6.67%
22. 29.75
23. $110.40
24. 1 : 16
25. 9 : 100

24. 6.8 kilograms
25. 6 teaspoons

Unit 8: pp. 253–254

1. 100
2. 1000000
3. 1000
4. Weight
5. Volume
6. c. 12.5 kilograms

Unit 6: p. 250

1–15.

Fraction	Decimal	Ratio	Percent
$\frac{1}{100}$	0.01	1 : 100	1
$\frac{2}{25}$	0.08	2 : 25	8
$\frac{2}{5}$	0.4	2 : 5	40
$\frac{21}{400}$	0.0525	21 : 400	$5\frac{1}{4}$
$\frac{1}{10}$	0.1	1 : 10	10

16. $4\frac{1}{3}$ tablespoons
17. 18.9 inches
18. 116 ounces
19. 47.5 milliliters
20. $1\frac{1}{2}$ pounds
21. 31.8 kilograms
22. 39 inches
23. 6 quarts

7. c. 105 micrograms
8. 0.06 milliliter
9. 0.2 milligram
10. 0.093 milligram
11. 0.12 kilogram
12. 0.00276
13. 250
14. 0.1208
15. 0.0047
16. 0.095

17. 12000
18. 0.00905
19. 0.01
20. 5.4
21. 500000
22. 1.2
23. 0.0238
24. 3370
25. 3.1 kilogram

Index

Brief Contents

 # Building Medical Terms from Word Parts

Four different word parts or elements can be used to construct medical terms:

1. The **word root** is the foundation of the word.
2. A prefix is at the beginning of the word.
3. A **suffix** is at the end of the word.
4. The **combining vowel** is a vowel (usually *o*) that links the word root to another word root or a suffix.

cardiogram = record of the heart

pericardium = around the heart
card**itis** = inflammation of the heart
cardi**o**my**o**pathy = disease of the heart muscle

The following sections on word roots, combining vowels and forms, prefixes, and suffixes will consider each of these word parts in more detail and present examples of some of those most commonly used.

Word Roots

The word root is the foundation of a medical term and provides the general meaning of the word. The word root often indicates the body system or part of the body being discussed, such as *cardi* for heart. At other times the word root may be an action. For example, the word root *cis* means to cut (as in incision).

A term may have more than one word root. For example, **osteoarthritis** (oss-tee-oh-ar-THRY-tis) combines the word root *oste* meaning bone and *arthr* meaning the joints. When the suffix *-itis*, meaning inflammation, is added, we have the entire word, meaning an inflammation involving bone at the joints.

Combining Vowel/Form

To make it possible to pronounce long medical terms with ease and to combine several word parts, a combining vowel is used. This is most often the vowel *o*. Combining vowels are utilized in two places: between a word root and a suffix or between two word roots.

To decide whether or not to use a combining vowel between a word root and a suffix, first look at the suffix. If it begins with a vowel, do not use the combining vowel. If, however, the suffix begins with a consonant, then use a combining vowel. For example: To combine *arthr* with *-scope* will require a combining vowel: **arthroscope** (AR-throh-scope). But to combine *arthr* with *-itis* does not require a combining vowel: **arthritis** (ar-THRY-tis).

The combining vowel is typically kept between two word roots, even if the second word root begins with a vowel. For example, in forming the term **gastroenteritis** (gas-troh-en-ter-EYE-tis) the combining vowel is kept between the two word roots *gastr* and *enter* (gastrenteritis is incorrect). As you can tell from pronouncing these two terms, the combining vowel makes the pronunciation easier.

When writing a word root by itself, its **combining form** is typically used. This consists of the word root and its combining vowel written in a word root/vowel form, for example, *cardi/o*. Since it is often simpler to pronounce word roots when they appear in their combining form, this format is used throughout this book.

Common Combining Forms

Some commonly used word roots in their combining form, their meaning, and examples of their use follow. Review the examples to observe when a combining vowel was kept and when it was dropped according to the rules presented on the preceding page.

COMBINING FORM	MEANING	EXAMPLE (DEFINITION)
aden/o	gland	adenopathy (gland disease)
carcin/o	cancer	carcinoma (cancerous tumor)
cardi/o	heart	cardiac (pertaining to the heart)
chem/o	chemical	chemotherapy (treatment with chemicals)
cis/o	to cut	incision (process of cutting into)
dermat/o	skin	dermatology (study of the skin)
enter/o	small intestine	enteric (pertaining to the small intestine)
gastr/o	stomach	gastric (pertaining to the stomach)
gynec/o	female	gynecology (study of females)
hemat/o	blood	hematic (pertaining to the blood)
hydr/o	water	hydrocele (protrusion of water [in the scrotum])
immun/o	immunity	immunology (study of immunity)
laryng/o	voice box	laryngeal (pertaining to the voice box)
nephr/o	kidney	nephromegaly (enlarged kidney)
neur/o	nerve	neural (pertaining to a nerve)
ophthalm/o	eye	ophthalmic (pertaining to the eye)
ot/o	ear	otic (pertaining to the ear)
path/o	disease	pathology (study of disease)
pulmon/o	lung	pulmonary (pertaining to the lungs)
rhin/o	nose	rhinoplasty (surgical repair of the nose)

Prefixes

A new medical term is formed when a prefix is added to the front of the term. Prefixes frequently give information about the location of an organ, the number of parts, or the time (frequency). For example, the prefix *bi-* stands for two of something, such as **bilateral** (bye-LAH-ter-al), meaning to have two sides. However, not every term will have a prefix.

Common Prefixes

Some of the more common prefixes, their meanings, and examples of their use follow. When written by themselves, prefixes are followed by a hyphen.

PREFIX	MEANING	EXAMPLE (DEFINITION)
a-	without, away from	aphasia (without speech)
an-	without	anoxia (without oxygen)
ante-	before, in front of	antepartum (before birth)
anti-	against	antibiotic (against life)
auto-	self	autograft (a graft from one's own body)
brady-	slow	bradycardia (slow heartbeat)
contra-	against	contraception (against conception)
de-	without	depigmentation (without pigment)
dys-	painful, difficult, abnormal	dyspnea (difficulty breathing)
endo-	within, inner	endoscope (instrument to view within)
epi-	upon, over	epigastric (upon or over the stomach)
eso-	inward	esotropia (inward turning)
eu-	normal, good	eupnea (normal breathing)
ex-	external, outward	exostosis (condition of external bone)
exo-	outward	exotropia (outward turning)
extra-	outside of	extracorporeal (outside of the body)
hetero-	different	heterograft (graft [like a skin graft] from another species)
homo-	same	homograft (graft [like a skin graft] from the same species)
hydro-	water	hydrotherapy (water therapy)
hyper-	over, above	hypertrophy (overdevelopment)
hypo-	under, below	hypodermic (under the skin)
in-	not; inward	infertility (not fertile); inhalation (to breathe in)
inter-	among, between	intervertebral (between the vertebrae)
intra-	within, inside	intravenous (inside, within a vein)
macro-	large	macrotia (having large ears)
micro-	small	microtia (having small ears)
myo-	~~to shut~~ (muscle)	myopia (to shut eyes/squint)
neo-	new	neonatology (study of the newborn)
pan-	all	pansinusitis (inflammation of all the sinuses)
para-	beside, near; abnormal; two like parts of a pair	paranasal (beside the nose); paresthesia (abnormal sensation); paraplegia (paralysis of two like parts of a pair/the legs)
per-	through	percutaneous (through the skin)
peri-	around	pericardial (around the heart)
post-	after	postpartum (after birth)
pre-	before, in front of	preoperative (before a surgical operation)
pro-	before	prolactin (before milk)
pseudo-	false	pseudocyesis (false pregnancy)

MED TERM TIP

Be very careful with prefixes; many have similar spellings but very different meanings. For example:

anti- means "against"; *ante-* means "before"

inter- means "between"; *intra-* means "inside"

per- means "through"; *peri-* means "around"

PREFIX	MEANING	EXAMPLE (DEFINITION)
retro-	backward, behind	retroperitoneal (behind the peritoneum)
sub-	below, under	subcutaneous (under, below the skin)
supra-	above	suprapubic (above the pubic bone)
tachy-	rapid, fast	tachycardia (fast heartbeat)
trans-	through, across	transurethral (across the urethra)
ultra-	beyond, excess	ultrasound (high-frequency sound waves)
un-	not	unconscious (not conscious)

Number Prefixes

Some common prefixes pertaining to the number of items or measurement, their meanings, and examples of their use follow.

PREFIX	MEANING	EXAMPLE (DEFINITION)
bi-	two	bilateral (two sides)
hemi-	half	hemiplegia (paralysis of one side/half of the body)
mono-	one	monoplegia (paralysis of one extremity)
multi-	many	multigravida (woman pregnant more than once)
nulli-	none	nulligravida (woman with no pregnancies)
poly-	many	polyuria (large amounts of urine)
primi-	first	primigravida (first pregnancy)
quadri-	four	quadriplegia (paralysis of all four limbs)
semi-	partial, half	semiconscious (partially conscious)
tetra-	four	tetraplegia (paralysis of all four limbs)
tri-	three	triceps (muscle with three heads)

Suffixes

A suffix is attached to the end of a word to add meaning, such as a condition, disease, or procedure. For example, the suffix *-itis*, meaning inflammation, when added to *cardi-* forms the new word **carditis** (car-DYE-tis), meaning inflammation of the heart. Every medical term *must* have a suffix. Most often the suffix is added to a word root, as in carditis above; however, terms can also be built from a suffix added directly to a prefix, without a word root. For example, the term **dystrophy** (DIS-troh-fee), meaning abnormal development, is built from the prefix *dys-* (meaning abnormal) and the suffix *-trophy* (meaning development).

Common Suffixes

Some common suffixes, their meanings, and examples of their use follow. When written by themselves, suffixes are preceded by a hyphen.

SUFFIX	MEANING	EXAMPLE (DEFINITION)
-algia	pain	gastralgia (stomach pain)
-cele	hernia, protrusion	cystocele (protrusion of the bladder)

MED TERM TIP

Remember, if a suffix begins with a vowel, the combining vowel is dropped; for example, *mastitis* rather than *mastoitis*.

SUFFIX	MEANING	EXAMPLE (DEFINITION)
-cyte	cell	erythrocyte (red cell)
-dynia	pain	cardiodynia (heart pain)
-ectasis	dilation	bronchiectasis (dilated bronchi)
-gen	that which produces	pathogen (that which produces disease)
-genesis	produces, generates	spermatogenesis (produces sperm)
-genic	producing, produced by	carcinogenic (producing cancer)
-ia	state, condition	bradycardia (condition of slow heart)
-iasis	abnormal condition	lithiasis (abnormal condition of stones)
-iatry	medical treatment	podiatry (medical treatment for the foot)
-ism	state of	hypothyroidism (state of low thyroid)
-itis	inflammation	dermatitis (inflammation of skin)
-logist	one who studies	cardiologist (one who studies the heart)
-logy	study of	cardiology (study of the heart)
-lysis	destruction	hemolysis (blood destruction)
-lytic	destruction	thrombolytic (clot destruction)
-malacia	abnormal softening	chondromalacia (abnormal cartilage softening)
-megaly	enlargement, large	cardiomegaly (enlarged heart)
-oid	resembling	fibroid (resembling fibers)
-oma	tumor, mass, swelling	carcinoma (cancerous tumor)
-osis	abnormal condition	cyanosis (abnormal condition of being blue)
-pathy	disease	myopathy (muscle disease)
-phobia	fear	photophobia (fear of light)
-plasia	development, growth	hyperplasia (excessive development)
-plasm	formation, development	neoplasm (new formation)
-ptosis	drooping	blepharoptosis (drooping eyelid)
-rrhage	excessive, abnormal flow	hemorrhage (excessive bleeding)
-rrhagia	abnormal flow condition	cystorrhagia (abnormal flow from the bladder)
-rrhea	discharge, flow	rhinorrhea (discharge from the nose)
-rrhexis	rupture	hysterorrhexis (ruptured uterus)
-sclerosis	hardening	arteriosclerosis (hardening of an artery)
-stenosis	narrowing	angiostenosis (narrowing of a vessel)
-therapy	treatment	chemotherapy (treatment with chemicals)
-trophy	nourishment, development	hypertrophy (excessive development)
-ule	small	venule (small vein)

Adjective Suffixes

The following suffixes are used to convert a word root into an adjective. These suffixes usually are translated as *pertaining to*.

SUFFIX	MEANING	EXAMPLE (DEFINITION)
-ac	pertaining to	cardiac (pertaining to the heart)
-al	pertaining to	duodenal (pertaining to the duodenum)
-an	pertaining to	ovarian (pertaining to the ovary)
-ar	pertaining to	ventricular (pertaining to a ventricle)
-ary	pertaining to	pulmonary (pertaining to the lungs)
-atic	pertaining to	lymphatic (pertaining to lymph)
-eal	pertaining to	esophageal (pertaining to the esophagus)
-iac	pertaining to	chondriac (pertaining to cartilage)
-ic	pertaining to	gastric (pertaining to the stomach)
-ile	pertaining to	penile (pertaining to the penis)
-ine	pertaining to	uterine (pertaining to the uterus)
-ior	pertaining to	superior (pertaining to above)
-nic	pertaining to	embryonic (pertaining to an embryo)
-ory	pertaining to	auditory (pertaining to hearing)
-ose	pertaining to	adipose (pertaining to fat)
-ous	pertaining to	intravenous (pertaining to within a vein)
-tic	pertaining to	acoustic (pertaining to hearing)

Surgical Suffixes

The following suffixes indicate surgical procedures.

SUFFIX	MEANING	EXAMPLE (DEFINITION)
-centesis	puncture to withdraw fluid	arthrocentesis (puncture to withdraw fluid from a joint)
-ectomy	surgical removal	gastrectomy (surgically remove the stomach)
-ostomy	surgically create an opening	colostomy (surgically create an opening for the colon [through the abdominal wall])
-otomy	cutting into	thoracotomy (cutting into the chest)
-pexy	surgical fixation	nephropexy (surgical fixation of a kidney)
-plasty	surgical repair	dermatoplasty (surgical repair of the skin)
-rrhaphy	suture	myorrhaphy (suture together muscle)

> **MED TERM TIP**
>
> Surgical suffixes have very specific meanings:
>
> *-otomy* means "to cut into"
> *-ostomy* means "to create a new opening"
> *-ectomy* means "to cut out" or "remove"

Procedural Suffixes

The following suffixes indicate procedural processes or instruments.

SUFFIX	MEANING	EXAMPLE (DEFINITION)
-gram	record or picture	electrocardiogram (record of heart's electricity)
-graph	instrument for recording	electrocardiograph (instrument for recording the heart's electrical activity)

SUFFIX	MEANING	EXAMPLE (DEFINITION)
-graphy	process of recording	electrocardiography (process of recording the heart's electrical activity)
-meter	instrument for measuring	audiometer (instrument to measure hearing)
-metry	process of measuring	audiometry (process of measuring hearing)
-scope	instrument for viewing	gastroscope (instrument to view stomach)
-scopy	process of visually examining	gastroscopy (process of visually examining the stomach)

Word Building

Word building consists of putting together two or more word elements to form a variety of terms. Prefixes and suffixes may be added to a combining form to create a new descriptive term. For example, adding the prefix *hypo-* (meaning below) and the suffix *-ic* (meaning pertaining to) to the combining form *derm/o* (meaning skin) forms **hypodermic** (high-poh-DER-mik), pertaining to below the skin.

Interpreting Medical Terms

The following strategy is a reliable method for puzzling out the meaning of an unfamiliar medical term.

STEP	EXAMPLE
1. Divide the term into its word parts.	gastr/o/enter/o/logy
2. Define each word part.	**gastr** = stomach
	o = combining vowel, no meaning
	enter = small intestine
	o = combining vowel, no meaning
	-logy = study
3. Combine the meaning of the word parts.	stomach, small intestine, study of

> **MED TERM TIP**
>
> To gain a quick understanding of a term, it may be helpful to you to read from the end of the word (or the suffix) back to the beginning (the prefix), and then pick up the word root. For example, *pericarditis* reads inflammation (*-itis*) surrounding (*peri-*) the heart (*cardi/o*).

Pronunciation

You will hear different pronunciations for the same terms depending on where people were born or educated. As long as it is clear which term people are discussing, differing pronunciations are acceptable. Some people are difficult to understand over the telephone or on a transcription tape. If you have any doubt about a term being discussed, ask for the term to be spelled. For example, it is often difficult to hear the difference between the terms **abduction** and **adduction.** However, since the terms refer to opposite directions of movement, it is very important to double-check if there is any question about which term was used.

Each new term in this book is introduced in boldface type, with the phonetic or "sounds like" pronunciation in parentheses immediately following. The part of the word that should receive the greatest emphasis during pronunciation appears in capital letters: for example, **pericarditis** (per-ih-car-DYE-tis). Each term presented in this book is also pronounced on the CD-ROM packaged with the book. Listen to each word, then pronounce it silently to yourself or out loud.

Spelling

Although you will hear differing pronunciations of the same term, there will be only one correct spelling. If you have any doubt about the spelling of a term or of its meaning, always look it up in a medical dictionary. If only one letter of the word is changed, it could make a critical difference for the patient. For example, imagine the problem that could arise if you note for insurance purposes that a portion of a patient's **ileum,** or small intestine, was removed when in reality he had surgery for removal of a piece of his **ilium,** or hip bone.

Some words have the same beginning sounds but are spelled differently. Examples include:

Sounds like *si*

| psy | **psychiatry** (sigh-KIGH-ah-tree) |
| cy | **cytology** (sigh-TALL-oh-gee) |

Sounds like *dis*

| dys | **dyspepsia** (dis-PEP-see-ah) |
| dis | **dislocation** (dis-low-KAY-shun) |

Singular and Plural Endings

Many medical terms originate from Greek and Latin words. The rules for forming the singular and plural forms of some words follow the rules of these languages rather than English. For example, the heart has a left atrium and a right atrium for a total of two *atria,* not two *atriums.* Other words, such as *virus* and *viruses,* are changed from singular to plural by following English rules. Each medical term needs to be considered individually when changing from the singular to the plural form. The following examples illustrate how to form plurals.

Words ending in	Singular	Plural
-a	vertebra	vertebrae
-ax	thorax	thoraces
-ex or -ix	appendix	appendices
-is	metastasis	metastases
-ma	sarcoma	sarcomata
-nx	phalanx	phalanges
-on	ganglion	ganglia
-us	nucleus	nuclei
-um	ovum	ova
-y	biopsy	biopsies

 Abbreviations

Abbreviations are commonly used in the medical profession as a way of saving time. However, some abbreviations can be confusing, such as *SM* for simple mastectomy and *sm* for small. Use of the incorrect abbreviation can result in problems for a patient, as well as with insurance records and processing. If you have any concern that you will confuse someone by using an abbreviation, spell out the word instead. It is never acceptable to use made-up abbreviations. All types of healthcare facilities will have a list of approved abbreviations, and it is extremely important that you become familiar with this list and follow it closely. Throughout the book abbreviations are included, when possible, immediately following terms. In addition, a list of common abbreviations for each body system is given in each chapter. Finally, Appendix I provides a complete alphabetical listing of all the abbreviations used in this text.

The Medical Record

The **medical record** or chart documents the details of a patient's hospital stay. Each healthcare professional who has contact with the patient in any capacity completes the appropriate report of that contact and adds it to the medical chart. This results in a permanent physical record of the patient's day-to-day condition, when and what services he or she received, and the response to treatment. Each institution adopts a specific format for each document and its location within the chart. This is necessary because each healthcare professional must be able to locate quickly and efficiently the information he or she needs in order to provide proper care for the patient. The medical record is also a legal document. Therefore, it is essential that all chart components be completely filled out and signed. Each page must contain the proper patient identification information: the patient's name, age, gender, physician, admission date, and identification number.

While the patient is still in the hospital, a unit clerk is usually responsible for placing documents in the proper place. After discharge, the medical records department ensures that all documents are present, complete, signed, and in the correct order. If a person is readmitted, especially for the same diagnosis, parts of this previous chart can be pulled and added to the current chart for reference (see Figure 1.2 ■). Physicians' offices and other outpatient care providers such as clinics and therapists also maintain a medical record detailing each patient's visit to their facility.

The digital revolution has also impacted healthcare with the increasing use of the **Electronic Medical Record** (EMR). A software program is used to enter patient information into a computer which then organizes and stores the information. Information may be entered either at a centralized workstation or by using mobile devices at the point of care. Once digitally stored, the information may be analyzed and monitored to detect and prevent potential errors. Since the records are digitally stored, they can be easily accessed and shared between healthcare providers which will reduce repeating tests unnecessarily and inadvertent medication errors. The following list includes the most common elements of a paper chart with a brief description.

History and Physical—Written or dictated by admitting physician; details patient's history, results of physician's examination, initial diagnoses, and physician's plan of treatment

Figure 1.2 Health information professionals maintain accurate, orderly, and permanent patient records. Medical records are securely stored and available for future reference.

Physician's Orders—Complete list of care, medications, tests, and treatments physician orders for patient

Nurse's Notes—Record of patient's care throughout the day; includes vital signs, treatment specifics, patient's response to treatment, and patient's condition

Physician's Progress Notes—Physician's daily record of patient's condition, results of physician's examinations, summary of test results, updated assessment and diagnoses, and further plans for patient's care

Consultation Reports—Reports given by specialists whom physician has asked to evaluate patient

Ancillary Reports—Reports from various treatments and therapies patient has received, such as rehabilitation, social services, or respiratory therapy

Diagnostic Reports—Results of diagnostic tests performed on patient, principally from clinical lab (e.g., blood tests) and medical imaging (e.g., X-rays and ultrasound)

Informed Consent—Document voluntarily signed by patient or a responsible party that clearly describes purpose, methods, procedures, benefits, and risks of a diagnostic or treatment procedure

Operative Report—Report from surgeon detailing an operation; includes pre- and postoperative diagnosis, specific details of surgical procedure itself, and how patient tolerated procedure

Anesthesiologist's Report—Relates details regarding substances (such as medications and fluids) given to patient, patient's response to anesthesia, and vital signs during surgery

Pathologist's Report—Report given by pathologist who studies tissue removed from patient (e.g., bone marrow, blood, or tissue biopsy)

Discharge Summary—Comprehensive outline of patient's entire hospital stay; includes condition at time of admission, admitting diagnosis, test results, treatments and patient's response, final diagnosis, and follow-up plans

Healthcare Settings

The use of medical terminology is widespread. It provides healthcare professionals with a precise and efficient method of communicating very specific patient information to one another, regardless of whether they are in the same type of facility (see Figure 1.3 ■). Descriptions follow of the different types of settings where medical terminology is used.

Acute Care or General Hospitals—Provide services to diagnose (laboratory, diagnostic imaging) and treat (surgery, medications, therapy) diseases for a short period of time; in addition, they usually provide emergency and obstetrical care

Specialty Care Hospitals—Provide care for very specific types of diseases; for example, a psychiatric hospital

Nursing Homes or Long-Term Care Facilities—Provide long-term care for patients needing extra time to recover from illness or injury before returning home, or for persons who can no longer care for themselves

Ambulatory Care Centers, Surgical Centers, or Outpatient Clinics—Provide services not requiring overnight hospitalization; services range from simple surgeries to diagnostic testing or therapy

Physicians' Offices—Provide diagnostic and treatment services in a private office setting

Health Maintenance Organization (HMO)—Provides wide range of services by a group of primary-care physicians, specialists, and other healthcare professionals in a prepaid system

Home Health Care—Provides nursing, therapy, personal care, or housekeeping services in patient's own home

Rehabilitation Centers—Provide intensive physical and occupational therapy; includes inpatient and outpatient treatment

Hospices—Provide supportive treatment to terminally ill patients and their families

■ **Figure 1.3** A nurse and medical assistant review a patient's chart and plan his or her daily care.

◪ Confidentiality

Anyone working with medical terminology and involved in the medical profession must have a firm understanding of confidentiality. Any information or record relating to a patient must be considered privileged. This means that you have a moral and legal responsibility to keep all information about the patient confidential. If you are asked to supply documentation relating to a patient, the proper authorization form must be signed by the patient. Give only the specific information that the patient has authorized. The Health Insurance Portability and Accountability Act of 1996 (HIPAA) set federal standards providing patients with more protection of their medical records and health information, better access to their own records, and greater control over how their health information is used and to whom it is disclosed.

Chapter Review

Practice Exercises

A. Complete the Statement

1. The combination of a word root and the combining vowel is called a(n) _____.

2. The vowel that connects two word roots or a suffix with a word root is usually a(n) _____.

3. A word part used at the end of a word root to change the meaning of the word is called a(n) _____.

4. A(n) _____ is used at the beginning of a word to indicate number, location, or time.

5. Although the pronunciation of medical terms may differ slightly from one person to another, the

   _____ must never change.

6. The four components of a medical term are _____, _____,

   _____, and _____.

B. Terminology Matching

Match each definition to its term.

1. _____ Provides services for a short period of time   a. rehabilitation center

2. _____ Complete outline of a patient's entire hospital stay   b. nurse's notes

3. _____ Describes purpose, methods, benefits, and risks of procedure   c. ancillary report

4. _____ Contains updated assessment, diagnoses, and further plans for care   d. hospice

5. _____ Provides supportive care to terminally ill patients and families   e. discharge summary

6. _____ Written by the admitting physician   f. physician's progress notes

7. _____ Reports results from study of tissue removed from the patient   g. ambulatory care center

8. _____ Written by the surgeon   h. diagnostic report

9. _____ Provides services not requiring overnight hospital stay   i. long-term care facility

10. _____ Report given by a specialist   j. informed consent

11. _____ Record of a patient's care through the day   k. history and physical

12. _____ Clinical lab and medical imaging reports   l. acute care hospital

13. _____ Provides intensive physical and occupational therapy   m. pathologist's report

14. _____ Report of treatment/therapy the patient received   n. consultation report

15. _____ Provides care for patients who need more time to recover   o. operative report

C. Define the Suffix

1. -plasty _____

2. -stenosis _____

3. -itis _____

4. -al _____

5. -algia _____

6. -otomy _____

7. -megaly _____

8. -ectomy _____

9. -rrhage _____

10. -centesis _____

11. -gram _____

12. -ac _____

13. -malacia _____

14. -ism _____

15. -rrhaphy _____

16. -ostomy _____

17. -pexy _____

18. -rrhea _____

19. -scopy _____

20. -oma _____

D. Combining Form and Suffix Practice

Join a combining form and a suffix to form words with the following meanings.

1. study of lungs _____

2. pain relating to a nerve _____

3. nose discharge or flow _____

4. abnormal softening of a kidney _____

5. enlarged heart _____

6. cutting into the stomach _____

7. inflammation of the skin _____

8. surgical removal of the voice box _____

9. surgical repair of a joint _____

10. gland disease _____

E. Name That Prefix

1. within, inside _____

2. large _____

3. before, in front of _____

4. around _____

5. new _____

6. without _____

7. half _____

8. painful, difficult _____

9. above _____

10. over, above _____

11. many _____

12. slow _____

13. self _____

14. across _____

15. two _____

F. Prefix Practice

Circle the prefixes in the following terms and define in the space provided.

1. tachycardia _____

2. pseudocyesis _____

3. hypoglycemia _____

4. intercostal _____

5. eupnea _____

6. postoperative _____

7. monoplegia _____

8. subcutaneous _____

G. Make It Plural

Change the following singular terms to plural terms.

1. metastasis _____

2. ovum _____

3. diverticulum _____

4. atrium _____

5. diagnosis _____

6. vertebra _____

H. Name That Term

Use the suffix -ology to write a term for each medical specialty.

1. heart _____

2. stomach _____

3. skin _____

4. eye _____

5. immunity _____

6. kidney _____

7. blood _____

8. female _____

9. nerve _____

10. disease _____

MEDICAL TERMINOLOGY INTERACTIVE

Medical Terminology Interactive is a premium online homework management system that includes a host of features to help you study. Registered users will find:

- Fun games and activities built within a virtual hospital
- Powerful tools that track and analyze your results—allowing you to create a personalized learning experience
- Videos, flashcards, and audio pronunciations to help enrich your progress
- Streaming lesson presentations and self-paced learning modules

www.pearsonhighered.com/mti

I. Building Medical Terms

Build a medical term by combining the word parts requested in each question.

For example, use the combining form for *spleen* with the suffix meaning *enlargement* to form a word meaning *enlargement of the spleen* (answer: *splenomegaly*).

1. combining form for *heart* _____

   suffix meaning *abnormal softening* _____

   term meaning *softening of the heart* _____

2. word root form for *stomach* _____

   suffix meaning *to surgically create an opening* _____

   term meaning *creating an opening into the stomach* _____

3. combining form for *nose* _____

   suffix meaning *surgical repair* _____

   term meaning *surgical repair of the nose* _____

4. prefix meaning *over, above* _____

   suffix meaning *nourishment, development* _____

   term meaning *overdevelopment* _____

5. combining form meaning *disease* _____

   suffix meaning *the study of* _____

   term meaning *the study of disease* _____

6. word root meaning *gland* _____

   suffix for *tumor/mass* _____

   term meaning *gland tumor or mass* _____

7. combining form meaning *stomach* _____

   combining form meaning *small intestine* _____

   suffix meaning *study of* _____

   term meaning *study of stomach and small intestine* _____

8. word root meaning *ear* _____

   suffix meaning *inflammation* _____

   term meaning *ear inflammation* _____

9. prefix meaning *water* _____

   suffix meaning *treatment* _____

   term meaning *water treatment* _____

10. combining form meaning *cancer* _____

    suffix meaning *that which produces* _____

    term meaning *that which produces cancer* _____

J. Define the Combining Form

1. aden/o _____

2. carcin/o _____

3. cardi/o _____

4. chem/o _____

5. cis/o _____

6. dermat/o _____

7. enter/o _____

8. gastr/o _____

9. gynec/o _____

10. hemat/o _____

11. hydr/o _____

12. immun/o _____

13. laryng/o _____

14. path/o _____

15. nephr/o _____

16. neur/o _____

17. ophthalm/o _____

18. ot/o _____

19. pulmon/o _____

20. rhin/o _____

2

BODY ORGANIZATION

Learning Objectives

Upon completion of this chapter, you will be able to

- Recognize the combining forms introduced in this chapter.

- Correctly spell and pronounce medical terms and anatomical structures relating to body structure.

- Discuss the organization of the body in terms of cells, tissues, organs, and systems.

- Describe the common features of cells.

- Define the four types of tissues.

- List the major organs found in the 12 organ systems.

- Describe the anatomical position.

- Define the body planes.

- Identify regions of the body.

- Define directional and positional terms.

- List the body cavities and their contents.

- Locate and describe the nine anatomical and four clinical divisions of the abdomen.

- Build body organization medical terms from word parts.

- Interpret abbreviations associated with body organization.

Body Organization at a Glance

Arrangement

The body is organized into levels; each is built from the one below it. In other words, the body as a whole is composed of systems, a system is composed of organs, an organ is composed of tissues, and tissues are composed of cells.

Levels

cells   tissues   organs   systems   body

Word Parts

Presented here are some of the more common combining forms used to build body organizational terms. For a list of the prefixes and suffixes used, refer to the Terminology section of this chapter.

Combining Forms

abdomin/o	abdomen	later/o	side
adip/o	fat	lumb/o	loin
anter/o	front	lymph/o	lymph
brachi/o	arm	medi/o	middle
cardi/o	heart	muscul/o	muscles
caud/o	tail	nephr/o	kidney
cephal/o	head	neur/o	nerve
cervic/o	neck	ophthalm/o	eye
chondr/o	cartilage	ot/o	ear
crani/o	skull	pelv/o	pelvis
crin/o	to secrete	peritone/o	peritoneum
crur/o	leg	pleur/o	pleura
cyt/o	cell	poster/o	back
dermat/o	skin	proct/o	rectum and anus
dist/o	away from	proxim/o	near to
dors/o	back of body	pub/o	genital region
enter/o	small intestine	pulmon/o	lung
epitheli/o	epithelium	rhin/o	nose
gastr/o	stomach	spin/o	spine
glute/o	buttock	super/o	above
gynec/o	woman	thorac/o	chest
hemat/o	blood	ur/o	urine
hist/o	tissue	vascul/o	blood vessel
immun/o	protection	ventr/o	belly
infer/o	below	vertebr/o	vertebra
laryng/o	larynx	viscer/o	internal organ

Body Organization Illustrated

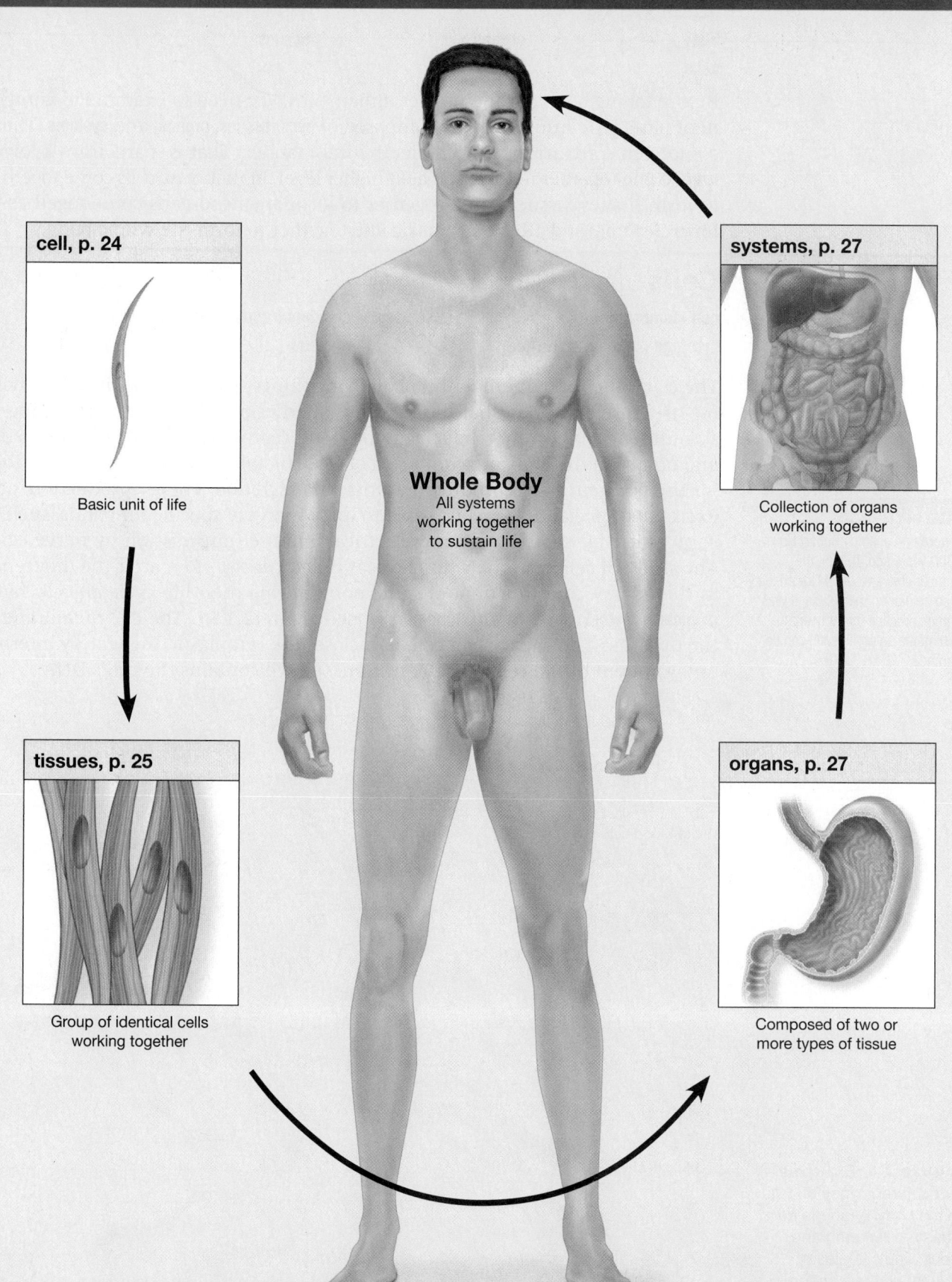

cell, p. 24

Basic unit of life

tissues, p. 25

Group of identical cells
working together

Whole Body
All systems
working together
to sustain life

systems, p. 27

Collection of organs
working together

organs, p. 27

Composed of two or
more types of tissue

Levels of Body Organization

body	organs	tissues
cells	systems	

Before taking a look at the whole human body, we need to examine its component parts. The human **body** is composed of **cells, tissues, organs,** and **systems.** These components are arranged in a hierarchical manner. That is, parts from a lower level come together to form the next higher level. In that way, cells come together to form tissues, tissues come together to form organs, organs come together to form systems, and all the systems come together to form the whole body.

Cells

cell membrane	cytoplasm (SIGH-toh-plazm)
cytology (sigh-TALL-oh-jee)	nucleus

The cell is the fundamental unit of all living things. That is to say, it is the smallest structure of a body that has all the properties of being alive: responding to stimuli, engaging in metabolic activities, and reproducing itself. All the tissues and organs in the body are composed of cells. Individual cells perform functions for the body such as reproduction, hormone secretion, energy production, and excretion. Special cells are also able to carry out very specific functions, such as contraction by muscle cells and electrical impulse transmission by nerve cells. The study of cells and their functions is called **cytology.** No matter the difference in their shape and function, at some point during their life cycle all cells have a **nucleus, cytoplasm,** and a **cell membrane** (see Figure 2.1 ■). The cell membrane is the outermost boundary of a cell. It encloses the cytoplasm, the watery internal environment of the cell, and the nucleus, which contains the cell's DNA.

MED TERM TIP

Cells were first seen by Robert Hooke over 300 years ago. To him, the rectangular shapes looked like prison cells, so he named them cells. It was a common practice for early anatomists to name an organ solely on its appearance.

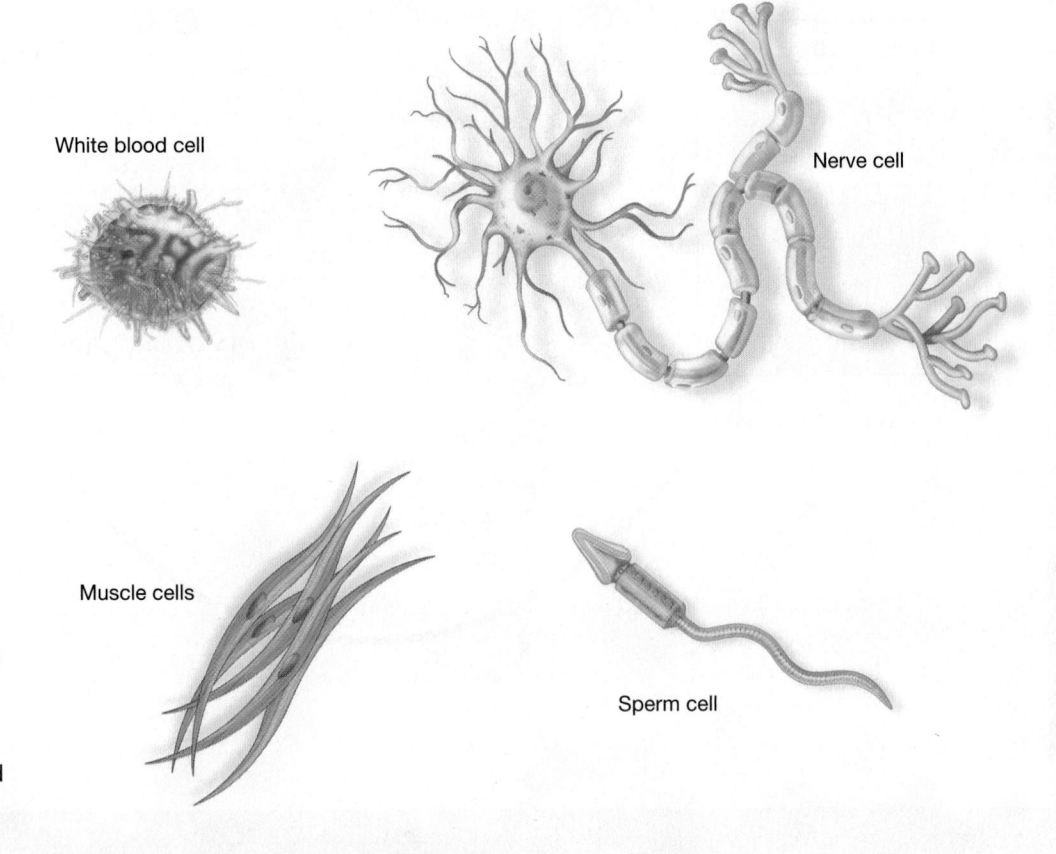

White blood cell

Nerve cell

Muscle cells

Sperm cell

■ **Figure 2.1** Examples of four different types of cells from the body. Although each cell has a cell membrane, nucleus, and cytoplasm, each has a unique shape depending on its location and function.

Tissues

connective tissue	muscle tissue
epithelial tissue (ep-ih-THEE-lee-al)	nervous tissue
histology (hiss-TALL-oh-jee)	

Histology is the study of tissue. A tissue is formed when like cells are grouped together and function together to perform a specific activity. The body has four types of tissue: **muscle tissue, epithelial tissue, connective tissue,** and **nervous tissue** (see Figure 2.2 ■).

Muscle Tissue

cardiac muscle	muscle fibers
smooth muscle	skeletal muscle

Muscle tissue produces movement in the body through contraction, or shortening in length, and is composed of individual muscle cells called **muscle fibers**. Muscle tissue forms one of three basic types of muscles: **skeletal muscle, smooth muscle,** or **cardiac muscle.** Skeletal muscle is attached to bone. Smooth muscle is found in internal organs such as the intestine, uterus, and blood vessels. Cardiac muscle is found only in the heart.

Epithelial Tissue

epithelium (ep-ih-THEE-lee-um)

Epithelial tissue, or **epithelium,** is found throughout the body and is composed of close-packed cells that form the covering for and lining of body structures. For example, both the top layer of skin and the lining of the stomach are epithelial tissue (see Figure 2.2). In addition to forming a protective barrier, epithelial tissue may be specialized to absorb substances (such as nutrients from the intestine), secrete substances (such as sweat glands), or excrete wastes (such as the kidney tubules).

> **MED TERM TIP**
>
> The term *epithelium* comes from the prefix *epi-* meaning "on top of" and the combining form *theli/o* meaning "nipple" (referring to any projection from the surface).

Connective Tissue

adipose (ADD-ih-pohs)	cartilage (CAR-tih-lij)
bone	tendons

Connective tissue is the supporting and protecting tissue in body structures. Because connective tissue performs many different functions depending on its location, it appears in many different forms so that each is able to perform the task required at that location. For example, **bone** provides structural support for the whole body. **Cartilage** is the shock absorber in joints. **Tendons** tightly connect skeletal muscles to bones. **Adipose** provides protective padding around body structures (see Figure 2.2).

Nervous Tissue

brain	neurons
nerves	spinal cord

Nervous tissue is composed of cells called **neurons** (see Figure 2.2). This tissue forms the **brain, spinal cord,** and a network of **nerves** throughout the entire body, allowing for the conduction of electrical impulses to send information between the brain and the rest of the body.

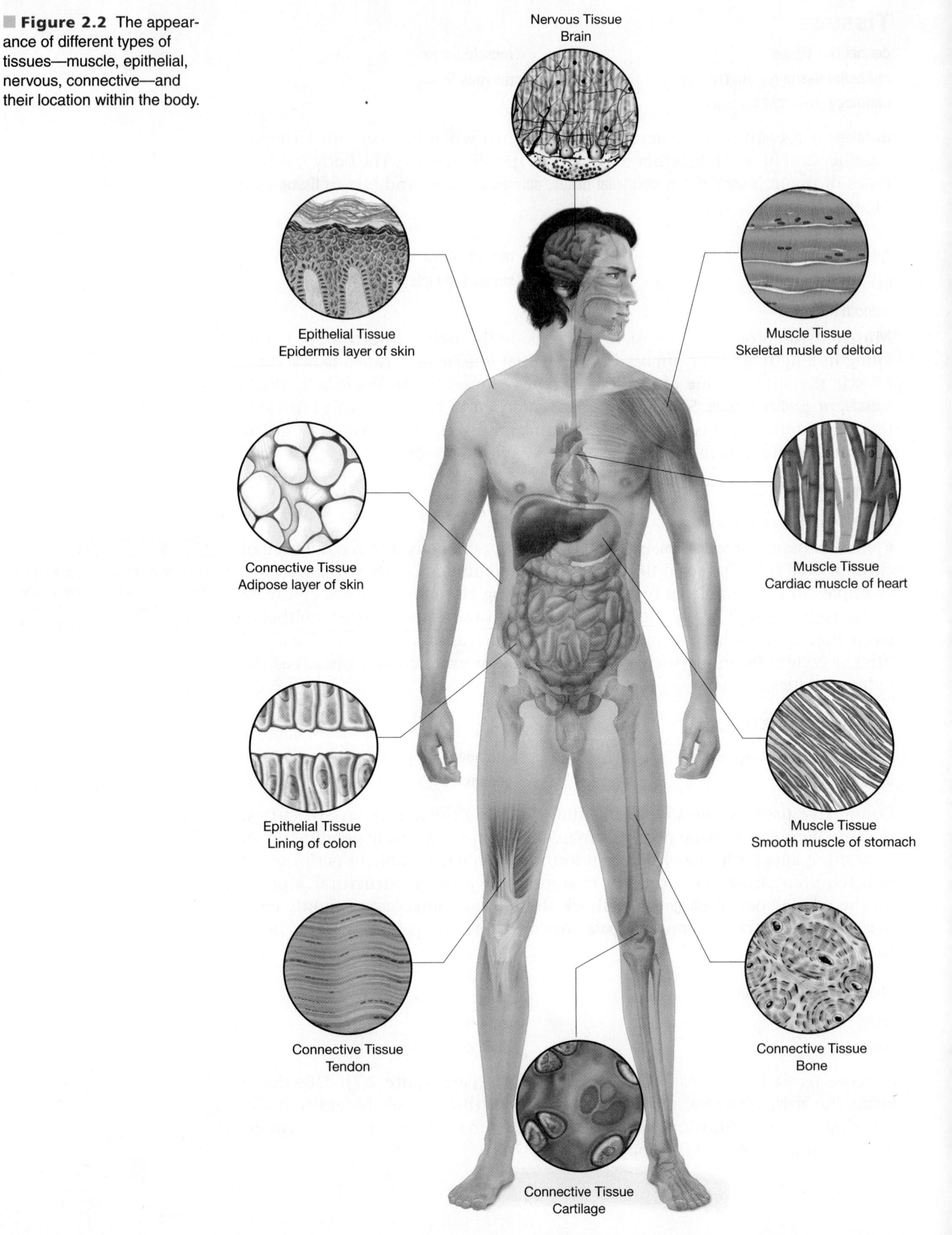

■ **Figure 2.2** The appearance of different types of tissues—muscle, epithelial, nervous, connective—and their location within the body.

Nervous Tissue
Brain

Epithelial Tissue
Epidermis layer of skin

Muscle Tissue
Skeletal musle of deltoid

Connective Tissue
Adipose layer of skin

Muscle Tissue
Cardiac muscle of heart

Epithelial Tissue
Lining of colon

Muscle Tissue
Smooth muscle of stomach

Connective Tissue
Tendon

Connective Tissue
Bone

Connective Tissue
Cartilage

Organs and Systems

Organs are composed of several different types of tissue that work as a unit to perform special functions. For example, the stomach contains smooth muscle tissue, nervous tissue, and epithelial tissue that allow it to contract to mix food with digestive juices.

A system is composed of several organs working in a coordinated manner to perform a complex function or functions. To continue our example, the stomach plus the other digestive system organs—the oral cavity, esophagus, liver, pancreas, small intestine, and colon—work together to ingest, digest, and absorb our food.

Table 2.1 ■ presents the organ systems that are discussed in this book along with the major organs found in each system, the system functions, and the medical specialties that treat conditions of that system.

Table 2.1	Organ Systems of the Human Body		
SYSTEM/MEDICAL SPECIALTY	**STRUCTURES**		**FUNCTIONS**
Integumentary System (in-teg-you-MEN-tah-ree) **dermatology** (der-mah-TALL-oh-jee)	• skin • hair • nails • sweat glands • sebaceous glands		Forms protective two-way barrier and aids in temperature regulation.
Musculoskeletal System (MS) (mus-qu-low-SKEL-et-all) **orthopedics** (or-thoh-PEE-diks) **orthopedic surgery** (or-the-PEE-dik)	• bones • joints • muscles		Skeleton supports and protects the body, forms blood cells, and stores minerals. Muscles produce movement.

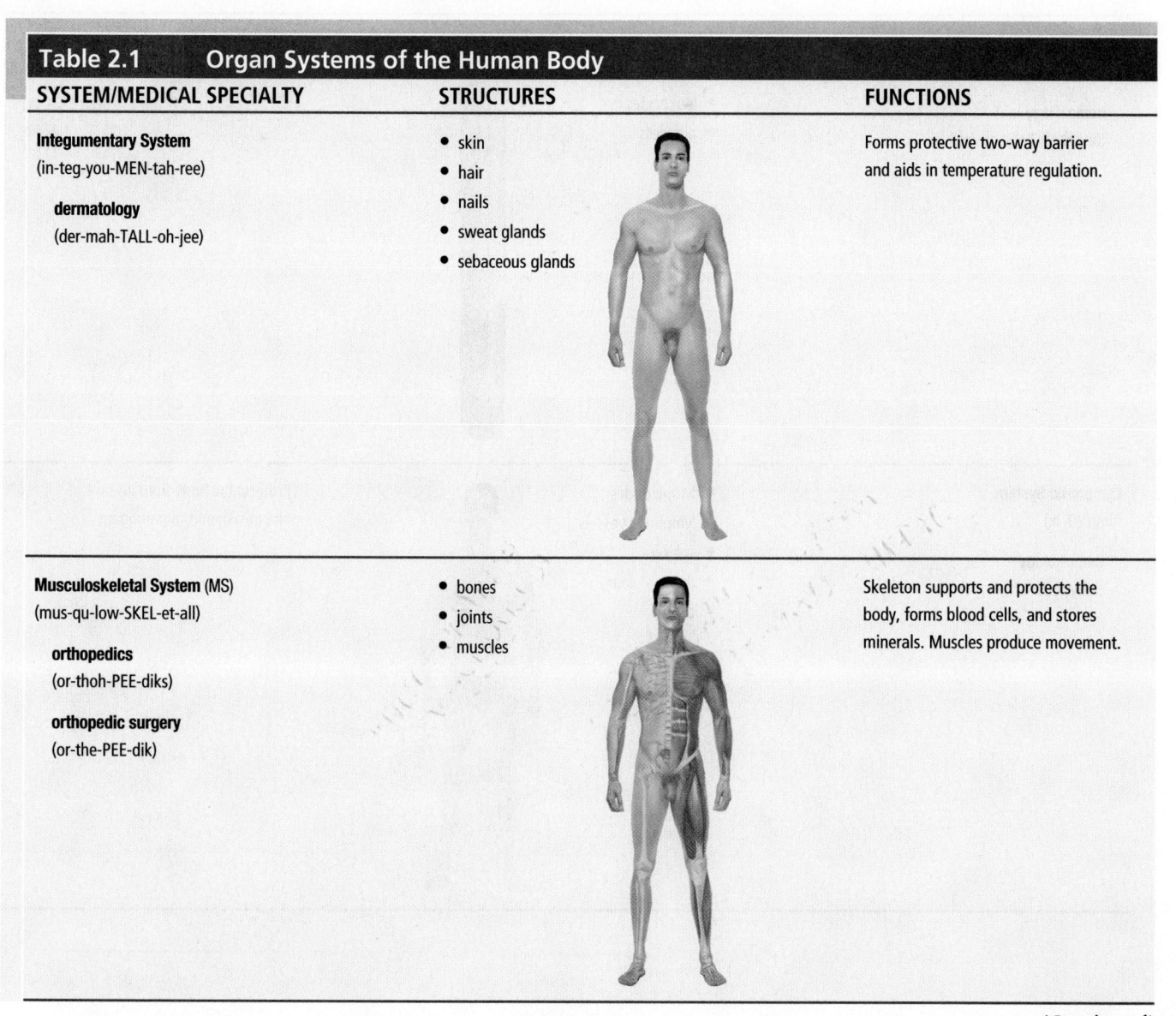

(Continued)

Table 2.1   Organ Systems of the Human Body (continued)

SYSTEM/MEDICAL SPECIALTY	STRUCTURES	FUNCTIONS
Cardiovascular System (CV) (car-dee-oh-VAS-kew-lar) **cardiology** (car-dee-ALL-oh-jee)	• heart • arteries • veins	Pumps blood throughout the entire body to transport nutrients, oxygen, and wastes.
Blood (Hematic System) (he-MAT-tik) **hematology** (hee-mah-TALL-oh-jee)	• plasma • erythrocytes • leukocytes • platelets	Transports oxygen, protects against pathogens, and controls bleeding.
Lymphatic System (lim-FAT-ik) **immunology** (im-yoo-NALL-oh-jee)	• lymph nodes • lymphatic vessels • spleen • thymus gland • tonsils	Protects the body from disease and invasion from pathogens.

Table 2.1	Organ Systems of the Human Body (continued)	
SYSTEM/MEDICAL SPECIALTY	**STRUCTURES**	**FUNCTIONS**
Respiratory System **otorhinolaryngology** (ENT) (oh-toh-rye-noh- lair-ing-GALL-oh-jee) **pulmonology** (pull-mon-ALL-oh-jee) **thoracic surgery** (tho-RASS-ik)	• nasal cavity • pharynx • larynx • trachea • bronchial tubes • lungs	Obtains oxygen and removes carbon dioxide from the body.
Digestive or **Gastrointestinal System** (GI) **gastroenterology** (gas-troh-en-ter-ALL-oh-jee) **proctology** (prok-TOL-oh-jee)	• oral cavity • pharynx • esophagus • stomach • small intestine • colon • liver • gallbladder • pancreas • salivary glands	Ingests, digests, and absorbs nutrients for the body.
Urinary System (YOO-rih-nair-ee) **nephrology** (neh-FROL-oh-jee) **urology** (yoo-RALL-oh-jee)	• kidneys • ureters • urinary bladder • urethra	Filters waste products out of the blood and removes them from the body.

(Continued)

Table 2.1 Organ Systems of the Human Body (continued)

SYSTEM/MEDICAL SPECIALTY	STRUCTURES	FUNCTIONS
Female Reproductive System **gynecology** (GYN) (gigh-neh-KOL- oh-jee) **obstetrics** (OB) (ob-STET-riks)	• ovary • fallopian tubes • uterus • vagina • vulva • breasts 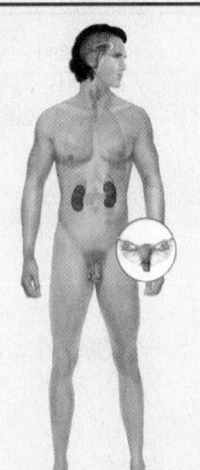	Produces eggs for reproduction and provides place for growing baby.
Male Reproductive System **urology** (yoo-RALL-oh-jee)	• testes • epididymis • vas deferens • penis • seminal vesicles • prostate gland • bulbourethral gland 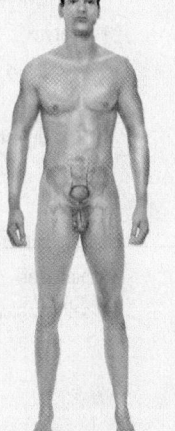	Produces sperm for reproduction.
Endocrine System (EN-doh-krin) **endocrinology** (en-doh-krin-ALL-oh-jee)	• pituitary gland • pineal gland • thyroid gland • parathyroid glands • thymus gland • adrenal glands • pancreas • ovaries • testes 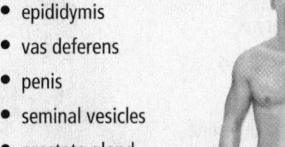	Regulates metabolic activities of the body.

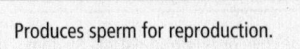

Table 2.1	Organ Systems of the Human Body (continued)	
SYSTEM/MEDICAL SPECIALTY	**STRUCTURES**	**FUNCTIONS**
Nervous System **neurology** (noo-RAL-oh-jee) **neurosurgery** (noo-roh-SIR-jer-ee)	• brain • spinal cord • nerves	Receives sensory information and coordinates the body's response.
Special Senses **ophthalmology** (off-thal-MALL-oh-jee)	• eye	Vision
otorhinolaryngology (ENT) (oh-toh-rye-noh-lair- ing-GALL-oh-jee)	• ear	Hearing and balance

Body

anatomical position

As seen from the previous sections, the body is the sum of all the systems, organs, tissues, and cells found in it. It is important to learn the anatomical terminology that applies to the body as a whole in order to correctly identify specific locations and directions when dealing with patients. The **anatomical position** is used when describing the positions and relationships of structures in the human body. A body in the anatomical position is standing erect with the arms at the sides of the body, the palms of the hands facing forward, and the eyes looking straight ahead. In addition, the legs are parallel with the feet, and the toes are pointing forward (see Figure 2.3 ■). For descriptive purposes the assumption is always that the person is in the anatomical position even if the body or parts of the body are in any other position.

Body Planes

coronal plane (kor-RONE-al)	**longitudinal section**
coronal section	**median plane**
cross-section	**sagittal plane** (SAJ-ih-tal)
frontal plane	**sagittal section**
frontal section	**transverse plane**
horizontal plane	**transverse section**

The terminology for body planes is used to assist medical personnel in describing the body and its parts. To understand body planes, imagine cuts slicing through the body at various angles. This imaginary slicing allows us to use more specific language when describing parts of the body. These body planes, illustrated in Figure 2.4 ■, include the following:

1. **Sagittal plane:** This vertical plane runs lengthwise from front to back and divides the body or any of its parts into right and left portions. The right and left sides do not have to be equal. If the sagittal plane passes through the middle of the body, thus dividing it into equal right and left halves, it is called a **midsagittal** or **median plane.** A cut along the sagittal plane yields a **sagittal section** view of the inside of the body.

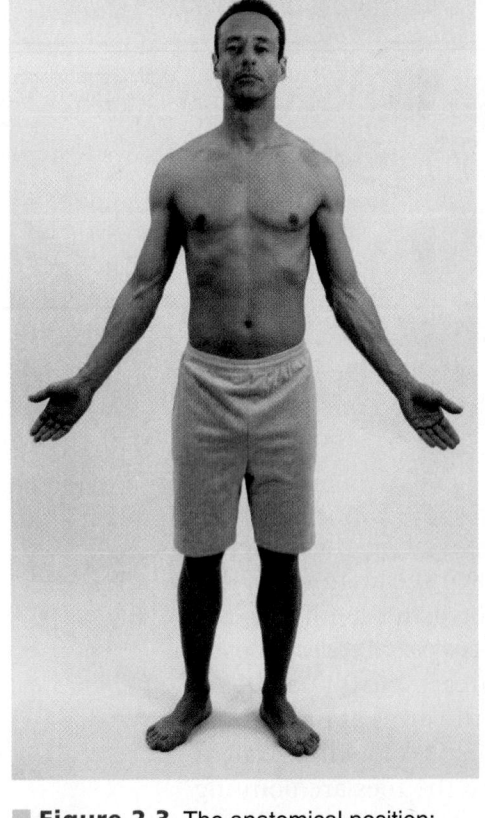

■ **Figure 2.3** The anatomical position: standing erect, gazing straight ahead, arms down at sides, palms facing forward, fingers extended, legs together, and toes pointing forward.

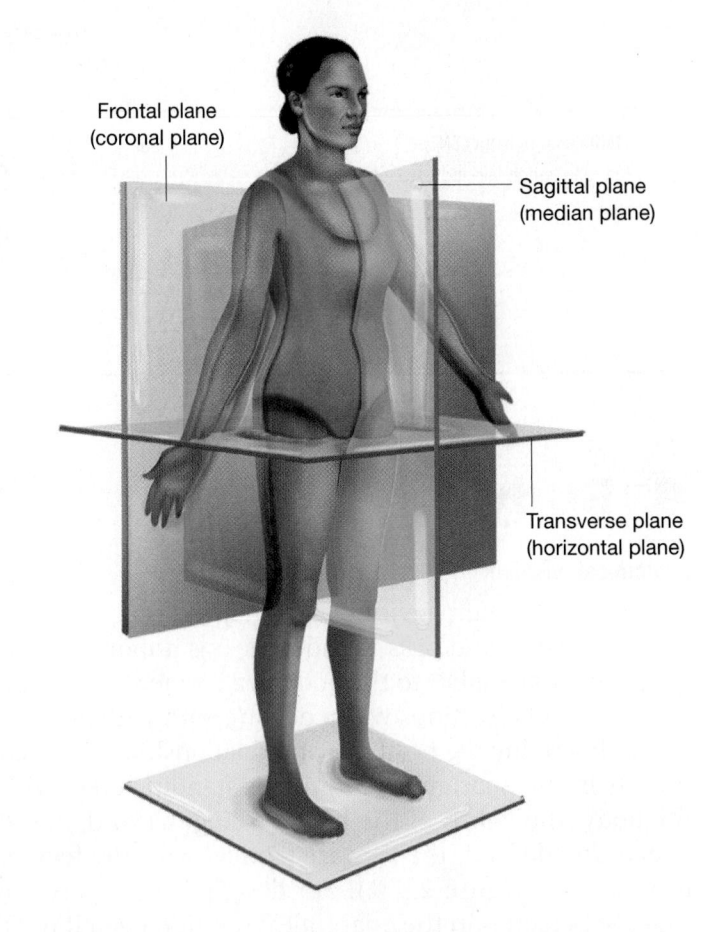

Frontal plane
(coronal plane)

Sagittal plane
(median plane)

Transverse plane
(horizontal plane)

■ **Figure 2.4** The planes of the body. The sagittal plane is vertical from front to back, the frontal plane is vertical from left to right, and the transverse plane is horizontal.

2. **Frontal plane:** The frontal, or **coronal plane,** divides the body into front and back portions; a vertical lengthwise plane is running from side to side. A cut along the frontal plane yields a **frontal** or **coronal section** view of the inside of the body.

3. **Transverse plane:** The transverse, or **horizontal plane,** is a crosswise plane that runs parallel to the ground. This imaginary cut would divide the body or its parts into upper and lower portions. A cut along the transverse plane yields a **transverse section** view of the inside of the body.

The terms **cross-section** and **longitudinal section** are frequently used to describe internal views of structures. A longitudinal section is produced by a lengthwise slice along the long axis of a structure. A cross-section view is produced by a slice perpendicular to the long axis of the structure.

Body Regions

abdominal region (ab-DOM-ih-nal)	**lower extremities**
brachial region (BRAY-kee-all)	**pelvic region** (PELL-vik)
cephalic region (she-FAL-ik)	**pubic region** (PEW-bik)
cervical region (SER-vih-kal)	**thoracic region** (tho-RASS-ik)
crural region (KREW-ral)	**trunk**
dorsum (DOOR-sum)	**upper extremities**
gluteal region (GLOO-tee-all)	**vertebral region** (VER-tee-bral)

The body is divided into large regions that can easily be identified externally. The **cephalic region** is the entire head. The neck is the **cervical region** and connects the head to the **trunk** (the torso). The trunk is further subdivided into different anterior and posterior regions. The anterior side consists of the **thoracic** (the chest), **abdominal, pelvic,** and **pubic** (genital) **regions.** The posterior side consists of the **dorsum** (the back), **vertebral region,** and **gluteal** (buttock) **region.** The **upper extremities** (UE) and **lower extremities** (LE) are attached to the trunk. The upper extremities or **brachial regions** are the arms. The lower extremities or **crural regions** are the legs. See Figure 2.5 ■ to locate each region on the body.

MED TERM TIP

As you learn medical terminology, it is important that you remember not to use common phrases and terms any longer. Many people commonly use the term *stomach* (an organ) when they actually mean *abdomen* (a body region).

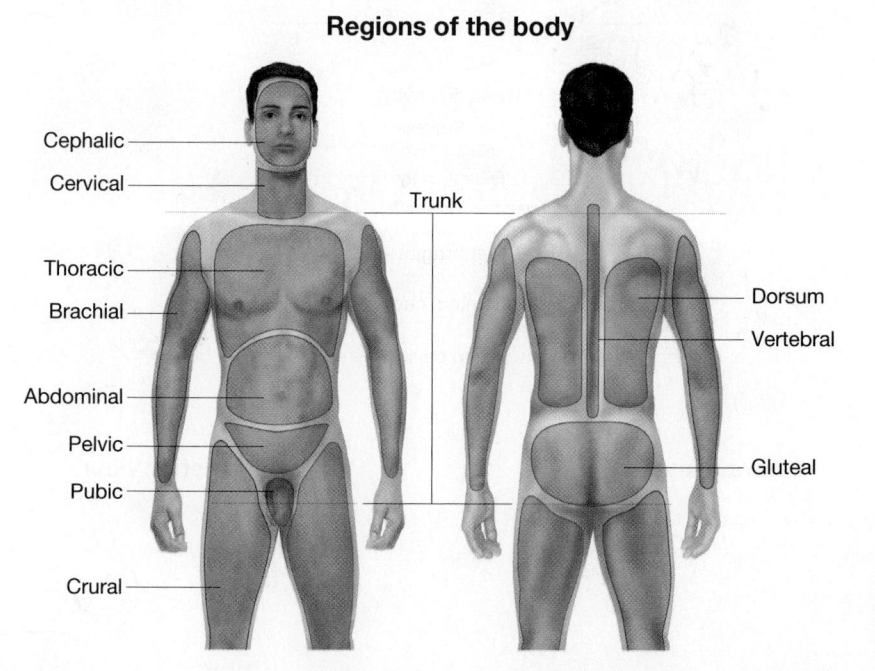

Regions of the body

Cephalic — Cervical — Trunk — Thoracic — Brachial — Abdominal — Pelvic — Pubic — Crural — Dorsum — Vertebral — Gluteal

■ **Figure 2.5** Anterior and posterior views of the body illustrating the location of various body regions.

Body Cavities

abdominal cavity	**pericardial cavity** (pair-ih-CAR-dee-al)
abdominopelvic cavity (ab-dom-ih-noh-PELL-vik)	**peritoneum** (pair-ih-toh-NEE-um)
	pleura (PLOO-rah)
cranial cavity (KRAY-nee-al)	**pleural cavity** (PLOO-ral)
diaphragm (DYE-ah-fram)	**spinal cavity**
mediastinum (mee-dee-ass-TYE-num)	**thoracic cavity**
parietal layer (pah-RYE-eh-tal)	**viscera** (VISS-er-ah)
parietal peritoneum	**visceral layer** (VISS-er-al)
parietal pleura	**visceral peritoneum**
pelvic cavity	**visceral pleura**

The body is not a solid structure; it has many open spaces or cavities. The cavities are part of the normal body structure and are illustrated in Figure 2.6 ■. We can divide the body into four major cavities—two dorsal cavities and two ventral cavities.

The dorsal cavities include the **cranial cavity,** containing the brain, and the **spinal cavity,** containing the spinal cord.

The ventral cavities include the **thoracic cavity** and the **abdominopelvic cavity.** The thoracic cavity contains the two lungs and a central region between them called the **mediastinum.** The heart, aorta, esophagus, trachea, and thymus gland are some of the structures located in the mediastinum. There is an actual physical wall between the thoracic cavity and the abdominopelvic cavity called the **diaphragm.** The diaphragm is a muscle used for breathing. The abdominopelvic cavity is generally subdivided into a superior **abdominal cavity** and an inferior **pelvic cavity.** The organs of the digestive, excretory, and reproductive systems are located in

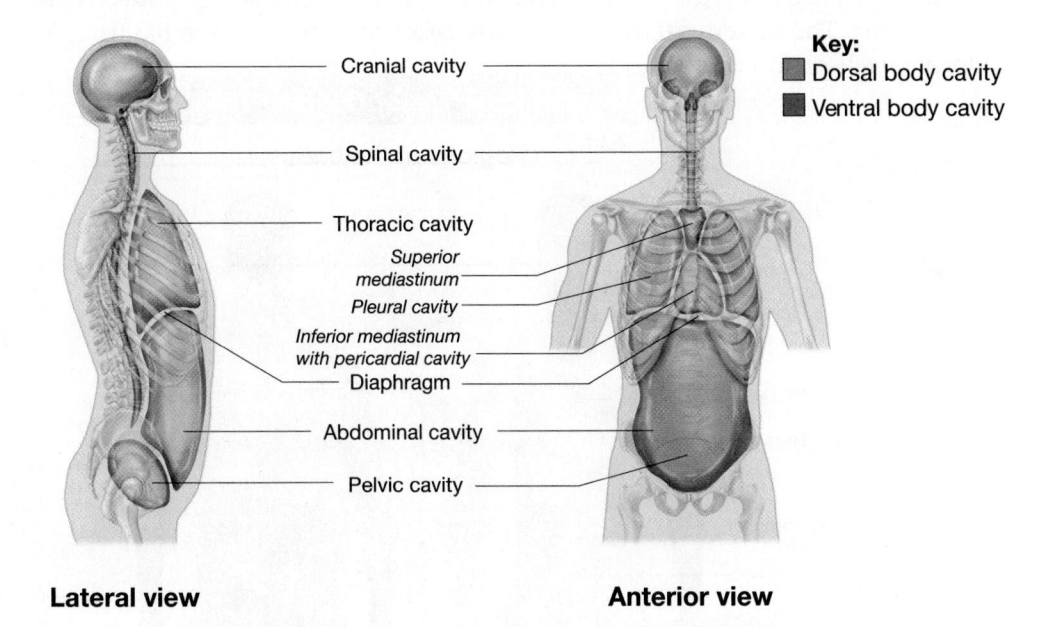

■ **Figure 2.6** The dorsal (red) and ventral (blue) body cavities.

these cavities. The organs within the ventral cavities are referred to as a group as the internal organs or **viscera.** Table 2.2 ■ describes the body cavities and their major organs.

All of the cavities are lined by, and the viscera are encased in, a two-layer membrane called the **pleura** in the thoracic cavity and the **peritoneum** in the abdominopelvic cavity. The outer layer that lines the cavities is called the **parietal layer** (i.e., **parietal pleura** and **parietal peritoneum**), and the inner layer that encases the viscera is called the **visceral layer** (i.e., **visceral pleura** and **visceral peritoneum**).

Within the thoracic cavity, the pleura is subdivided, forming the **pleural cavity,** containing the lungs, and the **pericardial cavity,** containing the heart. The larger abdominopelvic cavity is usually subdivided into regions so different areas can be precisely referred to. Two different methods of subdividing this cavity are used: the anatomical divisions and the clinical divisions. Choose a method partly on personal preference and partly on which system best describes the patient's condition. See Table 2.3 ■ for a description of these methods for dividing the abdominopelvic cavity.

Directional and Positional Terms

Directional terms assist medical personnel in discussing the position or location of a patient's complaint. Directional or positional terms also help to describe one process, organ, or system as it relates to another. Table 2.4 ■ presents commonly used terms for describing the position of the body or its parts. They are listed in pairs that have opposite meanings; for example, superior versus inferior, anterior versus posterior, medial versus lateral, proximal versus distal, superficial versus deep, and supine versus prone. Directional terms are illustrated in Figure 2.7 ■.

MED TERM TIP

The kidneys are the only major abdominopelvic organ located outside the sac formed by the peritoneum. Because they are found behind this sac, their position is referred to as *retroperitoneal* (retro- = behind; peritone/o = peritoneum; -al = pertaining to).

MED TERM TIP

Remember when using location or direction terms, it is assumed that the patient is in the anatomical position unless otherwise noted.

Table 2.2	Body Cavities and Their Major Organs
CAVITY	**MAJOR ORGANS**
Dorsal cavities	
Cranial cavity	Brain
Spinal cavity	Spinal cord
Ventral cavities	
Thoracic cavity	Pleural cavity: lungs
	Pericardial cavity: heart
	Mediastinum: heart, esophagus, trachea, thymus gland, aorta
Abdominopelvic cavity	
Abdominal cavity	Stomach, spleen, liver, gallbladder, pancreas, and portions of the small intestines and colon
Pelvic cavity	Urinary bladder, ureters, urethra, and portions of the small intestines and colon
	Female: uterus, ovaries, fallopian tubes, vagina
	Male: prostate gland, seminal vesicles, portion of the vas deferens

Table 2.3   Methods of Subdividing the Abdominopelvic Cavity

Anatomical Divisions of the Abdomen

- **Right hypochondriac** (high-poh-KON-dree-ak): Right lateral region of upper row beneath the lower ribs
- **Epigastric** (ep-ih-GAS-trik): Middle area of upper row above the stomach
- **Left hypochondriac:** Left lateral region of the upper row beneath the lower ribs
- **Right lumbar:** Right lateral region of the middle row at the waist
- **Umbilical** (um-BILL-ih-kal): Central area over the navel
- **Left lumbar:** Left lateral region of the middle row at the waist
- **Right iliac** (ILL-ee-ak): Right lateral region of the lower row at the groin
- **Hypogastric** (high-poh-GAS-trik): Middle region of the lower row beneath the navel
- **Left iliac:** Left lateral region of the lower row at the groin

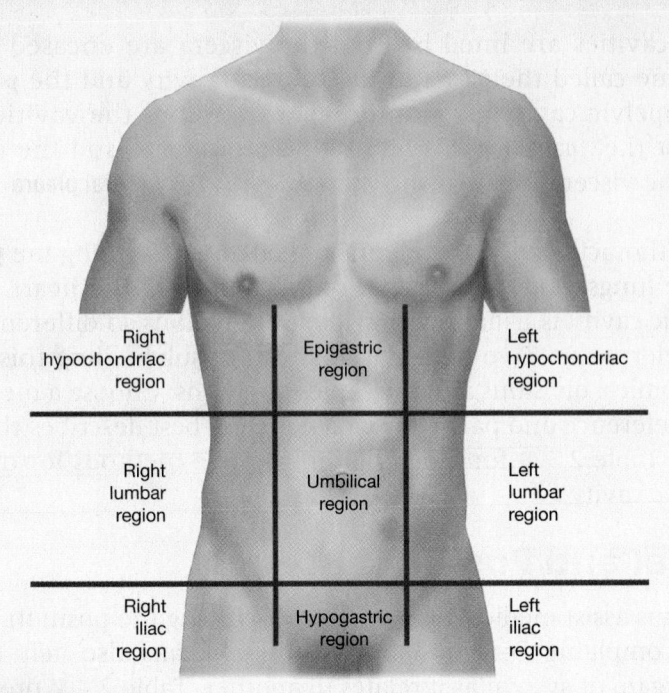

Right hypochondriac region | Epigastric region | Left hypochondriac region

Right lumbar region | Umbilical region | Left lumbar region

Right iliac region | Hypogastric region | Left iliac region

MED TERM TIP

To visualize the nine anatomical divisions, imagine a tic-tac-toe diagram over this region.

MED TERM TIP

The term *hypochondriac*, literally meaning "under the cartilage" (of the ribs), has come to refer to a person who believes he or she is sick when there is no obvious cause for illness. These patients commonly complain of aches and pains in the hypochondriac region.

Clinical Divisions of the Abdomen

- **Right upper quadrant (RUQ):** Contains majority of liver, gallbladder, small portion of pancreas, right kidney, small intestines, and colon
- **Right lower quadrant (RLQ):** Contains small intestines and colon, right ovary and fallopian tube, appendix, and right ureter
- **Left upper quadrant (LUQ):** Contains small portion of liver, spleen, stomach, majority of pancreas, left kidney, small intestines, and colon
- **Left lower quadrant (LLQ):** Contains small intestines and colon, left ovary and fallopian tube, and left ureter
- **Midline organs:** uterus, bladder, prostate gland

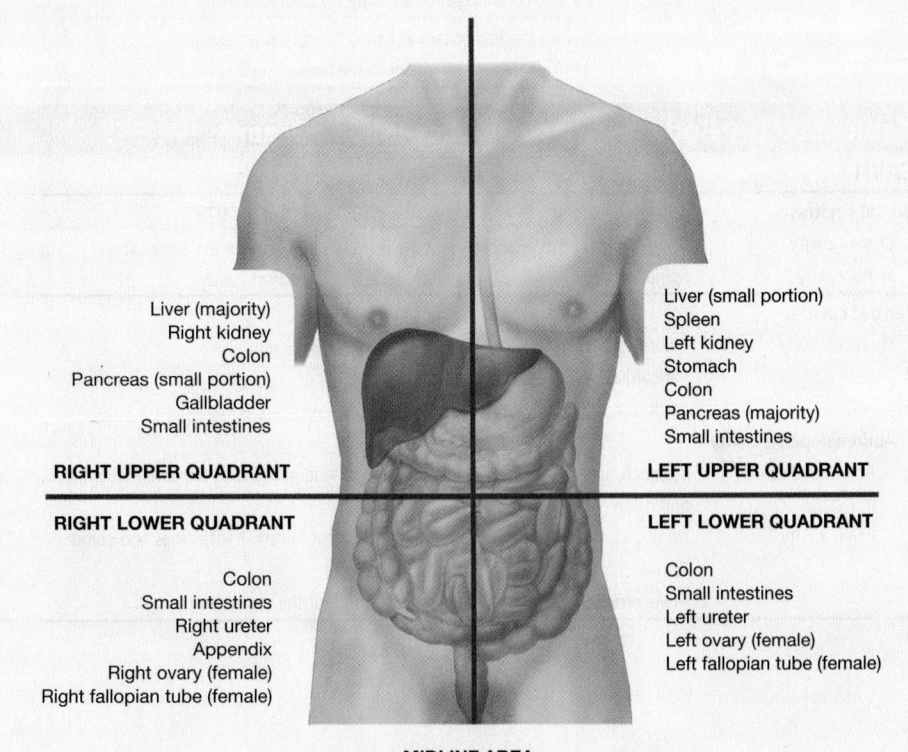

Liver (majority)
Right kidney
Colon
Pancreas (small portion)
Gallbladder
Small intestines

RIGHT UPPER QUADRANT

Liver (small portion)
Spleen
Left kidney
Stomach
Colon
Pancreas (majority)
Small intestines

LEFT UPPER QUADRANT

RIGHT LOWER QUADRANT

LEFT LOWER QUADRANT

Colon
Small intestines
Right ureter
Appendix
Right ovary (female)
Right fallopian tube (female)

Colon
Small intestines
Left ureter
Left ovary (female)
Left fallopian tube (female)

MIDLINE AREA

Bladder - Uterus (female) - Prostate (male)

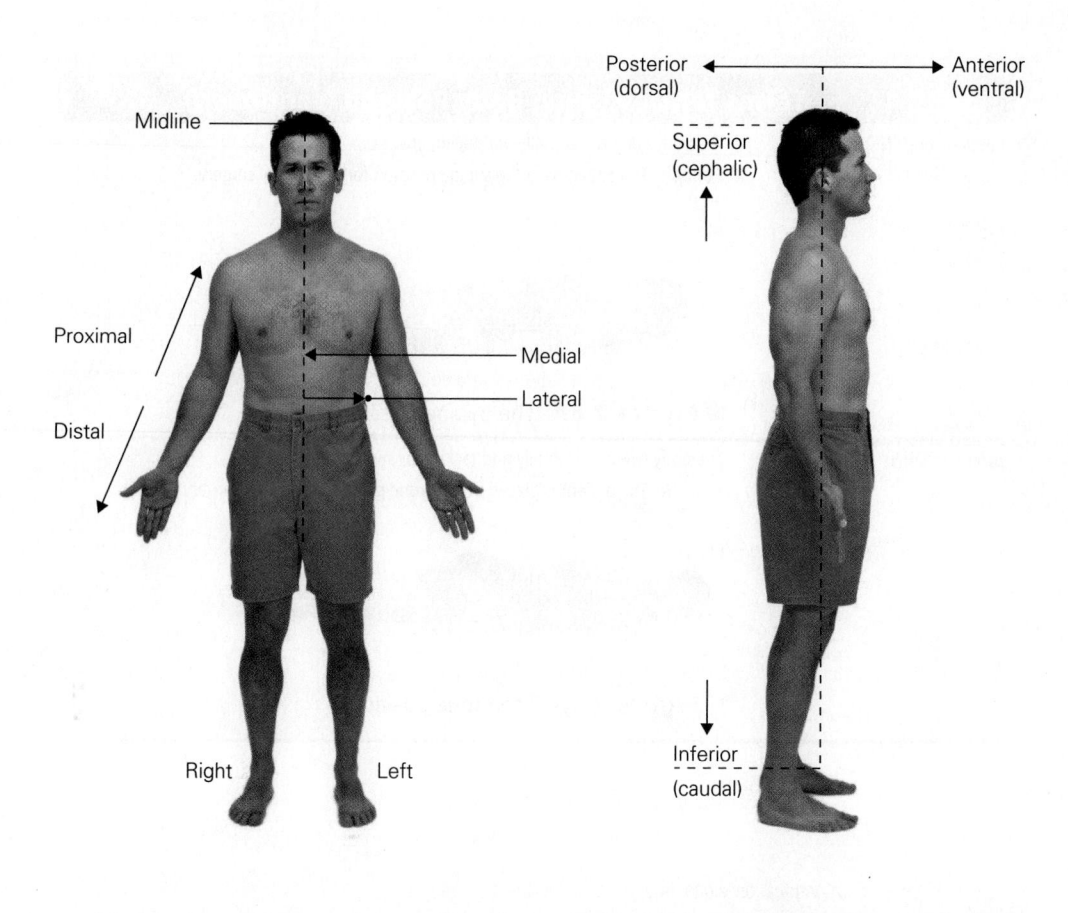

Table 2.4	Terms for Describing Body Position
superior (soo-PEE-ree-or) or **cephalic** (seh-FAL-ik)	More toward the head, or above another structure. *Example:* The adrenal glands are superior to the kidneys.
inferior (in-FEE-ree-or) or **caudal** (KAWD-al)	More toward the feet or tail, or below another structure. *Example:* The intestine is inferior to the heart.
anterior (an-TEE-ree-or) or **ventral** (VEN-tral)	More toward the front or belly-side of the body. *Example:* The navel is located on the anterior surface of the body.
posterior (poss-TEE-ree-or) or **dorsal** (DOR-sal)	More toward the back or spinal cord side of the body. *Example:* The posterior wall of the right kidney was excised.
medial (MEE-dee-al)	Refers to the middle or near the middle of the body or the structure. *Example:* The heart is medially located in the chest cavity.
lateral (lat) (LAT-er-al)	Refers to the side. *Example:* The ovaries are located lateral to the uterus.
proximal (PROK-sim-al)	Located nearer to the point of attachment to the body. *Example:* In the anatomical position, the elbow is proximal to the hand.
distal (DISS-tal)	Located farther away from the point of attachment to the body. *Example:* The hand is distal to the elbow.
apex (AY-peks)	Tip or summit of an organ. *Example:* We hear the heart beat by listening over the apex of the heart.
base	Bottom or lower part of an organ. *Example:* On the X-ray, a fracture was noted at the base of the skull.
superficial	More toward the surface of the body. *Example:* The cut was superficial.
deep	Further away from the surface of the body. *Example:* An incision into an abdominal organ is a deep incision.

(Continued)

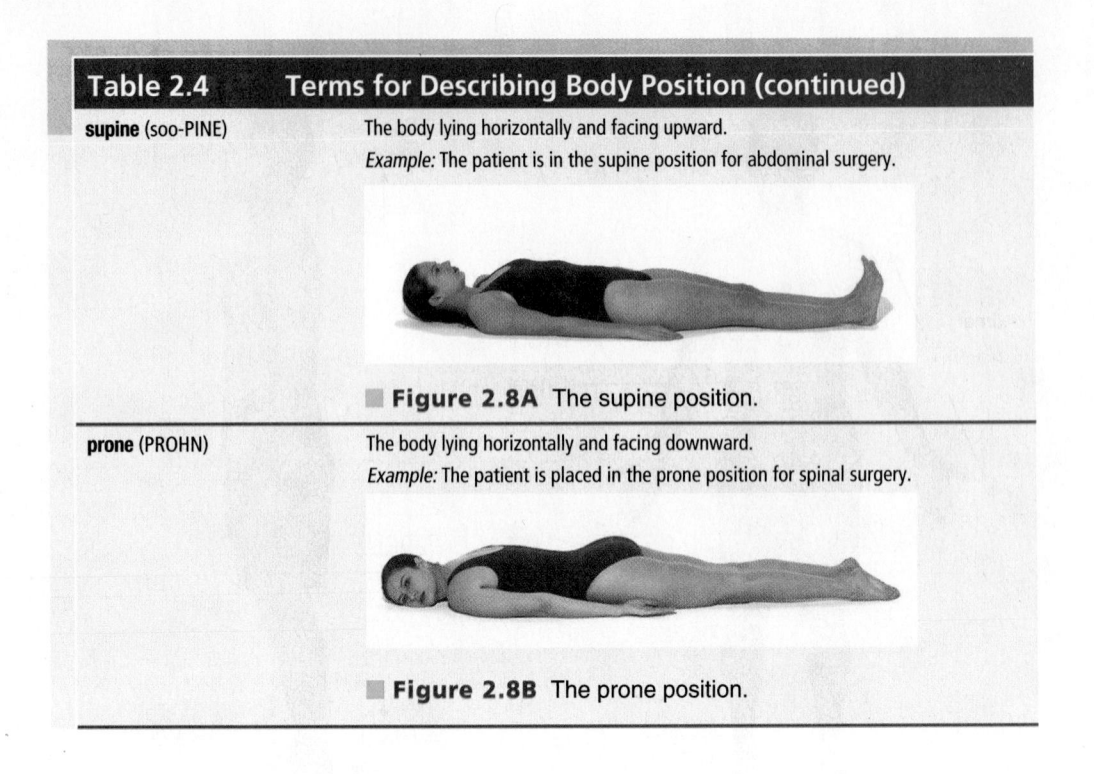

Table 2.4	Terms for Describing Body Position (continued)
supine (soo-PINE)	The body lying horizontally and facing upward. *Example:* The patient is in the supine position for abdominal surgery.
prone (PROHN)	The body lying horizontally and facing downward. *Example:* The patient is placed in the prone position for spinal surgery.

■ **Figure 2.8A** The supine position.

■ **Figure 2.8B** The prone position.

MED TERM TIP

The prefixes and suffixes introduced in Chapter 1 will be used over and over again in your medical terminology course, making it easier to recognize new terms more quickly.

 # Terminology

The following lists contain the suffixes and prefixes used to build terms in the remaining section of this chapter. The combining forms were introduced on page 22 of this of this chapter.

Suffixes

-ac	pertaining to	-atic	pertaining to	-logy	study of
-al	pertaining to	-iac	pertaining to	-ose	resembling
-ar	pertaining to	-ic	pertaining to		
-ary	pertaining to	-ior	pertaining to		

Prefixes

endo-	within	hypo-	under	retro-	behind
epi-	above	peri-	around		

The terms below, introduced in this chapter, are built directly from word parts following the rules given in Chapter 1. Review these terms in order to begin to familiarize yourself with how medical terms are built.

Anatomical Terms

TERM	WORD PARTS	DEFINITION
abdominal	abdomin/o = abdomen -al = pertaining to	pertaining to the abdomen
adipose	adip/o = fat -ose = resembling	resembling fat
anterior	anter/o = front -ior = pertaining to	pertaining to the front
brachial	brachi/o = arm -al = pertaining to	pertaining to the arm
cardiac	cardi/o = heart -ac = pertaining to	pertaining to the heart
cardiology	cardi/o = heart -logy = study of	study of the heart
cardiovascular	cardi/o = heart vascul/o = blood vessel -ar = pertaining to	pertaining to the heart and blood vessel
caudal	caud/o = tail -al = pertaining to	pertaining to the tail
cephalic	cephal/o = head -ic = pertaining to	pertaining to the head
cervical	cervic/o = neck -al = pertaining to	pertaining to the neck
cranial	crani/o = skull -al = pertaining to	pertaining to the skull
crural	crur/o = leg -al = pertaining to	pertaining to the leg
cytology	cyt/o = cell -logy = study of	study of the cell
dermatology	dermat/o = skin -logy = study of	study of the skin
distal	dist/o = away from -al = pertaining to	pertaining to away from
dorsal	dors/o = back of body -al = pertaining to	pertaining to the back of body
endocrinology	endo- = within crin/o = to secrete -logy = study of	study of secreting within [endocrine system]
epigastric	epi- = above gastr/o = stomach -ic = pertaining to	pertaining to above the stomach
epithelial	epitheli/o = epithelium -al = pertaining to	pertaining to the epithelium

Anatomical Terms *(continued)*

TERM	WORD PARTS	DEFINITION
gastroenterology	gastr/o = stomach enter/o = small intestine -logy = study of	study of the stomach and small intestine
gluteal	glute/o = buttock -al = pertaining to	pertaining to the buttocks
gynecology	gynec/o = woman -logy = study of	study of women
hematic	hemat/o = blood -ic = pertaining to	pertaining to the blood
hematology	hemat/o = blood -logy = study of	study of the blood
histology	hist/o = tissue -logy = study of	study of tissue
hypochondriac	hypo- = under chondr/o = cartilage -iac = pertaining to	pertaining to under the cartilage
hypogastric	hypo- = under gastr/o = stomach -ic = pertaining to	pertaining to under the stomach
immunology	immun/o = protection -logy = study of	study of protection [immune system]
inferior	infer/o = below -ior = pertaining to	pertaining to below
lateral	later/o = side -al = pertaining to	pertaining to the side
lumbar	lumb/o = loin -ar = pertaining to	pertaining to the loin [side and back between ribs and pelvic bones]
lymphatic	lymph/o = lymph -atic = pertaining to	pertaining to lymph
medial	medi/o = middle -al = pertaining to	pertaining to the middle
muscular	muscul/o = muscles -ar = pertaining to	pertaining to muscles
nephrology	nephr/o = kidney -logy = study of	study of the kidney
neurology	neur/o = nerve -logy = study of	study of nerves
ophthalmology	ophthalm/o = eye -logy = study of	study of the eye
otorhinolaryngology	ot/o = ear rhin/o = nose laryng/o = larynx -logy = study of	study of ear, nose, and larynx
pelvic	pelv/o = pelvis -ic = pertaining to	pertaining to the pelvis
peritoneal	peritone/o = peritoneum -al = pertaining to	pertaining to the peritoneum

Anatomical Terms *(continued)*

TERM	WORD PARTS	DEFINITION
pleural	pleur/o = pleura -al = pertaining to	pertaining to the pleura
posterior	poster/o = back -ior = pertaining to	pertaining to the back
proctology	proct/o = rectum and anus -logy = study of	study of the rectum and anus
proximal	proxim/o = near to -al = pertaining to	pertaining to near to
pubic	pub/o = genital region -ic = pertaining to	pertaining to the genital region
pulmonology	pulmon/o = lung -logy = study of	study of the lungs
spinal	spin/o = spine -al = pertaining to	pertaining to the spine
superior	super/o = above -ior = pertaining to	pertaining to above
thoracic	thorac/o = chest -ic = pertaining to	pertaining to the chest
urology	ur/o = urine -logy = study of	study of urine
ventral	ventr/o = belly -al = pertaining to	pertaining to the belly [side]
vertebral	vertebr/o = vertebra -al = pertaining to	pertaining to the vertebrae
visceral	viscer/o = internal organ -al = pertaining to	pertaining to internal organs

Abbreviations

(Flash cards)

AP	anteroposterior	LUQ	left upper quadrant
CV	cardiovascular	MS	musculoskeletal
ENT	ear, nose, and throat	OB	obstetrics
GI	gastrointestinal	PA	posteroanterior
GYN	gynecology	RLQ	right lower quadrant
lat	lateral	RUQ	right upper quadrant
LE	lower extremity	UE	upper extremity
LLQ	left lower quadrant		

Chapter Review

Practice Exercises

A. Complete the Statement

1. The levels of organization of the body in order from smallest to largest are: _____, _____, _____, _____, _____.

2. No matter its shape, all cells have a _____, _____, and _____.

3. _____ is the study of tissue.

4. _____ tissue lines internal organs and serves as a covering for the skin.

5. In the _____ position the body is standing erect with arms at sides and palms facing forward.

6. The _____ quadrant of the abdomen contains the appendix.

7. The dorsal cavities are the _____ cavity and the _____ cavity.

8. There are _____ anatomical divisions in the abdominal cavity.

9. The _____ region of the abdominal cavity is located in the right lower lateral region near the groin.

10. Within the thoracic cavity the lungs are found in the _____ cavity and the heart is found in the _____ cavity.

B. Body Plane Matching

Match each body plane to its definition.

1. _____ frontal plane   a. divides the body into right and left

2. _____ sagittal plane   b. divides the body into upper and lower

3. _____ transverse plane   c. divides the body into anterior and posterior

C. Prefix Practice

Circle the prefixes in the following terms and define in the space provided.

1. epigastric _____

2. pericardium _____

3. hypochondriac _____

4. retroperitoneal _____

D. Terminology Matching

Match each term to its definition.

1. _____ distal   a. away from the surface

2. _____ prone   b. toward the surface

3. _____ lateral   c. located closer to point of attachment to the body

4. _____ inferior   d. caudal

5. _____ deep   e. tip or summit of an organ

6. _____ apex   f. lying face down

7. _____ base   g. cephalic

8. _____ posterior   h. ventral

9. _____ superficial   i. dorsal

10. _____ supine   j. lying face up

11. _____ anterior   k. to the side

12. _____ medial   l. middle

13. _____ proximal   m. bottom or lower part of an organ

14. _____ superior   n. located further away from point of attachment to the body

E. What's the Abbreviation?

1. musculoskeletal _____

2. lateral _____

3. right upper quadrant _____

4. cardiovascular _____

5. gastrointestinal _____

6. anteroposterior _____

7. obstetrics _____

8. left lower quadrant _____

F. Build a Medical Term

Build terms for each expression using the correct prefixes, suffixes, and combining forms.

1. pertaining to spinal cord side _____

2. pertaining to the chest _____

3. pertaining to above _____

4. pertaining to the tail _____

5. pertaining to internal organs _____

6. pertaining to the side _____

7. pertaining to away from _____

8. pertaining to nerves _____

9. study of the lungs _____

10. pertaining to the muscles _____

11. pertaining to the belly side _____

12. pertaining to the front _____

13. pertaining to the head _____

14. pertaining to the middle _____

G. Define the Combining Form

1. **viscer/o** _____

2. **poster/o** _____

3. **abdomin/o** _____

4. **thorac/o** _____

5. **medi/o** _____

6. **ventr/o** _____

7. **anter/o** _____

8. **hist/o** _____

9. **epitheli/o** _____

10. **crani/o** _____

11. **cyt/o** _____

12. **proxim/o** _____

13. **cephal/o** _____

H. Organ System and Function Challenge

For each organ listed below, identify the name of the system it belongs to and then match it to its function.

	Organ	System		
1.	_____ skin	_____	a.	supports the body
2.	_____ heart	_____	b.	provides place for growing baby
3.	_____ stomach	_____	c.	filters waste products from blood
4.	_____ uterus	_____	d.	provides two-way barrier
5.	_____ bones	_____	e.	produces movement
6.	_____ lungs	_____	f.	produces sperm
7.	_____ kidney	_____	g.	ingest, digest, absorb nutrients
8.	_____ testes	_____	h.	coordinates body's response
9.	_____ brain	_____	i.	pumps blood through blood vessels
10.	_____ muscles	_____	j.	obtains oxygen

I. Body Region Practice

For each term below, write the corresponding body region.

1. head _____

2. genitals _____

3. leg _____

4. buttocks _____

5. neck _____

6. arm _____

7. back _____

8. chest _____

J. Terminology Matching

Match each organ to its body cavity.

1. _____ gallbladder
2. _____ appendix
3. _____ urinary bladder
4. _____ small intestines
5. _____ right kidney
6. _____ left ovary
7. _____ stomach
8. _____ colon
9. _____ right ureter
10. _____ pancreas (majority)

a. right upper quadrant
b. left upper quadrant
c. right lower quadrant
d. left lower quadrant
e. all quadrants
f. midline structure

K. Fill in the Blank

cardiology	otorhinolaryngology	urology	gynecology
ophthalmology	gastroenterology	dermatology	orthopedics

1. John is a musician who plays an electric bass guitar and is experiencing difficulty in hearing soft voices. He would consult a physician in _____.

2. Ruth is a stock trader with the Chicago Board of Trade. She has had a pounding and racing heartbeat. She would consult a physician specializing in _____.

3. Mary Ann is experiencing excessive bleeding from the uterus. She would consult a _____ doctor.

4. José has fractured his wrist in a fall. He would be seen for an examination by a physician in _____.

5. A physician who performs eye exams specializes in the field of _____.

6. When her daughter had repeated bladder infections, Mrs. Cortez sought the opinion of a specialist in

   _____.

7. Martha could not get rid of a persistent skin rash with over-the-counter creams. She decided to make an appointment with a specialist in _____.

8. After reviewing his X-ray, the specialist in _____ informed Mr. Sparks that he had a stomach ulcer.

Labeling Exercise

Image A

1. Write the labels for this figure on the numbered lines provided.

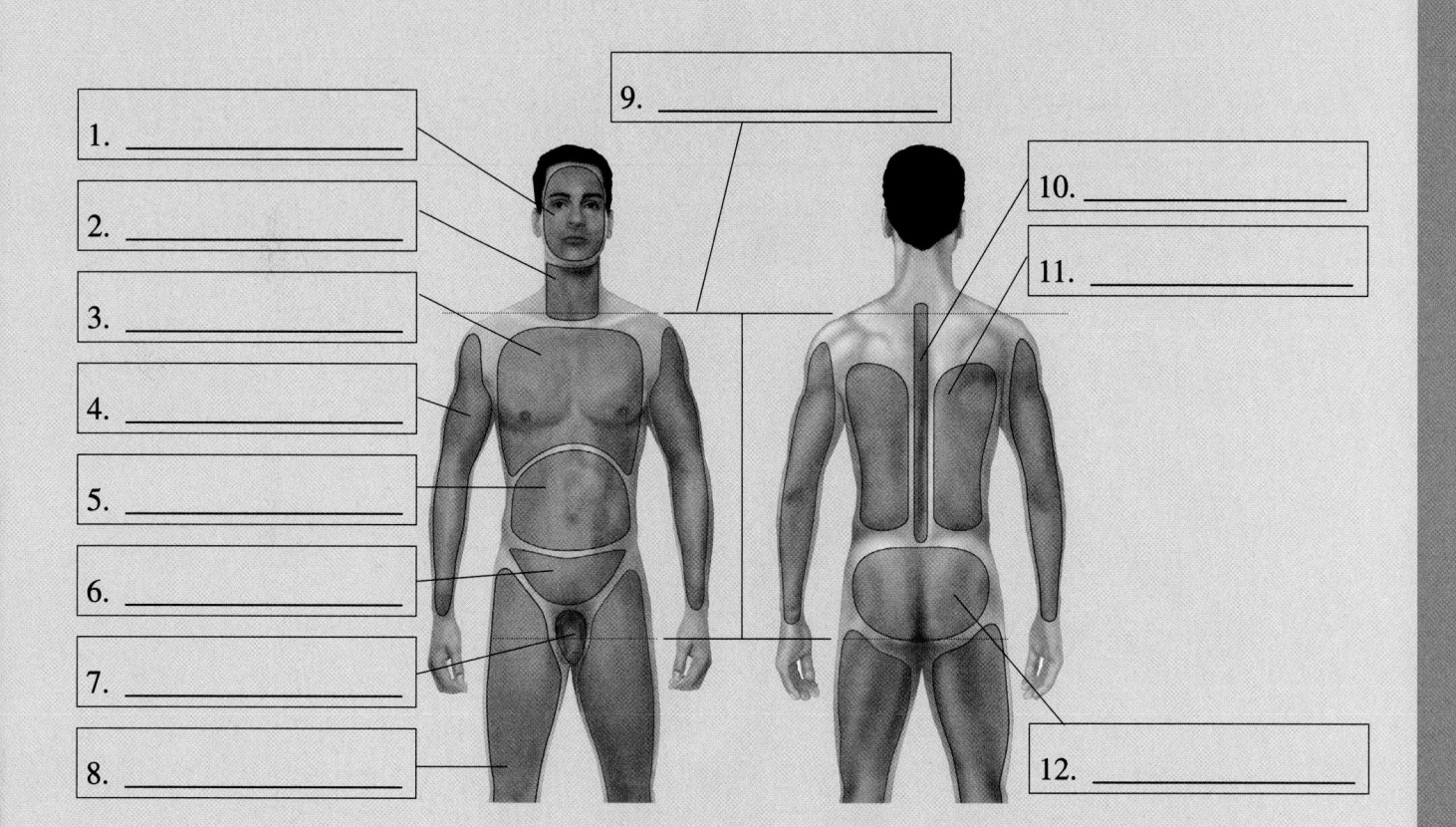

1. _____

2. _____

3. _____

4. _____

5. _____

6. _____

7. _____

8. _____

9. _____

10. _____

11. _____

12. _____

2. Write the labels for this figure on the numbered lines provided.

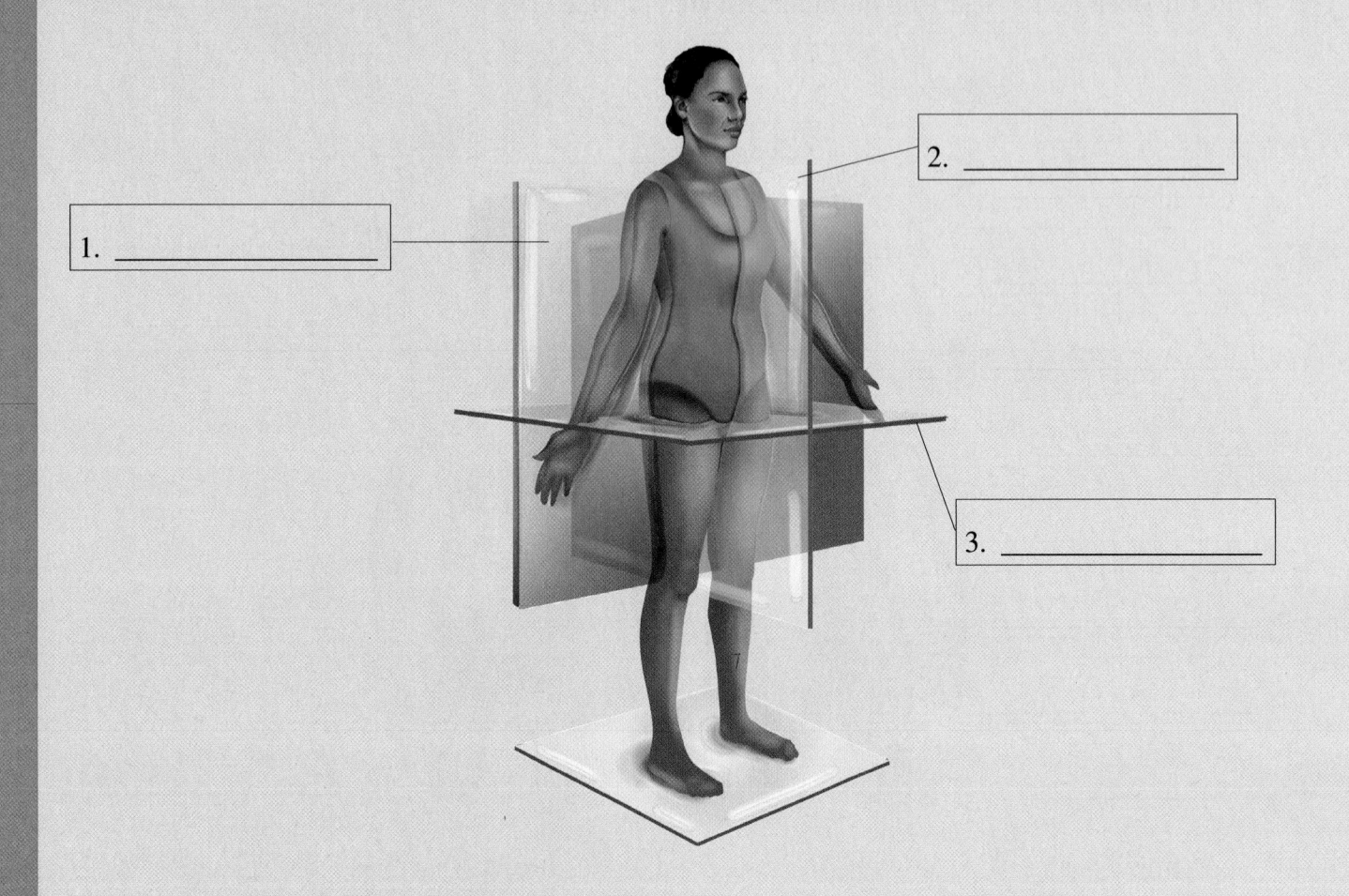

1. _____

2. _____

3. _____

MEDICAL **TERMINOLOGY** INTERACTIVE

Medical Terminology Interactive is a premium online homework management system that includes a host of features to help you study. Registered users will find:

- Fun games and activities built within a virtual hospital
- Powerful tools that track and analyze your results—allowing you to create a personalized learning experience
- Videos, flashcards, and audio pronunciations to help enrich your progress
- Streaming video lesson presentations and self-paced learning modules

www.pearsonhighered.com/mti

3

INTEGUMENTARY SYSTEM

Learning Objectives

Upon completion of this chapter, you will be able to

- Identify and define the combining forms, prefixes, and suffixes introduced in this chapter.

- Correctly spell and pronounce medical terms and major anatomical structures relating to the integumentary system.

- List and describe the three layers of skin and their functions.

- List and describe the four purposes of the skin.

- List and describe the accessory organs of the skin.

- Identify and define integumentary system anatomical terms.

- Identify and define selected integumentary system pathology terms.

- Identify and define selected integumentary system diagnostic procedures.

- Identify and define selected integumentary system therapeutic procedures.

- Identify and define selected medications relating to the integumentary system.

- Define selected abbreviations associated with the integumentary system.

Function

The skin provides a protective two-way barrier between our internal environment and the outside world. It also plays an important role in temperature regulation, houses sensory receptors to detect the environment around us, and secretes important fluids.

Organs

Here are the primary structures that comprise the integumentary system.

skin   **hair**   **nails**   **sebaceous glands**   **sweat glands**

Word Parts

Here are the most common word parts (with their meanings) used to build integumentary system terms. For a more comprehensive list, refer to the Terminology section of this chapter.

Combining Forms

albin/o	white	melan/o	black
bi/o	life	myc/o	fungus
cry/o	cold	necr/o	death
cutane/o	skin	onych/o	nail
cyan/o	blue	pedicul/o	lice
derm/o	skin	phot/o	light
dermat/o	skin	py/o	pus
diaphor/o	profuse sweating	rhytid/o	wrinkle
electr/o	electricity	scler/o	hard
erythr/o	red	seb/o	oil
hidr/o	sweat	trich/o	hair
ichthy/o	scaly, dry	ungu/o	nail
kerat/o	hard, horny	vesic/o	bladder
leuk/o	white	xer/o	dry
lip/o	fat	*xanth/o*	*yellow*
		chlor/o	*green*
		acr/o	*extremity*

Suffixes

-derma	skin condition
-opsy	view of
-tome	instrument used to cut

Prefixes

allo-	other, different from usual
xeno-	strange, foreign

Integumentary System Illustrated

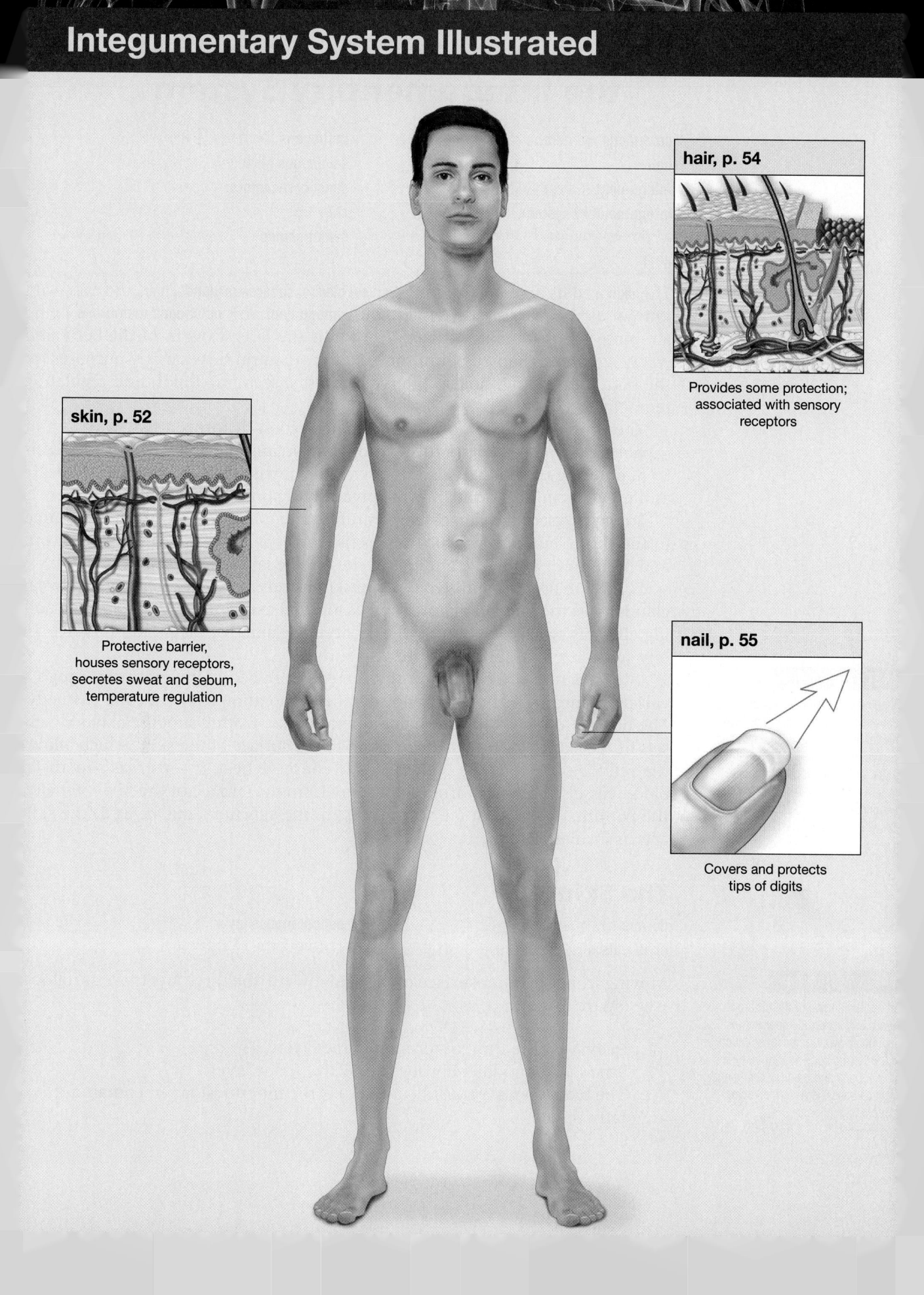

hair, p. 54

Provides some protection; associated with sensory receptors

skin, p. 52

Protective barrier, houses sensory receptors, secretes sweat and sebum, temperature regulation

nail, p. 55

Covers and protects tips of digits

Anatomy and Physiology of the Integumentary System

cutaneous membrane (kew-TAY-nee-us)

hair

integument (in-TEG-you-mint)

integumentary system
  (in-teg-you-MEN-tah-ree)

nails

pathogens (PATH-oh-jenz)

sebaceous glands (see-BAY-shus)

sensory receptors

skin

sweat glands

The **skin** and its accessory organs—**sweat glands, sebaceous glands, hair,** and **nails**—are known as the **integumentary system,** with **integument** and **cutaneous membrane** being alternate terms for skin. In fact, the skin is the largest organ of the body and can weigh more than 20 pounds in an adult. The skin serves many purposes for the body: protecting, housing nerve receptors, secreting fluids, and regulating temperature.

The primary function of the skin is protection. It forms a two-way barrier capable of keeping **pathogens** (disease-causing organisms) and harmful chemicals from entering the body. It also stops critical body fluids from escaping the body and prevents injury to the internal organs lying underneath the skin.

Sensory receptors that detect temperature, pain, touch, and pressure are located in the skin. The messages for these sensations are conveyed to the spinal cord and brain from the nerve endings in the middle layer of the skin.

Fluids are produced in two types of skin glands: sweat and sebaceous. Sweat glands assist the body in maintaining its internal temperature by creating a cooling effect as sweat evaporates. The sebaceous glands, or oil glands, produce an oily substance that lubricates the skin surface.

The structure of skin aids in the regulation of body temperature through a variety of means. As noted previously, the evaporation of sweat cools the body. The body also lowers its internal temperature by dilating superficial blood vessels in the skin. This brings more blood to the surface of the skin, which allows the release of heat. If the body needs to conserve heat, it constricts superficial blood vessels, keeping warm blood away from the surface of the body. Finally, the continuous layer of fat that makes up the subcutaneous layer of the skin acts as insulation.

MED TERM TIP

Flushing of the skin, a normal response to an increase in environmental temperature or to a fever, is caused by an increased blood flow to the skin of the face and neck. However, in some people, it is also a response to embarrassment called blushing and is not easily controlled.

The Skin

dermis (DER-mis)

epidermis (ep-ih-DER-mis)

subcutaneous layer
  (sub-kyoo-TAY-nee-us)

Moving from the outer surface of the skin inward, the three layers are as follows (see Figure 3.1 ■):

1. **Epidermis** is the thin, outer membrane layer.
2. **Dermis** is the middle, fibrous connective tissue layer.
3. The **subcutaneous layer** (Subcu, Subq) is the innermost layer, containing fatty tissue.

MED TERM TIP

An understanding of the different layers of the skin is important for healthcare workers because much of the terminology relating to types of injections and medical conditions, such as burns, is described using these designations.

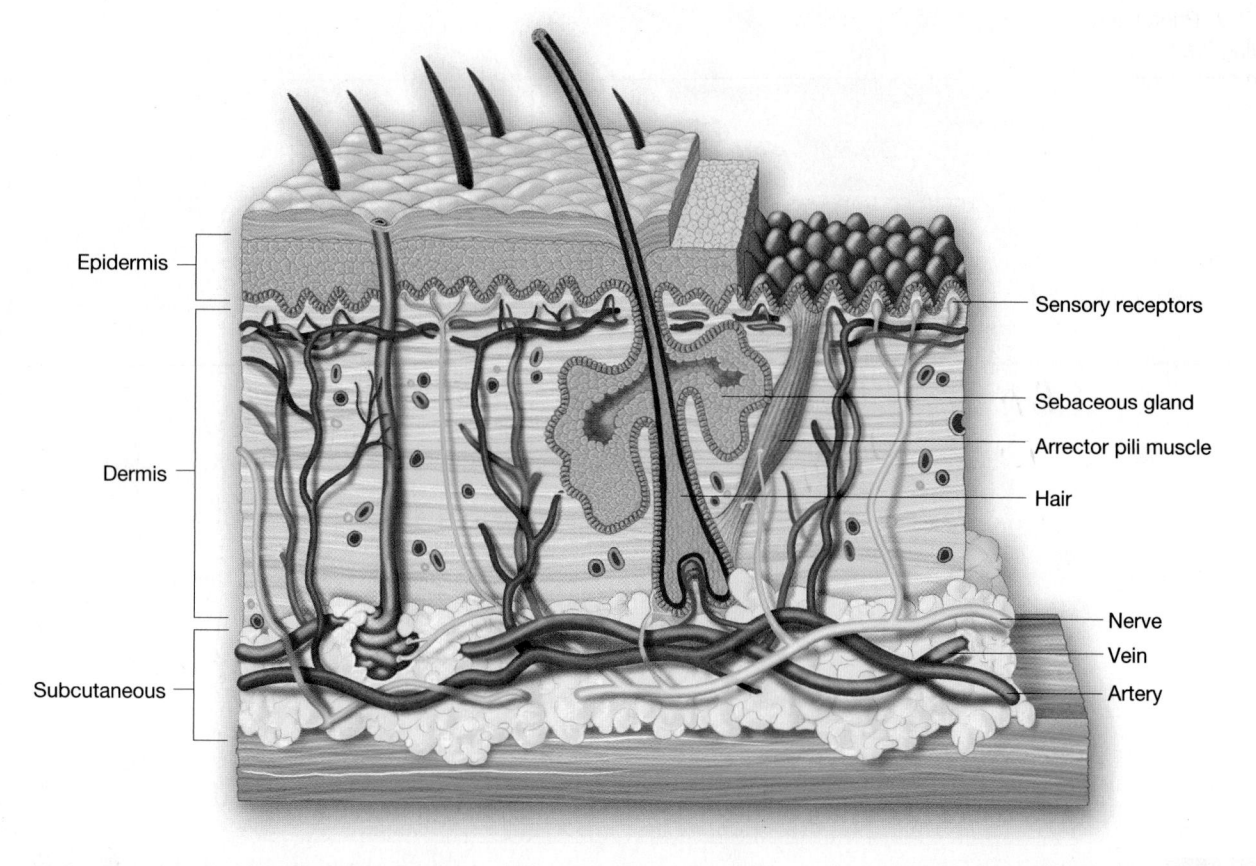

Figure 3.1 Skin structure, including the three layers of the skin and the accessory organs: sweat gland, sebaceous gland, and hair.

Epidermis

basal layer (BAY-sal)

keratin (KAIR-ah-tin)

melanin (MEL-ah-nin)

melanocytes (mel-AN-oh-sights)

stratified squamous epithelium (STRAT-ih-fyde / SKWAY-mus / ep-ih-THEE-lee-um)

The epidermis is composed of **stratified squamous epithelium** (see Figure 3.2 ■). This type of epithelial tissue consists of flat scale-like cells arranged in overlapping layers or strata. The epidermis does not have a blood supply or any connective tissue, so it is dependent for nourishment on the deeper layers of skin.

The deepest layer within the epidermis is called the **basal layer.** Cells in this layer continually grow and multiply. New cells that are forming push the old cells toward the outer layer of the epidermis. During this process the cells shrink, die, and become filled with a hard protein called **keratin.** These dead, overlapping, keratinized cells allow the skin to act as an effective barrier to infection and also make it waterproof.

The basal layer also contains special cells called **melanocytes,** which produce the black pigment **melanin.** Not only is this pigment responsible for the color of the skin, but it also protects against damage from the ultraviolet rays of the sun. This damage may be in the form of leatherlike skin and wrinkles, which are not hazardous, or it may be one of several forms of skin cancer. Dark-skinned people have more melanin and are generally less likely to get wrinkles or skin cancer.

> **MED TERM TIP**
>
> We lose 30,000-50,000 old, dead skin cells per minute and replace them with new, younger cells. In fact, because of this process, the epidermis is completely replaced every 25 days.

> **MED TERM TIP**
>
> A suntan can be thought of as a protective response to the rays of the sun. However, when the melanin in the skin is not able to absorb all the rays of the sun, the skin burns and DNA may be permanently and dangerously damaged.

Figure 3.2 Photomicrograph showing the three layers of the skin. *(Jubal Harshaw/Shutterstock)*

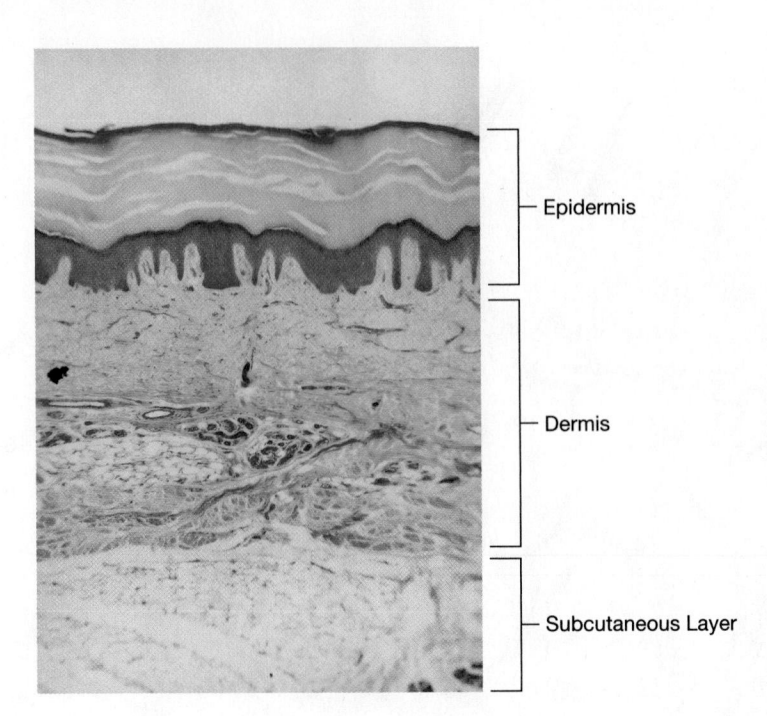

- Epidermis
- Dermis
- Subcutaneous Layer

Dermis

collagen fibers (KOL-ah-jen)   **corium** (KOH-ree-um)

The dermis, also referred to as the **corium,** is the middle layer of skin, located between the epidermis and the subcutaneous layer (see Figure 3.2). Its name means "true skin." Unlike the thinner epidermis, the dermis is living tissue with a very good blood supply. The dermis itself is composed of connective tissue and **collagen fibers.** Collagen fibers are made from a strong, fibrous protein present in connective tissue, forming a flexible "glue" that gives connective tissue its strength. The dermis houses hair follicles, sweat glands, sebaceous glands, blood vessels, lymph vessels, sensory receptors, nerve fibers, and muscle fibers.

Subcutaneous Layer

hypodermis (high-poh-DER-mis)   **lipocytes** (LIP-oh-sights)

The third and deepest layer of the skin is the subcutaneous layer, also called the **hypodermis.** This layer of tissue, composed of fat cells called **lipocytes,** protects the deeper tissues of the body and acts as insulation for heat and cold. (see Figure 3.2)

Accessory Organs

The accessory organs of the skin are the anatomical structures located within the dermis, including the hair, nails, sebaceous glands, and sweat glands.

Hair

arrector pili (ah-REK-tor / pee-lie)   **hair root**
hair follicle (FALL-ikl)   **hair shaft**

The fibers that make up hair are composed of the protein keratin, the same hard protein material that fills the cells of the epidermis. The process of hair formation is much like the process of growth in the epidermal layer of the skin. The deeper cells in the **hair root** force older keratinized cells to move upward, forming the **hair shaft.** The hair shaft grows toward the skin surface within the **hair follicle.** Melanin gives hair its color. Sebaceous glands release oil directly into the hair follicle. Each hair has a small slip of smooth muscle attached to it called the **arrector pili** muscle (see Figure 3.3 ■). When this muscle contracts the hair shaft stands up and results in "goose bumps."

Nails

cuticle (KEW-tikl)	**nail bed**
free edge	**nail body**
lunula (LOO-nyoo-lah)	**nail root**

Nails are a flat plate of keratin called the **nail body** that covers the ends of fingers and toes. The nail body is connected to the tissue underneath by the **nail bed.** Nails grow longer from the **nail root,** which is found at the base of the nail and is covered and protected by the soft tissue **cuticle.** The **free edge** is the exposed edge that is trimmed when nails become too long. The light-colored half-moon area at the base of the nail is the **lunula** (see Figure 3.4 ■).

Sebaceous Glands

sebum

Sebaceous glands, found in the dermis, secrete the oil **sebum,** which lubricates the hair and skin, thereby helping to prevent drying and cracking. These glands secrete sebum directly into hair follicles, rather than a duct (see Figure 3.1). Secretion from the sebaceous glands increases during adolescence, playing a role in the development of acne. Sebum secretion begins to diminish as age increases. A loss of sebum in old age, along with sun exposure, can account for wrinkles and dry skin.

> **MED TERM TIP**
>
> Because of its rich blood supply and light color, the nail bed is an excellent place to check patients for low oxygen levels in their blood. Deoxygenated blood is a very dark purple-red and gives skin a bluish tinge called *cyanosis.*

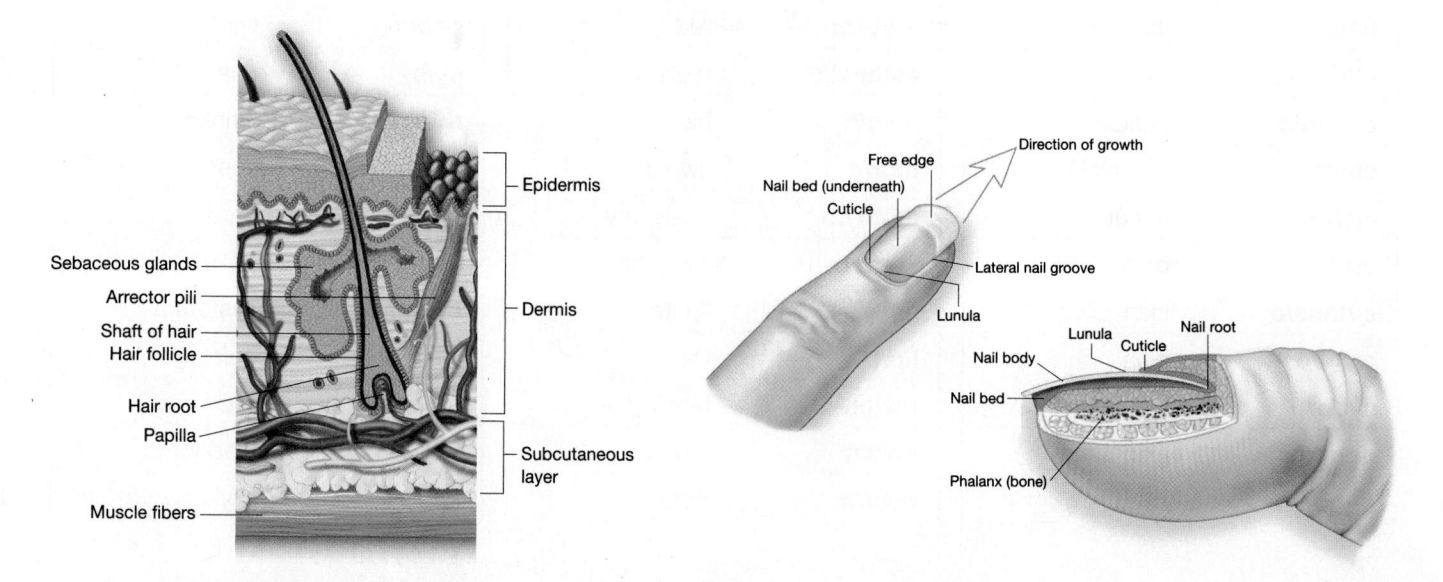

■ **Figure 3.3** Structure of a hair and its associated sebaceous gland.

■ **Figure 3.4** External and internal structures of nails.

Sweat Glands

apocrine glands (APP-oh-krin)   **sweat duct**

perspiration   **sweat pore**

sudoriferous glands (sue-doh-RIF-er-us)

About 2 million sweat glands, also called **sudoriferous glands,** are found throughout the body. These highly coiled glands are located in the dermis. Sweat travels to the surface of the skin in a **sweat duct.** The surface opening of a sweat duct is called a **sweat pore** (see Figure 3.1).

Sweat glands function to cool the body as sweat evaporates. Sweat or **perspiration** contains a small amount of waste product but is normally colorless and odorless. However, there are sweat glands called **apocrine glands** in the pubic and underarm areas that secrete a thicker sweat, which can produce an odor when it comes into contact with bacteria on the skin. This is what we recognize as body odor.

MED TERM TIP

Word Watch: Be careful when using *hydro-* meaning "water" and *hidr/o* meaning "sweat."

Terminology

Word Parts Used to Build Integumentary System Terms

The following lists contain the combining forms, suffixes, and prefixes used to build terms in the remaining sections of this chapter.

Combining Forms

albin/o	white
angi/o	vessel
bas/o	the base
bi/o	life
carcin/o	cancer
chem/o	chemical
cis/o	to cut
cry/o	cold
cutane/o	skin
cyan/o	blue
cyt/o	cell
derm/o	skin
dermat/o	skin

diaphor/o	profuse sweating
electr/o	electricity
erythr/o	red
esthesi/o	feeling
hem/o	blood
hidr/o	sweat
ichthy/o	scaly, dry
kerat/o	hard, horny
leuk/o	white
lip/o	fat
melan/o	black
myc/o	fungus
necr/o	death

onych/o	nail
pedicul/o	lice
phot/o	light
py/o	pus
rhytid/o	wrinkle
sarc/o	flesh
scler/o	hard
seb/o	oil
system/o	system
trich/o	hair
ungu/o	nail
vesic/o	bladder
xer/o	dry

Suffixes

-al	pertaining to		-itis	inflammation		-ous	pertaining to
-derma	skin condition		-logy	study of		-phagia	eating
-ectomy	surgical removal		-malacia	softening		-plasty	surgical repair
-emia	blood condition		-oma	mass		-rrhea	discharge
-ia	state, condition		-opsy	to view		-tic	pertaining to
-ic	pertaining to		-osis	abnormal condition		-tome	instrument to cut
-ism	state of					-ule	small

Prefixes

allo-	other		de-	without		intra-	within
an-	without		epi-	upon		para-	beside
anti-	against		hyper-	excessive		sub-	under
auto-	self		hypo-	under		xeno-	strange, foreign

Anatomical Terms

TERM	WORD PARTS	DEFINITION
cutaneous (kyoo-TAY-nee-us)	cutane/o = skin -ous = pertaining to	pertaining to the skin
dermal (DER-mal)	derm/o = skin -al = pertaining to	pertaining to the skin
epidermal (ep-ih-DER-mal)	epi- = upon derm/o = skin -al = pertaining to	pertaining to upon the skin
hypodermic (high-poh-DER-mik)	hypo- = under derm/o = skin -ic = pertaining to	pertaining to under the skin
intradermal (in-trah-DER-mal)	intra- = within derm/o = skin -al = pertaining to	pertaining to within the skin
subcutaneous (sub-kyoo-TAY-nee-us)	sub- = under cutane/o = skin -ous = pertaining to	pertaining to under the skin
ungual (UNG-gwal)	ungu/o = nail -al = pertaining to	pertaining to the nails

Pathology

TERM	WORD PARTS	DEFINITION
Medical Specialties		
dermatology (Derm, derm) (der-mah-TALL-oh-jee)	dermat/o = skin -logy = study of	Branch of medicine involving diagnosis and treatment of conditions and diseases of the integumentary system. Physician is a *dermatologist.*
plastic surgery		Surgical specialty involved in repair, reconstruction, or improvement of body structures such as the skin that are damaged, missing, or misshapen. Physician is a *plastic surgeon.*
Signs and Symptoms		
abrasion (ah-BRAY-zhun)		A scraping away of the skin surface by friction.
anhidrosis (an-hi-DROH-sis)	an- = without hidr/o = sweat -osis = abnormal condition	Abnormal condition of no sweat.
comedo (KOM-ee-do)		Collection of hardened sebum in hair follicle. Also called a *blackhead.*
contusion		Injury caused by a blow to the body; causes swelling, pain, and bruising. The skin is not broken.
cyanosis (sigh-ah-NOH-sis)	cyan/o = blue -osis = abnormal condition	Bluish tint to the skin caused by deoxygenated blood.

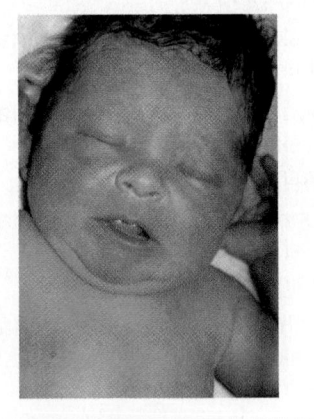

■ **Figure 3.5** A cyanotic infant. Note the bluish tinge to the skin around the lips, chin, and nose. *(St. Bartholomew's Hospital, London/Photo Researchers, Inc.)*

cyst (SIST)		Fluid-filled sac under the skin.

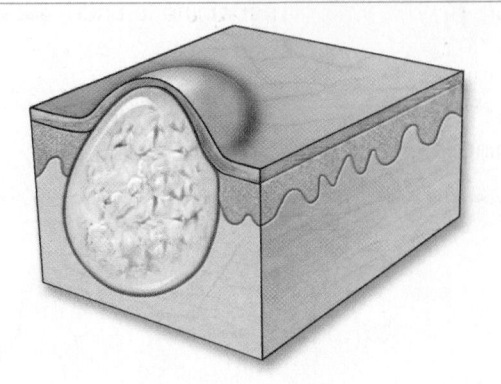

■ **Figure 3.6** Cyst.

Pathology *(continued)*

TERM	WORD PARTS	DEFINITION
depigmentation (dee-pig-men-TAY-shun)	de- = without	Loss of normal skin color or pigment.
diaphoresis (dye-ah-for-REE-sis)	diaphor/o = profuse sweating	Profuse sweating.
ecchymosis (ek-ih-MOH-sis)	-osis = abnormal condition	Skin discoloration caused by blood collecting under the skin following blunt trauma to the skin. A bruise.

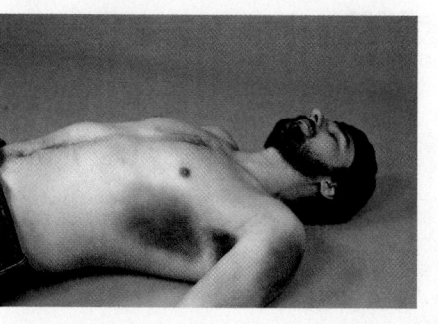

■ **Figure 3.7** Male lying supine with large ecchymosis on lateral rib cage and shoulder.

TERM	WORD PARTS	DEFINITION
erythema (er-ih-THEE-mah)	erythr/o = red hem/o = blood	Redness or flushing of the skin.
erythroderma (eh-rith-roh-DER-mah)	erythr/o = red -derma = skin condition	The condition of having reddened or flushed skin.
eschar (ESH-shar)		A thick layer of dead tissue and tissue fluid that develops over a deep burn area.
fissure (FISH-er)		Crack-like lesion or groove on the skin.

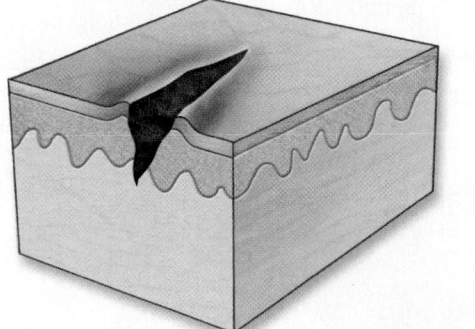

■ **Figure 3.8** Fissure.

TERM	WORD PARTS	DEFINITION
hirsutism (HER-soot-izm)		Excessive hair growth over the body.
hyperemia (high-per-EE-mee-ah)	hyper- = excessive -emia = blood condition	Redness of the skin due to increased blood flow.
hyperhidrosis (high-per-hi-DROH-sis)	hyper- = excessive hidr/o = sweat -osis = abnormal condition	Abnormal condition of excessive sweat.
hyperpigmentation (high-per-pig-men-TAY-shun)	hyper- = excessive	Abnormal amount of pigmentation in the skin.
ichthyoderma (ick-thee-oh-DER-mah)	ichthy/o = scaly, dry -derma = skin condition	The condition of having scaly and dry skin.

Pathology *(continued)*

TERM	WORD PARTS	DEFINITION
lesion (LEE-shun)		A general term for a wound, injury, or abnormality.
leukoderma (loo-koh-DER-mah)	leuk/o = white -derma = skin condition	Having skin that appears white because the normal skin pigment is absent. May be all the skin or just in some areas.
lipoma (lip-OH-mah)	lip/o = fat -oma = mass	Fatty mass.
macule (MACK-yool)	-ule = small	Flat, discolored area that is flush with the skin surface. An example would be a freckle or a birthmark.

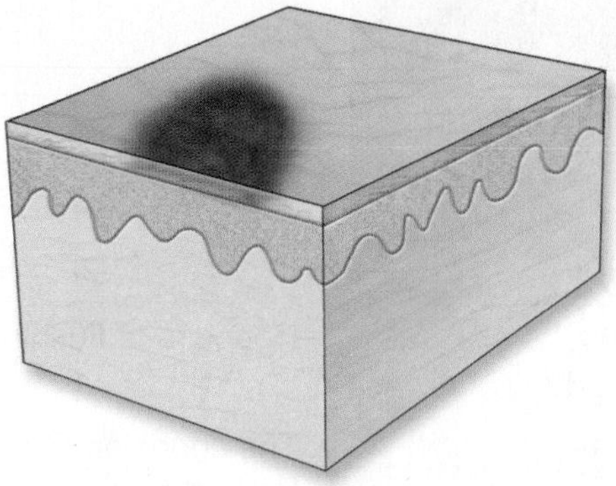

■ **Figure 3.9** Macule.

TERM	WORD PARTS	DEFINITION
necrosis (neh-KROH-sis)	necr/o = death -osis = abnormal condition	Abnormal condition of death.
nevus (NEV-us)		Pigmented skin blemish, birthmark, or mole. Usually benign but may become cancerous.
nodule (NOD-yool)	-ule = small	Firm, solid mass of cells in the skin larger than 0.5 cm in diameter.

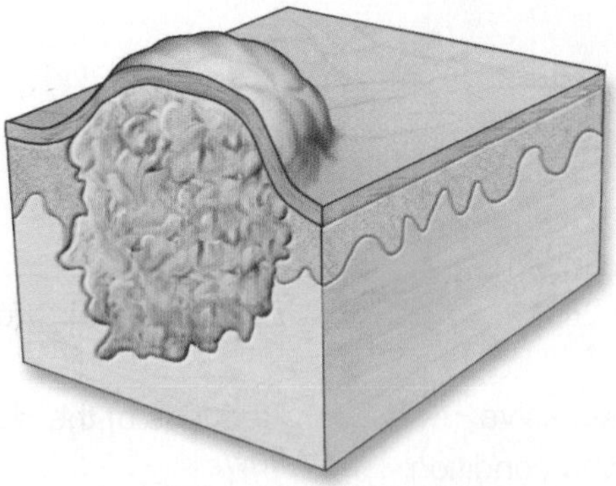

■ **Figure 3.10** Nodule.

TERM	WORD PARTS	DEFINITION
onychomalacia (on-ih-koh-mah-LAY-she-ah)	onych/o = nail -malacia = softening	Softening of the nails.
pallor (PAL-or)		Abnormal paleness of the skin.

Pathology *(continued)*

TERM	WORD PARTS	DEFINITION
papule (PAP-yool)	-ule = small	Small, solid, circular raised spot on the surface of the skin less than 0.5 cm in diameter.

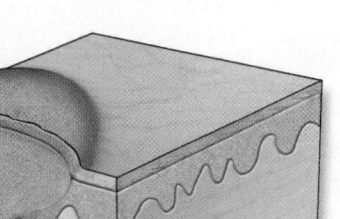

■ **Figure 3.11** Papule.

petechiae (peh-TEE-kee-eye)		Pinpoint purple or red spots from minute hemorrhages under the skin.

■ **Figure 3.12** Petechiae, pinpoint skin hemorrhages.
(Custom Medical Stock)

photosensitivity (foh-toh-sen-sih-TIH-vih-tee)	phot/o = light	Condition in which the skin reacts abnormally when exposed to light, such as the ultraviolet (UV) rays of the sun.
pruritus (proo-RIGH-tus)		Severe itching.
purpura (PER-pew-rah)		Hemorrhages into the skin due to fragile blood vessels. Commonly seen in older adults.

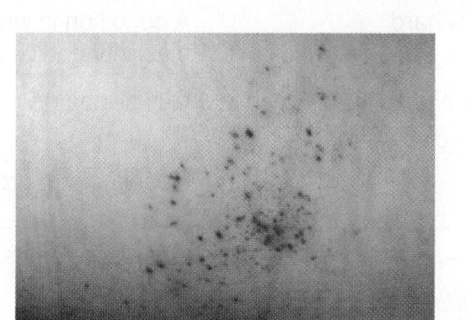

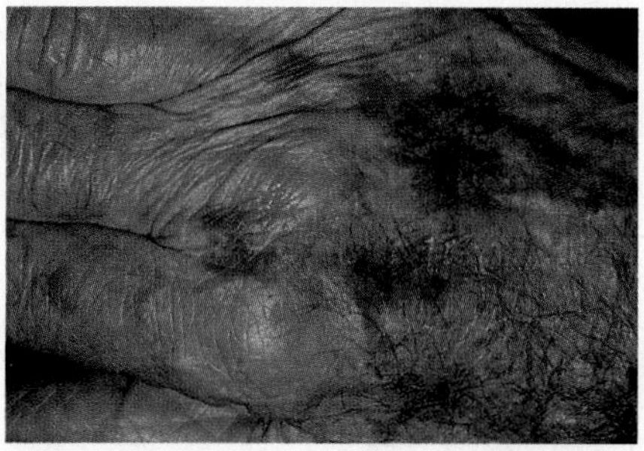

■ **Figure 3.13** Purpura, hemorrhaging into the skin due to fragile blood vessels.
(Caroll H. Weiss/Camera M.D. Studios)

MED TERM TIP

Purpura comes from the Latin word for "purple," which refers to the color of these pinpoint hemorrhages.

purulent (PYUR-yoo-lent)		Containing pus or an infection that is producing pus. Pus consists of dead bacteria, white blood cells, and tissue debris.

Pathology *(continued)*

TERM	WORD PARTS	DEFINITION
pustule (PUS-tyool) 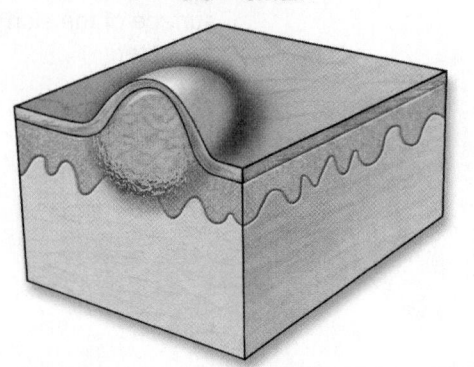 ■ **Figure 3.14** Pustule.	-ule = small	Raised spot on the skin containing pus.
pyoderma (pye-oh-DER-mah)	py/o = pus -derma = skin condition	The presence of pus on or in the layers of skin. A sign of a bacterial infection.
scleroderma (sklair-ah-DER-mah)	scler/o = hard -derma = skin condition	A condition in which the skin has lost its elasticity and become hardened.
seborrhea (seb-or-EE-ah)	seb/o = oil -rrhea = discharge	Oily discharge.
suppurative (SUP-pure-a-tiv)		Containing or producing pus.
ulcer (ULL-ser) 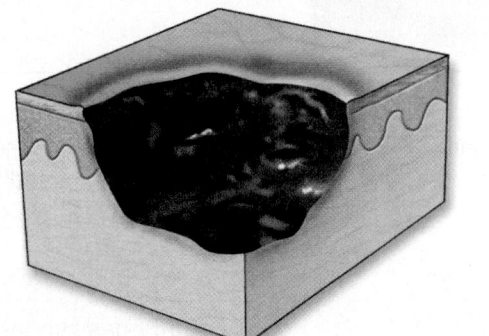 ■ **Figure 3.15** Ulcer.		Open sore or lesion in skin or mucous membrane.
urticaria (er-tih-KAY-ree-ah)		Also called *hives;* a skin eruption of pale reddish wheals with severe itching. Usually associated with food allergy, stress, or drug reactions.
vesicle (VESS-ikl) 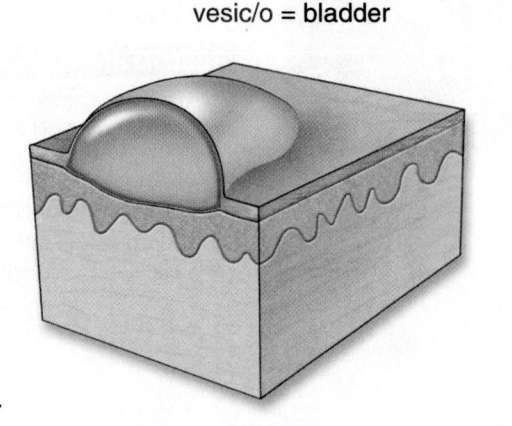 ■ **Figure 3.16** Vesicle.	vesic/o = bladder	A blister; small, fluid-filled raised spot on the skin.

Pathology *(continued)*

TERM	WORD PARTS	DEFINITION
wheal (WEEL)	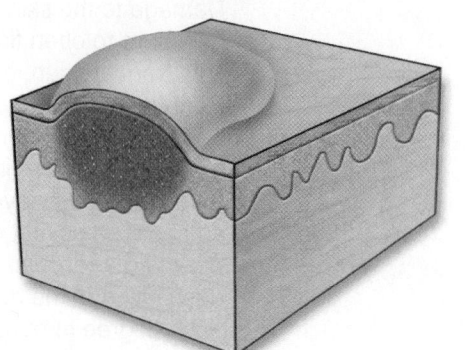 ■ **Figure 3.17** Wheal.	Small, round, swollen area on the skin; typically seen in allergic skin reactions such as *hives* and usually accompanied by urticaria.
xeroderma (zee-roh-DER-mah)	xer/o = dry -derma = skin condition	Condition in which the skin is abnormally dry.

Skin

TERM	WORD PARTS	DEFINITION
abscess (AB-sess)		A collection of pus in the skin.
acne (ACK-nee)		Inflammatory disease of the sebaceous glands and hair follicles resulting in papules and pustules.
acne rosacea (ACK-nee roh-ZAY-she-ah)		Chronic form of acne seen in adults involving redness, tiny pimples, and broken blood vessels, primarily on the nose and cheeks.
acne vulgaris (ACK-nee vul-GAY-ris)		Common form of acne seen in teenagers. Characterized by comedo, papules, and pustules.
albinism (al-BIH-nizm)	albin/o = white -ism = state of	A genetic condition in which the body is unable to make melanin. Characterized by white hair and skin and red pupils due to the lack of pigment. The person with albinism is called an *albino*.
basal cell carcinoma (BCC) (BAY-sal / sell / kar-sin-NOH-ma)	bas/o = the base -al = pertaining to carcin/o = cancer -oma = tumor	Cancerous tumor of the basal cell layer of the epidermis. A frequent type of skin cancer that rarely metastasizes or spreads. These cancers can arise on sun-exposed skin.

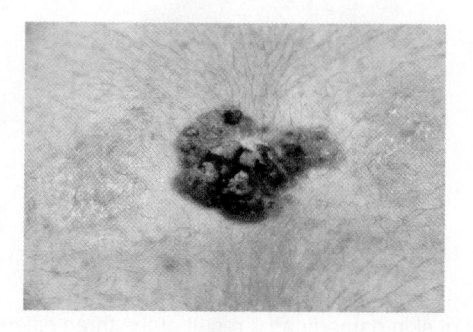

■ **Figure 3.18** Basal cell carcinoma, a frequent type of skin cancer that rarely metastasizes. *(Bob Craig/CDC)*

Pathology *(continued)*

TERM	WORD PARTS	DEFINITION
burn		Damage to the skin that can result from exposure to open fire, electricity, ultraviolet light from the sun, or caustic chemicals. Seriousness depends on the amount of body surface involved and the depth of the burn as determined by the amount of damage to each layer. Skin and burns are categorized as first degree, second degree, or third degree. See Figure 3.19 ■ for a description of the damage associated with each degree of burn. Extent of a burn is estimated using the Rule of Nines (see Figure 3.20 ■).

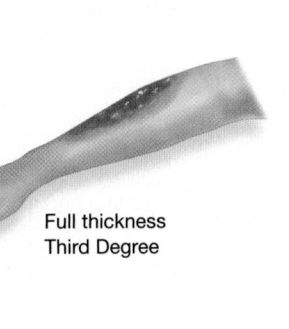
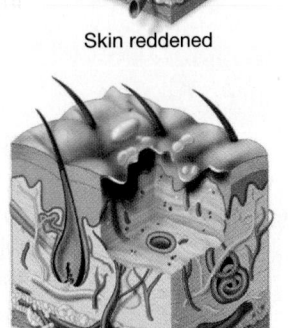
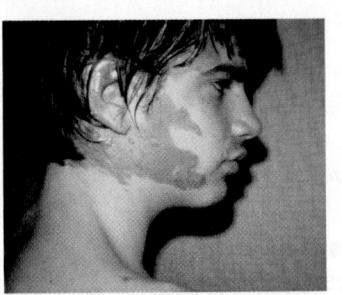

Superficial
First Degree

Skin reddened

(Moynahan Medical Center)

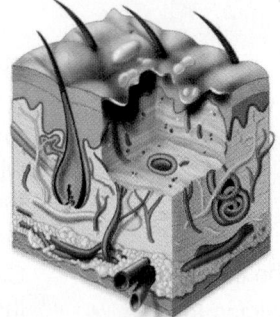
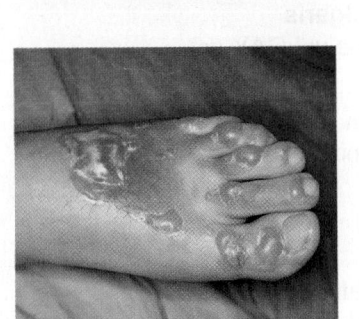

Partial thickness
Second Degree

Blisters

(Charles Stewart MD FACEP, FAAEM)

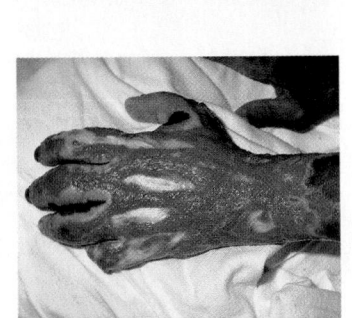

Full thickness
Third Degree

Charring

■ **Figure 3.19** Comparison of the level of skin damage as a result of the three different degrees of burns.

Pathology *(continued)*

TERM	WORD PARTS	DEFINITION

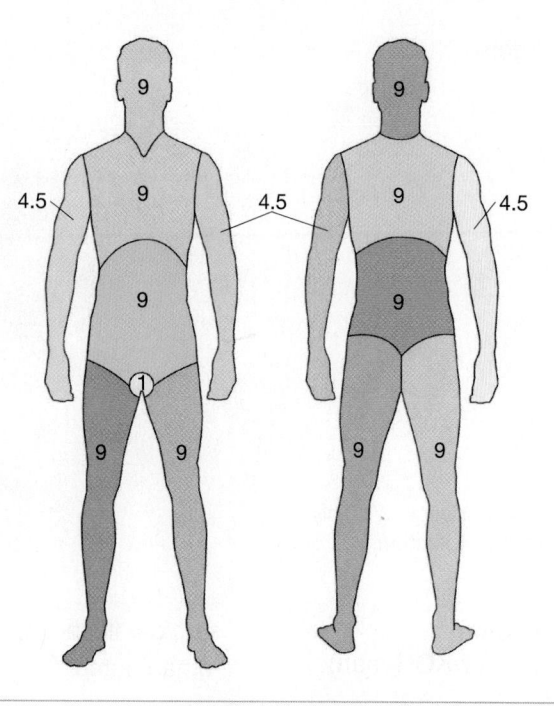

■ **Figure 3.20** Rule of Nines. A method for determining percentage of body burned. Each different-colored section represents a percentage of the body surface. All sections added together will equal 100%.

TERM	WORD PARTS	DEFINITION
cellulitis (sell-you-LYE-tis)	-itis = inflammation	A diffuse, acute infection and inflammation of the connective tissue found in the skin.
decubitus ulcer (decub) (dee-KYOO-bih-tus)	**MED TERM TIP** *Decubitus* comes from the Latin word *decumbo,* meaning "lying down," which leads to the use of the term for a bedsore or pressure sore.	Open sore caused by pressure over bony prominences cutting off the blood flow to the overlying skin. These can appear in bedridden patients who lie in one position too long and can be difficult to heal. Also called *bedsore* or *pressure sore.*
dermatitis (der-mah-TYE-tis)	dermat/o = skin -itis = inflammation	Inflammation of the skin.
dermatosis (der-mah-TOH-sis)	dermat/o = skin -osis = abnormal condition	A general term indicating the presence of an abnormal skin condition.
dry gangrene (GANG-green)		Late stages of gangrene characterized by the affected area becoming dried, blackened, and shriveled; referred to as *mummified.*
eczema (EK-zeh-mah)		Superficial dermatitis of unknown cause accompanied by redness, vesicles, itching, and crusting.
gangrene (GANG-green)		Tissue necrosis usually due to deficient blood supply.
ichthyosis (ick-thee-OH-sis)	ichthy/o = scaly, dry -osis = abnormal condition	Condition in which the skin becomes dry, scaly, and keratinized.

Pathology *(continued)*

TERM	WORD PARTS	DEFINITION
impetigo (im-peh-TYE-goh)		A highly infectious bacterial infection of the skin with pustules that rupture and become crusted over.

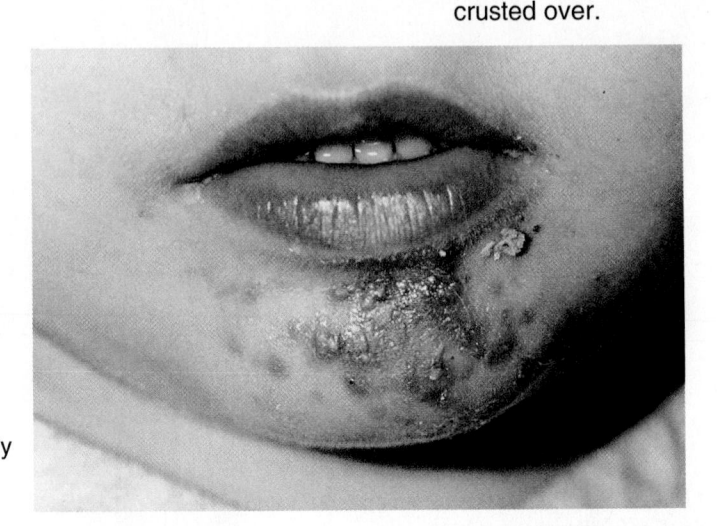

■ **Figure 3.21** Impetigo, a highly contagious bacterial infection. *(Dr. Jason L. Smith)*

TERM	WORD PARTS	DEFINITION
Kaposi's sarcoma (KAP-oh-seez / sar-KOH-mah)	sarc/o = flesh -oma = tumor	Form of skin cancer frequently seen in acquired immunodeficiency syndrome (AIDS) patients. Consists of brownish-purple papules that spread from the skin and metastasize to internal organs.
keloid (KEE-loyd)		Formation of a raised and thickened hypertrophic scar after an injury or surgery.

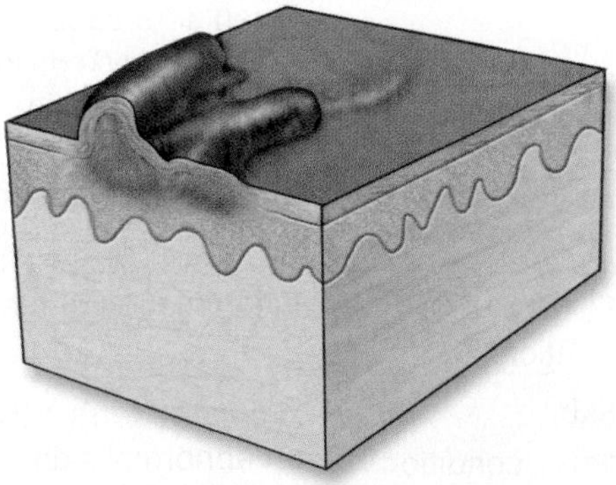

■ **Figure 3.22** Keloid.

TERM	WORD PARTS	DEFINITION
keratosis (kair-ah-TOH-sis)	kerat/o = hard, horny -osis = abnormal condition	Term for any skin condition involving an over-growth and thickening of the epidermis layer.
laceration		A torn or jagged wound; incorrectly used to describe a cut.
malignant melanoma (MM) (mah-LIG-nant / mel-a-NOH-ma)	melan/o = black -oma = tumor	Dangerous form of skin cancer caused by an uncontrolled growth of melanocytes. May quickly metastasize or spread to internal organs.

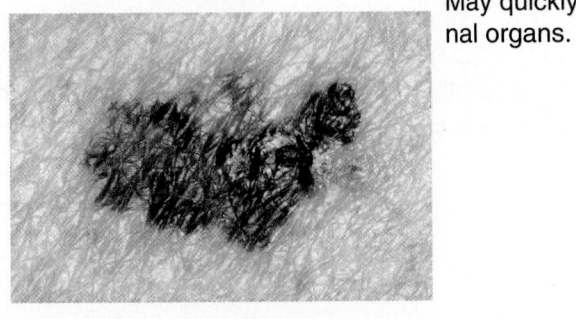

■ **Figure 3.23** Malignant melanoma. This photograph demonstrates the highly characteristic color of this tumor. *(Skin Cancer Foundation/National Cancer Institute)*

Pathology *(continued)*

TERM	WORD PARTS	DEFINITION
pediculosis (peh-dik-you-LOH-sis)	pedicul/o = lice -osis = abnormal condition	Infestation with lice. The eggs laid by the lice are called nits and cling tightly to hair.
psoriasis (soh-RYE-ah-sis)		Chronic inflammatory condition consisting of papules forming "silvery scale" patches with circular borders.

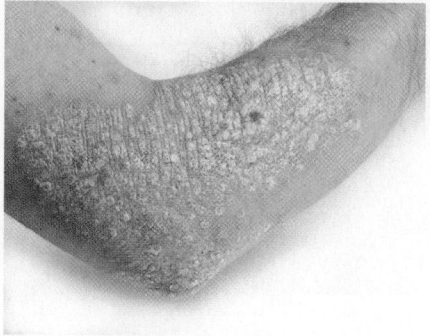

■ **Figure 3.24** Psoriasis. This photograph demonstrates the characteristic white skin patches of this condition. *(kenxro/Shutterstock)*

TERM	WORD PARTS	DEFINITION
rubella (roo-BELL-ah)		Contagious viral skin infection. Commonly called *German measles.*
scabies (SKAY-bees)		Contagious skin disease caused by an egg-laying mite that burrows through the skin and causes redness and intense itching; often seen in children.
sebaceous cyst (see-BAY-shus / SIST)	seb/o = oil	Sac under the skin filled with sebum or oil from a sebaceous gland. This can grow to a large size and may need to be excised.
cicatrix (SICK-ah-trix)		A scar.
squamous cell carcinoma (SCC) (SKWAY-mus / sell / kar-sih-NOH-mah)	carcin/o = cancer -oma = tumor	Cancer of the epidermis layer of skin that may invade deeper tissue and metastasize. Often begins as a sore that does not heal.

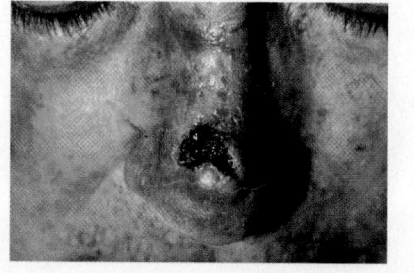

■ **Figure 3.25** Squamous cell carcinoma. *(National Cancer Institute)*

Pathology *(continued)*

TERM	WORD PARTS	DEFINITION
strawberry hemangioma (hee-man-jee-OH-ma)	hem/o = blood angi/o = vessel -oma = tumor	Congenital collection of dilated blood vessels causing a red birthmark that fades a few months after birth.

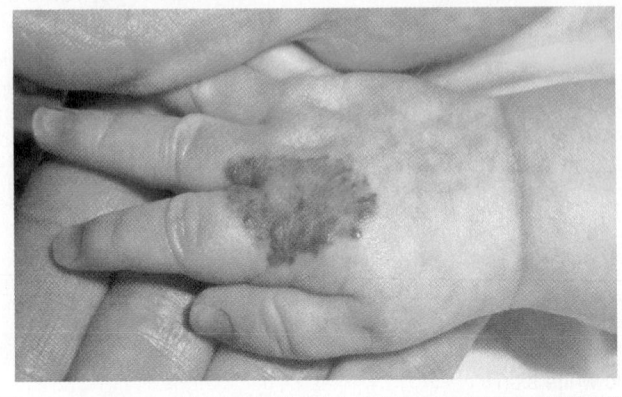

■ **Figure 3.26** Strawberry hemangioma, a birthmark caused by a collection of blood vessels in the skin. *(H.C. Robinson/Science Photo Library/ Photo Researchers)*

TERM	WORD PARTS	DEFINITION
systemic lupus erythematosus (SLE) (sis-TEM-ik / LOO-pus / air-ih-them-ah-TOH-sis)	system/o = system -ic = pertaining to erythr/o = red	Chronic disease of the connective tissue that injures the skin, joints, kidneys, nervous system, and mucous membranes. This is an autoimmune condition meaning that the body's own immune system attacks normal tissue of the body. May produce a characteristic red, scaly butterfly rash across the cheeks and nose.
tinea (TIN-ee-ah)		Fungal skin disease resulting in itching, scaling lesions.
tinea capitis (TIN-ee-ah / CAP-it-is)	*capitis* is the Latin term for the head	Fungal infection of the scalp. Commonly called *ringworm.*
tinea pedis (TIN-ee-ah / PED-is)	*pedis* is the Latin term for the foot	Fungal infection of the foot. Commonly called *athlete's foot.*
varicella (VAIR-ih-chell-a)		Contagious viral skin infection. Commonly called *chickenpox.*

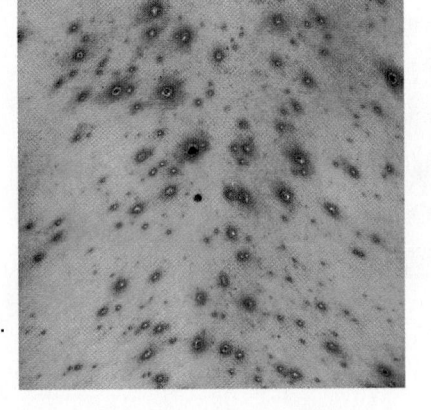

■ **Figure 3.27** Varicella or chickenpox, a viral skin infection. In this photograph, the rash is beginning to form scabs.

TERM	WORD PARTS	DEFINITION
verruca (ver-ROO-kah)		Commonly called *warts;* a benign growth caused by a virus. Has a rough surface that is removed by chemicals and/or laser therapy.

Pathology *(continued)*

TERM	WORD PARTS	DEFINITION
vitiligo (vit-ill-EYE-go)		Disappearance of pigment from the skin in patches, causing a milk-white appearance. Also called *leukoderma*.
wet gangrene (GANG-green)		An area of gangrene that becomes secondarily infected by pus-producing bacteria.
Hair		
alopecia (al-oh-PEE-she-ah)		Absence or loss of hair, especially of the head. Commonly called *baldness*.
carbuncle (CAR-bung-kl)		Furuncle involving several hair follicles.
furuncle (FOO-rung-kl)		Bacterial infection of a hair follicle. Characterized by redness, pain, and swelling. Also called a *boil*.
trichomycosis (trik-oh-my-KOH-sis)	trich/o = hair myc/o = fungus -osis = abnormal condition	Abnormal condition of hair fungus.
Nails		
onychia (oh-NICK-ee-ah)	onych/o = nail -ia = state, condition	Infected nail bed.
onychomycosis (on-ih-koh-my-KOH-sis)	onych/o = nail myc/o = fungus -osis = abnormal condition	Abnormal condition of nail fungus.
onychophagia (on-ih-koh-FAY-jee-ah)	onych/o = nail -phagia = eating	Nail eating (nail biting).
paronychia (pair-oh-NICK-ee-ah)	para- = beside onych/o = nail -ia = state, condition	Infection of the skin fold around a nail.

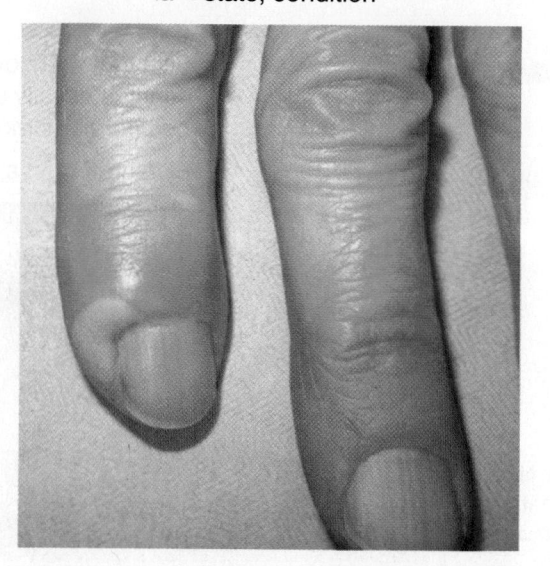

Figure 3.28 Paronychia.
(Local Images Inc.)

Diagnostic Procedures

TERM	WORD PARTS	DEFINITION
Clinical Laboratory Tests		
culture and sensitivity (C&S)		Laboratory test that grows a colony of bacteria removed from an infected area in order to identify the specific infecting bacteria and then determine its sensitivity to a variety of antibiotics.
Biopsy Procedures		
biopsy (BX, bx) (BYE-op-see) **MED TERM TIP** Word Watch: Be careful when using *bi-* meaning "two" and *bi/o* meaning "life."	bi/o = life -opsy = to view	Piece of tissue removed by syringe and needle, knife, punch, or brush to examine under a microscope. Used to aid in diagnosis.
exfoliative cytology (ex-FOH-lee-ah-tiv / sigh-TALL-oh-jee)	cyt/o = cell -logy = study of	Scraping cells from tissue and then examining them under a microscope.
frozen section (FS)		Thin piece of tissue cut from a frozen specimen for rapid examination under a microscope.
fungal scrapings	-al = pertaining to	Scrapings, taken with a curette or scraper, of tissue from lesions are placed on a growth medium and examined under a microscope to identify fungal growth.

Therapeutic Procedures

TERM	WORD PARTS	DEFINITION
Skin Grafting		
allograft (AL-oh-graft)	allo- = other	Skin graft from one person to another; donor is usually a cadaver. Also called *homograft* (homo = same).
autograft (AW-toh-graft)	auto- = self	Skin graft from a person's own body.

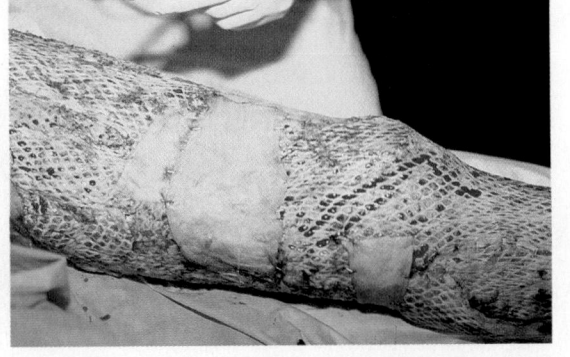

■ **Figure 3.29** A freshly applied autograft. Note that the donor skin has been perforated so that it can be stretched to cover a larger burned area. *(Courtesy of Dr. William Dominic, Community Regional Medical Center)*

dermatome (DER-mah-tohm)	derm/o = skin -tome = instrument to cut	Instrument for cutting the skin or thin transplants of skin.

■ Therapeutic Procedures *(continued)*

TERM	WORD PARTS	DEFINITION
dermatoplasty (DER-mah-toh-plas-tee)	dermat/o = skin -plasty = surgical repair	Skin grafting; transplantation of skin.
skin graft (SG)		Transfer of skin from a normal area to cover another site. Used to treat burn victims and after some surgical procedures. Also called *dermatoplasty.*
xenograft (ZEN-oh-graft)	xeno- = strange, foreign	Skin graft from an animal of another species (usually a pig) to a human. Also called *heterograft* (hetero- = other).

Surgical Procedures

TERM	WORD PARTS	DEFINITION
cauterization (kaw-ter-ih-ZAY-shun)		Destruction of tissue by using caustic chemicals, electric currents, heat, or by freezing.
cryosurgery (cry-oh-SER-jer-ee)	cry/o = cold	Use of extreme cold to freeze and destroy tissue.
curettage (koo-REH-tahz)		Removal of superficial skin lesions with a curette (surgical instrument shaped like a spoon) or scraper.
debridement (de-BREED-mint)		Removal of foreign material and dead or damaged tissue from a wound.
electrocautery (ee-leck-troh-KAW-teh-ree)	electr/o = electricity	To destroy tissue with an electric current.
incision and drainage (I&D)	cis/o = to cut	Making an incision to create an opening for the drainage of material such as pus.
onychectomy (on-ee-KECK-toh-mee)	onych/o = nail -ectomy = surgical removal	Removal of a nail.

Plastic Surgery Procedures

TERM	WORD PARTS	DEFINITION
chemabrasion (kee-moh-BRAY-zhun)	chem/o = chemical	Abrasion using chemicals. Also called a *chemical peel.*
dermabrasion (DERM-ah-bray-shun)	derm/o = skin	Abrasion or rubbing using wire brushes or sandpaper. Performed to remove acne scars, tattoos, and scar tissue.
laser therapy		Removal of skin lesions and birthmarks using a laser beam that emits intense heat and power at a close range. The laser converts frequencies of light into one small, powerful beam.
liposuction (LIP-oh-suck-shun)	lip/o = fat	Removal of fat beneath the skin by means of suction.
rhytidectomy (rit-ih-DECK-toh-mee)	rhytid/o = wrinkle -ectomy = surgical removal	Surgical removal of excess skin to eliminate wrinkles. Commonly referred to as a *face lift.*

Pharmacology

CLASSIFICATION	WORD PARTS	ACTION	EXAMPLES
anesthetic (an-es-THET-tic)	an- = without esthesi/o = feeling -ic = pertaining to	Applied to the skin to deaden pain.	lidocaine, Xylocaine; procaine, Novocain
antibiotic (an-tye-bye-AW-tic)	anti- = against bi/o = life -tic = pertaining to	Kill bacteria causing skin infections.	bacitracin/neomycin/polymixinB, Neosporin ointment
antifungal (an-tye-FUNG-all)	anti- = against -al = pertaining to	Kill fungi infecting the skin.	miconazole, Monistat; clotrimazole, Lotrimin
antiparasitic (an-tye-pair-ah-SIT-tic)	anti- = against -ic = pertaining to	Kill mites or lice.	lindane, Kwell; permethrin, Nix
antipruritic (an-tye-proo-RIGH-tik)	anti- = against -ic = pertaining to	Reduce severe itching.	diphenhydramine, Benadryl; camphor/pramoxine/zinc, Caladryl
antiseptic (an-tye-SEP-tic)	anti- = against -tic = pertaining to	Used to kill bacteria in skin cuts and wounds or at a surgical site.	isopropyl alcohol; hydrogen peroxide
antivirals	anti- = against	Treats herpes simplex infection.	valacyclovir, Valtrex; famcyclovir, Famvir; acyclovir, Zovirax
corticosteroid cream		Specific type of powerful anti-inflammatory cream.	hydrocortisone, Cortaid; triamcinolone, Kenalog

Abbreviations

BCC	basal cell carcinoma	**MM**	malignant melanoma
BX, bx	biopsy	**SCC**	squamous cell carcinoma
C&S	culture and sensitivity	**SG**	skin graft
decub	decubitus ulcer	**SLE**	systemic lupus erythematosus
Derm, derm	dermatology	**STSG**	split-thickness skin graft
FS	frozen section	**subcu, SC,**	subcutaneous
HSV	herpes simplex virus	**sc, subq**	
I&D	incision and drainage	**UV**	ultraviolet
ID	intradermal		

MED TERM TIP

Word Watch: Be careful when using the abbreviation *ID* meaning "intradermal" and *I&D* meaning "incision and drainage."

Chapter Review

Real-World Applications

Medical Record Analysis

This Dermatology Consultation Report contains 11 medical terms. Underline each term and write it in the list below the report. Then define each term.

Dermatology Consultation Report

Reason for Consultation: Possible recurrence of basal cell carcinoma, left cheek.

History of Present Illness: Patient is a 74-year-old male first seen by his regular physician 5 years ago for persistent facial lesions. Biopsies revealed basal cell carcinoma in two lesions, one on the nasal tip and the other on the left cheek. These were successfully excised. The patient noted that the left cheek lesion returned approximately one year ago. Patient reports pruritus and states the lesion is growing larger.

Results of Physical Exam: Examination revealed a 10 × 14 mm lesion on left cheek 20 mm anterior to the ear. The lesion displays marked erythema and poorly defined borders. The area immediately around the lesion shows depigmentation with vesicles.

Assessment: Recurrence of basal cell carcinoma.

Recommendations: Due to the lesion's size, shape, and reoccurrence, deep excision of the carcinoma through the epidermis and dermis layers followed by dermatoplasty is recommended.

Term	Definition
❶ _____	_____
❷ _____	_____
❸ _____	_____
❹ _____	_____
❺ _____	_____
❻ _____	_____
❼ _____	_____
❽ _____	_____
❾ _____	_____
❿ _____	_____
⓫ _____	_____

Chart Note Transcription

The chart note below contains 10 phrases that can be reworded with a medical term that you learned in this chapter. Each phrase is identified with an underline. Determine the medical term and write your answers in the spaces provided.

Current Complaint:	A 64-year-old female with an <u>open sore</u> ❶ on her right leg is seen by the <u>specialist in treating diseases of the skin.</u> ❷
Past History:	Patient states she first noticed an area of pain, <u>severe itching,</u> ❸ and <u>redness of the skin</u> ❹ just below her right knee about 6 weeks ago. One week later <u>raised spots containing pus</u> ❺ appeared. Patient states the raised spots containing pus ruptured and the open sore appeared.
Signs and Symptoms:	Patient has a deep open sore 5 × 3 cm: It is 4 cm distal to the knee on the lateral aspect of the right leg. It appears to extend into the <u>middle skin layer,</u> ❻ and the edges show signs of <u>tissue death.</u> ❼ The open sore has a small amount of drainage but there is no odor. A <u>sample of the drainage that was grown in the lab to identify the microorganism and determine the best antibiotic</u> ❽ of the drainage revealed *Staphylococcus* bacteria in the open sore.
Diagnosis:	<u>Inflammation of connective tissue in the skin.</u> ❾
Treatment:	<u>Removal of damaged tissue</u> ❿ of the open sore followed by application of an antibiotic cream. Patient was instructed to return to the skin disease specialist's office in 2 weeks, or sooner if the open sore does not heal, or if it begins draining pus.

❶ _____

❷ _____

❸ _____

❹ _____

❺ _____

❻ _____

❼ _____

❽ _____

❾ _____

❿ _____

Case Study

Below is a case study presentation of a patient with a condition discussed in this chapter. Read the case study and answer the questions below. Some questions will ask for information not included within this chapter. Use your text, a medical dictionary, or any other reference material you choose to answer these questions.

A 40-year-old female is seen in the dermatologist's office, upon the recommendation of her internist, for a workup for suspected SLE. Her presenting symptoms include erythema rash across her cheeks and nose, photosensitivity resulting in raised rash in sun-exposed areas, patches of alopecia, and pain and stiffness in her joints. The dermatologist examines the patient and orders exfoliative cytology and fungal scrapings to rule out other sources of the rash. Her internist had already placed the patient on oral anti-inflammatory medication for joint pain. The dermatologist orders corticosteroid cream for the rash. The patient is advised to use a sunscreen and make a follow-up appointment for results of the biopsy.

(Monkey Business Images/Shutterstock)

1. What pathological condition does the internist think this patient might have? Look this condition up in a reference source, and include a short description of it. SLE is an autoimmune disease. Use a reference source to look up the name of another autoimmune disease.

    _____

    _____

2. List and define each of the patient's presenting symptoms in your own words.

    _____

    _____

3. What diagnostic tests did the dermatologist perform? Describe it in your own words. Why were they important in helping the dermatologist make a diagnosis?

    _____

    _____

4. Each physician initiated a treatment. Describe them in your own words.

    _____

    _____

5. What do you think the term "workup" means?

    _____

    _____

Practice Exercises

A. Complete the Statement

1. The three layers of skin in order starting with the most superficial layer are _____,
   _____, and _____.

2. The _____ layer is the only living layer of the epidermis.

3. The subcutaneous layer of skin is composed primarily of _____.

4. Sensory receptors are located in the _____ layer of skin.

5. Nails and hair are composed of a hard protein called _____.

6. _____ is the pigment that gives skin its color.

7. Another name for the dermis is _____.

8. The nail body is connected to underlying tissue by the _____.

9. _____ glands release their product directly into hair follicles while _____ glands
   release their product into a duct.

10. _____ glands are sweat glands found in the underarm and pubic areas.

B. Define the Combining Form

	Definition	Example from Chapter
1. **cry/o**		
2. **cutane/o**		
3. **diaphor/o**		
4. **py/o**		
5. **cyan/o**		
6. **ungu/o**		
7. **lip/o**		
8. **hidr/o**		
9. **rhytid/o**		
10. **seb/o**		
11. **trich/o**		
12. **necr/o**		

C. Describe the Type of Burn

1. first degree _____

2. second degree _____

3. third degree _____

D. Terminology Matching

Match each term to its definition.

1. _____ eczema

2. _____ nevus

3. _____ lipoma

4. _____ urticaria

5. _____ bedsore

6. _____ acne rosacea

7. _____ acne vulgaris

8. _____ hirsutism

9. _____ alopecia

10. _____ gangrene

11. _____ scleroderma

12. _____ albinism

a. decubitus ulcer

b. lack of skin pigment

c. acne commonly seen in adults

d. hardened skin

e. redness, vesicles, itching, crusts

f. birthmark

g. excessive hair growth

h. caused by deficient blood supply

i. fatty tumor

j. hives

k. baldness

l. acne of adolescence

E. Define the Term

1. macule _____

2. papule _____

3. cyst _____

4. fissure _____

5. pustule _____

6. wheal _____

7. vesicle _____

8. ulcer _____

9. nodule _____

10. laceration _____

F. Combining Form Practice

The combining form **dermat/o** refers to the skin. Use it to write a term that means:

1. inflammation of the skin _____

2. any abnormal skin condition _____

3. an instrument for cutting the skin _____

4. specialist in skin _____

5. surgical repair of the skin _____

6. study of the skin _____

The combining form **melan/o** means black. Use it to write a term that means a:

7. black tumor _____

8. black cell _____

The suffix **-derma** means skin. Use it to write a term that means:

9. scaly skin _____

10. white skin _____

11. red skin _____

The combining form **onych/o** refers to the nail. Use it to write a term that means:

12. softening of the nails _____

13. infection around the nail _____

14. nail eating (biting) _____

15. removal of the nail _____

G. Procedure Matching

Match each procedure to its definition.

1.	_____ debridement	a.	surgical removal of wrinkled skin
2.	_____ cauterization	b.	instrument to cut thin slices of skin
3.	_____ chemabrasion	c.	removal of fat with suction
4.	_____ dermatoplasty	d.	use of extreme cold to destroy tissue
5.	_____ liposuction	e.	skin grafting
6.	_____ rhytidectomy	f.	removal of lesions with scraper
7.	_____ curettage	g.	removal of skin with brushes
8.	_____ dermabrasion	h.	removal of damaged skin
9.	_____ dermatome	i.	destruction of tissue with electric current
10.	_____ cryosurgery	j.	chemical peel

H. What's the Abbreviation?

1. frozen section _____

2. incision and drainage _____

3. intradermal _____

4. subcutaneous _____

5. ultraviolet _____

6. biopsy _____

I. What Does it Stand For?

1. C&S _____

2. BCC _____

3. derm _____

4. SG _____

5. decub _____

6. MM _____

J. Fill in the Blank

| impetigo | tinea | keloid | exfoliative cytology | xeroderma |
| petechiae | frozen section | paronychia | scabies | Kaposi's sarcoma |

1. The winter climates can cause dry skin. The medical term for this is _____ .

2. Kim has experienced small pinpoint purplish spots caused by bleeding under the skin. This is called _____ .

3. Janet has a fungal skin disease. This is called _____ .

4. A contagious skin disease caused by a mite is _____ .

5. An infection around the entire nail is called _____ .

6. A form of skin cancer affecting AIDS patients is called _____ .

7. Latrivia has a bacterial skin infection that results in pustules crusting and rupturing. It is called _____ .

8. James's burn scar became a hypertrophic _____ .

9. For a(n) _____ test, cells scraped off the skin are examined under a microscope.

10. During surgery a _____ was ordered for a rapid exam of tissue cut from a tumor.

K. Pharmacology Challenge

Fill in the classification for each drug description, then match the brand name.

Drug Description	Classification	Brand Name
1. _____ kills fungi	_____	a. Kwell
2. _____ reduces severe itching	_____	b. Cortaid
3. _____ kills mites and lice	_____	c. Valtrex
4. _____ treats herpes simplex infection	_____	d. Benadryl
5. _____ powerful anti-inflammatory	_____	e. Neosporin
6. _____ deadens pain	_____	f. Monistat
7. _____ kills bacteria	_____	g. Xylocaine

MEDICAL TERMINOLOGY INTERACTIVE

Medical Terminology Interactive is a premium online homework management system that includes a host of features to help you study. Registered users will find:

- Fun games and activities built within a virtual hospital
- Powerful tools that track and analyze your results—allowing you to create a personalized learning experience
- Videos, flashcards, and audio pronunciations to help enrich your progress
- Streaming video lesson presentations and self-paced learning modules

www.pearsonhighered.com/mti

Labeling Exercise

Image A

Write the labels for this figure on the numbered lines provided.

5. _____

6. _____

7. _____

8. _____

1. _____

2. _____

3. _____

9. _____

4. _____

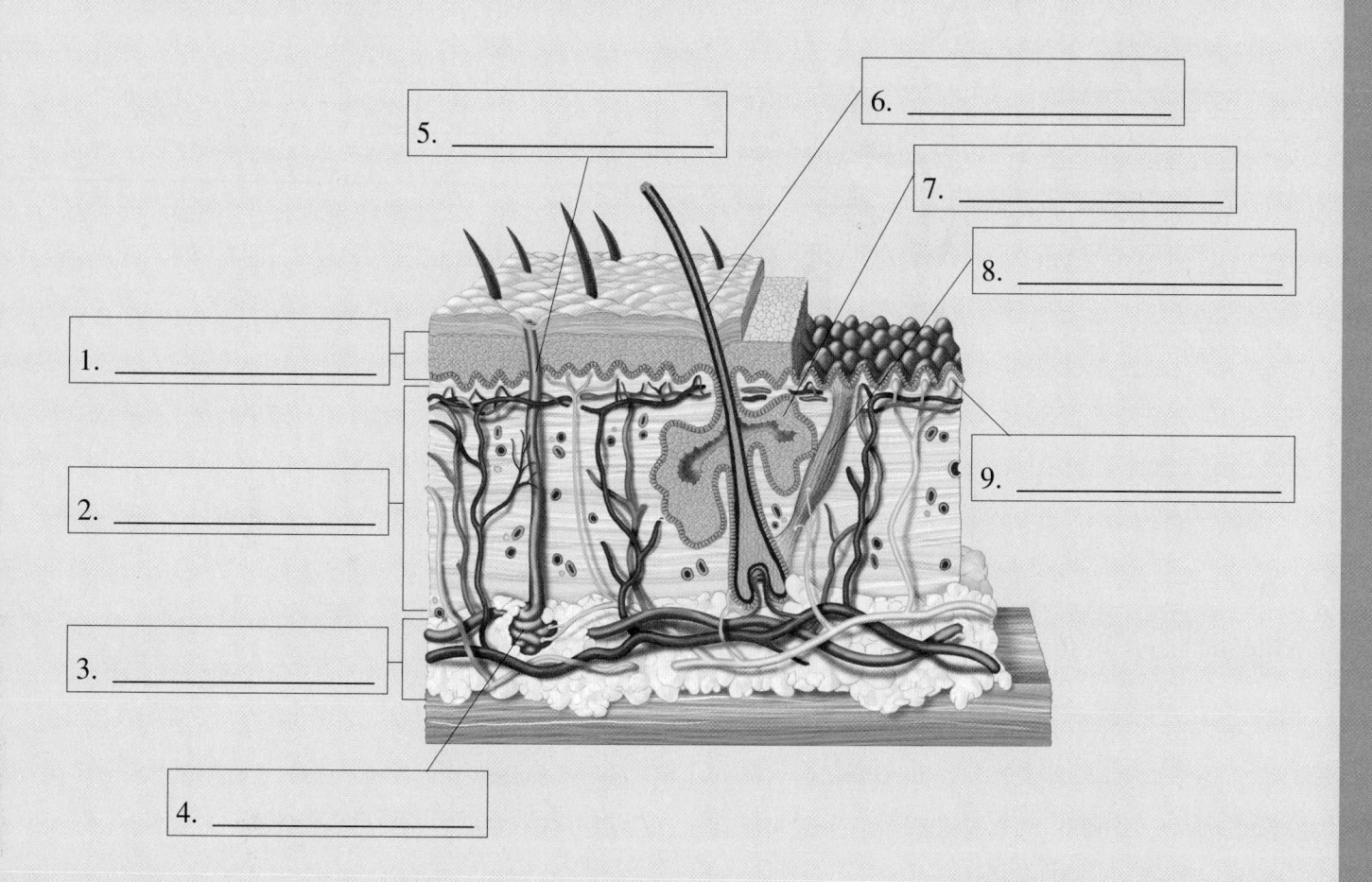

Image B

Write the labels for this figure on the numbered lines provided.

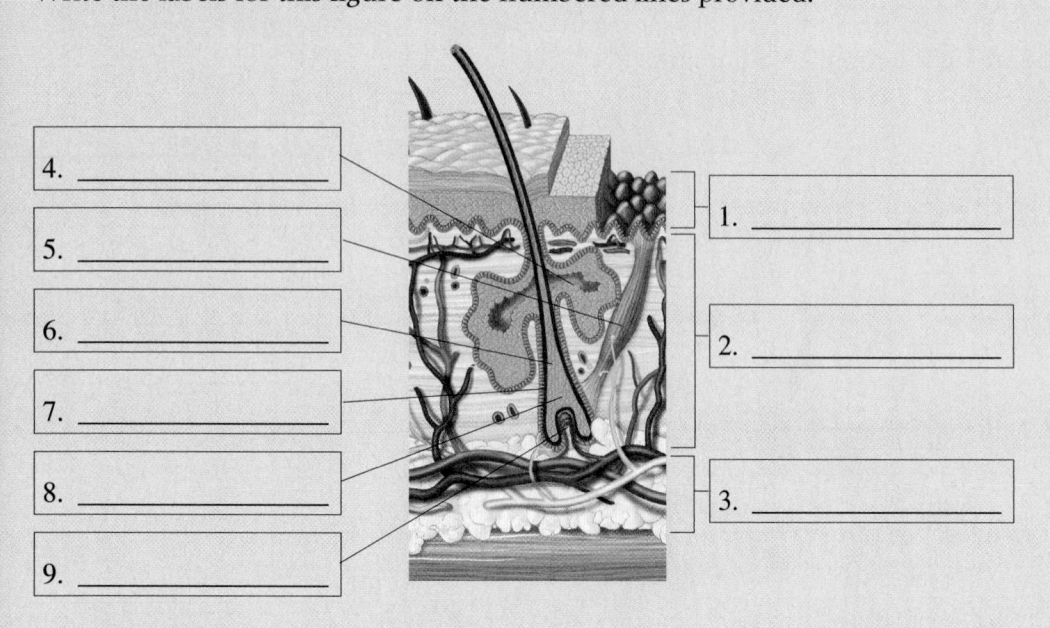

4. _____

5. _____

6. _____

7. _____

8. _____

9. _____

1. _____

2. _____

3. _____

Image C

Write the labels for this figure on the numbered lines provided.

1. _____

2. _____

3. _____

4. _____

5. _____

6. _____

7. _____

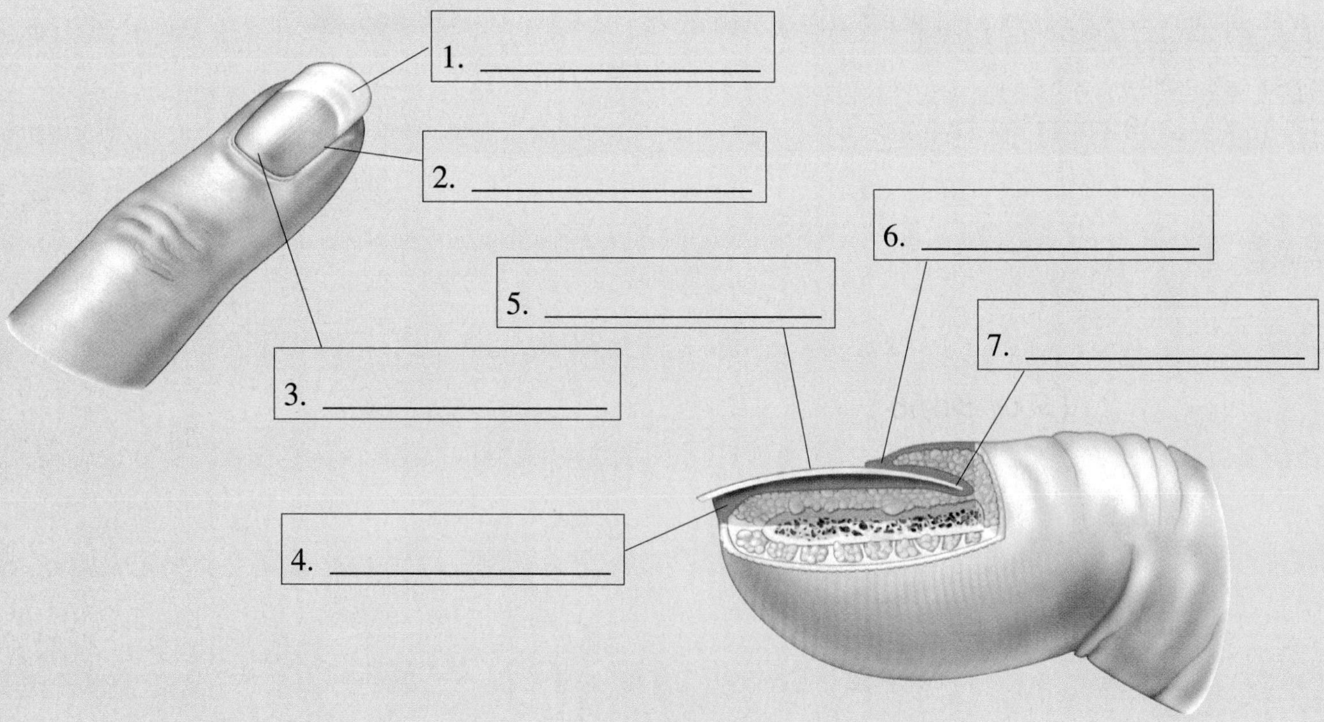

MUSCULOSKELETAL SYSTEM

4

Learning Objectives

Upon completion of this chapter, you will be able to

- Identify and define the combining forms, prefixes, and suffixes introduced in this chapter.

- Correctly spell and pronounce medical terms and major anatomical structures relating to the musculoskeletal system.

- Locate and describe the major organs of the musculoskeletal system and their functions.

- Correctly place bones in either the axial or the appendicular skeleton.

- List and describe the components of a long bone.

- Identify bony projections and depressions.

- Identify the parts of a synovial joint.

- Describe the characteristics of the three types of muscle tissue.

- Use movement terminology correctly.

- Identify and define musculoskeletal system anatomical terms.

- Identify and define selected musculoskeletal system pathology terms.

- Identify and define selected musculoskeletal system diagnostic procedures.

- Identify and define selected musculoskeletal system therapeutic procedures.

- Identify and define selected medications relating to the musculoskeletal system.

- Define selected abbreviations associated with the musculoskeletal system.

Section I: Skeletal System at a Glance

Function

The skeletal system consists of 206 bones that make up the internal framework of the body, called the skeleton. The skeleton supports the body, protects internal organs, serves as a point of attachment for skeletal muscles for body movement, produces blood cells, and stores minerals.

Organs

Here are the primary structures that comprise the skeletal system.

bones   joints

Word Parts

Here are the most common word parts (with their meanings) used to build skeletal system terms. For a more comprehensive list, refer to the Terminology section of this chapter.

Combining Forms

ankyl/o	stiff joint	myel/o	bone marrow, spinal cord
arthr/o	joint	orth/o	straight
articul/o	joint	oste/o	bone
burs/o	sac	patell/o	patella
carp/o	wrist	ped/o	child, foot
cervic/o	neck	pelv/o	pelvis
chondr/o	cartilage	phalang/o	phalanges
clavicul/o	clavicle	pod/o	foot
coccyg/o	coccyx	prosthet/o	addition
cortic/o	outer portion	pub/o	pubis
cost/o	rib	radi/o	radius, ray (X-ray)
crani/o	skull	sacr/o	sacrum
femor/o	femur	sarc/o	flesh (muscular substance)
fibul/o	fibula	scapul/o	scapula
humer/o	humerus	scoli/o	crooked, bent
ili/o	ilium	spin/o	spine
ischi/o	ischium	spondyl/o	vertebrae
kyph/o	hump	stern/o	sternum (breast bone)
lamin/o	lamina, part of vertebra	synovi/o	synovial membrane
lord/o	bent backwards	synov/o	synovial membrane
lumb/o	low back, loin	tars/o	ankle
mandibul/o	mandible	thorac/o	chest
maxill/o	maxilla	tibi/o	tibia
medull/o	inner portion	uln/o	ulna
metacarp/o	metacarpals	vertebr/o	vertebra
metatars/o	metatarsals		

Suffixes

-blast	immature, embryonic	-listhesis	slipping
-clasia	to surgically break	-porosis	porous
-desis	stabilize, fuse		

Skeletal System Illustrated

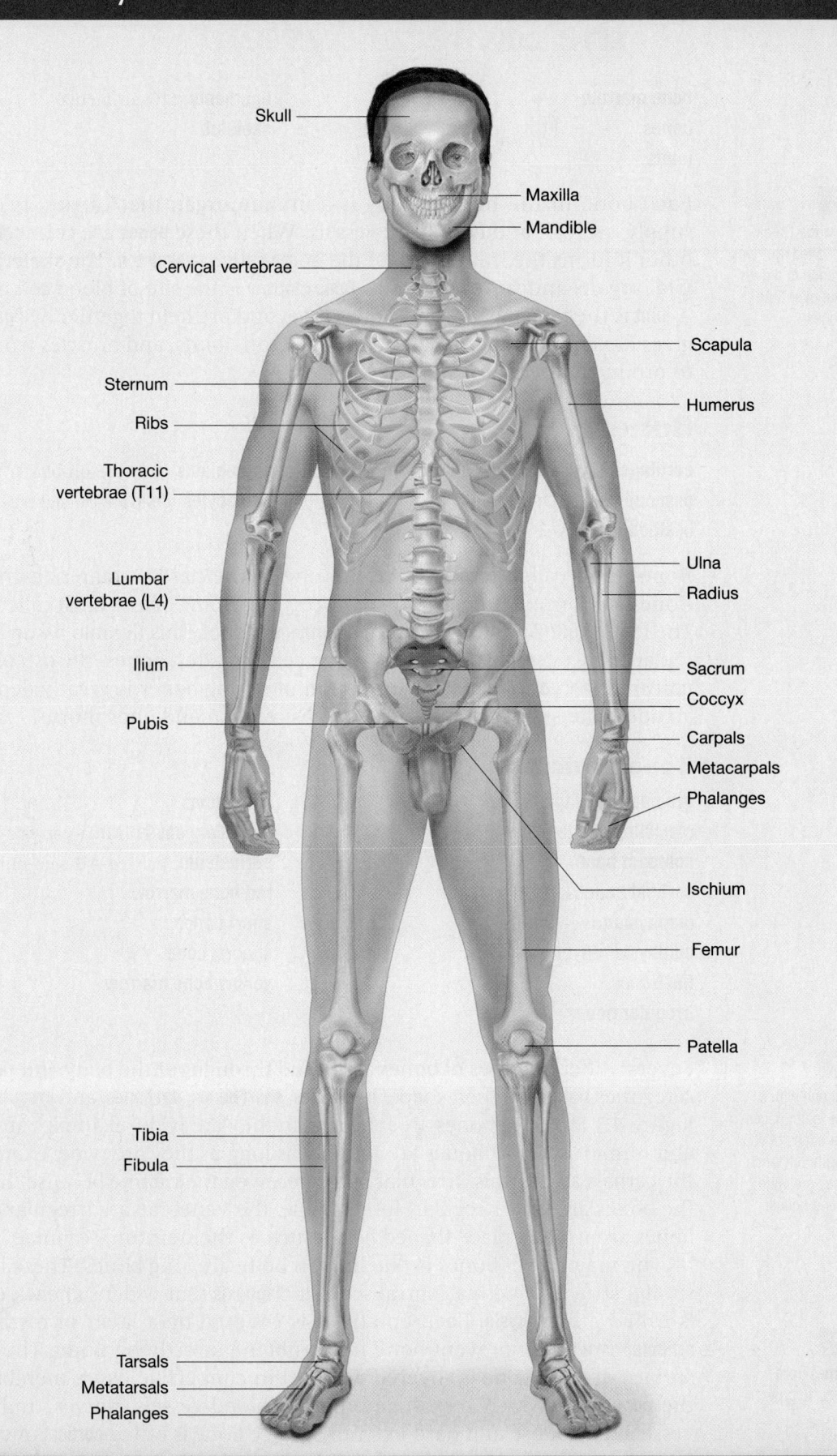

Skull

Maxilla

Mandible

Cervical vertebrae

Scapula

Sternum

Humerus

Ribs

Thoracic
vertebrae (T11)

Lumbar
vertebrae (L4)

Ulna

Radius

Ilium

Sacrum

Coccyx

Pubis

Carpals

Metacarpals

Phalanges

Ischium

Femur

Patella

Tibia

Fibula

Tarsals

Metatarsals

Phalanges

◼ Anatomy and Physiology of the Skeletal System

bone marrow	**ligaments** (LIG-ah-ments)
bones	**skeleton**
joints	

MED TERM TIP

The term *skeleton*, from the Greek word *skeltos* meaning "dried up," was originally used in reference to a dried-up mummified body, but over time came to be used for bones.

Each bone in the human body is a unique organ that carries its own blood supply, nerves, and lymphatic vessels. When these **bones** are connected to each other it forms the framework of the body called a **skeleton.** The skeleton protects vital organs and stores minerals. **Bone marrow** is the site of blood cell production. A **joint** is the place where two bones meet and are held together by **ligaments.** This gives flexibility to the skeleton. The skeleton, joints, and muscles work together to produce movement.

Bones

cartilage (CAR-tih-lij)	**osteoblasts** (OSS-tee-oh-blasts)
osseous tissue (OSS-ee-us)	**osteocytes** (OSS-tee-oh-sights)
ossification (oss-sih-fih-KAY-shun)	

Bones, also called **osseous tissue,** are one of the hardest materials in the body. Bones are formed from a gradual process beginning before birth called **ossification.** The fetal skeleton is formed from a **cartilage** model. This flexible tissue is gradually replaced by **osteoblasts,** immature bone cells. In adult bones, the osteoblasts have matured into **osteocytes.** The formation of strong bones is greatly dependent on an adequate supply of minerals such as calcium and phosphorus.

Bone Structure

articular cartilage (ar-TIK-yoo-lar)	**long bones**
cancellous bone (CAN-sell-us)	**medullary cavity** (MED-you-lair-ee)
compact bone	**periosteum** (pair-ee-AH-stee-um)
cortical bone (KOR-ti-kal)	**red bone marrow**
diaphysis (dye-AFF-ih-sis)	**short bones**
epiphysis (eh-PIFF-ih-sis)	**spongy bone**
flat bones	**yellow bone marrow**
irregular bones	

MED TERM TIP

Do not confuse a long bone with a large bone. A long bone is not necessarily a large bone. The bones of your fingers are short in length, but since they are longer than they are wide, they are classified as long bones.

Several different types of bones are found throughout the body and fall into four categories based on their shape: **long bones, short bones, flat bones,** and **irregular bones** (see Figure 4.1 ◼). Long bones are longer than they are wide; examples are the femur and humerus. Short bones are roughly as long as they are wide; examples being the carpals and tarsals. Irregular bones received their name because the shapes of the bones are very irregular; for example, the vertebrae are irregular bones. Flat bones are usually plate-shaped bones such as the sternum, scapulae, and pelvis.

The majority of bones in the human body are long bones. These bones have similar structure with a central shaft or **diaphysis** that widens at each end, which is called an **epiphysis.** Each epiphysis is covered by a layer of cartilage called **articular cartilage** to prevent bone from rubbing directly on bone. The remaining surface of each bone is covered with a thin connective tissue membrane called the **periosteum,** which contains numerous blood vessels, nerves, and lymphatic vessels. The dense and hard exterior surface bone is called **cortical** or **compact bone.** **Cancellous** or **spongy bone** is found inside the bone. As its name indicates, spongy

MED TERM TIP

The term *diaphysis* comes from the Greek term meaning "to grow between."

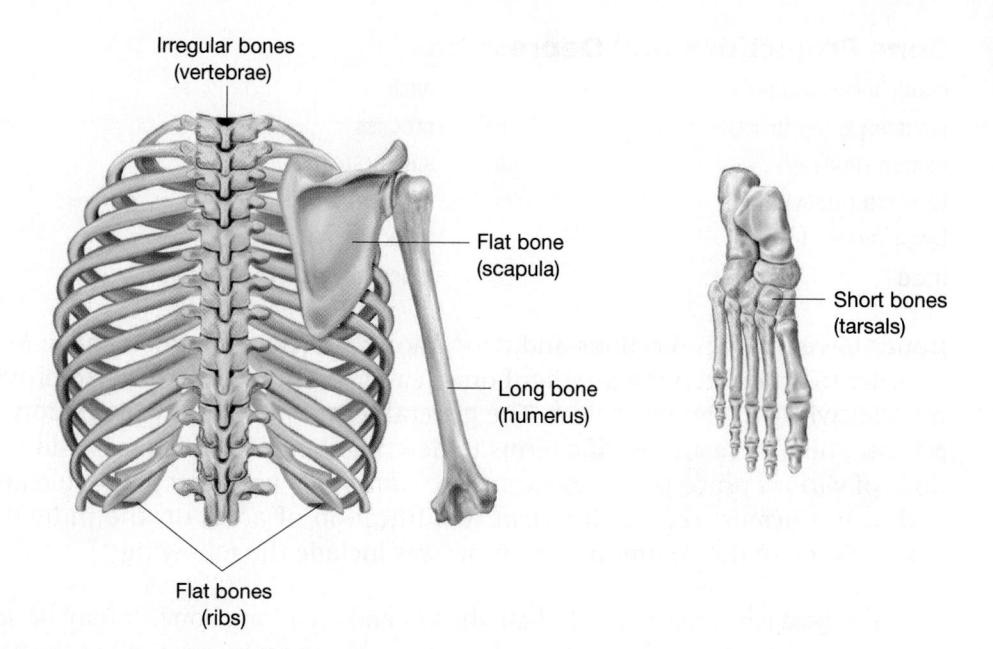

Irregular bones
(vertebrae)

Flat bone
(scapula)

Long bone
(humerus)

Short bones
(tarsals)

Flat bones
(ribs)

bone has spaces in it, giving it a spongelike appearance. These spaces contain **red bone marrow,** which manufactures most of the blood cells and is found in some parts of all bones.

The center of the diaphysis contains an open canal called the **medullary cavity.** Early in life this cavity also contains red bone marrow, but as we age the red bone marrow of the medullary cavity gradually converts to **yellow bone marrow,** which consists primarily of fat cells. Figure 4.2 ■ contains an illustration of the structure of long bones.

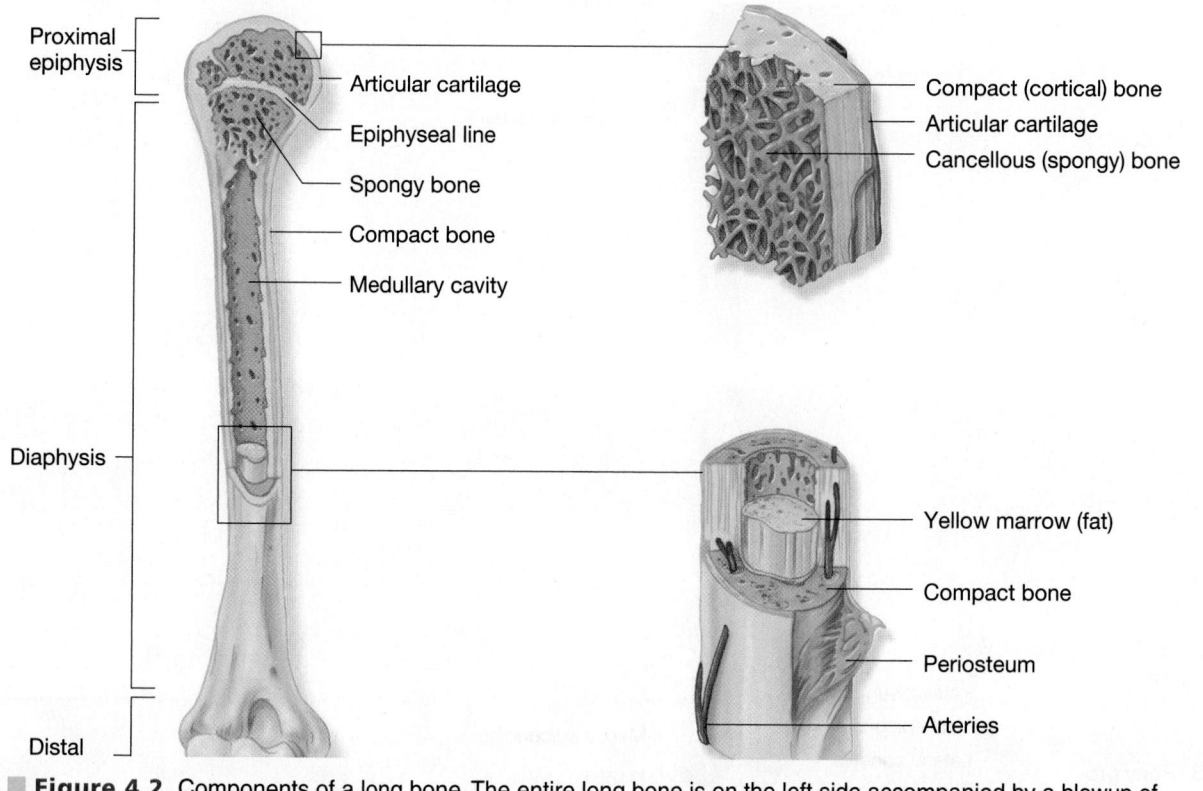

Proximal
epiphysis

Articular cartilage

Epiphyseal line

Spongy bone

Compact bone

Medullary cavity

Compact (cortical) bone
Articular cartilage
Cancellous (spongy) bone

Diaphysis

Yellow marrow (fat)

Compact bone

Periosteum

Arteries

Distal

■ **Figure 4.2** Components of a long bone. The entire long bone is on the left side accompanied by a blowup of the proximal epiphysis and a section of the diaphysis.

Bone Projections and Depressions

condyle (KON-dile)   **neck**

epicondyle (ep-ih-KON-dile)   **process**

fissure (FISH-er)   **sinus** (SIGH-nus)

foramen (for-AY-men)   **trochanter** (tro-KAN-ter)

fossa (FOSS-ah)   **tubercle** (TOO-ber-kl)

head   **tuberosity** (too-ber-OSS-ih-tee)

> **MED TERM TIP**
>
> The elbow, commonly referred to as the *funny bone*, is actually a projection of the ulna called the olecranon process.

Bones have many projections and depressions; some are rounded and smooth in order to articulate with another bone in a joint. Others are rough to provide muscles with attachment points. The general term for any bony projection is a **process**. Then there are specific terms to describe the different shapes and locations of various processes. These terms are commonly used on operative reports and in physicians' records for clear identification of areas on the individual bones. Some of the common bony processes include the following:

1. The **head** is a large, smooth, ball-shaped end on a long bone. It may be separated from the body or shaft of the bone by a narrow area called the **neck**.
2. A **condyle** refers to a smooth, rounded portion at the end of a bone.
3. The **epicondyle** is a projection located above or on a condyle.
4. The **trochanter** refers to a large rough process for the attachment of a muscle.
5. A **tubercle** is a small, rough process that provides the attachment for tendons and muscles.
6. The **tuberosity** is a large, rough process that provides the attachment of tendons and muscles.

See Figure 4.3 ■ for an illustration of the processes found on the femur.

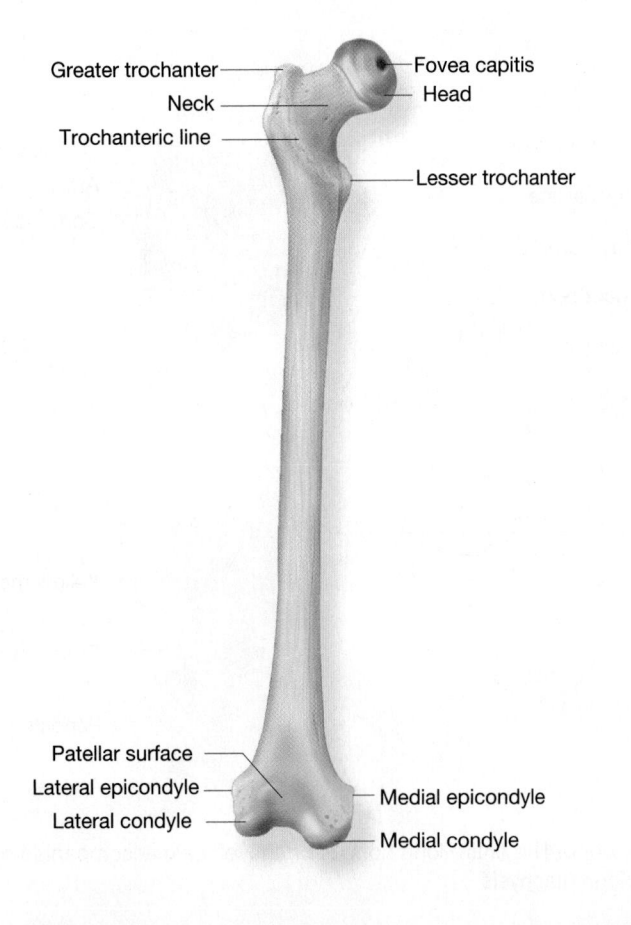

Greater trochanter —
Neck —
Trochanteric line —
Fovea capitis
Head
Lesser trochanter
Patellar surface —
Lateral epicondyle —
Lateral condyle —
Medial epicondyle
Medial condyle

■ **Figure 4.3** Bony processes found on the femur.

Additionally, bones have hollow regions or depressions. The most common depressions are the:

1. **Sinus** is a hollow cavity within a bone.
2. **Foramen** is a smooth, round opening for nerves and blood vessels.
3. **Fossa** consists of a shallow cavity or depression on the surface of a bone.
4. **Fissure** is a slit-type opening.

Skeleton

appendicular skeleton (app-en-DIK-yoo-lar)   **axial skeleton** (AK-see-al)

The human skeleton has two divisions: the **axial skeleton** and the **appendicular skeleton.** Figures 4.4 and 4.8 illustrate the axial and appendicular skeletons.

MED TERM TIP

Newborn infants have about 300 bones at birth that will fuse into 206 bones as an adult.

Axial Skeleton

cervical vertebrae

coccyx (COCK-six)

cranium (KRAY-nee-um)

ethmoid bone (ETH-moyd)

facial bones

frontal bone

hyoid bone (HIGH-oyd)

intervertebral disc (in-ter-VER-teh-bral)

lacrimal bone (LACK-rim-al)

lumbar vertebrae

mandible (MAN-dih-bl)

maxilla (mack-SIH-lah)

nasal bone

occipital bone (ock-SIP-eh-tal)

palatine bone (PAL-ah-tine)

parietal bone (pah-RYE-eh-tal)

rib cage

sacrum (SAY-crum)

sphenoid bone (SFEE-noyd)

sternum (STER-num)

temporal bone (TEM-por-al)

thoracic vertebrae

vertebral column (VER-teh-bral)

vomer bone (VOH-mer)

zygomatic bone (zeye-go-MAT-ik)

The axial skeleton includes the bones of the head, neck, spine, chest, and trunk of the body (see Figure 4.4 ■). These bones form the central axis for the whole body and protect many of the internal organs such as the brain, lungs, and heart.

The head or skull is divided into two parts consisting of the **cranium** and **facial bones.** These bones surround and protect the brain, eyes, ears, nasal cavity, and oral cavity from injury. The muscles for chewing and moving the head are attached to the cranial bones. The cranium encases the brain and consists of the **frontal, parietal, temporal, ethmoid, sphenoid,** and **occipital bones.** The facial bones surround the mouth, nose, and eyes and include the **mandible, maxilla, zygomatic, vomer, palatine, nasal,** and **lacrimal bones.** The cranial and facial bones are illustrated in Figure 4.5 ■ and described in Table 4.1 ■.

The **hyoid bone** is a single U-shaped bone suspended in the neck between the mandible and larynx. It is a point of attachment for swallowing and speech muscles.

Figure 4.4 Bones of the axial skeleton.

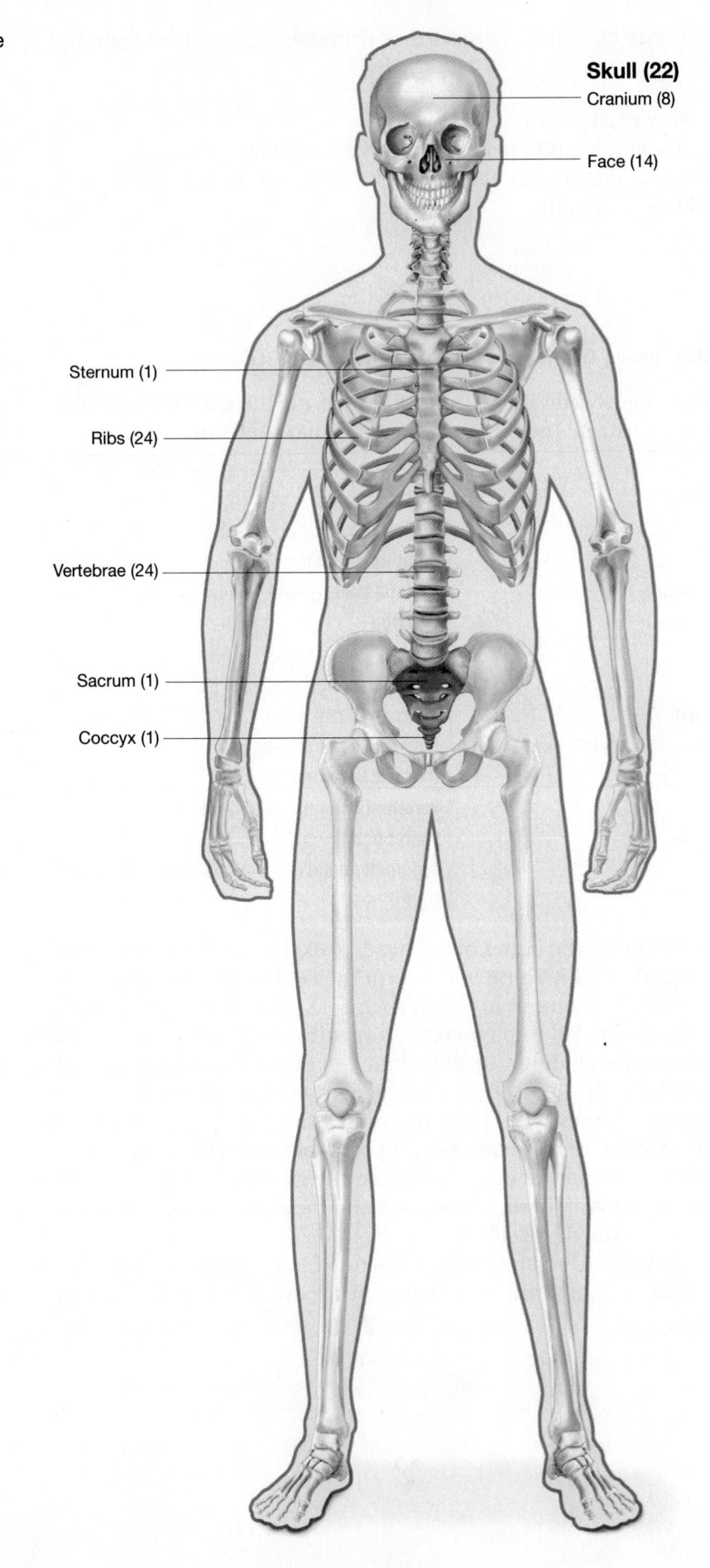

Skull (22)
Cranium (8)
Face (14)

Sternum (1)

Ribs (24)

Vertebrae (24)

Sacrum (1)

Coccyx (1)

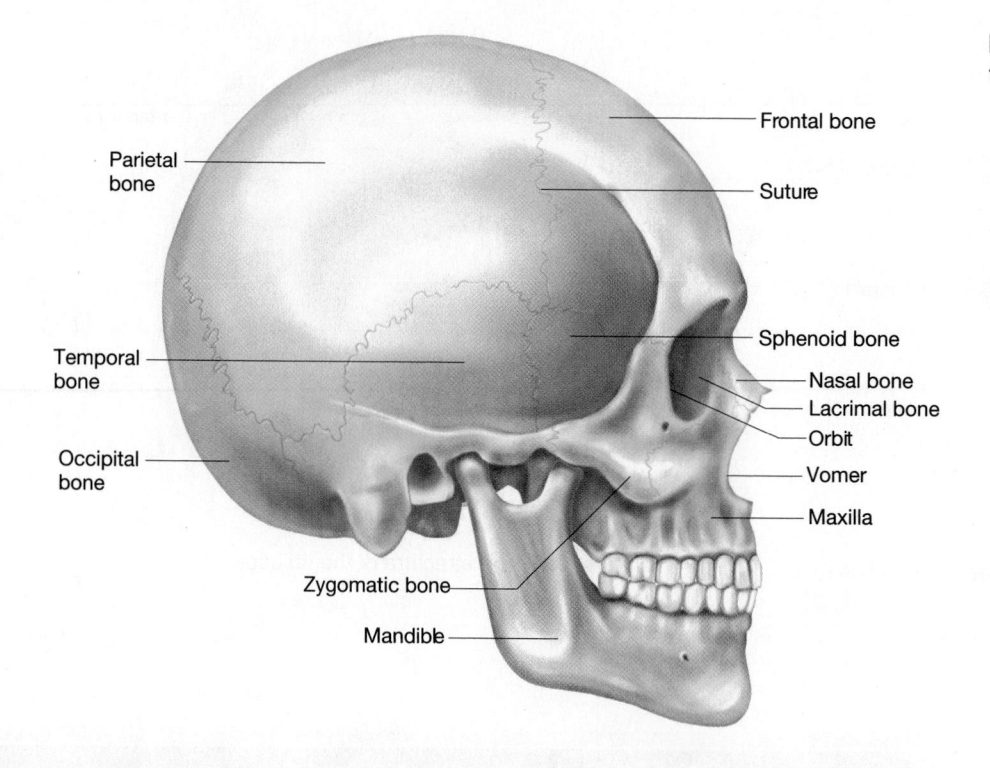

Table 4.1		Bones of the Skull
NAME	**NUMBER**	**DESCRIPTION**
Cranial Bones		
Frontal bone	1	Forehead
Parietal bone	2	Upper sides of cranium and roof of skull
Occipital bone	1	Back and base of skull
Temporal bone	2	Sides and base of cranium
Sphenoid bone	1	Bat-shaped bone that forms part of the base of the skull, floor, and sides of eye orbit
Ethmoid bone	1	Forms part of eye orbit, nose, and floor of cranium
Facial Bones		
Lacrimal bone	2	Inner corner of each eye
Nasal bone	2	Form part of nasal septum and support bridge of nose
Maxilla	1	Upper jaw
Mandible	1	Lower jawbone; only movable bone of the skull
Zygomatic bone	2	Cheekbones
Vomer bone	1	Base of nasal septum
Palatine bone	1	Hard palate (PAH lat) roof of oral cavity and floor of nasal cavity

The trunk of the body consists of the **vertebral column, sternum,** and **rib cage.** The vertebral or spinal column is divided into five sections: **cervical vertebrae, thoracic vertebrae, lumbar vertebrae, sacrum,** and **coccyx** (see Figure 4.6 ■ and Table 4.2 ■). Located between each pair of vertebrae, from the cervical through the lumbar regions, is an **intervertebral disc.** Each disc is composed of fibrocartilage to provide a cushion between the vertebrae. The rib cage has twelve pairs of ribs attached at the back to the vertebral column. Ten of the pairs are also attached to the sternum in the front (see Figure 4.7 ■). The lowest two pairs are called *floating ribs* and are attached only to the vertebral column. The rib cage serves to provide support for organs, such as the heart and lungs.

MED TERM TIP

The term *coccyx* comes from the Greek word for the cuckoo because the shape of these small bones extending off the sacrum resembles this bird's bill.

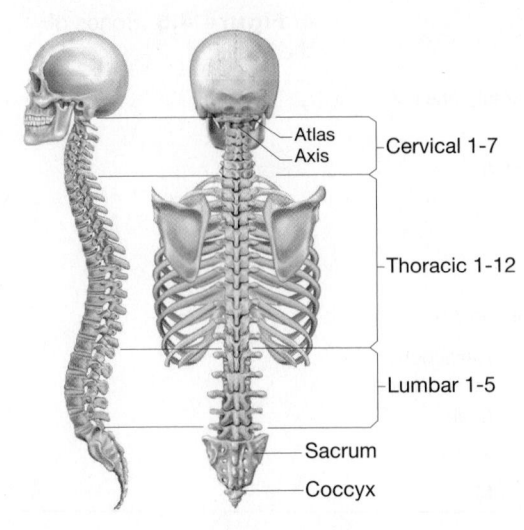

Figure 4.6 Divisions of the vertebral column.

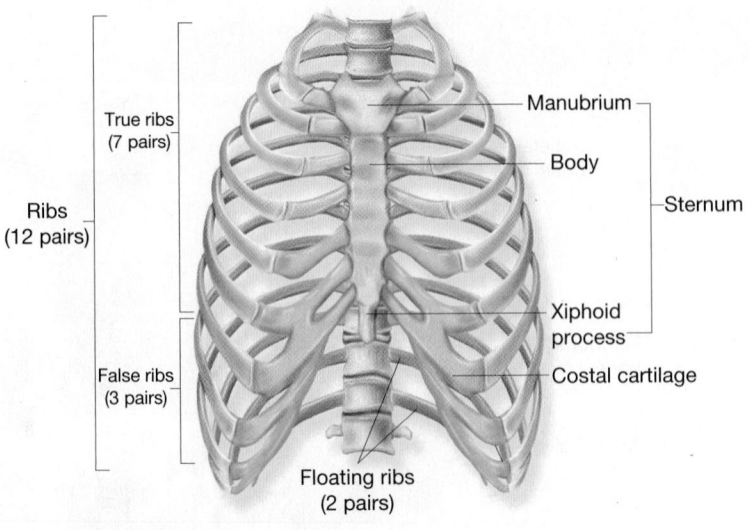

Figure 4.7 The structure of the rib cage.

Table 4.2	Bones of the Vertebral/Spinal Column	
NAME	**NUMBER**	**DESCRIPTION**
Cervical vertebra	7	Vertebrae in the neck region
Thoracic vertebra	12	Vertebrae in the chest region with ribs attached
Lumbar vertebra	5	Vertebrae in the small of the back, about waist level
Sacrum	1	Five vertebrae that become fused into one triangular-shaped flat bone at the base of the vertebral column
Coccyx	1	Three to five very small vertebrae attached to the sacrum, often become fused

Appendicular Skeleton

carpals (CAR-pals)
clavicle (CLAV-ih-kl)
femur (FEE-mer)
fibula (FIB-yoo-lah)
humerus (HYOO-mer-us)
ilium (ILL-ee-um)
innominate bone (ih-NOM-ih-nayt)
ischium (ISS-kee-um)
lower extremities
metacarpals (met-ah-CAR-pals)
metatarsals (met-ah-TAHR-sals)
os coxae (OSS / KOK-sigh)

patella (pah-TELL-ah)
pectoral girdle
pelvic girdle
phalanges (fah-LAN-jeez)
pubis (PYOO-bis)
radius (RAY-dee-us)
scapula (SKAP-yoo-lah)
tarsals (TAHR-sals)
tibia (TIB-ee-ah)
ulna (UHL-nah)
upper extremities

MED TERM TIP

The term *girdle,* meaning something that encircles or confines, refers to the entire bony structure of the shoulder and the pelvis. If just one bone from these areas is being discussed, like the ilium of the pelvis, it would be named as such. If, however, the entire pelvis is being discussed, it would be called the pelvic girdle.

The appendicular skeleton consists of the **pectoral girdle, upper extremities, pelvic girdle, and lower extremities** (see Figure 4.8 ■). These are the bones for our appendages or limbs and along with the muscles attached to them, they are responsible for body movement.

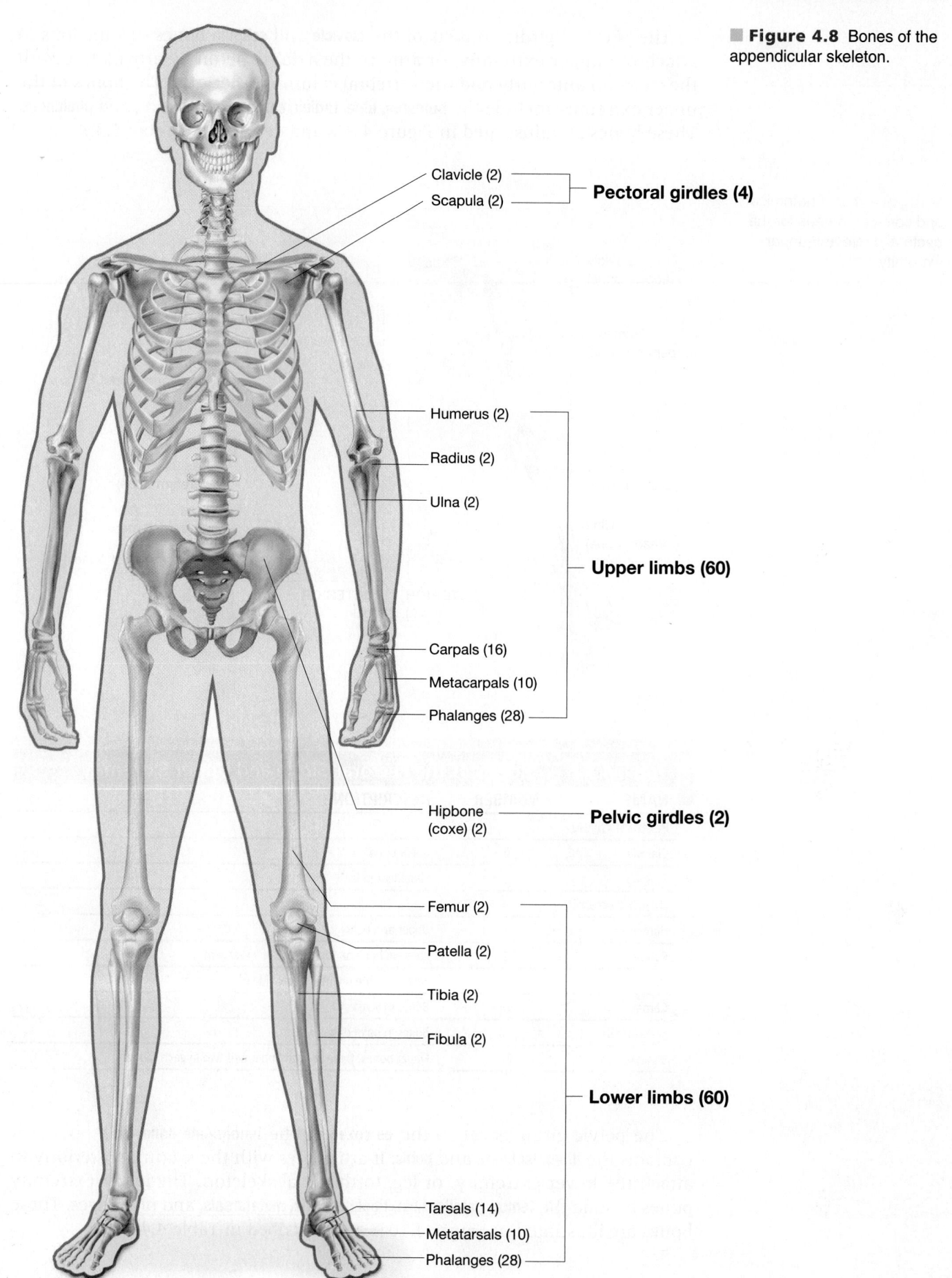

Clavicle (2)
Scapula (2)

Pectoral girdles (4)

Humerus (2)

Radius (2)

Ulna (2)

Upper limbs (60)

Carpals (16)

Metacarpals (10)

Phalanges (28)

Hipbone (coxe) (2)

Pelvic girdles (2)

Femur (2)

Patella (2)

Tibia (2)

Fibula (2)

Lower limbs (60)

Tarsals (14)

Metatarsals (10)

Phalanges (28)

The pectoral girdle consists of the **clavicle** and **scapula** bones. It functions to attach the upper extremity, or arm, to the axial skeleton by articulating with the sternum anteriorly and the vertebral column posteriorly. The bones of the upper extremity include the **humerus, ulna, radius, carpals, metacarpals,** and **phalanges.** These bones are illustrated in Figure 4.9 ■ and described in Table 4.3 ■.

■ **Figure 4.9** Anatomical and common names for the pectoral girdle and upper extremity.

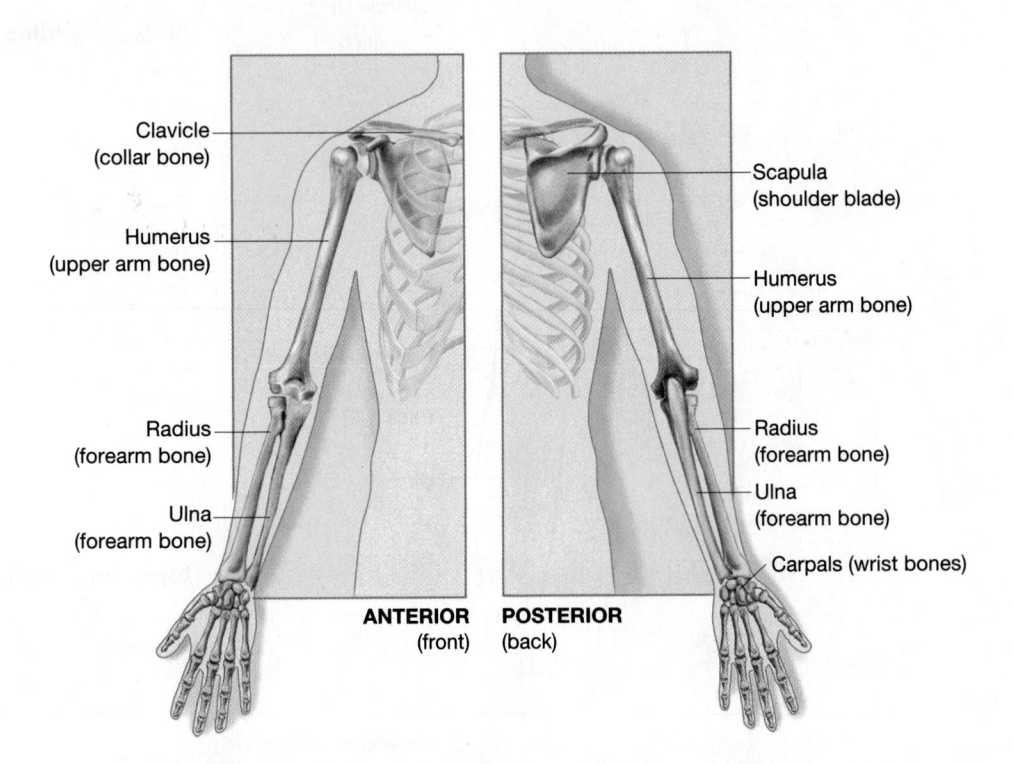

Table 4.3		Bones of the Pectoral Girdle and Upper Extremity
NAME	**NUMBER**	**DESCRIPTION**
Pectoral Girdle		
Clavicle	2	Collar bone
Scapula	2	Shoulder blade
Upper Extremity		
Humerus	2	Upper arm bone
Radius	2	Forearm bone on thumb side of lower arm
Ulna	2	Forearm bone on little finger side of lower arm
Carpal	16	Bones of wrist
Metacarpals	10	Bones in palm of hand
Phalanges	28	Finger bones; three in each finger and two in each thumb

The pelvic girdle is called the **os coxae** or the **innominate bone** or hipbone. It contains the **ilium, ischium,** and **pubis.** It articulates with the sacrum posteriorly to attach the lower extremity, or leg, to the axial skeleton. The lower extremity bones include the **femur, patella, tibia, fibula, tarsals, metatarsals,** and phalanges. These bones are illustrated in Figure 4.10 ■ and described in Table 4.4 ■.

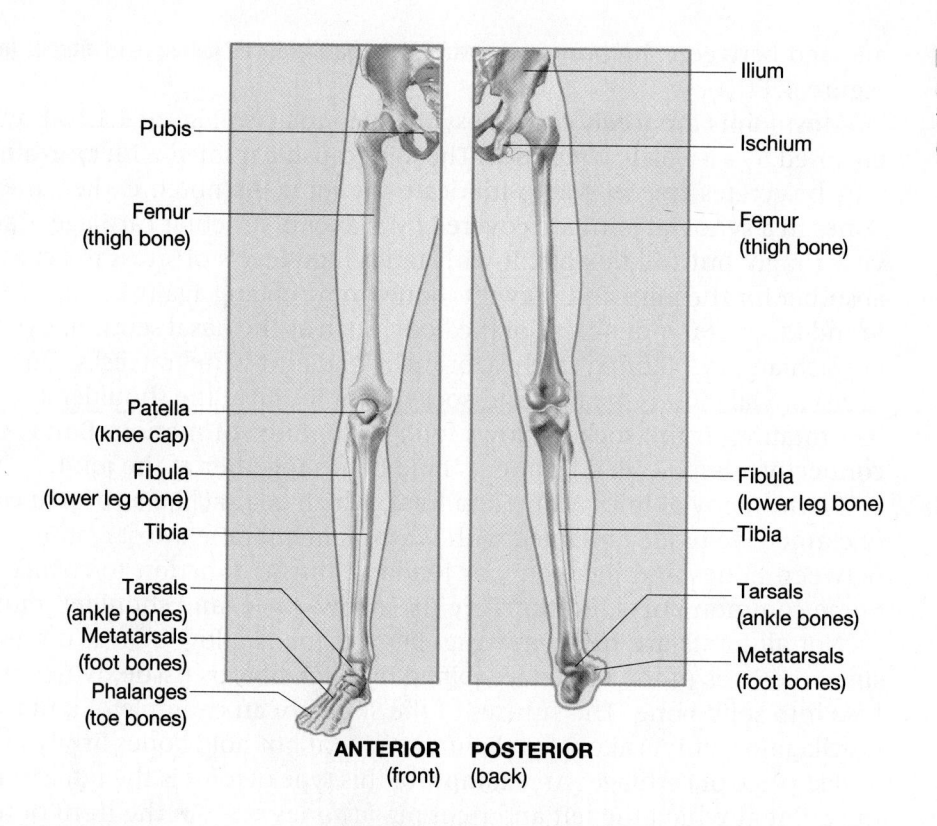

Pubis

Femur
(thigh bone)

Patella
(knee cap)

Fibula
(lower leg bone)

Tibia

Tarsals
(ankle bones)
Metatarsals
(foot bones)
Phalanges
(toe bones)

Ilium

Ischium

Femur
(thigh bone)

Fibula
(lower leg bone)

Tibia

Tarsals
(ankle bones)

Metatarsals
(foot bones)

ANTERIOR   **POSTERIOR**
(front)   (back)

Table 4.4	Bones of the Pelvic Girdle and Lower Extremity	
NAME	**NUMBER**	**DESCRIPTION**
Pelvic Girdle/Os Coxae		
Ilium	2	Part of the hipbone
Ischium	2	Part of the hipbone
Pubis	2	Part of the hipbone
Lower Extremity		
Femur	2	Upper leg bone; thigh bone
Patella	2	Knee cap
Tibia	2	Shin bone; thicker lower leg bone
Fibula	2	Thinner, long bone in lateral side of lower leg
Tarsals	14	Ankle and heel bones
Metatarsals	10	Forefoot bones
Phalanges	28	Toe bones; three in each toe and two in each great toe

Joints

articulation (ar-tik-yoo-LAY-shun)
bursa (BER-sah)
cartilaginous joints (car-tih-LAJ-ih-nus)
fibrous joints (FYE-bruss)

joint capsule
synovial fluid
synovial joint (sin-OH-vee-al)
synovial membrane

Joints are formed when two or more bones meet. This is also referred to as an **articulation.** There are three types of joints based on the amount of movement allowed between the bones: **synovial joints, cartilaginous joints,** and **fibrous joints** (see Figure 4.11 ■).

Most joints are freely moving synovial joints (see Figure 4.12 ■), which are enclosed by an elastic **joint capsule.** The joint capsule is lined with **synovial membrane,** which secretes **synovial fluid** to lubricate the joint. As noted earlier, the ends of bones in a synovial joint are covered by a layer of articular cartilage. Cartilage is very tough, but still flexible. It withstands high levels of stress to act as a shock absorber for the joint and prevents bone from rubbing against bone. Cartilage is found in several other areas of the body, such as the nasal septum, external ear, eustachian tube, larynx, trachea, bronchi, and intervertebral disks. One example of a synovial joint is the ball-and-socket joint found at the shoulder and hip. The ball rotating in the socket allows for a wide range of motion. Bands of strong connective tissue called ligaments bind bones together at the joint.

Some synovial joints contain a **bursa,** which is a saclike structure composed of connective tissue and lined with synovial membrane. Most commonly found between bones and ligaments or tendons, bursas function to reduce friction. Some common bursa locations are the elbow, knee, and shoulder joints.

Not all joints are freely moving. Fibrous joints allow almost no movement since the ends of the bones are joined by thick fibrous tissue, which may even fuse into solid bone. The sutures of the skull are an example of a fibrous joint. Cartilaginous joints allow for slight movement but hold bones firmly in place by a solid piece of cartilage. An example of this type of joint is the pubic symphysis, the point at which the left and right pubic bones meet in the front of the lower abdomen.

MED TERM TIP

Bursitis is an inflammation of the bursa located between bony prominences such as at the shoulder. Housemaid's knee, a term thought to have originated from the damage to the knees that occurred when maids knelt to scrub floors, is a form of bursitis and carries the medical name *prepatellar bursitis*.

Skull

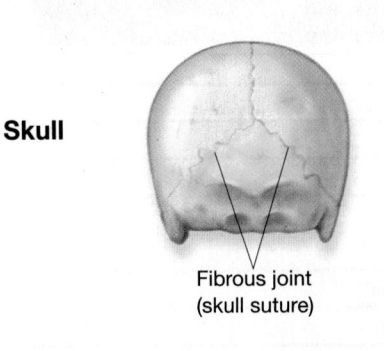

Fibrous joint
(skull suture)

Pelvis

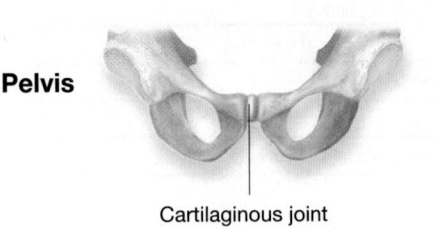

Cartilaginous joint

Hand

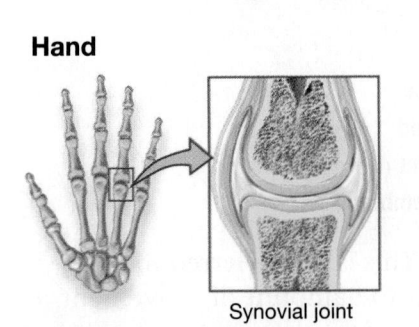

Synovial joint

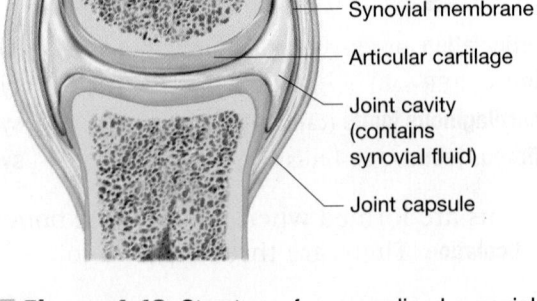

Medullary cavity

Periosteum

Spongy bone

Compact bone

Synovial membrane

Articular cartilage

Joint cavity
(contains
synovial fluid)

Joint capsule

■ **Figure 4.11** Examples of three types of joints found in the body.

■ **Figure 4.12** Structure of a generalized synovial joint.

■ Terminology

Word Parts Used to Build Skeletal System Terms

The following lists contain the combining forms, suffixes, and prefixes used to build terms in the remaining sections of this chapter.

Combining Forms

ankyl/o	stiff joint	**kyph/o**	hump	**prosthet/o**	addition
arthr/o	joint	**lamin/o**	lamina, part of vertebra	**pub/o**	pubis
articul/o	joint	**lord/o**	bent backwards	**radi/o**	radius, ray (X-ray)
burs/o	bursa	**lumb/o**	low back	**sacr/o**	sacrum
carp/o	carpus	**mandibul/o**	mandible	**sarc/o**	flesh
cervic/o	neck	**maxill/o**	maxilla	**scapul/o**	scapula
chondr/o	cartilage	**medull/o**	inner portion	**scoli/o**	crooked, bent
clavicul/o	clavicle	**metacarp/o**	metacarpus	**spin/o**	spine
coccyg/o	coccyx	**metatars/o**	metatarsus	**spondyl/o**	vertebra
cortic/o	outer portion	**myel/o**	bone marrow	**stern/o**	sternum
cost/o	rib	**orth/o**	straight	**synovi/o**	synovial membrane
crani/o	skull	**oste/o**	bone	**synov/o**	synovial membrane
cutane/o	skin	**patell/o**	patella	**system/o**	system
erythr/o	red	**path/o**	disease	**tars/o**	tarsus
femor/o	femur	**ped/o**	child, foot	**thorac/o**	thorax
fibul/o	fibula	**pelv/o**	pelvis	**tibi/o**	tibia
humer/o	humerus	**phalang/o**	phalanges	**uln/o**	ulna
ili/o	ilium	**pod/o**	foot	**vertebr/o**	vertebra
ischi/o	ischium				

Suffixes

-ac	pertaining to	-gram	record	-otomy	cutting into
-al	pertaining to	-graphy	process of recording	-ous	pertaining to
-algia	pain	-iatry	medical treatment	-pathy	disease
-ar	pertaining to	-ic	pertaining to	-plasty	surgical repair
-ary	pertaining to	-itis	inflammation	-porosis	porous
-centesis	puncture to withdraw fluid	-listhesis	slipping	-scope	instrument for viewing
-clasia	surgically break	-logy	study	-scopy	process of visually examining
-desis	fuse	-malacia	softening	-stenosis	narrowing
-eal	pertaining to	-metry	process of measuring	-tic	pertaining to
-ectomy	surgical removal	-oma	tumor	-tome	instrument used to cut
-genic	producing	-ory	pertaining to		
		-osis	abnormal condition		

Prefixes

anti-	against
bi-	two
ex-	external, outward

inter-	between
intra-	inside

per-	through
sub-	below, under

Anatomical Terms

TERM	WORD PARTS	DEFINITION
articular (ar-TIK-yoo-lar)	articul/o = joint -ar = pertaining to	pertaining to a joint
carpal (CAR-pal)	carp/o = carpus -al = pertaining to	pertaining to the carpus
cervical (CER-vih-kal)	cervic/o = neck -al = pertaining to	pertaining to the neck
clavicular (cla-VIK-yoo-lar)	clavicul/o = clavicle -ar = pertaining to	pertaining to the clavicle
coccygeal (cock-eh-JEE-all)	coccyg/o = coccyx -eal = pertaining to	pertaining to the coccyx
cortical (KOR-ti-kal)	cortic/o = outer portion -al = petaining to	pertaining to the outer portion
costal (COAST-all)	cost/o = rib -al = pertaining to	pertaining to the rib
cranial (KRAY-nee-all)	crani/o = skull -al = pertaining to	pertaining to the skull
femoral (FEM-or-all)	femor/o = femur -al = pertaining to	pertaining to the femur
fibular (FIB-yoo-lar)	fibul/o = fibula -ar = pertaining to	pertaining to the fibula
humeral (HYOO-mer-all)	humer/o = humerus -al = pertaining to	pertaining to the humerus
iliac (ILL-ee-ack)	ili/o = ilium -ac = pertaining to	pertaining to the ilium
intervertebral (in-ter-VER-teh-bral)	inter- = between vertebr/o = vertebra -al = pertaining to	pertaining to between vertebrae
intracranial (in-trah-KRAY-nee-al)	intra- = inside crani/o = skull -al = pertaining to	pertaining to inside the skull
ischial (ISH-ee-all)	ischi/o = ischium -al = pertaining to	pertaining to the ischium
lumbar (LUM-bar)	lumb/o = low back -ar = pertaining to	pertaining to the low back
mandibular (man-DIB-yoo-lar)	mandibul/o = mandible -ar = pertaining to	pertaining to the mandible
maxillary (mack-sih-LAIR-ree)	maxill/o = maxilla -ary = pertaining to	pertaining to the maxilla

Anatomical Terms *(continued)*

TERM	WORD PARTS	DEFINITION
medullary (MED-you-lair-ee)	medull/o = inner portion -ary = pertaining to	pertaining to the inner portion
metacarpal (met-ah-CAR-pal)	metacarp/o = metacarpus -al = pertaining to	pertaining to the metacarpus
metatarsal (met-ah-TAHR-sal)	metatars/o = metatarsus -al = pertaining to	pertaining to the metatarsus
patellar (pa-TELL-ar)	patell/o = patella -ar = pertaining to	pertaining to the patella
pelvic (PEL-vik)	pelv/o = pelvis -ic = pertaining to	pertaining to the pelvis
phalangeal (fay-lan-JEE-all)	phalang/o = phalanges -eal = pertaining to	pertaining to the phalanges
pubic (PYOO-bik)	pub/o = pubis -ic = pertaining to	pertaining to the pubis
radial (RAY-dee-all)	radi/o = radius -al = pertaining to	pertaining to the radius
sacral (SAY-kral)	sacr/o = sacrum -al = pertaining to	pertaining to the sacrum
scapular (SKAP-yoo-lar)	scapul/o = scapula -ar = pertaining to	pertaining to the scapula
sternal (STER-nal)	stern/o = sternum -al = pertaining to	pertaining to the sternum
synovial (sin-OH-vee-al)	synovi/o = synovial membrane -al = pertaining to	pertaining to the synovial membrane
tarsal (TAHR-sal)	tars/o = tarsus -al = pertaining to	pertaining to the tarsus
thoracic (tho-RASS-ik)	thorac/o = thorax -ic = pertaining to	pertaining to the thorax
tibial (TIB-ee-all)	tibi/o = tibia -al = pertaining to	pertaining to the tibia
ulnar (UHL-nar)	uln/o = ulna -ar = pertaining to	pertaining to the ulna

Pathology

TERM	WORD PARTS	DEFINITION
Medical Specialties		
chiropractic (ki-roh-PRAK-tik)	-tic = pertaining to	Healthcare profession concerned with diagnosis and treatment of malalignment conditions of the spine and musculoskeletal system with the intention of affecting the nervous system and improving health. Healthcare professional is a *chiropractor*.

◼◻ Pathology *(continued)*

TERM	WORD PARTS	DEFINITION
orthopedics (or-thoh-PEE-diks)	orth/o = straight ped/o = child, foot -ic = pertaining to	Branch of medicine specializing in the diagnosis and treatment of conditions of the musculoskeletal system; also called *orthopedic surgery*. Physician is an *orthopedist* or *orthopedic surgeon*. Name derived from straightening (*orth/o*) deformities in children (*ped/o*).
orthotics (or-THOT-iks)	orth/o = straight -tic = pertaining to	Healthcare profession specializing in making orthopedic appliances such as braces and splints. Person skilled in making and adjusting these appliances is an *orthotist*.
podiatry (po-DYE-ah-tree)	pod/o = foot -iatry = medical treatment	Healthcare profession specializing in diagnosis and treatment of disorders of the feet and lower legs. Healthcare professional is a *podiatrist*.
prosthetics (pross-THET-iks)	prosthet/o = addition -ic = pertaining to	Healthcare profession specializing in making artificial body parts. Person skilled in making and adjusting prostheses is a *prosthetist*.

Signs and Symptoms

TERM	WORD PARTS	DEFINITION
arthralgia (ar-THRAL-jee-ah)	arthr/o = joint -algia = pain	joint pain
bursitis (ber-SIGH-tis)	burs/o = bursa -itis = inflammation	inflammation of a bursa
callus (KAL-us)		The mass of bone tissue that forms at a fracture site during its healing.
chondromalacia (kon-droh-mah-LAY-she-ah)	chondr/o = cartilage -malacia = softening	softening of the cartilage
crepitation (krep-ih-TAY-shun)		The noise produced by bones or cartilage rubbing together in conditions such as arthritis. Also called *crepitus*.
ostealgia (oss-tee-AL-jee-ah)	oste/o = bone -algia = pain	bone pain
osteomyelitis (oss-tee-oh-mi-ell-EYE-tis)	oste/o = bone myel/o = bone marrow -itis = inflammation	inflammation of bone and bone marrow
synovitis (sih-no-VI-tis)	synov/o = synovial membrane -itis = inflammation	inflammation of synovial membrane

Fractures

TERM	WORD PARTS	DEFINITION
closed fracture		Fracture in which there is no open skin wound. Also called a *simple fracture*.

Pathology *(continued)*

TERM	WORD PARTS	DEFINITION

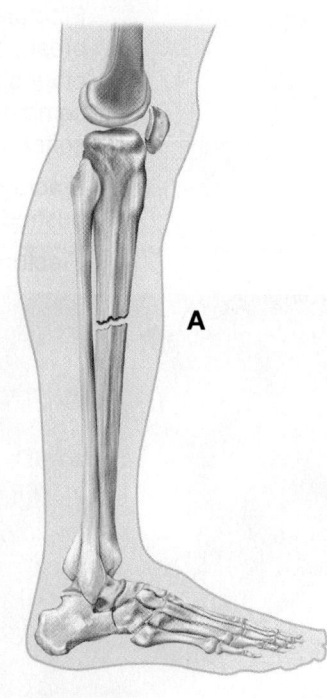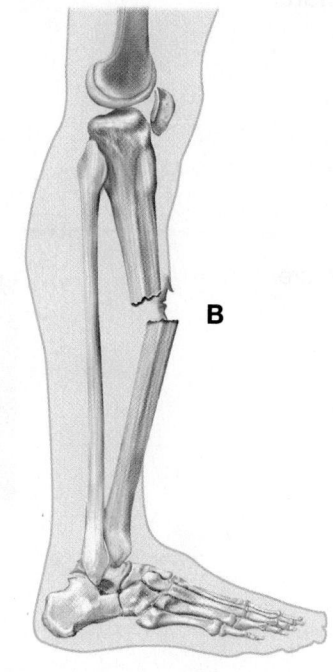

■ **Figure 4.13** (A) Closed (or simple) fracture and (B) open (or compound) fracture.

Colles' (COL-eez) **fracture**		A common type of wrist fracture.

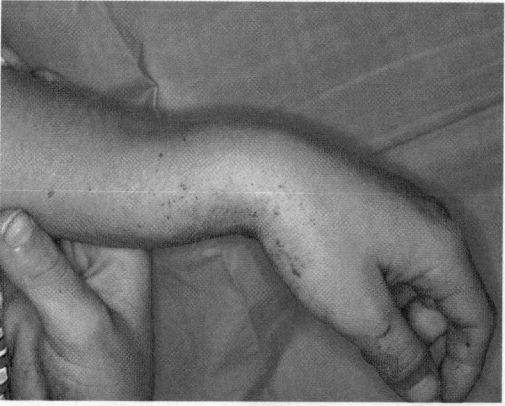

■ **Figure 4.14** Colles' fracture.
(Charles Stewart MD FACEP, FAAEM)

comminuted fracture (kom-ih-NYOOT-ed)		Fracture in which the bone is shattered, splintered, or crushed into many small pieces or fragments.
compound fracture		Fracture in which the skin has been broken through to the fracture. Also called an *open fracture* (see Figure 4.13B ■).
compression fracture		Fracture involving loss of height of a vertebral body. It may be the result of trauma, but in older people, especially women, it may be caused by conditions like osteoporosis.
fracture (FX, Fx)		A broken bone.

 Pathology *(continued)*

TERM	WORD PARTS	DEFINITION
greenstick fracture		Fracture in which there is an incomplete break; one side of bone is broken and the other side is bent. This type of fracture is commonly found in children due to their softer and more pliable bone structure.
impacted fracture		Fracture in which bone fragments are pushed into each other.
oblique (oh-BLEEK) **fracture**		Fracture at an angle to the bone.

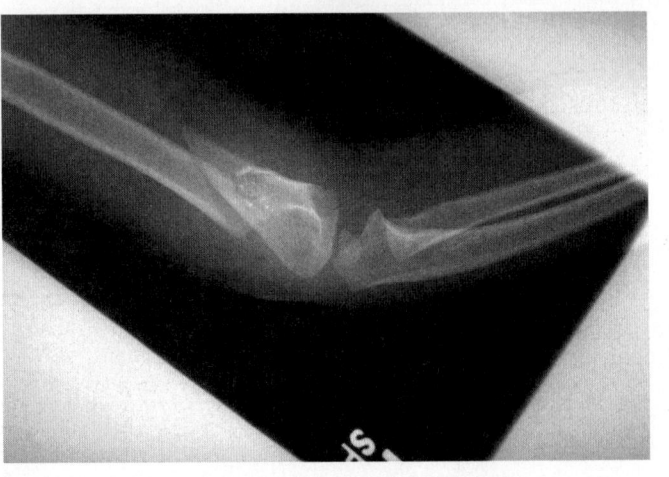

Figure 4.15 X-ray showing oblique fracture of the humerus. *(Charles Stewart MD)*

TERM	WORD PARTS	DEFINITION
pathologic (path-a-LOJ-ik) **fracture**	path/o = disease -logy = study -ic = pertaining to	Fracture caused by diseased or weakened bone.
spiral fracture		Fracture in which the fracture line spirals around the shaft of the bone. Can be caused by a twisting injury and is often slower to heal than other types of fractures.
stress fracture		A slight fracture caused by repetitive low-impact forces, like running, rather than a single forceful impact.
transverse fracture		Complete fracture that is straight across the bone at right angles to the long axis of the bone.

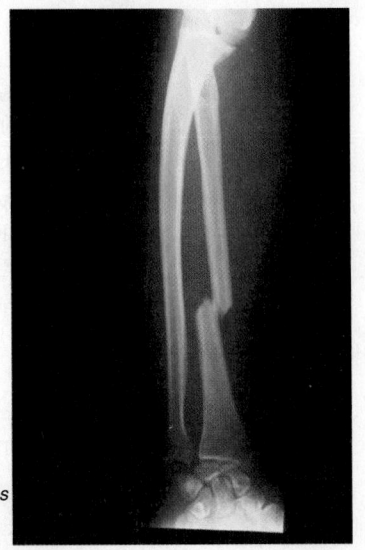

Figure 4.16 X-ray showing transverse fracture of radius. *(James Stevenson/Science Photo Library/Photo Researchers, Inc.)*

Pathology *(continued)*

TERM	WORD PARTS	DEFINITION
Bones		
chondroma (kon-DROH-mah)	chondr/o = cartilage -oma = tumor	A tumor, usually benign, that forms in cartilage.
Ewing's sarcoma (YOO-wings / sar-KOH-mah)	sarc/o = flesh -oma = tumor	Malignant growth found in the shaft of long bones that spreads through the periosteum. Removal is the treatment of choice because this tumor will metastasize or spread to other organs.
exostosis (eck-sos-TOH-sis)	ex- = external, outward oste/o = bone -osis = abnormal condition	A bone spur.
myeloma (my-ah-LOH-mah)	myel/o = bone marrow -oma = tumor	A tumor that forms in bone marrow tissue.
osteochondroma (oss-tee-oh-kon-DROH-mah)	oste/o = bone chondr/o = cartilage -oma = tumor	A tumor, usually benign, that consists of both bone and cartilage tissue.
osteogenic sarcoma (oss-tee-oh-GIN-ik / sark-OH-mah)	oste/o = bone -genic = producing sarc/o = flesh -oma = tumor	The most common type of bone cancer. Usually begins in osteocytes found at the ends of long bones.
osteomalacia (oss-tee-oh-mah-LAY-she-ah)	oste/o = bone -malacia = softening	Softening of the bones caused by a deficiency of calcium. It is thought to be caused by insufficient sunlight and vitamin D in children.
osteopathy (oss-tee-OPP-ah-thee)	oste/o = bone -pathy = disease	A general term for bone disease.
osteoporosis (oss-tee-oh-por-ROH-sis)	oste/o = bone -porosis = porous	Decrease in bone mass producing a thinning and weakening of the bone with resulting fractures. The bone becomes more porous, especially in the spine and pelvis.
Paget's disease (PAH-jets)		A fairly common metabolic disease of the bone from unknown causes. It usually attacks middle-aged and older adults and is characterized by bone destruction and deformity. Named for Sir James Paget, a British surgeon.
rickets (RIK-ets)		Deficiency in calcium and vitamin D found in early childhood that results in bone deformities, especially bowed legs.
Spinal Column		
ankylosing spondylitis (ang-kih-LOH-sing / spon-dih-LYE-tis)	ankyl/o = stiff joint spondyl/o = vertebra -itis = inflammation	Inflammatory spinal condition resembling rheumatoid arthritis and results in gradual stiffening and fusion of the vertebrae. More common in men than women.

Pathology *(continued)*

TERM	WORD PARTS	DEFINITION

herniated nucleus pulposus (HNP)
(HER-nee-ated / NOO-klee-us /
pull-POH-sus)

Herniation or protrusion of an intervertebral disk; also called *herniated disk* or *ruptured disk*. May require surgery.

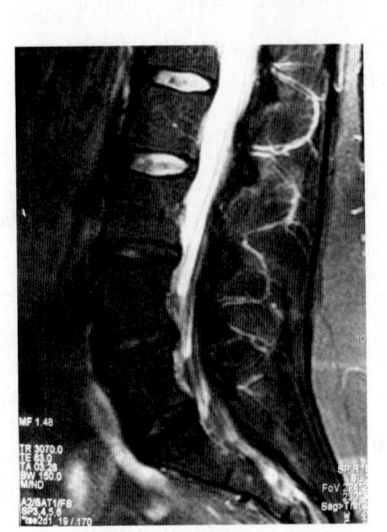

■ **Figure 4.17** Magnetic resonance imaging (MRI) image demonstrating a back herniated disk. *(Michelle Milano/Shutterstock)*

kyphosis
(ki-FOH-sis)

kyph/o = hump
-osis = abnormal condition

Abnormal increase in the outward curvature of the thoracic spine. Also known as *hunchback* or *humpback.* See Figure 4.18 ■ for an illustration of abnormal spine curvatures.

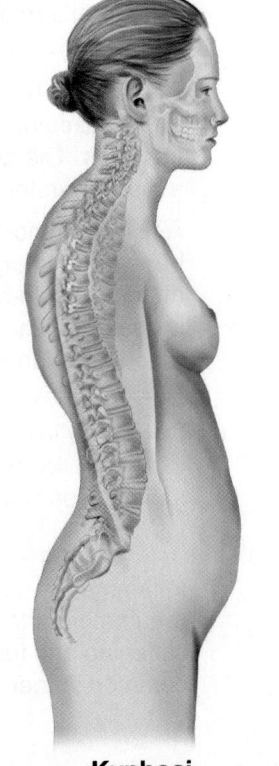
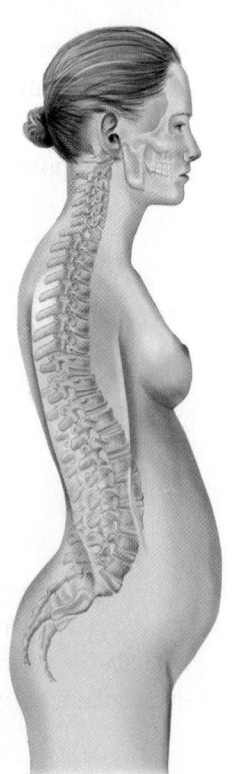
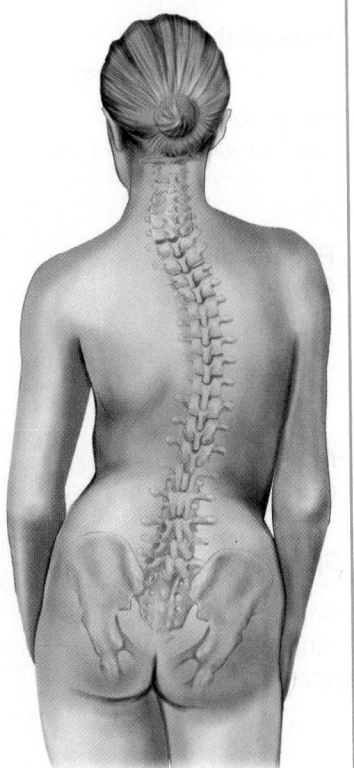

■ **Figure 4.18** Abnormal spinal curvatures: kyphosis, lordosis, and scoliosis.

Kyphosi
(excessive posterior thoracic curvature - hunchback)

Lordosis
(excessive anterior lumbar curvature - swayback)

Scoliosis
(lateral curvature)

◼ **Pathology** *(continued)*

TERM	WORD PARTS	DEFINITION
lordosis (lor-DOH-sis)	lord/o = bent backwards -osis = abnormal condition	Abnormal increase in the forward curvature of the lumbar spine. Also known as *swayback*. See again Figure 4.18 for an illustration of abnormal spine curvatures.
scoliosis (skoh-lee-OH-sis)	scoli/o = crooked, bent -osis = abnormal condition	Abnormal lateral curvature of the spine. See again Figure 4.18 for an illustration of abnormal spine curvatures.
spina bifida (SPY-nah / BIF-ih-dah)	spin/o = spine bi- = two	Congenital anomaly occurring when a vertebra fails to fully form around the spinal cord.
spinal stenosis (ste-NOH-sis)	spin/o = spine -al = pertaining to	Narrowing of the spinal canal causing pressure on the cord and nerves.
spondylolisthesis (spon-dih-loh-liss-THEE-sis)	spondyl/o = vertebra -listhesis = slipping	The forward sliding of a lumbar vertebra over the vertebra below it.
spondylosis (spon-dih-LOH-sis)	spondyl/o = vertebra -osis = abnormal condition	Specifically refers to ankylosing of the spine, but commonly used in reference to any degenerative condition of the vertebral column.
whiplash		Cervical muscle and ligament sprain or strain as a result of a sudden movement forward and backward of the head and neck. Can occur as a result of a rear-end auto collision.
Joints		
bunion (BUN-yun)		Inflammation of the bursa of the first metatarsophalangeal joint (base of the big toe).
dislocation		Occurs when the bones in a joint are displaced from their normal alignment and the ends of the bones are no longer in contact.
osteoarthritis (OA) (oss-tee-oh-ar-THRY-tis)	oste/o = bone arthr/o = joint -itis = inflammation	Arthritis resulting in degeneration of the bones and joints, especially those bearing weight. Results in bone rubbing against bone.
rheumatoid arthritis (RA) (ROO-mah-toyd / ar-THRY-tis)	arthr/o = joint -itis = inflammation	Chronic form of arthritis with inflammation of the joints, swelling, stiffness, pain, and changes in the cartilage that can result in crippling deformities; considered to be an autoimmune disease.

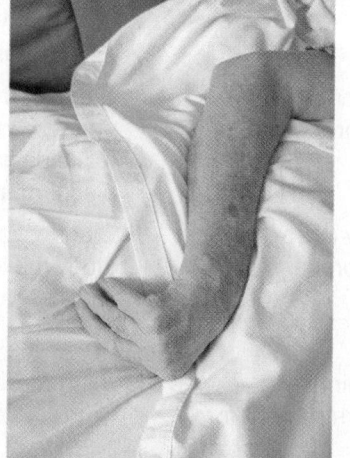

◼ **Figure 4.19** Patient with typical rheumatoid arthritis contractures.

Pathology *(continued)*

TERM	WORD PARTS	DEFINITION
sprain		Damage to the ligaments surrounding a joint due to overstretching, but no dislocation of the joint or fracture of the bone.
subluxation (sub-LUCKS-a-shun)	sub- = below, under	An incomplete dislocation, the joint alignment is disrupted, but the ends of the bones remain in contact.
systemic lupus erythematosus (SLE) (sis-TEM-ik / LOOP-us / air-ih-them-ah-TOH-sis)	system/o = system -ic = pertaining to erythr/o = red	Chronic inflammatory autoimmune disease of connective tissue affecting many systems that may include joint pain and arthritis. May be mistaken for rheumatoid arthritis.
talipes (TAL-ih-peez)		Congenital deformity causing misalignment of the ankle joint and foot. Also referred to as a *clubfoot.*

Diagnostic Procedures

TERM	WORD PART	DEFINITION
Diagnostic Imaging		
arthrogram (AR-throh-gram)	arthr/o = joint -gram = record	X-ray record of a joint; usually taken after the joint has been injected by a contrast medium.
arthrography (ar-THROG-rah-fee)	arthr/o = joint -graphy = process of recording	Process of X-raying a joint; usually after injection of a contrast medium into the joint space.
bone scan		Nuclear medicine procedure in which the patient is given a radioactive dye and then scanning equipment is used to visualize bones. It is especially useful in identifying stress fractures, observing progress of treatment for osteomyelitis, and locating cancer metastases to the bone.
dual-energy absorptiometry (DXA) (ab-sorp-she-AHM-eh-tree)	-metry = process of measuring	Measurement of bone density using low-dose X-ray for the purpose of detecting osteoporosis.
myelography (my-eh-LOG-rah-fee)	myel/o = bone marrow -graphy = process of recording	Study of the spinal column after injecting opaque contrast material; particularly useful in identifying herniated nucleus pulposus pinching a spinal nerve.
radiography	radi/o = ray (X-ray) -graphy = process of recording	Diagnostic imaging procedure using X-rays to study the internal structure of the body; especially useful for visualizing bones and joints.
Endoscopic Procedures		
arthroscope (AR-throw-skop)	arthr/o = joint -scope = instrument for viewing	Instrument used to view inside a joint.

Diagnostic Procedures *(continued)*

TERM	WORD PART	DEFINITION
arthroscopy (ar-THROS-koh-pee)	arthr/o = joint -scopy = process of visually examining	Examination of the interior of a joint by entering the joint with an *arthroscope.* The arthroscope contains a small television camera that allows the physician to view the interior of the joint on a monitor during the procedure. Some joint conditions can be repaired during arthroscopy.

Therapeutic Procedures

TERM	WORD PART	DEFINITION
Medical Treatments		
arthrocentesis (ar-thro-sen-TEE-sis)	arthr/o = joint -centesis = puncture to withdraw fluid	Involves the insertion of a needle into the joint cavity in order to remove or aspirate fluid. May be done to remove excess fluid from a joint or to obtain fluid for examination.
orthotic (or-THOT-ik)	orth/o = straight -tic = pertaining to	Orthopedic appliance, such as a brace or splint, used to prevent or correct deformities.
prosthesis (pross-THEE-sis)	prosthet/o = addition	Artificial device used as a substitute for a body part that is either congenitally missing or absent as a result of accident or disease. An example would be an artificial leg.
Surgical Procedures		
amputation (am-pew-TAY-shun)		Partial or complete removal of a limb for a variety of reasons, including tumors, gangrene, intractable pain, crushing injury, or uncontrollable infection.
arthroclasia (ar-throh-KLAY-see-ah)	arthr/o = joint -clasia = surgically break	To forcibly break loose a fused joint while the patient is under anesthetic. Fusion is usually caused by the buildup of scar tissue or adhesions.
arthrodesis (ar-throh-DEE-sis)	arthr/o = joint -desis = fuse	Procedure to stabilize a joint by fusing the bones together.
arthroscopic surgery (ar-throh-SKOP-ic)	arthr/o = joint -scopy = process of visually examining -ic = pertaining to	Performing a surgical procedure while using an arthroscope to view the internal structure, such as a joint.
arthrotomy (ar-THROT-oh-mee)	arthr/o = joint -otomy = cutting into	Surgical procedure that cuts into a joint capsule.
bone graft		Piece of bone taken from the patient used to take the place of a removed bone or a bony defect at another site.
bunionectomy (bun-yun-ECK-toh-mee)	-ectomy = surgical removal	Removal of the bursa at the joint of the great toe.

■ Therapeutic Procedures *(continued)*

TERM	WORD PART	DEFINITION
bursectomy (ber-SEK-toh-mee)	burs/o = bursa -ectomy = surgical removal	Surgical removal of a bursa.
chondrectomy (kon-DREK-toh-mee)	chondr/o = cartilage -ectomy = surgical removal	Surgical removal of cartilage.
chondroplasty (KON-droh-plas-tee)	chondr/o = cartilage -plasty = surgical repair	Surgical repair of cartilage.
craniotomy (kray-nee-OTT-oh-mee)	chondr/o = cartilage -otomy = cutting into	Surgical procedure that cuts into the skull.
laminectomy (lam-ih-NEK-toh-mee)	lamin/o = lamina, part of vertebra -ectomy = surgical removal	Removal of the vertebral posterior arch to correct severe back problems and pain caused by compression of a spinal nerve.
osteoclasia (oss-tee-oh-KLAY-see-ah)	oste/o = bone -clasia = surgically break	Surgical procedure involving the intentional breaking of a bone to correct a deformity.
osteotome (OSS-tee-oh-tohm)	oste/o = bone -tome = instrument used to cut	Instrument used to cut bone.
osteotomy (oss-tee-OTT-ah-me)	oste/o = bone -otomy = cutting into	Surgical procedure that cuts into a bone.
percutaneous diskectomy (per-kyou-TAY-nee-us / disk-EK-toh-mee)	per- = through cutane/o = skin -ous = pertaining to -ectomy = surgical removal	A thin catheter tube is inserted into the intervertebral disk through the skin and the herniated or ruptured disk material is sucked out or a laser is used to vaporize it.
spinal fusion	spin/o = spine -al = pertaining to	Surgical immobilization of adjacent vertebrae. This may be done for several reasons, including correction for a herniated disk.
synovectomy (sih-no-VEK-toh-mee)	synov/o = synovial membrane -ectomy = surgical removal	Surgical removal of the synovial membrane.
total hip arthroplasty (THA) (ar-thro-PLAS-tee)	arthr/o = joint -plasty = surgical repair	Surgical reconstruction of a hip by implanting a prosthetic or artificial hip joint. Also called *total hip replacement (THR)*.

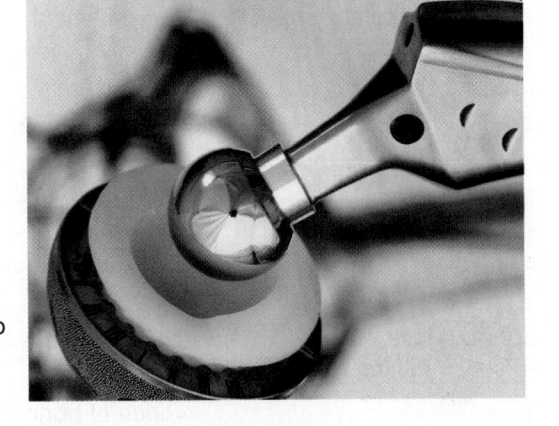

■ **Figure 4.20** Prosthetic hip joint. *(Lawrence Livermore National Library/Science Photo Library/Photo Researchers, Inc.)*

total knee arthroplasty (TKA) (ar-thro-PLAS-tee)	arthr/o = joint -plasty = surgical repair	Surgical reconstruction of a knee joint by implanting a prosthetic knee joint. Also called *total knee replacement (TKR)*.

Therapeutic Procedures (continued)

TERM	WORD PART	DEFINITION
Fracture Care		
cast		Application of a solid material to immobilize an extremity or portion of the body as a result of a fracture, dislocation, or severe injury. It may be made of plaster of Paris or fiberglass.
fixation		Procedure to stabilize a fractured bone while it heals. *External fixation* includes casts, splints, and pins inserted through the skin. *Internal fixation* includes pins, plates, rods, screws, and wires that are applied during an *open reduction.*
reduction		Correcting a fracture by realigning the bone fragments. *Closed reduction* is doing this manipulation without entering the body. *Open reduction* is the process of making a surgical incision at the site of the fracture to do the reduction. This is necessary when bony fragments need to be removed or *internal fixation* such as plates or pins are required.
traction		Applying a pulling force on a fractured or dislocated limb or the vertebral column in order to restore normal alignment.

Pharmacology

CLASSIFICATION	WORD PARTS	ACTION	EXAMPLES
bone reabsorption inhibitors		Conditions that result in weak and fragile bones, such as osteoporosis and Paget's disease, are improved by medications that reduce the reabsorption of bones.	alendronate, Fosamax; ibandronate, Boniva
calcium supplements and vitamin D therapy		Maintaining high blood levels of calcium in association with vitamin D helps maintain bone density; used to treat osteomalacia, osteoporosis, and rickets.	calcium carbonate, Oystercal, Tums; calcium citrate, Cal-Citrate, Citracal
corticosteroids	cortic/o = outer portion	A hormone produced by the adrenal cortex that has very strong anti-inflammatory properties. It is particularly useful in treating rheumatoid arthritis.	prednisone; methylprednisolone, Medrol; dexamethasone, Decadron
nonsteroidal anti-inflammatory drugs (NSAIDs)	-al = pertaining to anti- = against -ory = pertaining to	A large group of drugs that provide mild pain relief and anti-inflammatory benefits for conditions such as arthritis.	ibuprofen, Advil, Motrin; naproxen, Aleve, Naprosyn; salicylates, Aspirin

Abbreviations

AE	above elbow		LLE	left lower extremity
AK	above knee		LUE	left upper extremity
BDT	bone density testing		NSAID	nonsteroidal anti-inflammatory drug
BE	below elbow		OA	osteoarthritis
BK	below knee		ORIF	open reduction–internal fixation
BMD	bone mineral density		Orth, ortho	orthopedics (straight)
C1, C2, etc.	first cervical vertebra, second cervical vertebra, etc.		RA	rheumatoid arthritis
Ca	calcium		RLE	right lower extremity
DJD	degenerative joint disease		RUE	right upper extremity
DXA	dual-energy absorptiometry		SLE	systemic lupus erythematosus
FX, Fx	fracture		T1, T2, etc.	first thoracic vertebra, second thoracic vertebra, etc.
HNP	herniated nucleus pulposus		THA	total hip arthroplasty
JRA	juvenile rheumatoid arthritis		THR	total hip replacement
L1, L2, etc.	first lumbar vertebra, second lumbar vertebra, etc.		TKA	total knee arthroplasty
			TKR	total knee replacement
LE	lower extremity		UE	upper extremity

Section II: Muscular System at a Glance

Function

Muscles are bundles, sheets, or rings of tissue that produce movement by contracting and pulling on the structures to which they are attached.

Organs

Here is the primary structure that comprises the muscular system.
muscles

Word Parts

Here are the most common word parts (with their meanings) used to build muscular system terms. For a more comprehensive list, refer to the Terminology section of this chapter.

Combining Forms

duct/o	to bring	myocardi/o	heart muscle
extens/o	to stretch out	myos/o	muscle
fasci/o	fibrous band	plant/o	sole of foot
fibr/o	fibers	rotat/o	to revolve
flex/o	to bend	ten/o	tendon
kinesi/o	movement	tend/o	tendon
muscul/o	muscle	tendin/o	tendon
my/o	muscle	vers/o	to turn

Suffixes

-asthenia	weakness
-ion	action, condition
-kinesia	movement
-tonia	tone

Prefixes

ab-	away from
ad-	toward
circum-	around
e-	outward, without
in-	inward, without

Muscular System Illustrated

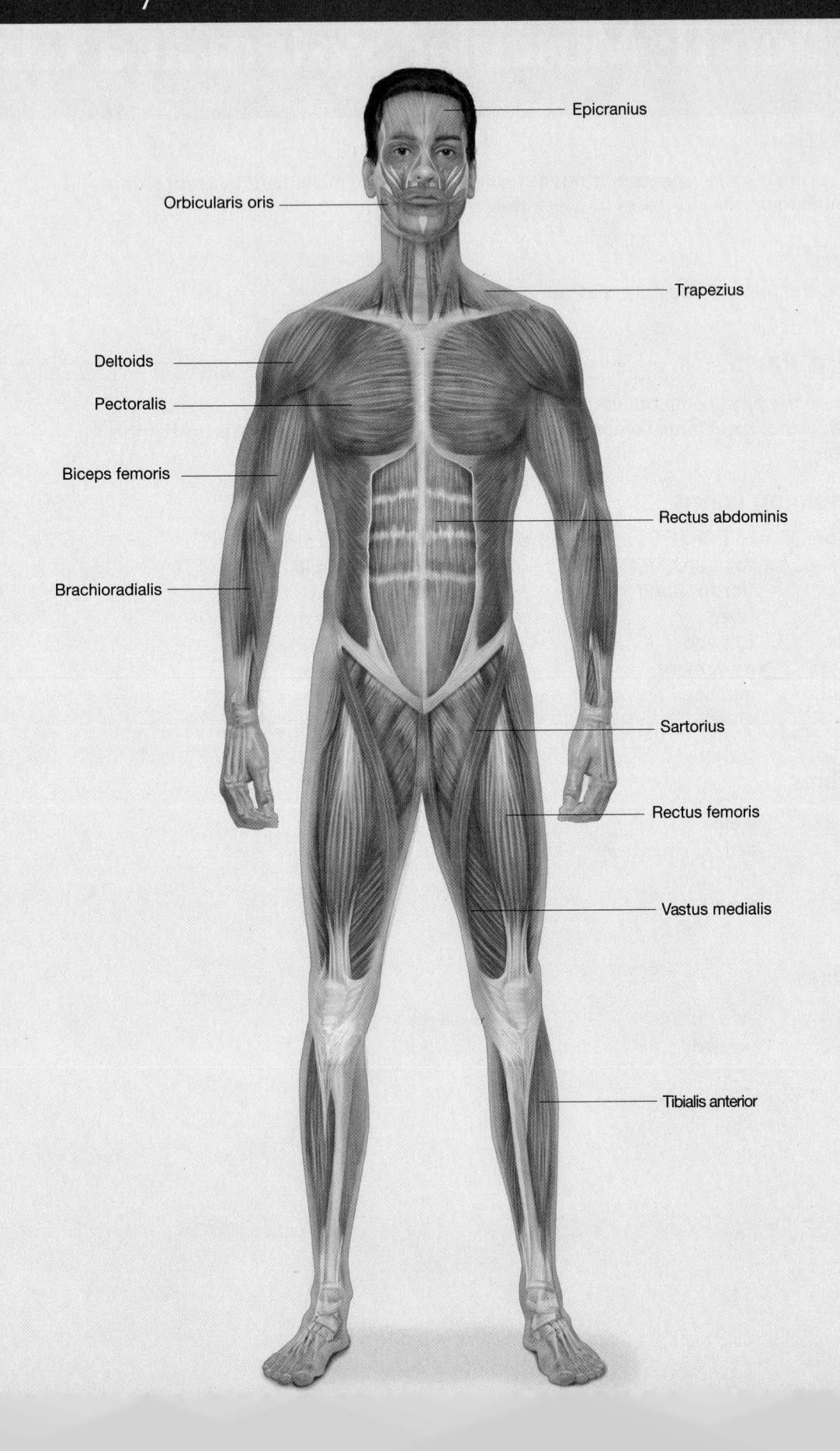

Epicranius

Orbicularis oris

Trapezius

Deltoids

Pectoralis

Biceps femoris

Rectus abdominis

Brachioradialis

Sartorius

Rectus femoris

Vastus medialis

Tibialis anterior

J. Terminology Matching

Match each term to its definition.

1. _____ abduction

a. backward bending of the foot

2. _____ rotation

b. bending the foot to point toes toward the ground

3. _____ plantar flexion

c. straightening motion

4. _____ extension

d. motion around a central axis

5. _____ dorsiflexion

e. motion away from the body

6. _____ flexion

f. moving the thumb away from the palm

7. _____ adduction

g. motion toward the body

8. _____ opposition

h. bending motion

K. Fill in the Blank

carpal tunnel syndrome	rickets	lateral epicondylitis	systemic lupus
scoliosis	osteogenic sarcoma	pseudohypertrophic muscular dystrophy	erythematosus
herniated nucleus pulposus	osteoporosis		
	spondylolisthesis		

1. Mrs. Lewis, age 84, broke her hip. Her physician will be running tests for what potential ailment? _____

2. Jamie, age 6 months, is being given orange juice and vitamin supplements to avoid what condition? _____

3. George has severe elbow pain after playing tennis four days in a row. He may have _____ .

4. Marshall's doctor told him that he had a ruptured disk. The medical term for this is _____ .

5. Mr. Jefferson's physician has discovered a tumor at the end of his femur. He has been admitted to the hospital for a biopsy to rule out what type of bone cancer? _____

6. The school nurse has asked Janelle to bend over so that she may examine her back to see if she is developing a lateral curve. What is the nurse looking for? _____

7. Gerald has experienced a gradual loss of muscle strength over the past 5 years even though his muscles look large and healthy. The doctors believe he has an inherited muscle disease. What is that disease? _____

8. Roberta has suddenly developed arthritis in her hands and knees. Rheumatoid arthritis had been ruled out, but what other auto-immune disease might Roberta have? _____

9. Mark's X-ray demonstrated forward sliding of a lumbar vertebra; the radiologist diagnosed _____ .

10. The orthopedist determined that Marcia's repetitive wrist movements at work caused her to develop _____ .

L. Fracture Type Matching

Match each fracture type to its definition.

1. _____ comminuted   a. fracture line is at an angle

2. _____ greenstick   b. fracture line curves around the bone

3. _____ compound   c. bone is splintered or crushed

4. _____ simple   d. bone is pressed into itself

5. _____ impacted   e. fracture line is straight across bone

6. _____ transverse   f. skin has been broken

7. _____ oblique   g. no open wound

8. _____ spiral   h. bone only partially broken

M. Name That Anatomical Name

1. knee cap _____

2. ankle bones _____

3. collar bone _____

4. thigh bone _____

5. toe bones _____

6. wrist bones _____

7. shin bone _____

8. shoulder blade _____

9. finger bones _____

N. What Does it Stand For?

1. DJD _____

2. EMG _____

3. C1 _____

4. T6 _____

5. IM _____

6. DTR _____

7. JRA _____

8. LLE _____

9. ortho _____

10. CTS _____

O. Define the Term

1. chondroplasty _____

2. bradykinesia _____

3. osteoporosis _____

4. lordosis _____

5. atrophy _____

6. myeloma _____

7. prosthesis _____

8. craniotomy _____

9. arthrocentesis _____

10. bursitis _____

P. Pharmacology Challenge

Fill in the classification for each drug description, then match the brand name.

Drug Description	Classification	Brand Name
1. _____ Treats mild pain and anti-inflammatory	_____	a. Flexeril
2. _____ Hormone with anti-inflammatory properties	_____	b. Aleve
3. _____ Reduces muscle spasms	_____	c. Fosamax
4. _____ Treats conditions of weakened bones	_____	d. Oystercal
5. _____ Maintains blood calcium levels	_____	e. Medrol

Labeling Exercise

Image A

Write the labels for this figure on the numbered lines provided.

1. _____

2. _____

3. _____

4. _____

5. _____

6. _____

7. _____

8. _____

9. _____

10. _____

11. _____

12. _____

13. _____

14. _____

15. _____

16. _____

17. _____

18. _____

19. _____

20. _____

21. _____

22 _____

23. _____

24. _____

25. _____

26. _____

27. _____

Image B

Write the labels for this figure on the numbered lines provided.

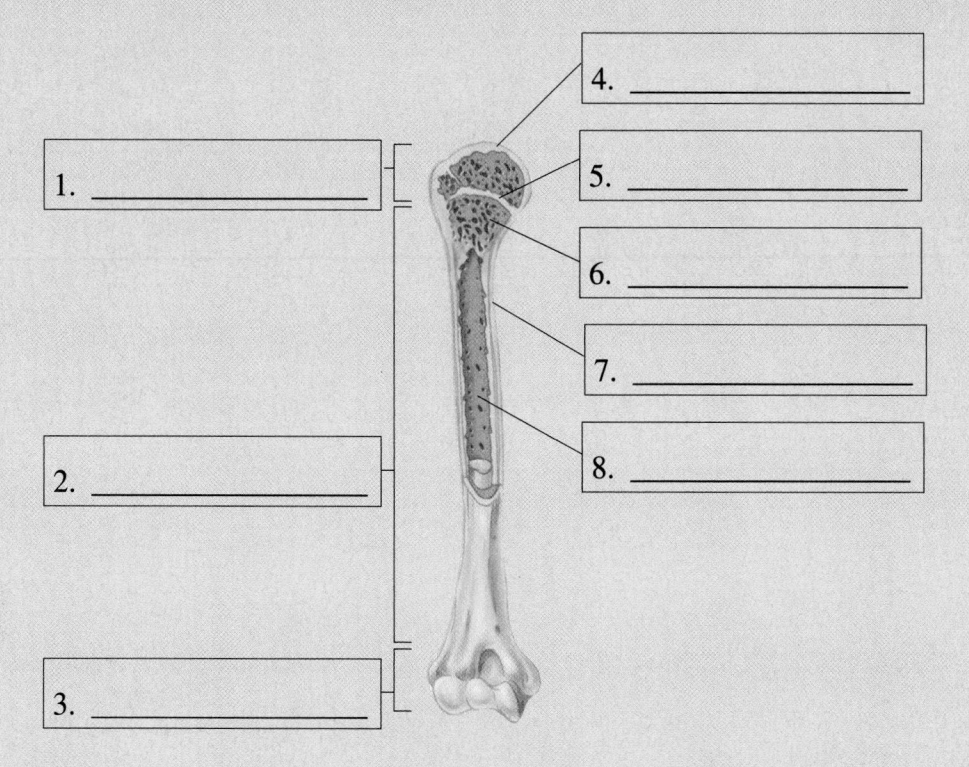

1. _____

2. _____

3. _____

4. _____

5. _____

6. _____

7. _____

8. _____

Image C

Write the labels for this figure on the numbered lines provided.

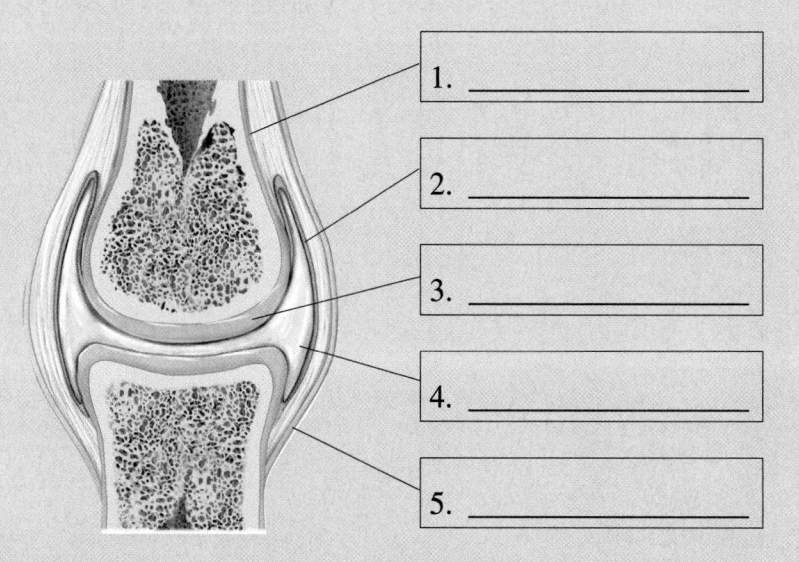

1. _____

2. _____

3. _____

4. _____

5. _____

5

CARDIOVASCULAR SYSTEM

Learning Objectives

Upon completion of this chapter, you will be able to

- Identify and define the combining forms and suffixes introduced in this chapter.

- Correctly spell and pronounce medical terms and major anatomical structures relating to the cardiovascular system.

- Describe the major organs of the cardiovascular system and their functions.

- Describe the anatomy of the heart.

- Describe the flow of blood through the heart.

- Explain how the electrical conduction system controls the heartbeat.

- List and describe the characteristics of the three types of blood vessels.

- Define pulse and blood pressure.

- Identify and define cardiovascular system anatomical terms.

- Identify and define selected cardiovascular system pathology terms.

- Identify and define selected cardiovascular system diagnostic procedures.

- Identify and define selected cardiovascular system therapeutic procedures.

- Identify and define selected medications relating to the cardiovascular system.

- Define selected abbreviations associated with the cardiovascular system.

Cardiovascular System at a Glance

Function

The cardiovascular system consists of the pump and vessels that distribute blood to all areas of the body. This system allows for the delivery of needed substances to the cells of the body as well as for the removal of wastes.

Organs

Here are the primary structures that comprise the cardiovascular system.

blood vessels   **heart**
- arteries
- capillaries
- veins

Word Parts

Here are the most common word parts (with their meanings) used to build cardiovascular system terms. For a more comprehensive list, refer to the Terminology section of this chapter.

Combining Forms

angi/o	vessel	phleb/o	vein
aort/o	aorta	sphygm/o	pulse
arteri/o	artery	steth/o	chest
ather/o	fatty substance	thromb/o	clot
atri/o	atrium	valv/o	valve
cardi/o	heart	valvul/o	valve
coron/o	heart	varic/o	dilated vein
corpor/o	body	vascul/o	blood vessel
embol/o	plug	vas/o	vessel, duct
isch/o	to hold back	ven/o	vein
myocardi/o	heart muscle	ventricul/o	ventricle
pect/o	chest		

Suffixes

-manometer	instrument to measure pressure
-ole	small
-tension	pressure
-tonic	pertaining to tone
-ule	small

Cardiovascular System Illustrated

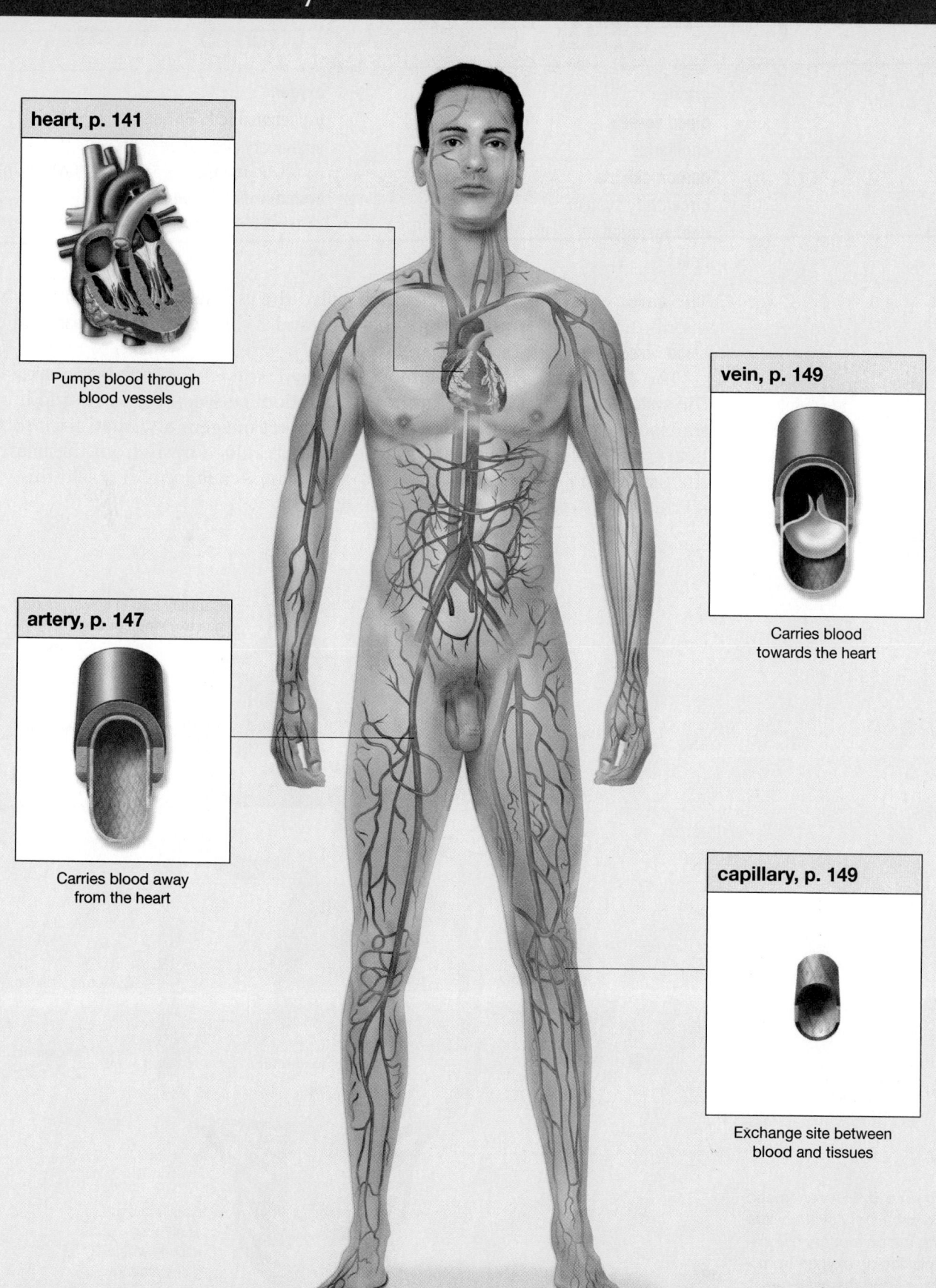

heart, p. 141

Pumps blood through blood vessels

artery, p. 147

Carries blood away from the heart

vein, p. 149

Carries blood towards the heart

capillary, p. 149

Exchange site between blood and tissues

 Anatomy and Physiology of the Cardiovascular System

arteries	**oxygen**
blood vessels	**oxygenated** (OK-sih-jen-ay-ted)
capillaries	**pulmonary circulation**
carbon dioxide	(PULL-mon-air-ee / ser-kew-LAY-shun)
circulatory system	**systemic circulation**
deoxygenated (dee-OK-sih-jen-ay-ted)	(sis-TEM-ik / ser-kew-LAY-shun)
heart	**veins**

The cardiovascular (CV) system, also called the **circulatory system,** maintains the distribution of blood throughout the body and is composed of the **heart** and the **blood vessels—arteries, capillaries,** and **veins.**

The circulatory system is composed of two parts: the **pulmonary circulation** and the **systemic circulation.** The pulmonary circulation, between the heart and lungs, transports **deoxygenated** blood to the lungs to get oxygen, and then back to the heart. The systemic circulation carries **oxygenated** blood away from the heart to the tissues and cells, and then back to the heart (see Figure 5.1 ■). In this way all the body's cells receive blood and oxygen.

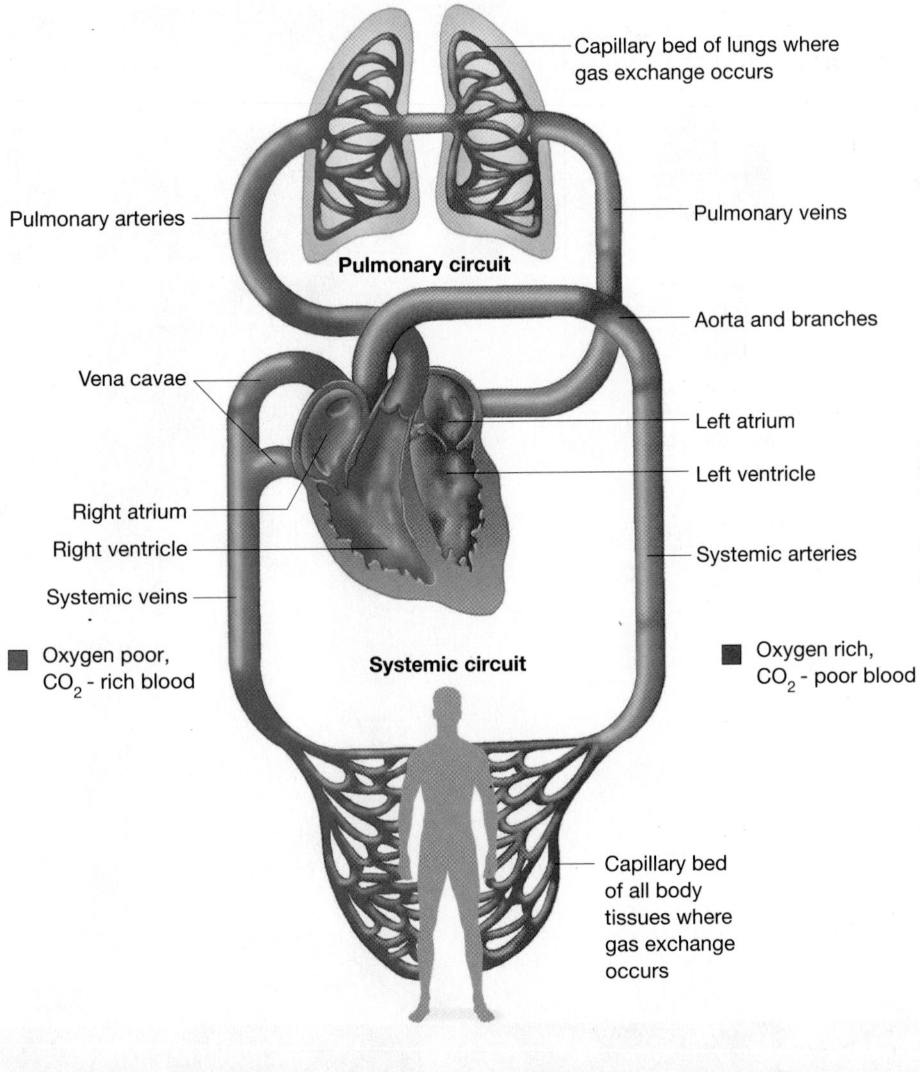

Capillary bed of lungs where gas exchange occurs

Pulmonary arteries

Pulmonary circuit

Pulmonary veins

Aorta and branches

Vena cavae

Left atrium

Left ventricle

Right atrium

Right ventricle

Systemic arteries

Systemic veins

Oxygen poor, CO_2 - rich blood

Systemic circuit

Oxygen rich, CO_2 - poor blood

Capillary bed of all body tissues where gas exchange occurs

■ **Figure 5.1** A schematic of the circulatory system illustrating the pulmonary circulation picking up oxygen from the lungs and the systemic circulation delivering oxygen to the body.

In addition to distributing **oxygen** and other nutrients, such as glucose and amino acids, the cardiovascular system also collects the waste products from the body's cells. **Carbon dioxide** and other waste products produced by metabolic reaction are transported by the cardiovascular system to the lungs, liver, and kidneys where they are eliminated from the body.

Heart

apex (AY-peks)   **cardiac muscle** (CAR-dee-ak)

The heart is a muscular pump made up of **cardiac muscle** fibers that could be considered a muscle rather than an organ. It has four chambers, or cavities, and beats an average of 60–100 beats per minute (bpm) or about 100,000 times in one day. Each time the cardiac muscle contracts, blood is ejected from the heart and pushed throughout the body within the blood vessels.

The heart is located in the mediastinum in the center of the chest cavity; however, it is not exactly centered; more of the heart is on the left side of the mediastinum than the right (see Figure 5.2 ▇). At about the size of a fist and shaped like an upside-down pear, the heart lies directly behind the sternum. The tip of the heart at the lower edge is called the **apex**.

> **MED TERM TIP**
>
> Your heart is approximately the size of your clenched fist and pumps 4,000 gallons of blood each day. It will beat at least three billion times during your lifetime.

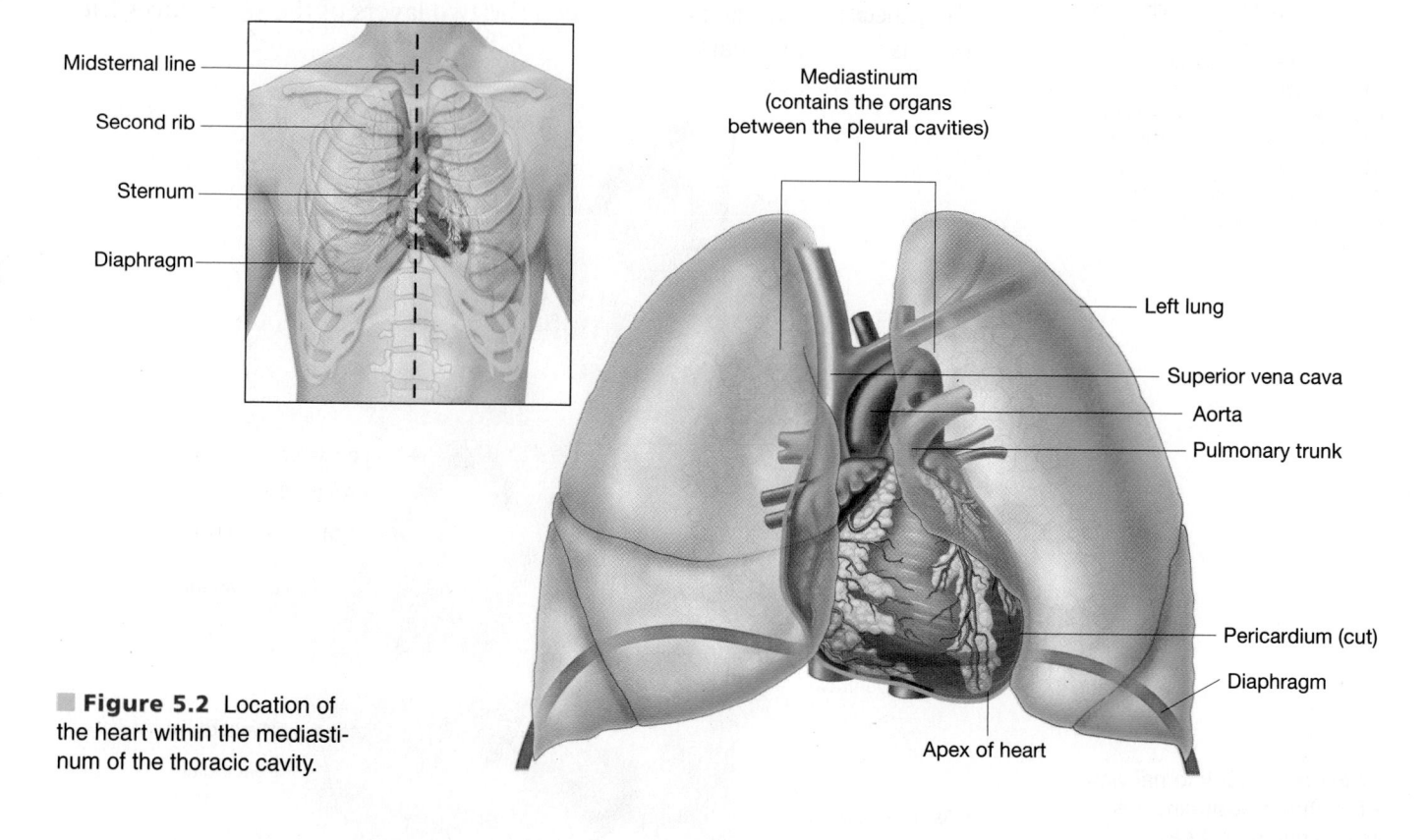

▇ **Figure 5.2** Location of the heart within the mediastinum of the thoracic cavity.

Labels: Midsternal line, Second rib, Sternum, Diaphragm, Mediastinum (contains the organs between the pleural cavities), Left lung, Superior vena cava, Aorta, Pulmonary trunk, Pericardium (cut), Diaphragm, Apex of heart

Heart Layers

endocardium (en-doh-CAR-dee-um)

epicardium (ep-ih-CAR-dee-um)

myocardium (my-oh-CAR-dee-um)

parietal pericardium
  (pah-RYE-eh-tal / pair-ih-CAR-dee-um)

pericardium (pair-ih-CAR-dee-um)

visceral pericardium
  (VISS-er-al / pair-ih-CAR-dee-um)

The wall of the heart is quite thick and composed of three layers (see Figure 5.3 ■):

1. The **endocardium** is the inner layer of the heart lining the heart chambers. It is a very smooth, thin layer that serves to reduce friction as the blood passes through the heart chambers.
2. The **myocardium** is the thick, muscular middle layer of the heart. Contraction of this muscle layer develops the pressure required to pump blood through the blood vessels.
3. The **epicardium** is the outer layer of the heart. The heart is enclosed within a double-layered pleural sac, called the **pericardium.** The epicardium is the **visceral pericardium,** or inner layer of the sac. The outer layer of the sac is the **parietal pericardium.** Fluid between the two layers of the sac reduces friction as the heart beats.

MED TERM TIP

These layers become important when studying the disease conditions affecting the heart. For instance, when the prefix *endo-* is added to *carditis*, forming *endocarditis*, we know that the inflammation is within the "inner layer of the heart." In discussing the muscular action of the heart, the prefix *myo-*, meaning "muscle," is added to *cardium* to form the word *myocardium*. The diagnosis *myocardial infarction* (MI), or heart attack, means that the patient has an infarct or "dead tissue in the muscle of the heart." The prefix *peri-*, meaning "around," when added to the word *cardium* refers to the sac "surrounding the heart." Therefore, *pericarditis* is an "inflammation of the outer sac of the heart."

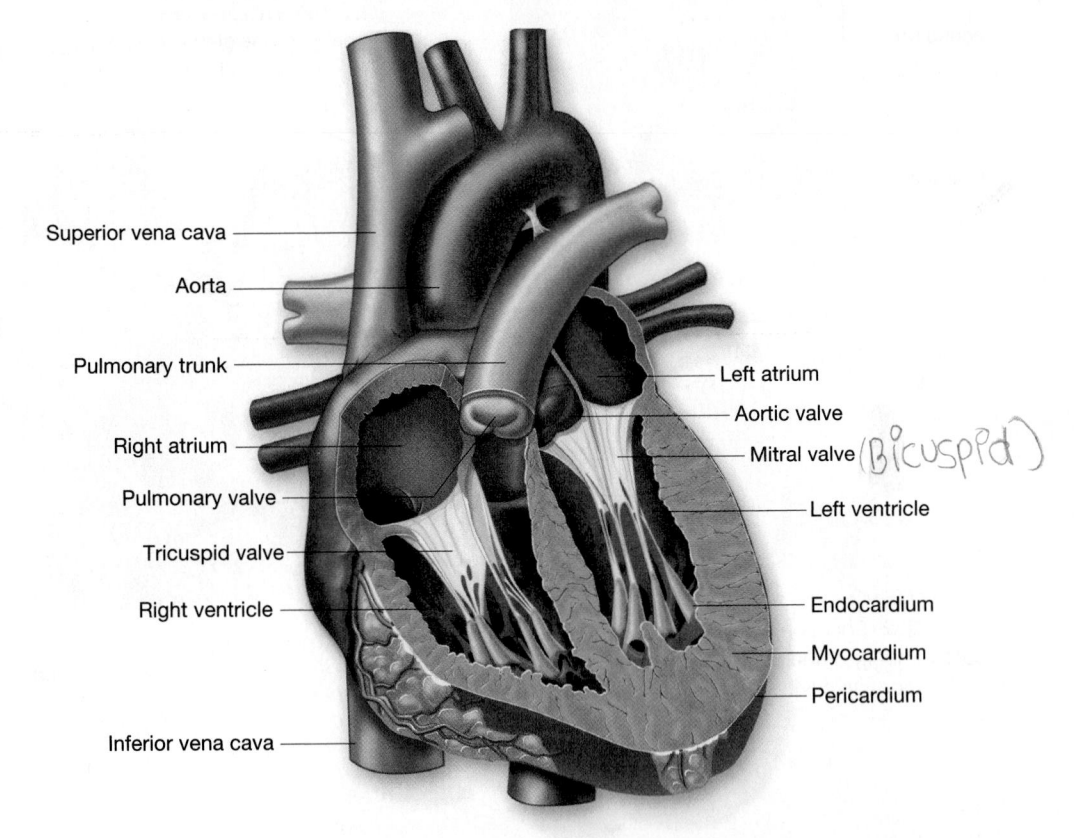

Superior vena cava

Aorta

Pulmonary trunk

Right atrium

Pulmonary valve

Tricuspid valve

Right ventricle

Inferior vena cava

Left atrium

Aortic valve

Mitral valve (Bicuspid)

Left ventricle

Endocardium

Myocardium

Pericardium

■ **Figure 5.3** Internal view of the heart illustrating the heart chambers, heart layers, and major blood vessels associated with the heart.

Heart Chambers

atria (AY-tree-ah)

interatrial septum
   (in-ter-AY-tree-al / SEP-tum)

interventricular septum
   (in-ter-ven-TRIK-yoo-lar / SEP-tum)

ventricles (VEN-trik-lz)

The heart is divided into four chambers or cavities (see Figures 5.3 and 5.4). There are two **atria,** or upper chambers, and two **ventricles,** or lower chambers. These chambers are divided into right and left sides by walls called the **interatrial septum** and the **interventricular septum.** The atria are the receiving chambers of the heart. Blood returning to the heart via veins first collects in the atria. The ventricles are the pumping chambers. They have a much thicker myocardium and their contraction ejects blood out of the heart and into the great arteries.

Heart Valves

aortic valve (ay-OR-tik)

atrioventricular valve
   (ay-tree-oh-ven-TRIK-yoo-lar)

bicuspid valve (bye-CUSS-pid)

cusps

mitral valve (MY-tral)

pulmonary valve (PULL-mon-air-ee)

semilunar valve (sem-ih-LOO-nar)

tricuspid valve (try-CUSS-pid)

Four valves act as restraining gates to control the direction of blood flow. They are situated at the entrances and exits to the ventricles (see Figure 5.4 ■). Properly functioning valves allow blood to flow only in the forward direction by blocking it from returning to the previous chamber.

The four valves are as follows:

1. **Tricuspid valve:** an **atrioventricular valve** (AV), meaning that it controls the opening between the right atrium and the right ventricle. Once the blood enters the right ventricle, it cannot go back up into the atrium again. The prefix *tri-,* meaning three, indicates that this valve has three leaflets or **cusps.**
2. **Pulmonary valve:** a **semilunar valve.** The prefix *semi-,* meaning half, and the term **lunar,** meaning moon, indicate that this valve looks like a half moon. Located between the right ventricle and the pulmonary artery, this valve prevents blood that has been ejected into the pulmonary artery from returning to the right ventricle as it relaxes.
3. **Mitral valve:** also called the **bicuspid valve,** indicating that it has two cusps. Blood flows through this atrioventricular valve to the left ventricle and cannot go back up into the left atrium.
4. **Aortic valve:** a semilunar valve located between the left ventricle and the aorta. Blood leaves the left ventricle through this valve and cannot return to the left ventricle.

MED TERM TIP

The term *ventricle* comes from the Latin term *venter,* which means "little belly." Although it originally referred to the abdomen and then the stomach, it came to stand for any hollow region inside an organ.

MED TERM TIP

The heart makes two distinct sounds referred to as "lub-dupp." These sounds are produced by the forceful snapping shut of the heart valves. *Lub* is the closing of the atrioventricular valves. *Dupp* is the closing of the semilunar valves.

■ Figure 5.4 Superior view of heart valves illustrating position, size, and shape of each valve.

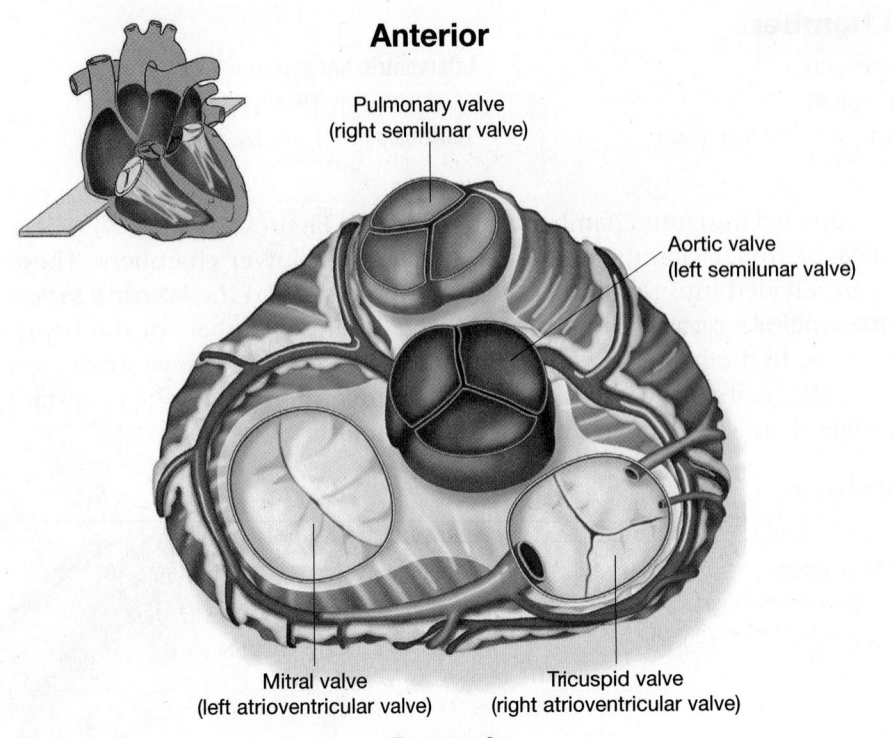

■ Figure 5.4 Superior view of heart valves illustrating position, size, and shape of each valve.

Anterior

Pulmonary valve
(right semilunar valve)

Aortic valve
(left semilunar valve)

Mitral valve
(left atrioventricular valve)

Tricuspid valve
(right atrioventricular valve)

Posterior

Blood Flow Through the Heart

aorta (ay-OR-tah)
diastole (dye-ASS-toe-lee)
inferior vena cava (VEE-nah / KAY-vah)
pulmonary artery (PULL-mon-air-ee)

pulmonary veins
superior vena cava
systole (SIS-toe-lee)

The flow of blood through the heart is very orderly (see Figure 5.5 ■). It progresses through the heart to the lungs, where it receives oxygen; then goes back to the heart; and then out to the body tissues and parts. The normal process of blood flow is:

1. Deoxygenated blood from all the tissues in the body enters a relaxed right atrium via two large veins called the **superior vena cava** and **inferior vena cava.**
2. The right atrium contracts and blood flows through the tricuspid valve into the relaxed right ventricle.
3. The right ventricle then contracts and blood is pumped through the pulmonary valve into the **pulmonary artery,** which carries it to the lungs for oxygenation.
4. The left atrium receives blood returning to the heart after being oxygenated by the lungs. This blood enters the relaxed left atrium from the four **pulmonary veins.**
5. The left atrium contracts and blood flows through the mitral valve into the relaxed left ventricle.
6. When the left ventricle contracts, the blood is pumped through the aortic valve and into the **aorta,** the largest artery in the body. The aorta carries blood to all parts of the body.

It can be seen that the heart chambers alternate between relaxing in order to fill and contracting to push blood forward. The period of time a chamber is relaxed is **diastole.** The contraction phase is **systole.**

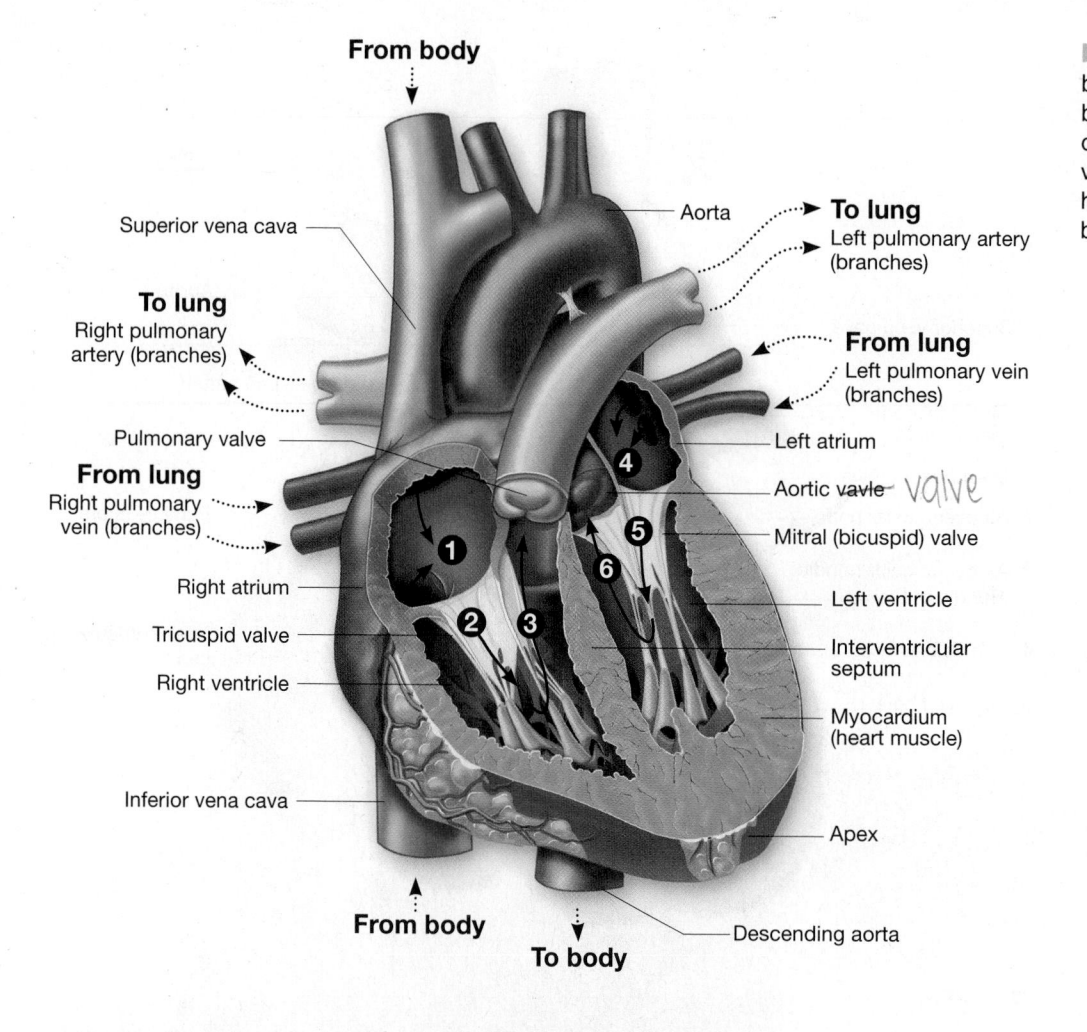

Figure 5.5 The path of blood flow through the chambers of the left and right side of the heart, including the veins delivering blood to the heart and arteries receiving blood ejected from the heart.

Conduction System of the Heart

atrioventricular bundle

atrioventricular node

autonomic nervous system
(aw-toh-NOM-ik / NER-vus / SIS-tem)

bundle branches

bundle of His

pacemaker

Purkinje fibers (per-KIN-gee)

sinoatrial node (sigh-noh-AY-tree-al)

The heart rate is regulated by the **autonomic nervous system;** therefore, we have no voluntary control over the beating of our heart. Special tissue within the heart is responsible for conducting an electrical impulse stimulating the different chambers to contract in the correct order.

The path that the impulses travel is as follows (see Figure 5.6 ■):

1. The **sinoatrial (SA) node,** or **pacemaker,** is where the electrical impulses begin. From the sinoatrial node a wave of electricity travels through the atria, causing them to contract, or go into systole.
2. The **atrioventricular node** is stimulated.
3. This node transfers the stimulation wave to the **atrioventricular bundle** (formerly called **bundle of His**).
4. The electrical signal next travels down the **bundle branches** within the interventricular septum.
5. The **Purkinje fibers** out in the ventricular myocardium are stimulated, resulting in ventricular systole.

■ **Figure 5.6** The conduction system of the heart; traces the path of the electrical impulse that stimulates the heart chambers to contract in the correct sequence.

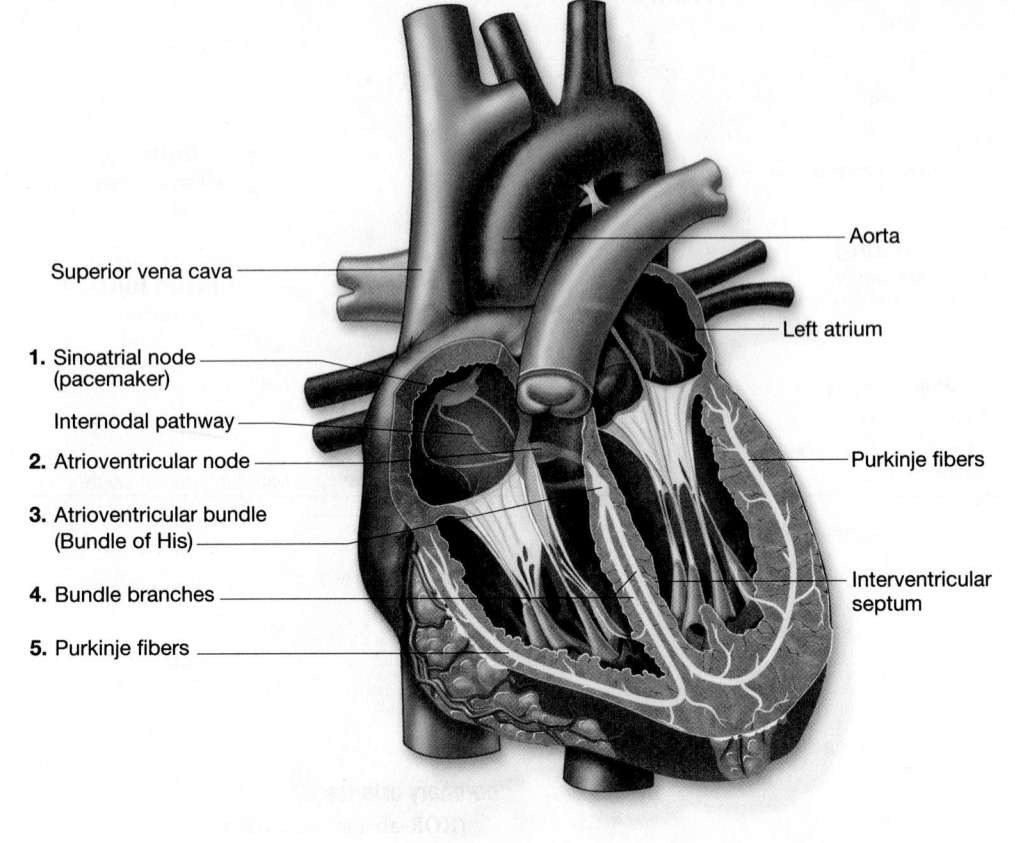

Superior vena cava

1. Sinoatrial node (pacemaker)

Internodal pathway

2. Atrioventricular node

3. Atrioventricular bundle (Bundle of His)

4. Bundle branches

5. Purkinje fibers

Aorta

Left atrium

Purkinje fibers

Interventricular septum

■ **Figure 5.7** An electrocardiogram (EKG) wave, a record of the electrical signal as it moves through the conduction system of the heart. This signal stimulates the chambers of the heart to contract and relax in the proper sequence.

MED TERM TIP

The electrocardiogram, referred to as an EKG or ECG, is a measurement of the electrical activity of the heart (see Figure 5.7 ■). This can give the physician information about the health of the heart, especially the myocardium.

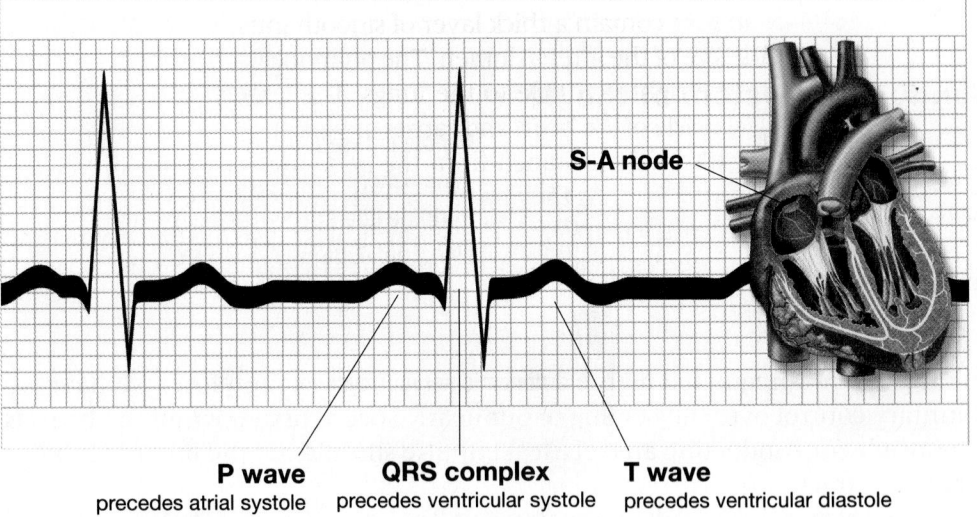

S-A node

P wave
precedes atrial systole

QRS complex
precedes ventricular systole

T wave
precedes ventricular diastole

Blood Vessels

lumen (LOO-men)

There are three types of blood vessels: arteries, capillaries, and veins (see Figure 5.8 ■). These are the pipes that circulate blood throughout the body. The **lumen** is the channel within these vessels through which blood flows.

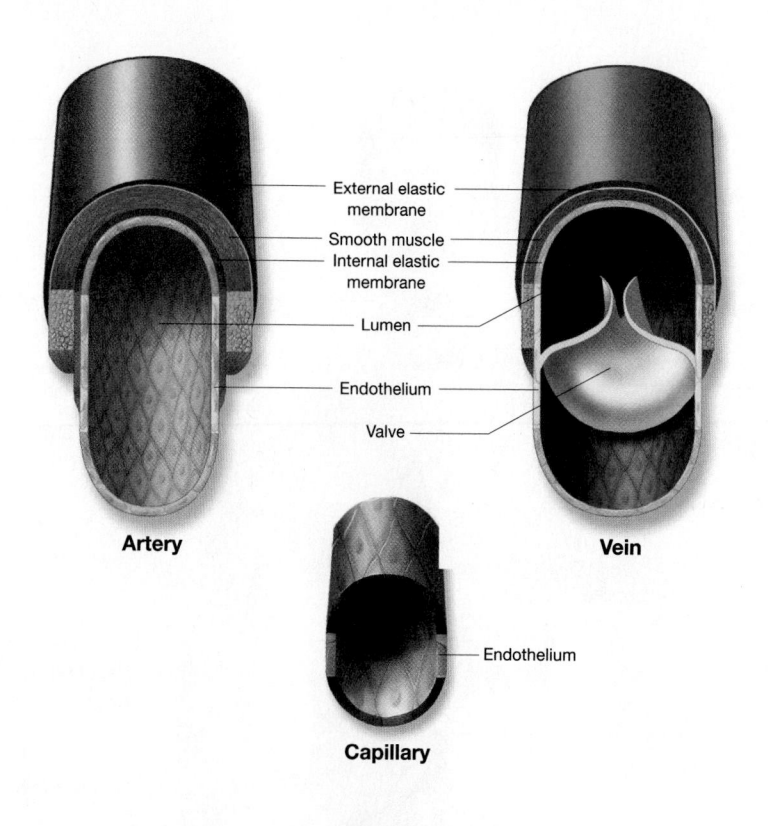

Arteries

arterioles (ar-TEE-ree-ohlz)

coronary arteries
(KOR-ah-nair-ee / AR-te-reez)

The arteries are the large, thick-walled vessels that carry the blood away from the heart. The walls of arteries contain a thick layer of smooth muscle that can contract or relax to change the size of the arterial lumen. The pulmonary artery carries deoxygenated blood from the right ventricle to the lungs. The largest artery, the aorta, begins from the left ventricle of the heart and carries oxygenated blood to all the body systems. The **coronary arteries** then branch from the aorta and provide blood to the myocardium (see Figure 5.9 ■). As they travel through the body, the arteries branch into progressively smaller sized arteries. The smallest of the arteries, called **arterioles,** deliver blood to the capillaries. Figure 5.10 ■ illustrates the major systemic arteries.

> **MED TERM TIP**
>
> The term *coronary*, from the Latin word for crown, describes how the great vessels encircle the heart as they emerge from the top of the heart.

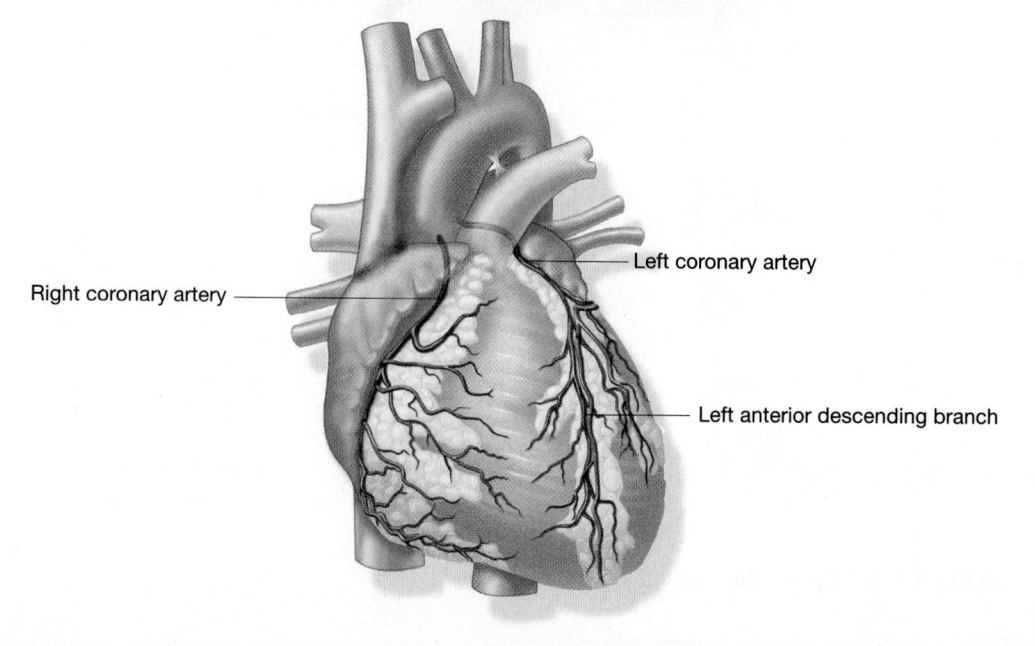

■ **Figure 5.9** The coronary arteries.

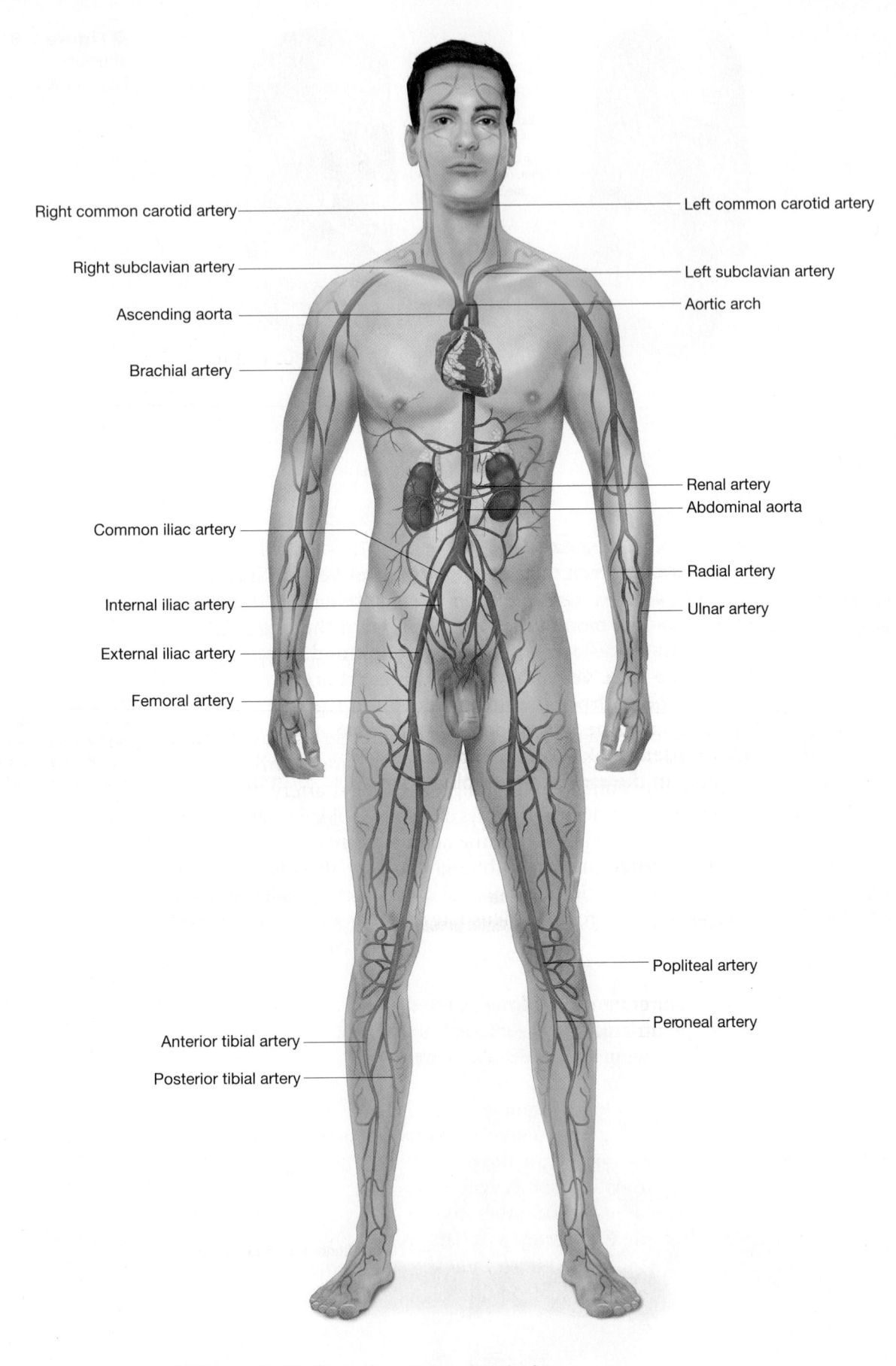

Right common carotid artery

Right subclavian artery

Ascending aorta

Brachial artery

Left common carotid artery

Left subclavian artery

Aortic arch

Renal artery

Abdominal aorta

Common iliac artery

Internal iliac artery

External iliac artery

Femoral artery

Radial artery

Ulnar artery

Popliteal artery

Peroneal artery

Anterior tibial artery

Posterior tibial artery

Figure 5.10 The major arteries of the body.

Capillaries

capillary bed

Capillaries are a network of tiny blood vessels referred to as a **capillary bed.** Arterial blood flows into a capillary bed, and venous blood flows back out. Capillaries are very thin walled, allowing for the diffusion of the oxygen and nutrients from the blood into the body tissues (see Figure 5.8). Likewise, carbon dioxide and waste products are able to diffuse out of the body tissues and into the bloodstream to be carried away. Since the capillaries are so small in diameter, the blood will not flow as quickly through them as it does through the arteries and veins. This means that the blood has time for an exchange of nutrients, oxygen, and waste material to take place. As blood exits a capillary bed, it returns to the heart through a vein.

Veins

venules (VEN-yools)

The veins carry blood back to the heart (see Figure 5.8). Blood leaving capillaries first enters small **venules,** which then merge into larger veins. Veins have much thinner walls than arteries, causing them to collapse easily. The veins also have valves that allow the blood to move only toward the heart. These valves prevent blood from backflowing, ensuring that blood always flows toward the heart. The two large veins that enter the heart are the superior vena cava, which carries blood from the upper body, and the inferior vena cava, which carries blood from the lower body. Blood pressure in the veins is much lower than in the arteries. Muscular action against the veins and skeletal muscle contractions help in the movement of blood. Figure 5.11 ■ illustrates the major systemic veins.

Pulse and Blood Pressure

blood pressure (BP)	**pulse**
diastolic pressure (dye-ah-STOL-ik)	**systolic pressure** (sis-TOL-ik)

Blood pressure (BP) is a measurement of the force exerted by blood against the wall of a blood vessel. During ventricular systole, blood is under a lot of pressure from the ventricular contraction, giving the highest blood pressure reading—the **systolic pressure.** The **pulse** felt at the wrist or throat is the surge of blood caused by the heart contraction. This is why pulse rate is normally equal to heart rate. During ventricular diastole, blood is not being pushed by the heart at all and the blood pressure reading drops to its lowest point—the **diastolic pressure.** Therefore, to see the full range of what is occurring with blood pressure, both numbers are required. Blood pressure is also affected by several other characteristics of the blood and the blood vessels. These include the elasticity of the arteries, the diameter of the blood vessels, the viscosity of the blood, the volume of blood flowing through the vessels, and the amount of resistance to blood flow.

MED TERM TIP

The instrument used to measure blood pressure is called a *sphygmomanometer.* The combining form *sphygm/o* means "pulse" and the suffix *-manometer* means "instrument to measure pressure." A blood pressure reading is reported as two numbers, for example, 120/80. The 120 is the systolic pressure and the 80 is the diastolic pressure. There is no one "normal" blood pressure number. The normal blood pressure for an adult is a systolic pressure less than 120 and diastolic pressure less than 80.

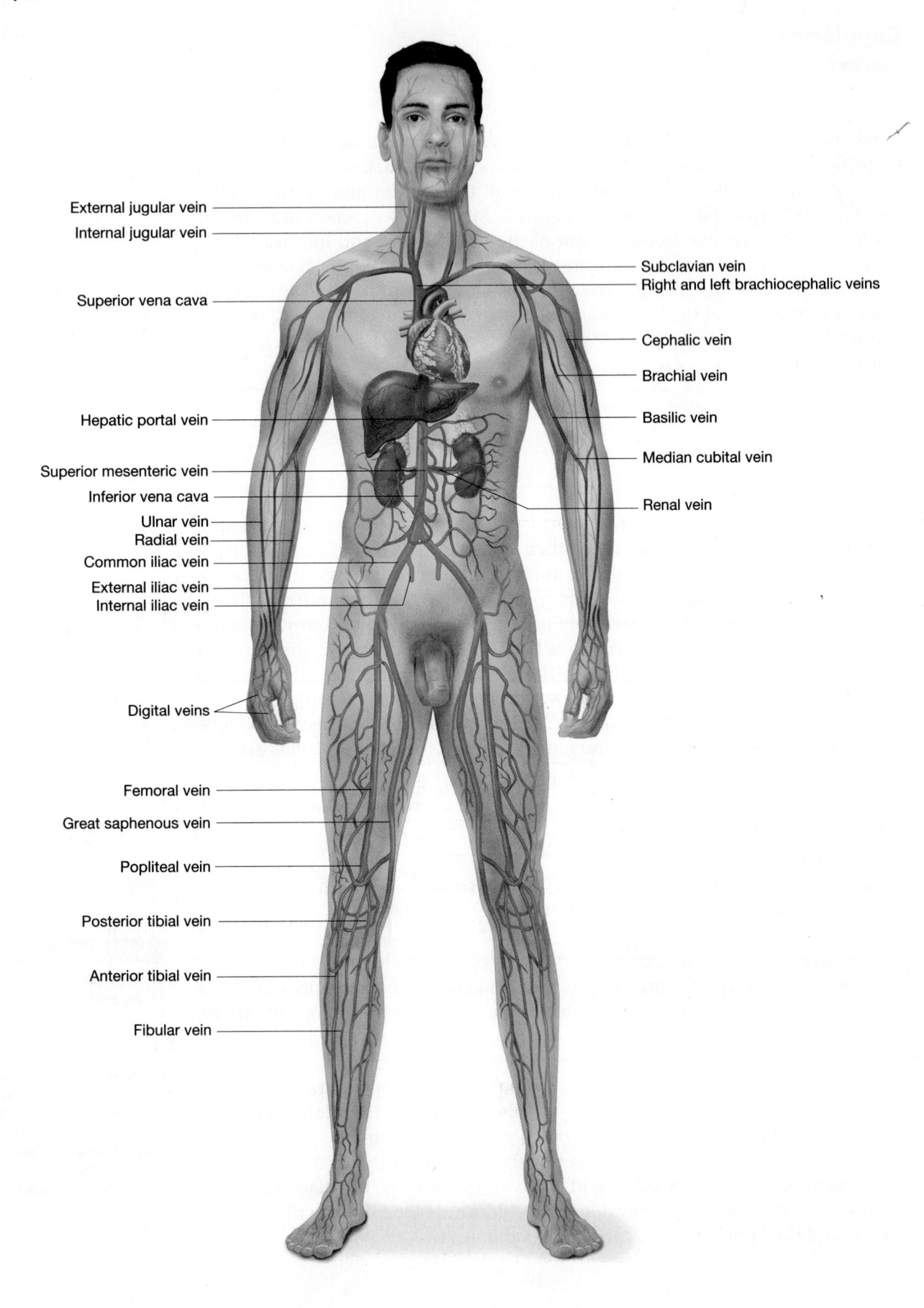

External jugular vein

Internal jugular vein

Subclavian vein

Right and left brachiocephalic veins

Superior vena cava

Cephalic vein

Brachial vein

Hepatic portal vein

Basilic vein

Superior mesenteric vein

Median cubital vein

Inferior vena cava

Renal vein

Ulnar vein

Radial vein

Common iliac vein

External iliac vein

Internal iliac vein

Digital veins

Femoral vein

Great saphenous vein

Popliteal vein

Posterior tibial vein

Anterior tibial vein

Fibular vein

Figure 5.11 The major veins of the body.

Terminology

Word Parts Used to Build Cardiovascular System Terms

The following lists contain the combining forms, suffixes, and prefixes used to build terms in the remaining sections of this chapter.

Combining Forms

aort/o	aorta	**embol/o**	plug	**son/o**	sound
angi/o	vessel	**hem/o**	blood	**sphygm/o**	pulse
arteri/o	artery	**isch/o**	to hold back	**steth/o**	chest
ather/o	fatty substance	**lip/o**	fat	**thromb/o**	clot
atri/o	atrium	**my/o**	muscle	**valv/o**	valve
cardi/o	heart	**myocardi/o**	heart muscle	**valvul/o**	valve
coron/o	heart	**orth/o**	straight	**varic/o**	dilated vein
corpor/o	body	**pect/o**	chest	**vas/o**	vessel
cutane/o	skin	**phleb/o**	vein	**vascul/o**	blood vessel
duct/o	to bring	**pulmon/o**	lung	**ven/o**	vein
electr/o	electricity	**sept/o**	a wall	**ventricul/o**	ventricle

Suffixes

-ac	pertaining to	-logy	study of	-rrhexis	rupture
-al	pertaining to	-lytic	destruction	-sclerosis	hardening
-ar	pertaining to	-manometer	instrument to measure pressure	-scope	instrument for viewing
-ary	pertaining to	-megaly	enlarged	-spasm	involuntary muscle contraction
-eal	pertaining to	-ole	small	-stenosis	narrowing
-ectomy	surgical removal	-oma	growth	-tension	pressure
-gram	record	-ose	pertaining to	-tic	pertaining to
-graphy	process of recording	-ous	pertaining to	-tonic	pertaining to tone
-ia	condition	-pathy	disease	-ule	small
-ic	pertaining to	-plasty	surgical repair		
-itis	inflammation				

Prefixes

a-	without	hyper-	excessive	poly-	many
anti-	against	hypo-	insufficient	tachy-	fast
brady-	slow	inter-	between	tetra-	four
de-	without	intra-	within	trans-	across
endo-	inner	per-	through	ultra-	beyond
extra-	outside of	peri-	around		

Anatomical Terms

TERM	WORD PARTS	DEFINITION
aortic (ay-OR-tik)	aort/o = aorta -ic = pertaining to	Pertaining to the aorta
arterial (ar-TEE-ree-al)	arteri/o = artery -al = pertaining to	Pertaining to an artery
arteriole (ar-TEE-ree-ohl)	arteri/o = artery -ole = small	A small (narrow in diameter) artery
atrial (AY-tree-al)	atri/o = atrium -al = pertaining to	Pertaining to the atrium
cardiac (CAR-dee-ak)	cardi/o = heart -ac = pertaining to	Pertaining to the heart
coronary (KOR-ah-nair-ee)	coron/o = heart -ary = pertaining to	Pertaining to the heart
interatrial (in-ter-AY-tree-al)	inter- = between atri/o = atrium -al = pertaining to	Pertaining to between the atria
interventricular (in-ter-ven-TRIK-yoo-lar)	inter- = between ventricul/o = ventricle -ar = pertaining to	Pertaining to between the ventricles
myocardial (my-oh-CAR-dee-al)	myocardi/o = heart muscle -al = pertaining to	Pertaining to heart muscle
valvular (VAL-view-lar)	valvul/o = valve -ar = pertaining to	Pertaining to a valve
vascular (VAS-kwee-lar)	vascul/o = blood vessel -ar = pertaining to	Pertaining to a blood vessel
venous (VEE-nus)	ven/o = vein -ous = pertaining to	Pertaining to a vein
ventricular (ven-TRIK-yoo-lar)	ventricul/o = ventricle -ar = pertaining to	Pertaining to a ventricle
venule (VEN-yool)	ven/o = vein -ule = small	A small (narrow in diameter) vein

Pathology

TERM	WORD PARTS	DEFINITION
Medical Specialties		
cardiology (car-dee-ALL-oh-jee)	cardi/o = heart -logy = study of	The branch of medicine involving diagnosis and treatment of conditions and diseases of the cardiovascular system. Physician is a *cardiologist.*
cardiovascular technician	cardi/o = heart vascul/o = blood vessel -ar = pertaining to	Healthcare professional trained to perform a variety of diagnostic and therapeutic procedures including electrocardiography, echocardiography, and exercise stress tests.

Pathology *(continued)*

TERM	WORD PARTS	DEFINITION
Signs and Symptoms		
angiitis (an-jee-EYE-tis)	angi/o = vessel -itis = inflammation	Inflammation of a vessel.
angiospasm (AN-jee-oh-spazm)	angi/o = vessel -spasm = involuntary muscle contraction	An involuntary muscle contraction of the smooth muscle in the wall of a vessel; narrows the vessel.
angiostenosis (an-jee-oh-sten-OH-sis)	angi/o = vessel -stenosis = narrowing	The narrowing of a vessel.
bradycardia (brad-ee-CAR-dee-ah)	brady- = slow cardi/o = heart -ia = condition	The condition of having a slow heart rate; typically less than 60 beats/minute; highly trained aerobic persons may normally have a slow heart rate.
embolus (EM-boh-lus)	embol/o = plug	The obstruction of a blood vessel by a blood clot that has broken off from a thrombus somewhere else in the body and traveled to the point of obstruction. If it occurs in a coronary artery, it may result in a myocardial infarction.

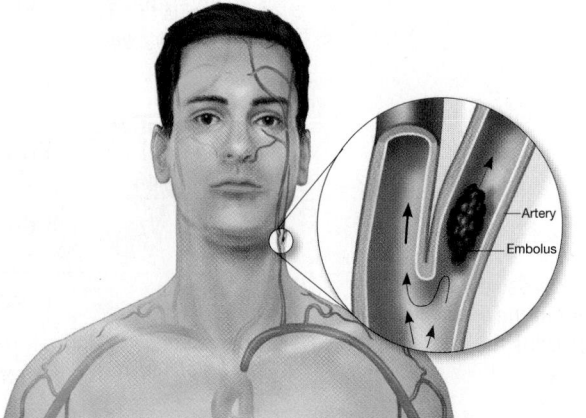

Artery
Embolus

■ **Figure 5.12** Illustration of an embolus floating in an artery. The embolus will become lodged in a blood vessel that is smaller than it is, resulting in occlusion of that artery.

TERM	WORD PARTS	DEFINITION
infarct (IN-farkt)		An area of tissue within an organ or part that undergoes necrosis (death) following the loss of its blood supply.
ischemia (is-KEYH-mee-ah)	isch/o = to hold back hem/o = blood -ia = condition	The localized and temporary deficiency of blood supply due to an obstruction to the circulation.
murmur (MUR-mur)		A sound, in addition to the normal heart sounds, arising from blood flowing through the heart. This extra sound may or may not indicate a heart abnormality.
orthostatic hypotension (or-thoh-STAT-ik)	orth/o = straight hypo- = insufficient -tension = pressure	The sudden drop in blood pressure a person experiences when standing straight up suddenly.
palpitations (pal-pih-TAY-shunz)		Pounding, racing heartbeats.

Pathology (continued)

TERM	WORD PARTS	DEFINITION
plaque (plak)		A yellow, fatty deposit of lipids in an artery that is the hallmark of atherosclerosis. Also called an *atheroma*.
regurgitation (re-ger-gih-TAY-shun)		To flow backwards. In the cardiovascular system this refers to the backflow of blood through a valve.
tachycardia (tak-ee-CAR-dee-ah)	tachy- = fast cardi/o = heart -ia = condition	The condition of having a fast heart rate; typically more than 100 beats/minute while at rest.
thrombus (THROM-bus)	thromb/o = clot	A blood clot forming within a blood vessel. May partially or completely occlude the blood vessel.

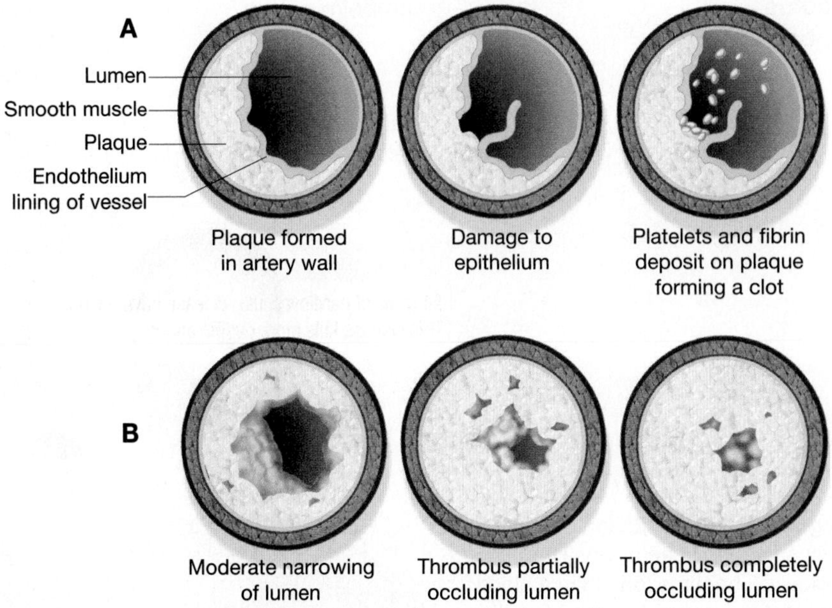

Figure 5.13 Development of an atherosclerotic plaque that progressively narrows the lumen of an artery to the point that a thrombus fully occludes the lumen.

Heart

TERM	WORD PARTS	DEFINITION
angina pectoris (an-JYE-nah / PECK-tor-is)	pect/o = chest	Condition in which there is severe pain with a sensation of constriction around the heart. Caused by a deficiency of oxygen to the heart muscle.
arrhythmia (ah-RITH-mee-ah)	a- = without -ia = condition	Irregularity in the heartbeat or action. Comes in many different forms; some are not serious, while others are life-threatening.
bundle branch block (BBB)		Occurs when the electrical impulse is blocked from traveling down the bundle of His or bundle branches. Results in the ventricles beating at a different rate than the atria. Also called a *heart block*.
cardiac arrest	cardi/o = heart -ac = pertaining to	Complete stopping of heart activity.
cardiomegaly (car-dee-oh-MEG-ah-lee)	cardi/o = heart -megaly = enlarged	An enlarged heart.

Pathology *(continued)*

TERM	WORD PARTS	DEFINITION
cardiomyopathy (car-dee-oh-my-OP-ah-thee)	cardi/o = heart my/o = muscle -pathy = disease	General term for a disease of the myocardium. Can be caused by alcohol abuse, parasites, viral infection, and congestive heart failure. One of the most common reasons a patient may require a heart transplant.
congenital septal defect (CSD)	sept/o = a wall -al = pertaining to	A hole, present at birth, in the septum between two heart chambers; results in a mixture of oxygenated and deoxygenated blood. There can be an *atrial septal defect* (ASD) and a *ventricular septal defect* (VSD).
congestive heart failure (CHF) (kon-JESS-tiv)		Pathological condition of the heart in which there is a reduced outflow of blood from the left side of the heart because the left ventricle myocardium has become too weak to efficiently pump blood. Results in weakness, breathlessness, and edema.
coronary artery disease (CAD) (KOR-ah-nair-ee)	coron/o = heart -ary = pertaining to	Insufficient blood supply to the heart muscle due to an obstruction of one or more coronary arteries. May be caused by atherosclerosis and may cause angina pectoris and myocardial infarction.

MED TERM TIP

All types of cardiovascular disease have been the number one killer of Americans since the 19th century. This disease kills more people annually than the next six causes of death combined.

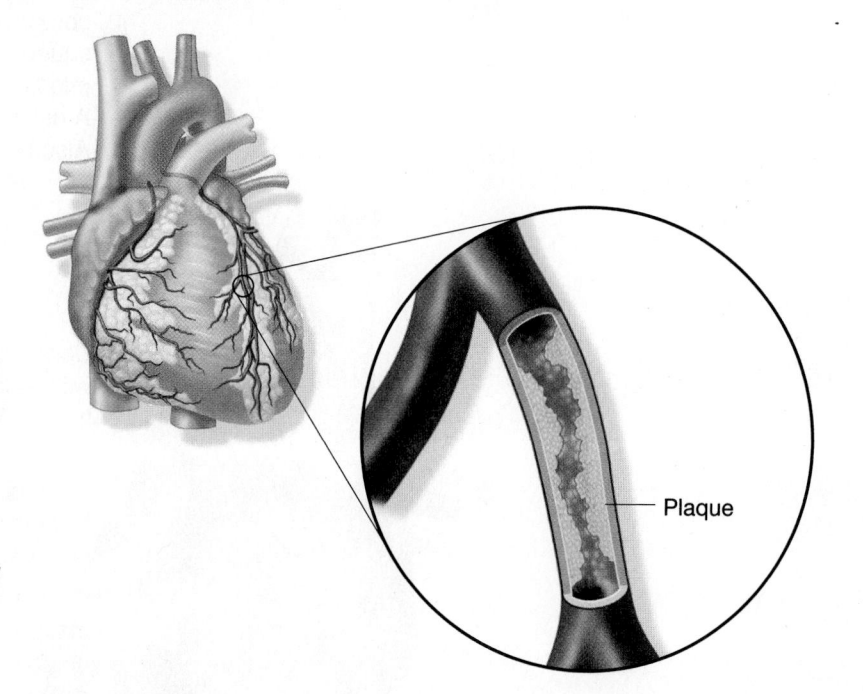

Plaque

■ **Figure 5.14** Formation of an atherosclerotic plaque within a coronary artery; may lead to coronary artery disease, angina pectoris, and myocardial infarction.

| **endocarditis** (en-doh-car-DYE-tis) | endo- = inner cardi/o = heart -itis = inflammation | Inflammation of the lining membranes of the heart. May be due to bacteria or to an abnormal immunological response. In bacterial endocarditis, the mass of bacteria that forms is referred to as *vegetation*. |

Pathology *(continued)*

TERM	WORD PARTS	DEFINITION
fibrillation (fih-brill-AY-shun)		An extremely serious arrhythmia characterized by an abnormal quivering or contraction of heart fibers. When this occurs in the ventricles, cardiac arrest and death can occur. Emergency equipment to defibrillate, or convert the heart to a normal beat, is necessary.
flutter		An arrhythmia in which the atria beat too rapidly, but in a regular pattern.
heart valve prolapse (PROH-laps)		Condition in which the cusps or flaps of the heart valve are too loose and fail to shut tightly, allowing blood to flow backward through the valve when the heart chamber contracts. Most commonly occurs in the mitral valve, but may affect any of the heart valves.
heart valve stenosis (steh-NOH-sis)	-stenosis = narrowing	The cusps or flaps of the heart valve are too stiff. Therefore, they are unable to open fully, making it difficult for blood to flow through, or shut tightly, allowing blood to flow backward. This condition may affect any of the heart valves.
myocardial infarction (MI) (my-oh-CAR-dee-al / in-FARC-shun)	myocardi/o = heart muscle -al = pertaining to	Condition caused by the partial or complete occlusion or closing of one or more of the coronary arteries. Symptoms include a squeezing pain or heavy pressure in the middle of the chest (angina pectoris). A delay in treatment could result in death. Also referred to as a *heart attack.*

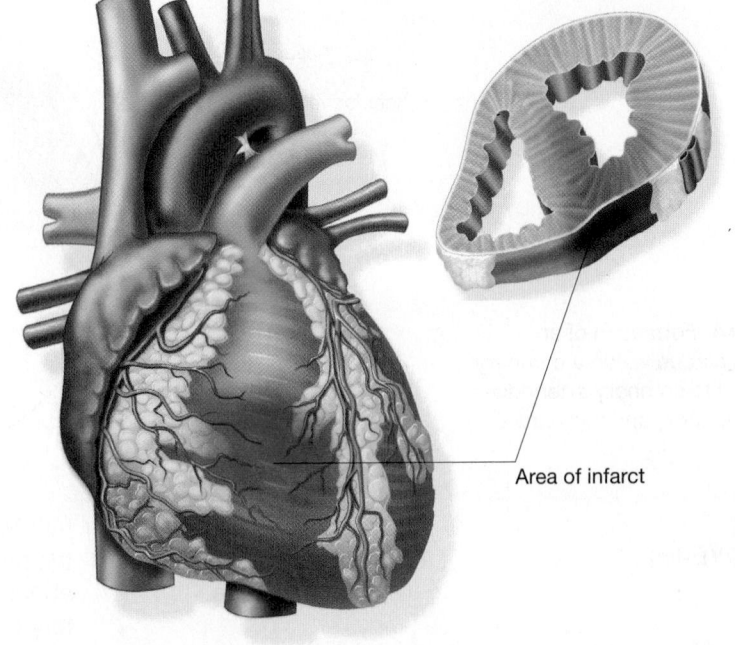

Area of infarct

■ **Figure 5.15** External and cross-sectional view of an infarct caused by a myocardial infarction.

Pathology *(continued)*

TERM	WORD PARTS	DEFINITION
myocarditis (my-oh-car-DYE-tis)	myocardi/o = heart muscle -itis = inflammation	Inflammation of the muscle layer of the heart wall.
pericarditis (pair-ih-car-DYE-tis)	peri- = around cardi/o = heart -itis = inflammation	Inflammation of the pericardial sac around the heart.
tetralogy of Fallot (teh-TRALL-oh-jee / fal-LOH)	tetra- = four -logy = study of	Combination of four congenital anomalies: pulmonary stenosis, an interventricular septal defect, improper placement of the aorta, and hypertrophy of the right ventricle. Needs immediate surgery to correct.
valvulitis (val-view-LYE-tis)	valvul/o = valve -itis = inflammation	The inflammation of a heart valve.

Blood Vessels

aneurysm (AN-yoo-rizm)		Weakness in the wall of an artery resulting in localized widening of the artery. Although an aneurysm may develop in any artery, common sites include the aorta in the abdomen and the cerebral arteries in the brain.

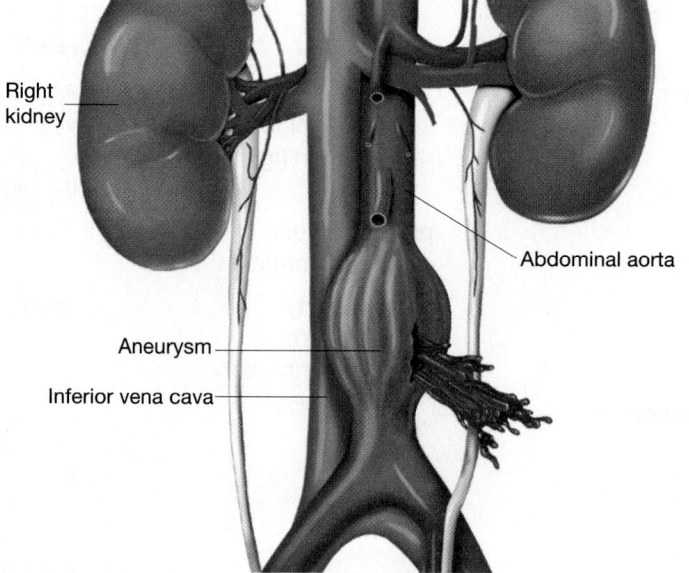

Right kidney

Abdominal aorta

Aneurysm

Inferior vena cava

Figure 5.16 Illustration of a large aneurysm in the abdominal aorta that has ruptured.

TERM	WORD PARTS	DEFINITION
arteriorrhexis (ar-tee-ree-oh-REK-sis)	arteri/o = artery -rrhexis = rupture	A ruptured artery; may occur if an aneurysm ruptures an arterial wall.
arteriosclerosis (ar-tee-ree-oh-skleh-ROH-sis)	arteri/o = artery -sclerosis = hardening	Thickening, hardening, and loss of elasticity of the walls of the arteries. Most often due to atherosclerosis.
atheroma (ath-er-OH-mah)	ather/o = fatty substance -oma = growth	A deposit of fatty substance in the wall of an artery that bulges into and narrows the lumen of the artery; a characteristic of atherosclerosis. Also called a *plaque.*

Pathology *(continued)*

TERM	WORD PARTS	DEFINITION
atherosclerosis (ath-er-oh-skleh-ROH-sis)	ather/o = fatty substance -sclerosis = hardening	The most common form of arteriosclerosis. Caused by the formation of yellowish plaques of cholesterol on the inner walls of arteries (see again Figures 5.13 & 5.14).
coarctation of the aorta (CoA) (koh-ark-TAY-shun)		Severe congenital narrowing of the aorta.
hemorrhoid (HIM-oh-royd)	hem/o = blood	Varicose veins in the anal region.
hypertension (HTN) (high-per-TEN-shun)	hyper- = excessive -tension = pressure	Blood pressure above the normal range. *Essential* or *primary hypertension* occurs directly from cardiovascular disease. *Secondary hypertension* refers to high blood pressure resulting from another disease such as kidney disease.
hypotension (high-poh-TEN-shun)	hypo- = insufficient -tension = pressure	Decrease in blood pressure. Can occur in shock, infection, cancer, anemia, or as death approaches.
patent ductus arteriosus (PDA) (PAY-tent / DUCK-tus / ar-tee-ree-OH-sis)	duct/o = to bring arteri/o = artery	Congenital heart anomaly in which the fetal connection between the pulmonary artery and the aorta fails to close at birth. This condition may be treated with medication and resolve with time. However, in some cases surgery is required.
peripheral vascular disease (PVD)	-al = pertaining to vascul/o = blood vessel -ar = pertaining to	Any abnormal condition affecting blood vessels outside the heart. Symptoms may include pain, pallor, numbness, and loss of circulation and pulses.
phlebitis (fleh-BYE-tis)	phleb/o = vein -itis = inflammation	The inflammation of a vein.
polyarteritis (pol-ee-ar-ter-EYE-tis)	poly- = many arteri/o = artery -itis = inflammation	Inflammation of several arteries.
Raynaud's phenomenon (ray-NOZ)		Periodic ischemic attacks affecting the extremities of the body, especially the fingers, toes, ears, and nose. The affected extremities become cyanotic and very painful. These attacks are brought on by arterial constriction due to extreme cold or emotional stress.
thrombophlebitis (throm-boh-fleh-BYE-tis)	thromb/o = clot phleb/o = vein -itis = inflammation	Inflammation of a vein resulting in the formation of blood clots within the vein.
varicose veins (VAIR-ih-kohs)	varic/o = dilated vein -ose = pertaining to	Swollen and distended veins, usually in the legs.

Diagnostic Procedures

TERM	WORD PARTS	DEFINITION
Medical Procedures		
auscultation (oss-kul-TAY-shun)		Process of listening to the sounds within the body by using a stethoscope.
sphygmomanometer (sfig-moh-mah-NOM-eh-ter)	sphygm/o = pulse -manometer = instrument to measure pressure	Instrument for measuring blood pressure. Also referred to as a *blood pressure cuff*.

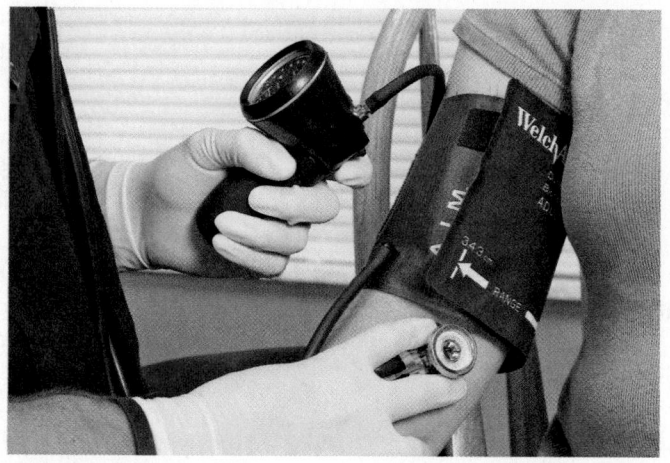

■ **Figure 5.17** Using a sphygmomanometer to measure blood pressure.

TERM	WORD PARTS	DEFINITION
stethoscope (STETH-oh-scope)	steth/o = chest -scope = instrument for viewing	Instrument for listening to body sounds (auscultation), such as the chest, heart, or intestines.
Clinical Laboratory Tests		
cardiac enzymes (CAR-dee-ak / EN-zyms)	cardi/o = heart -ac = pertaining to	Blood test to determine the level of enzymes specific to heart muscles in the blood. An increase in the enzymes may indicate heart muscle damage such as a myocardial infarction. These enzymes include creatine phosphokinase (CPK), lactate dehydrogenase (LDH), and glutamic oxaloacetic transaminase (GOT).
serum lipoprotein level (SEE-rum / lip-oh-PROH-teen)	lip/o = fat	Blood test to measure the amount of cholesterol and triglycerides in the blood. An indicator of atherosclerosis risk.
Diagnostic Imaging		
angiogram (AN-jee-oh-gram)	angi/o = vessel -gram = record	X-ray record of a vessel taken during angiography.
angiography (an-jee-OG-rah-fee)	angi/o = vessel -graphy = process of recording	X-rays taken after the injection of an opaque material into a blood vessel. Can be performed on the aorta as an aortic angiography, on the heart as angiocardiography, and on the brain as a cerebral angiography.
cardiac scan	cardi/o = heart -ac = pertaining to	Patient is given radioactive thallium intravenously and then scanning equipment is used to visualize the hear. It is especially useful in determining myocardial damage.

Diagnostic Procedures *(continued)*

TERM	WORD PARTS	DEFINITION
Doppler ultrasonography (DOP-ler / ul-trah-son-OG-rah-fee)	ultra- = beyond son/o = sound -graphy = process of recording	Measurement of sound-wave echoes as they bounce off tissues and organs to produce an image. In this system, used to measure velocity of blood moving through blood vessels to look for blood clots or deep vein thromboses.
echocardiography (ek-oh-car-dee-OG-rah-fee)	cardi/o = artery -graphy = process of recording	Noninvasive diagnostic method using ultrasound to visualize internal cardiac structures. Cardiac valve activity can be evaluated using this method.
Cardiac Function Tests		
catheter (KATH-eh-ter)		Flexible tube inserted into the body for the purpose of moving fluids into or out of the body. In the cardiovascular system a catheter is used to place dye into blood vessels so they may be visualized on x-rays.
cardiac catheterization (CAR-dee-ak / cath-eh-ter-ih-ZAY-shun)	cardi/o = heart -ac = pertaining to	Passage of a thin tube catheter through a blood vessel leading to the heart. Done to detect abnormalities, to collect cardiac blood samples, and to determine the blood pressure within the heart.
electrocardiogram (ee-lek-tro-CAR-dee-oh-gram)	electr/o = electricity cardi/o = heart -gram = record	Hard copy record produced by electrocardiography.
electrocardiography (ECG, EKG) (ee-lek-troh-car-dee-OG-rah-fee)	electr/o = electricity cardi/o = heart -graphy = process of recording	Process of recording the electrical activity of the heart. Useful in the diagnosis of abnormal cardiac rhythm and heart muscle (myocardium) damage.
Holter monitor		Portable ECG monitor worn by a patient for a period of a few hours to a few days to assess the heart and pulse activity as the person goes through the activities of daily living. Used to assess a patient who experiences chest pain and unusual heart activity during exercise and normal activities.
stress testing	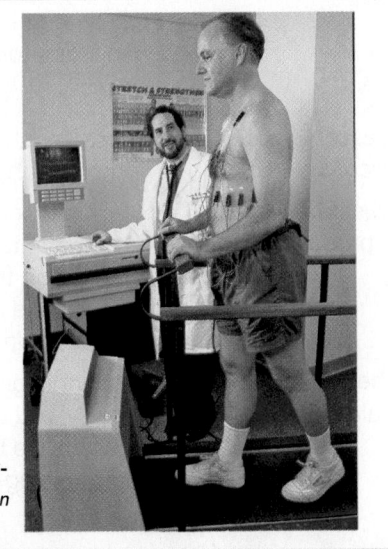	Method for evaluating cardiovascular fitness. The patient is placed on a treadmill or a bicycle and then subjected to steadily increasing levels of work. An EKG and oxygen levels are taken while the patient exercises. The test is stopped if abnormalities occur on the EKG. Also called an *exercise test* or a *treadmill test*.

■ **Figure 5.18** Man undergoing a stress test on a treadmill while physician monitors his condition. *(Jonathan Nourok/PhotoEdit Inc.)*

Therapeutic Procedures

TERM	WORD PARTS	DEFINITION
Medical Procedures		
cardiopulmonary resuscitation (CPR) (car-dee-oh-PULL-mon-air-ee / ree-suss-ih-TAY-shun)	cardi/o = heart pulmon/o = lung -ary = pertaining to	Procedure to restore cardiac output and oxygenated air to the lungs for a person in cardiac arrest. A combination of chest compressions (to push blood out of the heart) and artificial respiration (to blow air into the lungs) performed by one or two CPR-trained rescuers.
defibrillation (dee-fib-rih-LAY-shun)	de- = without	Procedure that converts serious irregular heartbeats, such as fibrillation, by giving electric shocks to the heart using an instrument called a defibrillator. Also called *cardioversion.* Automated external defibrillators (AED) are portable devices that automatically detect life-threatening arrhythmias and deliver the appropriate electrical shock. They are designed to be used by nonmedical personnel and are found in public places such as shopping malls and schools.

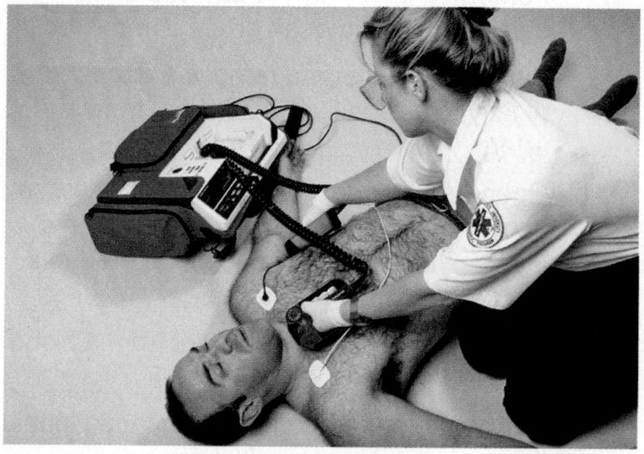

■ **Figure 5.19** An emergency medical technician positions defibrillator paddles on the chest of a supine male patient.

TERM	WORD PARTS	DEFINITION
extracorporeal circulation (ECC) (EX-tra-core-poor-EE-al)	extra- = outside of corpor/o = body -eal = pertaining to	During open-heart surgery, the routing of blood to a heart-lung machine so it can be oxygenated and pumped to the rest of the body.
implantable cardioverter-defibrillator (ICD) (CAR-dee-oh-ver-ter / de-FIB-rih-lay-tor)	cardi/o = heart de- = without	Device implanted in the heart that delivers an electrical shock to restore a normal heart rhythm. Particularly useful for persons who experience ventricular fibrillation.
pacemaker implantation		Electrical device that substitutes for the natural pacemaker of the heart. It controls the beating of the heart by a series of rhythmic electrical impulses. An external pacemaker has the electrodes on the outside of the body. An internal pacemaker has the electrodes surgically implanted within the chest wall.

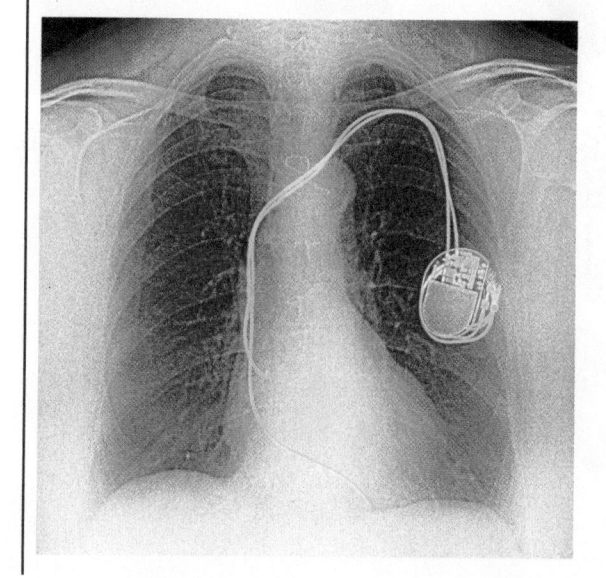

■ **Figure 5.20** Color enhanced X-ray showing a pacemaker implanted in the left side of the chest and the electrode wires running to the heart muscle. *(UHB Trust/Getty Images)*

◼ Therapeutic Procedures *(continued)*

TERM	WORD PARTS	DEFINITION
thrombolytic therapy (throm-boh-LIT-ik / THAIR-ah-pee)	thromb/o = clot -lytic = destruction	Process in which drugs, such as streptokinase (SK) or tissue-type plasminogen activator (tPA), are injected into a blood vessel to dissolve clots and restore blood flow.
Surgical Procedures		
aneurysmectomy (an-yoo-riz-MEK-toh-mee)	-ectomy = surgical removal	Surgical removal of the sac of an aneurysm.
arterial anastomosis (ar-TEE-ree-all / ah-nas-toe-MOE-sis)	arteri/o = artery -al = pertaining to	Surgical joining together of two arteries. Performed if an artery is severed or if a damaged section of an artery is removed.
atherectomy (ath-er-EK-toh-mee)	ather/o = fatty substance -ectomy = surgical removal	Surgical procedure to remove a deposit of fatty substance, an atheroma, from an artery.
coronary artery bypass graft (CABG) (KOR-ah-nair-ee)	coron/o = heart -ary = pertaining to	Open-heart surgery in which a blood vessel from another location in the body (often a leg vein) is grafted to route blood around a blocked coronary artery.
embolectomy (em-boh-LEK-toh-mee)	embol/o = plug -ectomy = surgical removal	Removal of an embolus or clot from a blood vessel.
endarterectomy (end-ar-teh-REK-toh-mee)	endo- = inner arteri/o = artery -ectomy = surgical removal	Removal of the diseased or damaged inner lining of an artery. Usually performed to remove atherosclerotic plaques.
heart transplantation		Replacement of a diseased or malfunctioning heart with a donor's heart.
intracoronary artery stent (in-trah-KOR-ah-nair-ee / AR-ter-ee)	intra- = within coron/o = heart -ary = pertaining to	Placement of a stent within a coronary artery to treat coronary ischemia due to atherosclerosis.

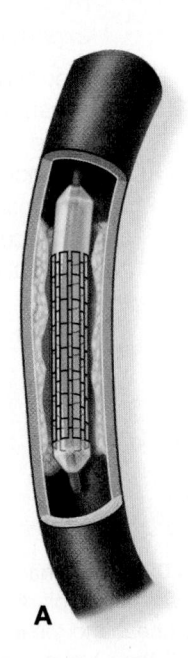
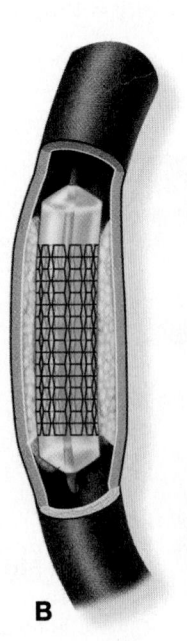
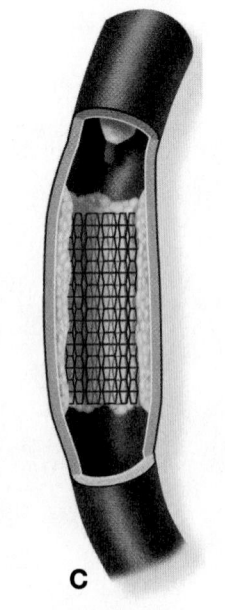

◼ Figure 5.21 The process of placing a stent in a blood vessel. (A) A catheter is used to place a collapsed stent next to an atherosclerotic plaque; (B) stent is expanded; (C) catheter is removed, leaving the expanded stent behind.

A   B   C

Therapeutic Procedures *(continued)*

TERM	WORD PARTS	DEFINITION
ligation and stripping (lye-GAY-shun)		Surgical treatment for varicose veins. The damaged vein is tied off (ligation) and removed (stripping).
percutaneous transluminal coronary angioplasty (PTCA) (per-kyoo-TAY-nee-us / trans-LOO-mih-nal / KOR-ah-nair-ee / AN-jee-oh-plas-tee)	per- = through cutane/o = skin -ous = pertaining to trans- = across -al = pertaining to angi/o = vessel -plasty = surgical repair	Method for treating localized coronary artery narrowing. A balloon catheter is inserted through the skin into the coronary artery and inflated to dilate the narrow blood vessel.

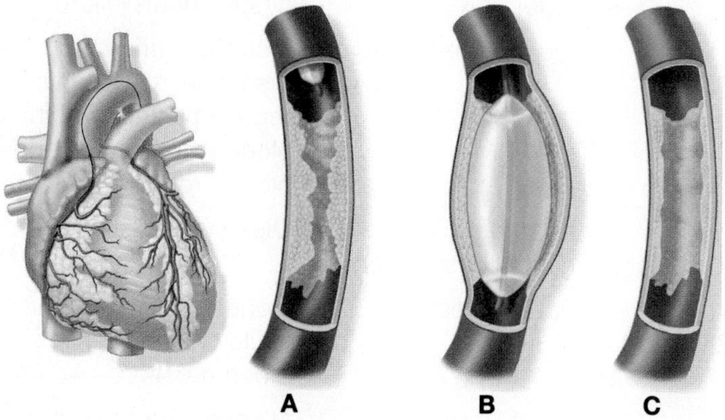

■ **Figure 5.22** Balloon angioplasty: (A) deflated balloon catheter is approaching an atherosclerotic plaque; (B) plaque is compressed by inflated balloon; (C) plaque remains compressed after balloon catheter is removed.

A   **B**   **C**

stent		Stainless steel tube placed within a blood vessel or a duct to widen the lumen (see again Figure 5.21).
valve replacement		Removal of a diseased heart valve and replacement with an artificial valve.
valvoplasty (VAL-voh-plas-tee)	valv/o = valve -plasty = surgical repair	Surgical procedure to repair a heart valve.

Pharmacology

CLASSIFICATION	WORD PARTS	ACTION	EXAMPLES
ACE inhibitor drugs		Produce vasodilation and decrease blood pressure.	benazepril, Lotensin; catopril, Capoten
antiarrhythmic (an-tye-a-RHYTH-mik)	anti- = against a- = without -ic = pertaining to	Reduces or prevents cardiac arrhythmias.	flecainide, Tambocor; ibutilide, Corvert
anticoagulant (an-tye-koh-AG-you-lant)	anti- = against	Prevents blood clot formation.	warfarin sodium, Coumadin, Warfarin
antilipidemic (an-tye-lip-ih-DEM-ik)	anti- = against lip/o = fat -ic = pertaining to	Reduces amount of cholesterol and lipids in the bloodstream; treats hyperlipidemia.	atorvastatin, Lipitor; simvastatin, Zocor
antiplatelet agents	anti- = against	Inhibits the ability of platelets to clump together as part of a blood clot.	clopidogrel, Plavix; aspirin; ticlopidine, Ticlid

Pharmacology *(continued)*

CLASSIFICATION	WORD PARTS	ACTION	EXAMPLES
beta-blocker drugs		Treats hypertension and angina pectoris by lowering the heart rate.	metoprolol, Lopressor; propranolol, Inderal
calcium channel blocker drugs		Treats hypertension, angina pectoris, and congestive heart failure by causing the heart to beat less forcefully and less often.	diltiazem, Cardizem; nifedipine, Procardia
cardiotonic (card-ee-oh-TAHN-ik)	cardi/o = heart -tonic = pertaining to tone	Increases the force of cardiac muscle contraction; treats congestive heart failure.	digoxin, Lanoxin
diuretic (dye-you-RET-ik)	-tic = pertaining to	Increases urine production by the kidneys, which works to reduce plasma and therefore blood volume, resulting in lower blood pressure.	furosemide, Lasix
thrombolytic (throm-boh-LIT-ik)	thromb/o = clot -lytic = destruction	Dissolves existing blood clots.	tissue plasminogen activator (tPA); alteplase, Activase
vasoconstrictor (vaz-oh-kon-STRICK-tor)	vas/o = vessel	Contracts smooth muscle in walls of blood vessels; raises blood pressure.	metaraminol, Aramine
vasodilator (vaz-oh-DYE-late-or)	vas/o = vessel	Relaxes the smooth muscle in the walls of arteries, thereby increasing diameter of the blood vessel. Used for two main purposes: increasing circulation to an ischemic area; reducing blood pressure.	nitroglycerine, Nitro-Dur; isoxsuprine, Vasodilan

Abbreviations

AED	automated external defibrillator	**CHF**	congestive heart failure
AF	atrial fibrillation	**CoA**	coarctation of the aorta
AMI	acute myocardial infarction	**CP**	chest pain
AS	arteriosclerosis	**CPR**	cardiopulmonary resuscitation
ASD	atrial septal defect	**CSD**	congenital septal defect
ASHD	arteriosclerotic heart disease	**CV**	cardiovascular
AV, A-V	atrioventricular	**DVT**	deep vein thrombosis
BBB	bundle branch block (L for left; R for right)	**ECC**	extracorporeal circulation
BP	blood pressure	**ECG, EKG**	electrocardiogram
bpm	beats per minute	**ECHO**	echocardiogram
CABG	coronary artery bypass graft	**GOT**	glutamic oxaloacetic transaminase
CAD	coronary artery disease	**HTN**	hypertension
cath	catheterization	**ICD**	implantable cardioverter-defibrillator
CC	cardiac catheterization, chief complaint	**ICU**	intensive care unit
CCU	coronary care unit	**IV**	intravenous

Abbreviations *(continued)*

LVAD	left ventricular assist device	**PDA**	patent ductus arteriosus
LVH	left ventricular hypertrophy	**PTCA**	percutaneous transluminal coronary angioplasty
MI	myocardial infarction, mitral insufficiency	**PVC**	premature ventricular contraction
mm Hg	millimeters of mercury	**S1**	first heart sound
MR	mitral regurgitation	**S2**	second heart sound
MS	mitral stenosis	**SA, S-A**	sinoatrial
		SK	streptokinase
		tPA	tissue-type plasminogen activator
MVP	mitral valve prolapse	**V fib**	ventricular fibrillation
P	pulse	**VSD**	ventricular septal defect
PAC	premature atrial contraction	**VT**	ventricular tachycardia

MED TERM TIP

Word Watch: Be careful using the abbreviation *MS,* which can mean either "mitral stenosis" or "multiple sclerosis."

Chapter Review

Real-World Applications

Medical Record Analysis

This Discharge Summary contains 12 medical terms. Underline each term and write it in the list below the report. Then define each term.

PEARSON GENERAL HOSPITAL

PGH

5500 University Avenue, Metropolis, TX
Phone: (211) 594-4000 • Fax: (211) 594-4001

Medical Consultation Osteology
Date 6/1/2013
Patient Jorge Johnson
Patient complaint: Sever pain in the right ankle with any movement of lower limb.

Discharge Summary

Admitting Diagnosis:	Difficulty breathing, hypertension, tachycardia
Final Diagnosis:	CHF secondary to mitral valve prolapse
History of Present Illness:	Patient was brought to the Emergency Room by her family because of difficulty breathing and palpitations. Patient reports that she has experienced these symptoms for the past 6 months, but this episode is more severe than any previous. Upon admission in the ER, heart rate was 120 beats per minute and blood pressure was 180/110. The results of an EKG and cardiac enzyme blood tests were normal. She was admitted for a complete workup for tachycardia and hypertension.
Summary of Hospital Course:	Patient underwent a full battery of diagnostic tests. A prolapsed mitral valve was observed by echocardiography. A stress test had to be stopped early due to onset of severe difficulty in breathing. Angiocardiography failed to demonstrate significant CAD. Blood pressure and tachycardia were controlled with medications. At discharge, HR was 88 beats per minute and blood pressure was 165/98.
Discharge Plans:	There was no evidence of a myocardial infarction or significant CAD. Patient was placed on a low-salt and low-cholesterol diet. She received instructions on beginning a carefully graded exercise program. She is to continue her medications. If symptoms are not controlled by these measures, a mitral valve replacement will be considered.

Term	Definition
1 _____	_____
2 _____	_____
3 _____	_____
4 _____	_____
5 _____	_____
6 _____	_____
7 _____	_____
8 _____	_____
9 _____	_____
10 _____	_____
11 _____	_____
12 _____	_____

Chart Note Transcription

The chart note below contains 11 phrases that can be reworded with a medical term that you learned in this chapter. Each phrase is identified with an underline. Determine the medical term and write your answers in the space provided.

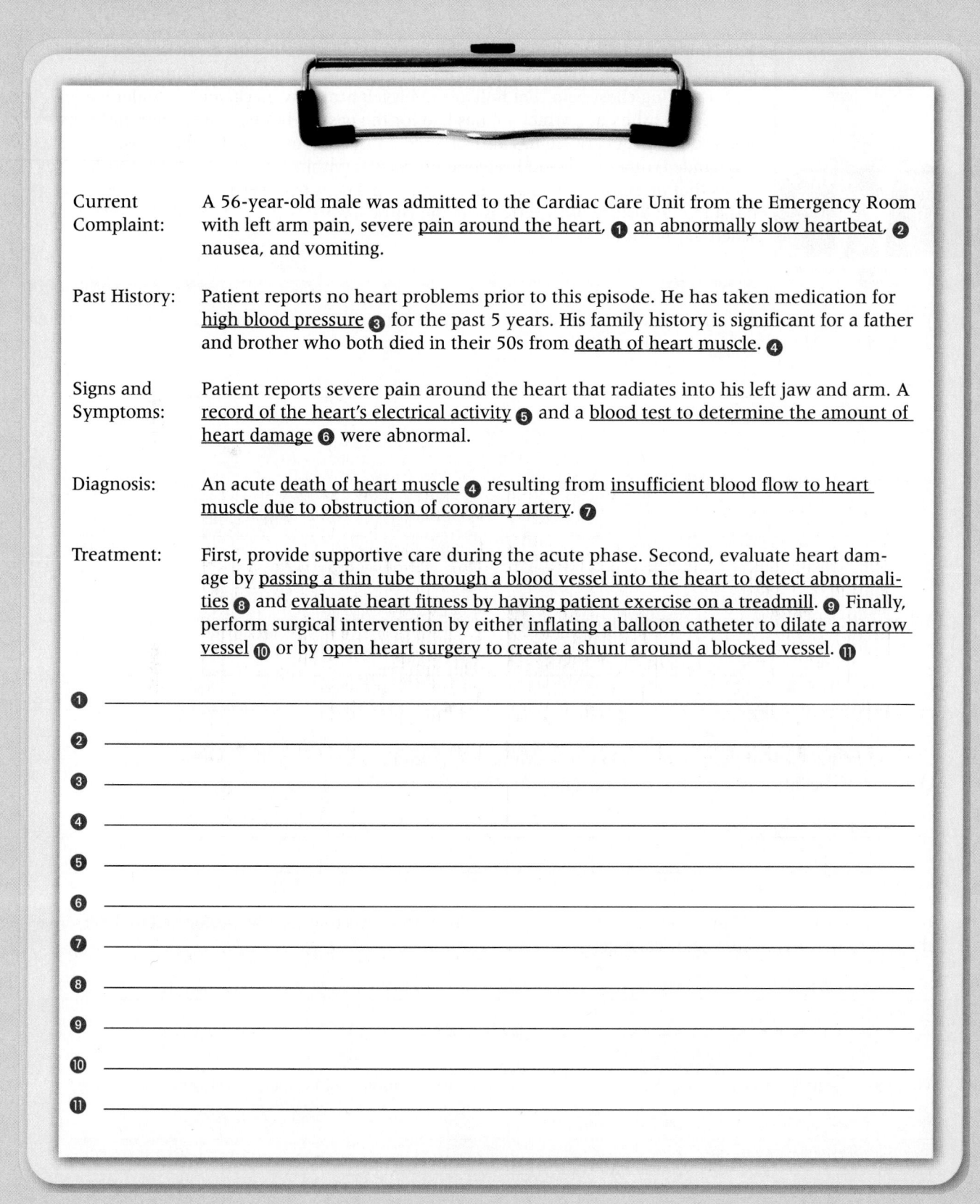

Current Complaint: A 56-year-old male was admitted to the Cardiac Care Unit from the Emergency Room with left arm pain, severe <u>pain around the heart</u>, **1** <u>an abnormally slow heartbeat</u>, **2** nausea, and vomiting.

Past History: Patient reports no heart problems prior to this episode. He has taken medication for <u>high blood pressure</u> **3** for the past 5 years. His family history is significant for a father and brother who both died in their 50s from <u>death of heart muscle</u>. **4**

Signs and Symptoms: Patient reports severe pain around the heart that radiates into his left jaw and arm. A <u>record of the heart's electrical activity</u> **5** and a <u>blood test to determine the amount of heart damage</u> **6** were abnormal.

Diagnosis: An acute <u>death of heart muscle</u> **4** resulting from <u>insufficient blood flow to heart muscle due to obstruction of coronary artery</u>. **7**

Treatment: First, provide supportive care during the acute phase. Second, evaluate heart damage by <u>passing a thin tube through a blood vessel into the heart to detect abnormalities</u> **8** and <u>evaluate heart fitness by having patient exercise on a treadmill</u>. **9** Finally, perform surgical intervention by either <u>inflating a balloon catheter to dilate a narrow vessel</u> **10** or by <u>open heart surgery to create a shunt around a blocked vessel</u>. **11**

1 _____

2 _____

3 _____

4 _____

5 _____

6 _____

7 _____

8 _____

9 _____

10 _____

11 _____

Case Study

Below is a case study presentation of a patient with a condition covered by this chapter. Read the case study and answer the questions below. Some questions will ask for information not included within this chapter. Use your text, a medical dictionary, or any other reference material you choose to answer these questions.

Mr. Thomas is a 62-year-old man who has been diagnosed with an acute myocardial infarction with the following symptoms and history. His chief complaint is a persistent, crushing chest pain that radiates to his left arm, jaw, neck, and shoulder blade. He describes the pain, which he has had for the past 12 hours, as a "squeezing" sensation around his heart. He has also suffered nausea, dyspnea, and diaphoresis. He has a low-grade temperature and his blood pressure is within a normal range at 130/82. He states that he smokes two packs of cigarettes a day, is overweight by 50 pounds, and has a family history of hypertension and coronary artery disease. He leads a relatively sedentary lifestyle.

(Galushko Sergey/Shutterstock)

1. What is the common name for Mr. Thomas's acute condition? Look this condition up in a reference source and include a short description of it.

   _____

   _____

2. What do you think the phrase "chief complaint" means?

   _____

   _____

3. What is the medical term for this patient's chief complaint? Define this term.

   _____

   _____

4. List and define each of the patient's additional symptoms in your own words. (These terms appear in other chapters of the book or use a medical dictionary.)

   _____

   _____

5. Using your text as a resource, name and describe three diagnostic tests that may be performed to determine the extent of the patient's heart damage.

   _____

   _____

6. What risk factors for developing heart disease does Mr. Thomas have? What changes should he make?

   _____

   _____

Practice Exercises

A. Complete the Statement

1. The study of the heart is called _____.

2. The three layers of the heart are _____, _____, and _____.

3. The impulse for the heartbeat (the pacemaker) originates in the _____.

4. Arteries carry blood _____ the heart.

5. The four heart valves are _____, _____, _____, and _____.

6. The _____ are the receiving chambers of the heart and the _____ are the pumping chambers.

7. The _____ circulation carries blood to and from the lungs.

8. The pointed tip of the heart is called the _____.

9. The _____ divides the heart into left and right halves.

10. _____ is the contraction phase of the heartbeat and _____ is the relaxation phase.

B. Combining Form Practice

The combining form **cardi/o** refers to the heart. Use it to write a term that means:

1. pertaining to the heart _____

2. disease of the heart muscle _____

3. enlargement of the heart _____

4. abnormally fast heart rate _____

5. abnormally slow heart rate _____

6. record of heart electricity _____

The combining form **angi/o** refers to the vessel. Use it to write a term that means:

7. vessel narrowing _____

8. vessel inflammation _____

9. involuntary muscle contraction of a vessel _____

The combining form **arteri/o** refers to the artery. Use it to write a term that means:

10. pertaining to an artery _____

11. hardening of an artery _____

12. small artery _____

C. Prefix Practice

Add the appropriate prefix to -carditis to form the term that matches each definition.

1. inflammation of the inner lining of the heart _____

2. inflammation of the outer layer of the heart _____

3. inflammation of the muscle of the heart _____

D. Define the Combining Form

	Definition	Example from Chapter
1. cardi/o	_____	_____
2. valvul/o	_____	_____
3. steth/o	_____	_____
4. arteri/o	_____	_____
5. phleb/o	_____	_____
6. angi/o	_____	_____
7. ventricul/o	_____	_____
8. thromb/o	_____	_____
9. atri/o	_____	_____
10. ather/o	_____	_____

E. Name That Term

1. pertaining to a vein _____

2. study of the heart _____

3. record of a vein _____

4. process of recording electrical activity of the heart _____

5. high blood pressure _____

6. low blood pressure _____

7. surgical repair of valve _____

8. pertaining to between ventricles _____

9. removal of fatty substance _____

10. narrowing of the arteries _____

F. Name That Suffix

	Suffix	Example from Chapter
1. pressure	_____	_____
2. abnormal narrowing	_____	_____
3. instrument to measure pressure	_____	_____
4. small	_____	_____
5. hardening	_____	_____

G. Terminology Matching

Match each term to its definition.

1. _____ arrhythmia   a. swollen, distended veins

2. _____ thrombus   b. inflammation of vein

3. _____ bradycardia   c. serious congenital anomaly

4. _____ murmur   d. slow heart rate

5. _____ phlebitis   e. insertion of thin tubing

6. _____ hypotension   f. irregular heartbeat

7. _____ varicose vein   g. an abnormal heart sound

8. _____ tetralogy of Fallot h. clot in blood vessel

9. _____ catheterization   i. low blood pressure

10. _____ sphygmomanometer   j. blood pressure cuff

H. What Does it Stand For?

1. BP _____

2. CHF _____

3. MI _____

4. CCU _____

5. PVC _____

6. CPR _____

7. CAD _____

8. CP _____

9. EKG _____

10. S1 _____

I. What's the Abbreviation?

1. mitral valve prolapse _____

2. ventricular septal defect _____

3. percutaneous transluminal coronary angioplasty _____

4. ventricular fibrillation _____

5. deep vein thrombosis _____

6. lactate dehydrogenase _____

7. coarctation of the aorta _____

8. tissue-type plasminogen activator _____

9. cardiovascular _____

10. extracorporeal circulation _____

J. Procedure Matching

Match each procedure to its definition.

1. _____ cardiac enzymes   a. visualizes heart after patient is given radioactive thallium

2. _____ Doppler ultrasound   b. uses ultrasound to visualize heart beating

3. _____ Holter monitor   c. blood test that indicates heart muscle damage

4. _____ cardiac scan   d. uses treadmill to evaluate cardiac fitness

5. _____ stress testing   e. removes varicose veins

6. _____ echocardiography   f. clot-dissolving drugs

7. _____ extracorporeal circulation   g. measures velocity of blood moving through blood vessels

8. _____ ligation and stripping   h. balloon angioplasty

9. _____ thrombolytic therapy   i. use of a heart-lung machine

10. _____ PTAC   j. portable EKG monitor

K. Define the Term

1. catheter _____

2. infarct _____

3. thrombus _____

4. palpitation _____

5. regurgitation _____

6. aneurysm _____

7. cardiac arrest _____

8. fibrillation _____

9. myocardial infarction _____

10. hemorrhoid _____

L. Fill in the Blank

angiography	murmur	varicose veins	echocardiogram
pacemaker	CHF	defibrillation	angina pectoris
Holter monitor	hypertension	MI	CCU

1. Tiffany was born with a congenital condition resulting in an abnormal heart sound called a(n) _____.

2. Joseph suffered an arrhythmia resulting in cardiac arrest. The emergency team used an instrument to give electric shocks to the heart to create a normal heart rhythm. This procedure is called _____.

3. Marguerite has been placed on a low-sodium diet and medication to bring her blood pressure down to a normal range. She suffers from _____.

4. Tony has had an artificial device called a(n) _____ inserted to control the beating of his heart by producing rhythmic electrical impulses.

5. Derrick's physician determined that he had _____ after examining his legs and finding swollen, tortuous veins.

6. Laura has persistent chest pains that require medication. The term for the pain is _____.

7. La Tonya will be admitted to what hospital unit after surgery to correct her heart condition? _____

8. Stephen is going to have a coronary artery bypass graft to correct the blockage in his coronary arteries. He recently suffered a heart attack as a result of this occlusion. His attack is called a(n) _____.

9. Stephen's physician scheduled a(n) _____, an X-ray to determine the extent of his blood vessel damage.

10. A patient scheduled to have a diagnostic procedure that uses ultrasound to produce an image of the heart valves is going to have a(n) _____.

11. Eric must wear a device for 24 hours that will keep track of his heart activity as he performs his normal daily routine. This device is called a(n) _____.

12. Lydia is 82 years old and is suffering from a heart condition that causes weakness, edema, and breathlessness. Her heart failure is the cause of her lung congestion. This condition is called _____.

M. Pharmacology Challenge

Fill in the classification for each drug description, then match the brand name.

	Drug Description	Classification	Brand Name
1.	_____ prevents arrhthymia	_____	a. tPA
2.	_____ reduces cholesterol	_____	b. Coumadin
3.	_____ increases force of heart contraction	_____	c. Cardizem
4.	_____ increases urine production	_____	d. Nitro-Dur
5.	_____ prevents blood clots	_____	e. Tambocor
6.	_____ dissolves blood clots	_____	f. Lanoxin
7.	_____ relaxes smooth muscle in artery wall	_____	g. Lipitor
8.	_____ cause heart to beat less forcefully	_____	h. Lasix

MEDICAL TERMINOLOGY INTERACTIVE

Medical Terminology Interactive is a premium online homework management system that includes a host of features to help you study. Registered users will find:

- Fun games and activities built within a virtual hospital
- Powerful tools that track and analyze your results—allowing you to create a personalized learning experience
- Videos, flashcards, and audio pronunciations to help enrich your progress
- Streaming video lesson presentations and self-paced learning modules

www.pearsonhighered.com/mti

Labeling Exercise

Image A

Write the labels for this figure on the numbered lines provided.

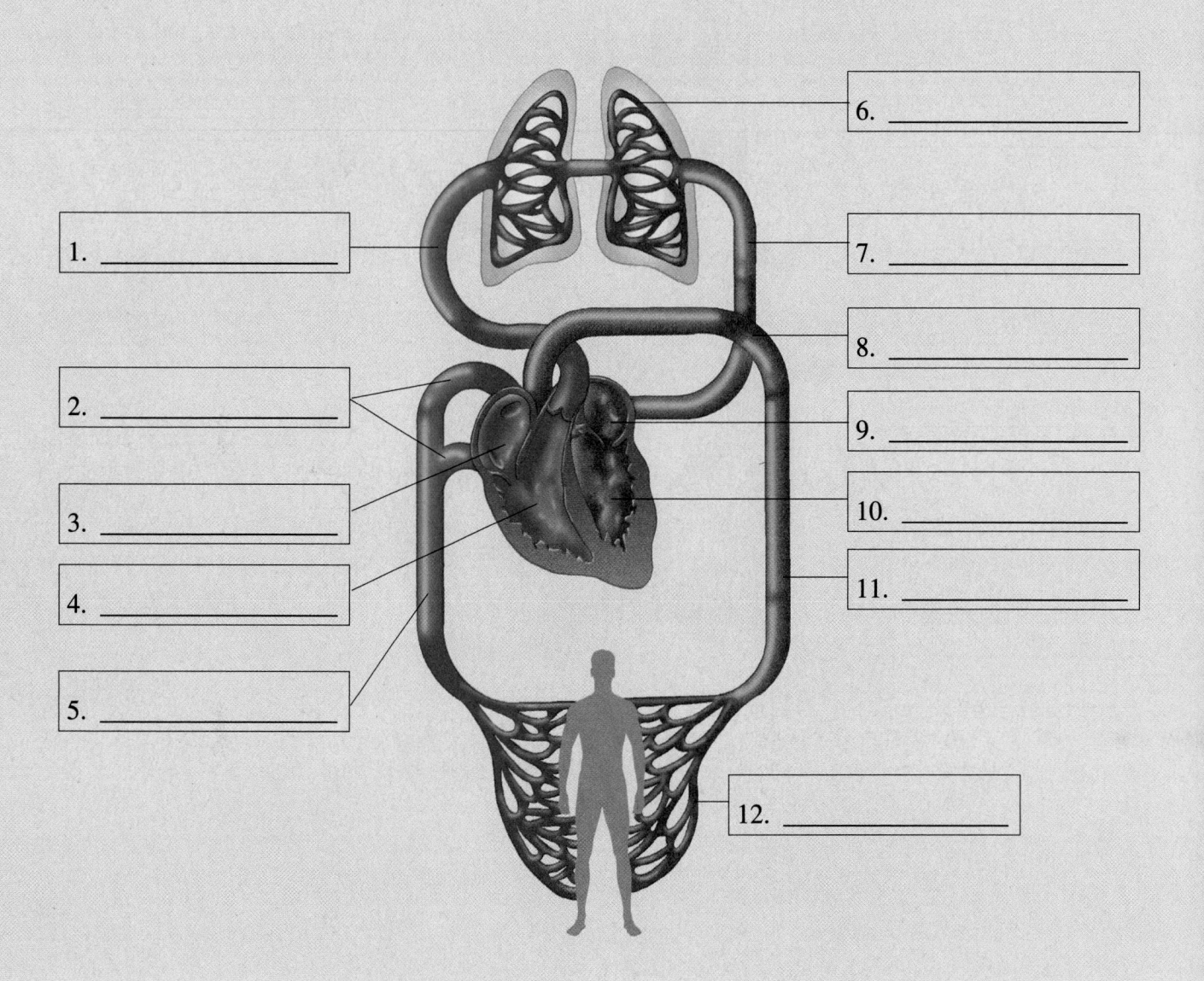

1. _____

2. _____

3. _____

4. _____

5. _____

6. _____

7. _____

8. _____

9. _____

10. _____

11. _____

12. _____

Image B

Write the labels for this figure on the numbered lines provided.

1. _____

2. _____

3. _____

4. _____

5. _____

6. _____

7. _____

8. _____

9. _____

10. _____

11. _____

12. _____

13. _____

14. _____

15. _____

16. _____

17. _____

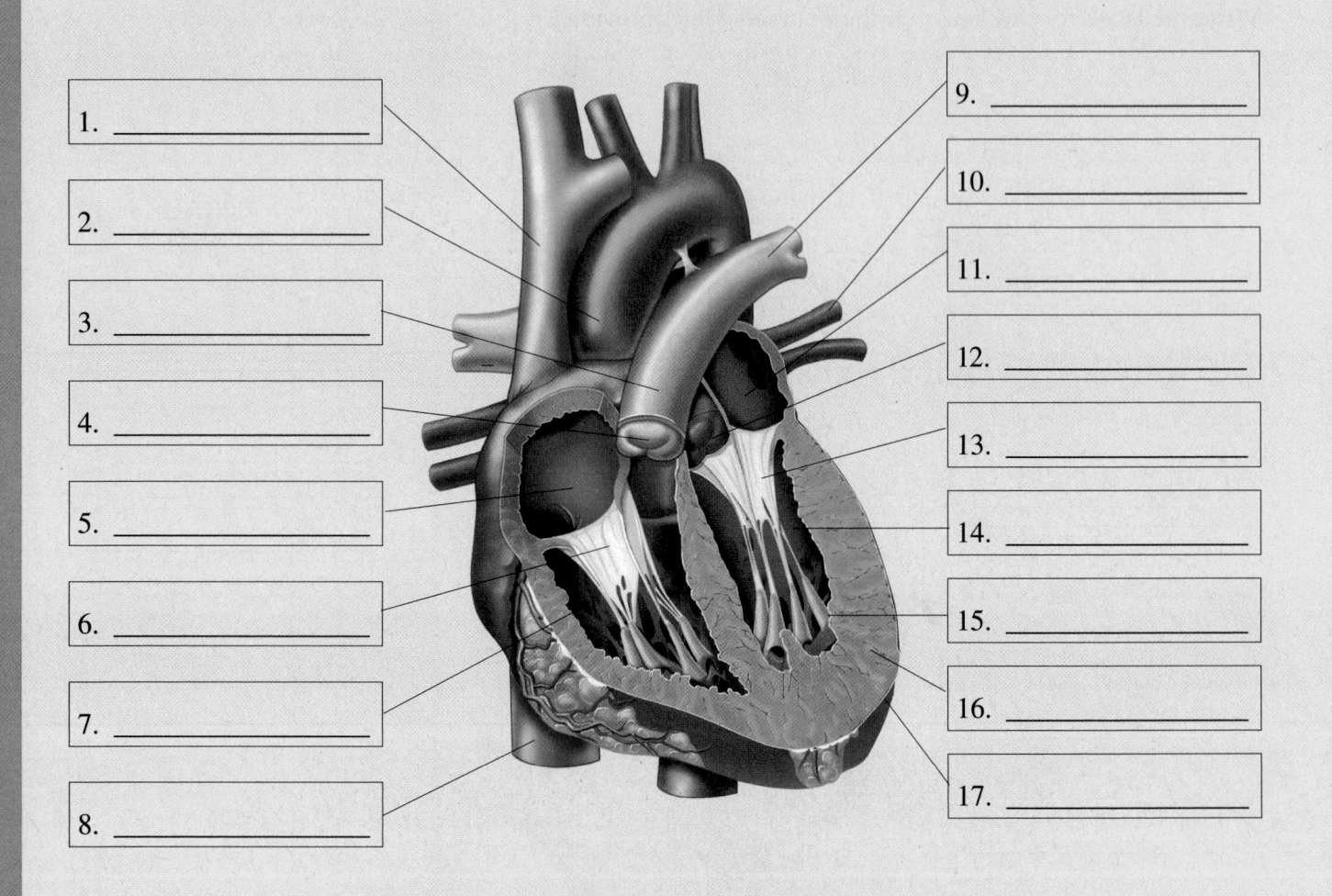

6

BLOOD AND THE LYMPHATIC AND IMMUNE SYSTEMS

Learning Objectives

Upon completion of this chapter, you will be able to

- Recognize the combining forms and suffixes introduced in this chapter.

- Gain the ability to pronounce medical terms and major anatomical structures.

- List the major components, structures, and organs of the blood and lymphatic and immune systems and their functions.

- Describe the blood typing systems.

- Discuss immunity, the immune response, and standard precautions.

- Identify and define blood and lymphatic and immune system anatomical terms.

- Identify and define selected blood and lymphatic and immune system pathology terms.

- Identify and define selected blood and lymphatic and immune system diagnostic procedures.

- Identify and define selected blood and lymphatic and immune system therapeutic procedures.

- Identify and define selected medications associated with blood and the lymphatic and immune systems.

- Define selected abbreviations associated with blood and the lymphatic and immune systems.

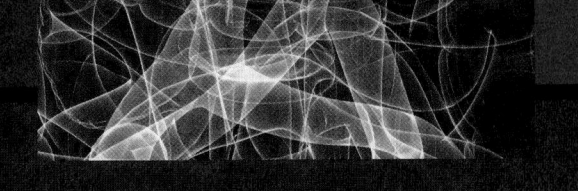

Section I: Blood at a Glance

Function

Blood transports gases, nutrients, and wastes to all areas of the body either attached to red blood cells or dissolved in the plasma. White blood cells fight infection and disease, and platelets initiate the blood clotting process.

Organs

Here are the primary components that comprise blood.

formed elements　　　　　　　**plasma**
- **erythrocytes**
- **leukocytes**
- **platelets**

Word Parts

Here are the most common word parts (with their meanings) used to build blood terms. For a more comprehensive list, refer to the Terminology section of this chapter.

Combining Forms

agglutin/o	clumping	**hem/o**	blood
bas/o	base	**hemat/o**	blood
chrom/o	color	**leuk/o**	white
coagul/o	clotting	**lymph/o**	lymph
cyt/o	cell	**morph/o**	shape
eosin/o	rosy red	**neutr/o**	neutral
erythr/o	red	**phag/o**	eat, swallow
fibrin/o	fibers, fibrous	**sanguin/o**	blood
fus/o	pouring	**septic/o**	infection
granul/o	granules	**thromb/o**	clot

Suffixes

-apheresis	removal, carry away
-crit	separation of
-cytosis	more than the normal number of cells
-emia	blood condition
-globin	protein
-penia	abnormal decrease, too few
-phil	attracted to
-poiesis	formation
-stasis	standing still

Blood Illustrated

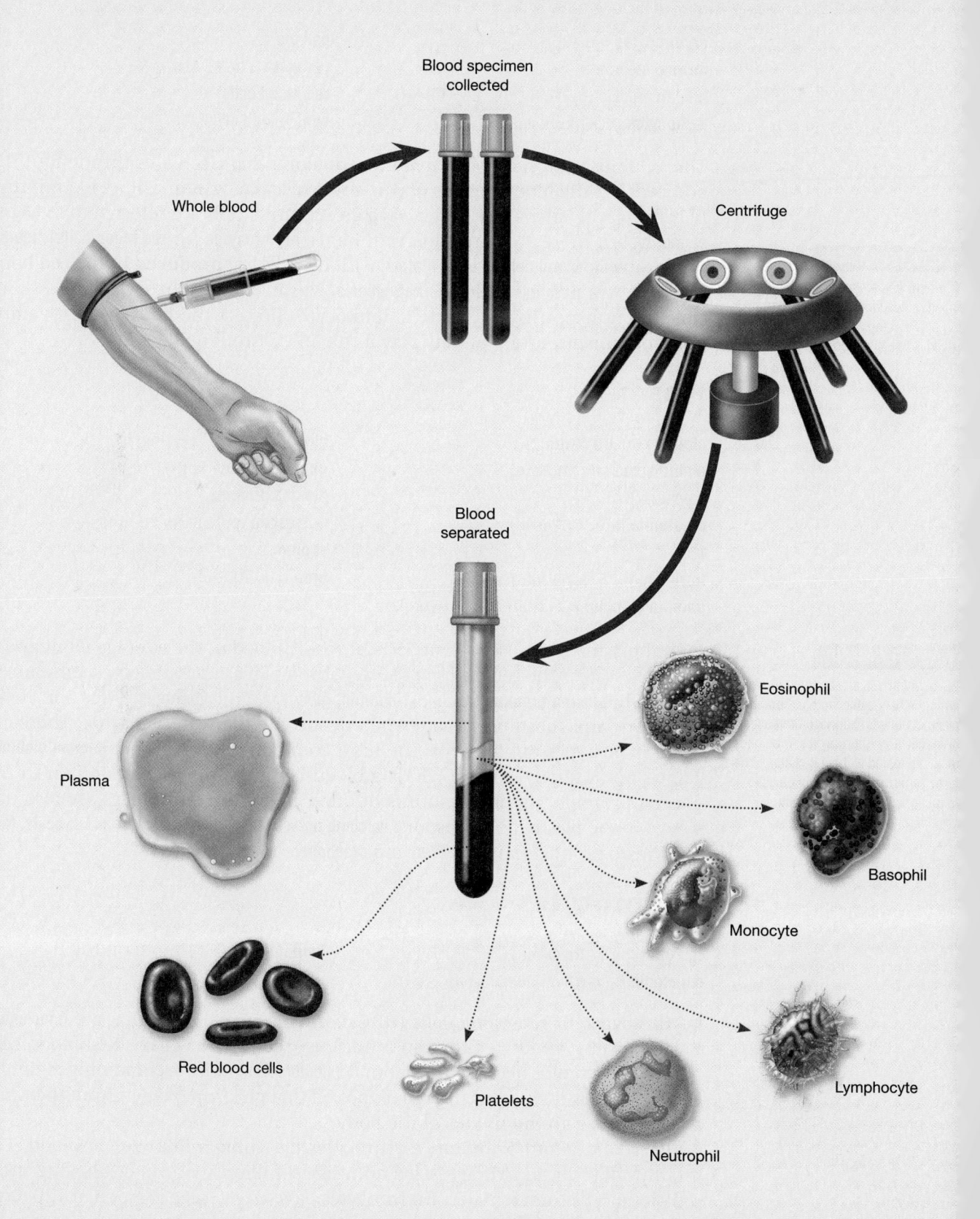

Blood specimen collected

Whole blood

Centrifuge

Blood separated

Plasma

Eosinophil

Basophil

Monocyte

Red blood cells

Platelets

Neutrophil

Lymphocyte

■ Anatomy and Physiology of Blood

erythrocytes (eh-RITH-roh-sights)

formed elements

hematopoiesis (hee-mah-toh-poy-EE-sis)

leukocytes (LOO-koh-sights)

plasma (PLAZ-mah)

platelets (PLAYT-lets)

red blood cells

white blood cells

The average adult has about five liters of blood that circulates throughout the body within the blood vessels of the cardiovascular system. Blood is a mixture of cells floating in watery **plasma.** As a group, these cells are referred to as **formed elements,** but there are three different kinds: **erythrocytes** (or **red blood cells**), **leukocytes** (or **white blood cells**), and **platelets.** Blood cells are produced in the red bone marrow by a process called **hematopoiesis.** Plasma and erythrocytes are responsible for transporting substances, leukocytes protect the body from invading microorganisms, and platelets play a role in controlling bleeding.

MED TERM TIP

The term *hematopoiesis* literally means "blood formation" by combining hemat/o (meaning blood) with -poiesis (meaning formation).

Plasma

albumin (al-BEW-min)

amino acids (ah-MEE-noh)

calcium (KAL-see-um)

creatinine (kree-AT-in-in)

fats

fibrinogen (fye-BRIN-oh-jen)

gamma globulin (GAM-ah / GLOB-yoo-lin)

globulins (GLOB-yew-lenz)

glucose (GLOO-kohs)

plasma proteins

potassium (poh-TASS-ee-um)

sodium

urea (yoo-REE-ah)

MED TERM TIP

Word Watch: *Plasma* and *serum* are not interchangeable words. Serum is plasma, but with fibrinogen removed or inactivated. This way it can be handled and tested without it clotting. The term *serum* is also sometimes used to mean antiserum or antitoxin.

Liquid plasma composes about 55% of whole blood in the average adult and is 90–92% water. The remaining 8–10% portion of plasma is dissolved substances, especially **plasma proteins** such as **albumin, globulins,** and **fibrinogen.** Albumin helps transport fatty substances that cannot dissolve in the watery plasma. There are three main types of globulins; the most commonly known one, **gamma globulin,** acts as an antibody. Fibrinogen is a blood-clotting protein. In addition to the plasma proteins, smaller amounts of other important substances are also dissolved in the plasma for transport: **calcium, potassium, sodium, glucose, amino acids, fats,** and waste products such as **urea** and **creatinine.**

Erythrocytes

bilirubin (bil-ly-ROO-bin)

enucleated (ee-NEW-klee-ate-ed)

hemoglobin (hee-moh-GLOH-bin)

Erythrocytes, or red blood cells (RBCs), are biconcave disks that are **enucleated,** meaning they no longer contain a nucleus (see Figure 6.1 ■). Red blood cells appear red in color because they contain **hemoglobin,** an iron-containing pigment. Hemoglobin is the part of the red blood cell that picks up oxygen from the lungs and delivers it to the tissues of the body.

There are about 5 million erythrocytes per cubic millimeter of blood. The total number in an average-sized adult is 35 trillion, with males having more red blood cells than females. Erythrocytes have an average lifespan of 120 days,

Erythrocytes

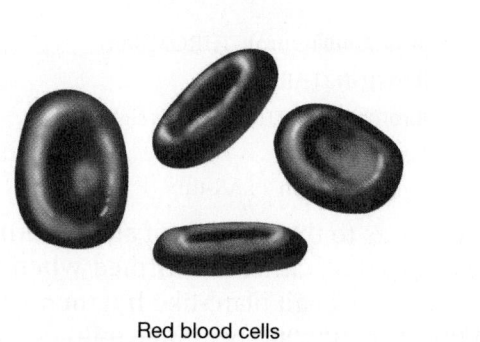

Leukocyctes

Basophil

Eosinophil

Monocyte

Neutrophil

Lymphocyte

■ **Figure 6.1** The biconcave disk shape of erythrocytes (red blood cells).

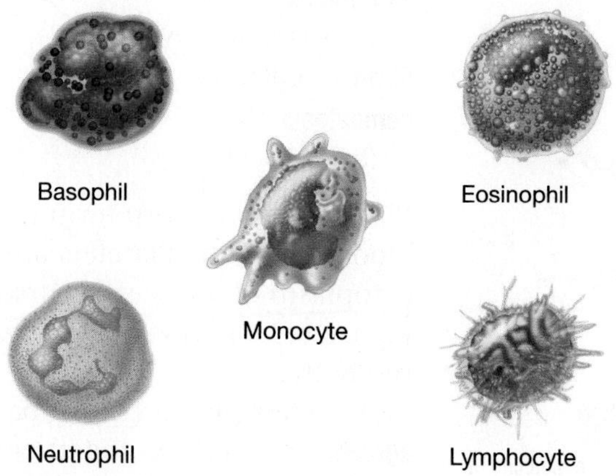

■ **Figure 6.2** The five different types of leukocytes (white blood cells).

and then the spleen removes the worn-out and damaged ones from circulation. Much of the red blood cell, such as the iron, can be reused, but one portion, **bilirubin,** is a waste product disposed of by the liver.

Leukocytes

agranulocytes (ah-GRAN-yew-loh-sights) **pathogens** (PATH-oh-ginz)
granulocytes (GRAN-yew-loh-sights)

Leukocytes, also referred to as white blood cells (WBCs), provide protection against the invasion of **pathogens** such as bacteria, viruses, and other foreign material. In general, white blood cells have a spherical shape with a large nucleus, and there are about 8,000 per cubic millimeter of blood (see Figure 6.2 ■). There are five different types of white blood cells, each with its own strategy for protecting the body. The five can be subdivided into two categories: **granulocytes** (with granules in the cytoplasm) and **agranulocytes** (without granules in the cytoplasm). The name and function of each type is presented in Table 6.1 ■.

> **MED TERM TIP**
>
> Your body makes about 2 million erythrocytes every second. Of course, it must then destroy 2 million every second to maintain a relatively constant 30 trillion red blood cells.

> **MED TERM TIP**
>
> A *phagocyte* is a cell that has the ability to ingest (phag/o = eat; -cyte = cell) and digest bacteria and other foreign particles. This process, *phagocytosis,* is critical for the control of bacteria within the body.

Table 6.1	Leukocyte Classification
LEUKOCYTE	**FUNCTION**
Granulocytes	
Basophils (basos) (BAY-soh-fillz)	Release histamine and heparin to damaged tissues
Eosinophils (eosins) (ee-oh-SIN-oh-fillz)	Destroy parasites and increase during allergic reactions
Neutrophils (NOO-troh-fillz)	Engulfs foreign and damaged cells (phagocytosis); most numerous of the leukocytes
Agranulocytes	
Monocytes (monos) (MON-oh-sights)	Engulfs foreign and damaged cells (phagocytosis)
Lymphocytes (lymphs) (LIM-foh-sights)	Plays several different roles in immune response

Platelets

agglutinate	**prothrombin** (proh-THROM-bin)
(ah-GLOO-tih-nayt)	**thrombin** (THROM-bin)
fibrin (FYE-brin)	**thrombocyte** (THROM-boh-sight)
hemostasis	**thromboplastin**
(hee-moh-STAY-sis)	(throm-boh-PLAS-tin)

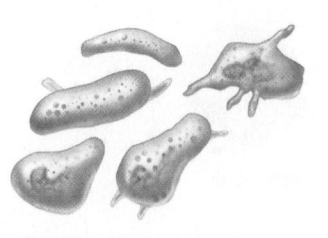

■ **Figure 6.3** Platelet structure.

Platelet, the modern term for **thrombocyte,** refers to the smallest of all the formed blood elements. Platelets are not whole cells, but rather are formed when the cytoplasm of a large precursor cell shatters into small plate-like fragments (see Figure 6.3 ■). There are between 200,000 and 300,000 per cubic millimeter in the body.

Platelets play a critical part in the blood-clotting process or **hemostasis.** They **agglutinate** or clump together into small clusters when a blood vessel is cut or damaged. Platelets also release a substance called **thromboplastin,** which, in the presence of calcium, reacts with **prothrombin** (a clotting protein in the blood) to form **thrombin.** Then thrombin, in turn, works to convert fibrinogen to **fibrin,** which eventually becomes the meshlike blood clot.

MED TERM TIP

You can find a clue to the meaning of many terms associated with platelets because they contain word parts:

- fibrinogen: fibrin/o = fibers + -gen = that which produces
- hemostasis: hem/o = blood + -stasis = standing still
- agglutinate: agglutin/o = clumping
- prothrombin: pro- = before + thromb/o = clot
- thromboplastin: thromb/o = clot + -plastin = formation

Blood Typing

ABO system	**Rh factor**
blood typing	

Each person's blood is different due to the presence of antigens or markers on the surface of erythrocytes. Before a person receives a blood transfusion, it is important to do **blood typing.** This laboratory test determines if the donated blood is compatible with the recipient's blood. There are many different subgroups of blood markers, but the two most important ones are the **ABO system** and **Rh factor.**

ABO System

type A	**type O**
type AB	**universal donor**
type B	**universal recipient**

In the ABO blood system there are two possible red blood cell markers, A and B. A marker is one method by which cells identify themselves. A person with an A marker is said to have **type A** blood. Type A blood produces anti-B antibodies that will attack type B blood. The presence of a B marker gives **type B** blood and anti-A antibodies (that will attack type A blood). If both markers are present, the blood is **type AB** and does not contain any antibodies. Therefore, type AB blood will not attack any other blood type. The absence of either an A or a B marker results in **type O** blood, which contains both anti-A and anti-B antibodies. Type O blood will attack all other blood types (A, B, and AB). For further information on antibodies, refer to the lymphatic section later in this chapter.

Because type O blood does not have either marker A or B, it will not react with anti-A or anti-B antibodies. For this reason, a person with type O blood is referred to as a **universal donor.** In extreme cases, type O blood may be given to a person with any of the other blood types. Similarly, type AB blood is the **universal recipient.** A person with type AB blood has no antibodies against the other blood types and, therefore, in extreme cases, can receive any type of blood.

Rh Factor

Rh-negative   **Rh-positive**

Rh factor is not as difficult to understand as the ABO system. A person with the Rh factor on his or her red blood cells is said to be **Rh-positive** (Rh+). Since this person has the factor, he or she will not make anti-Rh antibodies. A person without the Rh factor is **Rh-negative** (Rh–) and will produce anti-Rh antibodies. Therefore, an Rh+ person may receive both an Rh+ and an Rh– transfusion, but an Rh– person can receive only Rh– blood.

▣ Terminology

Word Parts Used to Build Blood Terms

The following lists contain the combining forms, suffixes, and prefixes used to build terms in the remaining sections of this chapter.

Combining Forms

bas/o	base	**fibrin/o**	fibers	**lymph/o**	lymph
chrom/o	color	**fus/o**	pouring	**morph/o**	shape
coagul/o	clotting	**granul/o**	granules	**neutr/o**	neutral
cyt/o	cell	**hem/o**	blood	**phleb/o**	vein
eosin/o	rosy red	**hemat/o**	blood	**sanguin/o**	blood
erythr/o	red	**leuk/o**	white	**septic/o**	infection
		lip/o	fat	**thromb/o**	clot

Suffixes

-apheresis	removal, carry away	**-ia**	condition	**-ous**	pertaining to
-crit	separation of	**-ic**	pertaining to	**-penia**	too few
-cyte	cell	**-ion**	action	**-phil**	attracted to
-cytosis	more than the normal number of cells	**-logy**	study of	**-plastic**	pertaining to development
		-lytic	destruction		
-emia	blood condition	**-oma**	growth	**-rrhage**	abnormal flow
-globin	protein	**-otomy**	cutting into	**-rrhagic**	pertaining to abnormal flow

Prefixes

a–	without	dys–	abnormal	mono–	one
an–	without	homo–	same	pan–	all
anti–	against	hyper–	excessive	poly–	many
auto–	self	hypo–	insufficient	trans–	across

Anatomical Terms

TERM	WORD PARTS	DEFINITION
agranulocyte (ah-GRAN-yew-loh-sight)	a- = without granul/o = granules -cyte = cell	A leukocyte without granules in its cytoplasm; monocytes and lymphocytes.
basophil (BAY-soh-fill)	bas/o = base -phil = attracted to	A granulocytic leukocyte that attracts a basic pH stain.
eosinophil (ee-oh-SIN-oh-fill)	eosin/o = rosy red -phil = attracted to	A granulocytic leukocyte that attracts a rosy red stain.
erythrocyte (eh-RITH-roh-sight)	erythr/o = red -cyte = cell	A red blood cell.
fibrinous (fye-brin-us)	fibrin/o = fibers -ous = pertaining to	Pertaining to fibers.
granulocyte (GRAN-yew-loh-sight)	granul/o = granules -cyte = cell	A leukocyte with granules in its cytoplasm; basophils, eosinophils, neutrophils.
hematic (hee-MAT-ik)	hemat/o = blood -ic = pertaining to	Pertaining to blood.
leukocyte (LOO-koh-sight)	leuk/o = white -cyte = cell	A white blood cell.
lymphocyte (LIM-foh-sight)	lymph/o = lymph -cyte = cell	An agranulocytic leukocyte formed in lymphatic tissue.
monocyte (MON-oh-sight)	mono- = one -cyte = cell	An agranulocytic leukocyte with a single, large nucleus.
neutrophil (NOO-troh-fill)	neutr/o = neutral -phil = attracted to	A granulocytic leukocyte that attracts a neutral pH stain.
sanguinous (SANG-gwih-nus)	sanguin/o = blood -ous = pertaining to	Pertaining to blood.
thrombocyte (THROM-boh-sight)	thromb/o = clot -cyte = cell	A clotting cell; a platelet.

Pathology

TERM	WORD PARTS	DEFINITION
Medical Specialties		
hematology (hee-mah-TALL-oh-jee)	hemat/o = blood -logy = study of	The branch of medicine specializing in treatment of diseases and conditions of the blood. Physician is a *hematologist*.
Signs and Symptoms		
blood clot		The hard collection of fibrin, blood cells, and tissue debris that is the end result of hemostasis or the blood-clotting process (see Figure 6.4 ■).

■ **Pathology** *(continued)*

TERM	WORD PARTS	DEFINITION
	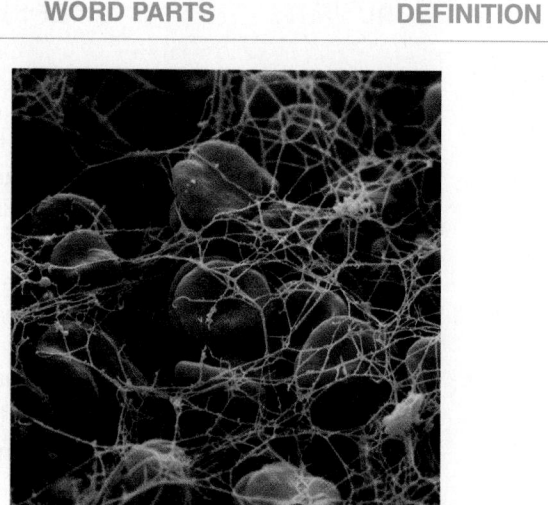 ■ **Figure 6.4** Electronmicrograph showing a blood clot composed of fibrin, red blood cells, and tissue debris. *(Eye of Science/Photo Researchers, Inc.)*	
coagulate (koh-ag-YOO-late)	coagul/o = clotting	To convert from a liquid to a gel or solid, as in blood coagulation.
dyscrasia (dis-CRAZ-ee-ah)	dys- = abnormal -ia = condition	A general term indicating the presence of a disease affecting blood.
hematoma (hee-mah-TOH-mah)	hemat/o = blood -oma = growth	The collection of blood under the skin as the result of blood escaping into the tissue from damaged blood vessels. Commonly referred to as a *bruise*.

> **MED TERM TIP**
>
> Word Watch: The term *hematoma* is confusing. Its simple translation is "blood tumor." However, it is used to refer to blood that has leaked out of a blood vessel and has pooled in the tissues.

TERM	WORD PARTS	DEFINITION
hemorrhage (HEM-er-rij)	hem/o = blood -rrhage = abnormal flow	Rapid flow of blood.

Blood

TERM	WORD PARTS	DEFINITION
hemophilia (hee-moh-FILL-ee-ah)	hem/o = blood -phil = attracted to -ia = condition	Hereditary blood disease in which blood-clotting time is prolonged due to a lack of one vital clotting factor. It is transmitted by a sex-linked trait from females to males, appearing almost exclusively in males.
hyperlipidemia (HYE-per-lip-id-ee-mee-ah)	hyper- = excessive lip/o = fat -emia = blood condition	Condition of having too high a level of lipids such as cholesterol in the bloodstream. A risk factor for developing atherosclerosis and coronary artery disease.
pancytopenia (pan-sigh-toe-PEN-ee-ah)	pan- = all cyt/o = cell -penia = too few	Having too few of all cells.
septicemia (sep-tih-SEE-mee-ah)	septic/o = infection -emia = blood condition	Having bacteria or their toxins in the bloodstream. *Sepsis* is a term that means putrefaction or infection. Commonly referred to as *blood poisoning*.

Pathology *(continued)*

TERM	WORD PARTS	DEFINITION
Erythrocytes		
anemia (an-NEE-mee-ah)	an- = without -emia = blood condition	A large group of conditions characterized by a reduction in the number of red blood cells or the amount of hemoglobin in the blood; results in less oxygen reaching the tissues.
aplastic anemia (a-PLAS-tik / an-NEE-mee-ah)	a- = without -plastic = pertaining to development an- = without -emia = blood condition	Severe form of anemia that develops as a consequence of loss of functioning red bone marrow. Results in a decrease in the number of all the formed elements. Treatment may eventually require a bone marrow transplant.
erythrocytosis (ee-RITH-row-sigh-toe-sis)	erythr/o = red -cytosis = more than normal number of cells	The condition of having too many red blood cells.
erythropenia (ee-RITH-row-pen-ee-ah)	erythr/o = red -penia = too few	The condition of having too few red blood cells.
hemolytic anemia (hee-moh-LIT-ik / an-NEE-mee-ah)	hem/o = blood -lytic = destruction an- = without -emia = blood condition	An anemia that develops as the result of the destruction of erythrocytes.
hemolytic reaction (hee-moh-LIT-ik)	hem/o = blood -lytic = destruction	The destruction of a patient's erythrocytes that occurs when receiving a transfusion of an incompatible blood type. Also called a *transfusion reaction.*
hypochromic anemia (hi-poe-CHROME-ik / an-NEE-mee-ah)	hypo- = insufficient chrom/o = color -ic = pertaining to an- = without -emia = blood condition	Anemia resulting from having insufficient hemoglobin in the erythrocytes. Named because the hemoglobin molecule is responsible for the dark red color of the erythrocytes.
iron-deficiency anemia	an- = without -emia = blood condition	Anemia resulting from not having sufficient iron to manufacture hemoglobin.
pernicious anemia (PA) (per-NISH-us / an-NEE-mee-ah)	an- = without -emia = blood condition	Anemia associated with insufficient absorption of vitamin B_{12} by the digestive system. Vitamin B_{12} is necessary for erythrocyte production.
polycythemia vera (pol-ee-sigh-THEE-mee-ah / VAIR-rah)	poly- = many cyt/o = cell hem/o = blood -ia = condition	Production of too many red blood cells by the bone marrow. Blood becomes too thick to easily flow through the blood vessels.
sickle cell anemia	an- = without -emia = blood condition	A genetic disorder in which erythrocytes take on an abnormal curved or "sickle" shape. These cells are fragile and are easily damaged, leading to a hemolytic anemia (see Figure 6.5 ■).

Pathology *(continued)*

TERM	WORD PARTS	DEFINITION
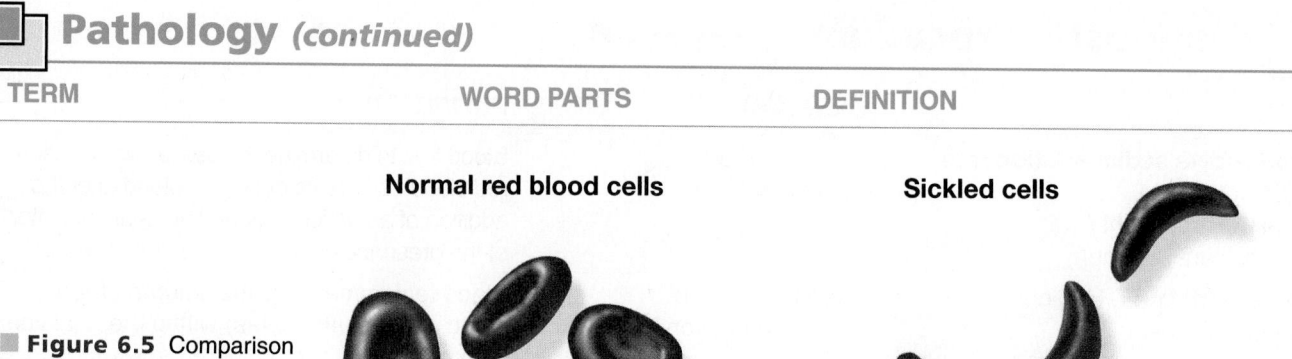 **Figure 6.5** Comparison of normal-shaped erythrocytes and the abnormal sickle shape noted in patients with sickle cell anemia.		
thalassemia (thal-ah-SEE-mee-ah)	-emia = blood condition	A genetic disorder in which the body is unable to make functioning hemoglobin, resulting in anemia.
Leukocytes		
leukemia (loo-KEE-mee-ah)	leuk/o = white -emia = blood condition	Cancer of the white blood cell–forming red bone marrow resulting in a large number of abnormal and immature white blood cells circulating in the blood.
leukocytosis (LOO-koh-sigh-toh-sis)	leuk/o = white -cytosis = more than normal number of cells	The condition of having too many white blood cells.
leukopenia (LOO-koh-pen-ee-ah)	leuk/o = white -penia = too few	The condition of having too few white blood cells.
Platelets		
thrombocytosis (throm-boh-sigh-TOH-sis)	thromb/o = clot -cytosis = more than normal number of cells	The condition of having too many platelets.
thrombopenia (THROM-boh-pen-ee-ah)	thromb/o = clot -penia = too few	The condition of having too few platelets.

Diagnostic Procedures

TERM	WORD PARTS	DEFINITION
Clinical Laboratory Tests		
blood culture and sensitivity (C&S)		Sample of blood is incubated in the laboratory to check for bacterial growth. If bacteria are present, they are identified and tested to determine which antibiotics they are sensitive to.
complete blood count (CBC)		Combination of blood tests including red blood cell count (RBC), white blood cell count (WBC), hemoglobin (Hgb), hematocrit (Hct), white blood cell differential, and platelet count.

◼ Diagnostic Procedures *(continued)*

TERM	WORD PARTS	DEFINITION
erythrocyte sedimentation rate (ESR, sed rate) (eh-RITH-roh-sight / sed-ih-men-TAY-shun)	erythr/o = red -cyte = cell	Blood test to determine the rate at which mature red blood cells settle out of the blood after the addition of an anticoagulant. This is an indicator of the presence of an inflammatory disease.
hematocrit (HCT, Hct, crit) (hee-MAT-oh-krit)	hemat/o = blood -crit = separation of	Blood test to measure the volume of red blood cells (erythrocytes) within the total volume of blood.
hemoglobin (Hgb, hb) (hee-moh-GLOH-bin)	hem/o = blood -globin = protein	A blood test to measure the amount of hemoglobin present in a given volume of blood.
platelet count (PLAYT-let)		Blood test to determine the number of platelets in a given volume of blood.
prothrombin time (Pro time, PT) (proh-THROM-bin)	thromb/o = clot	A measure of the blood's coagulation abilities by measuring how long it takes for a clot to form after prothrombin has been activated.
red blood cell count (RBC)		Blood test to determine the number of erythrocytes in a volume of blood. A decrease in red blood cells may indicate anemia; an increase may indicate polycythemia.
red blood cell morphology	morph/o = shape -logy = study of	Examination of a specimen of blood for abnormalities in the shape (morphology) of the erythrocytes. Used to determine diseases like sickle cell anemia.
sequential multiple analyzer computer (SMAC)		Machine for doing multiple blood chemistry tests automatically.
white blood cell count (WBC)		Blood test to measure the number of leukocytes in a volume of blood. An increase may indicate the presence of infection or a disease such as leukemia. A decrease in white blood cells may be caused by radiation therapy or chemotherapy.
white blood cell differential (diff) (diff-er-EN-shal)		Blood test to determine the number of each variety of leukocytes.
Medical Procedures		
bone marrow aspiration (as-pih-RAY-shun)		Sample of bone marrow is removed by aspiration with a needle and examined for diseases such as leukemia or aplastic anemia.
phlebotomy (fleh-BOT-oh-me)	phleb/o = vein -otomy = cutting into	Incision into a vein in order to remove blood for a diagnostic test. Also called *venipuncture*.

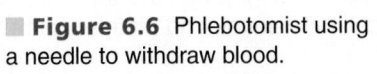

◼ **Figure 6.6** Phlebotomist using a needle to withdraw blood.

Therapeutic Procedures

TERM	WORD PARTS	DEFINITION
Medical Procedures		
autologous transfusion (aw-TALL-oh-gus / trans-FYOO-zhun)	auto- = self	Procedure for collecting and storing a patient's own blood several weeks prior to the actual need. It can then be used to replace blood lost during a surgical procedure.
blood transfusion (trans-FYOO-zhun)	trans- = across fus/o = pouring -ion = action	Artificial transfer of blood into the bloodstream.

MED TERM TIP

Before a patient receives a blood transfusion, the laboratory performs a **type and cross-match**. This test first double-checks the blood type of both the donor's and recipient's blood. Then a cross-match is performed. This process mixed together small samples of both bloods and observes the mixture for adverse reactions.

TERM	WORD PARTS	DEFINITION
bone marrow transplant (BMT)		Patient receives red bone marrow from a donor after the patient's own bone marrow has been destroyed by radiation or chemotherapy.
homologous transfusion (hoh-MALL-oh-gus / trans-FYOO-zhun)	homo- = same	Replacement of blood by transfusion of blood received from another person.
packed red cells		A transfusion in which most of the plasma, leukocytes, and platelets have been removed, leaving on erythrocytes.
plasmapheresis (plaz-mah-fah-REE-sis)	-apheresis = removal, carry away	Method of removing plasma from the body without depleting the formed elements. Whole blood is removed and the cells and plasma are separated. The cells are returned to the patient along with a donor plasma transfusion.
whole blood		Refers to the mixture of both plasma and formed elements.

Pharmacology

CLASSIFICATION	WORD PARTS	ACTION	EXAMPLES
anticoagulant (an-tih-koh-AG-yoo-lant)	anti- = against coagul/o = clotting	Substance that prevents blood clot formation. Commonly referred to as *blood thinners*.	heparin, HepLock; warfarin, Coumadin
antihemorrhagic (an-tih-hem-er-RAJ-ik)	anti- = against hem/o = blood -rrhagic = pertaining to abnormal flow	Substance that prevents or stops hemorrhaging; a *hemostatic agent*.	aminocaproic acid, Amicar; vitamin K
antiplatelet agents (an-tih-PLATE-let)	anti- = against	Substance that interferes with the action of platelets. Prolongs bleeding time. Used to prevent heart attacks and strokes.	clopidogrel, Plavix; ticlopidine, Ticlid

Pharmacology *(continued)*

CLASSIFICATION	WORD PARTS	ACTION	EXAMPLES
hematinic (hee-mah-TIN-ik)	hemat/o = blood -ic = pertaining to	Substance that increases the number of erythrocytes or the amount of hemoglobin in the blood.	epoetin alfa, Procrit; darbepoetin alfa, Aranesp
thrombolytic (throm-boh-LIT-ik)	thromb/o = clot -lytic = destruction	Term meaning able to dissolve existing blood clots.	alteplase, Activase; streptokinase, Streptase

Abbreviations

ALL	acute lymphocytic leukemia		**lymphs**	lymphocytes
AML	acute myelogenous leukemia		**monos**	monocytes
basos	basophils		**PA**	pernicious anemia
BMT	bone marrow transplant		**PCV**	packed cell volume
CBC	complete blood count		**PMN, polys**	polymorphonuclear neutrophil
CLL	chronic lymphocytic leukemia		**PT,**	prothrombin time
CML	chronic myelogenous leukemia		**pro-time**	
diff	differential		**RBC**	red blood cell
eosins, eos	eosinophils		**Rh+**	Rh-positive
ESR, SR,	erythrocyte sedimentation rate		**Rh–**	Rh-negative
sed rate			**segs**	segmented neutrophils
HCT, Hct,	hematocrit		**SMAC**	sequential multiple analyzer computer
crit			**WBC**	white blood cell
Hgb, Hb, **HGB**	hemoglobin			

Section II: The Lymphatic and Immune Systems at a Glance

Function

The lymphatic system consists of a network of lymph vessels that pick up excess tissue fluid, cleanse it, and return it to the circulatory system. It also picks up fats that have been absorbed by the digestive system. The immune system fights disease and infections.

Organs

Here are the primary structures that comprise the lymphatic and immune system.

lymph nodes
lymphatic vessels
spleen
thymus gland
tonsils

Word Parts

Here are the most common word parts (with their meanings) used to build lymphatic and immune system terms. For a more comprehensive list, refer to the Terminology section of this chapter.

Combining Forms

adenoid/o	adenoids	nucle/o	nucleus
axill/o	axilla, underarm	path/o	disease
immun/o	protection	splen/o	spleen
inguin/o	groin region	thym/o	thymus gland
lymph/o	lymph	tonsill/o	tonsils
lymphaden/o	lymph node	tox/o	poison
lymphangi/o	lymph vessel		

Suffixes

-edema	swelling
-globulin	protein

The Lymphatic and Immune Systems Illustrated

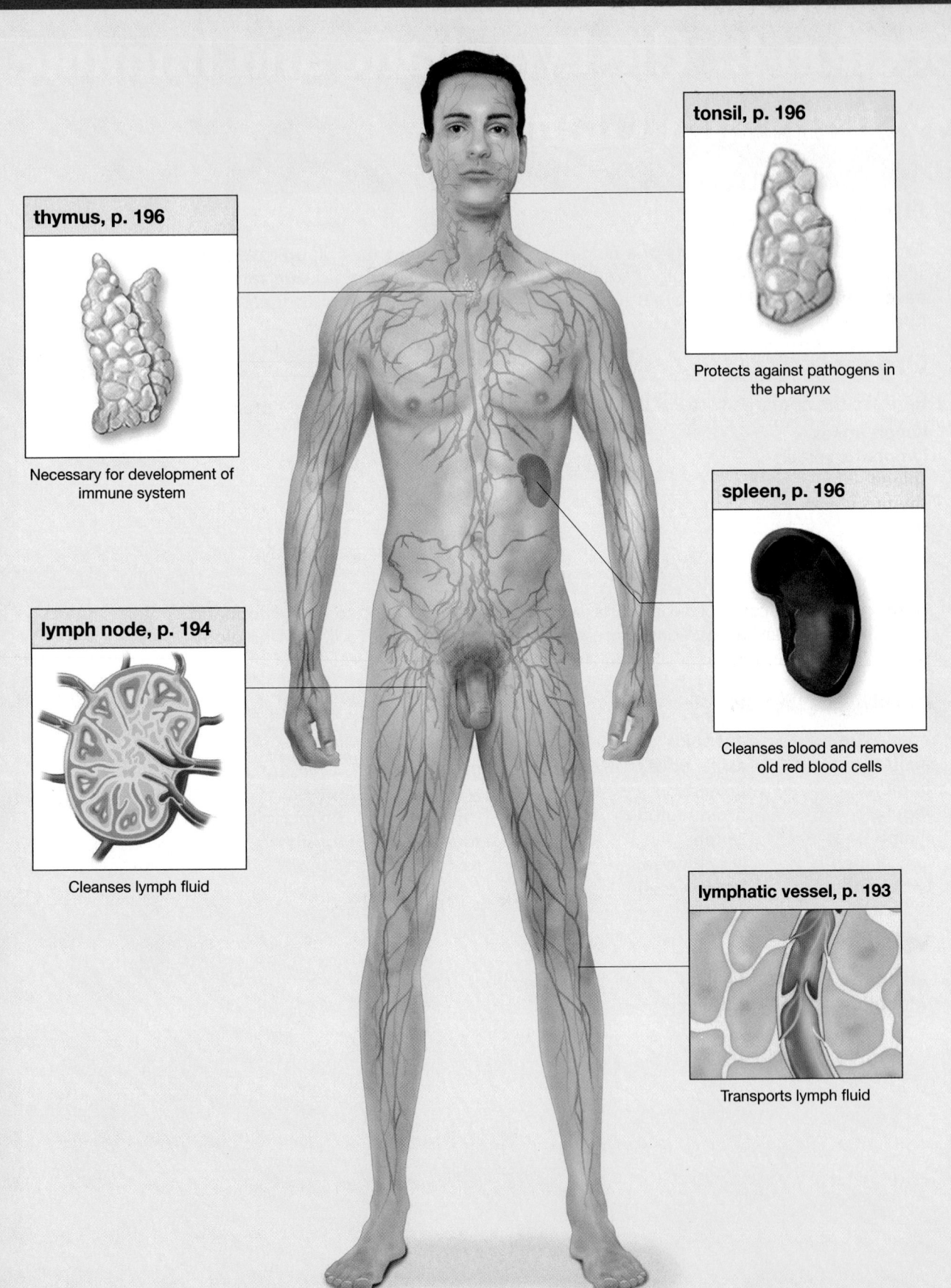

thymus, p. 196

Necessary for development of immune system

tonsil, p. 196

Protects against pathogens in the pharynx

spleen, p. 196

Cleanses blood and removes old red blood cells

lymph node, p. 194

Cleanses lymph fluid

lymphatic vessel, p. 193

Transports lymph fluid

Anatomy and Physiology of the Lymphatic and Immune Systems

lacteals (lack-TEE-als)
lymph (LIMF)
lymph nodes
lymphatic vessels (lim-FAT-ik)

spleen
thymus gland (THIGH-mus)
tonsils (TON-sulls)

The lymphatic system consists of a network of **lymphatic vessels, lymph nodes,** the **spleen,** the **thymus gland,** and the **tonsils.** These organs perform several quite diverse functions for the body. First, they collect excess tissue fluid throughout the body and return it to the circulatory system. The fluid, once inside a lymphatic vessel, is referred to as **lymph.** Lymph vessels located around the small intestines, called **lacteals,** are able to pick up absorbed fats for transport. Additionally, the lymphatic system works with the immune system to form the groups of cells, tissues, organs, and molecules that serve as the body's primary defense against the invasion of pathogens. These systems work together defending the body against foreign invaders and substances, as well as removing our own cells that have become diseased.

Lymphatic Vessels

lymphatic capillaries (CAP-ih-lair-eez)
lymphatic ducts
right lymphatic duct

thoracic duct
valves

The lymphatic vessels form an extensive network of ducts throughout the entire body. However, unlike the circulatory system, these vessels are not in a closed loop. Instead, they serve as one-way pipes conducting lymph from the tissues toward the thoracic cavity (see Figure 6.7 ■). These vessels begin as very small

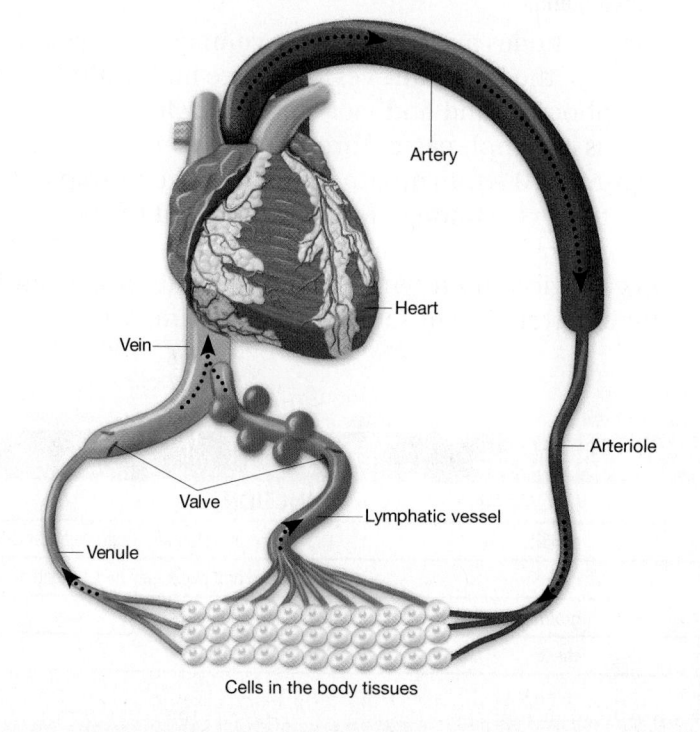

Artery

Heart

Vein

Arteriole

Valve

Lymphatic vessel

Venule

Cells in the body tissues

■ **Figure 6.7** Lymphatic vessels (green) pick up excess tissue fluid, purify it in lymph nodes, and return it to the circulatory system.

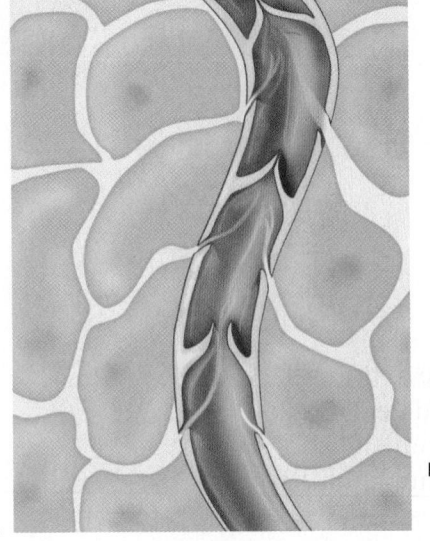

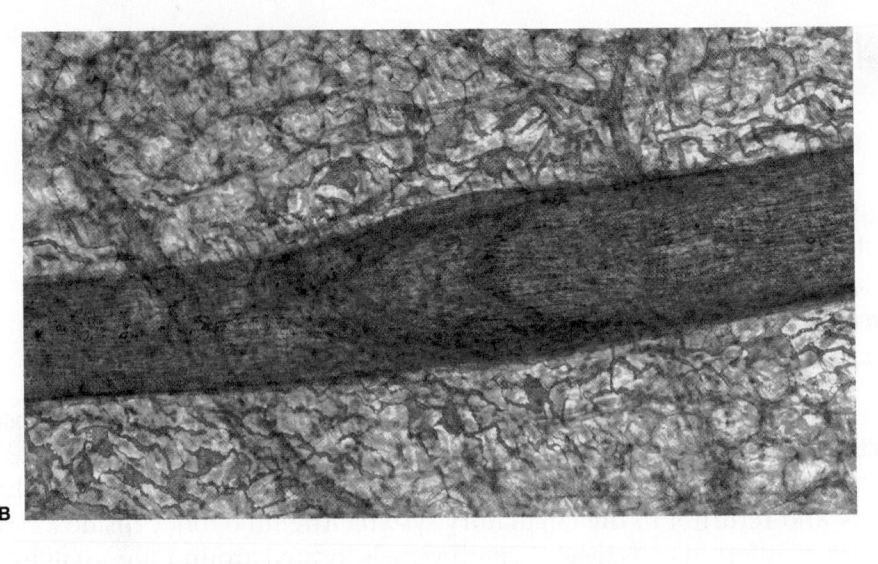

Figure 6.8 (A) Lymphatic vessel with valves within tissue cells; (B) photomicrograph of lymphatic vessel with valve clearly visible. *(Michael Abbey/Photo Researchers, Inc.)*

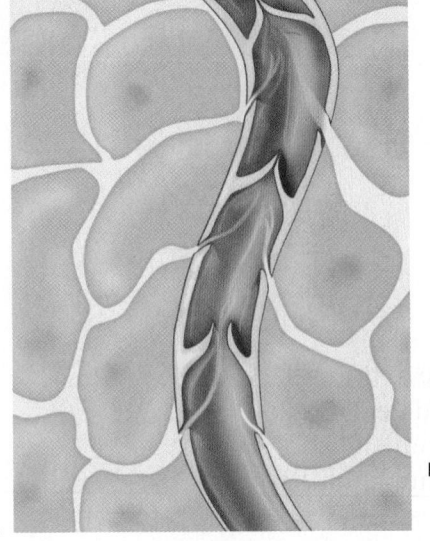 A

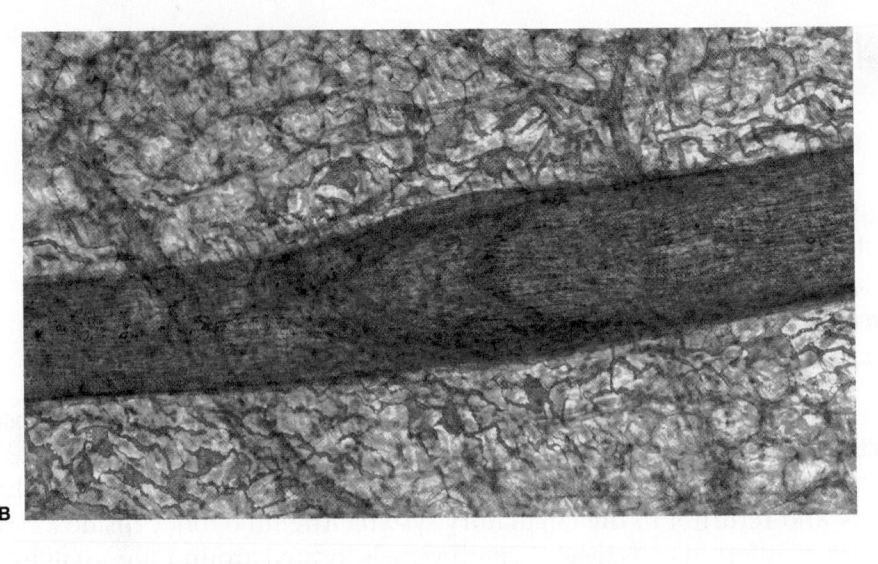 B

> **MED TERM TIP**
>
> The term *capillary* is also used to describe the minute blood vessels within the circulatory system. This is one of several general medical terms, such as valves, cilia, and hair, that are used in several systems.

lymphatic capillaries in the tissues. Excessive tissue fluid enters these capillaries to begin the trip back to the circulatory system. The capillaries merge into larger lymphatic vessels. This is a very low pressure system, so these vessels have **valves** along their length to ensure that lymph can only move forward toward the thoracic cavity (see Figure 6.8 ■). These vessels finally drain into one of two large **lymphatic ducts,** the **right lymphatic duct** or the **thoracic duct.** The smaller right lymphatic duct drains the right arm and the right side of the head, neck, and chest. This duct empties lymph into the right subclavian vein. The larger thoracic duct drains lymph from the rest of the body and empties into the left subclavian vein (see Figure 6.9 ■).

Lymph Nodes

lymph glands

> **MED TERM TIP**
>
> In surgical procedures to remove a malignancy from an organ, such as a breast, the adjacent lymph nodes are also tested for cancer. If cancerous cells are found in the tested lymph nodes, the disease is said to have spread or *metastasized.* Tumor cells may then spread to other parts of the body by means of the lymphatic system.

Lymph nodes are small organs composed of lymphatic tissue located along the route of the lymphatic vessels. These nodes, also referred to as **lymph glands,** house lymphocytes and antibodies and therefore work to remove pathogens and cell debris as lymph passes through them on its way back to the thoracic cavity (see Figure 6.10 ■). Lymph nodes also serve to trap and destroy cells from cancerous tumors. Although found throughout the body, lymph nodes are particularly concentrated in several regions. For example, lymph nodes concentrated in the neck region drain lymph from the head. See again Figure 6.9 and Table 6.2 ■ for a description of some of the most important sites for lymph nodes.

Table 6.2	Sites for Lymph Nodes	
NAME	**LOCATION**	**FUNCTION**
axillary (AK-sih-lair-ee)	armpits	Drain arms and shoulder region; cancer cells from breasts may be present
cervical (SER-vih-kal)	neck	Drain head and neck; may be enlarged during upper respiratory infections
inguinal (ING-gwih-nal)	groin	Drain legs and lower pelvis
mediastinal (mee-dee-ass-TYE-nal)	chest	Drain chest cavity

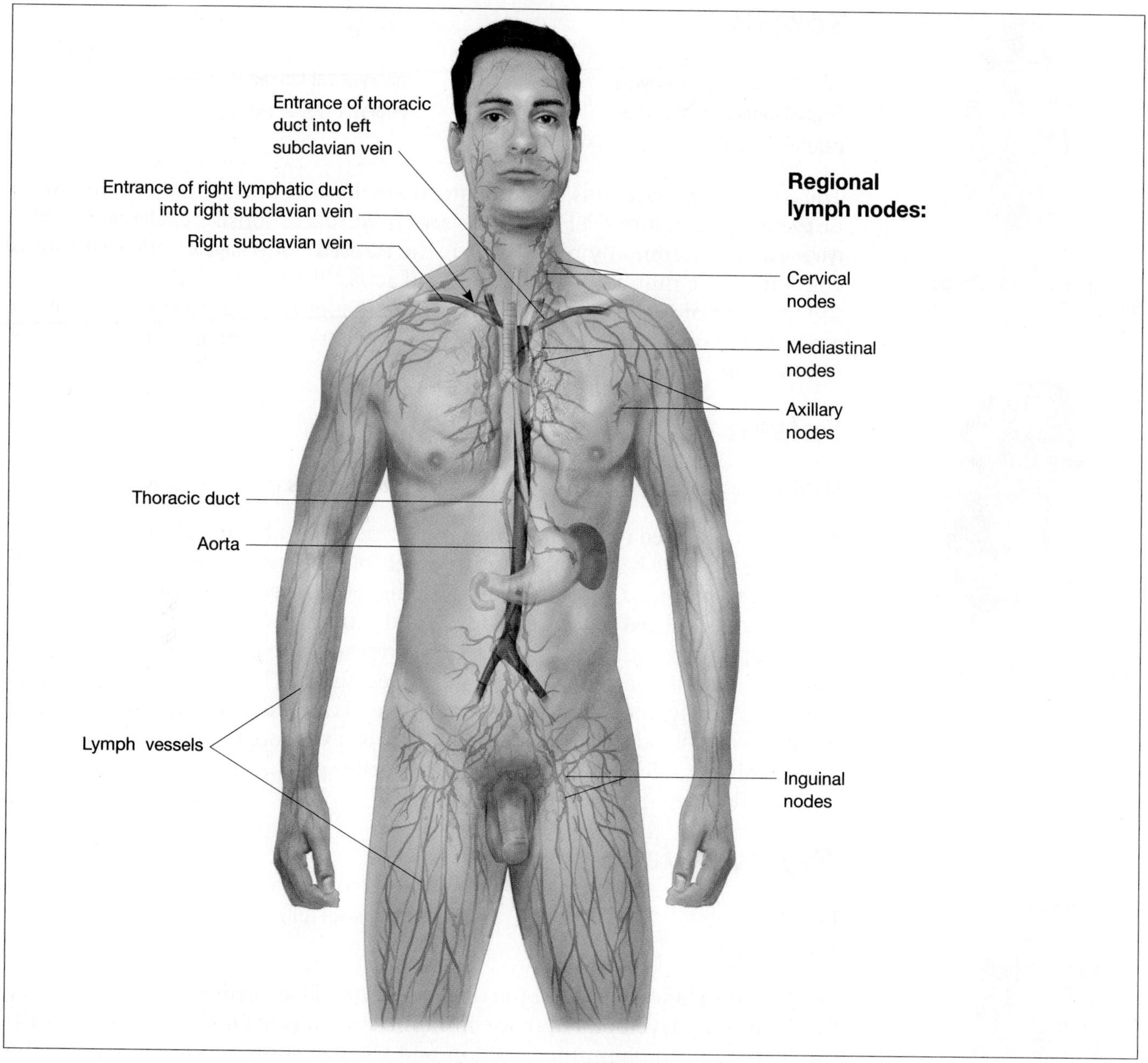

Entrance of thoracic
duct into left
subclavian vein

Entrance of right lymphatic duct
into right subclavian vein

Right subclavian vein

**Regional
lymph nodes:**

Cervical
nodes

Mediastinal
nodes

Axillary
nodes

Thoracic duct

Aorta

Lymph vessels

Inguinal
nodes

■ **Figure 6.9** Location of lymph vessels, lymphatic ducts, and areas of lymph node concentrations.

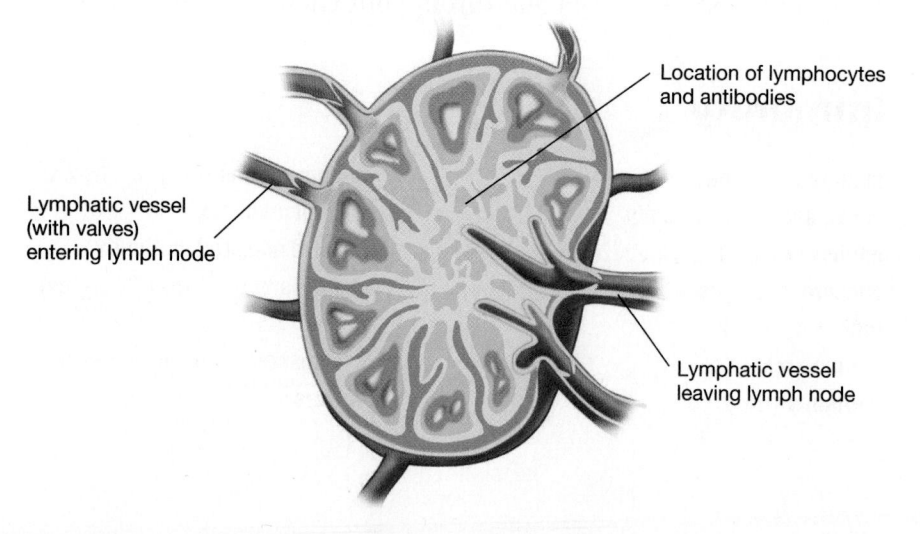

Location of lymphocytes
and antibodies

Lymphatic vessel
(with valves)
entering lymph node

Lymphatic vessel
leaving lymph node

■ **Figure 6.10** Structure of
a lymph node.

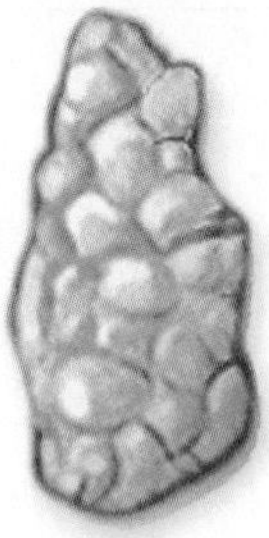

Figure 6.11 Shape of a tonsil.

Tonsils

adenoids (ADD-eh-noydz)   **pharyngeal tonsils** (fair-IN-jee-al)
lingual tonsils (LING-gwal)   **pharynx** (FAIR-inks)
palatine tonsils (PAL-ah-tyne)

The tonsils are collections of lymphatic tissue located on each side of the throat or **pharynx** (see Figure 6.11 ■). There are three sets of tonsils: **palatine tonsils, pharyngeal tonsils** (commonly referred to as the **adenoids**), and **lingual tonsils.** All tonsils contain a large number of leukocytes and act as filters to protect the body from the invasion of pathogens through the digestive or respiratory systems. Tonsils are not vital organs and can safely be removed if they become a continuous site of infection.

Spleen

blood sinuses   **macrophages** (MACK-roh-fayj-ez)

The spleen, located in the upper left quadrant of the abdomen, consists of lymphatic tissue that is highly infiltrated with blood vessels (see Figure 6.12 ■). These vessels spread out into slow-moving **blood sinuses.** The spleen filters out and destroys old red blood cells, recycles the iron, and also stores some of the blood supply for the body. Phagocytic **macrophages** line the blood sinuses in the spleen to engulf and remove pathogens. Because the blood is moving through the organ slowly, the macrophages have time to carefully identify pathogens and worn-out red blood cells. The spleen is also not a vital organ and can be removed due to injury or disease. However, without the spleen, a person's susceptibility to a bloodstream infection may be increased.

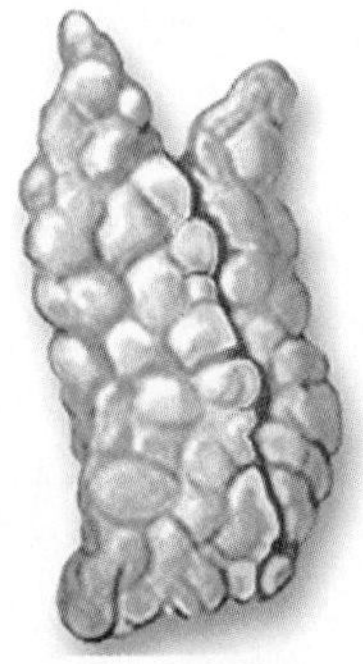

Figure 6.12 Shape of the spleen.

Thymus Gland

T cells   **thymosin** (thigh-MOH-sin)
T lymphocytes

The thymus gland, located in the upper portion of the mediastinum, is essential for the proper development of the immune system (see Figure 6.13 ■). It assists the body with the immune function and the development of antibodies. This organ's hormone, **thymosin,** changes lymphocytes to **T lymphocytes** (simply called **T cells**), which play an important role in the immune response. The thymus is active in the unborn child and throughout childhood until adolescence, when it begins to shrink in size.

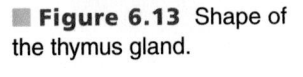

Figure 6.13 Shape of the thymus gland.

Immunity

acquired immunity   **immunizations** (im-yoo-nih-ZAY-shuns)
active acquired immunity   **natural immunity**
bacteria (bak-TEE-ree-ah)   **passive acquired immunity**
cancerous tumors   **protozoans** (proh-toh-ZOH-anz)
fungi (FUN-jee)   **toxins**
immune response   **vaccinations** (vak-sih-NAY-shuns)
immunity (im-YOO-nih-tee)   **viruses**

Immunity is the body's ability to defend itself against pathogens, such as **bacteria, viruses, fungi, protozoans, toxins,** and **cancerous tumors.** Immunity comes in two forms: **natural immunity** and **acquired immunity.** Natural immunity, also called *innate immunity,* is not specific to a particular disease and does not require prior exposure to the pathogenic agent. A good example of natural immunity is the macrophage. These leukocytes are present throughout all the tissues of the body, but are concentrated in areas of high exposure to invading bacteria, like the lungs and digestive system. They are very active phagocytic cells, ingesting and digesting any pathogen they encounter (see Figure 6.14 ■).

Acquired immunity is the body's response to a specific pathogen and may be established either passively or actively. **Passive acquired immunity** results when a person receives protective substances produced by another human or animal. This may take the form of maternal antibodies crossing the placenta to a baby or an antitoxin or gamma globulin injection. **Active acquired immunity** develops following direct exposure to the pathogenic agent. The agent stimulates the body's **immune response,** a series of different mechanisms all geared to neutralize the agent. For example, a person typically can catch chickenpox only once because once the body has successfully fought the virus, it will be able to more quickly recognize and kill it in the future. **Immunizations** or **vaccinations** are special types of active acquired immunity. Instead of actually being exposed to the infectious agent and having the disease, a person is exposed to a modified or weakened pathogen that is still capable of stimulating the immune response but not actually causing the disease.

Immune Response

antibody (AN-tih-bod-ee)

antibody-mediated immunity

antigen–antibody complex

antigens (AN-tih-jens)

B cells

B lymphocytes

cell-mediated immunity

cellular immunity

cytotoxic (sigh-toh-TOK-sik)

humoral immunity (HYOO-mor-al)

natural killer (NK) cells

Disease-causing agents are recognized as being foreign because they display proteins that are different from a person's own natural proteins. Those foreign proteins, called **antigens,** stimulate the immune response. The immune response consists of two distinct and different processes: **humoral immunity** (also called **antibody-mediated immunity**) and **cellular immunity** (also called **cell-mediated immunity**).

> **MED TERM TIP**
>
> The term *humoral* comes from the Latin word for "liquid." It is the old-fashioned term to refer to the fluids of the body.

■ **Figure 6.14** Enhanced photomicrograph showing a macrophage (purple) attacking bacillus *Escherichia coli* (green). *(Sebastian Kaulitzki/ Shutterstock)*

Humoral immunity refers to the production of **B lymphocytes,** also called **B cells,** which respond to antigens by producing a protective protein, an **antibody.** Antibodies combine with the antigen to form an **antigen–antibody complex.** This complex either targets the foreign substance for phagocytosis or prevents the infectious agent from damaging healthy cells.

Cellular immunity involves the production of T cells and **natural killer** (NK) **cells.** These defense cells are **cytotoxic,** meaning that they physically attack and destroy pathogenic cells.

Standard Precautions

cross-infection	**reinfection**
nosocomial infection (no-so-KOH-mee-all)	**self-inoculation**
Occupational Safety and Health Administration (OSHA)	

Hospitals and other healthcare settings contain a large number of infective pathogens. Patients and healthcare workers are exposed to each other's pathogens and sometimes become infected. An infection acquired in this manner, as a result of hospital exposure, is referred to as a **nosocomial infection.** Nosocomial infections can spread in several ways. **Cross-infection** occurs when a person, either a patient or healthcare worker, acquires a pathogen from another patient or healthcare worker. **Reinfection** takes place when a patient becomes infected again with the same pathogen that originally brought him or her to the hospital. **Self-inoculation** occurs when a person becomes infected in a different part of the body by a pathogen from another part of his or her own body—such as intestinal bacteria spreading to the urethra.

With the appearance of the hepatitis B virus (HBV) in the mid-1960s and the human immunodeficiency virus (HIV) in the mid-1980s, the fight against spreading infections took on even greater significance. In 1987 the **Occupational Safety and Health Administration** (OSHA) issued mandatory guidelines to ensure that all employees at risk of exposure to body fluids are provided with personal protective equipment. These guidelines state that all human blood, tissue, and body fluids must be treated as if they were infected with HIV, HBV, or other bloodborne pathogens. These guidelines were expanded in 1992 and 1996 to encourage the fight against not just bloodborne pathogens, but all nosocomial infections spread by contact with blood, mucous membranes, nonintact skin, and all body fluids (including amniotic fluid, vaginal secretions, pleural fluid, cerebrospinal fluid, peritoneal fluid, pericardial fluid, and semen). These guidelines are commonly referred to as the Standard Precautions:

1. Wash hands before putting on and after removing gloves and before and after working with each patient or patient equipment.
2. Wear gloves when in contact with any body fluid, mucous membrane, or nonintact skin or if you have chapped hands, a rash, or open sores.
3. Wear a nonpermeable gown or apron during procedures that are likely to expose you to any body fluid, mucous membrane, or nonintact skin.
4. Wear a mask and protective equipment or a face shield when patients are coughing often or if body fluid droplets or splashes are likely.
5. Wear a facemask and eyewear that seal close to the face during procedures that cause body tissues to be vaporized.
6. Remove for proper cleaning any shared equipment—such as a thermometer, stethoscope, or blood pressure cuff—that has come into contact with body fluids, mucous membrane, or nonintact skin.

MED TERM TIP

Analyzing the word parts that make up the term *cytotoxic* gives you a quick idea of this cell's function.
- cyt/o = cell
- tox/o = poison
- -ic = pertaining to

MED TERM TIP

The simple act of thoroughly washing your hands is the most effective method of preventing the spread of infectious diseases.

◼ Terminology

Word Parts Used to Build Lymphatic and Immune System Terms

The following lists contain the combining forms, suffixes, and prefixes used to build terms in the remaining sections of this chapter.

Combining Forms

adenoid/o	adenoids	**lymph/o**	lymph	**pneumon/o**	lung
axill/o	axilla, underarm	**lymphaden/o**	lymph node	**sarc/o**	flesh
cortic/o	outer region, cortex	**lymphangi/o**	lymph vessel	**splen/o**	spleen
immun/o	protection	**nucle/o**	nucleus	**thym/o**	thymus gland
inguin/o	groin	**path/o**	disease	**tonsill/o**	tonsils

Suffixes

-al	pertaining to	**-globulin**	protein	**-logy**	study of
-ar	pertaining to	**-gram**	record	**-megaly**	enlarged
-ary	pertaining to	**-graphy**	process of recording	**-oma**	tumor
-atic	pertaining to	**-ia**	condition	**-osis**	abnormal condition
-ectomy	surgical removal	**-iasis**	abnormal condition	**-pathy**	disease
-edema	swelling	**-ic**	pertaining to	**-therapy**	treatment
-genic	producing	**-itis**	inflammation		

Prefixes

anti-	against	auto-	self	mono-	one

◼ Anatomical Terms

TERM	WORD PARTS	DEFINITION
axillary (AK-sih-lair-ee)	axill/o = axilla, underarm -ary = pertaining to	Pertaining to the underarm region.
immunoglobulins (im-yoo-noh-GLOB-yoo-linz)	immun/o = protection -globulin = protein	Antibodies secreted by the B cells. All antibodies are immunoglobulins and assist in protecting the body and its surfaces from the invasion of bacteria. For example, the immunoglobulin IgA in colostrum, the first milk from the mother, helps to protect the newborn from infection.
inguinal (ING-gwih-nal)	inguin/o = groin -al = pertaining to	Pertaining to the groin region.
lymphangial (lim-FAN-gee-al)	lymphangi/o = lymph vessel -al = pertaining to	Pertaining to lymph vessels.

Anatomical Terms *(continued)*

TERM	WORD PARTS	DEFINITION
lymphatic (lim-FAT-ik)	lymph/o = lymph -atic = pertaining to	Pertaining to lymph.
splenic (SPLEN-ik)	splen/o = spleen -ic = pertaining to	Pertaining to the spleen.
thymic (THIGH-mik)	thym/o = thymus gland -ic = pertaining to	Pertaining to the thymus gland.
tonsillar (ton-sih-lar)	tonsill/o = tonsils -ar = pertaining to	Pertaining to the tonsils.

Pathology

TERM	WORD PARTS	DEFINITION
Medical Specialties		
allergist (AL-er-jist)		A physician who specializes in testing for and treating allergies.
immunology (im-yoo-NALL-oh-jee)	immun/o = protection -logy = study of	A branch of medicine concerned with diagnosis and treatment of infectious diseases and other disorders of the immune system. Physician is an *immunologist*.
pathology (path-OL-oh-gee)	path/o = disease -logy = study of	A branch of medicine concerned with determining the underlying causes and development of diseases. Physician is an *immunologist*.
Signs and Symptoms		
hives		Appearance of wheals as part of an allergic reaction.
inflammation (in-flah-MA-shun)		The tissues' response to injury from pathogens or physical agents. Characterized by redness, pain, swelling, and feeling hot to touch.

MED TERM TIP

Word Watch: The terms *inflammation* and *inflammatory* are spelled with two *m*'s, while *inflame* and *inflamed* each have only one *m*. These may be the most commonly misspelled terms by medical terminology students.

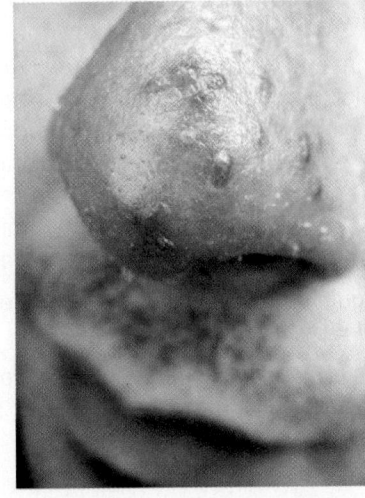

■ **Figure 6.15** Inflammation as illustrated by cellulitis of the nose. Note that the area is red and swollen. It is also painful and hot to touch.

Pathology *(continued)*

TERM	WORD PARTS	DEFINITION
lymphedema (limf-eh-DEE-mah)	lymph/o = lymph -edema = swelling	Edema appearing in the extremities due to an obstruction of the lymph flow through the lymphatic vessels.
pathogenic (path-oh-JEN-ik)	path/o = disease -genic = producing	An adjective term to describe something—such as bacteria, viruses, or toxins—that produce disease.
splenomegaly (splee-noh-MEG-ah-lee)	splen/o = spleen -megaly = enlarged	An enlarged spleen.
urticaria (er-tih-KAY-ree-ah)		Severe itching associated with hives, usually linked to food allergy, stress, or drug reactions.
Allergic Reactions		
allergy (AL-er-jee)		Hypersensitivity to a common substance in the environment or to a medication. The substance causing the allergic reaction is called an *allergen.*
anaphylactic shock (an-ah-fih-LAK-tik)		Life-threatening condition resulting from a severe allergic reaction. Examples of instances that may trigger this reaction include bee stings, medications, or the ingestion of foods. Circulatory and respiratory problems occur, including respiratory distress, hypotension, edema, tachycardia, and convulsions. Also called **anaphylaxis.**
Lymphatic System		
adenoiditis (add-eh-noyd-EYE-tis)	adenoid/o = adenoids -itis = inflammation	Inflammation of the adenoids.
autoimmune disease	auto- = self	A disease resulting from the body's immune system attacking its own cells as if they were pathogens. Examples include systemic lupus erythematosus, rheumatoid arthritis, and multiple sclerosis.
elephantiasis (el-eh-fan-TYE-ah-sis)	-iasis = abnormal condition	Inflammation, obstruction, and destruction of the lymph vessels resulting in enlarged tissues due to edema.
Hodgkin's disease (HD) (HOJ-kins)		Also called *Hodgkin's lymphoma.* Cancer of the lymphatic cells found in concentration in the lymph nodes. Named after Thomas Hodgkin, a British physician, who first described it.
lymphadenitis (lim-fad-en-EYE-tis)	lymphaden/o = lymph node -itis = inflammation	Inflammation of the lymph nodes. Referred to as *swollen glands.*
lymphadenopathy (lim-fad-eh-NOP-ah-thee)	lymphaden/o = lymph node -pathy = disease	A general term for lymph node diseases.
lymphangioma (lim-fan-jee-OH-mah)	lymphangi/o = lymph vessel -oma = tumor	A tumor in a lymphatic vessel.

Pathology (continued)

TERM	WORD PARTS	DEFINITION
lymphoma (lim-FOH-mah)	lymph/o = lymph -oma = tumor	A tumor in lymphatic tissue.
mononucleosis (mono) (mon-oh-nook-lee-OH-sis)	mono- = one nucle/o = nucleus -osis = abnormal condition	Acute infectious disease with a large number of abnormal mononuclear lymphocytes. Caused by the Epstein–Barr virus. Abnormal liver function may occur.
non-Hodgkin's lymphoma (NHL)	lymph/o = lymph -oma = tumor	Cancer of the lymphatic tissues other than Hodgkin's lymphoma.
thymoma (thigh-MOH-mah)	thym/o = thymus gland -oma = tumor	A tumor of the thymus gland.
tonsillitis (ton-sil-EYE-tis)	tonsill/o = tonsils -itis = inflammation	Inflammation of the tonsils.

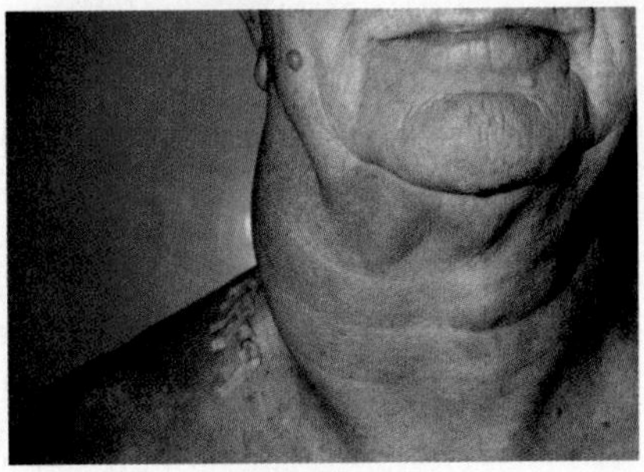

■ Figure 6.16 Photo of the neck of a patient with non-Hodgkin's lymphoma showing the swelling associated with enlarged lymph nodes.

Immune System

acquired immunodeficiency syndrome (AIDS) (ac-quired / im-you-noh-dee-FIH-shen-see / SIN-drohm)	immun/o = protection	Disease involving a defect in the cell-mediated immunity system. A syndrome of opportunistic infections occurring in the final stages of infection with the human immunodeficiency virus (HIV). This virus attacks T4 lymphocytes and destroys them, reducing the person's ability to fight infection.
AIDS-related complex (ARC)		Early stage of AIDS. There is a positive test for the virus, but only mild symptoms of weight loss, fatigue, skin rash, and anorexia.
graft versus host disease (GVHD)		Serious complication of bone marrow transplant (graft). Immune cells from the donor bone marrow attack the recipient's (host's) tissues.
human immunodeficiency virus (HIV) (im-yoo-noh-dee-FIH-shen-see)	immun/o = protection	Virus that causes AIDS; also known as a **retrovirus**.

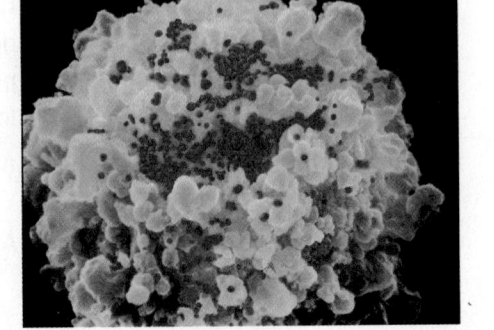

■ Figure 6.17 Color-enhanced scanning electron micrograph of HIV virus (red) infecting T-helper cells (green). *(National Institute for Biological Standards and Control (U.K.)/Science Photo Library/Photo Researchers, Inc.)*

Pathology *(continued)*

TERM	WORD PARTS	DEFINITION
immunocompromised (im-you-noh-KOM-pro-mized)	immun/o = protection	Having an immune system that is unable to respond properly to pathogens. Also called *immunodeficiency disorder.*
Kaposi's sarcoma (KS) (KAP-oh-seez / sar-KOH-mah)	sarc/o = flesh -oma = tumor	Form of skin cancer frequently seen in patients with AIDS. It consists of brownish-purple papules that spread from the skin and metastasize to internal organs. Named for Moritz Kaposi, an Austrian dermatologist.
opportunistic infections		Infectious diseases associated with patients who have compromised immune systems and therefore a lowered resistance to infections and parasites. May be the result of HIV infection.
pneumocystis pneumonia (PCP) (noo-moh-SIS-tis / new-MOH-nee-ah)	pneumon/o = lung -ia = condition	Pneumonia common in patients with weakened immune systems, such as AIDS patients, caused by the *Pneumocystis jirovecii* fungus.
sarcoidosis (sar-koyd-OH-sis)	-osis = abnormal condition	Disease of unknown cause that forms fibrous lesions commonly appearing in the lymph nodes, liver, skin, lungs, spleen, eyes, and small bones of the hands and feet.
severe combined immunodeficiency syndrome (SCIDS)	immun/o = protection	Disease seen in children born with a nonfunctioning immune system. Often these children are forced to live in sealed sterile rooms.

Diagnostic Procedures

TERM	WORD PARTS	DEFINITION
Clinical Laboratory Tests		
enzyme-linked immunosorbent assay (ELISA) (EN-zym / LINK'T / im-yoo-noh-sor-bent / ASS-say)	immun/o = protection	Blood test for an antibody to the HIV virus. A positive test means that the person has been exposed to the virus. There may be a false-positive reading, and then the Western blot test would be used to verify the results.
Western blot		Test used as a backup to the ELISA blood test to detect the presence of the antibody to HIV (AIDS virus) in the blood.
Diagnostic Imaging		
lymphangiogram (lim-FAN-jee-oh-gram)	lymphangi/o = lymph vessel -gram = record	X-ray record of the lymphatic vessels produced by lymphangiography.
lymphangiography (lim-FAN-jee-oh-graf-ee)	lymphangi/o = lymph vessel -graphy = process of recording	X-ray taken of the lymph vessels after the injection of dye into the foot. The lymph flow through the chest is traced.

Diagnostic Procedures *(continued)*

TERM	WORD PARTS	DEFINITION
Additional Diagnostic Procedures		
Monospot		Blood test for infectious mononucleosis.
scratch test		Form of allergy testing in which the body is exposed to an allergen through a light scratch on the skin.

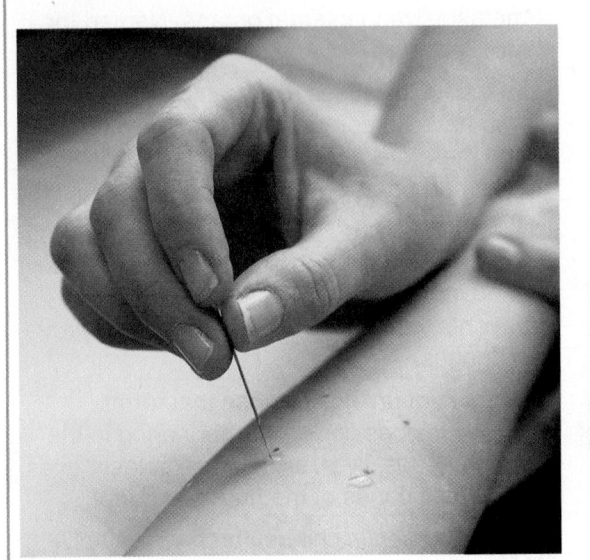

A

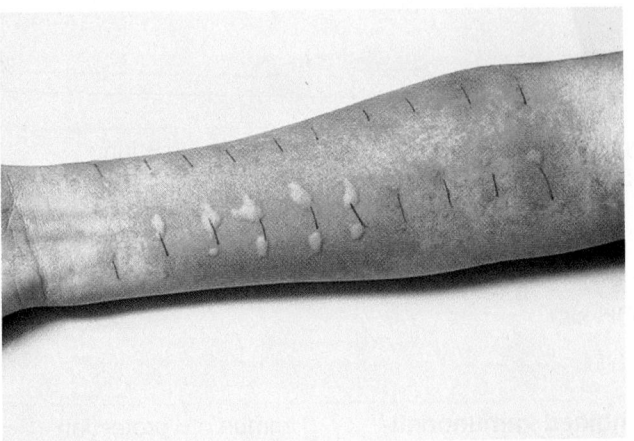

B

Figure 6.18 (A) Scratch test; patient is exposed to allergens through a light scratch on the skin; (B) Positive scratch test results. Inflammation indicates person is allergic to that substance. *(A. James King-Holmes/ Science Photo Library/Photo Researchers, Inc. B. SUI/Photo Researchers, Inc.)*

Therapeutic Procedures

TERM	WORD PARTS	DEFINITION
Medical Procedures		
immunotherapy (IM-yoo-noh-thair-ah-pee)	immun/o = protection -therapy = treatment	Giving a patient an injection of immunoglobulins or antibodies in order to treat a disease. The antibodies may be produced by another person or animal, for example, antivenom for snake bites. More recent developments include treatments to boost the activity of the immune system, especially to treat cancer and AIDS.
vaccination (vak-sih-NAY-shun)		Exposure to a weakened pathogen that stimulates the immune response and antibody production in order to confer protection against the full-blown disease. Also called *immunization*.

Therapeutic Procedures *(continued)*

TERM	WORD PARTS	DEFINITION
Surgical Procedures		
adenoidectomy (add-eh-noyd-EK-toh-mee)	adenoid/o = adenoids -ectomy = surgical removal	Surgical removal of the adenoids.
lymphadenectomy (lim-fad-eh-NEK-toh-mee)	lymphaden/o = lymph node -ectomy = surgical removal	Removal of a lymph node. This is usually done to test for malignancy.
splenectomy (splee-NEK-toh-mee)	splen/o = spleen -ectomy = surgical removal	Surgical removal of the spleen.
thymectomy (thigh-MEK-toh-mee)	thym/o = thymus gland -ectomy = surgical removal	Surgical removal of the thymus gland.
tonsillectomy (ton-sih-LEK-toh-mee)	tonsill/o = tonsils -ectomy = surgical removal	Surgical removal of the tonsils.

Pharmacology

CLASSIFICATION		ACTION	EXAMPLES
antihistamine (an-tih-HIST-ah-meen)	anti- = against	Blocks the effects of histamine released by the body during an allergic reaction.	cetirizine, Zyrtec; diphenhydramine, Benadryl
corticosteroids (core-tih-koh-STARE-royds)	cortic/o = outer region, cortex	A hormone produced by the adrenal cortex that has very strong anti-inflammatory properties. Particularly useful in treating autoimmune diseases.	prednisone; methylprednisolone, Solu-Medrol
immunosuppressants (im-yoo-noh-sue-PRESS-antz)	immun/o = protection	Blocks certain actions of the immune system. Required to prevent rejection of a transplanted organ.	mycophenolate mofetil, CellCept; cyclosporine, Neoral
protease inhibitor drugs (PROH-tee-ace)		Inhibits protease, an enzyme viruses need to reproduce.	indinavir, Crixivan; saquinavir, Fortovase
reverse transcriptase inhibitor drugs (trans-KRIP-tays)		Inhibits reverse transcriptase, an enzyme needed by viruses to reproduce.	lamivudine, Epivir; zidovudine, Retrovir

Abbreviations

AIDS	acquired immunodeficiency syndrome	**KS**	Kaposi's sarcoma
ARC	AIDS-related complex	**mono**	mononucleosis
ELISA	enzyme-linked immunosorbent assay	**NHL**	non-Hodgkin's lymphoma
GVHD	graft versus host disease	**NK**	natural killer cells
HD	Hodgkin's disease	**PCP**	pneumocystis pneumonia
HIV	human immunodeficiency virus	**SCIDS**	severe combined immunodeficiency syndrome
Ig	immunoglobulins (IgA, IgD, IgE, IgG, IgM)		

Chapter Review

Real-World Applications

Medical Record Analysis

This Discharge Summary contains 11 medical terms. Underline each term and write it in the list below the report. Then define each term. Note: Some terms are defined in other chapters; use your glossary-index to locate and define these terms.

Discharge Summary

Admitting Diagnosis:	Splenomegaly, weight loss, diarrhea, fatigue, chronic cough
Final Diagnosis:	Non-Hodgkin's lymphoma of spleen; splenectomy
History of Present Illness:	Patient is a 36-year-old businessman who was first seen in the office with complaints of feeling generally "run down," intermittent diarrhea, weight loss, and, more recently, a dry cough. He states he has been aware of these symptoms for approximately six months. Monospot and ELISA are both negative. In spite of a 35-pound weight loss, he has abdominal swelling and splenomegaly was detected. He was admitted to the hospital for further evaluation and treatment.
Summary of Hospital Course:	Full-body MRI confirmed splenomegaly and located a 3-cm encapsulated tumor in the spleen. Biopsies taken from the splenic tumor confirmed the diagnosis of non-Hodgkin's lymphoma. The patient underwent splenectomy for removal of the tumor.
Discharge Plans:	Patient was discharged home following recovery from the splenectomy. The abdominal swelling and diarrhea were resolved, but the dry cough persisted. He was referred to an oncologist for evaluation and surveillance for metastases.

	Term	Definition
1	_____	_____
2	_____	_____
3	_____	_____
4	_____	_____
5	_____	_____
6	_____	_____
7	_____	_____
8	_____	_____
9	_____	_____
10	_____	_____
11	_____	_____

Chart Note Transcription

The chart note below contains 10 phrases that can be reworded with a medical term that you learned in this chapter. Each phrase is identified with an underline. Determine the medical term and write your answers in the space provided.

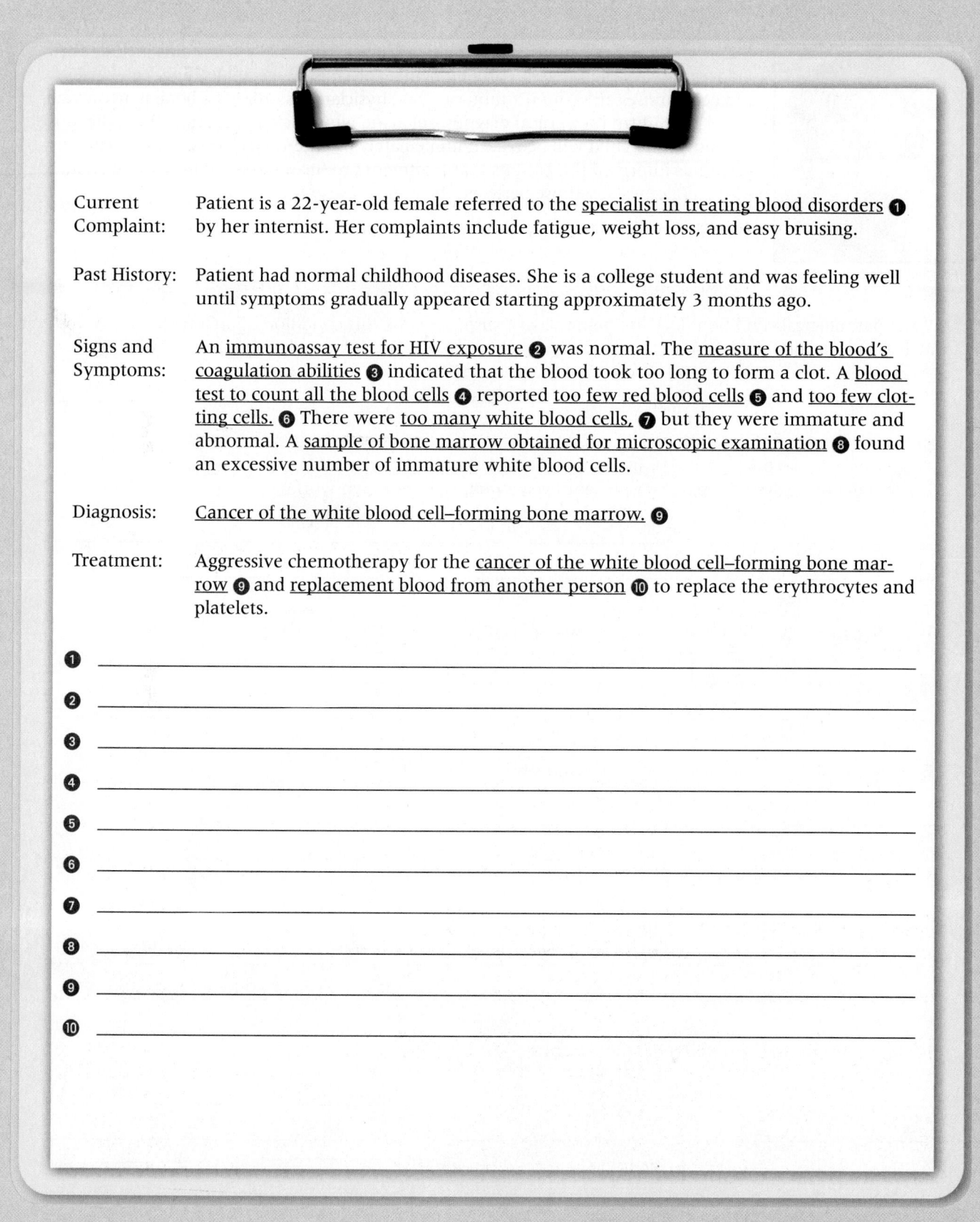

Current Complaint:	Patient is a 22-year-old female referred to the <u>specialist in treating blood disorders</u> ❶ by her internist. Her complaints include fatigue, weight loss, and easy bruising.
Past History:	Patient had normal childhood diseases. She is a college student and was feeling well until symptoms gradually appeared starting approximately 3 months ago.
Signs and Symptoms:	An <u>immunoassay test for HIV exposure</u> ❷ was normal. The <u>measure of the blood's coagulation abilities</u> ❸ indicated that the blood took too long to form a clot. A <u>blood test to count all the blood cells</u> ❹ reported <u>too few red blood cells</u> ❺ and <u>too few clotting cells.</u> ❻ There were <u>too many white blood cells,</u> ❼ but they were immature and abnormal. A <u>sample of bone marrow obtained for microscopic examination</u> ❽ found an excessive number of immature white blood cells.
Diagnosis:	<u>Cancer of the white blood cell–forming bone marrow.</u> ❾
Treatment:	Aggressive chemotherapy for the <u>cancer of the white blood cell–forming bone marrow</u> ❾ and <u>replacement blood from another person</u> ❿ to replace the erythrocytes and platelets.

❶ _____

❷ _____

❸ _____

❹ _____

❺ _____

❻ _____

❼ _____

❽ _____

❾ _____

❿ _____

Case Study

Below is a case study presentation of a patient with a condition covered in this chapter. Read the case study and answer the questions below. Some questions will ask for information not included within this chapter. Use your text, a medical dictionary, or any other reference material you choose to answer these questions.

A 2-year-old boy is being seen by a hematologist. The child's symptoms include the sudden onset of high fevers, thrombopenia, epistaxis, gingival bleeding, petechiae, and ecchymoses after minor traumas. The physician has ordered a bone marrow aspiration to confirm the clinical diagnosis of acute lymphocytic leukemia. If the diagnosis is positive, the child will be placed immediately on intensive chemotherapy. The physician has informed the parents that treatment produces remission in 90% of children with ALL, especially those between the ages of 2 and 8.

(Flashon Studio/Shutterstock)

1. What pathological condition does the hematologist suspect? Look this condition up in a reference source and include a short description of it.

_____

_____

2. List and define each of the patient's presenting symptoms in your own words.

_____

_____

3. What diagnostic test did the physician perform? Describe it in your own words.

_____

_____

4. Explain the phrase "clinical diagnosis" in your own words.

_____

_____

5. If the suspected diagnosis is correct, explain the treatment that will begin.

_____

_____

6. What do you think the term "remission" means?

_____

_____

Practice Exercises

A. Complete the Statement

1. The study of the blood is called _____.

2. The organs of the lymphatic system other than lymphatic vessels and lymph nodes are the _____, _____, and _____.

3. The two lymph ducts are the _____ and _____.

4. The primary concentrations of lymph nodes are the _____, _____, _____, and _____ regions.

5. The process whereby cells ingest and destroy bacteria within the body is _____.

6. The formed elements of blood are the _____, _____, and _____.

7. The fluid portion of blood is called _____.

8. _____ immunity develops following direct exposure to a pathogen.

9. Humoral immunity is also referred to as _____ immunity.

10. The medical term for blood clotting is _____.

B. Suffix Practice

Use the following suffixes to create medical terms for the following definitions.

-penia	-globin	-cytosis	-cyte	–globulin

1. too few white (cells) _____

2. too few red (cells) _____

3. too few clotting (cells) _____

4. too few of all cells _____

5. increase in white cells _____

6. increase in red cells _____

7. increase in clotting cells _____

8. blood protein _____

9. immunity protein _____

10. red cell _____

11. white cell _____

12. lymph cell _____

C. Combining Form Practice

The combining form **splen/o** refers to the spleen. Use it to write a term that means:

1. enlargement of the spleen _____

2. surgical removal of the spleen _____

3. cutting into the spleen _____

The combining form **lymph/o** refers to the lymph. Use it to write a term that means:

4. lymph cells _____

5. tumor of the lymph system _____

The combining form **lymphaden/o** refers to the lymph nodes. Use it to write a term that means:

6. disease of a lymph gland _____

7. tumor of a lymph gland _____

8. inflammation of a lymph gland _____

The combining form **immun/o** refers to the immune system. Use it to write a term that means:

9. specialist in the study of the immune system _____

10. immune protein _____

11. study of the immune system _____

The combining form **hemat/o** refers to blood. Use it to write a term that means:

12. relating to the blood _____

13. blood tumor or mass _____

14. blood formation _____

The combining form **hem/o** refers to blood. Use it to write a term that means:

15. blood destruction _____

16. blood protein _____

D. What Does it Stand For?

1. basos _____

2. CBC _____

3. Hgb _____

4. PT _____

5. GVHD _____

6. RBC _____

7. PCV _____

8. ESR _____

9. diff _____

10. lymphs _____

E. Terminology Matching

Match each term to its definition.

1. _____ thalassemia

a. fluid portion of blood

2. _____ lacteals

b. disease in which blood does not clot

3. _____ A, B, AB, O

c. conditions with reduced number of RBCs

4. _____ plasma

d. mass of blood

5. _____ dyscrasia

e. blood type

6. _____ hematoma

f. blood-clotting protein

7. _____ anemia

g. type of anemia

8. _____ serum

h. general term for blood disorders

9. _____ hemophilia

i. lymph vessels around intestine

10. _____ fibrinogen

j. plasma with inactivated fibrinogen

F. What's the Abbreviation?

1. acquired immunodeficiency syndrome _____

2. AIDS-related complex _____

3. human immunodeficiency virus _____

4. acute lymphocytic leukemia _____

5. bone marrow transplant _____

6. mononucleosis _____

7. Kaposi's sarcoma _____

8. eosinophils _____

9. immunoglobulin _____

10. severe combined immunodeficiency syndrome _____

G. Define the Combining Form

	Combining Form	Example from Chapter
1. lymph node	_____	_____
2. clot	_____	_____
3. blood	_____	_____
4. tonsil	_____	_____
5. poison	_____	_____
6. eat/swallow	_____	_____
7. lymph vessel	_____	_____
8. disease	_____	_____
9. spleen	_____	_____
10. lymph	_____	_____

H. Fill in the Blank

Kaposi's sarcoma	mononucleosis	Hodgkin's disease	aplastic
polycythemia vera	anaphylactic shock	AIDS	pernicious
pneumocystis	HIV		

1. The condition characterized by the production of too many red blood cells is called _____ .

2. The Epstein–Barr virus is thought to be responsible for what infectious disease? _____ .

3. A life-threatening allergic reaction is _____ .

4. The virus responsible for causing AIDS is _____ .

5. A cancer that is seen frequently in AIDS patients is _____ .

6. An ELISA is used to test for _____ .

7. Malignant tumors concentrate in lymph nodes with this disease: _____ .

8. A type of pneumonia seen in AIDS patients is _____ pneumonia.

9. _____ anemia is a severe form of anemia caused by nonfunctioning red bone marrow.

10. _____ anemia is the result of a vitamin B_{12} deficiency.

I. Terminology Matching

Match each term to its definition.

1. _____ allergy
2. _____ nosocomial
3. _____ phagocytosis
4. _____ hives
5. _____ antibody
6. _____ antigen
7. _____ Hodgkin's disease
8. _____ sarcoidosis
9. _____ vaccination
10. _____ ELISA

a. seen in an allergic reaction
b. substance that stimulates antibody formation
c. a hypersensitivity reaction
d. engulfing
e. protective blood protein
f. a type of cancer
g. autoimmune disease
h. infection acquired in the hospital
i. blood test for AIDS
j. immunization

J. Pharmacology Challenge

Fill in the classification for each drug description, then match the brand name.

	Drug Description	Classification	Brand Name
1. _____	inhibits enzyme needed for viral reproduction	_____	a. HepLock
2. _____	prevents blood clot formation	_____	b. Activase
3. _____	stops bleeding	_____	c. Solu-Medrol
4. _____	blocks effects of histamine	_____	d. Amicar
5. _____	prevents rejection of a transplanted organ	_____	e. Epivir
6. _____	dissolves existing blood clots	_____	f. CellCept
7. _____	increases number of erythrocytes	_____	g. Procrit
8. _____	strong anti-inflammatory properties	_____	h. Zyrtec
9. _____	interferes with action of platelets	_____	i. Plavix

K. Terminology Matching

Match each term to its definition.

1. _____ culture and sensitivity

2. _____ hematocrit

3. _____ complete blood count

4. _____ erythrocyte sedimentation rate

5. _____ prothrombin time

6. _____ white cell differential

7. _____ red cell morphology

a. measure of blood's clotting ability

b. counts number of each type of blood cell

c. examines cells for abnormal shape

d. checks blood for bacterial growth and best antibiotic to use

e. determines number of each type of white blood cell

f. measures percent of whole blood that is red blood cells

g. an indicator of the presence of an inflammatory condition

MEDICAL **TERMINOLOGY** INTERACTIVE

Medical Terminology Interactive is a premium online homework management system that includes a host of features to help you study. Registered users will find:

- Fun games and activities built within a virtual hospital
- Powerful tools that track and analyze your results—allowing you to create a personalized learning experience
- Videos, flashcards, and audio pronunciations to help enrich your progress
- Streaming video lesson presentations and self-paced learning modules

www.pearsonhighered.com/mti

Labeling Exercise

Image A

Write the labels for this figure on the numbered lines provided.

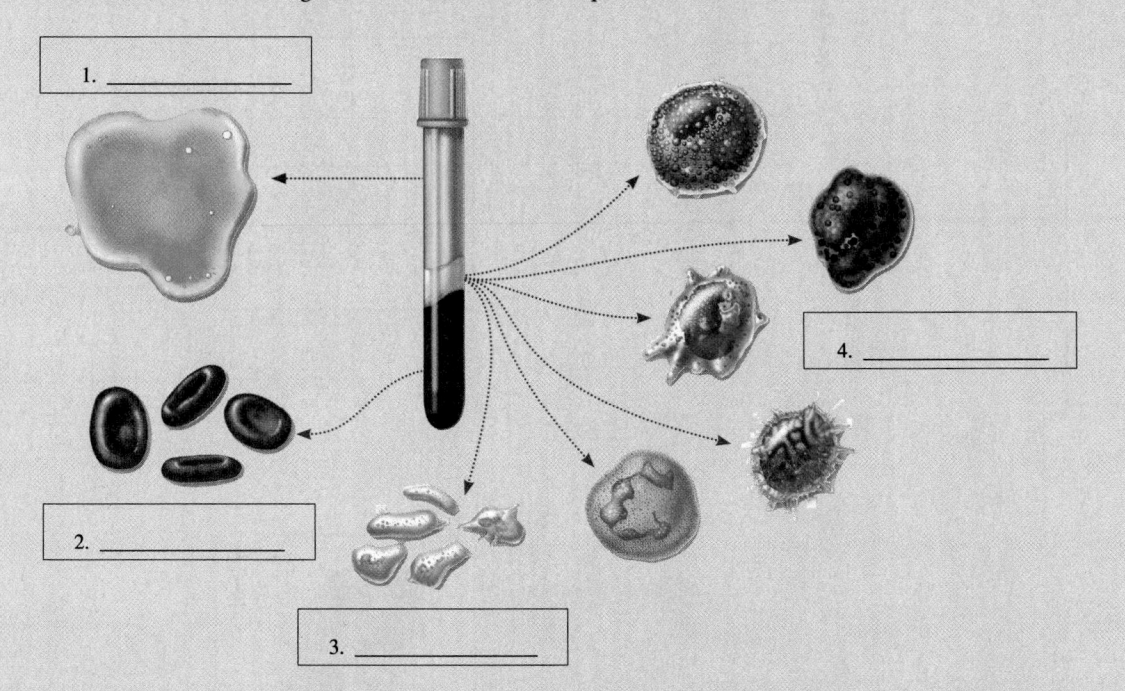

1. _____

2. _____

3. _____

4. _____

Image B

Write the labels for this figure on the numbered lines provided.

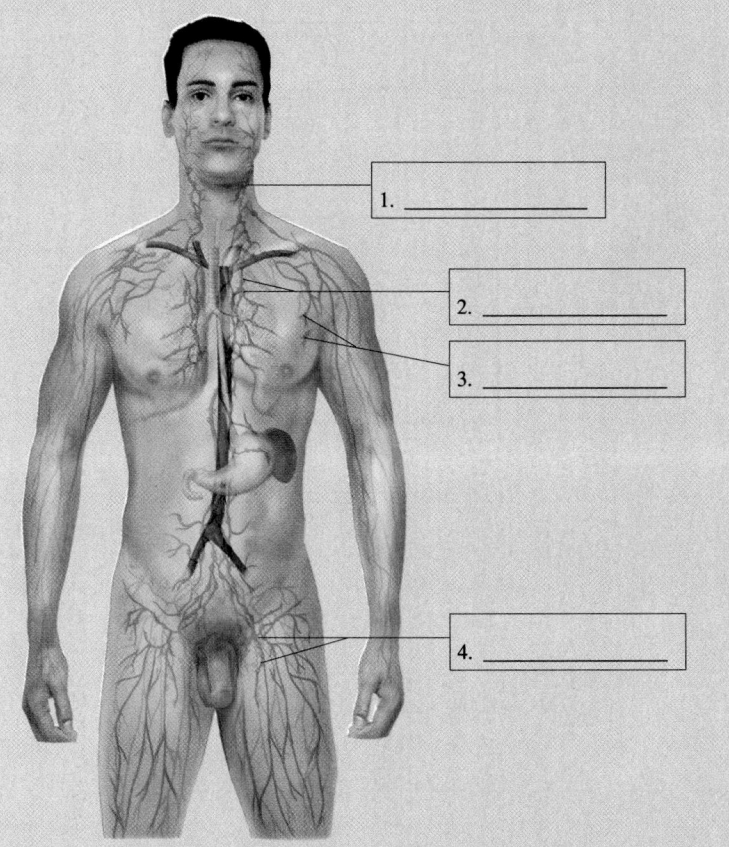

1. _____

2. _____

3. _____

4. _____

Image C

Write the labels for this figure on the numbered lines provided.

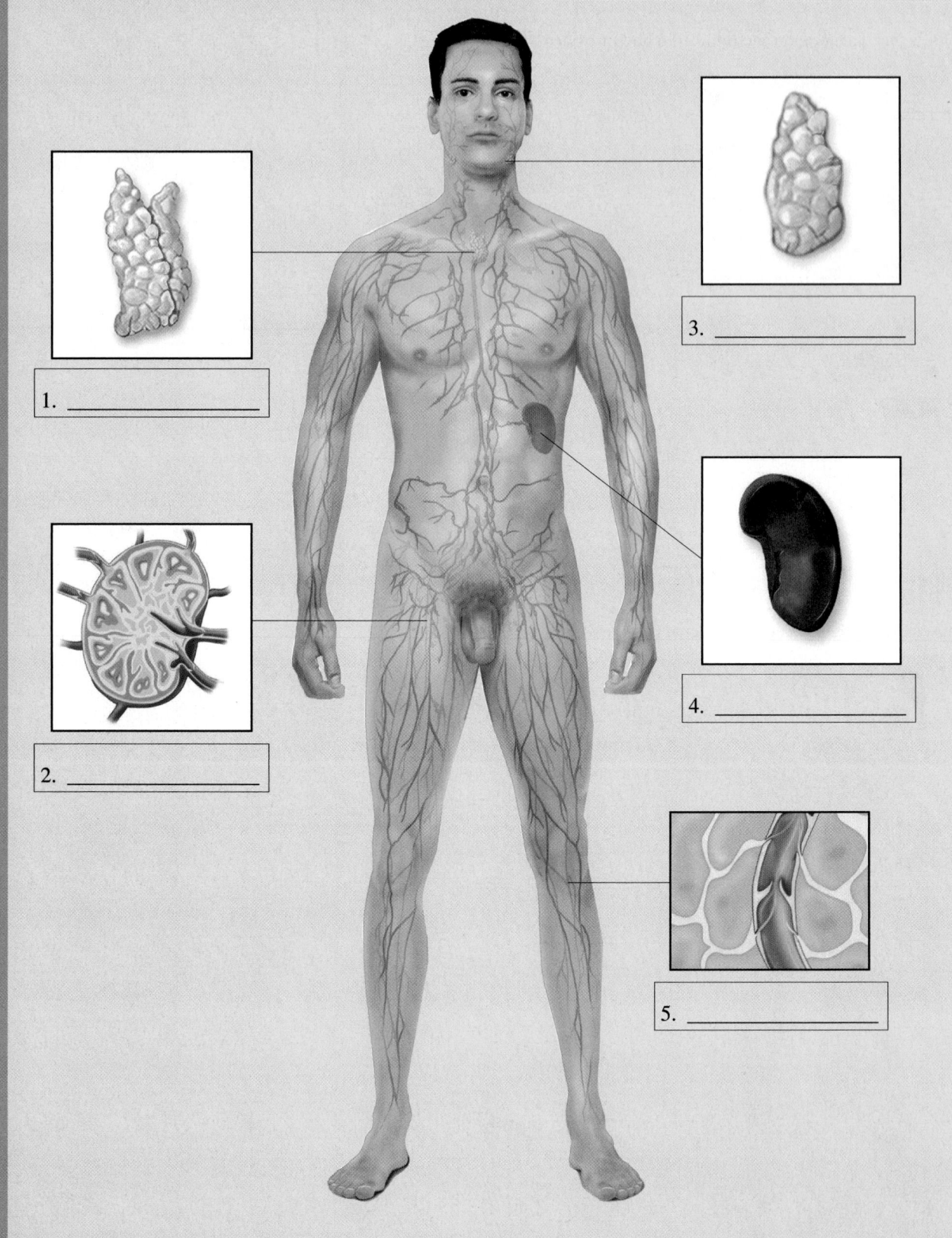

1. _____

2. _____

3. _____

4. _____

5. _____

7

RESPIRATORY SYSTEM

Learning Objectives

Upon completion of this chapter, you will be able to

- Identify and define the combining forms and suffixes introduced in this chapter.

- Correctly spell and pronounce medical terms and major anatomical structures relating to the respiratory system.

- Locate and describe the major organs of the respiratory system and their functions.

- List and describe the lung volumes and capacities.

- Describe the process of respiration.

- Identify and define respiratory system anatomical terms.

- Identify and define selected respiratory system pathology terms.

- Identify and define selected respiratory system diagnostic procedures.

- Identify and define selected respiratory system therapeutic procedures.

- Identify and define selected medications relating to the respiratory system.

- Define selected abbreviations associated with the respiratory system.

Respiratory System at a Glance

Function

The organs of the respiratory system are responsible for bringing fresh air into the lungs, exchanging oxygen for carbon dioxide between the air sacs of the lungs and the blood stream, and exhaling the stale air.

Organs

Here are the primary structures that comprise the respiratory system.

nasal cavity   **trachea**
pharynx   **bronchial tubes**
larynx   **lungs**

Word Parts

Here are the most common word parts (with their meanings) used to build respiratory system terms. For a more comprehensive list, refer to the Terminology section of this chapter.

Combining Forms

aer/o	air	**orth/o**	straight, upright
alveol/o	alveolus; air sac	**ox/o, ox/i**	oxygen
anthrac/o	coal	**pharyng/o**	pharynx
atel/o	incomplete	**pleur/o**	pleura
bronch/o	bronchus	**pneum/o**	lung, air
bronchi/o	bronchus	**pneumon/o**	lung, air
bronchiol/o	bronchiole	**pulmon/o**	lung
coni/o	dust	**rhin/o**	nose
diaphragmat/o	diaphragm	**sept/o**	wall
epiglott/o	epiglottis	**sinus/o**	sinus, cavity
laryng/o	larynx	**spir/o**	breathing
lob/o	lobe	**trache/o**	trachea, windpipe
nas/o	nose	**tuss/o**	cough
muc/o	mucus		

Suffixes

-capnia	carbon dioxide	**-pnea**	breathing
-osmia	smell	**-ptysis**	spitting
-phonia	voice	**-spasm**	involuntary muscle contraction
-plegia	paralysis	**-thorax**	chest

Respiratory System Illustrated

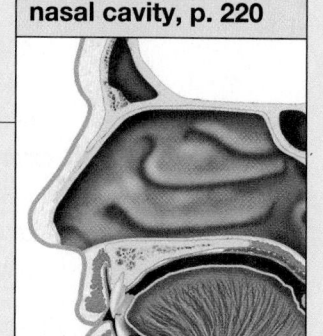

nasal cavity, p. 220

Cleanses, warms, and humidifies inhaled air

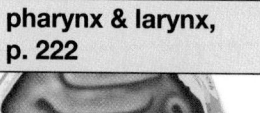

pharynx & larynx, p. 222

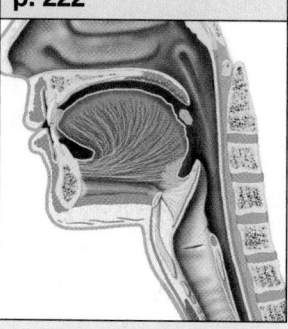

Carries air to the trachea through the voice box

bronchial tubes, p. 223

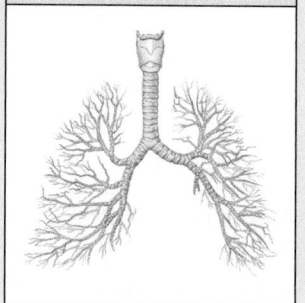

Air passageways inside the lung

trachea, p. 223

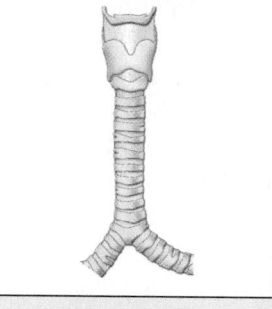

Transports air to and from lungs

lungs, p. 224

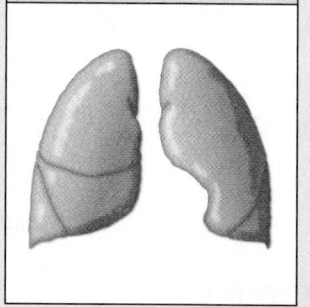

Site of gas exchange between air and blood

▪ Anatomy and Physiology of the Respiratory System

bronchial tubes (BRONG-key-all)	**lungs**
carbon dioxide	**nasal cavity** (NAY-zl)
exhalation (eks-hah-LAY-shun)	**oxygen** (OK-sih-jen)
external respiration	**pharynx** (FAIR-inks)
inhalation (in-hah-LAY-shun)	**trachea** (TRAY-kee-ah)
internal respiration	**ventilation**
larynx (LAIR-inks)	

The organs of the respiratory system include the **nasal cavity, pharynx, larynx, trachea, bronchial tubes,** and **lungs.** These organs function together to perform the mechanical and, for the most part, unconscious mechanism of respiration. The cells of the body require the continuous delivery of oxygen and removal of carbon dioxide. The respiratory system works in conjunction with the cardiovascular system to deliver oxygen to all the cells of the body. The process of respiration must be continuous; interruption for even a few minutes can result in brain damage and/or death.

The process of respiration can be subdivided into three distinct parts: **ventilation, external respiration,** and **internal respiration.** Ventilation is the flow of air between the outside environment and the lungs. **Inhalation** is the flow of air into the lungs, and **exhalation** is the flow of air out of the lungs. Inhalation brings fresh **oxygen** (O_2) into the air sacs, while exhalation removes **carbon dioxide** (CO_2) from the body.

External respiration refers to the exchange of oxygen and carbon dioxide that takes place in the lungs. These gases diffuse in opposite directions between the air sacs of the lungs and the bloodstream. Oxygen enters the bloodstream from the air sacs to be delivered throughout the body. Carbon dioxide leaves the bloodstream and enters the air sacs to be exhaled from the body.

Internal respiration is the process of oxygen and carbon dioxide exchange at the cellular level when oxygen leaves the bloodstream and is delivered to the tissues. Oxygen is needed for the body cells' metabolism, all the physical and chemical changes within the body that are necessary for life. The by-product of metabolism is the formation of a waste product, carbon dioxide. The carbon dioxide enters the bloodstream from the tissues and is transported back to the lungs for disposal.

> **MED TERM TIP**
>
> The terms *inhalation* and *inspiration* (in- = inward + spir/o = breathing) can be used interchangeably. Similarly, the terms *exhalation* and *expiration* (ex- = outward + spir/o = breathing) are interchangeable.

Nasal Cavity

cilia (SIL-ee-ah)	**nasal septum**
mucus (MYOO-kus)	**palate** (PAL-at)
mucous membrane	**paranasal sinuses** (pair-ah-NAY-zl)
nares (NAIR-eez)	

The process of ventilation begins with the nasal cavity. Air enters through two external openings in the nose called the **nares.** The nasal cavity is divided down the middle by the **nasal septum,** a cartilaginous plate. The **palate** in the roof of the mouth separates the nasal cavity above from the mouth below. The walls of the nasal cavity and the nasal septum are made up of flexible cartilage covered with **mucous membrane** (see Figure 7.1 ▪). In fact, much of the respiratory tract

> **MED TERM TIP**
>
> Anyone who has experienced a nosebleed, or *epistaxis,* is aware of the plentiful supply of blood vessels in the nose.

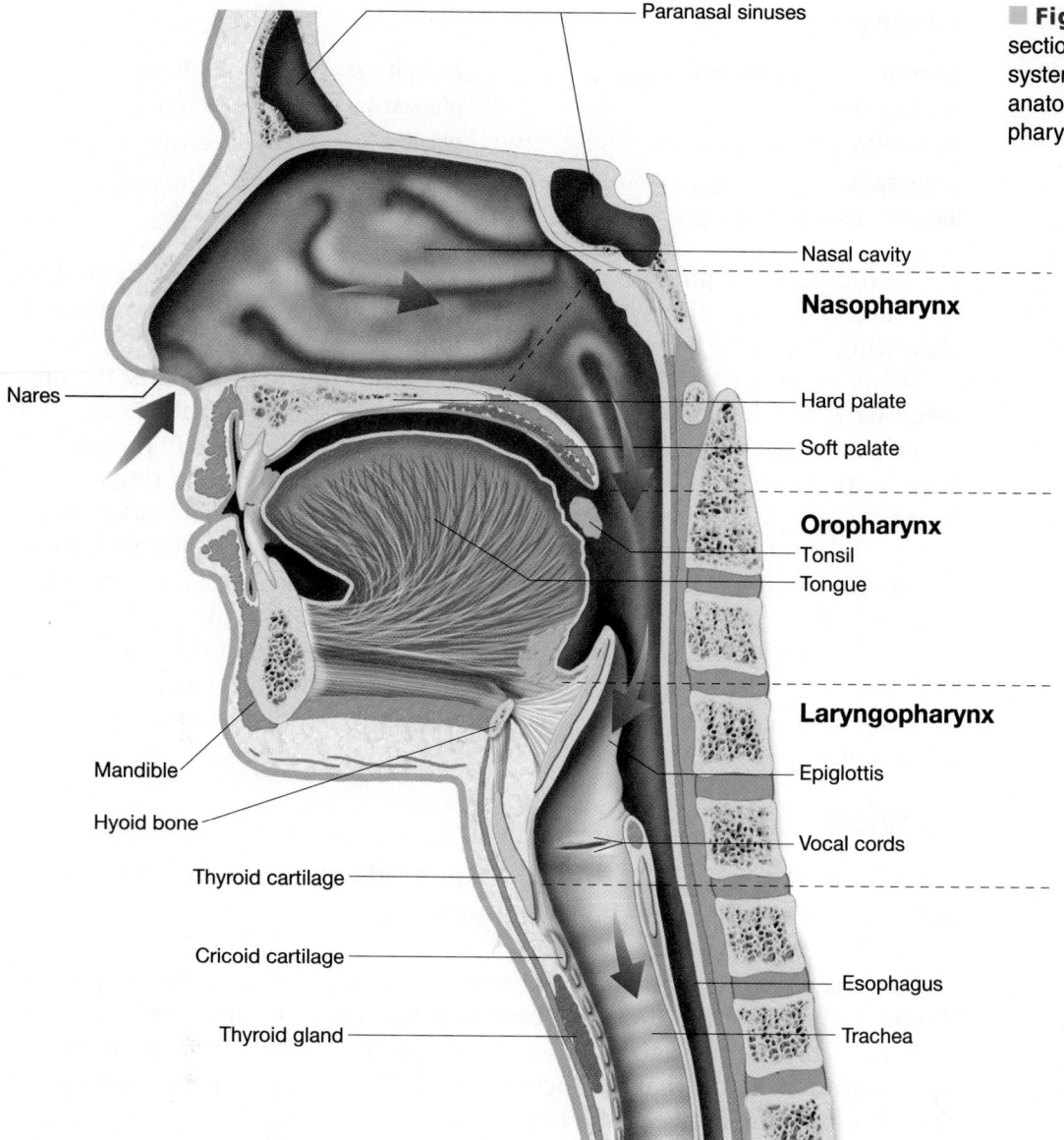

Figure 7.1 Sagittal section of upper respiratory system illustrating the internal anatomy of the nasal cavity, pharynx, larynx, and trachea.

Paranasal sinuses

Nasal cavity

Nasopharynx

Nares

Hard palate

Soft palate

Oropharynx

Tonsil

Tongue

Laryngopharynx

Mandible

Epiglottis

Hyoid bone

Vocal cords

Thyroid cartilage

Cricoid cartilage

Esophagus

Thyroid gland

Trachea

is covered with mucous membrane, which secretes a sticky fluid, **mucus,** to help cleanse the air by trapping dust and bacteria. Since this membrane is also wet, it moisturizes inhaled air as it passes by the surface of the cavity. Very small hairs or **cilia** line the opening to the nose (as well as much of the airways), and filter out large dirt particles before they can enter the lungs. Capillaries in the mucous membranes warm inhaled air as it passes through the airways. Additionally, several **paranasal sinuses,** or air-filled cavities, are located within the facial bones. The sinuses act as an echo chamber during sound production and give resonance to the voice.

MED TERM TIP

Word Watch: The term *cilia* means hair, and there are other body systems that have cilia or cilia-like processes. For example, when discussing the eye, *cilia* means eyelashes.

Pharynx

adenoids (ADD-eh-noydz)

auditory tube

eustachian tube (yoo-STAY-she-en)

laryngopharynx (lair-ring-goh-FAIR-inks)

lingual tonsils (LING-gwal)

nasopharynx (nay-zoh-FAIR-inks)

oropharynx (or-oh-FAIR-inks)

palatine tonsils (PAL-ah-tine)

pharyngeal tonsils (fair-IN-jee-al)

Air next enters the pharynx, also called the *throat,* which is used by both the respiratory and digestive systems. At the end of the pharynx, air enters the trachea while food and liquids are shunted into the esophagus.

The pharynx is roughly a 5-inch-long tube consisting of three parts: the upper **nasopharynx,** middle **oropharynx,** and lower **laryngopharynx** (see again Figure 7.1). Three pairs of tonsils (collections of lymphatic tissue) are located in the pharynx. Tonsils are strategically placed to help keep pathogens from entering the body through either the air breathed or food and liquid swallowed. The nasopharynx, behind the nose, contains the **adenoids** or **pharyngeal tonsils.** The oropharynx, behind the mouth, contains the **palatine tonsils** and the **lingual tonsils.** Tonsils are considered a part of the lymphatic system and are discussed in Chapter 6.

The opening of the **eustachian** or **auditory tube** is also found in the nasopharynx. The other end of this tube is in the middle ear. Each time you swallow, this tube opens to equalize air pressure between the middle ear and the outside atmosphere.

Larynx

epiglottis (ep-ih-GLOT-iss)

glottis (GLOT-iss)

thyroid cartilage (THIGH-royd / CAR-tih-lij)

vocal cords

The larynx, or *voice box,* is a muscular structure located between the pharynx and the trachea and contains the **vocal cords** (see again Figure 7.1 and Figure 7.2 ■). The vocal cords are not actually cordlike in structure, but rather they are folds of membranous tissue that produce sound by vibrating as air passes through the **glottis,** the opening between the two vocal cords.

A flap of cartilaginous tissue, the **epiglottis,** sits above the glottis and provides protection against food and liquid being inhaled into the lungs. The epiglottis covers the larynx and trachea during swallowing and shunts food and liquid from the pharynx into the esophagus. The walls of the larynx are composed of several cartilage plates held together with ligaments and muscles. One of these cartilages, the **thyroid cartilage,** forms what is known as the *Adam's apple.* The thyroid cartilage is generally larger in males than in females and helps to produce the deeper male voice.

MED TERM TIP

In the early 1970s it was common practice to remove the tonsils and adenoids in children suffering from repeated infections. However, it is now understood how important these organs are to remove pathogens from the air we breathe and the food we eat. Antibiotic treatment has also reduced the severity of infections.

MED TERM TIP

Stuttering may actually result from faulty neuromuscular control of the larynx. Some stutterers can sing or whisper without difficulty. Both singing and whispering involve movements of the larynx that differ from those required for regular speech.

MED TERM TIP

The term *Adam's apple* is thought to come from a fable that when Adam realized he had sinned in the Garden of Eden, he was unable to swallow the apple in his throat.

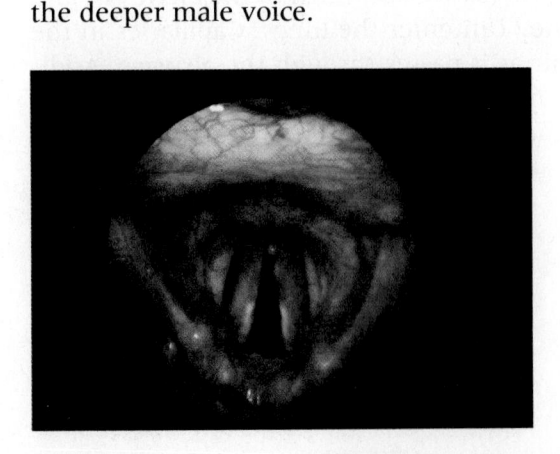

■ **Figure 7.2** The vocal cords within the larynx, superior view from the pharynx. *(CNRI/Photo Researchers, Inc.)*

Trachea

The trachea, also called the *windpipe,* is the passageway for air that extends from the pharynx and larynx down to the main bronchi (see Figure 7.3 ■). Measuring approximately 4 inches in length, it is composed of smooth muscle and cartilage rings and is lined by mucous membrane and cilia. Therefore, it also assists in cleansing, warming, and moisturizing air as it travels to the lungs.

Bronchial Tubes

alveoli (al-VEE-oh-lye)
bronchioles (BRONG-key-ohlz)
bronchus (BRONG-kus)

pulmonary capillaries
respiratory membrane

The distal end of the trachea divides to form the left and right main (primary) bronchi. Each **bronchus** enters one of the lungs and branches repeatedly to form secondary and tertiary bronchi. Each branch becomes narrower until the narrowest branches, the **bronchioles,** are formed (see Figure 7.4 ■). Each bronchiole terminates in a small group of air sacs, called **alveoli.** Each lung has approximately 150 million alveoli. The walls of alveoli are elastic, giving them the ability to expand to hold air and then recoil to their original size. A network of **pulmonary capillaries** from the pulmonary blood vessels tightly encases each alveolus (see Figure 7.5 ■). In fact, the walls of the alveoli and capillaries are so tightly associated with each other they are referred to as a single unit, the **respiratory membrane.** The exchange of oxygen and carbon dioxide between the air within the alveolus and the blood inside the capillaries takes place across the respiratory membrane.

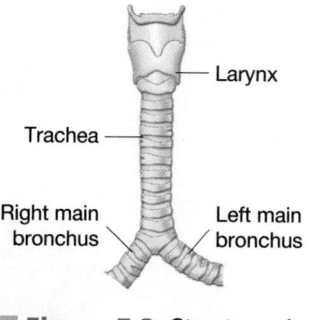

■ **Figure 7.3** Structure of the trachea, which extends from the larynx above to the main bronchi below.

MED TERM TIP

The respiratory system can be thought of as an upside-down tree and its branches. The trunk of the tree consists of the pharynx, larynx, and trachea. The trachea then divides into two branches, the bronchi. Each bronchus divides into smaller and smaller branches. In fact, this branching system of tubes is referred to as the *bronchial tree.*

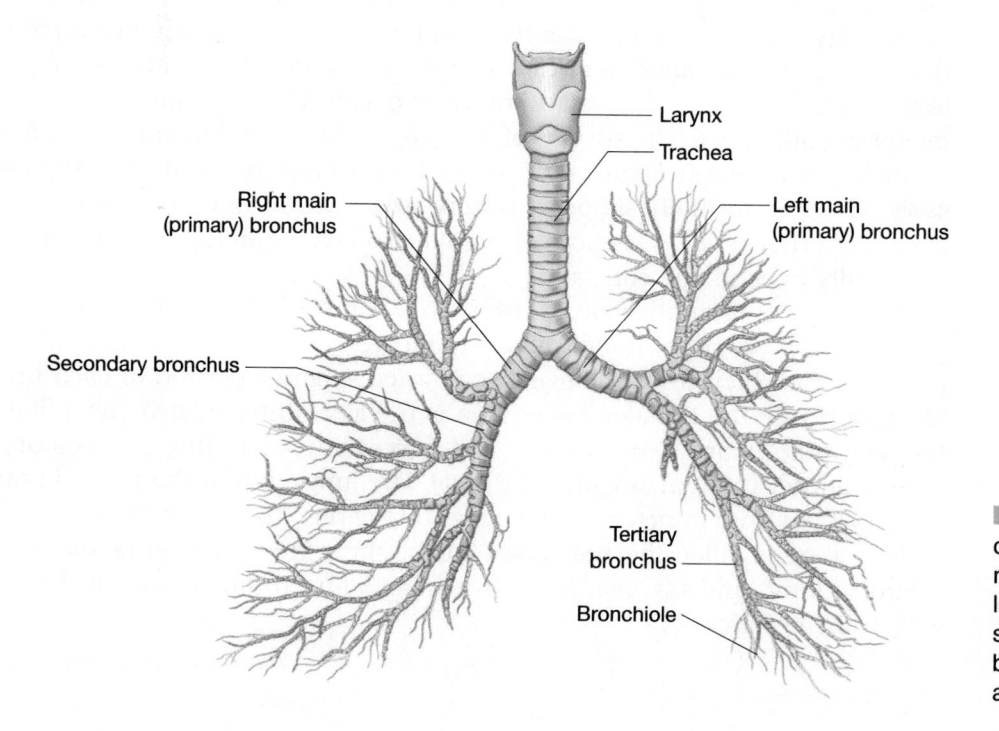

■ **Figure 7.4** The bronchial tree. Note how each main bronchus enters a lung and then branches into smaller and smaller primary bronchi, secondary bronchi, and bronchioles.

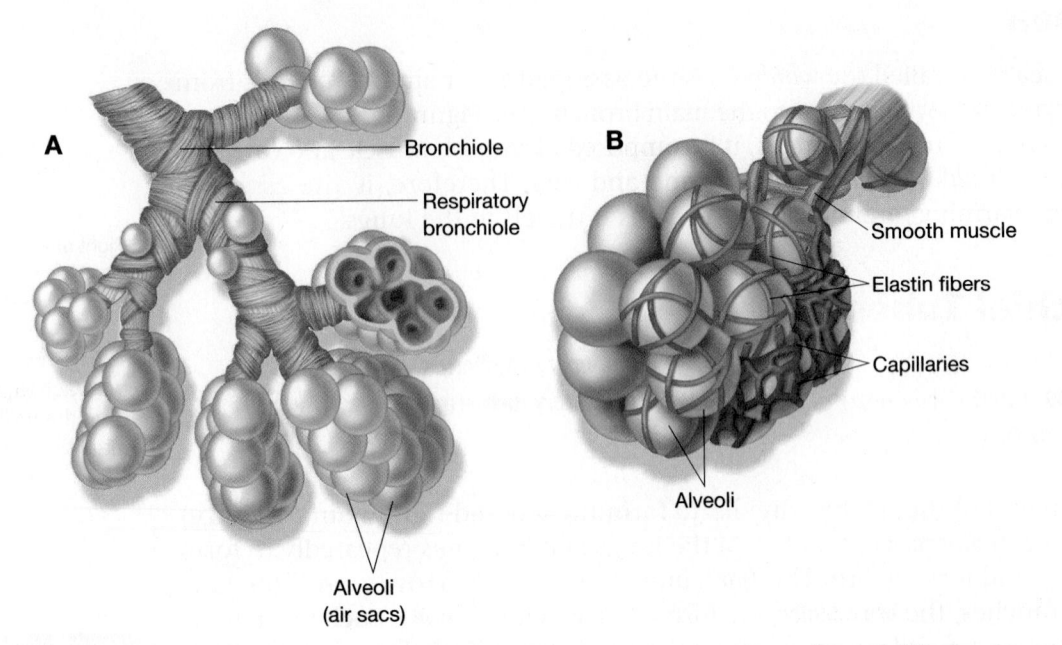

Figure 7.5 (A) Each bronchiole terminates in an alveolar sac, a group of alveoli; (B) alveoli encased by network capillaries, forming the respiratory membrane.

Lungs

apex	**parietal pleura** (pah-RYE-eh-tal)
base	**pleura** (PLOO-rah)
hilum (HYE-lum)	**pleural cavity**
lobes	**serous fluid** (SEER-us)
mediastinum (mee-dee-ass-TYE-num)	**visceral pleura** (VISS-er-al)

Each lung is the total collection of the bronchi, bronchioles, and alveoli. They are spongy to the touch because they contain air. The lungs are protected by a double membrane called the **pleura.** The pleura's outer membrane is the **parietal pleura,** which also lines the wall of the chest cavity. The inner membrane, or **visceral pleura,** adheres to the surface of the lungs. The pleural membrane is folded in such a way that it forms a sac around each lung, referred to as the **pleural cavity.** There is normally slippery, watery **serous fluid** between the two layers of the pleura that reduces friction when the two layers rub together as the lungs repeatedly expand and contract.

The lungs contain divisions or **lobes.** There are three lobes in the larger right lung (right upper, right middle, and right lower lobes) and two in the left lung (left upper and left lower lobes). The pointed superior portion of each lung is the **apex,** while the broader lower area is the **base.** Entry of structures like the bronchi, pulmonary blood vessels, and nerves into each lung occurs along its medial border in an area called the **hilum.** The lungs within the thoracic cavity are protected from puncture and damage by the ribs. The area between the right and left lung is called the **mediastinum** and contains the heart, aorta, esophagus, thymus gland, and trachea. See Figure 7.6 ■ for an illustration of the lungs within the chest cavity.

MED TERM TIP

Some of the abnormal lung sounds heard with a stethoscope, such as crackling and rubbing, are made when the parietal and/or visceral pleura become inflamed and rub against one another.

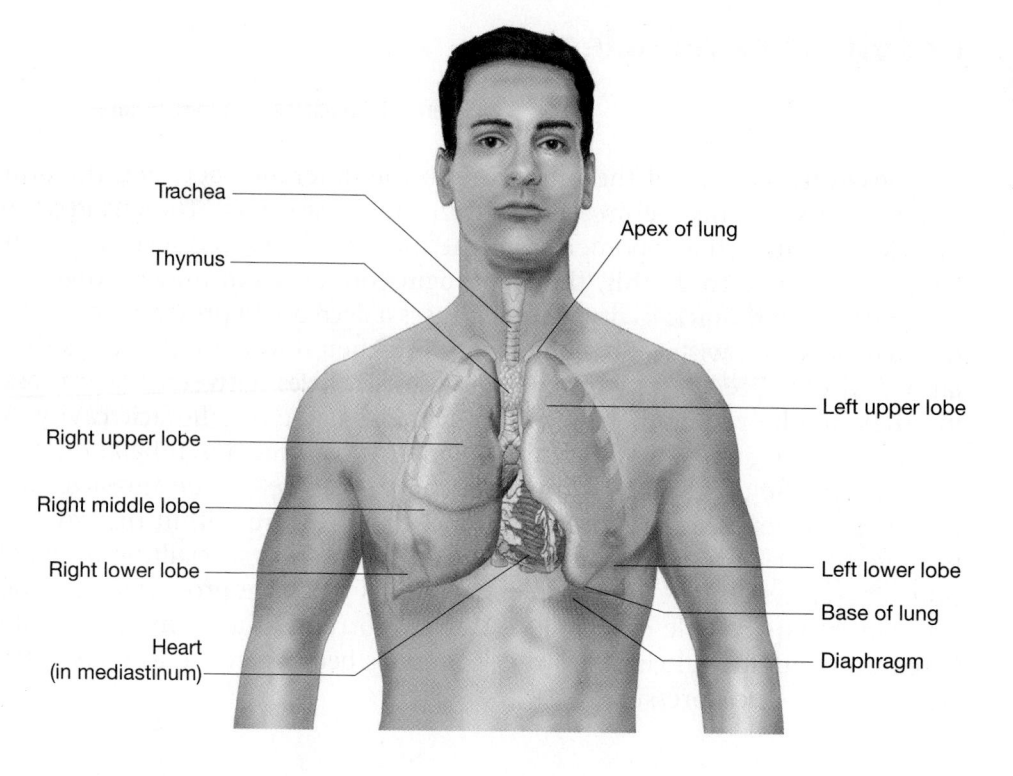

Lung Volumes and Capacities

pulmonary function test   **respiratory therapist**

For some types of medical conditions, like emphysema, it is important to measure the volume of air flowing in and out of the lungs to determine lung capacity. Lung volumes are measured by **respiratory therapists** to aid in determining the functioning level of the respiratory system. Collectively, these measurements are called **pulmonary function tests.** Table 7.1 ■ lists and defines the four lung volumes and four lung capacities.

Table 7.1	Lung Volumes and Capacities
TERM	**DEFINITION**
Tidal volume (TV)	The amount of air that enters the lungs in a single inhalation or leaves the lungs in a single exhalation of quiet breathing. In an adult this is normally 500 mL.*
Inspiratory reserve volume (IRV)	The amount of air that can be forcibly inhaled after a normal inspiration. Also called *complemental air;* generally measures around 3,000 mL.*
Expiratory reserve volume (ERV)	The amount of air that can be forcibly exhaled after a normal quiet exhalation. This is also called *supplemental air;* approximately 1,000 mL.*
Residual volume (RV)	The air remaining in the lungs after a forced exhalation; about 1,500 mL* in the adult.
Inspiratory capacity (IC)	The volume of air inhaled after a normal exhale.
Functional residual capacity (FRC)	The air that remains in the lungs after a normal exhalation has taken place.
Vital capacity (VC)	The total volume of air that can be exhaled after a maximum inhalation. This amount will be equal to the sum of TV, IRV, and ERV.
Total lung capacity (TLC)	The volume of air in the lungs after a maximal inhalation.

*There is a normal range for measurements of the volume of air exchanged. The numbers given are for the average measurement.

Respiratory Muscles

diaphragm   **intercostal muscles** (in-ter-COS-tal)

Air moves in and out of the lungs due to the difference between the atmospheric pressure and the pressure within the chest cavity. The **diaphragm,** the muscle separating the abdomen from the thoracic cavity, produces this difference in pressure. To do this, the diaphragm contracts and moves downward. This increase in thoracic cavity volume causes a decrease in pressure, or negative thoracic pressure, within the chest cavity. Air then flows into the lungs (inhalation) to equalize the pressure. The **intercostal muscles** between the ribs assist in inhalation by raising the rib cage to further enlarge the thoracic cavity. See Figure 7.7 ■ for an illustration of the role of the diaphragm in inhalation. Similarly, when the diaphragm and intercostal muscles relax, the thoracic cavity becomes smaller. This produces an increase in pressure within the cavity, or positive thoracic pressure, and air flows out of the lungs, resulting in exhalation. Therefore, a quiet, unforced exhalation is a passive process since it does not require any muscle contraction. When a forceful inhalation or exhalation is required, additional chest and neck muscles become active to create larger changes in thoracic pressure.

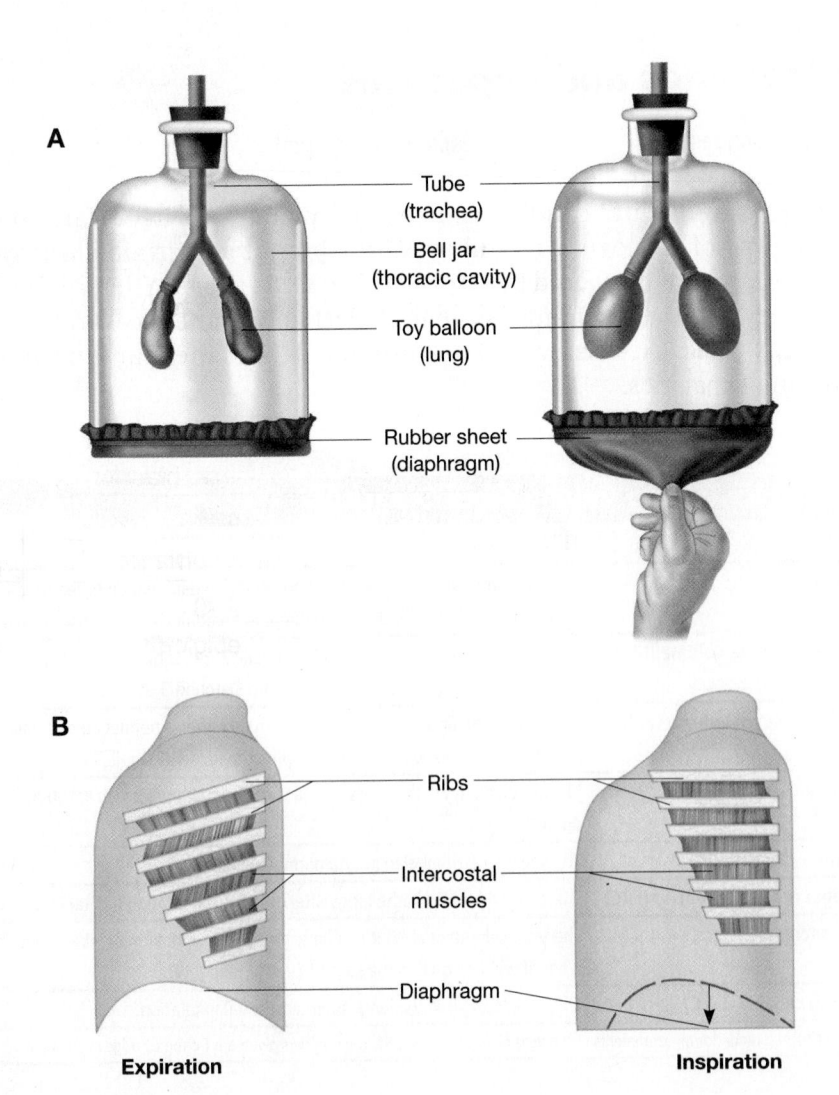

■ **Figure 7.7** (A) Bell jar apparatus demonstrating how downward movement of the diaphragm results in air flowing into the lungs; (B) action of the intercostal muscles lifts the ribs to assist the diaphragm in enlarging the volume of the thoracic cavity.

Respiratory Rate

vital signs

Respiratory rate (measured in breaths per minute) is one of our **vital signs** (VS), along with heart rate, temperature, and blood pressure. The respiratory rate is normally regulated by the level of CO_2 in the blood. When the CO_2 level is high, we breathe more rapidly to expel the excess. Likewise, when CO_2 levels drop, our respiratory rate will also drop.

When the respiratory rate falls outside the range of normal, it may indicate an illness or medical condition. For example, when a patient is running an elevated temperature and has shortness of breath (SOB) due to pneumonia, the respiratory rate may increase dramatically. Or a brain injury or some medications, such as those for pain, can cause a decrease in the respiratory rate. See Table 7.2 ■ for normal respiratory rate ranges for different age groups.

MED TERM TIP

Diaphragmatic breathing is taught to singers and public speakers. You can practice this type of breathing by allowing your abdomen to expand during inhalation and contract during exhalation while your shoulders remain motionless.

MED TERM TIP

When divers wish to hold their breath longer, they first hyperventilate (breath faster and deeper) in order to get rid of as much CO_2 as possible. This will hold off the urge to breathe longer, allowing a diver to stay submerged longer.

Table 7.2	Respiratory Rates for Different Age Groups
AGE	**RESPIRATIONS PER MINUTE**
Newborn	30–60
1-year-old	18–30
16-year-old	16–20
Adult	12–20

■ Terminology

Word Parts Used to Build Respiratory System Terms

The following lists contain the combining forms, suffixes, and prefixes used to build terms in the remaining sections of this chapter.

Combining Forms

aer/o	air	**cyst/o**	cyst, bladder	**ox/o**	oxygen
alveol/o	alveolus	**cyt/o**	cell	**pharyng/o**	pharynx
angi/o	vessel	**diaphragmat/o**	diaphragm	**pleur/o**	pleura
anthrac/o	coal	**embol/o**	plug	**pneum/o**	air
arteri/o	artery	**epiglott/o**	epiglottis	**pneumon/o**	lung
atel/o	incomplete	**fibr/o**	fibers	**pulmon/o**	lung
bi/o	life	**hem/o**	blood	**py/o**	pus
bronch/o	bronchus	**hist/o**	tissue	**/rhin/o**	nose
bronchi/o	bronchus	**laryng/o**	larynx	**sept/o**	wall
bronchiol/o	bronchiole	**lob/o**	lobe	**sinus/o**	sinus
carcin/o	cancer	**muc/o**	mucus·	**somn/o**	sleep
cardi/o	heart	**nas/o**	nose	**spir/o**	breathing
coni/o	dust	**orth/o**	straight	**thorac/o**	chest
cortic/o	outer region, cortex	**ot/o**	ear	**trache/o**	trachea
cyan/o	blue	**ox/i**	oxygen	**tuss/o**	cough

Suffixes

-al	pertaining to
-algia	pain
-ar	pertaining to
-ary	pertaining to
-capnia	carbon dioxide
-centesis	puncture to withdraw fluid
-dynia	pain
-eal	pertaining to
-ectasis	dilation
-ectomy	surgical removal
-emia	blood condition
-genic	produced by
-gram	record
-graphy	process of recording
-ia	condition

-ial	pertaining to
-ic	pertaining to
-ism	state of
-itis	inflammation
-logy	study of
-lytic	destruction
-meter	instrument to measure
-metry	process of measuring
-oma	tumor
-osis	abnormal condition
-osmia	smell
-ostomy	surgically create an opening
-otomy	cutting into
-phonia	voice

-plasm	formation
-plasty	surgical repair
-plegia	paralysis
-pnea	breathing
-ptysis	spitting
-rrhagia	abnormal flow condition
-rrhea	discharge
-scope	instrument for viewing
-scopy	process of visually examining
-spasm	involuntary muscle spasm
-stenosis	narrowing
-thorax	chest
-tic	pertaining to

Prefixes

a-	without
an-	without
anti-	against
brady-	slow
de-	without

dys-	abnormal, difficult
endo-	within
eu-	normal
hyper-	excessive

hypo-	insufficient
pan-	all
poly-	many
tachy-	fast

Anatomical Terms

TERM	WORD PARTS	DEFINITION
alveolar (al-VEE-oh-lar)	alveol/o = alveolus -ar = pertaining to	Pertaining to the alveoli.
bronchial (BRONG-ee-all)	bronch/o = bronchus -ial = pertaining to	Pertaining to a bronchus.
bronchiolar (brong-KEY-oh-lar)	bronchiol/o = bronchiole -ar = pertaining to	Pertaining to a bronchiole.
diaphragmatic (dye-ah-frag-MAT-ik)	diaphragmat/o = diaphragm -ic = pertaining to	Pertaining to the diaphragm.
epiglottic (ep-ih-GLOT-ik)	epiglott/o = epiglottis -ic = pertaining to	Pertaining to the epiglottis.
laryngeal (lair-in-GEE-all)	laryng/o = larynx -eal = pertaining to	Pertaining to the larynx.

Anatomical Terms *(continued)*

TERM	WORD PARTS	DEFINITION
nasal (NAY-zal)	nas/o = nose -al = pertaining to	Pertaining to the nose or nasal cavity.
pharyngeal (fair-in-GEE-all)	pharyng/o = pharynx -eal = pertaining to	Pertaining to the pharynx.
pleural (PLOO-ral)	pleur/o = pleura -al = pertaining to	Pertaining to the pleura.
pulmonary (PULL-mon-air-ee)	pulmon/o = lung -ary = pertaining to	Pertaining to the lung.
septal (SEP-tal)	sept/o = wall -al = pertaining to	Pertaining to the nasal septum.
thoracic (tho-RASS-ik)	thorac/o = chest -ic = pertaining to	Pertaining to the chest.
tracheal (TRAY-key-al)	trache/o = trachea -al = pertaining to	Pertaining to the trachea.

Pathology

TERM	WORD PARTS	DEFINITION
Medical Specialties		
internal medicine		Branch of medicine involving the diagnosis and treatment of diseases and conditions of internal organs such as the respiratory system. The physician is an *internist*.
otorhinolaryngology (ENT) (oh-toh-rye-noh-lair-in-GOL-oh-jee)	ot/o = ear rhin/o = nose laryng/o = larynx -logy = study of	Branch of medicine involving the diagnosis and treatment of conditions and diseases of the ear, nose, and throat region. The physician is an *otorhinolaryngologist*. This medical specialty may also be referred to as *otolaryngology*.
pulmonology (pull-mon-ALL-oh-jee)	pulmon/o = lung -logy = study of	Branch of medicine involved in the diagnosis and treatment of diseases and disorders of the respiratory system. Physician is a *pulmonologist*.
respiratory therapy	spir/o = breathing	Allied health specialty that assists patients with respiratory and cardiopulmonary disorders. Duties of a *respiratory therapist* include conducting pulmonary function tests, monitoring oxygen and carbon dioxide levels in the blood, administering breathing treatments, and ventilator management.
thoracic surgery (tho-RASS-ik)	thorac/o = chest -ic = pertaining to	Branch of medicine involving the diagnosis and treatment of conditions and diseases of the respiratory system by surgical means. Physician is a *thoracic surgeon*.

Pathology *(continued)*

TERM	WORD PARTS	DEFINITION
Signs and Symptoms		
anosmia (ah-NOZ-mee-ah)	an- = without -osmia = smell	Lack of the sense of smell.
anoxia (ah-NOK-see-ah)	an- = without ox/o = oxygen -ia = condition	Condition of receiving almost no oxygen from inhaled air.
aphonia (a-FOH-nee-ah)	a- = without -phonia = voice	Condition of being unable to produce sounds.
apnea (AP-nee-ah)	a- = without -pnea = breathing	Not breathing.
asphyxia (as-FIK-see-ah)	a- = without -ia = condition	Lack of oxygen that can lead to unconsciousness and death if not corrected immediately; also called *asphyxiation* or *suffocation*. Common causes include drowning, foreign body in the respiratory tract, poisoning, and electric shock.
aspiration (as-peer-RAY-shun)	spir/o = breathing	Refers to withdrawing fluid from a body cavity using suction. For example, using a long needle and syringe to withdraw fluid from the pleural cavity, or using a vacuum pump to remove phlegm from a patient's airways. Additionally, it refers to inhaling food, liquid, or a foreign object into the airways, which may lead to the development of pneumonia.
bradypnea (bray-DIP-nee-ah)	brady- = slow -pnea = breathing	Breathing too slowly; a low respiratory rate.
bronchiectasis (brong-key-EK-tah-sis)	bronchi/o = bronchus -ectasis = dilation	Dilated bronchus.
bronchospasm (BRONG-koh-spazm)	bronch/o = bronchus -spasm = involuntary muscle spasm	Involuntary muscle spasm of the smooth muscle in the wall of the bronchus.
Cheyne–Stokes respiration (CHAIN / STOHKS / res-pir-AY-shun)	spir/o = breathing	Abnormal breathing pattern in which there are long periods (10–60 seconds) of apnea followed by deeper, more rapid breathing. Named for John Cheyne, a Scottish physician, and Sir William Stokes, an Irish surgeon.
clubbing		Abnormal widening and thickening of the ends of the fingers and toes associated with chronic oxygen deficiency. Seen in patients with chronic respiratory conditions or circulatory problems.
crackles		Abnormal sound made during inspiration. Usually indicates the presence of fluid or mucus in the small airways. Also called *rales*.

Pathology *(continued)*

TERM	WORD PARTS	DEFINITION
cyanosis (sigh-ah-NO-sis)	cyan/o = blue -osis = abnormal condition	Refers to the bluish tint of skin that is receiving an insufficient amount of oxygen or circulation.
dysphonia (dis-FOH-nee-ah)	dys- = difficult, abnormal -phonia = voice	Condition of having difficulty producing sounds or producing abnormal sounds.
dyspnea (DISP-nee-ah)	dys- = abnormal, difficult -pnea = breathing	Term describing difficult or labored breathing.
epistaxis (ep-ih-STAKS-is)		Nosebleed.
eupnea (yoop-NEE-ah)	eu- = normal -pnea = breathing	Normal breathing and respiratory rate.
hemoptysis (hee-MOP-tih-sis)	hem/o = blood -ptysis = spitting	To cough up blood or blood-stained sputum.
hemothorax (hee-moh-THOH-raks)	hem/o = blood -thorax = chest	Presence of blood in the chest cavity.
hypercapnia (high-per-CAP-nee-ah)	hyper- = excessive -capnia = carbon dioxide	Condition of having excessive carbon dioxide in the body.
hyperpnea (high-per-NEE-ah)	hyper- = excessive -pnea = breathing	Taking deep breaths.
hyperventilation (HYE-per-vent-ill-a-shun)	hyper- = excessive	Breathing both too fast (tachypnea) and too deep (hyperpnea).
hypocapnia (high-poh-CAP-nee-ah)	hypo- = insufficient -capnia = carbon dioxide	An insufficient level of carbon dioxide in the body; a very serious problem because it is the presence of carbon dioxide that stimulates respiration, not the absence of oxygen. Therefore, a person with low carbon dioxide levels would respond with an increased respiratory rate.
hypopnea (high-POP-nee-ah)	hypo- = insufficient -pnea = breathing	Taking shallow breaths.
hypoventilation (HYE-poh-vent-ill-a-shun)	hypo- = insufficient	Breathing both too slow (bradypnea) and too shallow (hypopnea).
hypoxemia (high-pox-EE-mee-ah)	hypo- = insufficient ox/o = oxygen -emia = blood condition	Condition of having an insufficient amount of oxygen in the bloodstream.
hypoxia (high-POX-ee-ah)	hypo- = insufficient ox/o = oxygen -ia = condition	Condition of receiving an insufficient amount of oxygen from inhaled air.
laryngoplegia (lair-RING-goh-plee-gee-ah)	laryng/o = larynx -plegia = paralysis	Paralysis of the muscles controlling the larynx.

▣ Pathology *(continued)*

TERM	WORD PARTS	DEFINITION
orthopnea (or-THOP-nee-ah)	orth/o = straight -pnea = breathing	Term describing dyspnea that is worsened by lying flat. The patient feels able to breath easier while sitting straight up; a common occurrence in those with pulmonary disease.
pansinusitis (pan-sigh-nus-EYE-tis)	pan- = all sinus/o = sinus -itis = inflammation	Inflammation of all the paranasal sinuses.
patent (PAY-tent)		Open or unblocked, such as a patent airway.
phlegm (FLEM)		Thick mucus secreted by the membranes lining the respiratory tract. When phlegm is coughed through the mouth, it is called *sputum.* Phlegm is examined for color, odor, and consistency and tested for the presence of bacteria, viruses, and fungi.
pleural rub (PLOO-ral)	pleur/o = pleura -al = pertaining to	Grating sound made when the two layers of the pleura rub together during respiration. It is caused when one of the surfaces becomes thicker as a result of inflammation or other disease conditions. This rub can be felt through the fingertips when placed on the chest wall or heard through a stethoscope.
pleurodynia (ploor-oh-DIN-ee-ah)	pleur/o = pleura -dynia = pain	Pleural pain.
pyothorax (pye-oh-THOH-raks)	py/o = pus -thorax = chest	Presence of pus in the chest cavity; indicates a bacterial infection.
rhinitis (rye-NYE-tis)	rhin/o = nose -itis = inflammation	Inflammation of the nasal cavity.
rhinorrhagia (rye-noh-RAH-jee-ah)	rhin/o = nose -rrhagia = abnormal flow condition	Rapid flow of blood from the nose.
rhinorrhea (rye-noh-REE-ah)	rhin/o = nose -rrhea = discharge	Discharge from the nose; commonly called a *runny nose.*
rhonchi (RONG-kigh)		Somewhat musical sound during expiration, often found in asthma or infection. Caused by spasms of the bronchial tubes. Also called *wheezing.*
shortness of breath (SOB)		Term used to indicate that a patient is having some difficulty breathing; also called *dyspnea.* The causes can range from mild SOB after exercise to SOB associated with heart disease.
sputum (SPEW-tum)		Mucus or phlegm coughed up from the lining of the respiratory tract.

MED TERM TIP

The term *sputum,* from the Latin word meaning "to spit," now refers to the material coughed up and spit out from the respiratory system.

Pathology *(continued)*

TERM	WORD PARTS	DEFINITION
stridor (STRIGH-dor)		Harsh, high-pitched, noisy breathing sound made when there is an obstruction of the bronchus or larynx. Found in conditions such as croup in children.
tachypnea (tak-ip-NEE-ah)	tachy- = fast -pnea = breathing	Breathing fast; a high respiratory rate.
thoracalgia (thor-ah-KAL-jee-ah)	thorac/o = chest -algia = pain	Chest pain. Does not refer to angina pectoris.
tracheostenosis (tray-kee-oh-steh-w-sis)	trache/o = trachea -stenosis = narrowing	Narrowing of the trachea.

Upper Respiratory System

TERM	WORD PARTS	DEFINITION
croup (KROOP)		Acute respiratory condition found in infants and children characterized by a barking type of cough or stridor.
diphtheria (dif-THEAR-ee-ah)	-ia = condition	Bacterial upper respiratory infection characterized by the formation of a thick membranous film across the throat and a high mortality rate. Rare now due to the DPT (diphtheria, pertussis, tetanus) vaccine.
laryngitis (lair-in-JYE-tis)	laryng/o = larynx -itis = inflammation	Inflammation of the larynx.
nasopharyngitis (nay-zoh-fair-in-JYE-tis)	nas/o = nose pharyng/o = pharynx -itis = inflammation	Inflammation of the nasal cavity and pharynx; commonly called the *common cold.*
pertussis (per-TUH-is)	tuss/o = cough	Commonly called *whooping cough,* due to the whoop sound made when coughing. An infectious bacterial disease of the upper respiratory system that children receive immunization against as part of their DPT shots.
pharyngitis (fair-in-JYE-tis)	pharyng/o = pharynx -itis = inflammation	Inflammation of the pharynx; commonly called a *sore throat.*
rhinomycosis (rye-noh-my-KOH-sis)	rhin/o = nose myc/o = fungus -osis = abnormal condition	Fungal infection of the nasal cavity.

Bronchial Tubes

TERM	WORD PARTS	DEFINITION
asthma (AZ-mah)		Disease caused by various conditions, like allergens, and resulting in constriction of the bronchial airways, dyspnea, coughing, and wheezing. Can cause violent spasms of the bronchi (bronchospasms) but is generally not a life-threatening condition. Medication can be very effective.

MED TERM TIP

The term *asthma,* from the Greek word meaning "panting," describes the breathing pattern of a person having an asthma attack.

Pathology *(continued)*

TERM	WORD PARTS	DEFINITION
bronchiectasis (brong-key-EK-tah-sis)	bronchi/o = bronchus -ectasis = dilation	Abnormal enlargement of bronchi; may be the result of a lung infection. This condition can be irreversible and result in destruction of the bronchial walls. Major symptoms include coughing up a large amount of purulent sputum, crackles, and hemoptysis.
bronchitis (brong-KIGH-tis)	bronch/o = bronchus -itis = inflammation	Inflammation of a bronchus.
bronchogenic carcinoma (brong-koh-JEN-ik / car-sin-OH-mah)	bronch/o = bronchus -genic = produced by carcin/o = cancer -oma = tumor	Malignant tumor originating in the bronchi. Usually associated with a history of cigarette smoking.

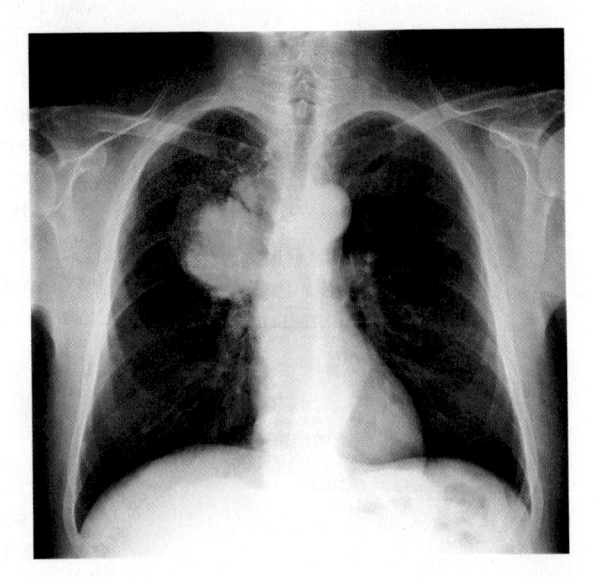

■ **Figure 7.8** Color-enhanced X-ray of large malignant tumor in the right lung. *(Du Cane Medical Imaging Ltd./Photo Researchers, Inc.)*

Lungs

TERM	WORD PARTS	DEFINITION
adult respiratory distress syndrome (ARDS)	spir/o = breathing -al = pertaining to	Acute respiratory failure in adults characterized by tachypnea, dyspnea, cyanosis, tachycardia, and hypoxemia. May follow trauma, pneumonia, or septic infections. Also called *acute respiratory distress syndrome.*
anthracosis (an-thra-KOH-sis)	anthrac/o = coal -osis = abnormal condition	Type of pneumoconiosis that develops from the collection of coal dust in the lung. Also called *black lung* or *miner's lung.*
asbestosis (az-bes-TOH-sis)	-osis = abnormal condition	Type of pneumoconiosis that develops from collection of asbestos fibers in the lungs. May lead to the development of lung cancer.

Pathology *(continued)*

TERM	WORD PARTS	DEFINITION
atelectasis (at-eh-LEK-tah-sis)	atel/o = incomplete -ectasis = dilation	Condition in which the alveoli in a portion of the lung collapse, preventing the respiratory exchange of oxygen and carbon dioxide. Can be caused by a variety of conditions, including pressure on the lung from a tumor or other object. Term also used to describe the failure of a newborn's lungs to expand.
chronic obstructive pulmonary disease (COPD) (PULL-mon-air-ee)	pulmon/o = lung -ary = pertaining to	Progressive, chronic, and usually irreversible group of conditions, like emphysema, in which the lungs have a diminished capacity for inspiration (inhalation) and expiration (exhalation). The person may have dyspnea upon exertion and a cough.
cystic fibrosis (CF) (SIS-tik / fye-BROH-sis)	cyst/o = cyst, bladder -ic = pertaining to fibr/o = fibers -osis = abnormal condition	Hereditary condition causing the exocrine glands to malfunction. The patient produces very thick mucus that causes severe congestion within the lungs and digestive system. Through more advanced treatment, many children are now living into adulthood with this disease. The term *cystic* in cystic fibrosis refers to cysts that form in the pancreas.
emphysema (em-fih-SEE-mah)		Pulmonary condition characterized by the destruction of the walls of the alveoli, resulting in fewer overexpanded air sacs. Can occur as a result of long-term heavy smoking. Air pollution also worsens this disease. The patient may not be able to breathe except in a sitting or standing position.
histoplasmosis (his-toh-plaz-MOH-sis)	hist/o = tissue -plasm = formation -osis = abnormal condition	Pulmonary infection caused by the fungus *Histoplasma capsulatum,* found in dust and in the droppings of pigeons and chickens. The translation of the name of this condition reflects the microscopic appearance of the fungus.
infant respiratory distress syndrome (IRDS)	spir/o = breathing	Lung condition most commonly found in premature infants that is characterized by tachypnea and respiratory grunting. The condition is caused by a lack of surfactant necessary to keep the lungs inflated. Also called *hyaline membrane disease* (HMD) and *respiratory distress syndrome of the newborn.*
influenza (in-floo-EN-za)		Viral infection of the respiratory system characterized by chills, fever, body aches, and fatigue. Commonly called the *flu.*
Legionnaire's disease (lee-jen-AYRZ)		Severe, often fatal bacterial infection characterized by pneumonia and liver and kidney damage. Named after people who came down with it at an American Legion convention in 1976.

Pathology *(continued)*

TERM	WORD PARTS	DEFINITION
***Mycoplasma* pneumonia** (MY-koh-plaz-ma)	myc/o = fungus -plasm = formation	Less severe but longer lasting form of pneumonia caused by the *Mycoplasma pneumoniae* bacteria. Also called *walking pneumonia*. The translation of the name of this condition reflects the microscopic appearance of the bacteria.
pneumoconiosis (noo-moh-koh-nee-OH-sis)	pneum/o = lung coni/o = dust -osis = abnormal condition	Condition that is the result of inhaling environmental particles that become toxic. Can be the result of inhaling coal dust (anthracosis) or asbestos (asbestosis).
pneumocystis pneumonia (PCP) (noo-moh-SIS-tis / new-MOH-nee-ah)	pneum/o = lung cyst/o = cyst, bladder pneumon/o = lung -ia = condition	Pneumonia with a nonproductive cough, very little fever, and dyspnea caused by the fungus *Pneumocystis jirovecii*. An opportunistic infection often seen in those with weakened immune systems, such as AIDS patients.
pneumonia (new-MOH-nee-ah)	pneumon/o = lung -ia = condition	Inflammatory condition of the lung that can be caused by bacteria, viruses, fungi, and aspirated substances. Results in the filling of the alveoli and air spaces with fluid.
pulmonary edema (PULL-mon-air-ee / eh-DEE-mah)	pulmon/o = lung -ary = pertaining to	Condition in which lung tissue retains an excessive amount of fluid, especially in the alveoli. Results in dyspnea.
pulmonary embolism (PULL-mon-air-ee / EM-boh-lizm)	pulmon/o = lung -ary = pertaining to embol/o = plug -ism = state of	Obstruction of the pulmonary artery or one of its branches by an embolus (often a blood clot broken away from another area of the body). May cause an infarct in the lung tissue.
pulmonary fibrosis (fi-BROH-sis)	pulmon/o = lung -ary = pertaining to fibr/o = fibers -osis = abnormal condition	Formation of fibrous scar tissue in the lungs that leads to decreased ability to expand the lungs. May be caused by infections, pneumoconiosis, autoimmune diseases, and toxin exposure.
severe acute respiratory syndrome (SARS)	spir/o = breathing	Acute viral respiratory infection that begins like the flu but quickly progresses to severe dyspnea; high fatality rate. First appeared in China in 2003.
silicosis (sil-ih-KOH-sis)	-osis = abnormal condition	Type of pneumoconiosis that develops from the inhalation of silica (quartz) dust found in quarrying, glass works, sandblasting, and ceramics.
sleep apnea (AP-nee-ah)	a- = without -pnea = breathing	Condition in which breathing stops repeatedly during sleep long enough to cause a drop in oxygen levels in the blood.
sudden infant death syndrome (SIDS)		Unexpected and unexplained death of an apparently well infant under 1 year of age. The child suddenly stops breathing for unknown reasons.

▇ Pathology *(continued)*

TERM	WORD PARTS	DEFINITION
tuberculosis (TB) (too-ber-kyoo-LOH-sis)	-osis = abnormal condition	Infectious disease caused by the bacteria *Mycobacterium tuberculosis*. Most commonly affects the respiratory system and causes inflammation and calcification in the lungs. Tuberculosis incidence is on the increase and is seen in many patients with weakened immune systems. Multidrug-resistant tuberculosis is a particularly dangerous form of the disease because some bacteria have developed a resistance to the standard drug therapy.

Pleural Cavity

TERM	WORD PARTS	DEFINITION
empyema (em-pye-EE-mah)	py/o = pus	Pus with in the pleural space usually associated with a bacterial infection. Also called *pyothorax*.
pleural effusion (PLOO-ral / eh-FYOO-zhun)	pleur/o = pleura -al = pertaining to	Abnormal accumulation of fluid in the pleural cavity preventing the lungs from fully expanding. Physicians can detect the presence of fluid by tapping the chest (percussion) or listening with a stethoscope (auscultation).
pleurisy (PLOOR-ih-see)	pleur/o = pleura	Inflammation of the pleura characterized by sharp chest pain with each breath. Also called *pleuritis*.
pneumothorax (new-moh-THOH-raks)	pneum/o = air -thorax = chest	Collection of air or gas in the pleural cavity, which may result in collapse of the lung.

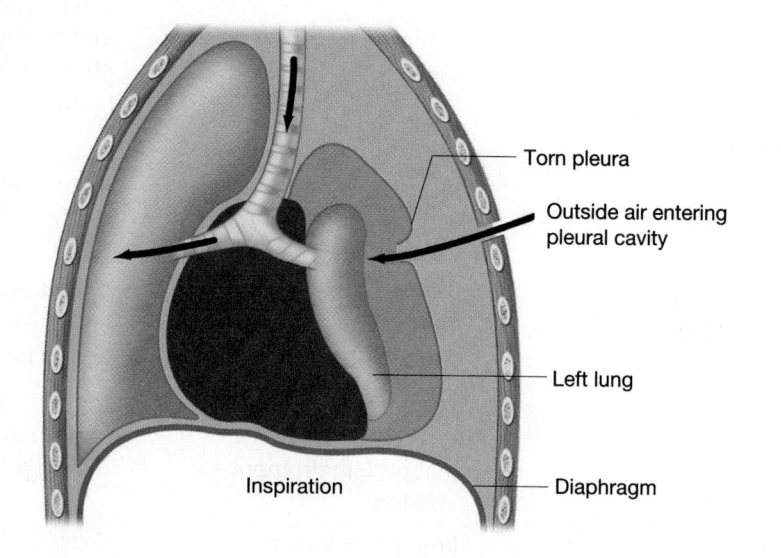

■ Figure 7.9 Pneumothorax. Figure illustrates how puncture of thoracic wall and tearing of pleural membrane allows air into lung and results in collapsed lung.

Diagnostic Procedures

TERM	WORD PARTS	DEFINITION
Clinical Laboratory Tests		
arterial blood gases (ABGs) (ar-TEE-ree-al)	arteri/o = artery -al = pertaining to	Testing for the gases present in the blood. Generally used to assist in determining the levels of oxygen (O_2) and carbon dioxide (CO_2) in the blood.
sputum culture and sensitivity (C&S) (SPEW-tum)		Testing sputum by placing it on a culture medium and observing any bacterial growth. The specimen is then tested to determine antibiotic effectiveness.
sputum cytology (SPEW-tum / sigh-TALL-oh-jee)	cyt/o = cell -logy = study of	Examining sputum for malignant cells.
Diagnostic Imaging		
bronchogram (BRONG-koh-gram)	bronch/o = bronchus -gram = record	X-ray record of the bronchus produced by bronchography.
bronchography (brong-KOG-rah-fee)	bronch/o = bronchus -graphy = process of recording	X-ray of the lung after a radiopaque substance has been inserted into the trachea or bronchial tube. Resulting X-ray is called a *bronchogram*.
chest X-ray (CXR)		Taking a radiographic picture of the lungs and heart from the back and sides.
pulmonary angiography (PULL-mon-air-ee / an-jee-OG-rah-fee)	pulmon/o = lung -ary = pertaining to angi/o = vessel -graphy = process of recording	Injecting dye into a blood vessel for the purpose of taking an X-ray of the arteries and veins of the lungs.
ventilation-perfusion scan (per-FUSE-shun)		Nuclear medicine diagnostic test that is especially useful in identifying pulmonary emboli. Radioactive air is inhaled for the ventilation portion to determine if air is filling the entire lung. Radioactive intravenous injection shows if blood is flowing to all parts of the lung.
Endoscopic Procedures		
bronchoscope (BRONG-koh-scope)	bronch/o = bronchus -scope = instrument for viewing	Instrument used to view inside a bronchus during a *bronchoscopy*.
bronchoscopy (Bronch) (brong-KOSS-koh-pee)	bronch/o = bronchus -scopy = process of visually examining	Visual examination of the inside of the bronchi; uses an instrument called a *bronchoscope* (see Figure 7.10 ■).
laryngoscope (lair-RING-go-scope)	laryng/o = larynx -scope = instrument for viewing	Instrument used to view inside the larynx during a *laryngoscopy*.
laryngoscopy (lair-in-GOSS-koh-pee)	laryng/o = larynx -scopy = process of visually examining	Examination of the interior of the larynx with a lighted instrument called a *laryngoscope*.

Diagnostic Procedures *(continued)*

TERM	WORD PARTS	DEFINITION

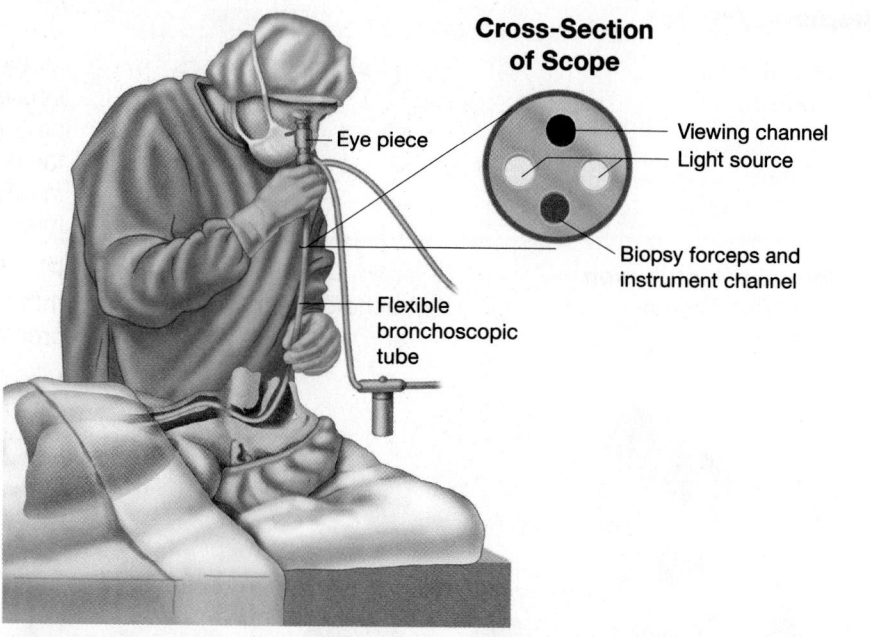

Cross-Section of Scope

Eye piece

Viewing channel
Light source

Biopsy forceps and instrument channel

Flexible bronchoscopic tube

■ **Figure 7.10** Bronchoscopy. Figure illustrates physician using a broncho-scope to inspect the patient's bronchial tubes. Advances in technology include using a videoscope, which projects the internal view of the bronchus onto a video screen.

Pulmonary Function Tests

TERM	WORD PARTS	DEFINITION
oximeter (ox-IM-eh-ter)	ox/i = oxygen -meter = instrument to measure	Instrument that measures the amount of oxygen in the bloodstream.
oximetry (ox-IM-eh-tree)	ox/i = oxygen -metry = process of measuring	Measures the oxygen level in the blood using a device, an *oximeter,* placed on the patient's fingertip or earlobe.
pulmonary function test (PFT) (PULL-mon-air-ee)	pulmon/o = lung -ary = pertaining to	Group of diagnostic tests that give information regarding air flow in and out of the lungs, lung volumes, and gas exchange between the lungs and bloodstream.
spirometer (spy-ROM-eh-ter)	spir/o = breathing -meter = instrument to measure	Instrument to measure lung capacity used for *spirometry.*
spirometry (spy-ROM-eh-tree)	spir/o = breathing -metry = process of measuring	Procedure to measure lung capacity using a *spirometer.*

Additional Diagnostic Procedures

TERM	WORD PARTS	DEFINITION
polysomnography (polly-som-NOG-rah-fee)	poly- = many somn/o = sleep -graphy = process of recording	Monitoring a patient while sleeping to identify sleep apnea. Also called *sleep apnea study.*
sweat test		Test for cystic fibrosis. Patients with this disease have an abnormally large amount of salt in their sweat.
tuberculin skin tests (TB test) (too-BER-kyoo-lin)		Applying the tuberculin purified protein derivative (PPD) under the surface of the skin to determine if the patient has been exposed to tuberculosis. Also called a *Mantoux test.*

Therapeutic Procedures

TERM	WORD PARTS	DEFINITION
Respiratory Therapy		
aerosol therapy (AIR-oh-sol)	aer/o = air	Medication suspended in a mist intended for inhalation. Delivered by a *nebulizer,* which provides the mist for a period of time while the patient breathes, or a *metered-dose inhaler* (MDI), which delivers a single puff of mist.
endotracheal intubation (en-doh-TRAY-kee-al / in-too-BAY-shun)	endo- = within trache/o = trachea -al = pertaining to	Placing of a tube through the mouth, through the glottis, and into the trachea to create a patent airway.

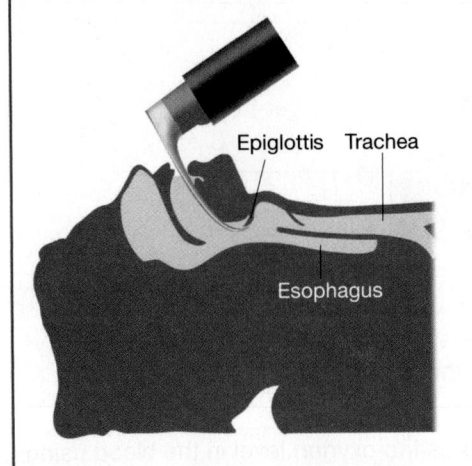 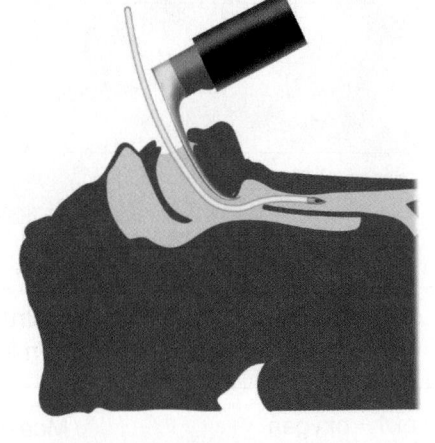 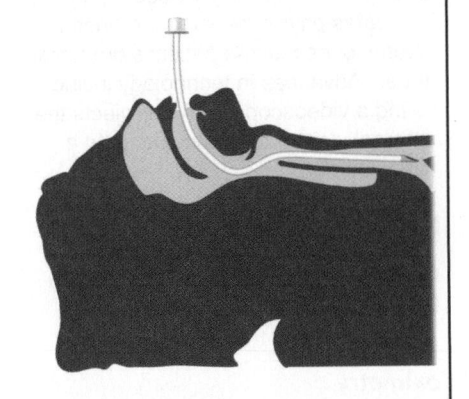

Epiglottis   Trachea

Esophagus

■ **Figure 7.11** Endotracheal intubation. First, a lighted scope is used to identify the trachea from the esophagus. Next, the tube is placed through the pharynx and into the trachea. Finally, the scope is removed, leaving the tube in place.

TERM	WORD PARTS	DEFINITION
intermittent positive pressure breathing (IPPB)		Method for assisting patients in breathing using a mask connected to a machine that produces an increased positive thoracic pressure.
nasal cannula (CAN-you-lah)	nas/o = nose -al = pertaining to	Two-pronged plastic device for delivering oxygen into the nose; one prong is inserted into each naris.
postural drainage	-al = pertaining to	Drainage of secretions from the bronchi by placing the patient in a position that uses gravity to promote drainage. Used for the treatment of cystic fibrosis and bronchiectasis.
supplemental oxygen therapy	-al = pertaining to	Providing a patient with additional concentration of oxygen to improve oxygen levels in the bloodstream. Oxygen may be provided by a mask or nasal cannula.
ventilator (VENT-ih-later)		Machine that provides artificial ventilation for a patient unable to breathe on his or her own. Also called a *respirator.*

Therapeutic Procedures *(continued)*

TERM	WORD PARTS	DEFINITION
Surgical Procedures		
bronchoplasty (BRONG-koh-plas-tee)	bronch/o = bronchus -plasty = surgical repair	Surgical repair of a bronchus.
laryngectomy (lair-in-JEK-toh-mee)	laryng/o = larynx -ectomy = surgical removal	Surgical removal of the larynx.
laryngoplasty (lair-RING-goh-plas-tee)	laryng/o = larynx -plasty = surgical repair	Surgical repair of the larynx.
lobectomy (loh-BEK-toh-mee)	lob/o = lobe -ectomy = surgical removal	Surgical removal of a lobe of a lung.
pleurectomy (ploor-EK-toh-mee)	pleur/o = pleura -ectomy = surgical removal	Surgical removal of the pleura.
pleurocentesis (ploor-oh-sen-TEE-sis)	pleur/o = pleura -centesis = puncture to withdraw fluid	Procedure involving insertion of a needle into the pleura space to withdraw fluid; may be a treatment for excess fluid accumulating or to obtain fluid for diagnostic examination.
rhinoplasty (RYE-noh-plas-tee)	rhin/o = nose -plasty = surgical repair	Surgical repair of the nose.
thoracentesis (thor-ah-sen-TEE-sis)	thorac/o = chest -centesis = puncture to withdraw fluid	Surgical puncture of the chest wall for the removal of fluids. Also called *thoracocentesis.*

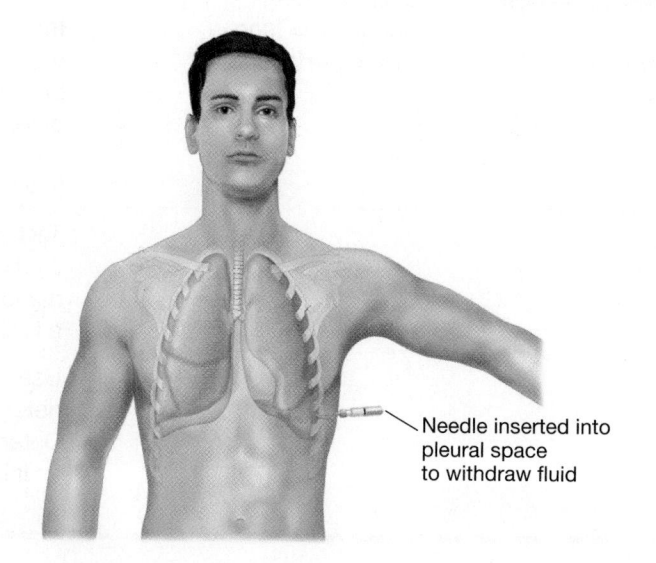

Needle inserted into pleural space to withdraw fluid

■ **Figure 7.12** Thoracentesis. A needle is inserted between the ribs to withdraw fluid from the pleural sac at the base of the left lung.

TERM	WORD PARTS	DEFINITION
thoracostomy (thor-ah-KOS-toh-mee)	thorac/o = chest -ostomy = surgically create an opening	Insertion of a tube into the chest cavity for the purpose of draining off fluid or air. Also called *chest tube.*
thoracotomy (thor-ah-KOT-oh-mee)	thorac/o = chest -otomy = cutting into	To cut into the chest cavity.

Therapeutic Procedures (continued)

TERM	WORD PARTS	DEFINITION
tracheotomy (tray-kee-OTT-oh-mee)	trache/o = trachea -otomy = cutting into	Surgical procedure often performed in an emergency that creates an opening directly into the trachea to allow the patient to breathe easier; also called *tracheostomy*.

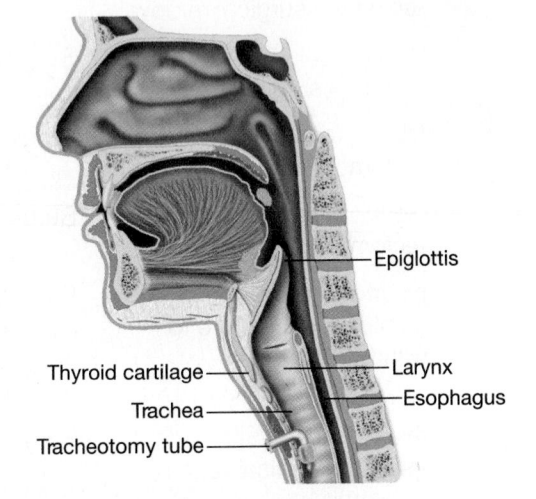

Epiglottis

Thyroid cartilage —

Trachea —

Tracheotomy tube —

Larynx

Esophagus

Figure 7.13 A tracheotomy tube in place, inserted through an opening in the front of the neck and anchored within the trachea.

Additional Procedures

cardiopulmonary resuscitation (CPR) (car-dee-oh-PULL-mon-air-ee / ree-suss-ih-TAY-shun)	cardi/o = heart pulmon/o = lung -ary = pertaining to	Emergency treatment provided by persons trained in CPR and given to patients when their respirations and heart stop. CPR provides oxygen to the brain, heart, and other vital organs until medical treatment can restore a normal heart and pulmonary function.
Heimlich maneuver (HYME-lik)		Technique for removing a foreign body from the trachea or pharynx by exerting diaphragmatic pressure. Named for Harry Heimlich, a U.S. thoracic surgeon.
percussion (per-KUH-shun)		Use of the fingertips to tap on a surface to determine the condition beneath the surface. Determined in part by the feel of the surface as it is tapped and the sound generated.

Pharmacology

CLASSIFICATION	WORD PARTS	ACTION	EXAMPLES
antibiotic (an-tih-bye-AW-tic)	anti- = against bi/o = life -tic = pertaining to	Kills bacteria causing respiratory infections.	ampicillin; amoxicillin, Amoxil; ciprofloxacin, Cipro
antihistamine (an-tih-HIST-ah-meen)	anti- = against	Blocks the effects of histamine that has been released by the body during an allergy attack.	fexofenadine, Allegra; loratadine, Claritin; diphenhydramine, Benadryl

Pharmacology *(continued)*

CLASSIFICATION	WORD PARTS	ACTION	EXAMPLES
antitussive (an-tih-TUSS-ive)	anti- = without tuss/o = cough	Relieves the urge to cough.	hydrocodon, Hycodan; dextromethorphan, Vicks Formula 44
bronchodilator (BRONG-koh-dye-late-or)	bronch/o = bronchus	Relaxes muscle spasms in bronchial tubes. Used to treat asthma.	albuterol, Proventil, Ventolin; theophyllin, Theo-Dur
corticosteroids (core-tih-koh-STAIR-ryods)	cortic/o = outer region, cortex	Reduces inflammation and swelling in the respiratory tract.	fluticasone, Flonase; mometasone, Nasonex; triamcinolone, Azmacort
decongestant (dee-kon-JES-tant)	de- = without	Reduces stuffiness and congestion throughout the respiratory system.	oxymetazoline, Afrin, Dristan, Sinex; pseudoephedrine, Drixoral, Sudafed
expectorant (ek-SPEK-toh-rant)		Improves the ability to cough up mucus from the respiratory tract.	guaifenesin, Robitussin, Mucinex
mucolytic (myoo-koh-LIT-ik)	muc/o = mucus -lytic = destruction	Liquefies mucus so it is easier to cough and clear it from the respiratory tract.	N-acetyl-cysteine, Mucomyst

Abbreviations

ABGs	arterial blood gases
ARDS	adult (or acute) respiratory distress syndrome
Bronch	bronchoscopy
CO₂	carbon dioxide
COPD	chronic obstructive pulmonary disease
CPR	cardiopulmonary resuscitation
C&S	culture and sensitivity
CTA	clear to auscultation
CXR	chest X-ray
DOE	dyspnea on exertion
DPT	diphtheria, pertussis, tetanus injection
ENT	ear, nose, and throat
ERV	expiratory reserve volume
FRC	functional residual capacity
HMD	hyaline membrane disease
IC	inspiratory capacity
IPPB	intermittent positive pressure breathing
IRDS	infant respiratory distress syndrome
IRV	inspiratory reserve volume
LLL	left lower lobe
LUL	left upper lobe

MDI	metered-dose inhaler
O₂	oxygen
PCP	pneumocystis pneumonia
PFT	pulmonary function test
PPD	purified protein derivative
R	respiration
RA	room air
RDS	respiratory distress syndrome
RLL	right lower lobe
RML	right middle lobe
RRT	registered respiratory therapist
RV	reserve volume
RUL	right upper lobe
SARS	severe acute respiratory syndrome
SIDS	sudden infant death syndrome
SOB	shortness of breath
TB	tuberculosis
TLC	total lung capacity
TPR	temperature, pulse, and respiration
TV	tidal volume
URI	upper respiratory infection
VC	vital capacity

Chapter Review

Real-World Applications

Medical Record Analysis

This Pulmonology Consultation Report contains 12 medical terms. Underline each term and write it in the list below the report. Then define each term.

Pulmonology Consultation Report

Reason for Consultation: Evaluation of increasingly severe asthma.

History of Present Illness: Patient is a 10-year-old male who first presented to the Emergency Room with dyspnea, coughing, and wheezing at 7 years of age. Attacks are increasing in frequency, and there do not appear to be any precipitating factors such as exercise. No other family members are asthmatics.

Results of Physical Examination: Patient is currently in the ER with marked dyspnea, cyanosis around the lips, prolonged expiration, and a hacking cough producing thick phlegm. Auscultation revealed rhonchi throughout lungs. ABGs indicate hypoxemia. Spirometry reveals moderately severe airway obstruction during expiration. This patient responded to Proventil and he is beginning to cough less and breathe with less effort.

Assessment: Acute asthma attack with severe airway obstruction. There is no evidence of infection. In view of increasing severity and frequency of attacks, all his medications should be reevaluated for effectiveness and all attempts to identify precipitating factors should be made.

Recommendations: Patient is to continue to use Proventil for relief of bronchospasms. Instructions for taking medications and controlling severity of asthma attacks were carefully reviewed with the patient and his family.

	Term	Definition
1	_____	_____
2	_____	_____
3	_____	_____
4	_____	_____
5	_____	_____
6	_____	_____
7	_____	_____
8	_____	_____
9	_____	_____
10	_____	_____
11	_____	_____
12	_____	_____

Chart Note Transcription

The chart note below contains 11 phrases that can be reworded with a medical term that you learned in this chapter. Each phrase is identified with an underline. Determine the medical term and write your answers in the space provided.

Current Complaint:	A 43-year-old female was brought to the Emergency Room by her family. She complained of <u>painful and labored breathing,</u> ❶ <u>rapid breathing,</u> ❷ and fever. Symptoms began 3 days ago, but have become much worse during the past 12 hours.
Past History:	Patient is a mother of three and a business executive. She has had no surgeries or previous serious illnesses.
Signs and Symptoms:	Temperature is 103°F, respiratory rate is 20 breaths/minute, blood pressure is 165/98, and heart rate is 90 bpm. <u>A blood test to measure the levels of oxygen in the blood</u> ❸ indicates a marked <u>low level of oxygen in the blood.</u> ❹ The <u>process of listening to body sounds</u> ❺ of the lungs revealed <u>abnormal crackling sounds</u> ❻ over the left lower chest. She is producing large amounts of <u>pus-filled</u> ❼ <u>mucus coughed up from the respiratory tract</u> ❽ and a <u>chest X-ray</u> ❾ shows a large cloudy patch in the lower lobe of the left lung.
Diagnosis:	Left lower lobe <u>inflammatory condition of the lungs caused by bacterial infection.</u> ❿
Treatment:	Patient was started on intravenous antibiotics. She also required a <u>tube placed through the mouth to create an airway</u> ⓫ for 3 days.

❶ _____

❷ _____

❸ _____

❹ _____

❺ _____

❻ _____

❼ _____

❽ _____

❾ _____

❿ _____

⓫ _____

Case Study

Below is a case study presentation of a patient with a condition discussed in this chapter. Read the case study and answer the questions below. Some questions will ask for information not included within this chapter. Use your text, a medical dictionary, or any other reference material you choose to answer these questions.

An 88-year-old female was seen in the physician's office complaining of dyspnea, dizziness, orthopnea, elevated temperature, and a cough. Lung auscultation revealed crackles over the right bronchus. CXR revealed fluid in the RUL. The patient was sent to the hospital with an admitting diagnosis of pneumonia. Vital signs upon admission were temperature 102°F, pulse 100 BPM and rapid, respirations 24 breaths/min and labored, blood pressure 180/110. She was treated with IV antibiotics and IPPB. She responded well to treatment and was released home to her family with oral antibiotics on the third day.

(© Francesco De Napoli/istockphoto.com)

1. What was this patient's admitting diagnosis? Look this condition up in a reference source and include a short description of it.

   _____

   _____

2. List and define each of the patient's presenting symptoms in your own words.

   _____

   _____

3. Define auscultation and CXR. Describe what each revealed in your own words.

   _____

   _____

4. What does the term "vital signs" mean? Describe this patient's vital signs.

   _____

   _____

5. Describe the treatments this patient received while in the hospital in your own words.

   _____

   _____

6. Explain the change in the patient's medication when she was discharged home.

   _____

   _____

Practice Exercises

A. Complete the Statement

1. The primary function of the respiratory system is _____.

2. The movement of air in and out of the lungs is called _____.

3. Define external respiration: _____.

4. Define internal respiration: _____.

5. The organs of the respiratory system are _____, _____, _____, _____, _____, and _____.

6. The passageway for food, liquids, and air is the _____.

7. The _____ helps to keep food out of the respiratory tract.

8. The function of the cilia in the nose is to _____.

9. The muscle that divides the thoracic cavity from the abdominal cavity is the _____.

10. The respiratory rate for an adult is _____ to _____ respirations per minute.

11. The respiratory rate for a newborn is _____ to _____ respirations per minute.

12. The right lung has _____ lobes; the left lung has _____ lobes.

13. The air sacs at the ends of the bronchial tree are called _____.

14. The term for the double membrane around the lungs is _____.

15. The nasal cavity is separated from the mouth by the _____.

16. The small branches of the bronchi are the _____.

B. Define the Suffix

	Definition	Example from Chapter
1. -ectasis	_____	_____
2. -capnia	_____	_____
3. -phonia	_____	_____
4. -thorax	_____	_____
5. -pnea	_____	_____
6. -ptysis	_____	_____
7. -osmia	_____	_____

C. Combining Form Practice

The combining form **rhin/o** refers to the nose. Use it to write a term that means:

1. inflammation of the nose _____

2. abnormal flow from the nose _____

3. discharge from the nose _____

4. surgical repair of the nose _____

The combining form **laryng/o** refers to the larynx or voice box. Use it to write a term that means:

5. inflammation of the larynx _____

6. spasm of the larynx _____

7. visual examination of the larynx _____

8. pertaining to the larynx _____

9. cutting into the larynx _____

10. removal of the larynx _____

11. surgical repair of the larynx _____

12. paralysis of the larynx _____

The combining form **bronch/o** refers to the bronchus. Use it to write a term that means:

13. pertaining to bronchus _____

14. inflammation of the bronchus _____

15. visually examine the interior of the bronchus _____

16. produced by bronchus _____

17. spasm of the bronchus _____

The combining form **thorac/o** refers to the chest. Use it to write a term that means:

18. surgical repair of the chest _____

19. cutting into the chest _____

20. chest pain _____

21. pertaining to chest _____

The combining form **trache/o** refers to the trachea. Use it to write a term that means:

22. cutting into the trachea _____

23. surgical repair of the trachea _____

24. narrowing of the trachea _____

25. pertaining to inside the trachea _____

26. inflammation of the trachea _____

D. Define the Combining Form

	Definition	Example from Chapter
1. **trache/o**	_____	_____
2. **laryng/o**	_____	_____
3. **bronch/o**	_____	_____
4. **spir/o**	_____	_____
5. **pneum/o**	_____	_____
6. **rhin/o**	_____	_____
7. **coni/o**	_____	_____
8. **pleur/o**	_____	_____
9. **epiglott/o**	_____	_____
10. **alveol/o**	_____	_____
11. **pulmon/o**	_____	_____
12. **ox/o**	_____	_____
13. **sinus/o**	_____	_____
14. **lob/o**	_____	_____
15. **nas/o**	_____	_____

E. Suffix Practice

The suffix **-pnea** means breathing. Use this suffix to write a medical term that means:

1. normal breathing _____

2. difficult or labored breathing _____

3. rapid breathing _____

4. can breathe only in an upright position _____

5. lack of breathing _____

F. Name That Term

1. the process of breathing in _____

2. spitting up of blood _____

3. blood clot in the pulmonary artery _____

4. inflammation of a sinus _____

5. sore throat _____

6. air in the pleural cavity _____

7. whooping cough _____

8. cutting into the pleura _____

9. pain in the pleural region _____

10. common cold _____

G. What's the Abbreviation?

1. upper respiratory infection _____

2. pulmonary function test _____

3. left lower lobe _____

4. oxygen _____

5. carbon dioxide _____

6. intermittent positive pressure breathing _____

7. chronic obstructive pulmonary disease _____

8. bronchoscopy _____

9. total lung capacity _____

10. tuberculosis _____

11. infant respiratory distress syndrome _____

H. What Does it Stand For?

1. CXR _____

2. TV _____

3. TPR _____

4. ABGs _____

5. DOE _____

6. RUL _____

7. SIDS _____

8. TLC _____

9. ARDS _____

10. MDI _____

11. CTA _____

12. SARS _____

I. Terminology Matching

Match each term to its definition.

1. _____ inhaling environmental particles

2. _____ whooping cough

3. _____ may result in collapsed lung

4. _____ test to identify sleep apnea

5. _____ respiratory tract mucus

6. _____ sweat test

7. _____ measures oxygen levels in blood

8. _____ *Mycoplasma* pneumonia

9. _____ disease with overexpanded air sacs

10. _____ tuberculin test

11. _____ nosebleed

12. _____ pus in the pleural space

a. polysomnography

b. Mantoux test

c. oximetry

d. epistaxis

e. pneumoconiosis

f. emphysema

g. walking pneumonia

h. pneumothorax

i. empyema

j. phlegm

k. pertussis

l. test for cystic fibrosis

J. Define the Term

1. total lung capacity _____

2. tidal volume _____

3. residual volume _____

K. Fill in the Blank

anthracosis	sputum cytology	cardiopulmonary resuscitation	patent
thoracentesis	respirator	ventilation-perfusion scan	rhonchi
supplemental oxygen	hyperventilation		

1. When the patient's breathing and heart stopped, the paramedics began _____.

2. The physician performed a _____ to remove fluid from the chest.

3. A _____ is also called a ventilator.

4. The patient received _____ through a nasal cannula.

5. An endotracheal intubation was performed to establish a _____ airway.

6. A _____ is a particularly useful test to identify a pulmonary embolus.

7. The result of the _____ was negative for cancer.

8. _____ involves tachypnea and hyperpnea.

9. _____ are wheezing lung sounds.

10. Miners are at risk of developing _____.

L. Pharmacology Challenge

Fill in the classification for each drug description, then match the brand name.

Drug Description	Classification	Brand Name
1. _____ Reduces stuffiness and congestion	_____	a. Hycodan
2. _____ Relieves the urge to cough	_____	b. Flonase
3. _____ Kills bacteria	_____	c. Cipro
4. _____ Improves ability to cough up mucus	_____	d. Ventolin
5. _____ Liquefies mucus	_____	e. Allegra
6. _____ Relaxes bronchial muscle spasms	_____	f. Afrin
7. _____ Blocks allergy attack	_____	g. Robitussin
8. _____ Reduces inflammation and swelling	_____	h. Mucomyst

Labeling Exercise

Image A

Write the labels for this figure on the numbered lines provided.

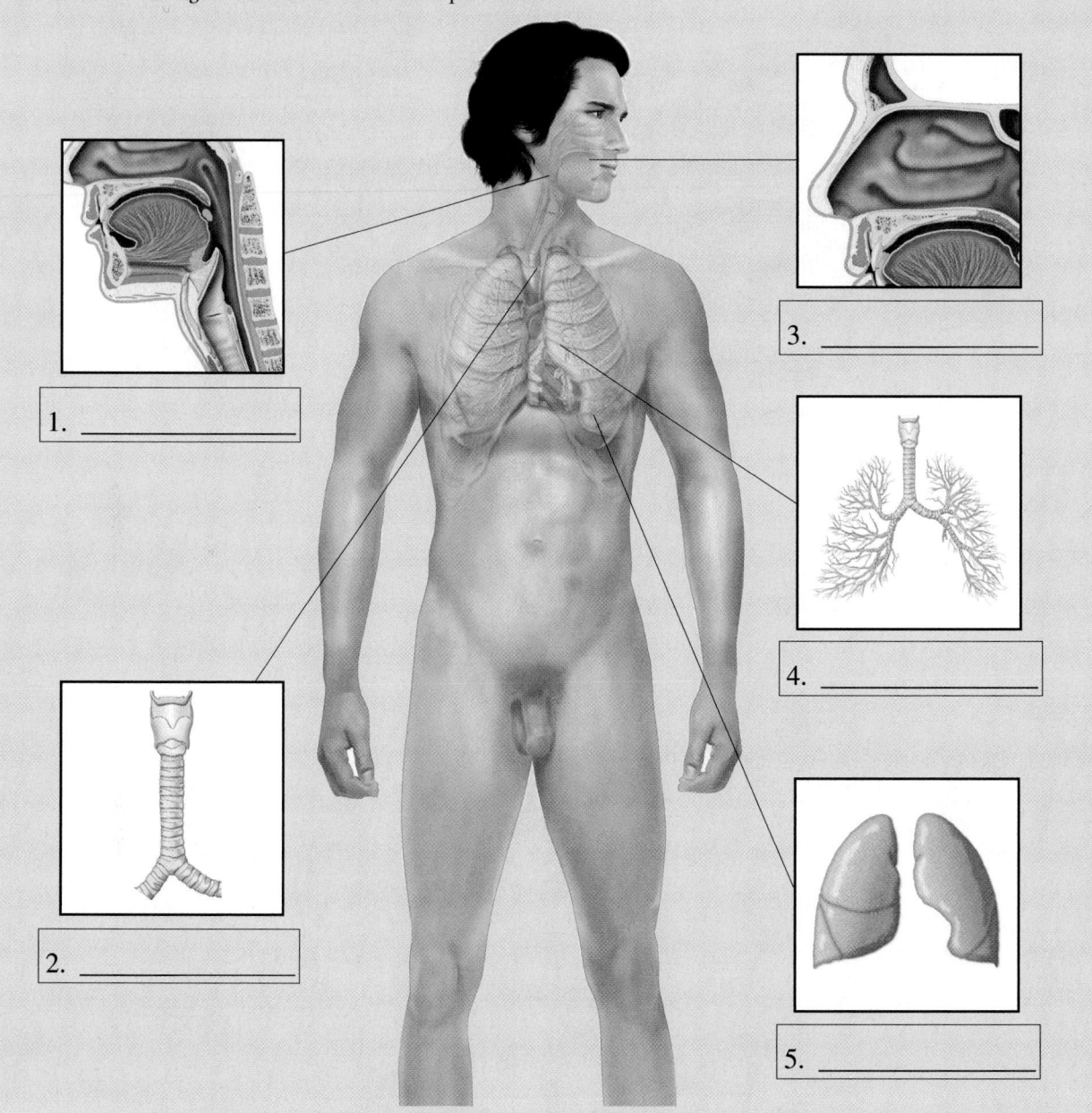

1. _____

2. _____

3. _____

4. _____

5. _____

MEDICAL TERMINOLOGY INTERACTIVE

Medical Terminology Interactive is a premium online homework management system that includes a host of features to help you study. Registered users will find:

- Fun games and activities built within a virtual hospital
- Powerful tools that track and analyze your results—allowing you to create a personalized learning experience
- Videos, flashcards, and audio pronunciations to help enrich your progress
- Streaming video lesson presentations and self-paced learning modules

www.pearsonhighered.com/mti

Image B

Write the labels for this figure on the numbered lines provided.

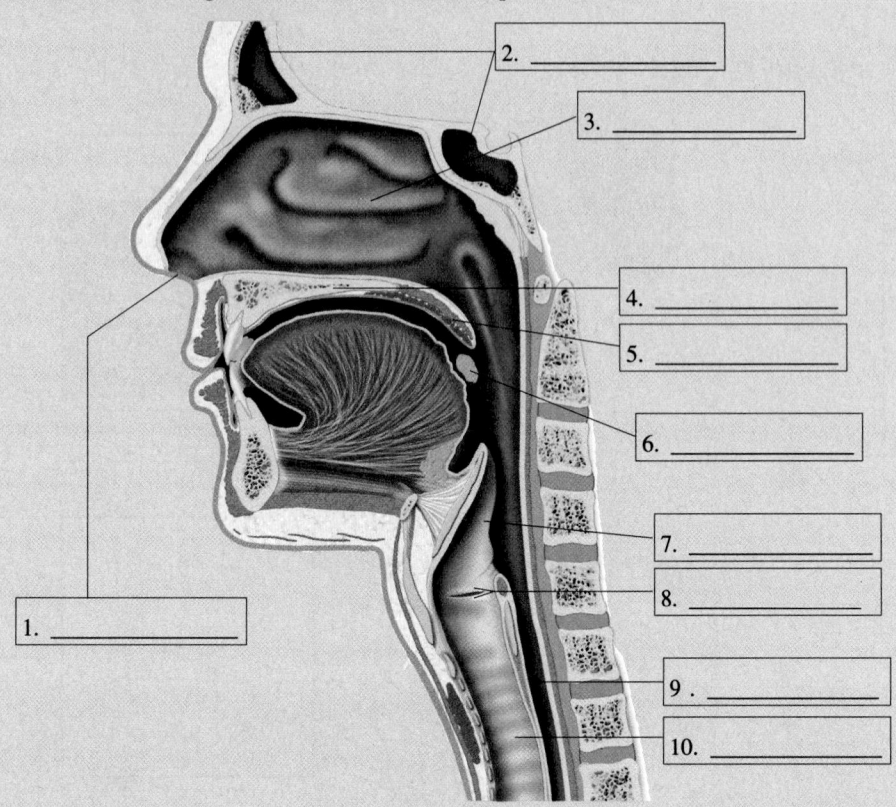

2. _____

3. _____

4. _____

5. _____

6. _____

7. _____

8. _____

1. _____

9. _____

10. _____

Image C

Write the labels for this figure on the numbered lines provided.

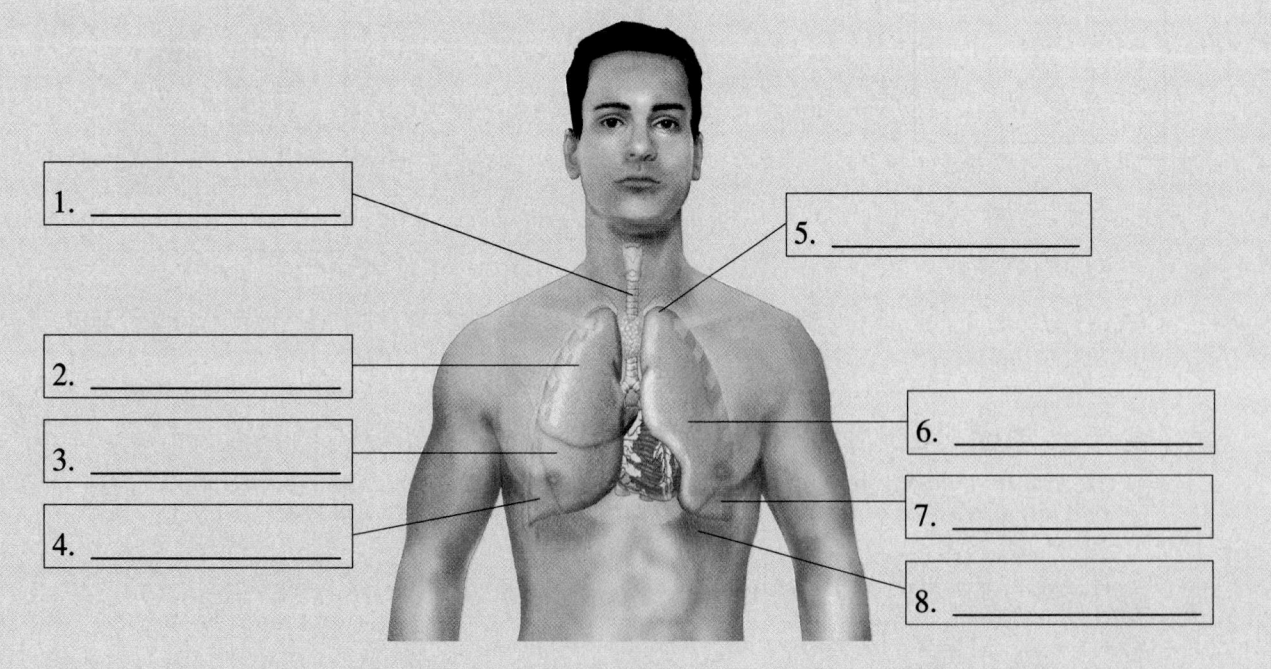

1. _____

5. _____

2. _____

3. _____

4. _____

6. _____

7. _____

8. _____

8

DIGESTIVE SYSTEM

Learning Objectives

Upon completion of this chapter, you will be able to

- Identify and define the combining forms and suffixes introduced in this chapter.

- Correctly spell and pronounce medical terms and major anatomical structures relating to the digestive system.

- Locate and describe the major organs of the digestive system and their functions.

- Describe the function of the accessory organs of the digestive system.

- Identify the shape and function of each type of tooth.

- Identify and define digestive system anatomical terms.

- Identify and define selected digestive system pathology terms.

- Identify and define selected digestive system diagnostic procedures.

- Identify and define selected digestive system therapeutic procedures.

- Identify and define selected medications relating to the digestive system.

- Define selected abbreviations associated with the digestive system.

Digestive System at a Glance

Function

The digestive system begins breaking down food through mechanical and chemical digestion. After being digested, nutrient molecules are absorbed into the body and enter the bloodstream; any food not digested or absorbed is eliminated as solid waste.

Organs

Here are the primary structures that comprise the digestive system.

colon
esophagus
gallbladder (GB)
liver
oral cavity

pancreas
pharynx
salivary glands
small intestine
stomach

Word Parts

Here are the most common word parts (with their meanings) used to build digestive system terms. For a more comprehensive list, refer to the Terminology section of this chapter.

Combining Forms

an/o	anus	gloss/o	tongue
append/o	appendix	hepat/o	liver
appendic/o	appendix	ile/o	ileum
bar/o	weight	jejun/o	jejunum
bucc/o	cheek	labi/o	lip
cec/o	cecum	lapar/o	abdomen
cholangi/o	bile duct	lingu/o	tongue
chol/e	bile, gall	lith/o	stone
cholecyst/o	gallbladder	odont/o	tooth
choledoch/o	common bile duct	or/o	mouth
cirrh/o	yellow	palat/o	palate
col/o	colon	pancreat/o	pancreas
colon/o	colon	pharyng/o	pharynx (throat)
dent/o	tooth	polyp/o	polyp
diverticul/o	pouch	proct/o	anus and rectum
duoden/o	duodenum	pylor/o	pylorus
enter/o	small intestine	pyr/o	fire
esophag/o	esophagus	rect/o	rectum
gastr/o	stomach	sialaden/o	salivary gland
gingiv/o	gums	sigmoid/o	sigmoid colon

Suffixes

-emesis	vomit	-pepsia	digestion
-istry	specialty of	-phagia	eat, swallow
-lithiasis	condition of stones	-prandial	pertaining to a meal
-orexia	appetite	-tripsy	surgical crushing

Digestive System Illustrated

salivary glands, p. 264

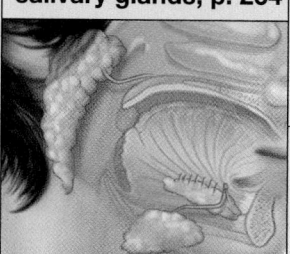

Produces saliva

oral cavity, p. 258

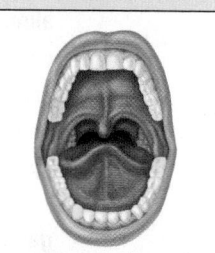

Ingests, chews, and swallows food

esophagus, p. 261

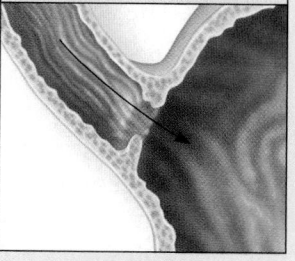

Transports food to the stomach

stomach, p. 262

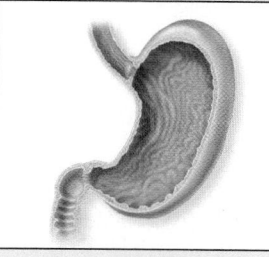

Secretes acid and mixes food to start digestion

pancreas, p. 265

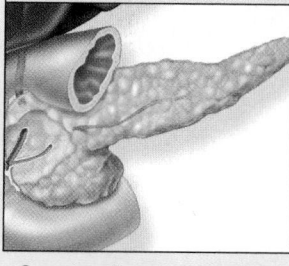

Secretes digestive enzymes and buffers

liver & gallbladder, p. 265

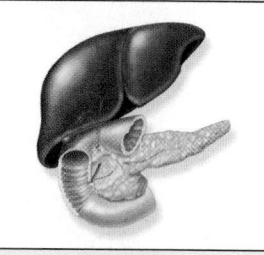

Produces and stores bile

small intestine, p. 262

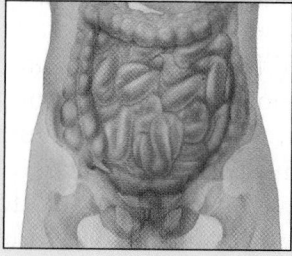

Digests and absorbs nutrients

colon, p. 263

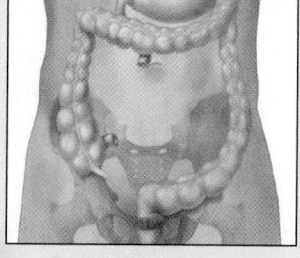

Reabsorbs water and stores feces

Anatomy and Physiology of the Digestive System

accessory organs	**gut**
alimentary canal (al-ih-MEN-tar-ree)	**liver**
colon (COH-lon)	**oral cavity**
esophagus (eh-SOFF-ah-gus)	**pancreas** (PAN-kree-ass)
gallbladder	**pharynx** (FAIR-inks)
gastrointestinal system	**salivary glands** (SAL-ih-vair-ee)
(gas-troh-in-TESS-tih-nal)	**small intestine**
gastrointestinal tract	**stomach** (STUM-ak)

The digestive system, also known as the **gastrointestinal (GI) system,** includes approximately 30 feet of a continuous muscular tube called the **gut, alimentary canal,** or **gastrointestinal tract** that stretches between the mouth and the anus. Most of the organs in this system are actually different sections of this tube. In order, beginning at the mouth and continuing to the anus, these organs are the **oral cavity, pharynx, esophagus, stomach, small intestine, colon, rectum,** and **anus.** The **accessory organs** of digestion are those that participate in the digestion process, but are not part of the continuous alimentary canal. These organs, which are connected to the gut by a duct, are the **liver, pancreas, gallbladder,** and **salivary glands.**

The digestive system has three main functions: digesting food, absorbing nutrients, and eliminating waste. Digestion includes the physical and chemical breakdown of large food particles into simple nutrient molecules like glucose, triglycerides, and amino acids. These simple nutrient molecules are absorbed from the intestines and circulated throughout the body by the cardiovascular system. They are used for growth and repair of organs and tissues. Any food that cannot be digested or absorbed by the body is eliminated from the gastrointestinal system as a solid waste.

Oral Cavity

cheeks	**saliva** (suh-LYE-vah)
gingiva (JIN-jih-veh)	**taste buds**
gums	**teeth**
lips	**tongue**
palate (PAL-at)	**uvula** (YU-vyu-lah)

Digestion begins when food enters the mouth and is mechanically broken up by the chewing movements of the **teeth.** The muscular **tongue** moves the food within the mouth and mixes it with **saliva** (see Figure 8.1 ■). Saliva contains digestive enzymes to break down carbohydrates and slippery lubricants to make food easier to swallow. **Taste buds,** found on the surface of the tongue, can distinguish the bitter, sweet, sour, and salty flavors in our food. The roof of the oral cavity is known as the **palate** and is subdivided into the hard palate (the bony anterior portion) and the soft palate (the flexible posterior portion). Hanging down from the posterior edge of the soft palate is the **uvula.** The uvula serves two important functions. First, it has a role in speech production, and second, it is the location of the gag reflex. This reflex is stimulated when food enters the throat without swallowing (e.g., laughing with food in your mouth). It is important because swallowing also results in the epiglottis covering the larynx to prevent food from entering the lungs (see Figure 8.2 ■). The **cheeks** form the

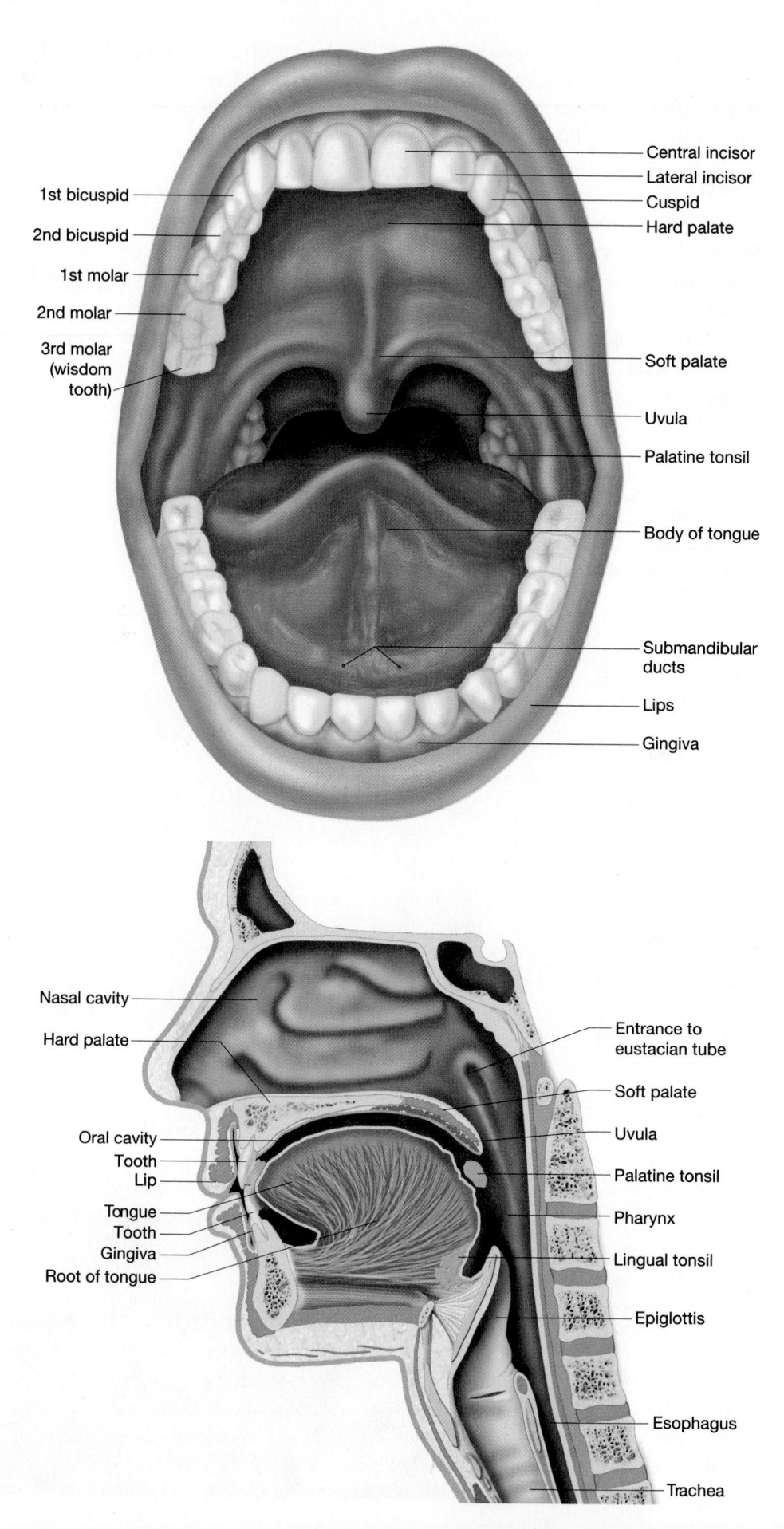

Figure 8.1 Anatomy of structures of the oral cavity.

Central incisor
Lateral incisor
Cuspid
Hard palate
1st bicuspid
2nd bicuspid
1st molar
2nd molar
3rd molar (wisdom tooth)
Soft palate
Uvula
Palatine tonsil
Body of tongue
Submandibular ducts
Lips
Gingiva

Figure 8.2 Structures of the oral cavity, pharynx, and esophagus.

Nasal cavity
Hard palate
Oral cavity
Tooth
Lip
Tongue
Tooth
Gingiva
Root of tongue
Entrance to eustacian tube
Soft palate
Uvula
Palatine tonsil
Pharynx
Lingual tonsil
Epiglottis
Esophagus
Trachea

lateral walls of this cavity and the **lips** are the anterior opening. The entire oral cavity is lined with mucous membrane, a portion of which forms the **gums,** or **gingiva,** that combine with connective tissue to cover the jaw bone and seal off the teeth in their bony sockets.

Teeth

bicuspids (bye-CUSS-pids)	**incisors** (in-SIGH-zors)
canines (KAY-nines)	**molars** (MOH-lars)
cementum (see-MEN-tum)	**periodontal ligaments** (pair-ee-on-DON-tal)
crown	**permanent teeth**
cuspids (CUSS-pids)	**premolars** (pree-MOH-lars)
deciduous teeth (dee-SID-yoo-us)	**pulp cavity**
dentin (DEN-tin)	**root**
enamel	**root canal**

Teeth are an important part of the first stage of digestion. The teeth in the front of the mouth bite, tear, or cut food into small pieces. These cutting teeth include the **cuspids** (or **canines**) and the **incisors** (see Figure 8.3 ■). The remaining posterior teeth grind and crush food into even finer pieces. These grinding teeth include the

---

MED TERM TIP

There are three different molars, simply referred to as the first, second, or third molars. However, the third molar has a more common name, the wisdom tooth. Not every person ever forms all four wisdom teeth. Unfortunately, most people do not have enough room in their jaws for the third molars to properly erupt through the gum, a condition requiring surgical removal of the third molar, referred to as an *impacted wisdom tooth.*

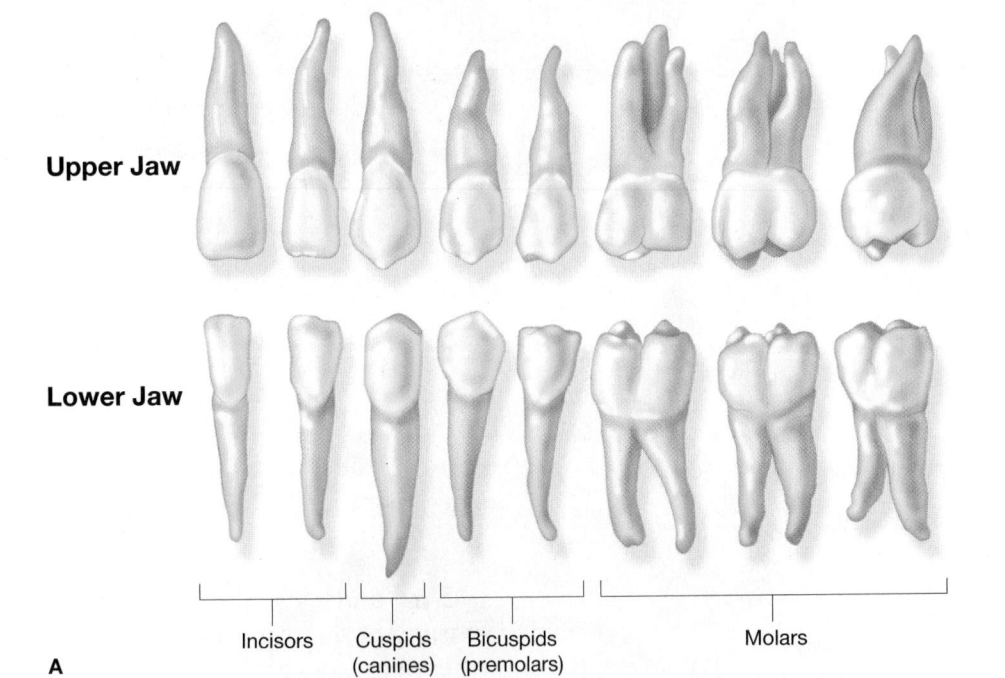

Upper Jaw

Lower Jaw

Incisors   Cuspids (canines)   Bicuspids (premolars)   Molars

A

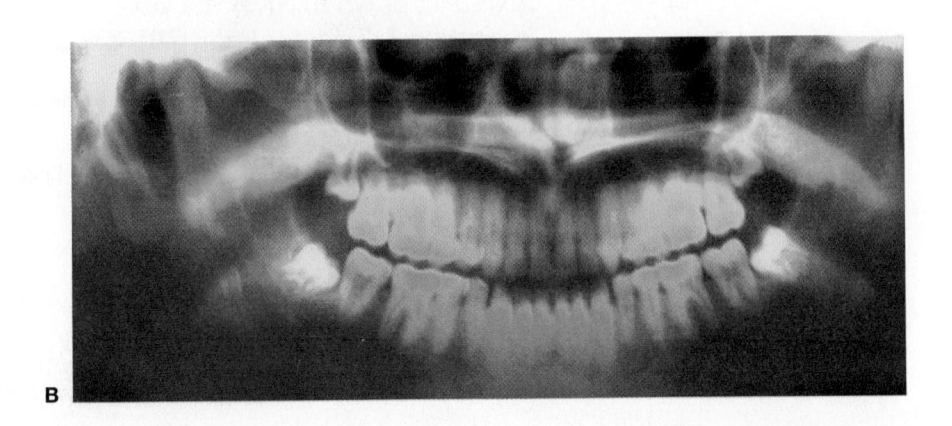

B

■ **Figure 8.3**   (A) The name and shape of the adult teeth. These teeth represent those found in the right side of the mouth. Those of the left side would be a mirror image. The incisors and cuspids are cutting teeth. The bicuspids and molars are grinding teeth. (B) Color-enhanced X-ray of all teeth. Note the four wisdom teeth (third molars) that have not erupted. *(Photo Researchers, Inc.)*

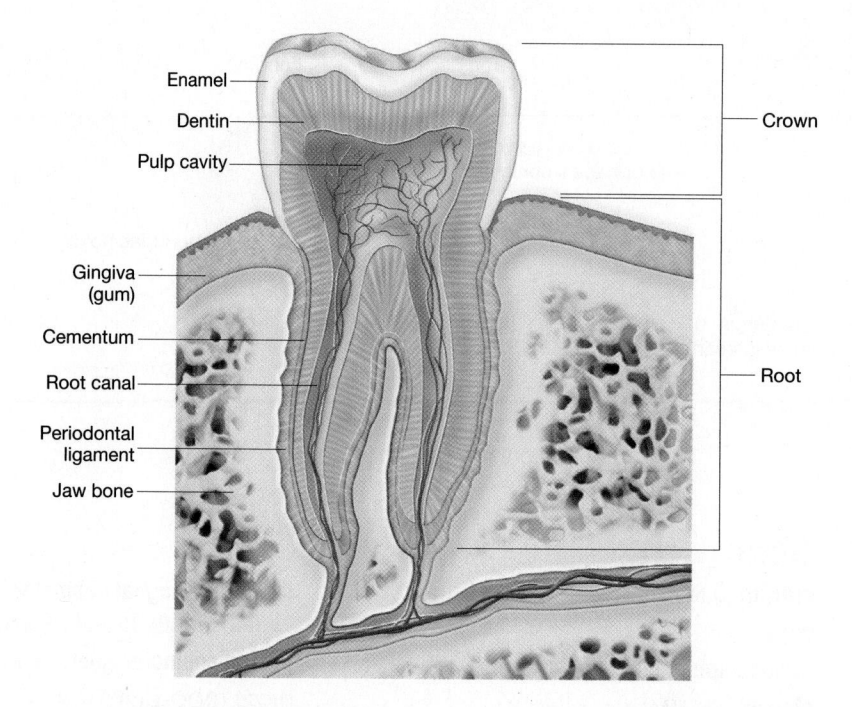

Enamel
Dentin
Pulp cavity
Crown

Gingiva (gum)
Cementum
Root canal
Periodontal ligament
Jaw bone
Root

Figure 8.4 An adult tooth, longitudinal view showing internal structures of the crown and root.

bicuspids (or **premolars**) and the **molars.** A tooth can be subdivided into the **crown** and the **root.** The crown is that part of the tooth visible above the gum line; the root is below the gum line. The root is anchored in the bony socket of the jaw by **cementum** and tiny **periodontal ligaments.** The crown of the tooth is covered by a layer of **enamel,** the hardest substance in the body. Under the enamel layer is **dentin,** the substance that makes up the main bulk of the tooth. The hollow interior of a tooth is called the **pulp cavity** in the crown and the **root canal** in the root. These cavities contain soft tissue made up of blood vessels, nerves, and lymph vessels (see Figure 8.4 ■).

Humans have two sets of teeth. The first set, often referred to as baby teeth, are **deciduous teeth.** There are 20 teeth in this set that erupt through the gums between the ages of 6 and 28 months. At approximately 6 years of age, these teeth begin to fall out and are replaced by the 32 **permanent teeth.** This replacement process continues until about 18–20 years of age.

Pharynx

epiglottis (ep-ih-GLOT-iss)   **laryngopharynx**
oropharynx

When food is swallowed, it enters the **oropharynx** and then the **laryngopharynx** (see again Figure 8.2). Remember from your study of the respiratory system in Chapter 7 that air is also traveling through these portions of the pharynx. The **epiglottis** is a cartilaginous flap that folds down to cover the larynx and trachea so that food is prevented from entering the respiratory tract and instead continues into the esophagus.

Esophagus

peristalsis (pair-ih-STALL-sis)

The esophagus is a muscular tube of about 10 inches long in adults. Food entering the esophagus is carried through the thoracic cavity and diaphragm and into the abdominal cavity where it enters the stomach (see Figure 8.5 ■). Food is propelled along the esophagus by wavelike muscular contractions called **peristalsis.** In fact, peristalsis works to push food through the entire gastrointestinal tract.

MED TERM TIP

The combining form *dent/o* means teeth. Hence we have terms such as dentist and dentistry. The combining form *odont/o* also means teeth and when combined with *orth/o*, which means straight, we have the specialty of *orthodontics*, or straightening teeth.

MED TERM TIP

It takes about 10 seconds for swallowed food to reach the stomach.

Figure 8.5 The stomach. Longitudinal view showing regions and internal structures.

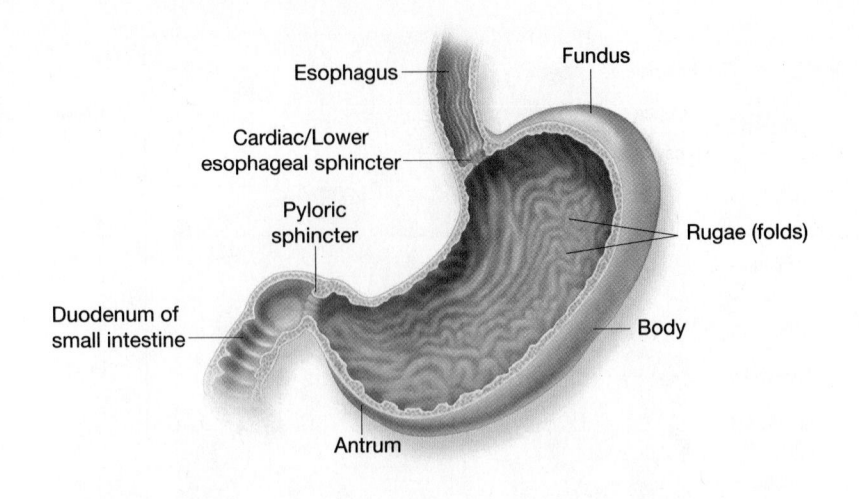

Stomach

antrum (AN-trum)
body
cardiac sphincter (CAR-dee-ak / SFINGK-ter)
chyme (KIGHM)
fundus (FUN-dus)
hydrochloric acid

lower esophageal sphincter
    (eh-soff-ah-JEE-al / SFINGK-ter)
pyloric sphincter (pigh-LOR-ik / SFINGK-ter)
rugae (ROO-gay)
sphincters (SFINGK-ters)

The stomach, a J-shaped muscular organ that acts as a bag or sac to collect and churn food with digestive juices, is composed of three parts: the **fundus** or upper region, the **body** or main portion, and the **antrum** or lower region (see again Figure 8.5). The folds in the lining of the stomach are called **rugae.** When the stomach fills with food, the rugae stretch out and disappear. **Hydrochloric acid** (HCl) is secreted by glands in the mucous membrane lining of the stomach. Food mixes with hydrochloric acid and other gastric juices to form a liquid mixture called **chyme,** which then passes through the remaining portion of the digestive system.

Entry into and exit from the stomach is controlled by muscular valves called **sphincters.** These valves open and close to ensure that food can only move forward down the gut tube. The **cardiac sphincter,** named for its proximity to the heart, is located between the esophagus and the fundus; also called the **lower esophageal sphincter** (LES), it keeps food from flowing backward into the esophagus.

The antrum tapers off into the **pyloric sphincter,** which regulates the passage of food into the small intestine. Only a small amount of the chyme is allowed to enter the small intestine with each opening of the sphincter for two important reasons. First, the small intestine is much narrower than the stomach and cannot hold as much as the stomach can. Second, the chyme is highly acidic and must be thoroughly neutralized as it leaves the stomach.

MED TERM TIP

It is easier to remember the function of the pyloric sphincter when you note that *pylor/o* means "gatekeeper." This gatekeeper controls the forward movement of food. Sphincters are rings of muscle that can be opened and closed to control entry and exit from hollow organs like the stomach, colon, and bladder.

Small Intestine

duodenum
    (doo-oh-DEE-num / doo-OD-eh-num)
ileocecal valve (ill-ee-oh-SEE-kal)

ileum (ILL-ee-um)
jejunum (jee-JOO-num)

MED TERM TIP

Word Watch: Be careful not to confuse the word root *ile/o* meaning "ileum," a portion of the small intestines, and *ili/o* meaning "ilium," a pelvic bone.

The small intestine, or small bowel, is the major site of digestion and absorption of nutrients from food. It is located between the pyloric sphincter and the colon (see Figure 8.6 ■). Because the small intestine is concerned with absorption of food products, an abnormality in this organ can cause malnutrition. The small intestine, with an average length of 20 feet, is the longest portion of the alimentary canal and has three sections: the **duodenum,** the **jejunum,** and the **ileum.**

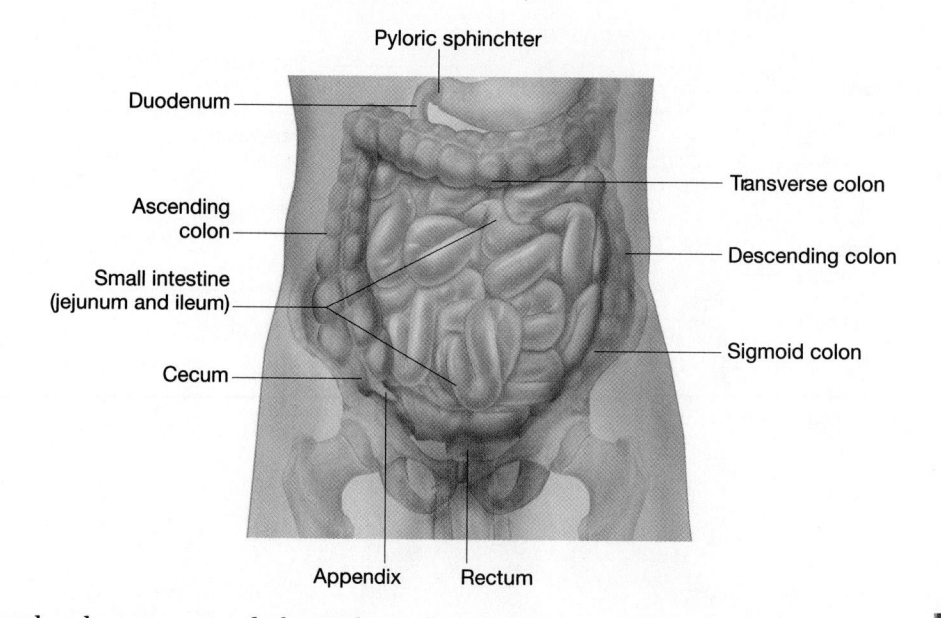

Pyloric sphinchter

Duodenum

Ascending colon

Small intestine (jejunum and ileum)

Cecum

Transverse colon

Descending colon

Sigmoid colon

Appendix   Rectum

■ Figure 8.6   The small intestine. Anterior view of the abdominopelvic cavity illustrating how the three sections of small intestine— duodenum, jejunum, and ileum—begin at the pyloric sphincter and end at the colon, but are not arranged in an orderly fashion.

- The duodenum extends from the pyloric sphincter to the jejunum, and is about 10–12 inches long. Digestion is completed in the duodenum after the liquid chyme from the stomach is mixed with digestive juices from the pancreas and gallbladder.
- The jejunum, or middle portion, extends from the duodenum to the ileum and is about 8 feet long.
- The ileum is the last portion of the small intestine and extends from the jejunum to the colon. At 12 feet in length, it is the longest portion of the small intestine. The ileum connects to the colon with a sphincter called the **ileocecal valve.**

Colon

anal sphincter (AY-nal / SFINGK-ter)

anus (AY-nus)

ascending colon

cecum (SEE-kum)

defecation

descending colon

feces (FEE-seez)

rectum (REK-tum)

sigmoid colon (SIG-moyd)

transverse colon

vermiform appendix (VER-mih-form / ah-PEN-diks)

Fluid that remains after the complete digestion and absorption of nutrients in the small intestine enters the colon or large intestine (see Figure 8.7 ■). Most of this fluid is water that is reabsorbed into the body. The material that remains after absorption is solid waste called **feces** (or stool). This is the product evacuated in bowel movements (BM).

The colon is approximately 5 feet long and extends from the **cecum** to the **anus**. The cecum is a pouch or saclike area in the first 2–3 inches at the beginning of the colon. The **vermiform appendix** is a small worm-shaped outgrowth at the end of the cecum. The remaining colon consists of the **ascending colon, transverse colon, descending colon,** and **sigmoid colon.** The ascending colon on the right side extends from the cecum to the lower border of the liver. The transverse colon begins where the ascending colon leaves off and moves horizontally across the upper abdomen toward the spleen. The descending colon then travels down the left side of the body to where the sigmoid colon begins. The sigmoid colon curves in an S-shape back to the midline of the body and ends at the **rectum.** The rectum, where feces is stored, leads into the anus, which contains the **anal sphincter.** This sphincter consists of rings of voluntary and involuntary muscles to control the evacuation of feces or **defecation.**

MED TERM TIP

We can survive without a portion of the small intestine. For example, in cases of cancer, much of the small intestine and/or colon may have to be removed. The surgeon then creates an opening between the remaining intestine and the abdominal wall. The combining form for the section of intestine connected to the abdominal wall and the suffix -*ostomy* are used to describe this procedure. For example, if a person has a *jejunostomy,* the jejunum is connected to the abdominal wall and the ileum (and remainder of the gut tube) has been removed.

MED TERM TIP

The term *colon* refers to the large intestine. However, you should be aware that many people use it incorrectly as a general term referring to the entire intestinal system, both small and large intestines.

■ **Figure 8.7**   The regions of the colon beginning with the cecum and ending at the anus.

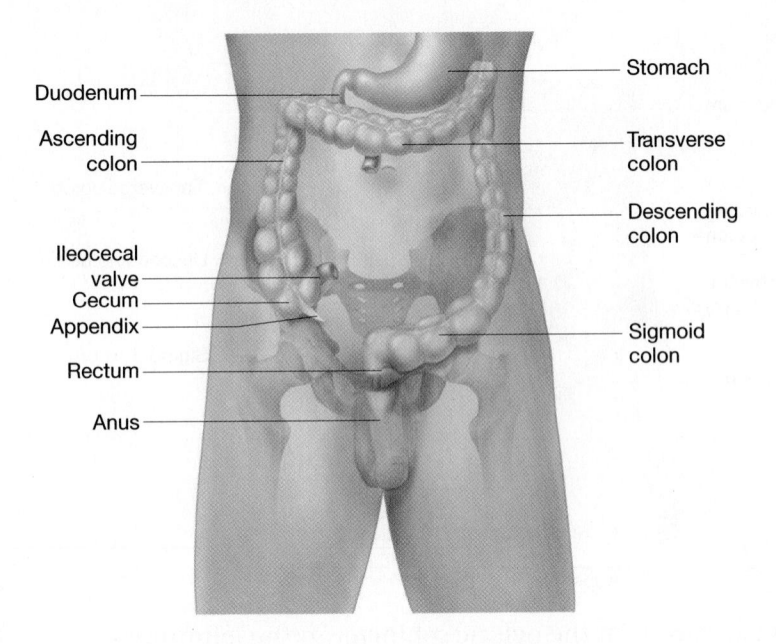

Accessory Organs of the Digestive System

As described earlier, the accessory organs of the digestive system are the salivary glands, the liver, the pancreas, and the gallbladder. In general, these organs function by producing much of the digestive fluids and enzymes necessary for the chemical breakdown of food. Each is attached to the gut tube by a duct.

Salivary Glands

amylase (AM-ill-ace)

bolus

parotid glands (pah-ROT-id)

sublingual glands (sub-LING-gwal)

submandibular glands
   (sub-man-DIB-yoo-lar)

Salivary glands in the oral cavity produce saliva. This very watery and slick fluid allows food to be swallowed with less danger of choking. Saliva mixed with food in the mouth forms a **bolus,** chewed food that is ready to swallow. Saliva also contains the digestive enzyme **amylase** that begins the digestion of carbohydrates. There are three pairs of salivary glands. The **parotid glands** are in front of the ears, and the **submandibular glands** and **sublingual glands** are in the floor of the mouth (see Figure 8.8 ■).

■ **Figure 8.8**   The salivary glands, parotid, sublingual, and submandibular. This image shows the position of each gland and its duct emptying into the oral cavity.

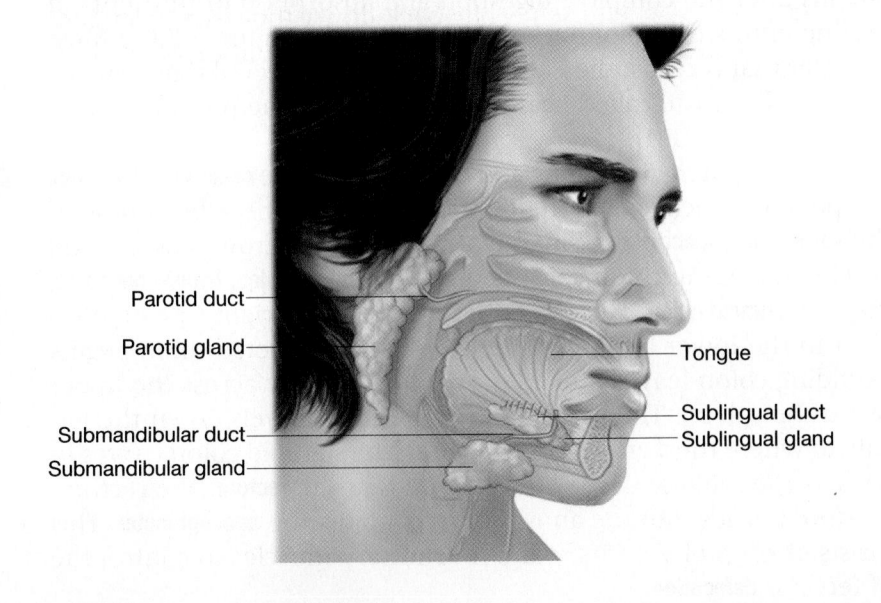

Liver

bile (BYE-al)   **emulsification** (ee-mull-sih-fih-KAY-shun)

The liver, a large organ located in the right upper quadrant of the abdomen, has several functions including processing the nutrients absorbed by the intestines, detoxifying harmful substances in the body, and producing **bile** (see Figure 8.9 ■). Bile is important for the digestion of fats and lipids because it breaks up large fat globules into much smaller droplets, making them easier to digest in the watery environment inside the intestines. The process is called **emulsification.**

MED TERM TIP

The liver weighs about 4 pounds and has so many important functions that people cannot live without it. It has become a major transplant organ. The liver is also able to regenerate itself. You can lose more than half of your liver, and it will regrow.

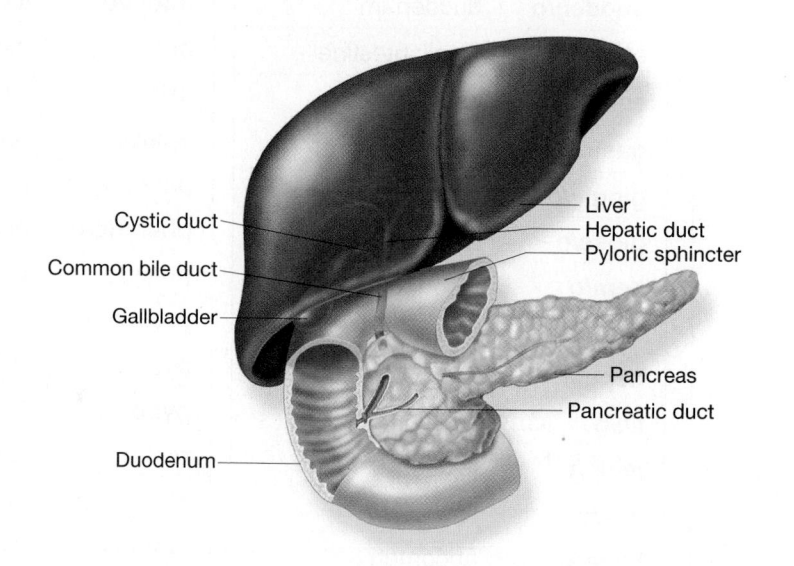

■ **Figure 8.9** The accessory organs of the digestive system: the liver, gallbladder, and pancreas. Image shows the relationship of these three organs and their ducts to the duodenum.

Gallbladder

common bile duct   **cystic duct** (SIS-tik)

hepatic duct (hep-PAT-tik)

Bile produced by the liver is stored in the gallbladder (GB). As the liver produces bile, it travels down the **hepatic duct** and up the **cystic duct** into the gallbladder (see again Figure 8.9). In response to the presence of fat in the chyme, the muscular wall of the gallbladder contracts and sends bile back down the cystic duct and into the **common bile duct** (CBD), which carries bile to the duodenum where it is able to emulsify the fat in chyme.

Pancreas

buffers   **pancreatic duct** (pan-kree-AT-ik)

pancreatic enzymes (pan-kree-AT-ik / EN-zimes)

The pancreas, connected to the duodenum by the **pancreatic duct,** produces two important secretions for digestion: **buffers** and **pancreatic enzymes** (see again Figure 8.9). Buffers neutralize acidic chyme that has just left the stomach, and pancreatic enzymes chemically digest carbohydrates, fats, and proteins. The pancreas is also an endocrine gland that produces the hormones insulin and glucagon, which play a role in regulating the level of glucose in the blood and are discussed in further detail in Chapter 11.

■ Terminology

Word Parts Used to Build Digestive System Terms

The following lists contain the combining forms, suffixes, and prefixes used to build terms in the remaining sections of this chapter.

Combining Forms

an/o	anus	**diverticul/o**	pouch	**nas/o**	nose
append/o	appendix	**duoden/o**	duodenum	**odont/o**	tooth
appendic/o	appendix	**enter/o**	small intestine	**or/o**	mouth
bar/o	weight	**esophag/o**	esophagus	**orth/o**	straight
bucc/o	cheek	**gastr/o**	stomach	**palat/o**	palate
carcin/o	cancer	**gingiv/o**	gums	**pancreat/o**	pancreas
cec/o	cecum	**gloss/o**	tongue	**pharyng/o**	pharynx
chol/e	bile	**hem/o**	blood	**polyp/o**	polyp
cholangi/o	bile duct	**hemat/o**	blood	**proct/o**	anus and rectum
cholecyst/o	gallbladder	**hepat/o**	liver	**pylor/o**	pylorus
choledoch/o	common bile duct	**ile/o**	ileum	**pyr/o**	fire
cirrh/o	yellow	**jejun/o**	jejunum	**rect/o**	rectum
col/o	colon	**labi/o**	lip	**sialaden/o**	salivary gland
colon/o	colon	**lapar/o**	abdomen	**sigmoid/o**	sigmoid colon
cutane/o	skin	**lingu/o**	tongue	**ven/o**	vein
dent/o	tooth	**lith/o**	stone		

Suffixes

-al	pertaining to	**-itis**	inflammation	**-pexy**	surgical fixation
-algia	pain	**-lithiasis**	condition of stones	**-phagia**	eating
-centesis	process of removing fluid	**-logy**	study of	**-plasty**	surgical repair
-eal	pertaining to	**-oma**	tumor	**-plegia**	paralysis
-ectomy	surgical removal	**-orexia**	appetite	**-prandial**	a meal
-emesis	vomiting	**-osis**	abnormal condition	**-ptosis**	drooping
-gram	record	**-ostomy**	create a new opening	**-scope**	instrument to view
-graphy	process of recording	**-otomy**	cutting into	**-scopy**	process of viewing
-ic	pertaining to	**-ous**	pertaining to	**-tic**	pertaining to
-istry	specialty of	**-pepsia**	digestion	**-tripsy**	surgical crushing

Prefixes

a-	without
an-	without
anti-	against
brady-	slow
dys-	abnormal
endo-	within

hyper-	excessive
hypo-	under
intra-	within
per-	through
peri-	around

poly-	many
post-	after
retro-	backwards
sub-	under
trans-	across

Anatomical Terms

TERM	WORD PARTS	DEFINITION
anal	an/o = anus -al = pertaining to	Pertaining to the anus. **MED TERM TIP** Word Watch: Be careful when using the combining form *an/o* meaning "anus" and the prefix *an* meaning "none."
buccal (BYOO-kal)	bucc/o = cheek -al = pertaining to	Pertaining to the cheeks.
buccolabial (BYOO-koh-labe-ee-all)	bucc/o = cheek labi/o = lip -al = pertaining to	Pertaining to the cheeks and lips.
cecal (SEE-kal)	cec/o = cecum -al = pertaining to	Pertaining to the cecum.
cholecystic (koh-lee-SIS-tik)	cholecyst/o = gallbladder -ic = pertaining to	Pertaining to the gallbladder.
colonic (koh-LON-ik)	colon/o = colon -ic = pertaining to	Pertaining to the colon.
colorectal (kohl-oh-REK-tall)	col/o = colon rect/o = rectum -al = pertaining to	Pertaining to the colon and rectum.
dental (DENT-all)	dent/o = tooth -al = pertaining to	Pertaining to the teeth.
duodenal (duo-DEN-all / do-ODD-in-all)	duoden/o = duodenum -al = pertaining to	Pertaining to the duodenum.
enteric (en-TARE-ik)	enter/o = small intestine -ic = pertaining to	Pertaining to the small intestine.
esophageal (eh-soff-ah-JEE-al)	esophag/o = esophagus -eal = pertaining to	Pertaining to the esophagus.
gastric (GAS-trik)	gastr/o = stomach -ic = pertaining to	Pertaining to the stomach.
gingival (JIN-jih-vul)	gingiv/o = gums -al = pertaining to	Pertaining to the gums.
glossal (GLOSS-all)	gloss/o = tongue -al = pertaining to	Pertaining to the tongue.

Anatomical Terms (continued)

TERM	WORD PARTS	DEFINITION
hepatic (hep-AT-ik)	hepat/o = liver -ic = pertaining to	Pertaining to the liver.
hypoglossal (high-poe-GLOSS-all)	hypo- = under gloss/o = tongue -al = pertaining to	Pertaining to under the tongue.
ileal (ILL-ee-all)	ile/o = ileum -al = pertaining to	Pertaining to the ileum.
jejunal (jih-JUNE-all)	jejun/o = jejunum -al = pertaining to	Pertaining to the jejunum.
nasogastric (nay-zoh-GAS-trik)	nas/o = nose gastr/o = stomach -ic = pertaining to	Pertaining to the nose and stomach.
oral (OR-ral)	or/o = mouth -al = pertaining to	Pertaining to the mouth.
pancreatic (pan-kree-AT-ik)	pancreat/o = pancreas -ic = pertaining to	Pertaining to the pancreas.
pharyngeal (fair-in-JEE-all)	pharyng/o = pharynx -eal = pertaining to	Pertaining to the pharynx.
pyloric (pie-LORE-ik)	pylor/o = pylorus -ic = pertaining to	Pertaining to the pylorus.
rectal (RECK-tall)	rect/o = rectum -al = pertaining to	Pertaining to the rectum.
sigmoidal (sig-MOYD-all)	sigmoid/o = sigmoid colon -al = pertaining to	Pertaining to the sigmoid colon.
sublingual (sub-LING-gwal)	sub- = under lingu/o = tongue -al = pertaining to	Pertaining to under the tongue.

Pathology

TERM	WORD PARTS	DEFINITION
Medical Specialties		
dentistry	dent/o = tooth -istry = specialty of	Branch of healthcare involved with the prevention, diagnosis, and treatment of conditions involving the teeth, jaw, and mouth. Practitioner is a *dentist*.
gastroenterology (gas-troh-en-ter-ALL-oh-jee)	gastr/o = stomach enter/o = small intestine -logy = study of	Branch of medicine involved in diagnosis and treatment of diseases and disorders of the digestive system. Physician is a *gastroenterologist*.
oral surgery	or/o = mouth -al = pertaining to	Branch of dentistry that uses surgical means to treat dental conditions. Specialist is an *oral surgeon*.

◾ Pathology *(continued)*

TERM	WORD PARTS	DEFINITION
orthodontics (or-thoh-DON-tiks)	orth/o = straight odont/o = tooth -ic = pertaining to	Branch of dentistry concerned with correction of problems with tooth alignment. Specialist is an *orthodontist*.
periodontics (pair-ee-oh-DON-tiks)	peri- = around odont/o = tooth -ic = pertaining to	Branch of dentistry concerned with treating conditions involving the gums and tissues surrounding the teeth. Specialist is a *periodontist*.
proctology (prok-TOL-oh-jee)	proct/o = anus and rectum -logy = study of	Branch of medicine involved in diagnosis and treatment of diseases and disorders of the anus and rectum. Physician is a *proctologist*.

Signs and Symptoms

TERM	WORD PARTS	DEFINITION
anorexia (an-oh-REK-see-ah)	an- = without -orexia = appetite	General term meaning loss of appetite that may accompany other conditions. Also used to refer to *anorexia nervosa,* which is an eating disorder involving the refusal to eat.
aphagia (ah-FAY-jee-ah)	a- = without -phagia = eating	Being unable to swallow or eat.
ascites (ah-SIGH-teez)		Collection or accumulation of fluid in the peritoneal cavity.
bradypepsia (brad-ee-PEP-see-ah)	brady- = slow -pepsia = digestion	Having a slow digestive system.
cachexia (ka-KEK-see-ah)		Loss of weight and generalized wasting that occurs during a chronic disease.
cholecystalgia (koh-lee-sis-TAL-jee-ah)	cholecyst/o = gallbladder -algia = pain	Having gallbladder pain.
constipation (kon-stih-PAY-shun)		Experiencing difficulty in defecation or infrequent defecation.
dentalgia (dent-AL-gee-ah)	dent/o = tooth -algia = pain	Tooth pain.
diarrhea (dye-ah-REE-ah)		Passing of frequent, watery, or bloody bowel movements. Usually accompanies gastrointestinal (GI) disorders.
dysorexia (dis-oh-REKS-ee-ah)	dys- = abnormal -orexia = appetite	Abnormal appetite; usually a diminished appetite.
dyspepsia (dis-PEP-see-ah)	dys- = difficult -pepsia = digestion	"Upset stomach"; indigestion.
dysphagia (dis-FAY-jee-ah)	dys- = abnormal -phagia = eating	Having difficulty swallowing or eating.
emesis (EM-eh-sis)		Vomiting.
gastralgia (gas-TRAL-jee-ah)	gastr/o = stomach -algia = pain	Stomach pain.
hematemesis (hee-mah-TEM-eh-sis)	hemat/o = blood -emesis = vomiting	Vomiting blood.
hematochezia (he-mat-oh-KEY-zee-ah)	hemat/o = blood	Passing bright red blood in the stools.

Pathology *(continued)*

TERM	WORD PARTS	DEFINITION
hyperemesis (high-per-EM-eh-sis)	hyper- = excessive -emesis = vomiting	Excessive vomiting.
jaundice (JAWN-diss)		Yellow cast to the skin, mucous membranes, and the whites of the eyes caused by the deposit of bile pigment from too much bilirubin in the blood. Bilirubin is a waste product produced when worn-out red blood cells are broken down. May be a symptom of a disorder such as gallstones blocking the common bile duct or carcinoma of the liver. Also called *icterus*.
melena (me-LEE-nah)		Passage of dark tarry stools. Color is the result of digestive enzymes working on blood in the gastrointestinal tract.
nausea (NAW-see-ah)	**MED TERM TIP** The term *nausea* comes from the Greek word for "seasickness."	Urge to vomit.
obesity		Body weight that is above a healthy level. A person whose weight interferes with normal activity and body function has *morbid obesity*.
polyphagia (pall-ee-FAY-jee-ah)	poly- = many -phagia = eating	Excessive eating; eating too much.
postprandial (post-PRAN-dee-all)	post- = after -prandial = a meal	After a meal.
pyrosis (pie-ROW-sis)	pyr/o = fire -osis = abnormal condition	Pain and burning sensation usually caused by stomach acid splashing up into the esophagus. Commonly called *heartburn*.
regurgitation (ree-gur-jih-TAY-shun)		Return of fluids and solids from the stomach into the mouth.
Oral Cavity		
aphthous ulcers (AF-thus)		Painful ulcers in the mouth of unknown cause. Commonly called *canker sores*.
cleft lip (CLEFT)		Congenital anomaly in which the upper lip and jaw bone fail to fuse in the midline, leaving an open gap. Often seen along with a cleft palate. Corrected with surgery.
cleft palate (CLEFT / PAL-at)		Congenital anomaly in which the roof of the mouth has a split or fissure. Corrected with surgery.
dental caries (KAIR-eez)	dent/o = tooth -al = pertaining to	Gradual decay and disintegration of teeth caused by bacteria; may lead to abscessed teeth. Commonly called a *tooth cavity*.
gingivitis (jin-jih-VIGH-tis)	gingiv/o = gums -itis = inflammation	Inflammation of the gums.

Pathology *(continued)*

TERM	WORD PARTS	DEFINITION
herpes labialis (HER-peez / lay-bee-AL-iz)	labi/o = lip	Infection of the lip by the herpes simplex virus type 1 (HSV-1). Also called *fever blisters* or *cold sores.*
periodontal disease (pair-ee-oh-DON-tal)	peri- = around odont/o = tooth -al = pertaining to	Disease of the supporting structures of the teeth, including the gums and bones; the most common cause of tooth loss.
sialadenitis (sigh-al-add-eh-NIGH-tis)	sialaden/o = salivary gland -itis = inflammation	Inflammation of a salivary gland.
Pharynx and Esophagus		
esophageal varices (eh-soff-ah-JEE-al / VAIR-ih-seez)	esophag/o = esophagus -eal = pertaining to	Enlarged and swollen varicose veins in the lower end of the esophagus. If these rupture, serious hemorrhage results; often related to liver disease.
gastroesophageal reflux disease (GERD) (gas-troh-ee-sof-ah-GEE-all / REE-fluks)	gastr/o = stomach esophag/o = esophagus -eal = pertaining to	Acid from the stomach flows backward up into the esophagus causing inflammation and pain.
pharyngoplegia (fair-in-goh-PLEE-jee-ah)	pharyng/o = pharynx -plegia = paralysis	Paralysis of the throat muscles.
Stomach		
gastric carcinoma (GAS-trik / car-si-NOH-mah)	gastr/o = stomach -ic = pertaining to	Cancerous tumor in the stomach.
gastritis (gas-TRY-tis)	gastr/o = stomach -itis = inflammation	Stomach inflammation.
gastroenteritis (gas-troh-en-ter-EYE-tis)	gastr/o = stomach enter/o = small intestines -itis = inflammation	Inflammation of stomach and small intestine.
hiatal hernia (high-AY-tal / HER-nee-ah)	-al = pertaining to	Protrusion of the stomach through the diaphragm (also called a *diaphragmatocele*) and extending into the thoracic cavity; gastroesophageal reflux disease is a common symptom.

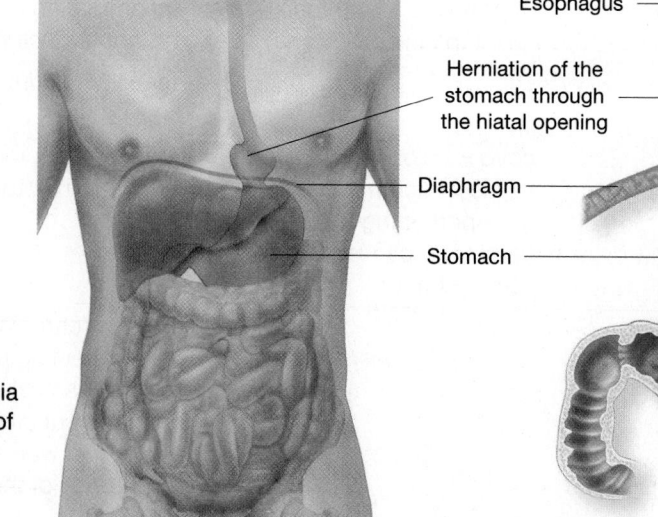

Esophagus

Herniation of the stomach through the hiatal opening

Diaphragm

Stomach

■ **Figure 8.10** A hiatal hernia or diaphragmatocele. A portion of the stomach protrudes through the diaphragm into the thoracic cavity.

Pathology *(continued)*

TERM	WORD PARTS	DEFINITION
peptic ulcer disease (PUD) (PEP-tik / ULL-sir)	-ic = pertaining to	Ulcer occurring in the lower portion of the esophagus, stomach, and/or duodenum; thought to be caused by the acid of gastric juices. Initial damage to the protective lining of the stomach may be caused by a *Helicobacter pylori* (*H. pylori*) bacterial infection. If the ulcer extends all the way through the wall of the stomach, it is called a *perforated ulcer,* which requires immediate surgery to repair.

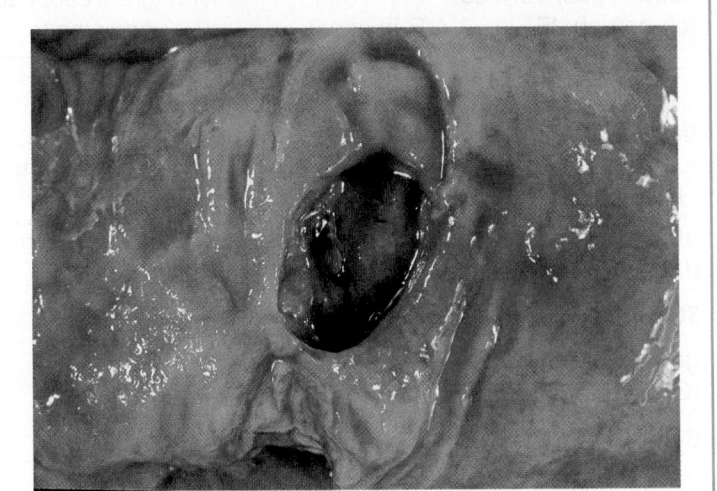

Gastric juices are released into the stomach

Gastric juices (acidic)

Duodenal ulcer

Acid secretions further break down the lining of the stomach, forming an ulcer

Gastric ulcer

A

B

■ **Figure 8.11**   (A) Figure illustrating the location and appearance of a peptic ulcer in both the stomach and the duodenum; (B) photomicrograph illustrating a gastric ulcer. *(Dr. E. Walker/Science Photo Library/Photo Researchers, Inc.)*

Small Intestine and Colon

anal fistula (FIH-styoo-lah)	-al = pertaining to	Abnormal tube-like passage from the surface around the anal opening directly into the rectum.
appendicitis (ah-pen-dih-SIGH-tis)	appendic/o = appendix -itis = inflammation	Inflammation of the appendix; may require an *appendectomy.*
bowel incontinence (in-CON-tih-nence)		Inability to control defecation.
colorectal carcinoma (kohl-oh-REK-tall / car-ci-NOH-mah)	col/o = colon rect/o = rectum -al = pertaining to carcin/o = cancer -oma = tumor	Cancerous tumor along the length of the colon and rectum.
Crohn's disease (KROHNZ)		Form of chronic inflammatory bowel disease affecting primarily the ileum and/or colon. Also called *regional ileitis.* This autoimmune condition affects all the layers of the bowel wall and results in scarring and thickening of the gut wall.

Pathology (continued)

TERM	WORD PARTS	DEFINITION
diverticulitis (dye-ver-tik-yoo-LYE-tis)	diverticul/o = pouch -itis = inflammation	Inflammation of a *diverticulum* (an out-pouching off the gut), especially in the colon. Inflammation often results when food becomes within the pouch.

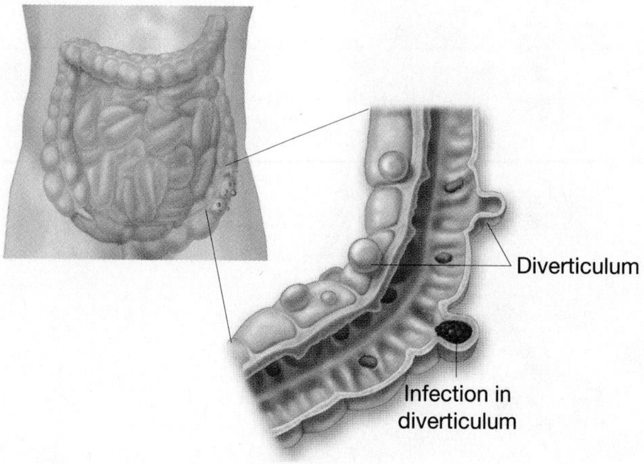

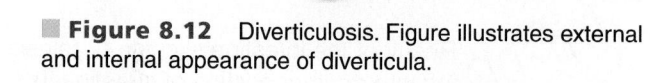

Figure 8.12 Diverticulosis. Figure illustrates external and internal appearance of diverticula.

TERM	WORD PARTS	DEFINITION
diverticulosis (dye-ver-tik-yoo-LOW-sis)	diverticul/o = pouch -osis = abnormal condition	Condition of having diverticula (outpouches off the gut). May lead to *diverticulitis* if one becomes inflamed.
dysentery (dis-in-TARE-ee)		Disease characterized by diarrhea, often with mucus and blood, severe abdominal pain, fever, and dehydration. Caused by ingesting food or water contaminated by chemicals, bacteria, protozoans, or parasites.
enteritis (en-ter-EYE-tis)	enter/o = small intestine -itis = inflammation	Inflammation of the small intestines.
hemorrhoids (HEM-oh-roydz)	hem/o = blood	Varicose veins in the rectum and anus.
ileus (ILL-ee-us)		Severe abdominal pain, inability to pass stools, vomiting, and abdominal distension as a result of an intestinal blockage. The blockage can be a physical block such as a tumor or the failure of bowel contents to move forward due to loss of peristalsis (a nonmechanical blockage). May require surgery to reverse the blockage.
inguinal hernia (ING-gwih-nal / HER-nee-ah)	-al = pertaining to	Hernia or protrusion of a loop of small intestines into the inguinal (groin) region through a weak spot in the abdominal muscle wall that develops into a hole. May become *incarcerated* or *strangulated* if the muscle tightens down around the loop of intestines and cuts off its blood flow. See Figure 8.13 ■.

Pathology *(continued)*

TERM	WORD PARTS	DEFINITION

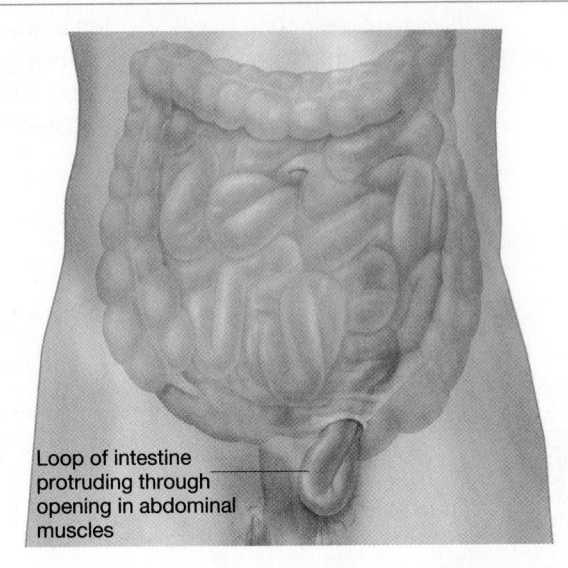

Figure 8.13 An inguinal hernia. A portion of the small intestine is protruding through the abdominal muscles into the groin region.

Loop of intestine protruding through opening in abdominal muscles

---

intussusception
(in-tuh-suh-SEP-shun)

Result of the intestine slipping or telescoping into another section of intestine just below it. More common in children.

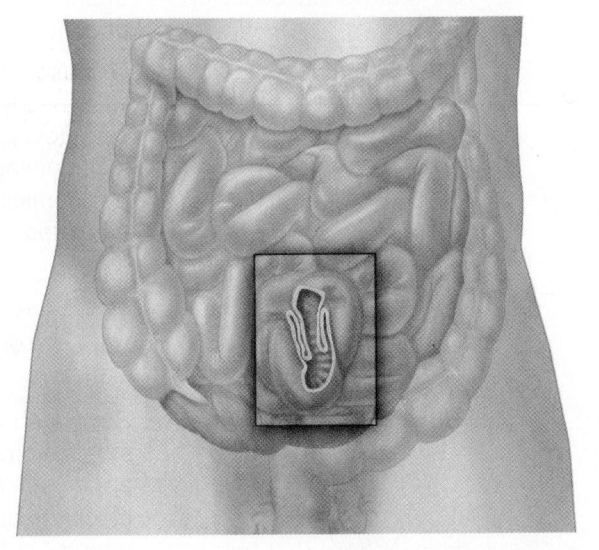

Figure 8.14 Intussusception. A short length of small intestine has telescoped into itself.

---

irritable bowel syndrome (IBS)

Disturbance in the functions of the intestine from unknown causes. Symptoms generally include abdominal discomfort and an alteration in bowel activity. Also called *spastic colon* or *functional bowel syndrome.*

---

polyposis
(pall-ee-POH-sis)

polyp/o = polyp
-osis = abnormal condition

Presence of small tumors, called **polyps**, containing a pedicle or stemlike attachment in the mucous membranes of the large intestine (colon); may be precancerous. See Figure 8.15 ∎.

Pathology *(continued)*

TERM	WORD PARTS	DEFINITION

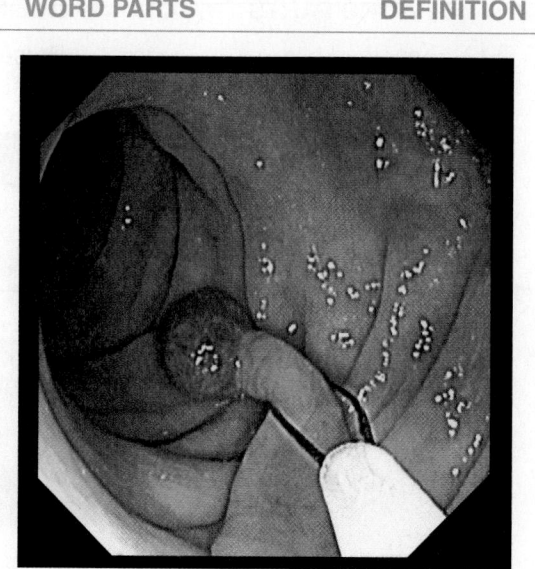

Figure 8.15 Endoscopic view of a polyp in the colon. Note the mushroom-like shape, an enlarged top growing at the end of a stem. It is being removed by means of a wire loop slipped over the polyp and then tightened to cut it off. *(David M. Martin, M.D./ Photo Researchers, Inc.)*

TERM	WORD PARTS	DEFINITION
proctoptosis (prok-top-TOH-sis)	proct/o = rectum and anus -ptosis = drooping	Prolapsed or drooping rectum.
ulcerative colitis (ULL-sir-ah-tiv / koh-LYE-tis)	col/o = colon -itis = inflammation	Chronic inflammatory condition resulting in numerous ulcers formed on the mucous membrane lining of the colon; the cause is unknown. Also known as *inflammatory bowel disease* (IBD).
volvulus (VOL-vyoo-lus)		Condition in which the bowel twists upon itself causing an obstruction; painful and requires immediate surgery.

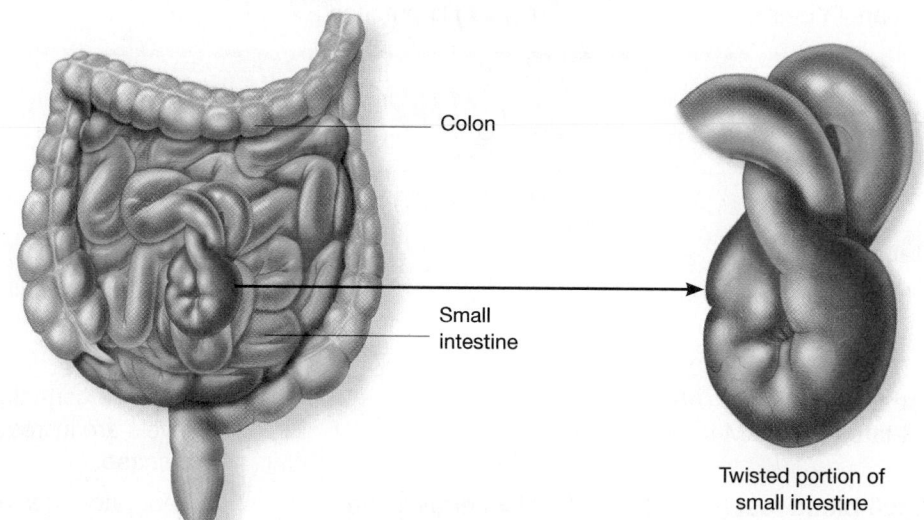

Colon

Small intestine

Twisted portion of small intestine

Figure 8.16 Volvulus. A length of small intestine has twisted around itself, cutting off blood circulation to the twisted loop.

Accessory Organs

TERM	WORD PARTS	DEFINITION
cholecystitis (koh-lee-sis-TYE-tis)	cholecyst/o = gallbladder -itis = inflammation	Inflammation of the gallbladder; most commonly caused by gallstones in the gallbladder or common bile duct that block the flow of bile.

Pathology *(continued)*

TERM	WORD PARTS	DEFINITION
cholelithiasis (koh-lee-lih-THIGH-ah-sis)	chol/e = bile -lithiasis = condition of stones	Presence of gallstones; may or may not cause symptoms such as *cholecystalgia*.

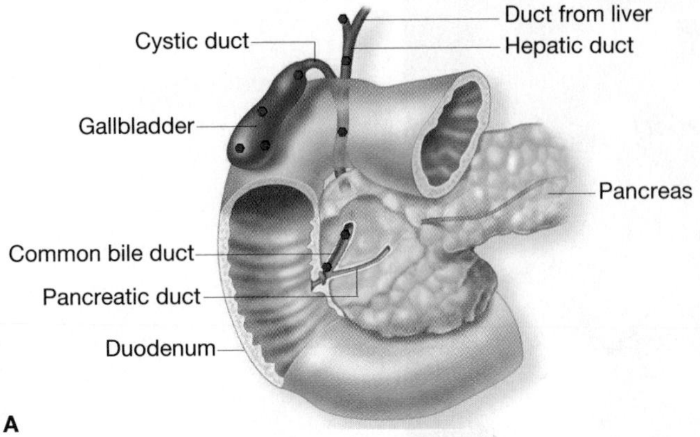

Cystic duct

Gallbladder

Common bile duct

Pancreatic duct

Duodenum

Duct from liver

Hepatic duct

Pancreas

A

B

■ **Figure 8.17**   (A) Common sites for cholelithiasis; (B) a gallbladder specimen with multiple gallstones *(Biophoto Associates/Photo Researchers, Inc.).*

TERM	WORD PARTS	DEFINITION
cirrhosis (sih-ROH-sis)	cirrh/o = yellow -osis = abnormal condition	Chronic disease of the liver associated with failure of the liver to function properly.
hepatitis (hep-ah-TYE-tis)	hepat/o = liver -itis = inflammation	Inflammation of the liver, usually due to a viral infection. Different viruses are transmitted by different routes, such as sexual contact or from exposure to blood or fecally contaminated water or food.
hepatoma (hep-ah-TOH-mah)	hepat/o = liver -oma = tumor	Liver tumor.
pancreatitis (pan-kree-ah-TYE-tis)	pancreat/o = pancreas -itis = inflammation	Inflammation of the pancreas.

Diagnostic Procedures

TERM	WORD PARTS	DEFINITION
Clinical Laboratory Tests		
alanine transaminase (ALT) (AL-ah-neen / trans-AM-in-nase)		Enzyme normally present in the blood. Blood levels are increased in persons with liver disease.
aspartate transaminase (AST) (ass-PAR-tate / trans-AM-in-nase)		Enzyme normally present in the blood. Blood levels are increased in persons with liver disease.
fecal occult blood test (FOBT) (uh-CULT)	-al = pertaining to	Laboratory test on the feces to determine if microscopic amounts of blood are present. Also called *hemoccult* or *stool guaiac*.
ova and parasites (O&P) (OH-vah / PAR-ah-sights)		Laboratory examination of feces with a microscope for the presence of parasites or their eggs.
serum bilirubin (SEE-rum / BILLY-rubin)		Blood test to determine the amount of the waste product bilirubin in the bloodstream. Elevated levels indicate liver disease.

Diagnostic Procedures *(continued)*

TERM	WORD PARTS	DEFINITION
stool culture		Laboratory test of feces to determine if any pathogenic bacteria are present.
Diagnostic Imaging		
bite-wing X-ray		X-ray taken with a part of the film holder held between the teeth and parallel to the teeth.
cholecystogram (koh-lee-SIS-toh-gram)	cholecyst/o = gallbladder -gram = record	X-ray image of the gallbladder.
intravenous cholecystography (in-trah-VEE-nus / koh-lee-sis-TOG-rah-fee)	intra- = within ven/o = vein -ous = pertaining to cholecyst/o = gallbladder -graphy = process of recording	Dye is administered intravenously to the patient allowing for X-ray visualization of the gallbladder and bile ducts.
lower gastrointestinal series (lower GI series)	gastr/o = stomach -al = pertaining to	X-ray image of the colon and rectum is taken after the administration of barium (a radiopaque dye) by enema. Also called a *barium enema (BE)*.

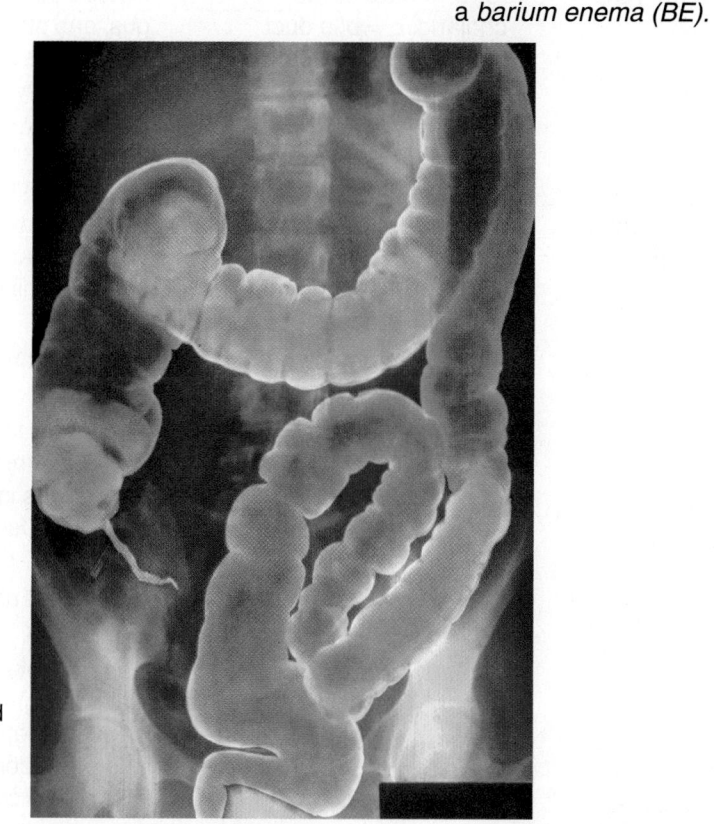

■ **Figure 8.18**   Color-enhanced X-ray of the colon taken during a barium enema. *(CNRI/Science Photo Library/Photo Researchers, Inc.)*

TERM	WORD PARTS	DEFINITION
percutaneous transhepatic cholangiography (PTC) (per-kyoo-TAY-nee-us / trans-heh-PAT-ik / koh-lan-jee-OG-rah-fee)	per- = through cutane/o = skin -ous = pertaining to trans- = across hepat/o = liver -ic = pertaining to cholangi/o = bile duct -graphy = process of recording	Procedure in which contrast medium is injected directly into the liver to visualize the bile ducts. Used to detect obstructions such as gallstones in the common bile duct.

Diagnostic Procedures *(continued)*

TERM	WORD PARTS	DEFINITION
upper gastrointestinal (UGI) **series**	gastr/o = stomach -al = pertaining to	Patient is administered a barium contrast material orally and then X-rays are taken to visualize the esophagus, stomach, and duodenum. Also called a *barium swallow*.
Endoscopic Procedures		
colonoscope (koh-LON-oh-scope)	colon/o = colon -scope = instrument to view	Instrument used to view the colon.
colonoscopy (koh-lon-OSS-koh-pee)	colon/o = colon -scopy = process of viewing	Flexible fiberscope called a *colonoscope* is passed through the anus, rectum, and colon; used to examine the upper portion of the colon. Polyps and small growths can be removed during this procedure (see again Figure 8.15).
endoscopic retrograde cholangiopancreatography (ERCP) (en-doh-SKOP-ik / RET-roh-grayd / koh-lan-jee-oh-pan-kree-ah-TOG-rah-fee)	endo- = within -scopy = process of viewing -ic = pertaining to retro- = backwards cholangi/o = bile duct pancreat/o = pancreas -graphy = process of recording	Procedure using an endoscope to visually examine the hepatic duct, common bile duct, and pancreatic duct. First an endoscope is passed through the patient's mouth, esophagus, and stomach until it reaches the duodenum where the pancreatic and common bile ducts empty. Then a thin catheter is passed through the endoscope and into the ducts (in the retrograde direction). Contrast dye is then used to visualize these ducts on an X-ray.
esophagogastroduodenoscopy (EGD) (eh-soff-ah-go-gas-troh-duo-den-OS-koh-pee)	esophag/o = esophagus gastr/o = stomach duoden/o = duodenum -scopy = process of viewing	Use of a flexible fiberoptic endoscope to visually examine the esophagus, stomach, and beginning of the duodenum.
gastroscope (GAS-troh-scope)	gastr/o = stomach -scope = instrument to view	Instrument used to view inside the stomach.
gastroscopy (gas-TROS-koh-pee)	gastr/o = stomach -scopy = process of viewing	Procedure in which a flexible *gastroscope* is passed through the mouth and down the esophagus in order to visualize inside the stomach. Used to diagnose peptic ulcers and gastric carcinoma.
laparoscope (LAP-ah-roh-scope)	lapar/o = abdomen -scope = instrument to view	Instrument used to view inside the abdomen.
laparoscopy (lap-ar-OSS-koh-pee)	lapar/o = abdomen -scopy = process of viewing	*Laparoscope* is passed into the abdominal wall through a small incision. The abdominal cavity is then visually examined for tumors and other conditions with this lighted instrument. Also called *peritoneoscopy*.
sigmoidoscope (sig-MOYD-oh-scope)	sigmoid/o = sigmoid colon -scope = instrument to view	Instrument used to view inside the sigmoid colon.
sigmoidoscopy (sig-moid-OS-koh-pee)	sigmoid/o = sigmoid colon -scopy = process of viewing	Procedure using a flexible *sigmoidoscope* to visually examine the sigmoid colon. Commonly done to diagnose cancer and polyps.
Additional Diagnostic Procedures		
paracentesis (pair-ah-sin-TEE-sis)	-centesis = process of removing fluid	Insertion of a needle into the abdominal cavity to withdraw fluid. Tests to diagnose diseases may be conducted on the fluid.

Therapeutic Procedures

TERM	WORD PARTS	DEFINITION
Dental Procedures		
bridge		Dental appliance to replace missing teeth. It is attached to adjacent teeth for support.
crown		Artificial covering for a tooth that is created to replace the original enamel covering of the tooth.
denture (DEN-chur)	dent/o = tooth	Partial or complete set of artificial teeth that are set in plastic materials. Acts as a substitute for the natural teeth and related structures.
extraction	ex- = outward	Removing or "pulling" of teeth.
implant (IM-plant)		Prosthetic device placed in the jaw to which a tooth or denture may be anchored.
root canal	-al = pertaining to	Dental treatment involving the pulp cavity of the root of a tooth. Procedure is used to save a tooth that is badly infected or abscessed.
Medical Procedures		
gavage (guh-VAHZH)		Use of a nasogastric (NG) tube to place liquid nourishment directly into the stomach.
lavage (lah-VAHZH)		Use of a nasogastric (NG) tube to wash out the stomach. For example, after ingestion of dangerous substances.
nasogastric intubation (NG tube) (NAY-zo-gas-trik / in-two-BAY-shun)	nas/o = nose gastr/o = stomach -ic = pertaining to	Procedure in which a flexible catheter is inserted into the nose and down the esophagus to the stomach. May be used for feeding or to suction out stomach fluids.
total parenteral nutrition (TPN) (pair-in-TARE-all)	-al = pertaining to	Providing 100% of a patient's nutrition intravenously. Used when a patient is unable to eat.
Surgical Procedures		
anastomosis (ah-nas-toh-MOH-sis)		To surgically create a connection between two organs or vessels. For example, joining together two cut ends of the intestines after a section is removed.
appendectomy (ap-en-DEK-toh-mee)	append/o = appendix -ectomy = surgical removal	Surgical removal of the appendix.
bariatric surgery (bear-ee-AT-rik)	bar/o = weight	Group of surgical procedures such as stomach stapling and restrictive banding to reduce the size of the stomach. A treatment for morbid (extreme) obesity.
cholecystectomy (koh-lee-sis-TEK-toh-mee)	cholecyst/o = gallbladder -ectomy = surgical removal	Surgical removal of the gallbladder.
choledocholithotripsy (koh-led-oh-koh-LITH-oh-trip-see)	choledoch/o = common bile duct lith/o = stone -tripsy = surgical crushing	Crushing of a gallstone in the common bile duct.
colectomy (koh-LEK-toh-mee)	col/o = colon -ectomy = surgical removal	Surgical removal of the colon.

Therapeutic Procedures *(continued)*

TERM	WORD PARTS	DEFINITION
colostomy (koh-LOSS-toh-mee)	col/o = colon -ostomy = create a new opening	Surgical creation of an opening of some portion of the colon through the abdominal wall to the outside surface. Fecal material (stool) drains into a bag worn on the abdomen.

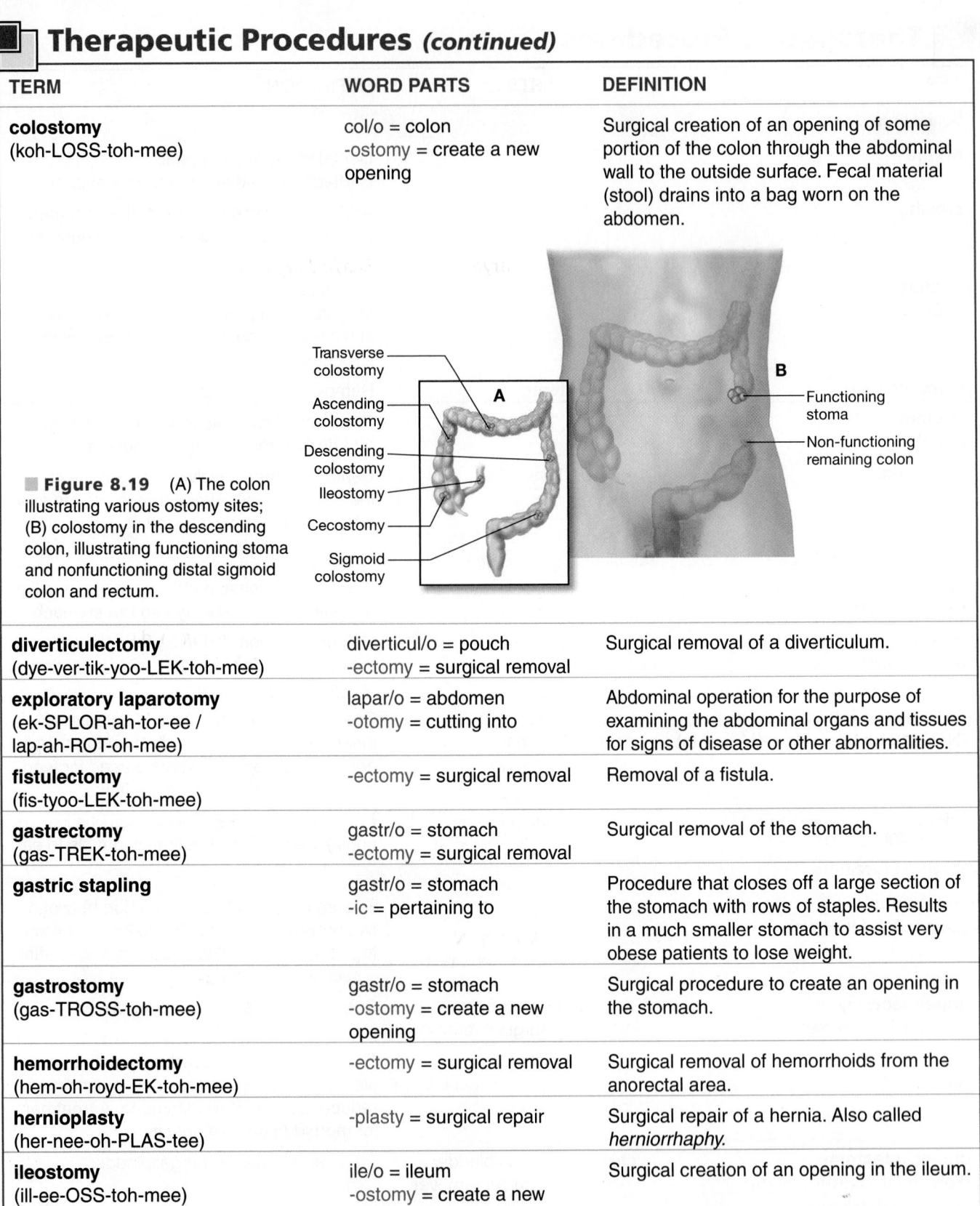

Figure 8.19 (A) The colon illustrating various ostomy sites; (B) colostomy in the descending colon, illustrating functioning stoma and nonfunctioning distal sigmoid colon and rectum.

TERM	WORD PARTS	DEFINITION
diverticulectomy (dye-ver-tik-yoo-LEK-toh-mee)	diverticul/o = pouch -ectomy = surgical removal	Surgical removal of a diverticulum.
exploratory laparotomy (ek-SPLOR-ah-tor-ee / lap-ah-ROT-oh-mee)	lapar/o = abdomen -otomy = cutting into	Abdominal operation for the purpose of examining the abdominal organs and tissues for signs of disease or other abnormalities.
fistulectomy (fis-tyoo-LEK-toh-mee)	-ectomy = surgical removal	Removal of a fistula.
gastrectomy (gas-TREK-toh-mee)	gastr/o = stomach -ectomy = surgical removal	Surgical removal of the stomach.
gastric stapling	gastr/o = stomach -ic = pertaining to	Procedure that closes off a large section of the stomach with rows of staples. Results in a much smaller stomach to assist very obese patients to lose weight.
gastrostomy (gas-TROSS-toh-mee)	gastr/o = stomach -ostomy = create a new opening	Surgical procedure to create an opening in the stomach.
hemorrhoidectomy (hem-oh-royd-EK-toh-mee)	-ectomy = surgical removal	Surgical removal of hemorrhoids from the anorectal area.
hernioplasty (her-nee-oh-PLAS-tee)	-plasty = surgical repair	Surgical repair of a hernia. Also called *herniorrhaphy.*
ileostomy (ill-ee-OSS-toh-mee)	ile/o = ileum -ostomy = create a new opening	Surgical creation of an opening in the ileum.
laparoscopic cholecystectomy (lap-ar-oh-SKOP-ik / koh-lee-sis-TEK-toh-mee)	lapar/o = abdomen -scopy = process of viewing -ic = pertaining to cholecyst/o = gallbladder -ectomy = surgical removal	Surgical removal of the gallbladder through a very small abdominal incision with the assistance of a laparoscope.

■ Therapeutic Procedures *(continued)*

TERM	WORD PARTS	DEFINITION
laparotomy (lap-ah-ROT-oh-mee)	lapar/o = abdomen -otomy = cutting into	Surgical incision into the abdomen.
liver transplant		Transplant of a liver from a donor.
palatoplasty (pa-LOT-toh-plas-tee)	palat/o = palate -plasty = surgical repair	Surgical repair of the palate.
pharyngoplasty (fair-ING-oh-plas-tee)	pharyng/o = pharynx -plasty = surgical repair	Surgical repair of the throat.
proctopexy (PROK-toh-pek-see)	proct/o = rectum and anus -pexy = surgical fixation	Surgical fixation of the rectum and anus.

■ Pharmacology

CLASSIFICATION	WORD PARTS	ACTION	EXAMPLES
anorexiant (an-oh-REKS-ee-ant)	an- = without -orexia = appetite	Treats obesity by suppressing appetite.	phendimetrazine, Adipost, Obezine; phentermine, Zantryl, Adipex
antacid	anti- = against	Used to neutralize stomach acids.	calcium carbonate, Tums; aluminum hydroxide and magnesium hydroxide, Maalox, Mylanta
antidiarrheal (an-tee-dye-ah-REE-all)	anti- = against -al = pertaining to	Used to control diarrhea.	loperamide, Imodium; diphenoxylate and atropine, Lomotil; kaolin/pectin, Kaopectate
antiemetic (an-tye-ee-MEH-tik)	anti- = against -emesis = vomit -tic = pertaining to	Treats nausea, vomiting, and motion sickness.	prochlorperazine, Compazine; promethazine, Phenergan
H₂-receptor antagonist	anti- = against	Used to treat peptic ulcers and gastroesophageal reflux disease. When stimulated, H₂-receptors increase the production of stomach acid. Using an antagonist to block these receptors results in a low acid level in the stomach.	ranitidine, Zantac; cimetidine, Tagamet; famotidine, Pepcid
laxative		Treats constipation by stimulating a bowel movement.	senosides, Senokot; psyllium, Metamucil
proton pump inhibitors		Used to treat peptic ulcers and gastroesophageal reflux disease. Blocks the stomach's ability to secrete acid.	esomeprazole, Nexium; omeprazole, Prilosec

MED TERM TIP

The term *laxative* refers to a medication to stimulate a bowel movement; comes from the Latin term meaning "to relax."

Abbreviations

ac	before meals	HDV	hepatitis D virus
ALT	alanine transaminase	HEV	hepatitis E virus
AST	aspartate transaminase	HSV-1	herpes simplex virus type 1
Ba	barium	IBD	inflammatory bowel disease
BE	barium enema	IBS	irritable bowel syndrome
BM	bowel movement	IVC	intravenous cholangiography
BS	bowel sounds *(blood sugar, breath sounds)*	n&v	nausea and vomiting
CBD	common bile duct	NG	nasogastric (tube)
EGD	esophagogastroduodenoscopy	NPO	nothing by mouth
ERCP	endoscopic retrograde cholangio-pancreatography	O&P	ova and parasites
		pc	after meals
FOBT	fecal occult blood test	PO	by mouth
GB	gallbladder	pp	postprandial
GERD	gastroesophageal reflux disease	PTC	percutaneous transhepatic cholangiography
GI	gastrointestinal		
HAV	hepatitis A virus	PUD	peptic ulcer disease
HBV	hepatitis B virus	TPN	total parenteral nutrition
HCl	hydrochloric acid	UGI	upper gastrointestinal series
HCV	hepatitis C virus		

Chapter Review

Real-World Applications

Medical Record Analysis

This Gastroenterology Consultation Report contains 12 medical terms. Underline each term and write it in the list below the report. Then define each term.

Gastroenterology Consultation Report

Reason for Consultation: Evaluation of recurrent epigastric pain with anemia and melena.

History of Present Illness: Patient is a 56-year-old male. He reports a long history of mild dyspepsia characterized by burning epigastric pain, especially when his stomach is empty. This pain has been relieved by over-the-counter antacids. Approximately two weeks ago, the pain became significantly worse and he noted that his stools were dark and tarry.

Results of Physical Examination: CBC indicates anemia, and a fecal occult blood test is positive for blood. A blood test for *Helicobacter pylori* is positive. Gastroscopy located an ulcer in the lining of the stomach. This ulcer is 1.5 cm in diameter and deep. There is evidence of active bleeding from the ulcer.

Assessment: Peptic ulcer disease.

Recommendations: A gastrectomy to remove the ulcerated portion of stomach is indicated because the ulcer is already bleeding.

	Term	Definition
1	_____	_____
2	_____	_____
3	_____	_____
4	_____	_____
5	_____	_____
6	_____	_____
7	_____	_____
8	_____	_____
9	_____	_____
10	_____	_____
11	_____	_____
12	_____	_____

Chart Note Transcription

The chart note below contains 12 phrases that can be reworded with a medical term that you learned in this chapter. Each phrase is identified with an underline. Determine the medical term and write your answers in the space provided.

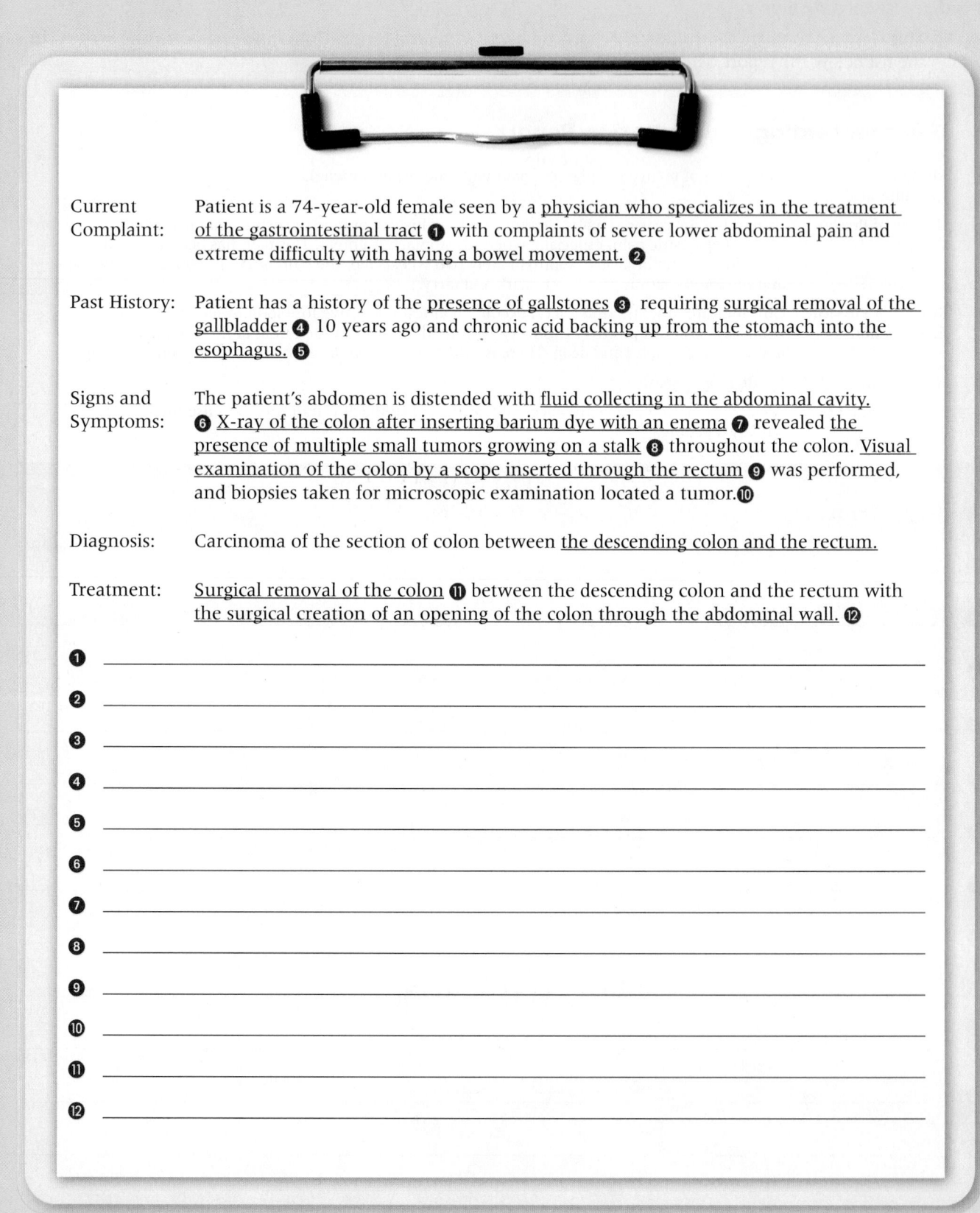

Current Complaint: Patient is a 74-year-old female seen by a <u>physician who specializes in the treatment of the gastrointestinal tract</u> ❶ with complaints of severe lower abdominal pain and extreme <u>difficulty with having a bowel movement.</u> ❷

Past History: Patient has a history of the <u>presence of gallstones</u> ❸ requiring <u>surgical removal of the gallbladder</u> ❹ 10 years ago and chronic <u>acid backing up from the stomach into the esophagus.</u> ❺

Signs and Symptoms: The patient's abdomen is distended with <u>fluid collecting in the abdominal cavity.</u> ❻ <u>X-ray of the colon after inserting barium dye with an enema</u> ❼ revealed <u>the presence of multiple small tumors growing on a stalk</u> ❽ throughout the colon. <u>Visual examination of the colon by a scope inserted through the rectum</u> ❾ was performed, and biopsies taken for microscopic examination located a tumor.❿

Diagnosis: Carcinoma of the section of colon between <u>the descending colon and the rectum.</u>

Treatment: <u>Surgical removal of the colon</u> ⓫ between the descending colon and the rectum with <u>the surgical creation of an opening of the colon through the abdominal wall.</u> ⓬

❶ _____

❷ _____

❸ _____

❹ _____

❺ _____

❻ _____

❼ _____

❽ _____

❾ _____

❿ _____

⓫ _____

⓬ _____

Case Study

Below is a case study presentation of a patient with a condition discussed in this chapter. Read the case study and answer the questions below. Some questions will ask for information not included within this chapter. Use your text, a medical dictionary, or any other reference material you choose to answer these questions.

A 60-year-old obese female has come into the ER due to severe RUQ pain for the past 2 hours. Patient also reports increasing nausea but denies emesis. Patient states she has been told she has cholelithiasis by her family physician following a milder episode of this pain 2 years ago. In addition to severe pain, patient displays a moderate degree of scleral jaundice. Abdominal ultrasound identified acute cholecystitis and a large number of gallstones. Because of the jaundice a PTC was performed and confirmed choledocholithiasis. Patient was sent to surgery for laparoscopic cholecystectomy to remove the gallbladder and all gallstones. She recovered without incident.

(© Rob Marmion/Shutterstock)

1. Define each of the patient's symptoms.

_____

_____

2. The patient has severe RUQ pain. What organs are located in the RUQ?

_____

_____

3. After reading the definition of jaundice, what is most likely causing this patient to have it?

_____

_____

4. Describe the diagnostic imaging procedures this patient received.

_____

_____

5. What is the difference between cholelithiasis and cholecystitis?

_____

_____

6. The patient's gallbladder was removed laparoscopically. What does that mean?

_____

_____

Practice Exercises

A. Complete the Statement

1. The digestive system is also known as the _____ system.

2. The continuous muscular tube of the digestive system is called the _____ or _____ and

   stretches between the _____ and _____.

3. The accessory organs of the digestive system are the _____, _____,

   _____, and _____.

4. The three main functions of the digestive system are _____, _____, and

   _____.

5. The incisors are examples of _____ teeth and the molars are examples of _____ teeth.

6. Food is propelled through the gut by wavelike muscular contractions called _____.

7. Food in the stomach is mixed with _____ and other gastric juices to form a watery mixture called

   _____.

8. The three sections of small intestine in order are the _____, _____, and

   _____.

9. The S-shaped section of colon that curves back toward the rectum is called the _____ colon.

10. _____ produced by the liver is responsible for the _____ of fats. It is stored in the

   _____.

B. Combining Form Practice

The combining form **gastr/o** refers to the stomach. Use it to write a term that means:

1. inflammation of the stomach_____

2. study of the stomach and small intestines_____

3. removal of the stomach _____

4. visual exam of the stomach _____

5. stomach pain_____

6. enlargement of the stomach_____

7. cutting into the stomach_____

The combining form **esophag/o** refers to the esophagus. Use it to write a term that means:

8. inflammation of the esophagus _____

9. visual examination of the esophagus _____

10. surgical repair of the esophagus _____

11. pertaining to the esophagus _____

12. stretched-out esophagus _____

The combining form **proct/o** refers to the rectum and anus. Use it to write a term that means:

13. surgical fixation of the rectum and anus _____

14. drooping of the rectum and anus _____

15. inflammation of the rectum and anus _____

16. specialist in the study of the rectum and anus _____

The combining form **cholecyst/o** refers to the gallbladder. Use it to write a term that means:

17. removal of the gallbladder _____

18. condition of having gallbladder stones _____

19. gallbladder stone surgical crushing _____

20. gallbladder inflammation _____

The combining form **lapar/o** refers to the abdomen. Use it to write a term that means:

21. instrument to view inside the abdomen _____

22. cutting into the abdomen _____

23. visual examination of the abdomen _____

The combining form **hepat/o** refers to the liver. Use it to write a term that means:

24. liver tumor _____

25. enlargement of the liver _____

26. pertaining to the liver _____

27. inflammation of the liver _____

The combining form **pancreat/o** refers to the pancreas. Use it to write a term that means:

28. inflammation of the pancreas _____

29. pertaining to the pancreas _____

The combining form **col/o** refers to the colon. Use it to write a term that means:

30. create an opening in the colon _____

31. inflammation of the colon _____

C. Define the Combining Form

	Definition	Example from Chapter
1. esophag/o		
2. hepat/o		
3. ile/o		
4. proct/o		
5. gloss/o		
6. labi/o		
7. jejun/o		
8. sigmoid/o		
9. rect/o		
10. gingiv/o		
11. cholecyst/o		
12. duoden/o		
13. an/o		
14. enter/o		
15. dent/o		

D. Suffix Practice

Use the following suffixes to create a medical term for the following definitions.

-orexia	-phagia	-pepsia	-prandial
-emesis	-lithiasis		

1. after meals

2. condition of having gallstones

3. no appetite

4. difficulty swallowing

5. vomiting blood

6. slow digestion

E. What Does it Stand For?

1. BM _____

2. UGI _____

3. BE _____

4. BS _____

5. n & v _____

6. O & P _____

7. PO _____

8. CBD _____

9. NPO _____

10. pp _____

F. Terminology Matching

Match each term to its definition.

1.	_____ dentures	a.	excess body weight
2.	_____ anorexia	b.	chronic liver disease
3.	_____ hematemesis	c.	heartburn
4.	_____ pyrosis	d.	small colon tumors
5.	_____ obesity	e.	fluid accumulation in abdominal cavity
6.	_____ constipation	f.	vomit blood
7.	_____ melena	g.	bowel twists on self
8.	_____ ascites	h.	set of artificial teeth
9.	_____ cirrhosis	i.	loss of appetite
10.	_____ spastic colon	j.	difficulty having BM
11.	_____ polyposis	k.	irritable bowel syndrome
12.	_____ volvulus	l.	black tarry stool
13.	_____ hiatal hernia	m.	yellow skin color
14.	_____ ulcerative colitis	n.	bloody diarrhea
15.	_____ dysentery	o.	diaphragmatocele
16.	_____ jaundice	p.	inflammatory bowel disease

G. What's the Abbreviation?

1. nasogastric _____

2. gastrointestinal _____

3. hepatitis B virus _____

4. fecal occult blood test _____

5. inflammatory bowel disease _____

6. herpes simplex virus type 1 _____

7. aspartate transaminase _____

8. after meals _____

9. peptic ulcer disease _____

10. gastroesophageal reflux disease _____

H. Define the Term

1. colonoscopy _____

2. bite wing X-ray _____

3. hematochezia _____

4. serum bilirubin _____

5. cachexia _____

6. lavage _____

7. hernioplasty _____

8. extraction _____

9. choledocholithotripsy _____

10. anastomosis _____

I. Fill in the Blank

colonoscopy	barium swallow	lower GI series
gastric stapling	colostomy	colectomy
total parenteral nutrition	choledocholithotripsy	liver biopsy
ileostomy	fecal occult blood test	intravenous cholecystography

1. Excising a small piece of hepatic tissue for microscopic examination is called a(n) _____.

2. When a surgeon performs a total or partial colectomy for cancer, she may have to create an opening on the surface of the skin for fecal matter to leave the body. This procedure is called a(n) _____.

3. Another name for an upper GI series is a(n) _____.

4. Mr. White has had a radiopaque material placed into his large bowel by means of an enema for the purpose of viewing his colon. This procedure is called a(n) _____.

5. A(n) _____ is the surgical removal of the colon.

6. Jessica has been on a red meat-free diet in preparation for a test of her feces for the presence of hidden blood. This test is called a(n) _____.

7. Dr. Mendez uses equipment to crush gallstones in the common bile duct. This procedure is called a(n) _____.

8. Mrs. Alcazar required _____ because she could not eat following her intestinal surgery.

9. Mr. Bright had a(n) _____ to treat his morbid obesity.

10. Visualizing the gallbladder and bile ducts by injecting a dye into the patient's arm is called a(n) _____.

11. Passing an instrument into the anus and rectum in order to see the colon is called a(n) _____.

12. Ms. Fayne suffers from Crohn's disease, which has necessitated the removal of much of her small intestine. She has had a surgical passage created for the external disposal of waste material from the ileum. This is called a(n) _____.

J. Terminology Matching

Match each term to its definition.

1. _____ dentures   a. tooth decay

2. _____ cementum   b. prosthetic device used to anchor a tooth

3. _____ root canal   c. inflammation of the gums

4. _____ crown   d. full set of artificial teeth

5. _____ bridge   e. portion of the tooth covered by enamel

6. _____ implant   f. replacement for missing teeth

7. _____ gingivitis   g. anchors root in bony socket of jaw

8. _____ dental caries   h. surgery on the tooth pulp

K. Pharmacology Challenge

Fill in the classification for each drug description, then match the brand name.

Drug Description	Classification	Brand Name
1. _____ Controls diarrhea	_____	a. Pepcid
2. _____ Blocks stomach's ability to secrete acid	_____	b. Obezine
3. _____ Treats motion sickness	_____	c. Metamucil
4. _____ Blocks acid-producing receptors	_____	d. Compazine
5. _____ Suppresses appetite	_____	e. Maalox
6. _____ Stimulates a bowel movement	_____	f. Imodium
7. _____ Neutralizes stomach acid	_____	g. Nexium

Labeling Exercise

Image A

Write the labels for this figure on the numbered lines provided.

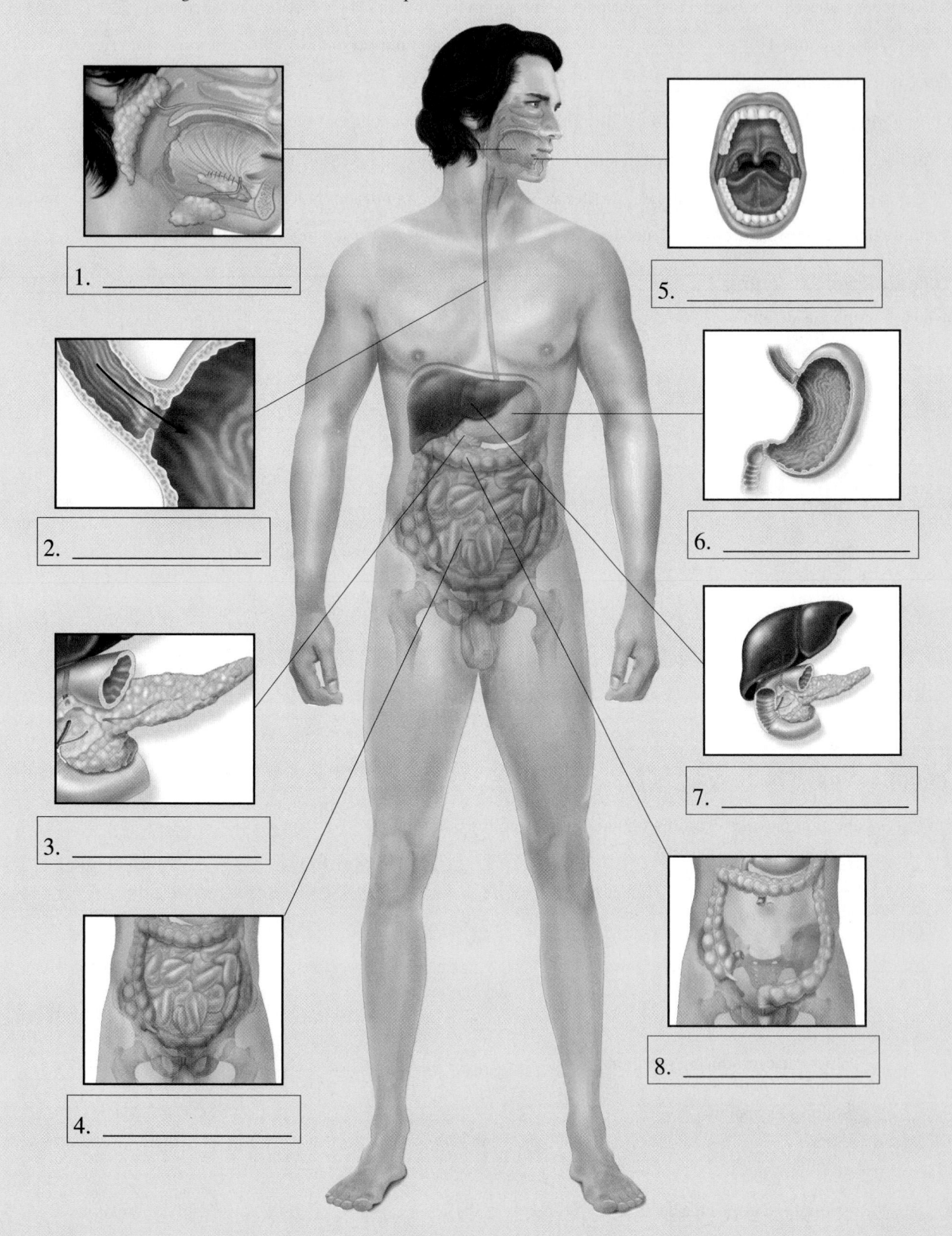

1. _____

2. _____

3. _____

4. _____

5. _____

6. _____

7. _____

8. _____

Image B

Write the labels for this figure on the numbered lines provided.

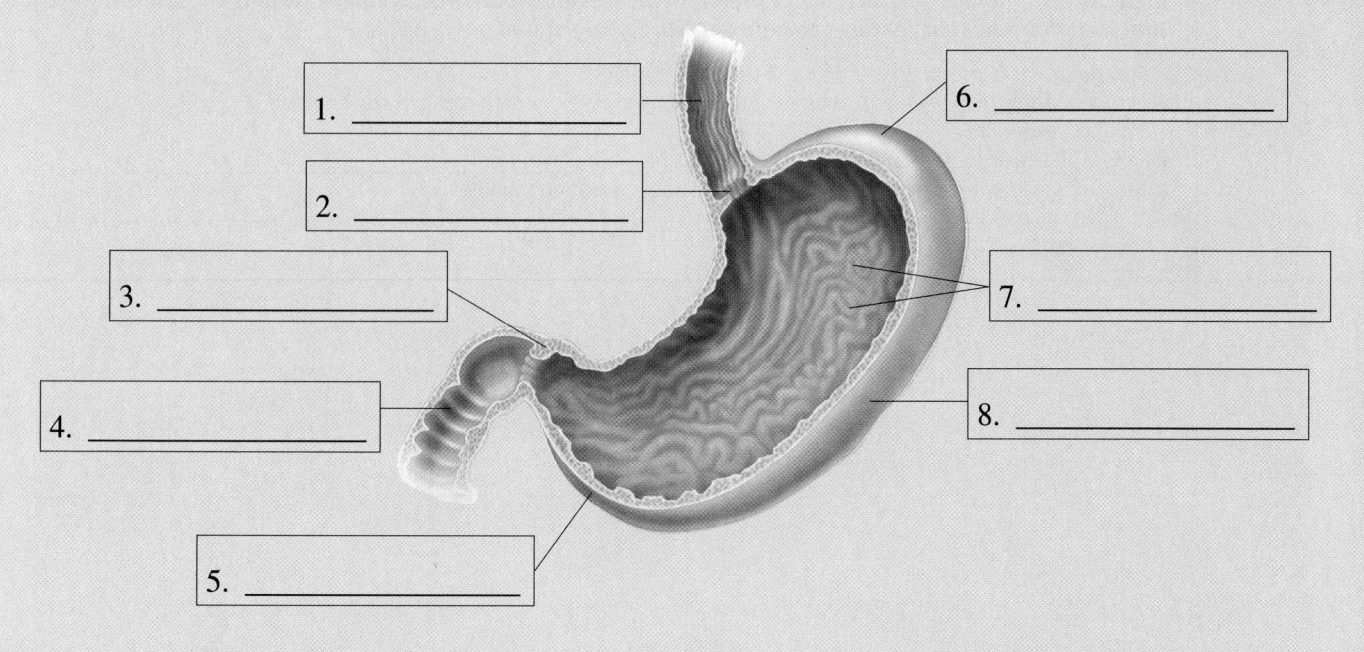

1. _____

2. _____

3. _____

4. _____

5. _____

6. _____

7. _____

8. _____

Image C

Write the labels for this figure on the numbered lines provided.

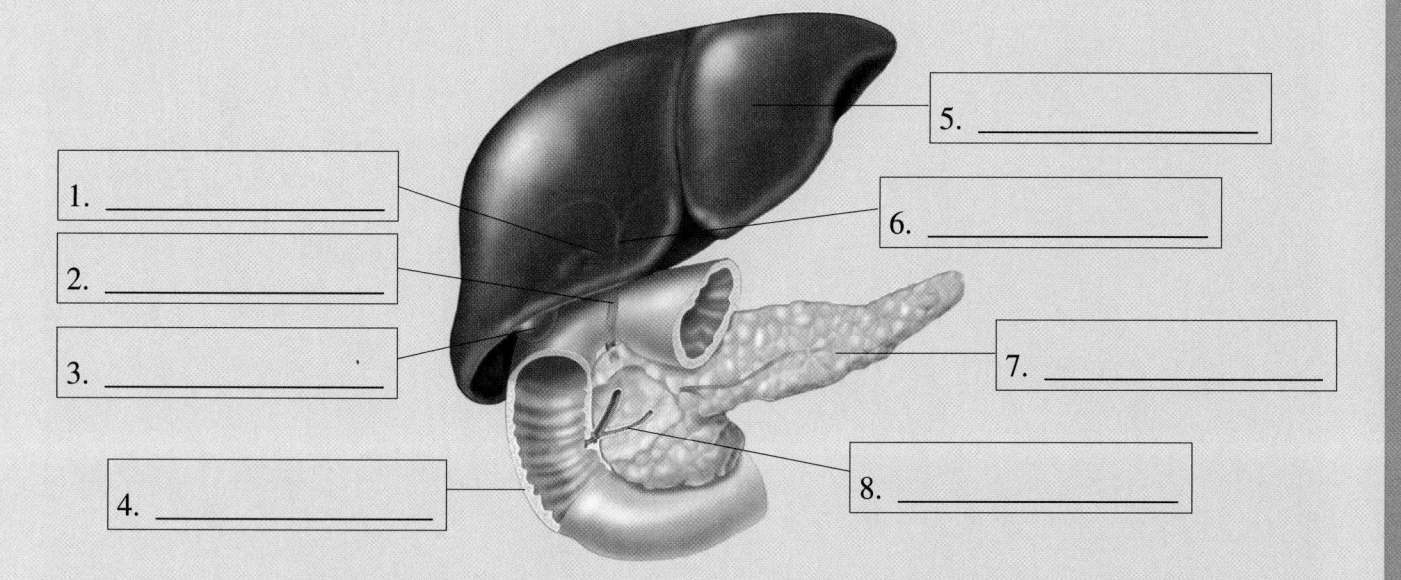

1. _____

2. _____

3. _____

4. _____

5. _____

6. _____

7. _____

8. _____

MEDICAL **TERMINOLOGY** INTERACTIVE

Medical Terminology Interactive is a premium online homework management system that includes a host of features to help you study. Registered users will find:

- Fun games and activities built within a virtual hospital
- Powerful tools that track and analyze your results—allowing you to create a personalized learning experience
- Videos, flashcards, and audio pronunciations to help enrich your progress
- Streaming video lesson presentations and self-paced learning modules

www.pearsonhighered.com/mti

9

URINARY SYSTEM

Learning Objectives

Upon completion of this chapter, you will be able to

- Identify and define the combining forms and suffixes introduced in this chapter.

- Correctly spell and pronounce medical terms and major anatomical structures relating to the urinary system.

- Locate and describe the major organs of the urinary system and their functions.

- Describe the nephron and the mechanisms of urine production.

- Identify the characteristics of urine and a urinalysis.

- Identify and define urinary system anatomical terms.

- Identify and define selected urinary system pathology terms.

- Identify and define selected urinary system diagnostic procedures.

- Identify and define selected urinary system therapeutic procedures.

- Identify and define selected medications relating to the urinary system.

- Define selected abbreviations associated with the urinary system.

Urinary System at a Glance

Function

The urinary system is responsible for maintaining a stable internal environment for the body. In order to achieve this state, the urinary system removes waste products, adjusts water and electrolyte levels, and maintains the correct pH.

Organs

Here are the primary structures that comprise the urinary system.

kidneys
ureters
urethra
urinary bladder

Word Parts

Here are the most common word parts (with their meanings) used to build urinary system terms. For a more comprehensive list, refer to the Terminology section of this chapter.

Combining Forms

azot/o	nitrogenous waste	noct/i	night
bacteri/o	bacteria	olig/o	scanty
cyst/o	bladder, pouch	protein/o	protein
glomerul/o	glomerulus	pyel/o	renal pelvis
glycos/o	sugar, glucose	ren/o	kidney
keton/o	ketones	ureter/o	ureter
lith/o	stone	urethr/o	urethra
meat/o	meatus	urin/o	urine
nephr/o	kidney	ur/o	urine

Suffixes

-lith	stone
-lithiasis	condition of stones
-ptosis	drooping
-tripsy	surgical crushing
-uria	condition of the urine

Urinary System Illustrated

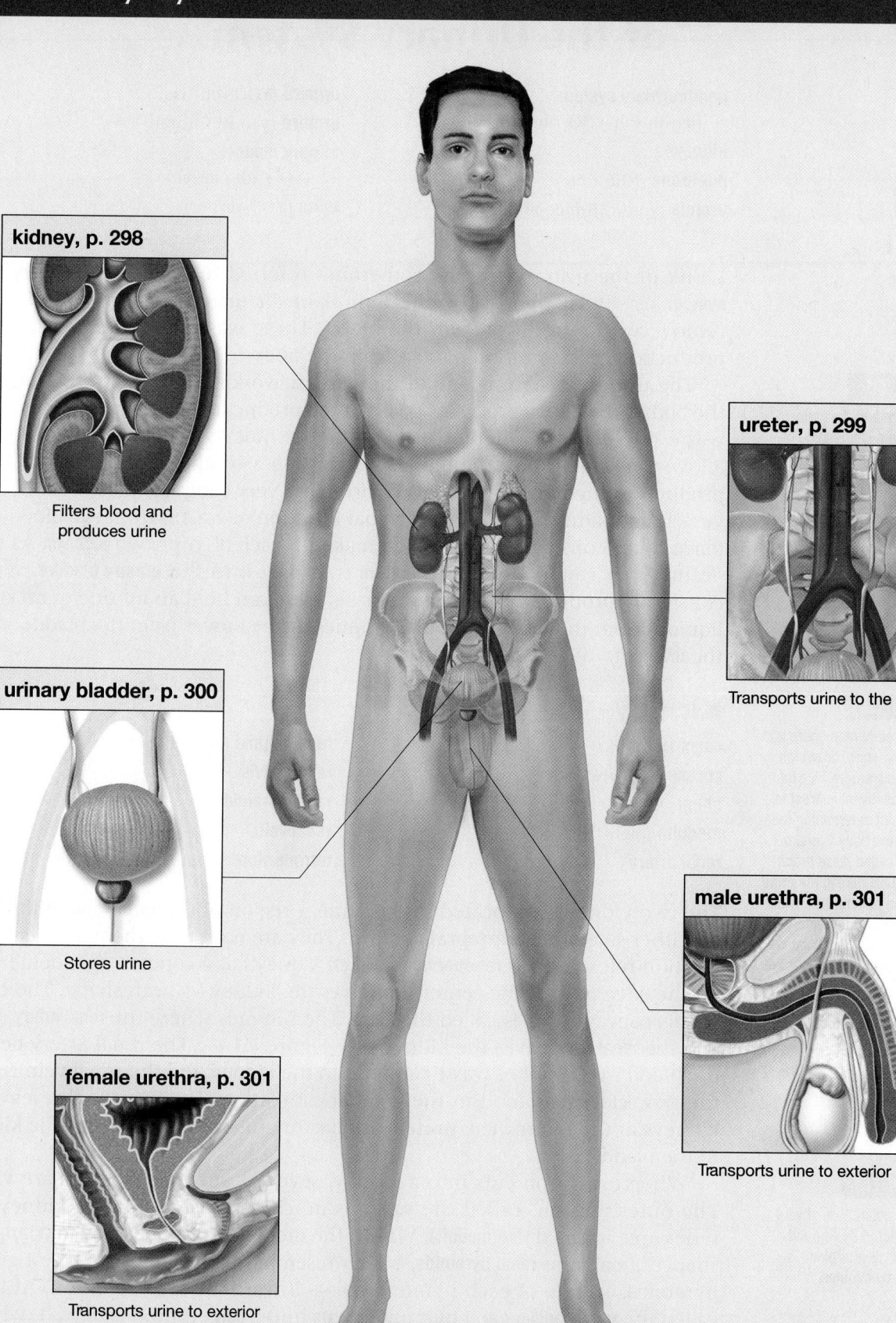

kidney, p. 298

Filters blood and
produces urine

ureter, p. 299

Transports urine to the bladder

urinary bladder, p. 300

Stores urine

male urethra, p. 301

Transports urine to exterior

female urethra, p. 301

Transports urine to exterior

Anatomy and Physiology of the Urinary System

genitourinary system
(jen-ih-toh-YOO-rih-nair-ee)
kidneys
nephrons (NEF-ronz)
uremia (yoo-REE-mee-ah)

ureters (YOO-reh-ters)
urethra (yoo-REE-thrah)
urinary bladder
(YOO-rih-nair-ee)
urine (YOO-rin)

Think of the urinary system, sometimes referred to as the **genitourinary** (GU) **system,** as similar to a water filtration plant. Its main function is to filter and remove waste products from the blood. These waste materials result in the production and excretion of **urine** from the body.

The urinary system is one of the hardest working systems of the body. All the body's metabolic processes result in the production of waste products. These waste products are a natural part of life but quickly become toxic if they are allowed to build up in the blood, resulting in a condition called **uremia.** Waste products in the body are removed through a very complicated system of blood vessels and kidney tubules. The actual filtration of wastes from the blood takes place in millions of **nephrons,** which make up each of your two **kidneys.** As urine drains from each kidney, the **ureters** transport it to the **urinary bladder.** We are constantly producing urine, and our bladders can hold about one quart of this liquid. When the urinary bladder empties, urine moves from the bladder down the **urethra** to the outside of the body.

Kidneys

calyx (KAY-liks)
cortex (KOR-teks)
hilum (HIGH-lum)
medulla (meh-DULL-ah)
renal artery

renal papilla (pah-PILL-ah)
renal pelvis
renal pyramids
renal vein
retroperitoneal (ret-roh-pair-ih-toh-NEE-al)

The two kidneys are located in the lumbar region of the back above the waist on either side of the vertebral column. They are not inside the peritoneal sac, a location referred to as **retroperitoneal.** Each kidney has a concave or indented area on the edge toward the center that gives the kidney its bean shape. The center of this concave area is called the **hilum.** The hilum is where the **renal artery** enters and the **renal vein** leaves the kidney (see Figure 9.1 ■). The renal artery delivers the blood that is full of waste products to the kidney and the renal vein returns the now cleansed blood to the general circulation. The ureters also leave the kidneys at the hilum. The ureters are narrow tubes that lead from the kidneys to the bladder.

When a surgeon cuts into a kidney, several structures or areas are visible. The outer portion, called the **cortex,** is much like a shell for the kidney. The inner area is called the **medulla.** Within the medulla are a dozen or so triangular-shaped areas, the **renal pyramids,** which resemble their namesake, the Egyptian pyramids. The tip of each pyramid points inward toward the hilum. At its tip, called the **renal papilla,** each pyramid opens into a **calyx** (plural is *calyces*), which is continuous with the **renal pelvis.** The calyces and ultimately the renal pelvis collect urine as it is formed. The ureter for each kidney arises from the renal pelvis (see Figure 9.2 ■).

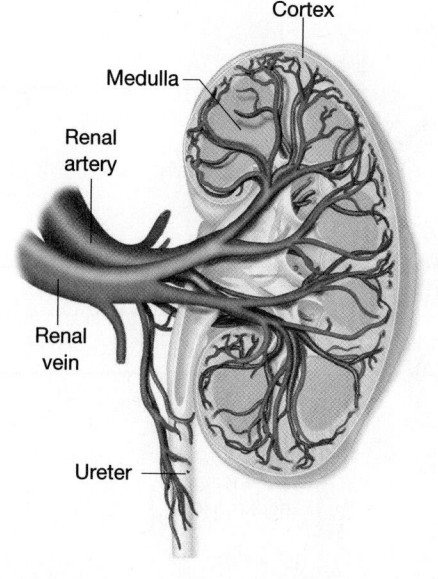

Figure 9.1 Kidney structure. Longitudinal section showing the renal artery entering and the renal vein and ureter exiting at the hilium of the kidney.

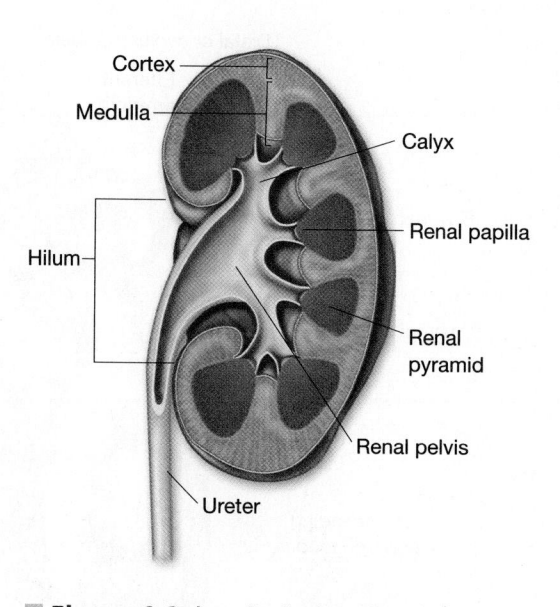

Figure 9.2 Longitudinal section of a kidney illustrating the internal structures.

Nephrons

afferent arteriole (AFF-er-ent)

Bowman's capsule

collecting tubule

distal convoluted tubule
　　(DISS-tall / con-voh-LOOT-ed)

efferent arteriole (EF-er-ent)

glomerular capsule (glom-AIR-yoo-lar)

renal tubule

glomerulus (glom-AIR-yoo-lus)

loop of Henle

nephron (NEF-ron)

nephron loop

proximal convoluted tubule
　　(PROK-sim-al / con-voh-LOOT-ed)

renal corpuscle (KOR-pus-ehl)

> **MED TERM TIP**
>
> The kidney bean is so named because it resembles a kidney in shape. Each organ weighs 4–6 ounces, is 2–3 inches wide and approximately 1 inch thick, and is about the size of your fist. In most people the left kidney is slightly higher and larger than the right kidney. Functioning kidneys are necessary for life, but it is possible to live with only one functioning kidney.

The functional or working unit of the kidney is the **nephron**. There are more than one million of these microscopic structures in each human kidney. Each nephron consists of the **renal corpuscle** and the **renal tubule** (see Figure 9.3 ▪). The renal corpuscle is the blood-filtering portion of the nephron. It has a double-walled cuplike structure called the **glomerular capsule** (also known as **Bowman's capsule**) that encases a ball of capillaries called the **glomerulus**. An **afferent arteriole** carries blood to the glomerulus, and an **efferent arteriole** carries blood away from the glomerulus.

Water and substances that were removed from the bloodstream in the renal corpuscle flow into the renal tubules to finish the urine production process. This continuous tubule is divided into four sections: the **proximal convoluted tubule**, followed by the narrow **nephron loop** (also known as the **loop of Henle**), then the **distal convoluted tubule,** and finally the **collecting tubule.**

> **MED TERM TIP**
>
> *Afferent*, meaning moving toward, and *efferent*, meaning moving away from, are terms used when discussing moving either toward or away from the central point in many systems. For example, there are afferent and efferent nerves in the nervous system.

Ureters

As urine drains out of the renal pelvis it enters the ureter, which carries it down to the urinary bladder (see Figure 9.4 ▪). Ureters are very narrow tubes measuring less than ¼-inch wide and 10–12 inches long that extend from the renal pelvis to the urinary bladder. Mucous membrane lines the ureters just as it lines most passages that open to the external environment.

■ **Figure 9.3** The structure of a nephron, illustrating the nephron structure in relation to the circulatory system.

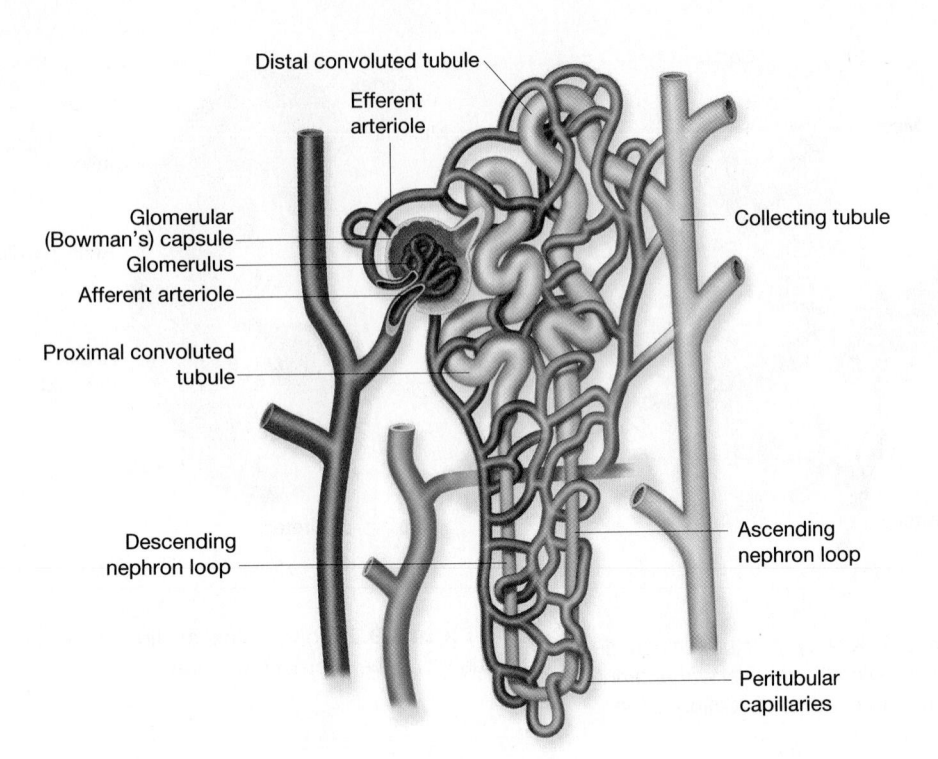

Distal convoluted tubule

Efferent arteriole

Glomerular (Bowman's) capsule

Glomerulus

Afferent arteriole

Proximal convoluted tubule

Collecting tubule

Descending nephron loop

Ascending nephron loop

Peritubular capillaries

Urinary Bladder

external sphincter (SFINGK-ter)
internal sphincter

rugae (ROO-gay)
urination

The urinary bladder is an elastic muscular sac that lies in the base of the pelvis just behind the pubic symphysis (see Figure 9.5 ■). It is composed of three layers of smooth muscle tissue lined with mucous membrane containing **rugae** or folds that allow it to stretch. The bladder receives the urine directly from the ureters, stores it, and excretes it by **urination** through the urethra.

Generally, an adult bladder will hold 250 mL of urine. This amount then creates an urge to void or empty the bladder. Involuntary muscle action causes the bladder to contract and the **internal sphincter** to relax. The internal sphincter protects us from having our bladder empty at the wrong time. Voluntary action

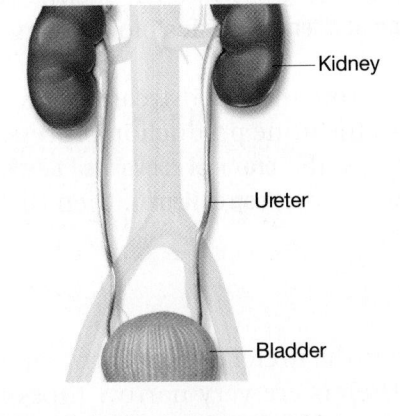

Kidney

Ureter

Bladder

■ **Figure 9.4** The ureters extend from the kidneys to the urinary bladder.

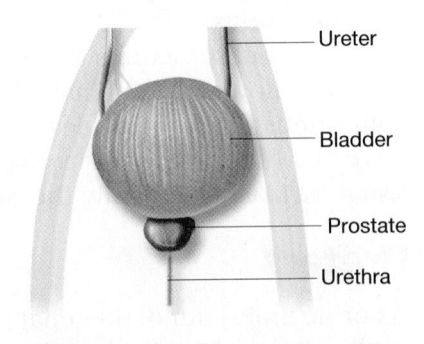

Ureter

Bladder

Prostate

Urethra

■ **Figure 9.5** The structure of the urinary bladder. (Note the prostate gland.)

controls the **external sphincter,** which opens on demand to allow the intentional emptying of the bladder. The act of controlling the emptying of urine is developed sometime after a child is 2 years of age.

Urethra

urinary meatus (mee-AY-tus)

The urethra is a tubular canal that carries the flow of urine from the bladder to the outside of the body (see Figure 9.6 ■ for the male urethra). The external opening through which urine passes out of the body is called the **urinary meatus.** Mucous membrane also lines the urethra as it does other structures of the urinary system. This is one of the reasons that infection spreads up the urinary tract. The urethra is 1–2 inches long in the female and 8 inches long in the male. In a woman it functions only as the outlet for urine and is in front of the vagina. In the male, however, it has two functions: an outlet for urine and the passageway for semen to leave the body.

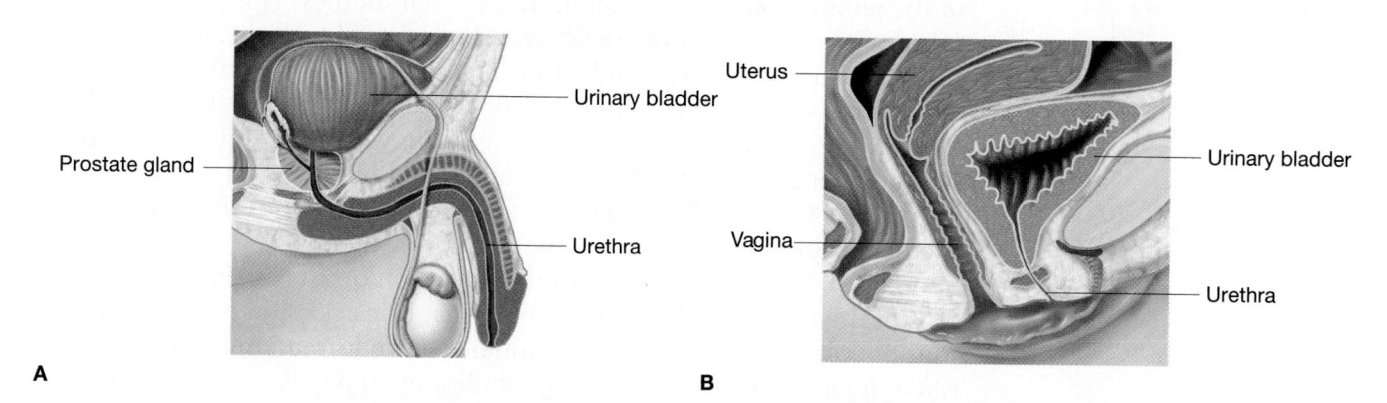

A   **B**

■ **Figure 9.6** (A) The male urethra extends from the urinary bladder in the floor of the pelvis through the penis to the urinary meatus; (B) the much shorter female urethra extends from the urinary bladder to the floor of the pelvis and exits just in front of the vaginal opening.

Role of Kidneys in Homeostasis

electrolytes (ee-LEK-troh-lites)   **homeostasis** (hoh-mee-oh-STAY-sis)

The kidneys are responsible for **homeostasis** or balance in the body. They continually adjust the chemical conditions in the body, allowing us to survive. Because of its interaction with the bloodstream and its ability to excrete substances from the body, the urinary system maintains the body's proper balance of water and chemicals. If the body is low on water, the kidneys conserve it, or in the opposite case, if there is excess water in the body, the kidneys excrete the excess. In adition to water, the kidneys regulate the level of **electrolytes**—small biologically important molecules such as sodium (Na^+), potassium (K^+), chloride (Cl), and bicarbonate (HCO_3^-). Finally, the kidneys play an important role in maintaining the correct pH range within the body, making sure we do not become too acidic or too alkaline. The kidneys accomplish these important tasks through the production of urine.

> **MED TERM TIP**
>
> Mucous membranes will carry infections up the urinary tract from the urinary meatus and urethra into the bladder and eventually up the ureters and the kidneys if not stopped. It is never wise to ignore a simple bladder infection or what is called *cystitis.*

Stages of Urine Production

filtration   **reabsorption**
glomerular filtrate   **secretion**
peritubular capillaries

As wastes and unnecessary substances are removed from the bloodstream by the nephrons, many desirable molecules are also removed initially. Waste products are eliminated from the body, but other substances such as water, electrolytes, and nutrients must be returned to the bloodstream. Urine, in its final form ready for elimination from the body, is the ultimate product of this entire process.

Urine production occurs in three stages: **filtration, reabsorption,** and **secretion.** Each of these steps is performed by a different section of the nephrons (see Figure 9.7 ■).

> **MED TERM TIP**
>
> The amount of water and other fluids processed by the kidneys each day is astonishing. Approximately 190 quarts of fluid are filtered out of the glomerular blood every day. Most of this fluid returns to the body through the reabsorption process. About 99% of the water that leaves the blood each day through the filtration process returns to the blood by proximal tubule reabsorption.

1. **Filtration.** The first stage is the filtering of particles, which occurs in the renal corpuscle. The pressure of blood flowing through the glomerulus forces material out of the bloodstream, through the wall of the glomerular capsule, and into the renal tubules. This fluid in the tubules is called the **glomerular filtrate** and consists of water, electrolytes, nutrients such as glucose and amino acids, wastes, and toxins.

2. **Reabsorption.** After filtration, the filtrate passes through the four sections of the tubule. As the filtrate moves along its twisted journey, most of the water and much of the electrolytes and nutrients are reabsorbed into the **peritubular capillaries,** a capillary bed that surrounds the renal tubules. They can then reenter the circulating blood.

3. **Secretion.** The final stage of urine production occurs when the special cells of the renal tubules secrete ammonia, uric acid, and other waste substances directly into the renal tubule. Urine formation is now finished; it passes into the collecting tubules, renal papilla, calyx, renal pelvis, and ultimately into the ureter.

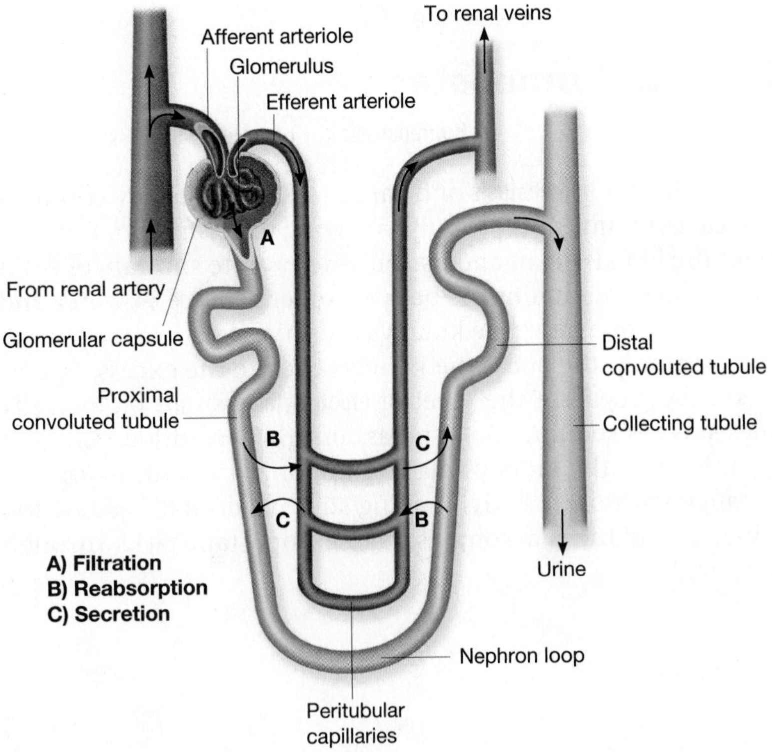

■ **Figure 9.7** The three stages of urine production: filtration, reabsorption, and secretion.

Urine

albumin (al-BEW-min)

nitrogenous wastes (nigh-TROJ-eh-nus)

specific gravity

urinalysis (yoo-rih-NAL-ih-sis)

Urine is normally straw-colored to clear, and sterile. Although it is 95% water, it also contains many dissolved substances, such as electrolytes, toxins, and **nitrogenous wastes,** the byproducts of muscle metabolism. At times the urine also contains substances that should not be there, such as glucose, blood, or **albumin,** a protein that should remain in the blood. This is the reason for performing a **urinalysis,** a physical and chemical analysis of urine, which gives medical personnel important information regarding disease processes occurring in a patient. Normally, during a 24-hour period the output of urine will be 1,000–2,000 mL, depending on the amount of fluid consumed and the general health of the person. Normal urine is acidic because this is one way our bodies dispose of excess acids. **Specific gravity** indicates the amount of dissolved substances in urine. The specific gravity of pure water is 1.000. The specific gravity of urine varies from 1.001 to 1.030. Highly concentrated urine has a higher specific gravity, while the specific gravity of very dilute urine is close to that of water. See Table 9.1 ■ for the normal values for urine testing and Table 9.2 ■ for abnormal findings.

> **MED TERM TIP**
>
> The color, odor, volume, and sugar content of urine have been examined for centuries. Color charts for urine were developed by 1140, and "taste testing" was common in the late seventeenth century. By the nineteenth century, urinalysis was a routine part of a physical examination.

Table 9.1	Values for Urinalysis Testing
ELEMENT	**NORMAL FINDINGS**
Color	Straw-colored, pale yellow to deep gold
Odor	Aromatic
Appearance	Clear
Specific gravity	1.001–1.030
pH	5.0–8.0
Protein	Negative to trace
Glucose	None
Ketones	None
Blood	Negative

Table 9.2	Abnormal Urinalysis Findings
ELEMENT	**IMPLICATIONS**
Color	Color varies depending on the patient's fluid intake and output or medication. Brown or black urine color indicates a serious disease process.
Odor	A fetid or foul odor may indicate infection. While a fruity odor may be found in diabetes mellitus, dehydration, or starvation. Other odors may be due to medication or foods.
Appearance	Cloudiness may mean that an infection is present.
Specific gravity	Concentrated urine has a higher specific gravity. Dilute urine, such as can be found with diabetes insipidus, acute tubular necrosis, or salt-restricted diets, has a lower specific gravity.
pH	A pH value below 7.0 (acidic) is common in urinary tract infections, metabolic or respiratory acidosis, diets high in fruits or vegetables, or administration of some drugs. A pH higher than 7.0 (basic or alkaline) is common in metabolic or respiratory alkalosis, fever, high-protein diets, and taking ascorbic acid.
Protein	Protein may indicate glomerulonephritis or preeclampsia in a pregnant woman.
Glucose	Small amounts of glucose may be present as the result of eating a high-carbohydrate meal, stress, pregnancy, and taking some medications, such as aspirin or corticosteroids. Higher levels may indicate poorly controlled diabetes, Cushing's syndrome, or infection.
Ketones	The presence of ketones may indicate poorly controlled diabetes, dehydration, starvation, or ingestion of large amounts of aspirin.
Blood	Blood may indicate glomerulonephritis, cancer of the urinary tract, some types of anemia, taking of some medications (such as blood thinners), arsenic poisoning, reactions to transfusion, trauma, burns, and convulsions.

▣ Terminology

Word Parts Used to Build Urinary System Terms

The following lists contain the combining forms, suffixes, and prefixes used to build terms in the remaining sections of this chapter.

Combining Forms

azot/o	nitrogenous waste	**keton/o**	ketones	**py/o**	pus
bacteri/o	bacteria	**lith/o**	stone	**pyel/o**	renal pelvis
bi/o	life	**meat/o**	meatus	**ren/o**	kidney
carcin/o	cancer	**necr/o**	death	**ur/o**	urine
corpor/o	body	**nephr/o**	kidney	**ureter/o**	ureter
cyst/o	bladder, pouch	**neur/o**	nerve	**urethr/o**	urethra
glomerul/o	glomerulus	**noct/i**	night	**urin/o**	urine
glycos/o	sugar	**olig/o**	scanty	**ven/o**	vein
hem/o	blood	**peritone/o**	peritoneum		
hemat/o	blood	**protein/o**	protein		

Suffixes

-al	pertaining to	**-lithiasis**	condition of stones	**-pathy**	disease
-algia	pain	**-logist**	one who studies	**-pexy**	surgical fixation
-ar	pertaining to	**-logy**	study of	**-plasty**	surgical repair
-ary	pertaining to	**-lysis**	to destroy (to break down)	**-ptosis**	drooping
-cele	protrusion			**-rrhagia**	abnormal flow condition
-eal	pertaining to	**-malacia**	softening		
-ectasis	dilated	**-megaly**	enlarged	**-sclerosis**	hardening
-ectomy	surgical removal	**-meter**	instrument to measure	**-scope**	instrument to visually examine
-emia	blood condition	**-oma**	tumor	**-scopy**	process of visually examining
-genic	produced by	**-ory**	pertaining to		
-gram	record	**-osis**	abnormal condition	**-stenosis**	narrowing
-graphy	process of recording	**-ostomy**	create a new opening	**-tic**	pertaining to
-ic	pertaining to	**-otomy**	cutting into	**-tripsy**	surgical crushing
-itis	inflammation	**-ous**	pertaining to	**-uria**	urine condition
-lith	stone				

Prefixes

an-	without	**extra-**	outside of	**poly-**	many
anti-	against	**hydro-**	water	**retro-**	backward
dys-	abnormal, difficult	**intra-**	within		

Anatomical Terms

TERM	WORD PARTS	DEFINITION
cystic (SIS-tik)	cyst/o = bladder -ic = pertaining to	Pertaining to the bladder.
renal (REE-nal)	ren/o = kidney -al = pertaining to	Pertaining to the kidney.
ureteral (yoo-REE-ter-all)	ureter/o = ureter -al = pertaining to	Pertaining to the ureter.

> **MED TERM TIP**
>
> Word Watch: Be particularly careful when using the three very similar combining forms: *uter/o* meaning "uterus," *ureter/o* meaning "ureter," and *urethr/o* meaning "urethra."

TERM	WORD PARTS	DEFINITION
urethral (yoo-REE-thral)	urethr/o = urethra -al = pertaining to	Pertaining to the urethra.
urinary (yoo-rih-NAIR-ee)	urin/o = urine -ary = pertaining to	Pertaining to urine.

Pathology

TERM	WORD PARTS	DEFINITION
Medical Specialties		
nephrology (neh-FROL-oh-jee)	nephr/o = kidney -logy = study of	Branch of medicine involved in diagnosis and treatment of diseases and disorders of the kidney. Physician is a *nephrologist*.
urology (yoo-RAL-oh-jee)	ur/o = urine -logy = study of	Branch of medicine involved in diagnosis and treatment of diseases and disorders of the urinary system (and male reproductive system). Physician is a *urologist*.
Signs and Symptoms		
anuria (an-YOO-ree-ah)	an- = without -uria = urine condition	Complete suppression of urine formed by the kidneys and a complete lack of urine excretion.
azotemia (a-zo-TEE-mee-ah)	azot/o = nitrogenous waste -emia = blood condition	Accumulation of nitrogenous waste in the bloodstream. Occurs when the kidney fails to filter these wastes from the blood.
bacteriuria (back-teer-ree-YOO-ree-ah)	bacteri/o = bacteria -uria = urine condition	Presence of bacteria in the urine.

Pathology (continued)

TERM	WORD PARTS	DEFINITION
calculus (KAL-kew-lus)		Stone formed within an organ by an accumulation of mineral salts. Found in the kidney, renal pelvis, ureters, bladder, or urethra. Plural is *calculi*.

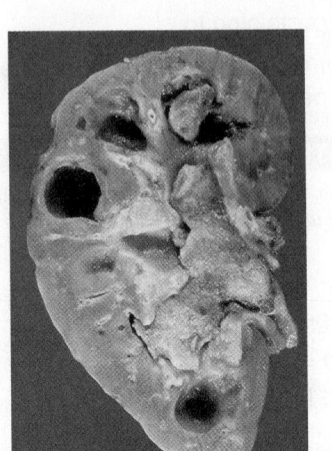

■ **Figure 9.8** Photograph of sectioned kidney specimen illustrating extensive renal calculi. *(Photo Researchers, Inc.)*

TERM	WORD PARTS	DEFINITION
cystalgia (sis-TAL-jee-ah)	cyst/o = bladder -algia = pain	Urinary bladder pain.

MED TERM TIP

Word Watch: Be careful using the combining forms *cyst/o* meaning "bladder" and *cyt/o* meaning "cell."

TERM	WORD PARTS	DEFINITION
cystolith (SIS-toh-lith)	cyst/o = bladder -lith = stone	Bladder stone.
cystorrhagia (sis-toh-RAH-jee-ah)	cyst/o = bladder -rrhagia = abnormal flow condition	Profuse bleeding from the urinary bladder.
diuresis (dye-yoo-REE-sis)		Increased formation and excretion of urine.
dysuria (dis-YOO-ree-ah)	dys- = abnormal, difficult -uria = urine condition	Difficult or painful urination.
enuresis (en-yoo-REE-sis)		Involuntary discharge of urine after the age by which bladder control should have been established. This usually occurs by the age of 5. *Nocturnal enuresis* refers to bed-wetting at night.
frequency		Greater-than-normal occurrence in the urge to urinate, without an increase in the total daily volume of urine. Frequency is an indication of inflammation of the bladder or urethra.
glycosuria (glye-kohs-YOO-ree-ah)	glycos/o = sugar -uria = urine condition	Presence of sugar in the urine.
hematuria (hee-mah-TOO-ree-ah)	hemat/o = blood -uria = urine condition	Presence of blood in the urine.

Pathology *(continued)*

TERM	WORD PARTS	DEFINITION
hesitancy		Decrease in the force of the urine stream, often with difficulty initiating the flow. It is often a symptom of a blockage along the urethra, such as an enlarged prostate gland.
ketonuria (key-tone-YOO-ree-ah)	keton/o = ketones -uria = urine condition	Presence of ketones in the urine. This occurs when the body burns fat instead of glucose for energy, such as in uncontrolled diabetes mellitus.
nephrolith (NEF-roh-lith)	nephr/o = kidney -lith = stone	Kidney stone.
nephromalacia (nef-roh-mah-LAY-she-ah)	nephr/o = kidney -malacia = softening	Kidney is abnormally soft.
nephromegaly (nef-roh-MEG-ah-lee)	nephr/o = kidney -megaly = enlarged	Kidney is enlarged.
nephrosclerosis (nef-roh-skleh-ROH-sis)	nephr/o = kidney -sclerosis = hardening	Kidney tissue has become hardened.
nocturia (nok-TOO-ree-ah)	noct/i = night -uria = urine condition	Having to urinate frequently during the night.
oliguria (ol-ig-YOO-ree-ah)	olig/o = scanty -uria = urine condition	Producing too little urine.
polyuria (pol-ee-YOO-ree-ah)	poly- = many -uria = urine condition	Producing an unusually large volume of urine.
proteinuria (pro-ten-YOO-ree-ah)	protein/o = protein -uria = urine condition	Presence of protein in the urine.
pyuria (pye-YOO-ree-ah)	py/o = pus -uria = urine condition	Presence of pus in the urine.
renal colic (KOL-ik)	ren/o = kidney -al = pertaining to -ic = pertaining to	Pain caused by a kidney stone. Can be an excruciating pain and generally requires medical treatment.
stricture (STRIK-chur)		Narrowing of a passageway in the urinary system.
uremia (yoo-REE-me-ah)	ur/o = urine -emia = blood condition	Accumulation of waste products (especially nitrogenous wastes) in the bloodstream. Associated with renal failure.
ureterectasis (yoo-ree-ter-EK-tah-sis)	ureter/o = ureter -ectasis = dilated	Ureter is stretched out or dilated.
ureterolith (yoo-REE-teh-roh-lith)	ureter/o = ureter -lith = stone	Stone in the ureter.
ureterostenosis (yoo-ree-ter-oh-sten-OH-sis)	ureter/o = ureter -stenosis = narrowing	Ureter has become narrow.
urethralgia (yoo-ree-THRAL-jee-ah)	urethr/o = urethra -algia = pain	Urethral pain.

Pathology *(continued)*

TERM	WORD PARTS	DEFINITION
urethrorrhagia (yoo-ree-throh-RAH-jee-ah)	urethr/o = urethra -rrhagia = abnormal flow condition	Profuse bleeding from the urethra.
urethrostenosis (yoo-ree-throh-steh-NOH-sis)	urethr/o = urethra -stenosis = narrowing	Urethra has become narrow.
urgency (ER-jen-see)		Feeling the need to urinate immediately.
urinary incontinence (in-CON-tin-ens)	urin/o = urine -ary = pertaining to	Involuntary release of urine. In some patients an indwelling catheter is inserted into the bladder for continuous urine drainage.

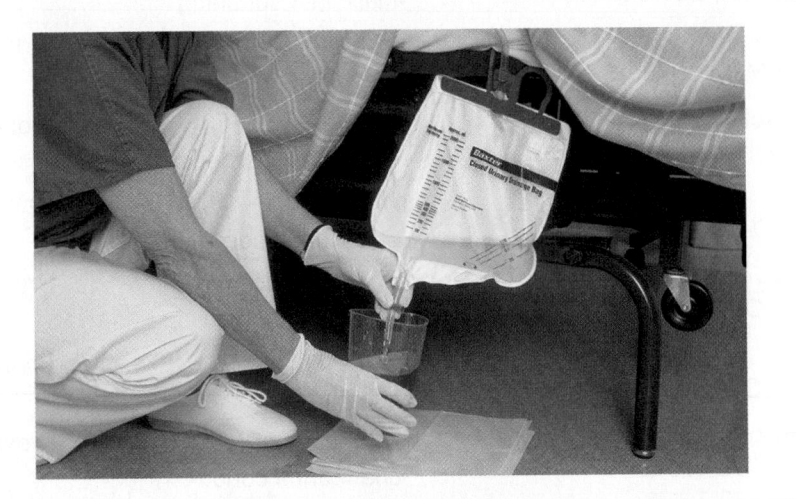

Figure 9.9 Healthcare worker draining urine from a bladder catheter bag.

TERM	WORD PARTS	DEFINITION
urinary retention	urin/o = urine -ary = pertaining to	Inability to fully empty the bladder, often indicates a blockage in the urethra.

Kidney

TERM	WORD PARTS	DEFINITION
acute tubular necrosis (ATN) (ne-KROH-sis)	-ar = pertaining to necr/o = death -osis = abnormal condition	Damage to the renal tubules due to presence of toxins in the urine or to ischemia. Results in oliguria.
diabetic nephropathy (ne-FROH-path-ee)	-ic = pertaining to nephr/o = kidney -pathy = disease	Accumulation of damage to the glomerulus capillaries due to the chronic high blood sugars of diabetes mellitus.
glomerulonephritis (gloh-mair-yoo-loh-neh-FRYE-tis)	glomerul/o = glomerulus nephr/o = kidney -itis = inflammation	Inflammation of the kidney (primarily of the glomerulus). Since the glomerular membrane is inflamed, it becomes more permeable and will allow protein and blood cells to enter the filtrate. Results in protein in the urine (proteinuria) and hematuria.
hydronephrosis (high-droh-neh-FROH-sis)	hydro- = water nephr/o = kidney -osis = abnormal condition	Distention of the renal pelvis due to urine collecting in the kidney; often a result of the obstruction of a ureter.
nephritis (neh-FRYE-tis)	nephr/o = kidney -itis = inflammation	Kidney inflammation.

Pathology *(continued)*

TERM	WORD PARTS	DEFINITION
nephrolithiasis (nef-roh-lith-EE-a-sis)	nephr/o = kidney -lithiasis = condition of stones	Presence of calculi in the kidney. Usually begins with the solidification of salts present in the urine.
nephroma (neh-FROH-ma)	nephr/o = kidney -oma = tumor	Kidney tumor.
nephropathy (neh-FROP-ah-thee)	nephr/o = kidney -pathy = disease	General term describing the presence of kidney disease.
nephroptosis (nef-rop-TOH-sis)	nephr/o = kidney -ptosis = drooping	Downward displacement of the kidney out of its normal location; commonly called a *floating kidney.*
nephrotic syndrome (NS)	nephr/o = kidney -tic = pertaining to	Damage to the glomerulus resulting in protein appearing in the urine, proteinuria, and the corresponding decrease in protein in the bloodstream. Also called *nephrosis.*
polycystic kidneys (POL-ee-sis-tik)	poly- = many cyst/o = pouch -tic = pertaining to	Formation of multiple cysts within the kidney tissue. Results in the destruction of normal kidney tissue and uremia.

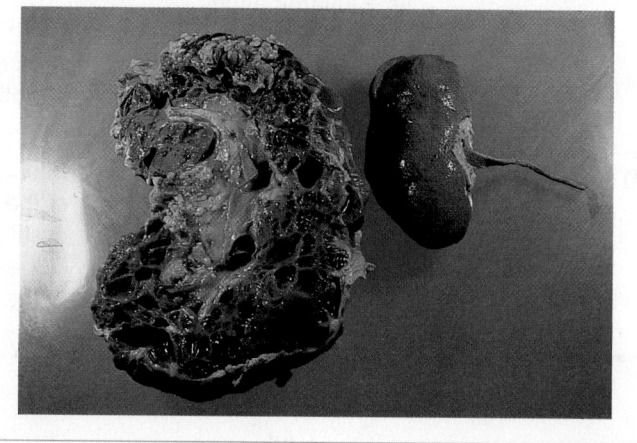

■ **Figure 9.10** Photograph of a polycystic kidney on the left compared to a normal kidney on the right. *(Simon Fraser/ Royal Victoria Infirmary, Newcastle/Science Photo Library/Photo Researchers, Inc.)*

TERM	WORD PARTS	DEFINITION
pyelitis (pye-eh-LYE-tis)	pyel/o = renal pelvis -itis = inflammation	Renal pelvis inflammation.
pyelonephritis (pye-eh-loh-neh-FRYE-tis)	pyel/o = renal pelvis nephr/o = kidney -itis = inflammation	Inflammation of the renal pelvis and the kidney. One of the most common types of kidney disease. It may be the result of a lower urinary tract infection that moved up to the kidney by way of the ureters. There may be large quantities of white blood cells and bacteria in the urine. Blood (hematuria) may even be present in the urine in this condition. Can occur with any untreated or persistent case of cystitis.
renal cell carcinoma	ren/o = kidney -al = pertaining to carcin/o = cancer -oma = tumor	Cancerous tumor that arises from kidney tubule cells.

■ Pathology *(continued)*

TERM	WORD PARTS	DEFINITION
renal failure	ren/o = kidney -al = pertaining to	Inability of the kidneys to filter wastes from the blood resulting in uremia. May be acute or chronic. Major reason for a patient being placed on dialysis.
Wilm's tumor (VILMZ)		Malignant kidney tumor found most often in children.
Urinary Bladder		
bladder cancer		Cancerous tumor that arises from the cells lining the bladder; major sign is hematuria.
bladder neck obstruction (BNO)		Blockage of the bladder outlet. Often caused by an enlarged prostate gland in males.
cystitis (sis-TYE-tis)	cyst/o = bladder -itis = inflammation	Urinary bladder inflammation.
cystocele (SIS-toh-seel)	cyst/o = bladder -cele = protrusion	Hernia or protrusion of the urinary bladder into the wall of the vagina.
interstitial cystitis (in-ter-STISH-al / sis-TYE-tis)	-al = pertaining to cyst/o = bladder -itis = inflammation	Disease of unknown cause in which there is inflammation and irritation of the bladder. Most commonly seen in middle-aged women.
neurogenic bladder (noo-roh-JEN-ik)	neur/o = nerve -genic = produced by	Loss of nervous control that leads to retention; may be caused by spinal cord injury or multiple sclerosis.
urinary tract infection (UTI)	urin/o = urine -ary = pertaining to	Infection, usually from bacteria, of any organ of the urinary system. Most often begins with cystitis and may ascend into the ureters and kidneys. Most common in women because of their shorter urethra.

■ Diagnostic Procedures

TERM	WORD PARTS	DEFINITION
Clinical Laboratory Tests		
blood urea nitrogen (BUN) (yoo-REE-ah / NIGH-troh-jen)		Blood test to measure kidney function by the level of nitrogenous waste (urea) that is in the blood.
clean catch specimen (CC)		Urine sample obtained after cleaning off the urinary opening and catching or collecting a urine sample in midstream (halfway through the urination process) to minimize contamination from the genitalia.

Diagnostic Procedures (continued)

TERM	WORD PARTS	DEFINITION
creatinine clearance (kree-AT-tih-neen)		Test of kidney function. Creatinine is a waste product cleared from the bloodstream by the kidneys. For this test, urine is collected for 24 hours, and the amount of creatinine in the urine is compared to the amount of creatinine that remains in the bloodstream.
urinalysis (U/A, UA) (yoo-rih-NAL-ih-sis)	urin/o = urine -lysis = to destroy (to break down)	Laboratory test consisting of the physical, chemical, and microscopic examination of urine.
urine culture and sensitivity (C&S)		Laboratory test of urine for bacterial infection. Attempt to grow bacteria on a culture medium in order to identify it and determine which antibiotics it is sensitive to.
urinometer (yoo-rin-OH-meter)	urin/o = urine -meter = instrument to measure	Instrument to measure the specific gravity of urine; part of a urinalysis.

Diagnostic Imaging

TERM	WORD PARTS	DEFINITION
cystogram (SIS-toh-gram)	cyst/o = bladder -gram = record	X-ray record of the urinary bladder.
cystography (sis-TOG-rah-fee)	cyst/o = bladder -graphy = process of recording	Process of instilling a contrast material or dye into the bladder by catheter to visualize the urinary bladder on X-ray.
excretory urography (EU) (EKS-kreh-tor-ee / yoo-ROG-rah-fee)	-ory = pertaining to ur/o = urine -graphy = process of recording	Injecting dye into the bloodstream and then taking an X-ray to trace the action of the kidney as it excretes the dye.
intravenous pyelography (IVP) (in-trah-VEE-nus / pye-eh-LOG-rah-fee)	intra- = within ven/o = vein -ous = pertaining to pyel/o = renal pelvis -graphy = process of recording	Diagnostic X-ray procedure in which a dye is injected into a vein and then X-rays are taken to visualize the renal pelvis as the dye is removed by the kidneys.
kidneys, ureters, bladder (KUB)		X-ray taken of the abdomen demonstrating the kidneys, ureters, and bladder without using any contrast dye. Also called a *flat-plate abdomen*.
nephrogram (NEH-fro-gram)	nephr/o = kidney -gram = record	X-ray record of the kidney.
pyelogram (PYE-eh-loh-gram)	pyel/o = renal pelvis -gram = record	X-ray record of the renal pelvis.

Diagnostic Procedures *(continued)*

TERM	WORD PARTS	DEFINITION
retrograde pyelography (RP) (RET-roh-grayd/ pye-eh-LOG-rah-fee)	retro- = backward pyel/o = renal pelvis -graphy = process of recording	Diagnostic X-ray procedure in which dye is inserted through the urethra to outline the bladder, ureters, and renal pelvis.
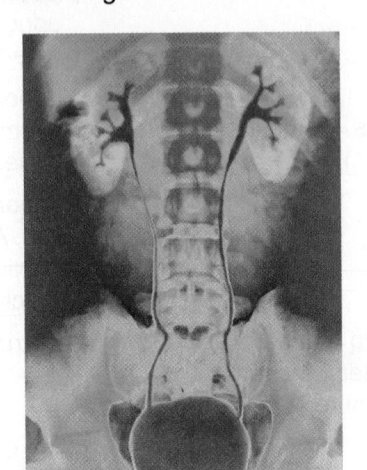 ▪ **Figure 9.11** Color-enhanced retrograde pyelogram X-ray. Radiopaque dye outlines urinary bladder, ureters, and renal pelvis. *(Clinique Ste. Catherine/CNRI/ Science Photo Library/Photo Researchers, Inc.)*		
voiding cystourethrography (VCUG) (sis-toh-yoo-ree-THROG-rah-fee)	cyst/o = bladder urethr/o = urethra -graphy = process of recording	X-ray taken to visualize the urethra while the patient is voiding after a contrast dye has been placed in the bladder.
Endoscopic Procedure		
cystoscope (SIS-toh-scope)	cyst/o = bladder -scope = instrument to visually examine	Instrument used to visually examine the inside of the urinary bladder.
cystoscopy (cysto) (sis-TOSS-koh-pee)	cyst/o = bladder -scopy = process of visually examining	Visual examination of the urinary bladder using an instrument called a *cystoscope*.
urethroscope (yoo-REE-throh-scope)	urethr/o = urethra -scope = instrument to visually examine	Instrument to visually examine the inside of the urethra.

Therapeutic Procedures

TERM	WORD PARTS	DEFINITION
Medical Treatments		
catheter (KATH-eh-ter)		Flexible tube inserted into the body for the purpose of moving fluids into or out of the body. Most commonly used to refer to a tube threaded through the urethra into the bladder to withdraw urine (see again Figure 9.9).
catheterization (cath) (kath-eh-ter-ih-ZAY-shun)		Insertion of a tube through the urethra and into the urinary bladder for the purpose of withdrawing urine or inserting dye.

Therapeutic Procedures *(continued)*

TERM	WORD PARTS	DEFINITION
extracorporeal shockwave lithotripsy (ESWL) (eks-trah-cor-POR-ee-al / shockwave / LITH-oh-trip-see)	extra- = outside of corpor/o = body -eal = pertaining to lith/o = stone -tripsy = surgical crushing	Use of ultrasound waves to break up stones. Process does not require invasive surgery.

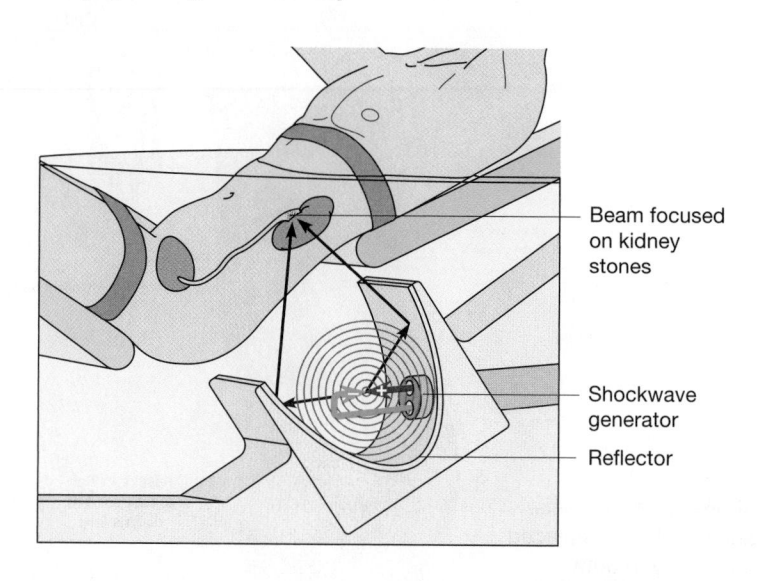

Beam focused on kidney stones

Shockwave generator

Reflector

■ **Figure 9.12** Extracorporeal shockwave lithotripsy, a noninvasive procedure using high-frequency sound waves to shatter kidney stones.

hemodialysis (HD) (hee-moh-dye-AL-ih-sis)	hem/o = blood	Use of an artificial kidney machine that filters the blood of a person to remove waste products. Use of this technique in patients who have defective kidneys is lifesaving.

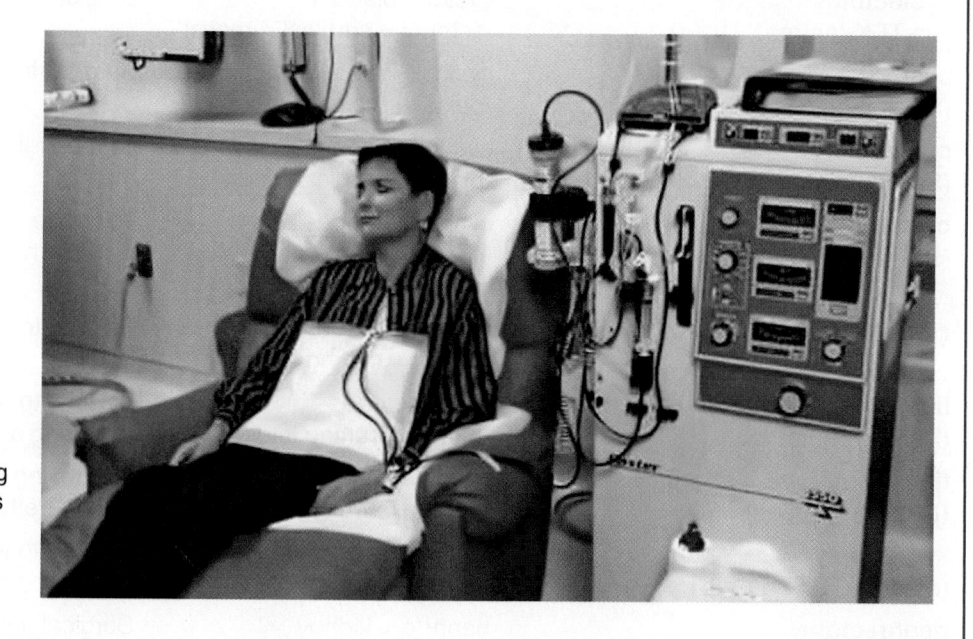

■ **Figure 9.13** Patient undergoing hemodialysis. Patient's blood passes through hemodialysis machine for cleansing and is then returned to her body.

Therapeutic Procedures *(continued)*

TERM	WORD PARTS	DEFINITION
peritoneal dialysis (pair-ih-TOH-nee-al / dye-AL-ih-sis)	peritone/o = peritoneum -eal = pertaining to	Removal of toxic waste substances from the body by placing warm chemically balanced solutions into the peritoneal cavity. Wastes are filtered out of the blood across the peritoneum. Used in treating renal failure and certain poisonings.

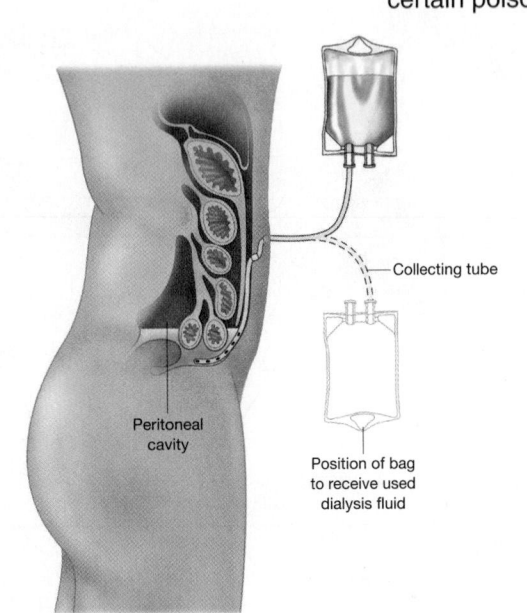

Collecting tube

Peritoneal cavity

Position of bag to receive used dialysis fluid

■ Figure 9.14 Peritoneal dialysis. Chemically balanced solution is placed into the abdominal cavity to draw impurities out of the bloodstream. It is removed after several hours.

Surgical Treatments

TERM	WORD PARTS	DEFINITION
cystectomy (sis-TEK-toh-me)	cyst/o = bladder -ectomy = surgical removal	Surgical removal of the urinary bladder.
cystopexy (SIS-toh-pek-see)	cyst/o = bladder -pexy = surgical fixation	Surgical fixation of the urinary bladder.
cystoplasty (SIS-toh-plas-tee)	cyst/o = bladder -plasty = surgical repair	To repair the urinary bladder by surgical means.
cystostomy (sis-TOSS-toh-mee)	cyst/o = bladder -ostomy = create a new opening	To create a new opening into the urinary bladder through the abdominal wall.
cystotomy (sis-TOT-oh-mee)	cyst/o = bladder -otomy = cutting into	To cut into the urinary bladder.
lithotomy (lith-OT-oh-me)	lith/o = stone -otomy = cutting into	To cut into an organ for the purpose of removing a stone.
lithotripsy (LITH-oh-trip-see)	lith/o = stone -tripsy = surgical crushing	Destroying or crushing stones in the bladder or urethra.
meatotomy (mee-ah-TOT-oh-me)	meat/o = meatus -otomy = cutting into	To cut into the meatus in order to enlarge the opening of the urethra.
nephrectomy (ne-FREK-toh-mee)	nephr/o = kidney -ectomy = surgical removal	Surgical removal of a kidney.
nephrolithotomy (nef-roh-lith-OT-oh-mee)	nephr/o = kidney lith/o = stone -otomy = cutting into	To cut into the kidney in order to remove stones.

Therapeutic Procedures *(continued)*

TERM	WORD PARTS	DEFINITION
nephropexy (NEF-roh-pek-see)	nephr/o = kidney -pexy = surgical fixation	Surgical fixation of a kidney; to anchor it in its normal anatomical position.
nephrostomy (neh-FROS-toh-mee)	nephr/o = kidney -ostomy = create a new opening	To create a new opening into the kidney through the abdominal wall.
nephrotomy (neh-FROT-oh-mee)	nephr/o = kidney -otomy = cutting into	To cut into the kidney.
pyeloplasty (PIE-ah-loh-plas-tee)	pyel/o = renal pelvis -plasty = surgical repair	To repair the renal pelvis by surgical means.
renal transplant	ren/o = kidney -al = pertaining to	Surgical placement of a donor kidney.

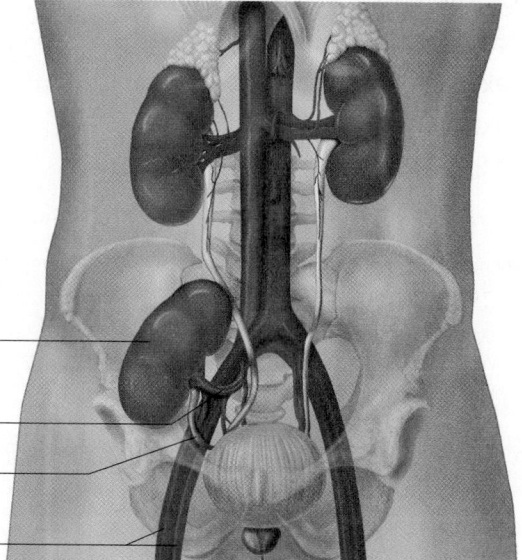

Transplanted kidney

Internal iliac artery and vein

Grafted ureter

External iliac artery and vein

■ **Figure 9.15** Figure illustrates location utilized for implantation of donor kidney.

Pharmacology

CLASSIFICATION	WORD PARTS	ACTION	EXAMPLES
antibiotic	anti- = against bi/o = life -tic = pertaining to	Used to treat bacterial infections of the urinary tract.	ciprofloxacin, Cipro; nitrofurantoin, Macrobid
antispasmodic (an-tye-spaz-MAH-dik)	anti- = against -ic = pertaining to	Medication to prevent or reduce bladder muscle spasms.	oxybutynin, Ditropan; neostigmine, Prostigmine
diuretic (dye-yoo-REH-tiks)	-tic = pertaining to	Medication that increases the volume of urine produced by the kidneys. Useful in the treatment of edema, kidney failure, heart failure, and hypertension.	furosemide, Lasix; spironolactone, Aldactone

Abbreviations

AGN	acute glomerulonephritis		HD	hemodialysis
ARF	acute renal failure		H₂O	water
ATN	acute tubular necrosis		I&O	intake and output
BNO	bladder neck obstruction		IPD	intermittent peritoneal dialysis
BUN	blood urea nitrogen		IVP	intravenous pyelogram
CAPD	continuous ambulatory peritoneal dialysis		K⁺	potassium
cath	catheterization		KUB	kidney, ureter, bladder
CC	clean catch urine specimen		mL	milliliter
Cl⁻	chloride		Na⁺	sodium
CRF	chronic renal failure		NS	nephrotic syndrome
C&S	culture and sensitivity		pH	acidity or alkalinity of urine
cysto	cystoscopy		RP	retrograde pyelogram
ESRD	end-stage renal disease		SG, sp. gr.	specific gravity
ESWL	extracorporeal shockwave lithotripsy		U/A, UA	urinalysis
EU	excretory urography		UC	urine culture
GU	genitourinary		UTI	urinary tract infection
HCO₃⁻	bicarbonate		VCUG	voiding cystourethrography

H_2O — water
Cl^- — chloride
K^+ — potassium
Na^+ — sodium
HCO_3^- — bicarbonate

Chapter Review

Real-World Applications

Medical Record Analysis

This Discharge Summary contains 13 medical terms. Underline each term and write it in the list below the report. Then define each term.

Discharge Summary

Admitting Diagnosis:	Severe right side pain and hematuria.
Final Diagnosis:	Pyelonephritis right kidney, complicated by chronic cystitis.
History of Present Illness:	Patient has long history of frequent bladder infections, but denies any recent lower pelvic pain or dysuria. Earlier today he had rapid onset of severe right side pain and is unable to stand fully erect. His temperature was 101°F, and his skin was sweaty and flushed. He was admitted from the ER for further testing and diagnosis.
Summary of Hospital Course:	Clean catch urinalysis revealed gross hematuria and pyuria, but no albuminuria. A culture and sensitivity was ordered to identify the pathogen and an antibiotic was started. Cystoscopy showed evidence of chronic cystitis, bladder irritation, and a bladder neck obstruction. The obstruction appears to be congenital and the probable cause of the chronic cystitis. The patient was catheterized to ensure complete emptying of the bladder, and fluids were encouraged. Patient responded well to the antibiotic therapy and fluids, and his symptoms improved.
Discharge Plans:	Patient was discharged home after 3 days in the hospital. He was switched to an oral antibiotic for the pyelonephritis and chronic cystitis. A repeat urinalysis is scheduled for next week. After all inflammation is corrected, will repeat cystoscopy to reevaluate bladder neck obstruction.

	Term		Definition
1	_____		_____
2	_____		_____
3	_____		_____
4	_____		_____
5	_____		_____
6	_____		_____
7	_____		_____
8	_____		_____
9	_____		_____
10	_____		_____
11	_____		_____
12	_____		_____
13	_____		_____

Chart Note Transcription

The chart note below contains 11 phrases that can be reworded with a medical term that you learned in this chapter. Each phrase is identified with an underline. Determine the medical term and write your answers in the space provided.

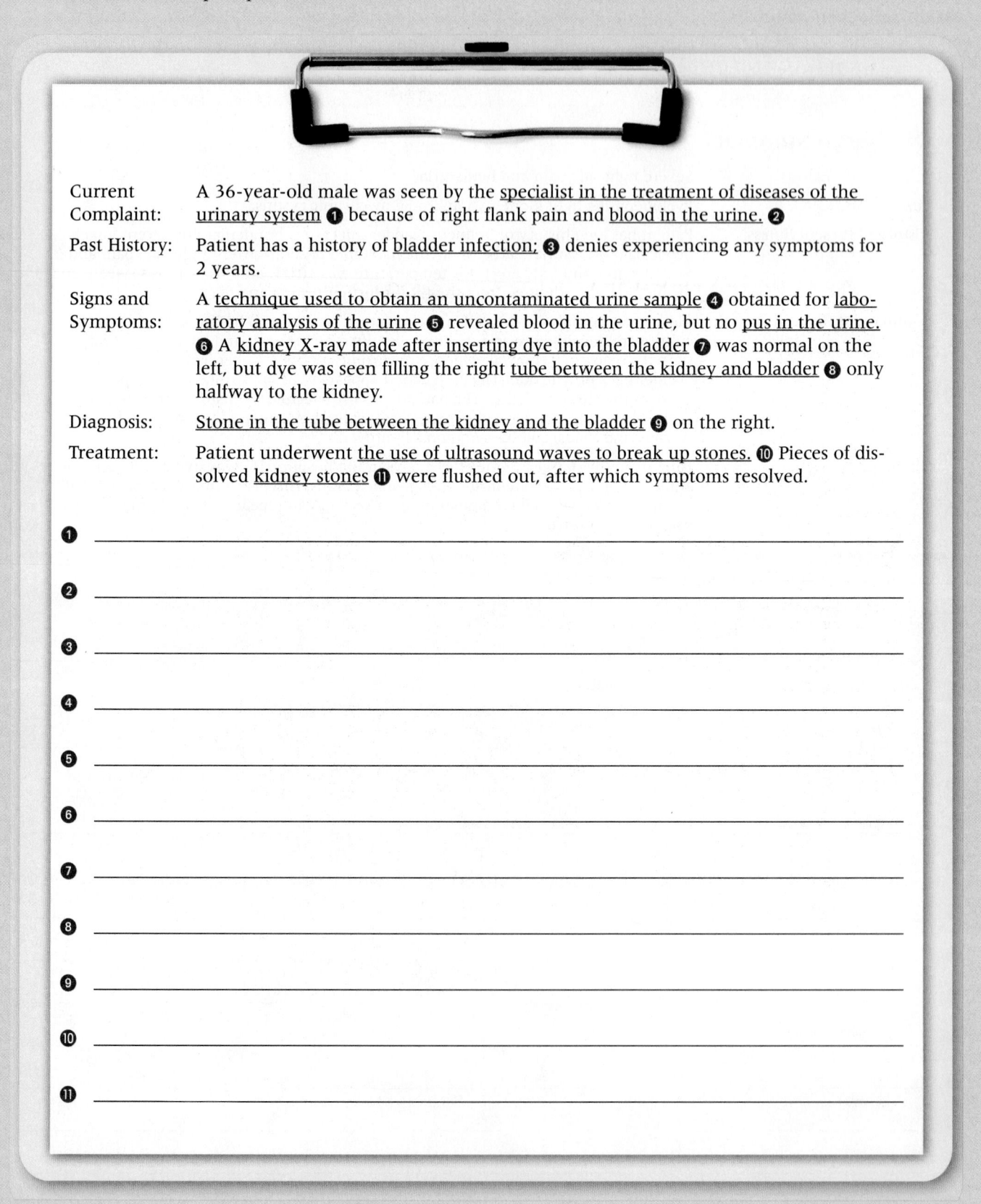

Current Complaint: A 36-year-old male was seen by the specialist in the treatment of diseases of the urinary system ❶ because of right flank pain and blood in the urine. ❷

Past History: Patient has a history of bladder infection; ❸ denies experiencing any symptoms for 2 years.

Signs and Symptoms: A technique used to obtain an uncontaminated urine sample ❹ obtained for laboratory analysis of the urine ❺ revealed blood in the urine, but no pus in the urine. ❻ A kidney X-ray made after inserting dye into the bladder ❼ was normal on the left, but dye was seen filling the right tube between the kidney and bladder ❽ only halfway to the kidney.

Diagnosis: Stone in the tube between the kidney and the bladder ❾ on the right.

Treatment: Patient underwent the use of ultrasound waves to break up stones. ❿ Pieces of dissolved kidney stones ⓫ were flushed out, after which symptoms resolved.

❶ _____

❷ _____

❸ _____

❹ _____

❺ _____

❻ _____

❼ _____

❽ _____

❾ _____

❿ _____

⓫ _____

Case Study

Below is a case study presentation of a patient with a condition discussed in this chapter. Read the case study and answer the questions below. Some questions will ask for information not included within this chapter. Use your text, a medical dictionary, or any other reference material you choose to answer these questions.

(Gina Smith/Shutterstock)

A 32-year-old female is seen in the urologist's office because of a fever, chills, and generalized fatigue. She also reported urgency, frequency, dysuria, and hematuria. In addition, she noticed that her urine was cloudy with a fishy odor. The physician ordered the following tests: a clean catch specimen for a U/A, a urine C&S, and a KUB. The U/A revealed pyuria, bacteriuria, and a slightly acidic pH. A common type of bacteria was grown in the culture. X-rays reveal acute pyelonephritis resulting from cystitis, which has spread up to the kidney from the bladder. The patient was placed on an antibiotic and encouraged to "push fluids" by drinking 2L of water a day.

Questions

1. This patient has two urinary system infections in different locations; name them. Which one caused the other and how?

   _____

   _____

2. List and define each of the patient's presenting symptoms in your own words.

   _____

   _____

3. What diagnostic tests did the urologist order? Describe them in your own words.

   _____

   _____

4. Explain the results of each diagnostic test in your own words.

   _____

   _____

5. What were the physician's treatment instructions for this patient? Explain the purpose of each treatment.

   _____

   _____

6. Describe the normal appearance of urine.

   _____

   _____

Practice Exercises

A. Complete the Statement

1. The functional or working units of the kidneys are the _____.

2. The three stages of urine production are _____, _____,

   and _____.

3. Na⁺, K⁺, and Cl⁻ are collectively known as _____.

4. The term that describes the location of the kidneys is _____.

5. The center of the concave side of the kidney is the _____.

6. The glomerular capsule surrounds the _____.

7. The tip of each renal pyramid opens into a(n) _____.

8. There are _____ ureters and _____ urethra.

9. Urination can also be referred to as _____ or _____.

10. A(n) _____ is the physical and chemical analysis of urine.

B. Combining Form Practice

The combining form **nephr/o** refers to the kidney. Use it to write a term that means:

1. surgical fixation of the kidney _____

2. X-ray record of the kidney _____

3. condition of kidney stones _____

4. removal of a kidney _____

5. inflammation of the kidney _____

6. kidney disease _____

7. hardening of the kidney _____

The combining form **cyst/o** refers to the urinary bladder. Use it to write a term that means:

8. inflammation of the bladder _____

9. abnormal flow condition from the bladder _____

10. surgical repair of the bladder _____

11. instrument to view inside the bladder _____

12. bladder pain _____

The combining form **pyel/o** refers to the renal pelvis. Use it to write a term that means:

13. surgical repair of the renal pelvis _____

14. inflammation of the renal pelvis _____

15. X-ray record of the renal pelvis _____

The combining form **ureter/o** refers to one or both of the ureters. Use it to write a term that means:

16. a ureteral stone _____

17. ureter dilation _____

18. ureter narrowing _____

The combining form **urethr/o** refers to the urethra. Use it to write a term that means:

19. urethra inflammation _____

20. instrument to view inside the urethra _____

C. Define the Combining Form

	Definition	Example from Chapter
1. **ur/o**		
2. **meat/o**		
3. **cyst/o**		
4. **ren/o**		
5. **pyel/o**		
6. **glycos/o**		
7. **noct/i**		
8. **olig/o**		
9. **ureter/o**		
10. **glomerul/o**		

D. Pharmacology Challenge

Fill in the classification for each drug description, then match the brand name.

Drug Description	Classification	Brand Name
1. _____ Reduces bladder muscle spasms	_____	a. Lasix
2. _____ Treats bacterial infections	_____	b. Ditropan
3. _____ Increases volume of urine produced	_____	c. Cipro

E. Define the Term

1. micturition _____

2. diuretic _____

3. renal colic _____

4. catheterization _____

5. pyelitis _____

6. glomerulonephritis _____

7. lithotomy _____

8. enuresis _____

9. meatotomy _____

10. diabetic nephropathy _____

11. urinalysis _____

12. hesitancy _____

F. Name That Term

1. absence of urine _____

2. blood in the urine _____

3. kidney stone _____

4. crushing a stone _____

5. inflammation of the urethra _____

6. pus in the urine _____

7. bacteria in the urine _____

8. painful urination _____

9. ketones in the urine _____

10. protein in the urine _____

11. (too) much urine _____

G. What's the Abbreviation?

1. potassium _____

2. sodium _____

3. urinalysis _____

4. blood urea nitrogen _____

5. specific gravity _____

6. intravenous pyelogram _____

7. bladder neck obstruction _____

8. intake and output _____

9. acute tubular necrosis _____

10. end stage renal disease _____

H. What Does it Stand For?

1. KUB _____

2. cath _____

3. cysto _____

4. GU _____

5. ESWL _____

6. UTI _____

7. UC _____

8. RP _____

9. ARF _____

10. BUN _____

11. CRF _____

12. H$_2$O _____

I. Terminology Matching

Match each term to its definition.

1.	_____ Wilm's tumor	a.	kidney stones
2.	_____ electrolytes	b.	feeling the need to urinate immediately
3.	_____ nephrons	c.	childhood malignant kidney tumor
4.	_____ nephron loop	d.	swelling of the kidney due to urine collecting in the renal pelvis
5.	_____ calyx	e.	involuntary release of urine
6.	_____ incontinence	f.	collects urine as it is produced
7.	_____ hydronephrosis	g.	sodium and potassium
8.	_____ urgency	h.	functional unit of the kidneys
9.	_____ nephrolithiasis	i.	part of the renal tubule
10.	_____ polycystic kidneys	j.	multiple cysts in the kidneys

J. Define the Suffix

	Definition	Example from Chapter
1. -ptosis	_____	_____
2. -uria	_____	_____
3. -lith	_____	_____
4. -tripsy	_____	_____
5. -lithiasis	_____	_____

K. Fill in the Blank

renal transplant	ureterectomy	intravenous pyelogram (IVP)
cystostomy	pyelolithectomy	nephropexy
renal biopsy	cystoscopy	urinary tract infection

1. Juan suffered from chronic renal failure. His sister, Maria, donated one of her normal kidneys to him, and he had a(n)

   _____.

2. Anesha's floating kidney needed surgical fixation. Her physician performed a surgical procedure known as

   _____.

3. Kenya's physician stated that she had a general infection that he referred to as a UTI. The full name for this infection is

   _____.

4. The surgeons operated on Robert to remove calculi from his renal pelvis. The name of this surgery is

   _____.

5. Charles had to have a small piece of his kidney tissue removed so that the physician could perform a microscopic evalua-

   tion. This procedure is called a(n) _____.

6. Naomi had to have one of her ureters removed due to a stricture. This procedure is called _____.

7. The physician had to create a temporary opening between Eric's bladder and his abdominal wall. This procedure is called

   _____.

8. Sally's bladder was visually examined using a special instrument. This procedure is called a(n) _____.

9. The doctors believe that Jacob has a tumor of the right kidney. They are going to do a test called a(n) _____

   that requires them to inject a radiopaque contrast medium intravenously so that they can see the kidney on X-ray.

Labeling Exercise

Image A

Write the labels for this figure on the numbered lines provided.

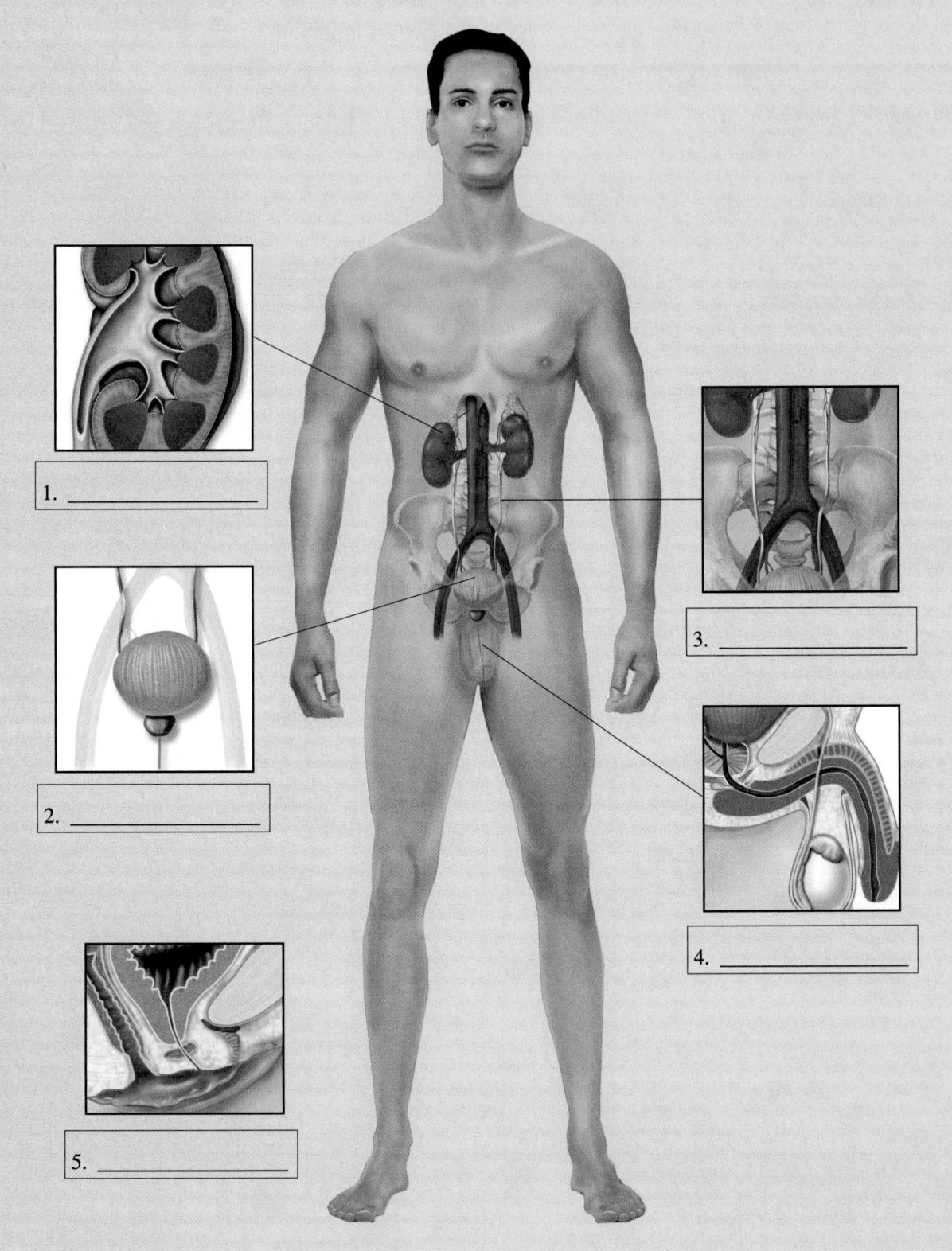

1. _____

2. _____

3. _____

4. _____

5. _____

Image B

Write the labels for this figure on the numbered lines provided.

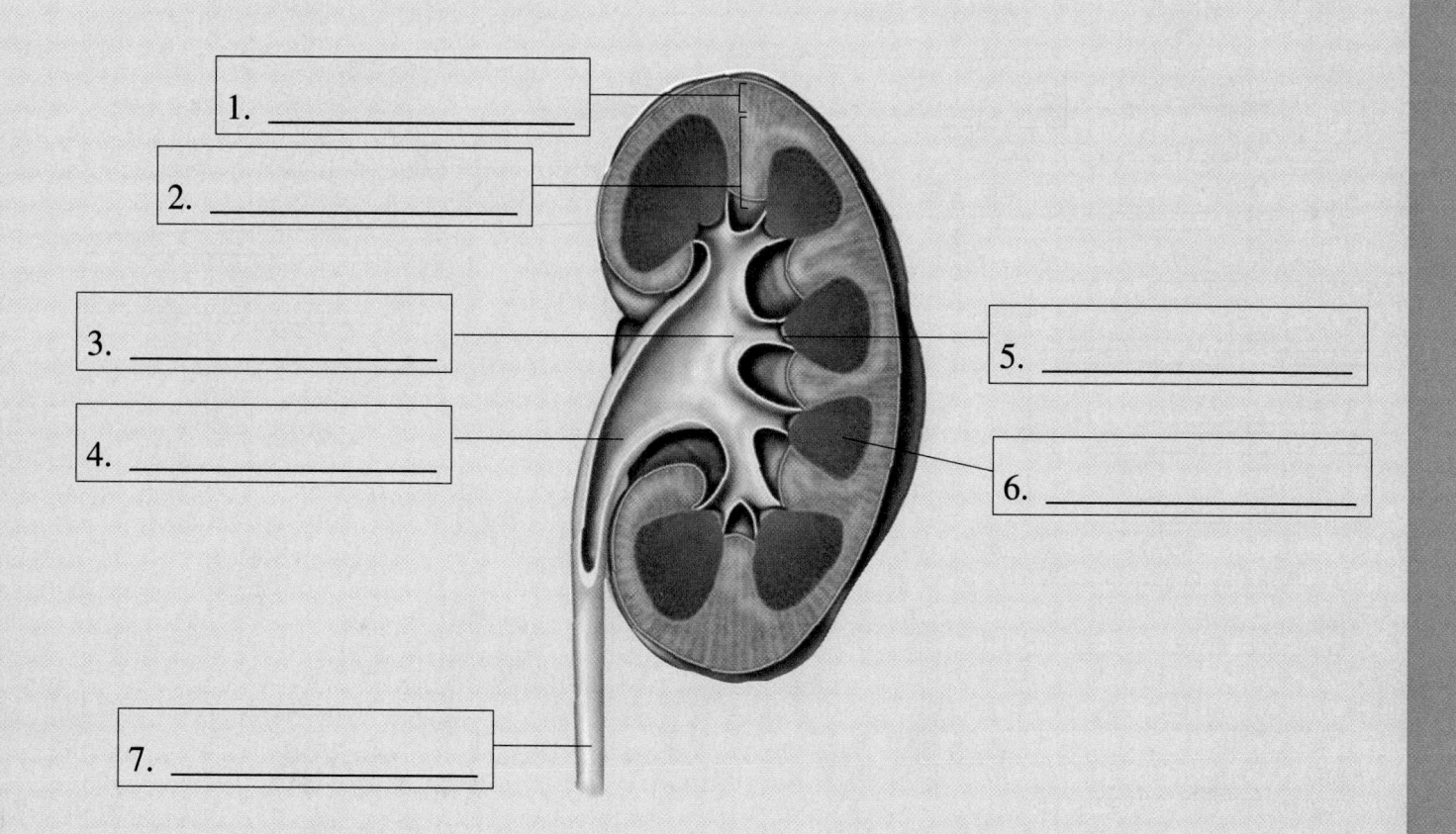

1. _____

2. _____

3. _____

4. _____

5. _____

6. _____

7. _____

Image C

Write the labels for this figure on the numbered lines provided.

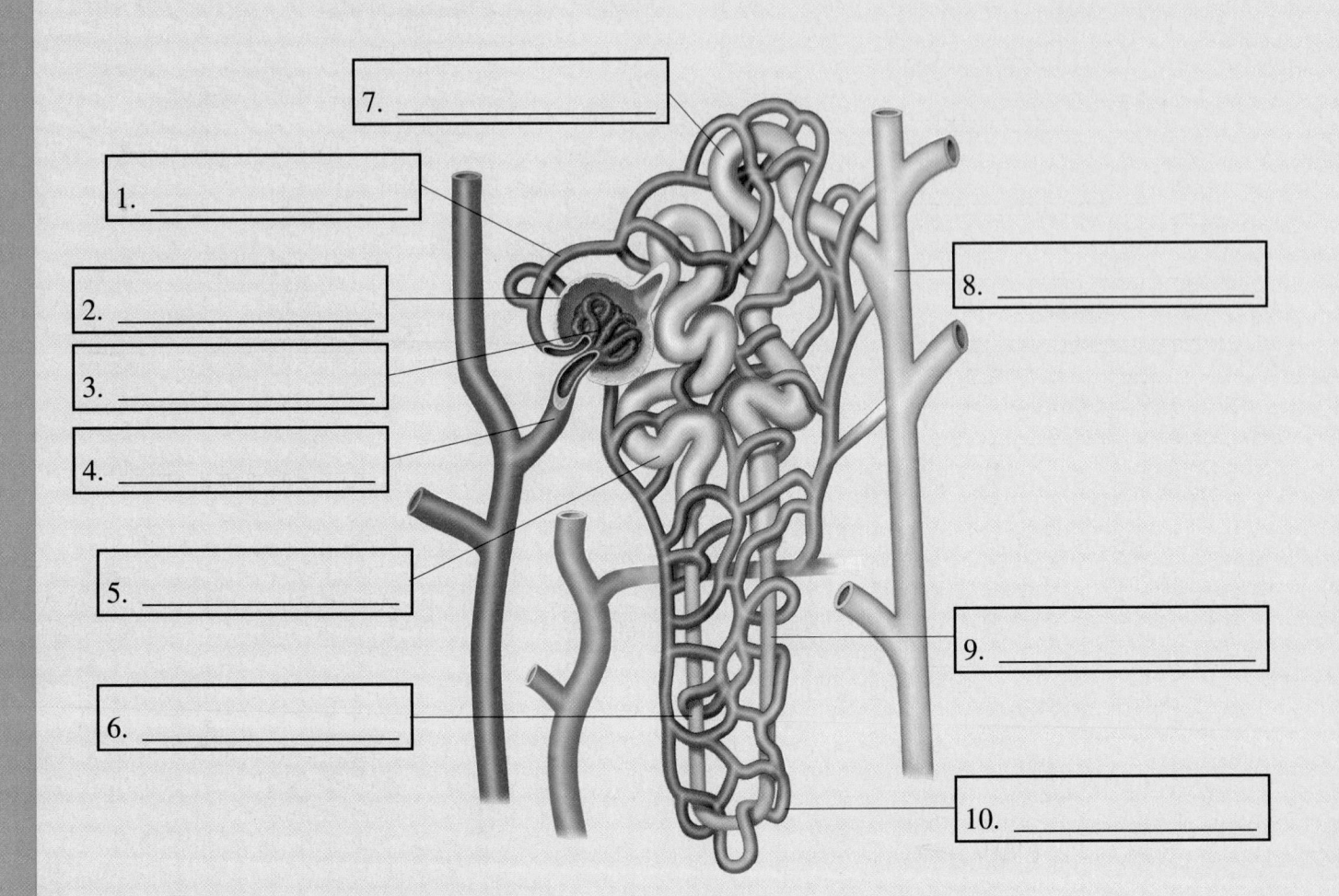

7. _____

1. _____

2. _____

3. _____

4. _____

5. _____

6. _____

8. _____

9. _____

10. _____

REPRODUCTIVE SYSTEM

Learning Objectives

Upon completion of this chapter, you will be able to

- Identify and define the combining forms and suffixes introduced in this chapter.

- Correctly spell and pronounce medical terms and major anatomical structures relating to the reproductive systems.

- Locate and describe the major organs of the reproductive systems and their functions.

- Use medical terms to describe circumstances relating to pregnancy.

- Identify the symptoms and origin of sexually transmitted diseases.

- Identify and define reproductive system anatomical terms.

- Identify and define selected reproductive system pathology terms.

- Identify and define selected reproductive system diagnostic procedures.

- Identify and define selected reproductive system therapeutic procedures.

- Identify and define selected medications relating to the reproductive systems.

- Define selected abbreviations associated with the reproductive systems.

Section I: Female Reproductive System at a Glance

Function

The female reproductive system produces ova (the female reproductive cells), provides a location for fertilization and growth of a baby, and secretes female sex hormones. In addition, the breasts produce milk to nourish the newborn.

Organs

Here are the primary structures that comprise the cardiovascular system.

breasts	uterus
uterine tubes	vagina
ovaries	vulva

Word Parts

Here are the most common word parts (with their meanings) used to build female reproductive system terms. For a more comprehensive list, refer to the Terminology section of this chapter.

Combining Forms

amni/o	amnion	men/o	menses, menstruation
cervic/o	neck, cervix		
chori/o	chorion	metr/o	uterus
colp/o	vagina	nat/o	birth
culd/o	cul-de-sac	o/o	egg ← (ov/o)
embry/o	embryo	oophor/o	ovary
episi/o	vulva	ovari/o	ovary
fet/o	fetus	perine/o	perineum
gynec/o	woman, female	salping/o	uterine tubes, fallopian tubes ~~uterine tubes~~
hymen/o	hymen		
hyster/o	uterus	uter/o	uterus
lact/o	milk ← (galact/o)	vagin/o	vagina
mamm/o	breast	vulv/o	vulva
mast/o	breast		

Suffixes

-arche	beginning
-cyesis	state of pregnancy
-gravida	pregnancy
-para	to bear (offspring)
-partum	childbirth
-salpinx	uterine tube (fallopian tube)
-tocia	labor, childbirth

Image B

Write the labels for this figure on the numbered lines provided.

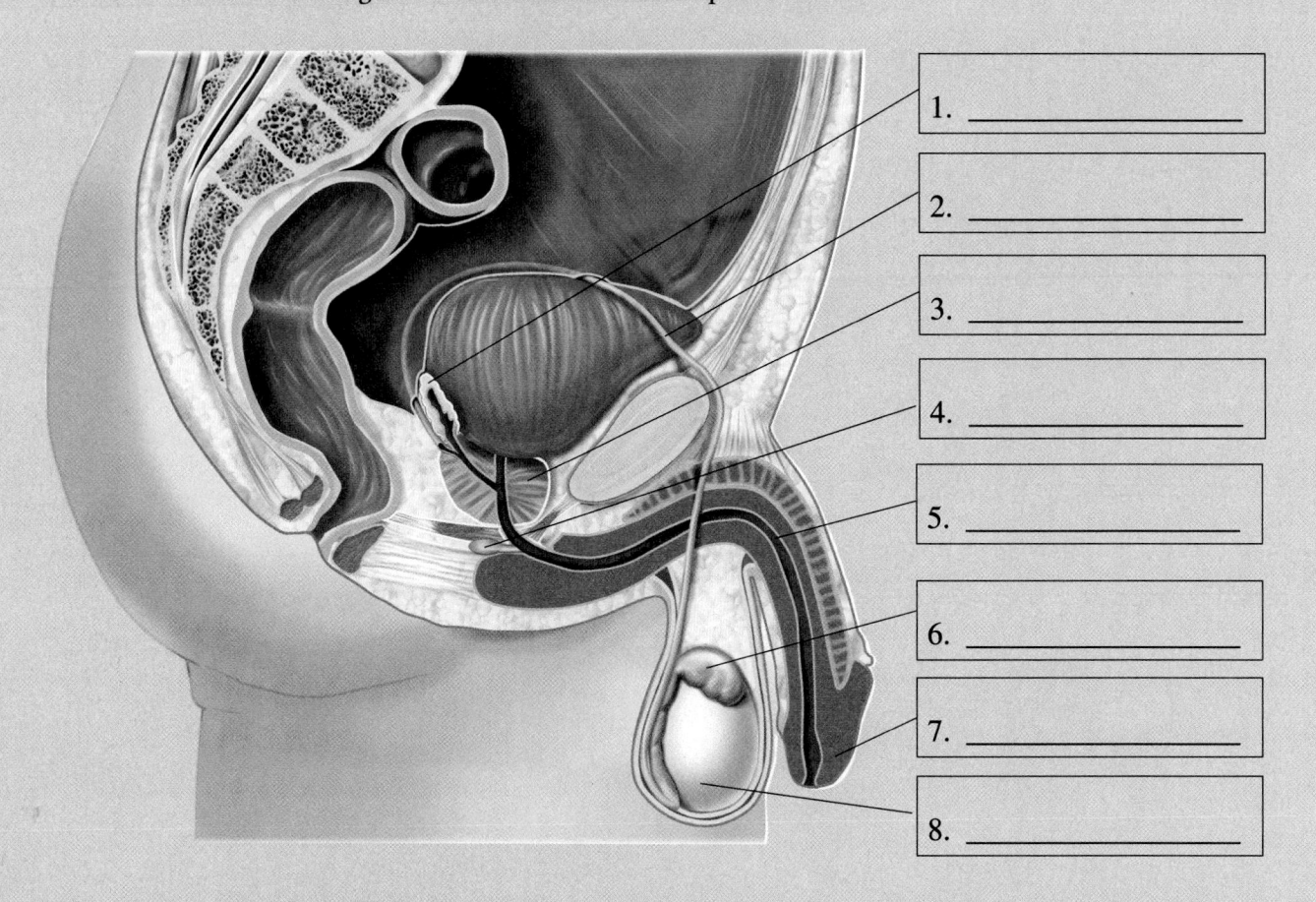

1. _____

2. _____

3. _____

4. _____

5. _____

6. _____

7. _____

8. _____

Image C

Write the labels for this figure on the numbered lines provided.

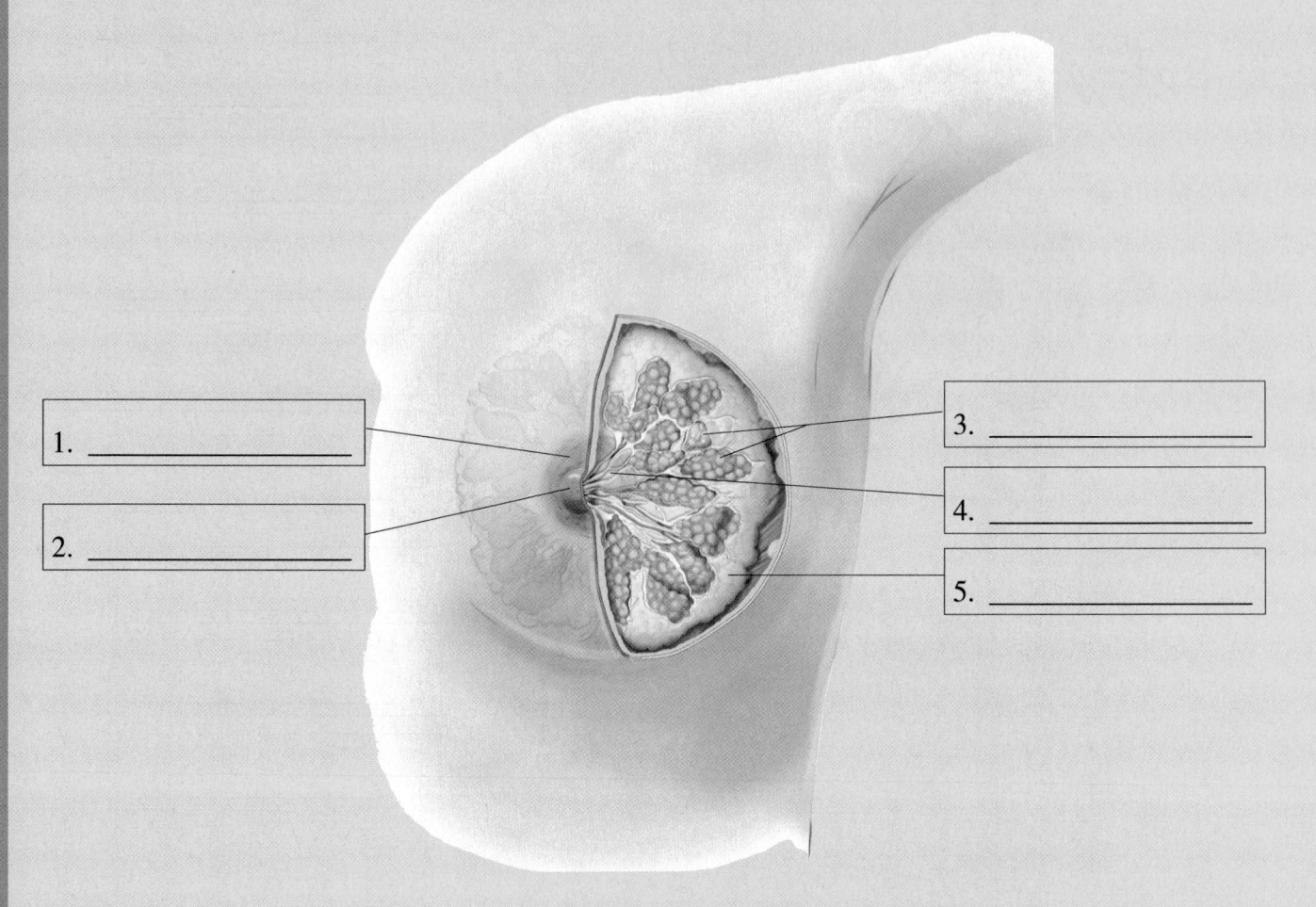

1. _____

2. _____

3. _____

4. _____

5. _____

ENDOCRINE SYSTEM

Learning Objectives

Upon completion of this chapter, you will be able to

- Identify and define the combining forms and suffixes introduced in this chapter.

- Correctly spell and pronounce medical terms and major anatomical structures relating to the endocrine system.

- Locate and describe the major organs of the endocrine system and their functions.

- List the major hormones secreted by each endocrine gland and describe their functions.

- Identify and define endocrine system anatomical terms.

- Identify and define selected endocrine system pathology terms.

- Identify and define selected endocrine system diagnostic procedures.

- Identify and define selected endocrine system therapeutic procedures.

- Identify and define selected medications relating to the endocrine system.

- Define selected abbreviations associated with the endocrine system.

Function

Endocrine glands secrete hormones that regulate many body activities such as metabolic rate, water and mineral balance, immune system reactions, and sexual functioning.

Organs

Here are the primary structures that comprise the endocrine system.

adrenal glands
ovaries
pancreas (islets of Langerhans)
parathyroid glands
pineal gland

pituitary gland
testes
thymus gland
thyroid gland

Word Parts

Here are the most common word parts used to build endocrine system terms. For a more comprehensive list, refer to the Terminology section of this chapter.

Combining Forms

acr/o	extremities	ket/o	ketones
adren/o	adrenal glands	mineral/o	minerals, electrolytes
adrenal/o	adrenal glands	natr/o	sodium
andr/o	male	ophthalm/o	eye
calc/o	calcium	ovari/o	ovary
crin/o	to secrete	pancreat/o	pancreas
estr/o	female	parathyroid/o	parathyroid gland
gluc/o	glucose	pineal/o	pineal gland
glyc/o	sugar	pituitar/o	pituitary gland
glycos/o	sugar	testicul/o	testes
gonad/o	sex glands	thym/o	thymus gland
home/o	sameness	thyr/o	thyroid gland
iod/o	iodine	thyroid/o	thyroid gland
kal/i	potassium	toxic/o	poison

Suffixes

-dipsia	thirst	-pressin	to press down
-prandial	relating to a meal	-tropin	to stimulate

Endocrine System Illustrated

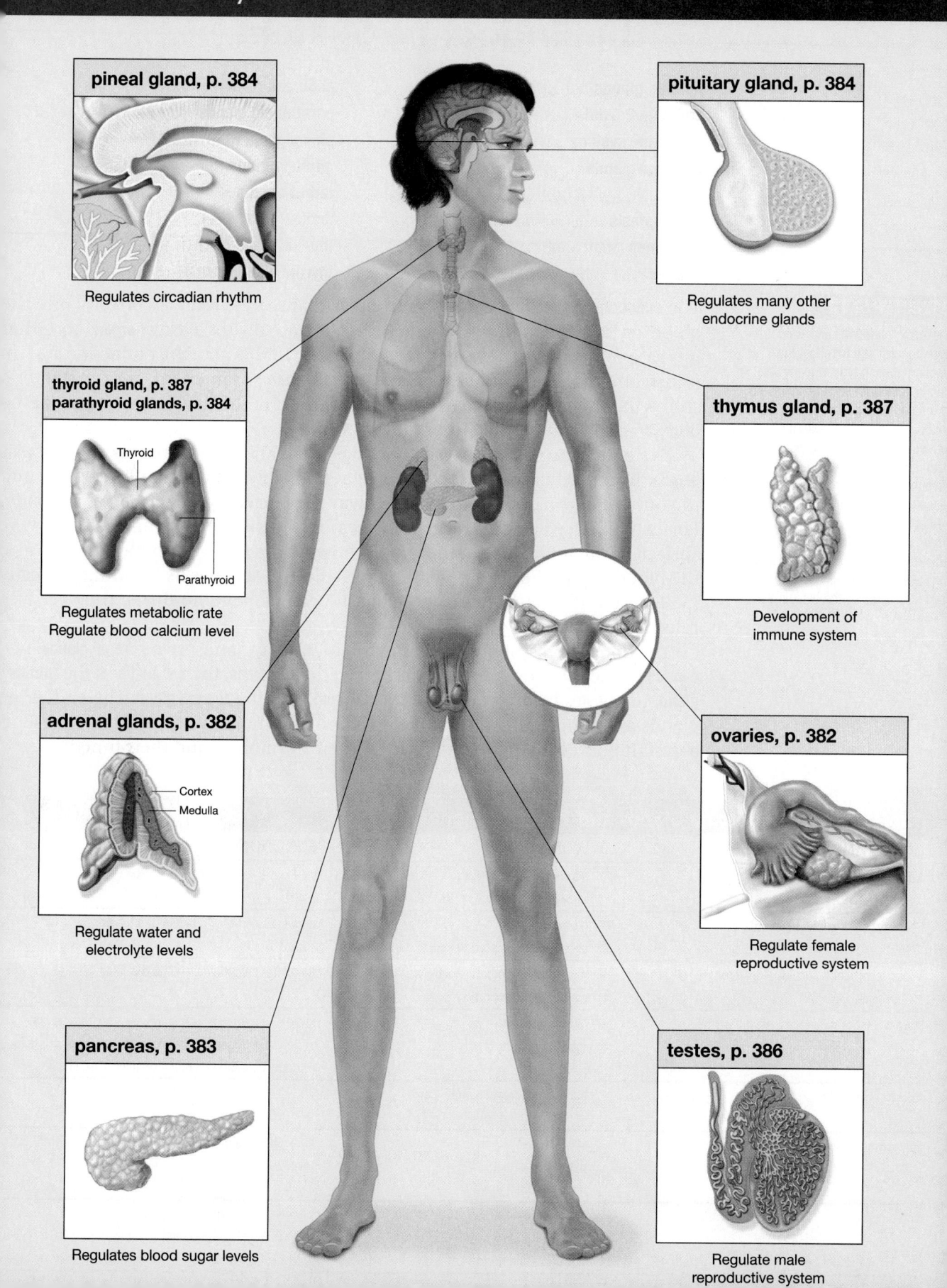

pineal gland, p. 384

Regulates circadian rhythm

pituitary gland, p. 384

Regulates many other endocrine glands

thyroid gland, p. 387
parathyroid glands, p. 384

Thyroid

Parathyroid

Regulates metabolic rate
Regulate blood calcium level

thymus gland, p. 387

Development of immune system

adrenal glands, p. 382

Cortex
Medulla

Regulate water and electrolyte levels

ovaries, p. 382

Regulate female reproductive system

pancreas, p. 383

Regulates blood sugar levels

testes, p. 386

Regulate male reproductive system

▣ Anatomy and Physiology of the Endocrine System

adrenal glands (ad-REE-nal)

endocrine glands (EN-doh-krin)

endocrine system

exocrine glands (EKS-oh-krin)

glands

homeostasis (hoe-me-oh-STAY-sis)

hormones (HOR-mohnz)

ovaries (OH-vah-reez)

pancreas (PAN-kree-ass)

parathyroid glands (pair-ah-THIGH-royd)

pineal gland (pih-NEAL)

pituitary gland (pih-TOO-ih-tair-ee)

target organs

testes (TESS-teez)

thymus gland (THIGH-mus)

thyroid gland (THIGH-royd)

MED TERM TIP

The terms *endocrine* and *exocrine* were constructed to reflect the function of each type of gland. As glands, they both secrete, indicated by the combining form *crin/o*. The prefix *exo-*, meaning "external" or "outward," tells us that exocrine gland secretions are carried to the outside of the body or to a passageway connected to the outside of the body. However, the prefix *endo-*, meaning "within" or "internal," indicates that endocrine gland secretions are carried to other internal body structures by the bloodstream.

The **endocrine system** is a collection of **glands** that secrete **hormones** directly into the bloodstream. Hormones are chemicals that act on their **target organs** to either increase or decrease the target's activity level. In this way the endocrine system is instrumental in maintaining **homeostasis** (*home/o* = sameness; *-stasis* = standing still)—that is, adjusting the activity level of most of the tissues and organs of the body to maintain a stable internal environment.

The body actually has two distinct types of glands: **exocrine glands** and **endocrine glands.** Exocrine glands release their secretions into a duct that carries them to the outside of the body or to a passageway connected to the outside of the body. For example, sweat glands release sweat into a sweat duct that travels to the surface of the body. Endocrine glands, however, release hormones directly into the bloodstream. For example, the thyroid gland secretes its hormones directly into the bloodstream. Because endocrine glands have no ducts, they are also referred to as *ductless glands.*

The endocrine system consists of the following glands: two **adrenal glands,** two **ovaries** in the female, four **parathyroid glands,** the **pancreas,** the **pineal gland,** the **pituitary gland,** two **testes** in the male, the **thymus gland,** and the **thyroid gland.** The endocrine glands as a whole affect the functions of the entire body. Table 11.1 ▣ presents a description of the endocrine glands, their hormones, and their functions.

Table 11.1 Endocrine Glands and Their Hormones

GLAND AND HORMONE	WORD PARTS	FUNCTION
Adrenal cortex	adren/o = adrenal gland -al = pertaining to	
Glucocorticoids such as cortisol	gluc/o = glucose cortic/o = outer portion	Regulates carbohydrate levels in the body.
Mineralocorticoids such as aldosterone	mineral/o = minerals, electrolytes cortic/o = outer portion	Regulates electrolytes and fluid volume in body.
Steroid sex hormones such as androgen	andr/o = male -gen = that which produces	Male sex hormones from adrenal cortex may be converted to estrogens in the bloodstream. Responsible for reproduction and secondary sexual characteristics.
Adrenal medulla	adren/o = adrenal gland -al = pertaining to	
Epinephrine (adrenaline)	epi- = above nephr/o = kidney -ine = pertaining to	Intensifies response during stress; "fight-or-flight" response.
Norepinephrine	epi- = above nephr/o = kidney -ine = pertaining to	Chiefly a vasoconstrictor.

Table 11.1   Endocrine Glands and Their Hormones (continued)

GLAND AND HORMONE	WORD PARTS	FUNCTION
Ovaries		
Estrogen	estr/o = female -gen = that which produces	Stimulates development of secondary sex characteristics in females; regulates menstrual cycle.
Progesterone	pro- = before estr/o = female	Prepares for conditions of pregnancy.
Pancreas		
Glucagon		Stimulates liver to release glucose into the blood.
Insulin		Regulates and promotes entry of glucose into cells.
Parathyroid glands		
Parathyroid hormone (PTH)		Stimulates bone breakdown; regulates calcium level in the blood.
Pituitary anterior lobe		
Adrenocorticotropin hormone (ACTH)	adren/o = adrenal gland cortic/o = outer portion -tropin = to stimulate	Regulates function of adrenal cortex.
Gonadotropins	gonad/o = gonads -tropin = to stimulate	
Follicle-stimulating hormone (FSH)		Stimulates growth of eggs in female and sperm in males.
Luteinizing hormone (LH)		Regulates function of male and female gonads and plays a role in releasing ova in females.
Growth hormone (GH)		Stimulates growth of the body.
Melanocyte-stimulating hormone (MSH)	melan/o = black -cyte = cell	Stimulates pigment in skin.
Prolactin	pro- = before lact/o = milk	Stimulates milk production.
Thyroid-stimulating hormone (TSH)		Regulates function of thyroid gland.
Pituitary posterior lobe		
Antidiuretic hormone (ADH)	anti- = against -tic = pertaining to	Stimulates reabsorption of water by the kidneys.
Oxytocin		Stimulates uterine contractions and releases milk into ducts.
Testes		
Testosterone		Promotes sperm production and development of secondary sex characteristics in males.
Thymus		
Thymosin	thym/o = thymus gland	Promotes development of cells in immune system.
Thyroid gland		
Calcitonin (CT)		Stimulates deposition of calcium into bone.
Thyroxine (T_4)	thyr/o = thyroid gland -ine = pertaining to	Stimulates metabolism in cells.
Triiodothyronine (T_3)	tri- = three iod/o = iodine thyr/o = thyroid gland -ine = pertaining to	Stimulates metabolism in cells.

Adrenal Glands

adrenal cortex (KOR-tex)

adrenal medulla (meh-DOOL-lah)

adrenaline (ah-DREN-ah-lin)

aldosterone (al-DOSS-ter-ohn)

androgens (AN-druh-jenz)

corticosteroids (kor-tih-koh-STAIR-oydz)

cortisol (KOR-tih-sal)

epinephrine (ep-ih-NEF-rin)

estrogen (ESS-troh-jen)

glucocorticoids (gloo-koh-KOR-tih-koydz)

mineralocorticoids
  (min-er-al-oh-KOR-tih-koydz)

norepinephrine (nor-ep-ih-NEF-rin)

progesterone (proh-JESS-ter-ohn)

steroid sex hormones (STAIR-oyd)

The two adrenal glands are located above each of the kidneys (see Figure 11.1 ■). Each gland is composed of two sections: **adrenal cortex** and **adrenal medulla.**

The outer adrenal cortex manufactures several different families of hormones: **mineralocorticoids, glucocorticoids,** and **steroid sex hormones.** However, because they are all produced by the cortex, they are collectively referred to as **corticosteroids.** The mineralocorticoid hormone, **aldosterone,** regulates sodium (Na⁺) and potassium (K⁺) levels in the body. The glucocorticoid hormone, **cortisol,** regulates carbohydrates in the body. The adrenal cortex of both men and women secretes steroid sex hormones, **androgens** (which may be converted to **estrogen** once released into the bloodstream). These hormones regulate secondary sexual characteristics. All hormones secreted by the adrenal cortex are steroid hormones.

The inner adrenal medulla is responsible for secreting the hormones **epinephrine,** also called **adrenaline,** and **norepinephrine.** These hormones are critical during emergency situations because they increase blood pressure, heart rate, and respiration levels. This helps the body perform better during emergencies or otherwise stressful times.

MED TERM TIP

The term *cortex* is frequently used in anatomy to indicate the outer portion of an organ such as the adrenal gland or the kidney. The term *cortex* means "bark," as in the bark of a tree. The term *medulla* means "marrow." Because marrow is found in the inner cavity of bones, the term came to stand for the middle of an organ.

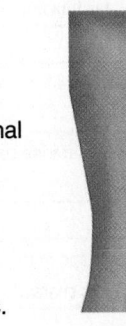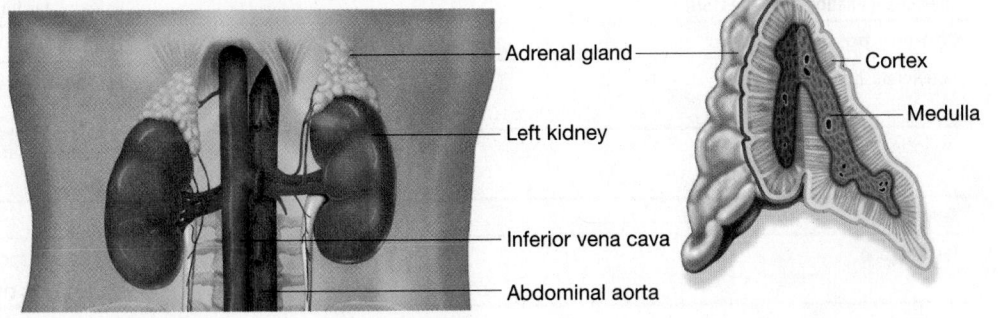

■ **Figure 11.1**   The adrenal glands. These glands sit on top of each kidney. Each adrenal is subdivided into an outer cortex and an inner medulla. Each region secretes different hormones.

Adrenal gland — Cortex

Left kidney — Medulla

Inferior vena cava

Abdominal aorta

Ovaries

estrogen

gametes (gam-EATS)

gonads (GOH-nadz)

menstrual cycle (men-STROO-all)

ova

progesterone

The two ovaries are located in the lower abdominopelvic cavity of the female (see Figure 11.2 ■). They are the female **gonads.** Gonads are organs that produce **gametes** or the reproductive sex cells. In the case of females, the gametes are the **ova.** Of importance to the endocrine system, the ovaries produce the female sex hormones, **estrogen** and **progesterone.** Estrogen is responsible for the appearance of the female sexual characteristics and regulation of the **menstrual cycle.** Progesterone helps to maintain a suitable uterine environment for pregnancy.

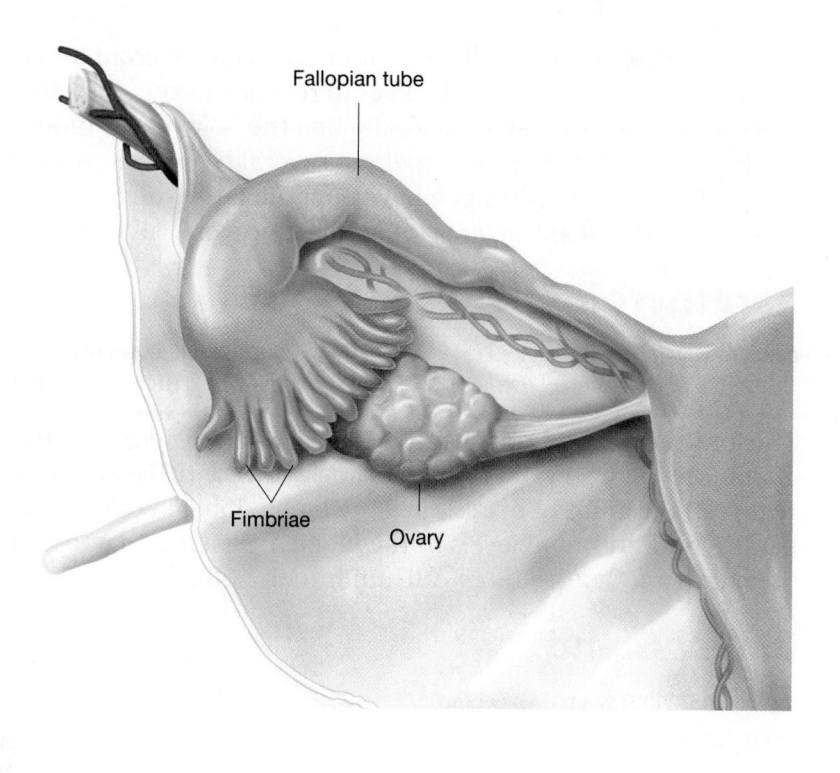

The ovaries. In addition to producing ova, the ovaries secrete the female sex hormones, estrogen and progesterone.

Pancreas

glucagon (GLOO-koh-gon)
insulin (IN-suh-lin)

islets of Langerhans
(EYE-lets / of / LAHNG-er-hahnz)

The pancreas is located along the lower curvature of the stomach (see Figure 11.3A ■). It is the only organ in the body that has both endocrine and exocrine functions. The exocrine portion of the pancreas releases digestive enzymes through a duct into the duodenum of the small intestine. The endocrine sections of the pancreas, **islets of Langerhans,** are named after Dr. Paul Langerhans, a German anatomist. The islets cells produce two different hormones: **insulin** and **glucagon** (see Figure 11.3B ■). Insulin, produced by beta (β) islet cells, stimulates the cells of the body to take in glucose from the bloodstream, lowering the body's blood sugar level. This occurs after a meal has been eaten and the carbohydrates are absorbed into the bloodstream. In this way the cells obtain the glucose they need for cellular respiration.

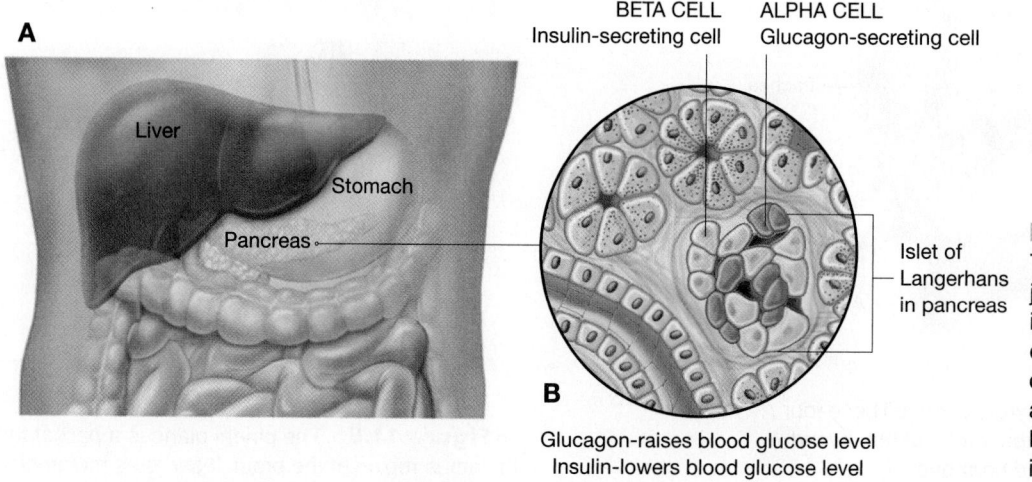

A

BETA CELL
Insulin-secreting cell

ALPHA CELL
Glucagon-secreting cell

Liver
Stomach
Pancreas

Islet of
Langerhans
in pancreas

B

Glucagon-raises blood glucose level
Insulin-lowers blood glucose level

■ Figure 11.3
The pancreas. This organ sits just below the stomach and is both an exocrine and an endocrine gland. The endocrine regions of the pancreas are called the islets of Langerhans and they secrete insulin and glucagon.

Another set of islet cells, the alpha (α) cells, secrete a different hormone, glucagon, which stimulates the liver to release glucose, thereby raising the blood glucose level. Glucagon is released when the body needs more sugar, such as at the beginning of strenuous activity or several hours after the last meal has been digested. Insulin and glucagon have opposite effects on blood sugar level. Insulin will reduce the blood sugar level, while glucagon will increase it.

Parathyroid Glands

calcium   **parathyroid hormone**
                                                      (pair-ah-THIGH-royd / HOR-mohn)

The four tiny parathyroid glands are located on the dorsal surface of the thyroid gland (see Figure 11.4 ■). The **parathyroid hormone** (PTH) secreted by these glands regulates the amount of **calcium** in the blood. If blood calcium levels fall too low, parathyroid hormone levels in the blood are increased and will stimulate bone breakdown to release more calcium into the blood.

Pineal Gland

circadian rhythm (seer-KAY-dee-an)   **melatonin** (mel-ah-TOH-nin)
thalamus (THALL-mus)

The pineal gland is a small pine cone-shaped gland that is part of the **thalamus** region of the brain (see Figure 11.5 ■). The pineal gland secretes **melatonin**, a hormone not well understood, but that plays a role in regulating the body's **circadian rhythm.** This is the 24-hour clock that governs our periods of wakefulness and sleepiness.

Pituitary Gland

adrenocorticotropin hormone   **follicle-stimulating hormone**
   (ah-dree-noh-kor-tih-koh-TROH-pin)   (FOLL-ih-kl / STIM-yoo-lay-ting)
anterior lobe   **gonadotropins** (go-nad-oh-TROH-pins)
antidiuretic hormone   **growth hormone**
   (an-tye-dye-yoo-RET-ik)   **hypothalamus** (high-poh-THAL-ah-mus)

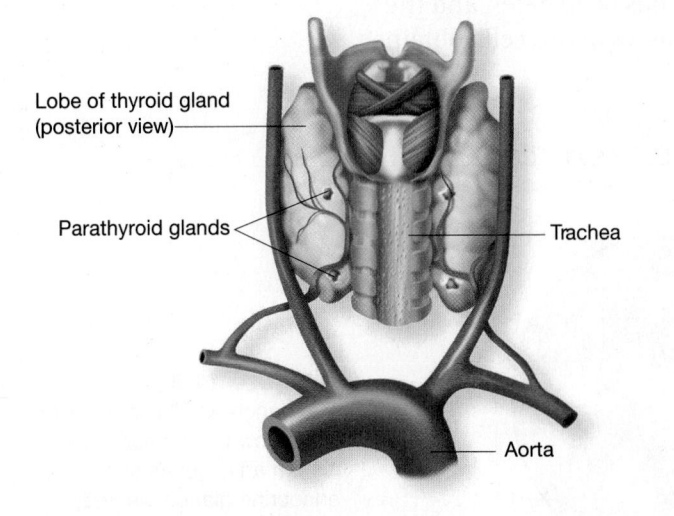

Lobe of thyroid gland
(posterior view)

Parathyroid glands

Trachea

Aorta

■ **Figure 11.4** The parathyroid glands. These four glands are located on the posterior side of the thyroid gland. They secrete parathyroid hormone.

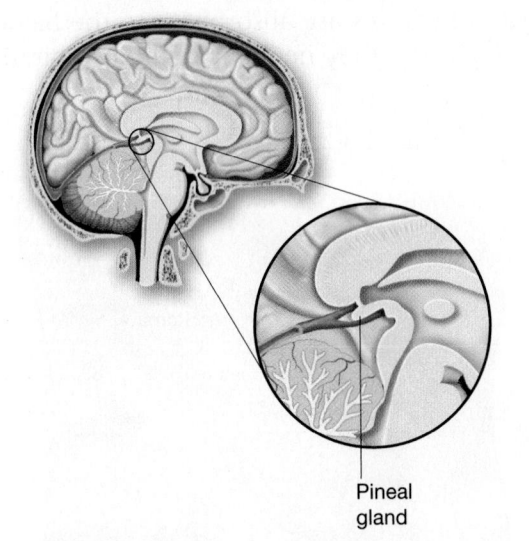

Pineal
gland

■ **Figure 11.5** The pineal gland is a part of the thalamus region of the brain. It secretes melatonin.

luteinizing hormone (LOO-tee-in-eye-zing)
melanocyte-stimulating hormone
oxytocin (ok-see-TOH-sin)
posterior lobe

prolactin (proh-LAK-tin)
somatotropin (so-mat-oh-TROH-pin)
thyroid-stimulating hormone

The pituitary gland is located underneath the brain (see Figure 11.6 ■). The small marble-shaped gland is divided into an **anterior lobe** and a **posterior lobe.** Both lobes are controlled by the **hypothalamus,** a region of the brain active in regulating automatic body responses.

The anterior pituitary secretes several different hormones (see Figure 11.7 ■). **Growth hormone** (GH), also called **somatotropin,** promotes growth of the body by stimulating cells to rapidly increase in size and divide. **Thyroid-stimulating hormone** (TSH) regulates the function of the thyroid gland. **Adrenocorticotropin hormone** (ACTH) regulates the function of the adrenal cortex. **Prolactin** (PRL) stimulates milk production in the breast following pregnancy and birth. **Follicle-stimulating hormone** (FSH) and **luteinizing hormone** (LH) both exert their influence on the male and female gonads. Therefore, these two hormones together are referred to as the **gonadotropins.** Follicle-stimulating hormone is responsible for the development of ova in ovaries and sperm in testes. It also stimulates the ovary to secrete estrogen. Luteinizing hormone stimulates secretion of sex hormones in both males and females and plays a role in releasing ova in females. **Melanocyte-stimulating hormone** (MSH) stimulates melanocytes to produce more melanin, thereby darkening the skin.

The posterior pituitary secretes two hormones, **antidiuretic hormone** (ADH) and **oxytocin.** Antidiuretic hormone promotes water reabsorption by the kidney tubules. Oxytocin stimulates uterine contractions during labor and delivery, and after birth the release of milk from the mammary glands.

MED TERM TIP
The pituitary gland is sometimes referred to as the "master gland" because several of its secretions regulate other endocrine glands.

MED TERM TIP
Many people use the term *diabetes* to refer to diabetes mellitus (DM). But there is another type of diabetes, called *diabetes insipidus* (DI), that is a result of the inadequate secretion of the antidiuretic hormone (ADH) from the pituitary gland.

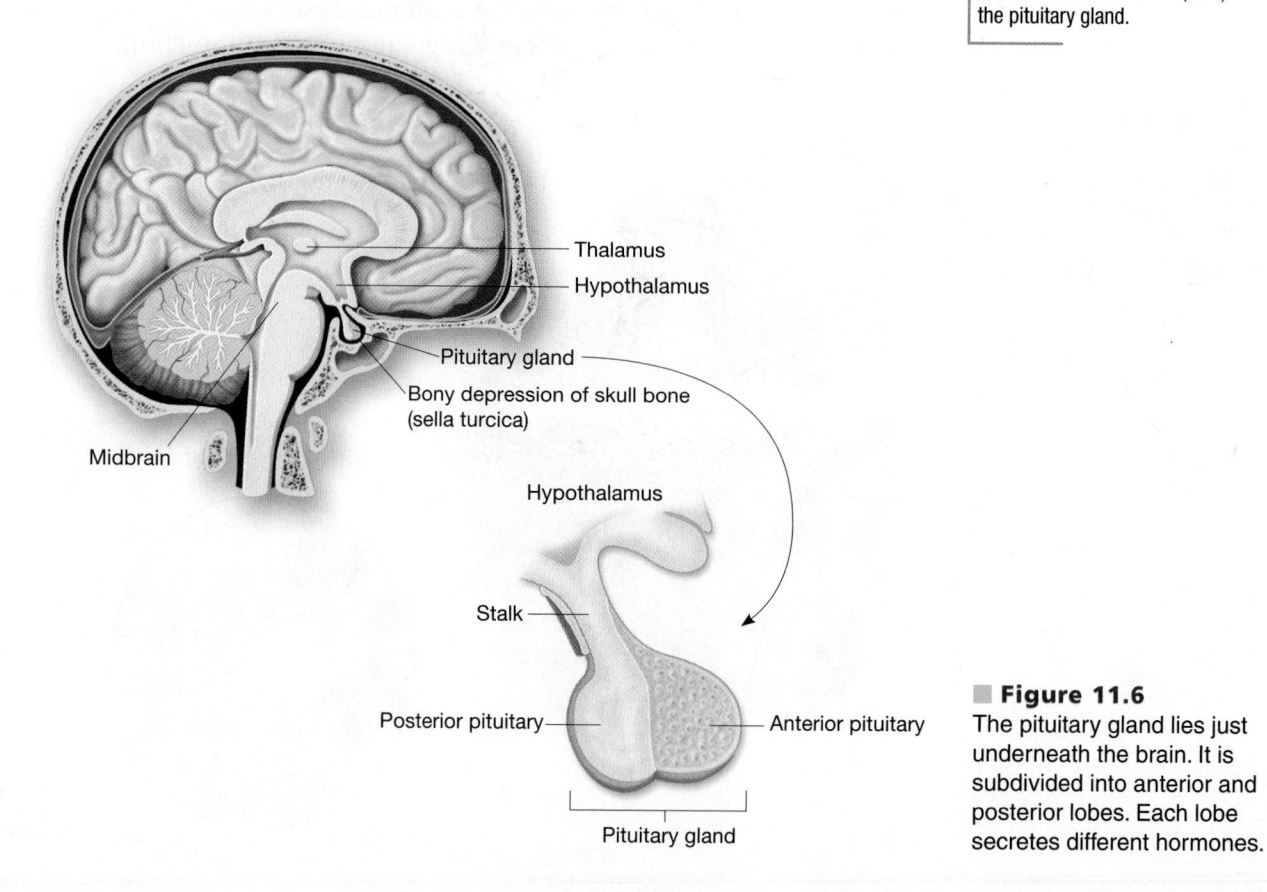

■ Figure 11.6
The pituitary gland lies just underneath the brain. It is subdivided into anterior and posterior lobes. Each lobe secretes different hormones.

■ **Figure 11.7**
The anterior pituitary is sometimes called the master gland because it secretes many hormones that regulate other glands. This figure illustrates the different hormones and target tissues for the anterior pituitary.

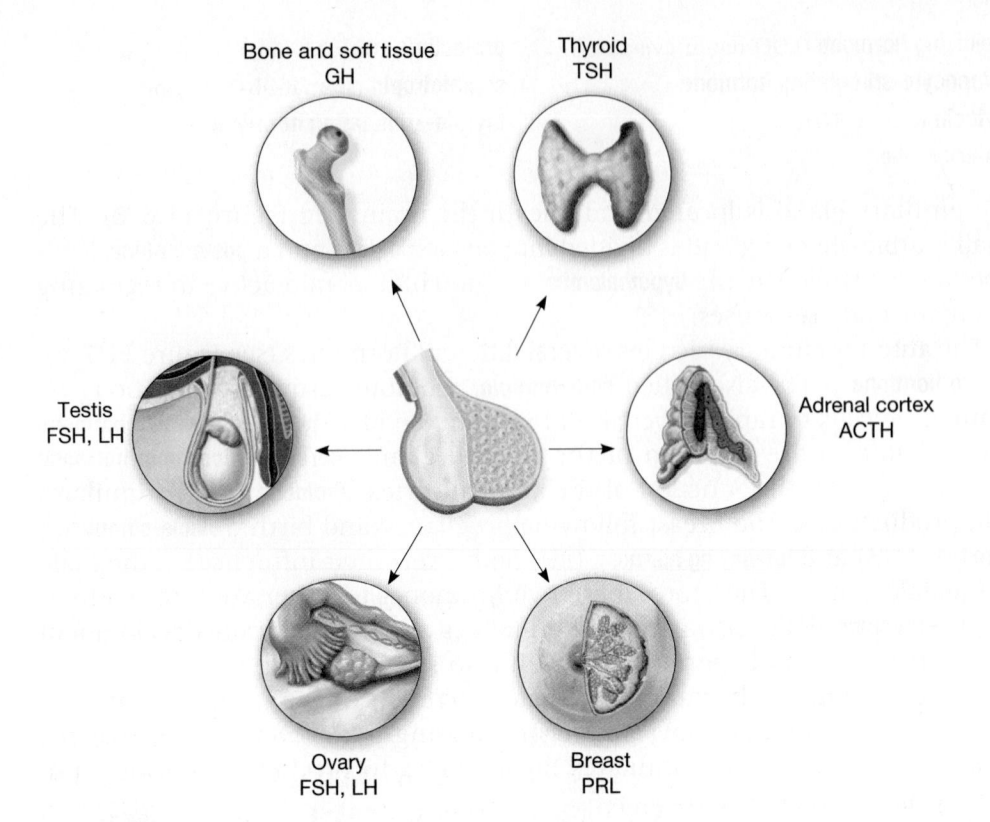

Bone and soft tissue
GH

Thyroid
TSH

Testis
FSH, LH

Adrenal cortex
ACTH

Ovary
FSH, LH

Breast
PRL

Testes

sperm   **testosterone** (tess-TOSS-ter-own)

The testes are two oval glands located in the scrotal sac of the male (see Figure 11.8 ■). They are the male gonads, which produce the male gametes, **sperm,** and the male sex hormone, **testosterone.** Testosterone produces the male secondary sexual characteristics and regulates sperm production.

■ **Figure 11.8**
The testes. In addition to producing sperm, the testes secrete the male sex hormones, primarily testosterone.

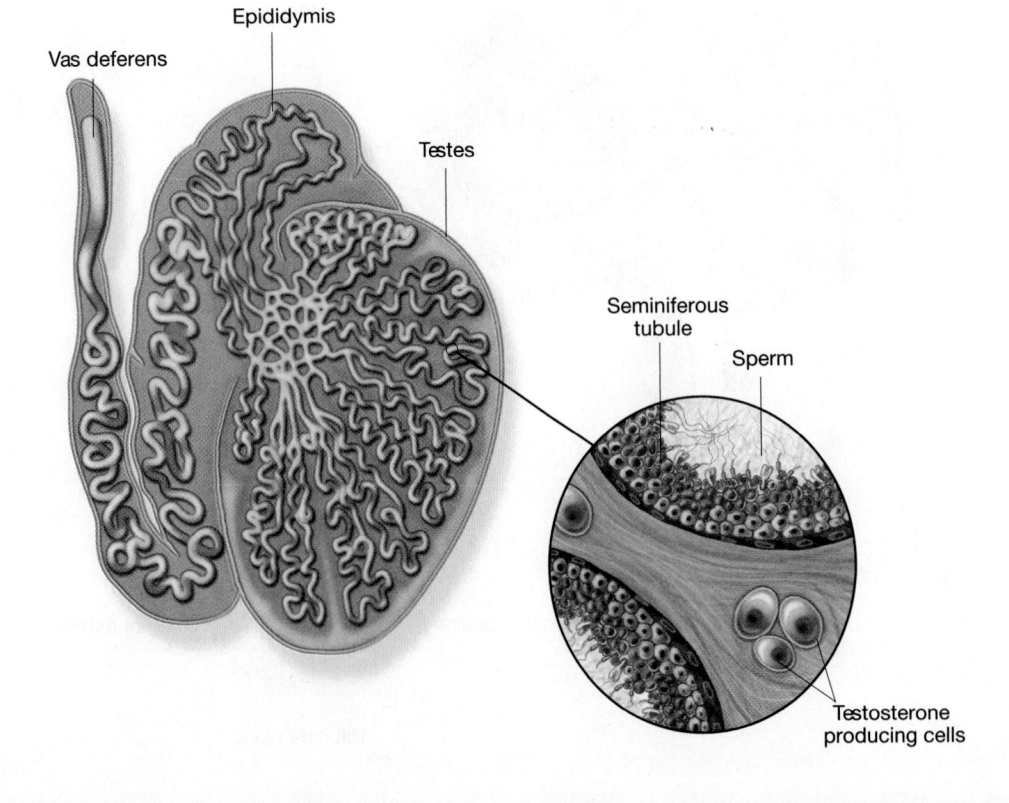

Vas deferens

Epididymis

Testes

Seminiferous
tubule

Sperm

Testosterone
producing cells

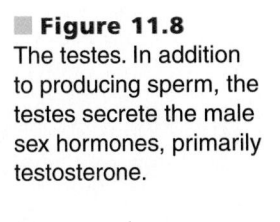

Thymus Gland

T cells   **thymosin** (thigh-MOH-sin)

In addition to its role as part of the immune system, the thymus is also one of the endocrine glands because it secretes the hormone **thymosin.** Thymosin, like the rest of the thymus gland, is important for proper development of the immune system. The thymus gland is located in the mediastinal cavity anterior and superior to the heart (see Figure 11.9 ■). The thymus is present at birth and grows to its largest size during puberty. At puberty it begins to shrink and eventually is replaced with connective and adipose tissue.

The most important function of the thymus is the development of the immune system in the newborn. It is essential to the growth and development of thymic lymphocytes or **T cells,** which are critical for the body's immune system.

Thyroid Gland

calcitonin (kal-sih-TOH-nin)   **triiodothyronine**
iodine (EYE-oh-dine)   (try-eye-oh-doh-THIGH-roh-neen)
thyroxine (thigh-ROKS-in)

The thyroid gland, which resembles a butterfly in shape, has right and left lobes (see Figure 11.10 ■). It is located on either side of the trachea and larynx. The thyroid cartilage, or Adam's apple, is located just above the thyroid gland. This gland produces the hormones **thyroxine** (T_4) and **triiodothyronine** (T_3). These hormones are produced in the thyroid gland from the mineral **iodine.** Thyroxine and triiodothyronine help to regulate the production of energy and heat in the body to adjust the body's metabolic rate.

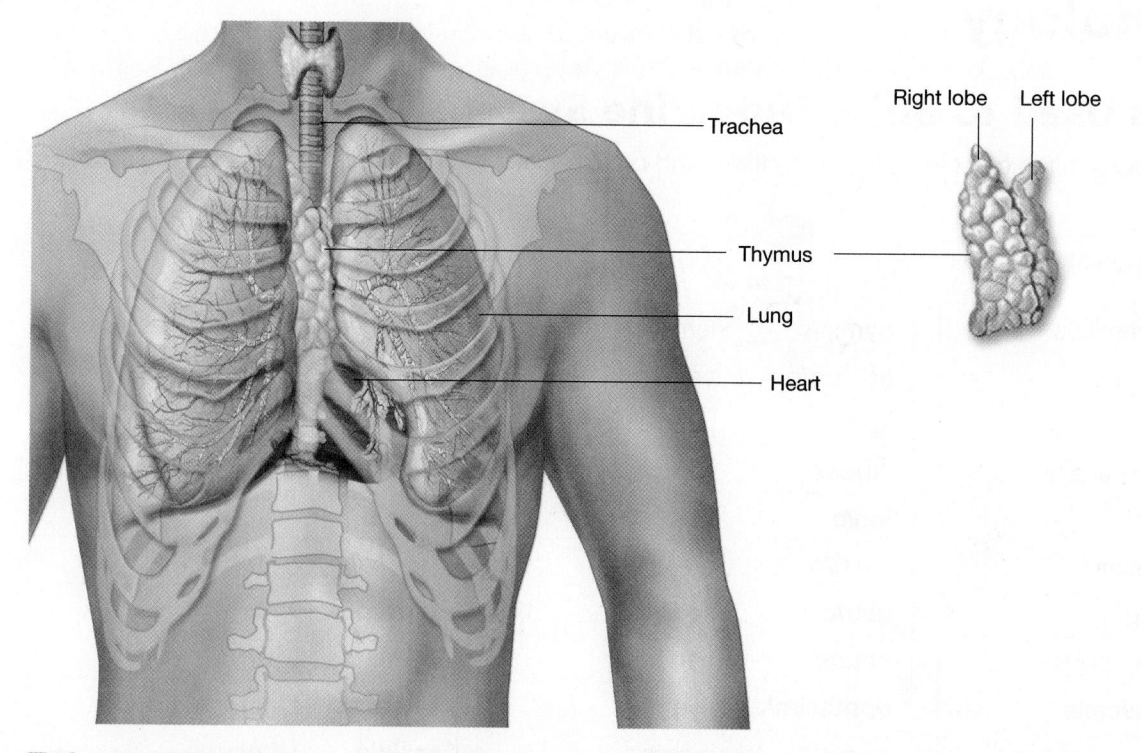

■ **Figure 11.9**   The thymus gland. This gland lies in the mediastinum of the thoracic cavity, just above the heart. It secretes thymosin.

■ **Figure 11.10** The thyroid gland is subdivided into two lobes, one on each side of the trachea.

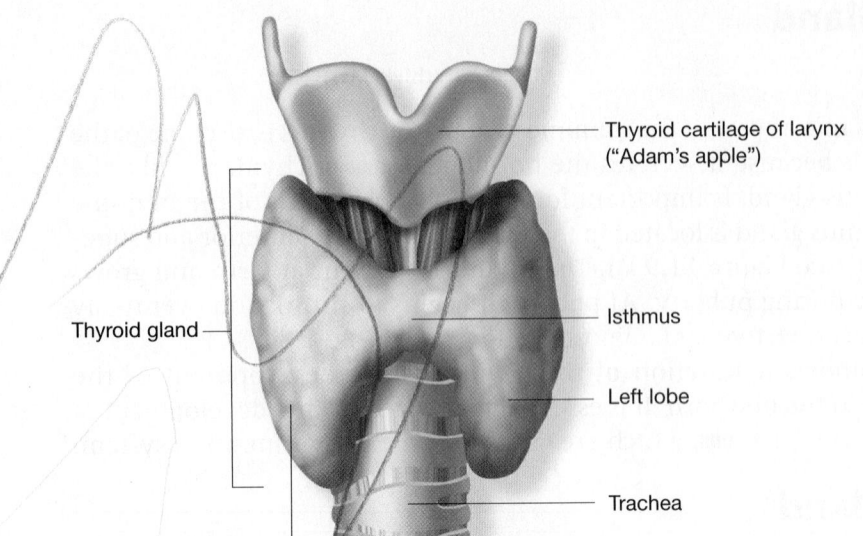

Thyroid cartilage of larynx ("Adam's apple")

Thyroid gland

Isthmus

Left lobe

Trachea

Right lobe

MED TERM TIP

Iodine is found in many foods, including vegetables and seafood. It is also present in iodized salt, which is one of the best sources of iodine for people living in the Goiter Belt, composed of states located away from saltwater. A lack of iodine in the diet can lead to thyroid disorders, including *goiter.*

The thyroid gland also secretes **calcitonin** (CT) in response to hypercalcemia (too high blood calcium level). Its action is the opposite of parathyroid hormone and stimulates the increased deposition of calcium into bone, thereby lowering blood levels of calcium.

■ Terminology

Word Parts Used to Build Endocrine System Terms

The following lists contain the combining forms, suffixes, and prefixes used to build terms in the remaining sections of this chapter.

Combining Forms

acr/o	extremities	**gynec/o**	female	**parathyroid/o**	parathyroid gland
aden/o	gland	**immun/o**	protection	**pineal/o**	pineal gland
adren/o	adrenal gland	**kal/i**	potassium	**pituitar/o**	pituitary gland
adrenal/o	adrenal gland	**lapar/o**	abdomen	**radi/o**	ray
calc/o	calcium	**lob/o**	lobe	**retin/o**	retina
carcin/o	cancer	**mast/o**	breast	**testicul/o**	testes
chem/o	drug	**natr/o**	sodium	**thym/o**	thymus gland
cortic/o	outer portion	**neur/o**	nerve	**thyr/o**	thyroid gland
crin/o	to secrete	**ophthalm/o**	eye	**thyroid/o**	thyroid gland
cyt/o	cell	**or/o**	mouth	**toxic/o**	poison
glyc/o	sugar	**ovari/o**	ovary	**vas/o**	vessel
glycos/o	sugar	**pancreat/o**	pancreas		

Suffixes

-al	pertaining to		-ic	pertaining to		-pathy	disease
-ary	pertaining to		-ism	state of		-prandial	relating to a meal
-dipsia	thirst		-itis	inflammation		-pressin	to press down
-ectomy	surgical removal		-logy	study of		-scopy	procedure to visually examine
-emia	blood condition		-megaly	enlarged			
-emic	relating to a blood condition		-meter	instrument to measure		-tic	pertaining to
-graphy	process of recording		-oma	tumor		-uria	urine condition
-ia	condition		-osis	abnormal condition			

Prefixes

anti-	against		hyper-	excessive		poly-	many
endo-	within		hypo-	insufficient		post-	after
ex-	outward		pan-	all			

Anatomical Terms

TERM	WORD PARTS	DEFINITION
adrenal (ah-DREE-nall)	adren/o = adrenal gland -al = pertaining to	Pertaining to the adrenal glands.
ovarian (oh-VAIR-ee-an)	ovari/o = ovary -ian = pertaining to	Pertaining to the ovary.
pancreatic (pan-kree-AT-ik)	pancreat/o = pancreas -ic = pertaining to	Pertaining to the pancreas.
parathyroidal (pair-ah-THIGH-roy-dall)	parathyroid/o = parathyroid gland -al = pertaining to	Pertaining to the parathyroid gland.
pituitary (pih-TOO-ih-tair-ee)	pituitar/o = pituitary gland -ary = pertaining to	Pertaining to the pituitary gland.
testicular (tes-TIK-yoo-lar)	testicul/o = testes -ar = pertaining to	Pertaining to the testes.
thymic (THIGH-mik)	thym/o = thymus gland -ic = pertaining to	Pertaining to the thymus gland.
thyroidal (thigh-ROYD-all)	thyroid/o = thyroid gland -al = pertaining to	Pertaining to the thyroid gland.

Pathology

TERM	WORD PARTS	DEFINITION
Medical Specialties		
endocrinology (en-doh-krin-ALL-oh-jee)	endo- = within crin/o = to secrete -logy = study of	Branch of medicine involving diagnosis and treatment of conditions and diseases of endocrine glands. Physician is an *endocrinologist*.
Signs and Symptoms		
adrenomegaly (ad-ree-noh-MEG-ah-lee)	adren/o = adrenal gland -megaly = enlarged	Having one or both adrenal glands enlarged.
adrenopathy (ad-ren-OP-ah-thee)	adren/o = adrenal gland -pathy = disease	General term for adrenal gland disease.
edema (eh-DEE-mah)		Condition in which the body tissues contain excessive amounts of fluid.
endocrinopathy (en-doh-krin-OP-ah-thee)	endo- = within crin/o = to secrete -pathy = disease	General term for diseases of the endocrine system.
exophthalmos (eks-off-THAL-mohs)	ex- = outward ophthalm/o = eye	Condition in which the eyeballs protrude, such as in Graves' disease. This is generally caused by an overproduction of thyroid hormone.

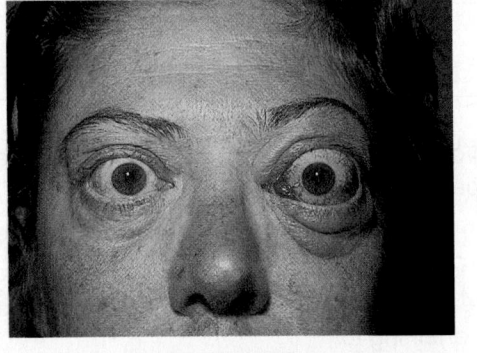

■ **Figure 11.11**
A photograph of a woman with exophthalmos. This condition is associated with hypersecretion of the thyroid gland. *(Custom Medical Stock Photo, Inc.)*

TERM	WORD PARTS	DEFINITION
glycosuria (glye-kohs-YOO-ree-ah)	glycos/o = sugar -uria = urine condition	Having a high level of sugar excreted in the urine.
gynecomastia (gigh-neh-koh-MAST-ee-ah)	gynec/o = female mast/o = breast -ia = condition	Development of breast tissue in males. May be a symptom of adrenal feminization.
hirsutism (HER-soot-izm)	-ism = state of	Condition of having an excessive amount of hair. Term generally used to describe females who have the adult male pattern of hair growth. Can be the result of a hormonal imbalance.
hypercalcemia (high-per-kal-SEE-mee-ah)	hyper- = excessive calc/o = calcium -emia = blood condition	Condition of having a high level of calcium in the blood; associated with hypersecretion of parathyroid hormone.
hyperglycemia (high-per-glye-SEE-mee-ah)	hyper- = excessive glyc/o = sugar -emia = blood condition	Condition of having a high level of sugar in the blood; associated with diabetes mellitus.

Pathology *(continued)*

TERM	WORD PARTS	DEFINITION
hyperkalemia (high-per-kal-EE-mee-ah)	hyper- = excessive kal/i = potassium -emia = blood condition	The condition of having a high level of potassium in the blood.
hypersecretion	hyper- = excessive	Excessive hormone production by an endocrine gland.
hypocalcemia (high-poh-kal-SEE-mee-ah)	hypo- = insufficient calc/o = calcium -emia = blood condition	The condition of having a low level of calcium in the blood; associated with hyposecretion of parathyroid hormone. Hypocalcemia may result in tetany.
hypoglycemia (high-poh-glye-SEE-mee-ah)	hypo- = insufficient glyc/o = sugar -emia = blood condition	Condition of having a low level of sugar in the blood.
hyponatremia (high-poh-nah-TREE-mee-ah)	hypo- = insufficient natr/o = sodium -emia = blood condition	Condition of having a low level of sodium in the blood.
hyposecretion	hypo- = insufficient	Deficient hormone production by an endocrine gland.
obesity (oh-BEE-sih-tee)		Having an abnormal amount of fat in the body.
polydipsia (pall-ee-DIP-see-ah)	poly- = many -dipsia = thirst	Excessive feeling of thirst.
polyuria (pall-ee-YOO-ree-ah)	poly- = many -uria = urine condition	Condition of producing an excessive amount of urine.
syndrome (SIN-drohm)		Group of symptoms and signs that, when combined, present a clinical picture of a disease or condition.
thyromegaly (thigh-roh-MEG-ah-lee)	thyr/o = thyroid gland -megaly = enlarged	Having an enlarged thyroid gland.

Adrenal Glands

TERM	WORD PARTS	DEFINITION
Addison's disease (AD-ih-sons)		Disease named for British physician Thomas Addison; results from a deficiency in adrenocortical hormones. There may be an increased pigmentation of the skin, generalized weakness, and weight loss.
adrenal feminization (ad-REE-nal / fem-ih-nigh-ZAY-shun)	adren/o = adrenal gland -al = pertaining to	Development of female secondary sexual characteristics (such as breasts) in a male. Often as a result of increased estrogen secretion by the adrenal cortex.
adrenal virilism (ad-REE-nal / VIR-ill-izm)	adren/o = adrenal gland -al = pertaining to -ism = state of	Development of male secondary sexual characteristics (such as deeper voice and facial hair) in a female. Often as a result of increased androgen secretion by the adrenal cortex.
adrenalitis (ad-ree-nal-EYE-tis)	adrenal/o = adrenal gland -itis = inflammation	Inflammation of one or both adrenal glands.

■ Pathology (continued)

TERM	WORD PARTS	DEFINITION
Cushing's syndrome (CUSH-ings / SIN-drohm) 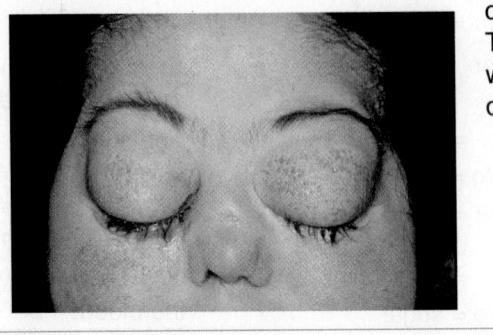 ■ **Figure 11.12** Cushing's syndrome. A photograph of a woman with the characteristic facial features of Cushing's syndrome. *(Biophoto Photo Associates/Photo Researchers, Inc.)*		Set of symptoms caused by excessive levels of cortisol due to high doses of corticosteroid drugs and adrenal tumors. The syndrome may present symptoms of weakness, edema, excess hair growth, skin discoloration, and osteoporosis.
pheochromocytoma (fee-oh-kroh-moh-sigh-TOH-ma)	cyt/o = cell -oma = tumor	Usually benign tumor of the adrenal medulla that secretes epinephrine. Symptoms include anxiety, heart palpitations, dyspnea, profuse sweating, headache, and nausea.

Pancreas

TERM	WORD PARTS	DEFINITION
diabetes mellitus (DM) (dye-ah-BEE-teez / MELL-ih-tus)		Chronic disorder of carbohydrate metabolism resulting in hyperglycemia and glycosuria. There are two distinct forms of diabetes mellitus: *insulin-dependent diabetes mellitus* (IDDM) or *type 1,* and *non-insulin-dependent diabetes mellitus* (NIDDM) or *type 2.*
diabetic retinopathy (dye-ah-BET-ik / ret-in-OP-ah-thee)	-tic = pertaining to retin/o = retina -pathy = disease	Secondary complication of diabetes that affects the blood vessels of the retina, resulting in visual changes and even blindness.
insulin-dependent diabetes mellitus (IDDM) (dye-ah-BEE-teez / MELL-ih-tus)		Also called *type 1 diabetes mellitus.* It develops early in life when the pancreas stops insulin production. Patient must take daily insulin injections.
insulinoma (in-sue-lin-OH-mah)	-oma = tumor	Tumor of the islets of Langerhans cells of the pancreas that secretes an excessive amount of insulin.
ketoacidosis (KEE-toh-ass-ih-DOH-sis)	ket/o = ketones -osis = abnormal condition	Acidosis due to an excess of acidic ketone bodies (waste products). A serious condition requiring immediate treatment that can result in death for the diabetic patient if not reversed. Also called *diabetic acidosis.*
non-insulin-dependent diabetes mellitus (dye-ah-BEE-teez / MELL-ih-tus)		Also called *type 2 diabetes mellitus.* It typically develops later in life. The pancreas produces normal to high levels of insulin, but the cells fail to respond to it. Patients may take oral hypoglycemics to improve insulin function, or may eventually have to take insulin.
peripheral neuropathy (per-IF-eh-rall / new-ROP-ah-thee)	-al = pertaining to neur/o = nerve -pathy = disease	Damage to the nerves in the lower legs and hands as a result of diabetes mellitus. Symptoms include either extreme sensitivity or numbness and tingling.

Pathology *(continued)*

TERM	WORD PARTS	DEFINITION
Parathyroid Glands		
hyperparathyroidism (HIGH-per-pair-ah-THIGH-royd-izm)	hyper- = excessive parathyroid/o = parathyroid gland -ism = state of	Hypersecretion of parathyroid hormone; may result in hypercalcemia and Recklinghausen disease.
hypoparathyroidism (HIGH-poh-pair-ah-THIGH-royd-izm)	hypo- = insufficient parathyroid/o = parathyroid gland -ism = state of	Hyposecretion of parathyroid hormone; may result in hypocalcemia and tetany.
Recklinghausen disease (REK-ling-how-zenz)		Excessive production of parathyroid hormone resulting in degeneration of the bones.
tetany (TET-ah-nee)		Nerve irritability and painful muscle cramps resulting from hypocalcemia. Hypoparathyroidism is one cause of tetany.
Pituitary Gland		
acromegaly (ak-roh-MEG-ah-lee)	acr/o = extremities -megaly = enlarged	Chronic disease of adults that results in an elongation and enlargement of the bones of the head and extremities. There can also be mood changes. Due to an excessive amount of growth hormone in an adult.

■ **Figure 11.13** Acromegaly. Photo of a woman illustrating the enlarged skull, jaw, and hands typical of acromegaly. *(Reprinted from American Journal of Medicine, Vol 20, Dr. William H. Daughaday, University of California/Irvine, ©1956. With permission from Excerpta Medica Inc.)*

diabetes insipidus (DI) (dye-ah-BEE-teez / in-SIP-ih-dus)		Disorder caused by the inadequate secretion of antidiuretic hormone by the posterior lobe of the pituitary gland. There may be polyuria and polydipsia.
dwarfism (DWARF-izm)	-ism = state of	Condition of being abnormally short in height. It may be the result of a hereditary condition or a lack of growth hormone.

Pathology (continued)

TERM	WORD PARTS	DEFINITION
gigantism (JYE-gan-tizm)	-ism = state of	Excessive development of the body due to the overproduction of the growth hormone by the pituitary gland in a child or teenager. The opposite of *dwarfism*.
hyperpituitarism (HIGH-per-pih-TOO-ih-tuh-rizm)	hyper- = excessive pituitar/o = pituitary gland -ism = state of	Hypersecretion of one or more pituitary gland hormones.
hypopituitarism (HIGH-poh-pih-TOO-ih-tuh-rizm)	hypo- = insufficient pituitar/o = pituitary gland -ism = state of	Hyposecretion of one or more pituitary gland hormones.
panhypopituitarism (pan-high-poh-pih-TOO-ih-tair-izm)	pan- = all hypo- = insufficient pituitar/o = pituitary gland -ism = state of	Deficiency in all the hormones secreted by the pituitary gland. Often recognized because of problems with the glands regulated by the pituitary–adrenal cortex, thyroid, ovaries, and testes.
Thymus Gland		
thymitis (thigh-MY-tis)	thym/o = thymus gland -itis = inflammation	Inflammation of the thymus gland.
thymoma (thigh-MOH-mah)	thym/o = thymus gland -oma = tumor	A tumor in the thymus gland.
Thyroid Gland		
cretinism (KREE-tin-izm)	-ism = state of	Congenital condition in which a lack of thyroid hormones may result in arrested physical and mental development.
goiter (GOY-ter)	 ■ **Figure 11.14** Goiter. A photograph of a male with an extreme goiter or enlarged thyroid gland.	Enlargement of the thyroid gland.
Graves' disease		Condition named for Irish physician Robert Graves that results in overactivity of the thyroid gland and can cause a crisis situation. Symptoms include exophthalmos and goiter. A type of *hyperthyroidism*.
Hashimoto's thyroiditis (hash-ee-MOH-tohz / thigh-roy-DYE-tis)	thyroid/o = thyroid gland -itis = inflammation	Chronic autoimmune form of thyroiditis; results in hyposecretion of thyroid hormones.

Pathology *(continued)*

TERM	WORD PARTS	DEFINITION
hyperthyroidism (hi-per-THIGH-royd-izm)	hyper- = excessive thyroid/o = thyroid gland -ism = state of	Hypersecretion of thyroid gland hormones.
hypothyroidism (high-poh-THIGH-royd-izm)	hypo- = insufficient thyroid/o = thyroid gland -ism = state of	Hyposecretion of thyroid gland hormones.
myxedema (miks-eh-DEE-mah)		Condition resulting from a hyposecretion of the thyroid gland in an adult. Symptoms can include anemia, slow speech, swollen facial features, edematous skin, drowsiness, and mental lethargy.
thyrotoxicosis (thigh-roh-toks-ih-KOH-sis)	thyr/o = thyroid gland toxic/o = poison -osis = abnormal condition	Condition resulting from marked overproduction of the thyroid gland. Symptoms include rapid heart action, tremors, enlarged thyroid gland, exophthalmos, and weight loss.
All Glands		
adenocarcinoma (ad-eh-no-car-sih-NO-mah)	aden/o = gland carcin/o = cancer -oma = tumor	Cancerous tumor in a gland that is capable of producing the hormones secreted by that gland. One cause of hypersecretion pathologies.

Diagnostic Procedures

TERM	WORD PARTS	DEFINITION
Clinical Laboratory Tests		
blood serum test		Blood test to measure the level of substances such as calcium, electrolytes, testosterone, insulin, and glucose. Used to assist in determining the function of various endocrine glands.
fasting blood sugar (FBS)		Blood test to measure the amount of sugar circulating throughout the body after a 12-hour fast.
glucose tolerance test (GTT) (GLOO-kohs)		Test to determine the blood sugar level. A measured dose of glucose is given to a patient either orally or intravenously. Blood samples are then drawn at certain intervals to determine the ability of the patient to use glucose. Used for diabetic patients to determine their insulin response to glucose.
protein-bound iodine test (PBI)		Blood test to measure the concentration of thyroxine (T_4) circulating in the bloodstream. The iodine becomes bound to the protein in the blood and can be measured. Useful in establishing thyroid function.

Diagnostic Procedures *(continued)*

TERM	WORD PARTS	DEFINITION
radioimmunoassay (RIA) (ray-dee-oh-im-yoo-noh-ASS-ay)	radi/o = ray immun/o = protection	Blood test that uses radioactively tagged hormones and antibodies to measure the quantity of hormone in the plasma.
thyroid function test (TFT) (THIGH-royd)		Blood test used to measure the levels of thyroxine, triiodothyronine, and thyroid-stimulating hormone in the bloodstream to assist in determining thyroid function.
total calcium		Blood test to measure the total amount of calcium to assist in detecting parathyroid and bone disorders.
two-hour postprandial glucose tolerance test (post-PRAN-dee-al)	post- = after -prandial = relating to a meal	Blood test to assist in evaluating glucose metabolism. The patient eats a high carbo-hydrate diet and then fasts overnight before the test. Then the blood sample is taken 2 hours after a meal.
Diagnostic Imaging		
thyroid echography (THIGH-royd / eh-KOG-rah-fee)	-graphy = process of recording	Ultrasound examination of the thyroid that can assist in distinguishing a thyroid nodule from a cyst.
thyroid scan (THIGH-royd)		Test in which radioactive iodine is adminis-tered that localizes in the thyroid gland. The gland can then be visualized with a scanning device to detect pathology such as tumors.

Therapeutic Procedures

TERM	WORD PARTS	DEFINITION
Medical Procedures		
chemical thyroidectomy (thigh-royd-EK-toh-mee)	chem/o = drug -al = pertaining to thyroid/o = thyroid gland -ectomy = surgical removal	Large dose of radioactive iodine is given in order to kill thyroid gland cells without hav-ing to actually do surgery.
glucometer	gluc/o = glucose -meter = instrument to measure	Device designed for a diabetic to use at home to measure the level of glucose in the bloodstream.
hormone replacement therapy		Artificial replacement of hormones in patients with hyposecretion disorders. May be oral pills, injections, or adhesive skin patches.
Surgical Procedures		
adrenalectomy (ad-ree-nal-EK-toh-mee)	adrenal/o = adrenal gland -ectomy = surgical removal	Surgical removal of one or both adrenal glands.
laparoscopic adrenalectomy (lap-row-SKOP-ik / ad-ree-nal-EK-toh-mee)	lapar/o = abdomen -scopy = procedure to visu-ally examine -ic = pertaining to adren/o = adrenal gland -ectomy = surgical removal	Removal of the adrenal gland through a small incision in the abdomen and using endoscopic instruments.

Therapeutic Procedures *(continued)*

TERM	WORD PARTS	DEFINITION
lobectomy (lobe-EK-toh-mee)	lob/o = lobe -ectomy = surgical removal	Removal of a lobe from an organ. In this case, one lobe of the thyroid gland.
parathyroidectomy (pair-ah-thigh-royd-EK-toh-mee)	parathyroid/o = parathyroid gland -ectomy = surgical removal	Surgical removal of one or more of the parathyroid glands.
pinealectomy (PIN-ee-ah-LEK-toh-mee)	pineal/o = pineal gland -ectomy = surgical removal	Surgical removal of the pineal gland.
thymectomy (thigh-MEK-toh-mee)	thym/o = thymus gland -ectomy = surgical removal	Surgical removal of the thymus gland.
thyroidectomy (thigh-royd-EK-toh-mee)	thyroid/o = thyroid gland -ectomy = surgical removal	Surgical removal of the thyroid gland.

Pharmacology

CLASSIFICATION	WORD PARTS	ACTION	EXAMPLES
antithyroid agents	anti- = against	Medication given to block production of thyroid hormones in patients with hypersecretion disorders.	methimazole, Tapazole; propylthiouracil
corticosteroids (kor-tih-koh-STAIR-oydz)	cortic/o = outer portion	Although the function of these hormones in the body is to regulate carbohydrate metabolism, they also have a strong anti-inflammatory action. Therefore they are used to treat severe chronic inflammatory diseases such as rheumatoid arthritis. Long-term use of corticosteroids has adverse side effects such as osteoporosis and the symptoms of Cushing's disease. Also used to treat adrenal cortex hyposecretion disorders such as Addison's disease.	prednisone, Deltasone
human growth hormone therapy		Hormone replacement therapy with human growth hormone in order to stimulate skeletal growth. Used to treat children with abnormally short stature.	somatropin, Genotropin; somatrem, Protropin
insulin (IN-suh-lin)		Administered to replace insulin for type 1 diabetics or to treat severe type 2 diabetics.	human insulin, Humulin L
oral hypoglycemic agents (high-poh-glye-SEE-mik)	or/o = mouth -al = pertaining to hypo- = insufficient glyc/o = sugar -emic = relating to a blood condition	Medications taken by mouth that cause a decrease in blood sugar; not used for insulin-dependent patients.	metformin, Glucophage; glipizide, Glucotrol

Pharmacology *(continued)*

CLASSIFICATION	WORD PARTS	ACTION	EXAMPLES
thyroid replacement hormone		Hormone replacement therapy for patients with hypothyroidism or who have had a thyroidectomy.	levothyroxine, Levo-T; liothyronine, Cytomel
vasopressin (vaz-oh-PRESS-in)	vas/o = vessel -pressin = to press down	Given to control diabetes insipidus and promote reabsorption of water in the kidney tubules.	desmopressin acetate, Desmopressin; conivaptan, Vaprisol

Abbreviations

α	alpha	LH	luteinizing hormone
ACTH	adrenocorticotropin hormone	MSH	melanocyte-stimulating hormone
ADH	antidiuretic hormone	Na⁺	sodium
β	beta	NIDDM	non-insulin-dependent diabetes mellitus
BMR	basal metabolic rate	NPH	neutral protamine Hagedorn (insulin)
CT	calcitonin	PBI	protein-bound iodine
DI	diabetes insipidus	PRL	prolactin
DM	diabetes mellitus	PTH	parathyroid hormone
FBS	fasting blood sugar	RAI	radioactive iodine
FSH	follicle-stimulating hormone	RIA	radioimmunoassay
GH	growth hormone	T_3	triiodothyronine
GTT	glucose tolerance test	T_4	thyroxine
IDDM	insulin-dependent diabetes mellitus	TFT	thyroid function test
K⁺	potassium	TSH	thyroid-stimulating hormone

Chapter Review

Real-World Applications

Medical Record Analysis

This Discharge Summary below contains 10 medical terms. Underline each term and write it in the list below the report. Then define each term.

Discharge Summary

Admitting Diagnosis:	Hyperglycemia, ketoacidosis, glycosuria
Final Diagnosis:	New-onset type 1 diabetes mellitus
History of Present Illness:	A 12-year-old female patient presented to her physician's office with a 2-month history of weight loss, fatigue, polyuria, and polydipsia. Her family history is significant for a grandfather, mother, and older brother with type 1 diabetes mellitus. The pediatrician found hyperglycemia with a fasting blood sugar and glycosuria with a urine dipstick. She is being admitted at this time for management of new-onset diabetes mellitus.
Summary of Hospital Course:	At the time of admission, the FBS was 300 mg/100 mL and she was in ketoacidosis. She rapidly improved after receiving insulin; her blood glucose level normalized. The next day a glucose tolerance test confirmed the diagnosis of diabetes mellitus. The patient was started on insulin injections. Patient and family were instructed on diabetes mellitus, insulin, diet, exercise, and long-term complications.
Discharge Plans:	Patient was discharged to home with her parents. Her parents are to check her blood glucose levels twice daily and call the office for insulin dosage. She is to return to the office in 2 weeks.

	Term	Definition
1	_____	_____
2	_____	_____
3	_____	_____
4	_____	_____
5	_____	_____
6	_____	_____
7	_____	_____
8	_____	_____
9	_____	_____
10	_____	_____

Chart Note Transcription

The chart note below contains 11 phrases that can be reworded with a medical term that you learned in this chapter. Each phrase is identified with an underline. Determine the medical term and write your answers in the space provided.

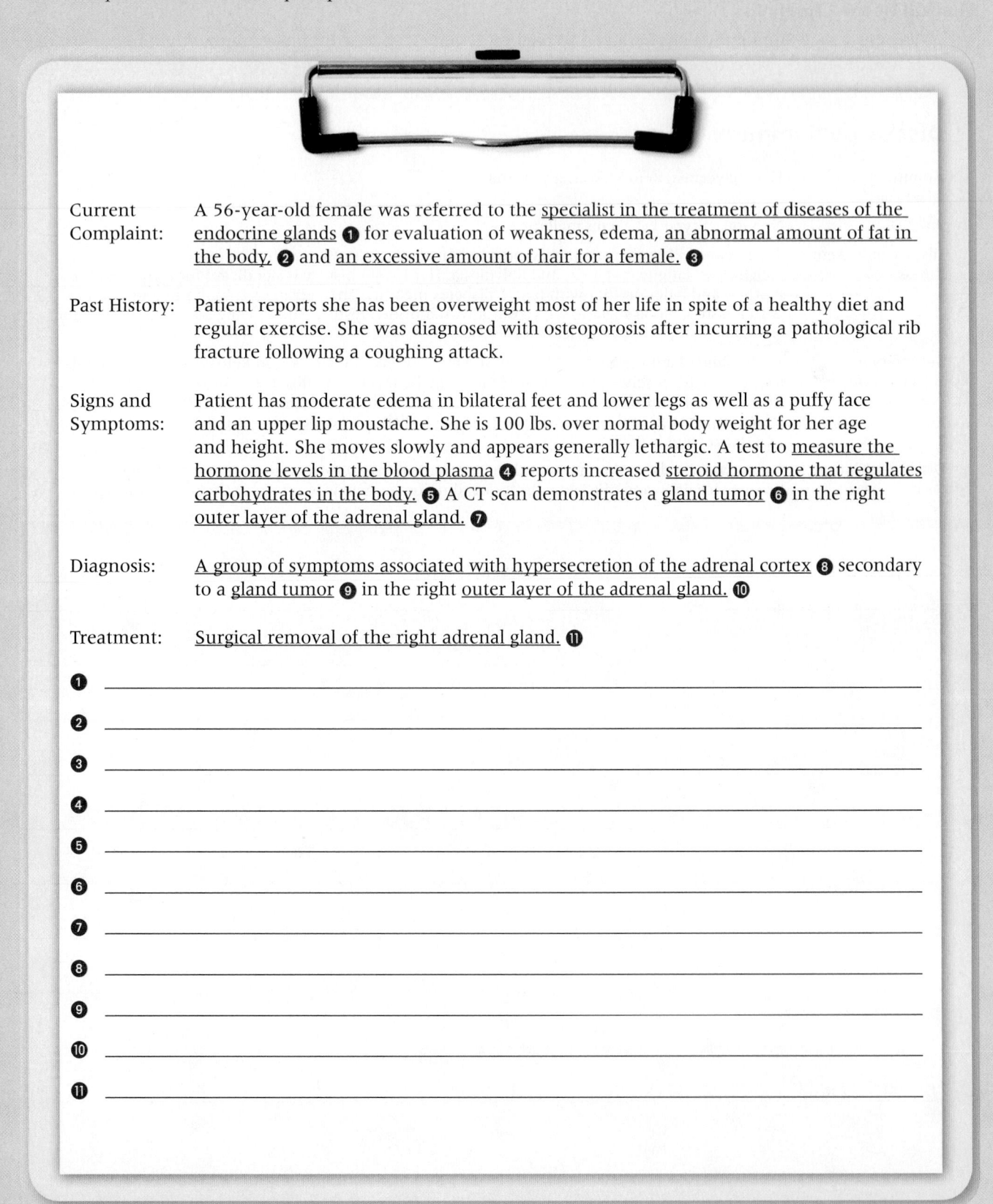

Current
Complaint: A 56-year-old female was referred to the <u>specialist in the treatment of diseases of the endocrine glands</u> ❶ for evaluation of weakness, edema, <u>an abnormal amount of fat in the body,</u> ❷ and <u>an excessive amount of hair for a female.</u> ❸

Past History: Patient reports she has been overweight most of her life in spite of a healthy diet and regular exercise. She was diagnosed with osteoporosis after incurring a pathological rib fracture following a coughing attack.

Signs and
Symptoms: Patient has moderate edema in bilateral feet and lower legs as well as a puffy face and an upper lip moustache. She is 100 lbs. over normal body weight for her age and height. She moves slowly and appears generally lethargic. A test to <u>measure the hormone levels in the blood plasma</u> ❹ reports increased <u>steroid hormone that regulates carbohydrates in the body.</u> ❺ A CT scan demonstrates a <u>gland tumor</u> ❻ in the right <u>outer layer of the adrenal gland.</u> ❼

Diagnosis: <u>A group of symptoms associated with hypersecretion of the adrenal cortex</u> ❽ secondary to a <u>gland tumor</u> ❾ in the right <u>outer layer of the adrenal gland.</u> ❿

Treatment: <u>Surgical removal of the right adrenal gland.</u> ⓫

❶ _____

❷ _____

❸ _____

❹ _____

❺ _____

❻ _____

❼ _____

❽ _____

❾ _____

❿ _____

⓫ _____

Case Study

Below is a case study presentation of a patient with a condition covered in this chapter. Read the case study and answer the questions below. Some questions will ask for information not included within this chapter. Use your text, a medical dictionary, or any other reference material you choose to answer these questions.

A 22-year-old college student was admitted to the emergency room after his friends called an ambulance when he passed out in a bar. He had become confused, developed slurred speech, and had difficulty walking after having only one beer to drink. In the ER he was noted to have diaphoresis, rapid respirations and pulse, and was disoriented. Upon examination, needle marks were found on his abdomen and outer thighs. The physician ordered blood serum tests that revealed hyperglycemia and ketoacidosis. Unknown to his friends, this young man has had diabetes mellitus since early childhood. The patient quickly recovered following an insulin injection.

(Flashon Studio/Shutterstock)

1. What pathological condition has this patient had since childhood? Look this condition up in a reference source and include a short description of it.

   _____

   _____

2. List and define each symptom noted in the ER in your own words.

   _____

   _____

3. What diagnostic test was performed? Describe it in your own words.

   _____

   _____

4. Explain the results of the test.

   _____

   _____

5. What specific type of diabetes does this young man probably have? Justify your answer.

   _____

   _____

6. Describe the other type of diabetes mellitus that this young man did not have.

   _____

   _____

Practice Exercises

A. Complete the Statement

1. The study of the endocrine system is called _____.

2. The master endocrine gland is the _____.

3. _____ is a general term for the sexual organs that produce gametes.

4. The term for the hormones produced by the outer portion of the adrenal cortex is _____.

5. The hormone produced by the testes is _____.

6. The two hormones produced by the ovaries are _____ and _____.

7. An inadequate supply of the hormone _____ causes diabetes insipidus.

8. The endocrine gland associated with the immune system is the _____.

9. The term for a protrusion of the eyeballs in Graves' disease is _____.

10. A general medical term for a hormone-secreting cancerous tumor is _____.

B. Combining Form Practice

The combining form **thyroid/o** refers to the thyroid. Use it to write a term that means:

1. removal of the thyroid _____

2. pertaining to the thyroid _____

3. state of excessive thyroid _____

The combining form **pancreat/o** refers to the pancreas. Use it to write a term that means:

4. pertaining to the pancreas _____

5. inflammation of the pancreas _____

6. removal of the pancreas _____

7. cutting into the pancreas _____

The combining form **adren/o** refers to the adrenal glands. Use it to write a term that means:

8. pertaining to the adrenal gland _____

9. enlargement of the adrenal glands _____

10. adrenal gland disease _____

The combining form **thym/o** refers to the thymus glands. Use it to write a term that means:

11. tumor of the thymus gland _____

12. removal of the thymus gland _____

13. pertaining to the thymus gland _____

14. inflammation of the thymus gland _____

C. Define the Combining Form

	Definition	Example from Chapter
1. natr/o	_____	_____
2. estr/o	_____	_____
3. pineal/o	_____	_____
4. pituitar/o	_____	_____
5. kal/i	_____	_____
6. calc/o	_____	_____
7. parathyroid/o	_____	_____
8. acr/o	_____	_____
9. glyc/o	_____	_____
10. gonad/o	_____	_____

D. Terminology Matching

Match the term to its definition.

1. _____ protein-bound iodine test

2. _____ fasting blood sugar

3. _____ radioimmunoassay

4. _____ thyroid scan

5. _____ 2-hour postprandial glucose tolerance test

6. _____ glucose tolerance test

a. measures levels of hormones in the blood

b. determines glucose metabolism after patient receives a measured dose of glucose

c. test of glucose metabolism 2 hours after eating a meal

d. measures blood sugar level after 12-hour fast

e. measures T4 concentration in the blood

f. uses radioactive iodine

E. What's the Abbreviation?

1. non-insulin-dependent diabetes mellitus _____

2. insulin-dependent diabetes mellitus _____

3. adrenocorticotropin hormone _____

4. parathyroid hormone _____

5. triiodothyronine _____

6. thyroid-stimulating hormone _____

7. fasting blood sugar _____

8. prolactin _____

F. Terminology Matching

Match each term to its definition.

1. _____ Cushing's disease   a. enlarged thyroid

2. _____ goiter   b. overactive adrenal cortex

3. _____ acromegaly   c. hyperthyroidism

4. _____ gigantism   d. underactive adrenal cortex

5. _____ cretinism   e. enlarged bones of head and extremities

6. _____ myxedema   f. may cause polyuria and polydipsia

7. _____ diabetes mellitus   g. an autoimmune disease

8. _____ diabetes insipidus   h. arrested physical and mental development

9. _____ Hashimoto's thyroiditis   i. disorder of carbohydrate metabolism

10. _____ Graves' disease   j. insufficient thyroid hormone in an adult

11. _____ Addison's disease   k. excessive growth hormone in a child

G. What Does it Stand For?

1. PBI _____

2. K^+ _____

3. T_4 _____

4. GTT _____

5. DM _____

6. BMR _____

7. Na^+ _____

8. ADH _____

H. Suffix Practice

Use the following suffixes to create medical terms for the following definitions.

-pressin	-uria	-tropin
-dipsia	-emia	-prandial

1. the presence of sugar or glucose in the urine _____

2. to press down a vessel _____

3. excessive urination _____

4. condition of excessive calcium in the blood _____

5. excessive thirst _____

6. stimulate adrenal cortex _____

7. after a meal _____

I. Define the Term

1. corticosteroid _____

2. hirsutism _____

3. tetany _____

4. diabetic retinopathy _____

5. hyperglycemia _____

6. hypoglycemia _____

7. adrenaline _____

8. insulin _____

9. thyrotoxicosis _____

10. hypersecretion _____

J. Fill in the Blank

insulinoma	ketoacidosis	pheochromocytoma
gynecomastia	panhypopituitarinism	Hashimoto's thyroiditis

1. The doctor found that Marsha's high level of insulin and hypoglycemia was caused by a(n) _____.

2. Kevin developed _____ as a result of his diabetes mellitus and required emergency treatment.

3. It was determined that Karen had _____ when doctors realized she had problems with her thyroid gland, adrenal cortex, and ovaries.

4. Luke's high epinephrine level was caused by a(n) _____.

5. When it was determined that Carl's thyroiditis was an autoimmune condition, it became obvious that he had

   _____.

6. Excessive sex hormones caused Jack to develop _____.

K. Pharmacology Challenge

Fill in the classification for each drug description, then match the brand name.

Drug Description	Classification	Brand Name
1. _____ strong anti-inflammatory	_____	a. genotropin
2. _____ stimulates skeletal growth	_____	b. Desmopressin
3. _____ treats type 1 diabetes mellitus	_____	c. Tapazole
4. _____ blocks production of thyroid hormone	_____	d. glucophage
5. _____ treats type 1 diabetes mellitus	_____	e. Deltasone
6. _____ controls diabetes insipidus	_____	f. Humulin

MEDICAL TERMINOLOGY INTERACTIVE

Medical Terminology Interactive is a premium online homework management system that includes a host of features to help you study. Registered users will find:

- Fun games and activities built within a virtual hospital
- Powerful tools that track and analyze your results—allowing you to create a personalized learning experience
- Videos, flashcards, and audio pronunciations to help enrich your progress
- Streaming video lesson presentations and self-paced learning modules

www.pearsonhighered.com/mti

Labeling Exercise

Image A

Write the labels for this figure on the numbered lines provided.

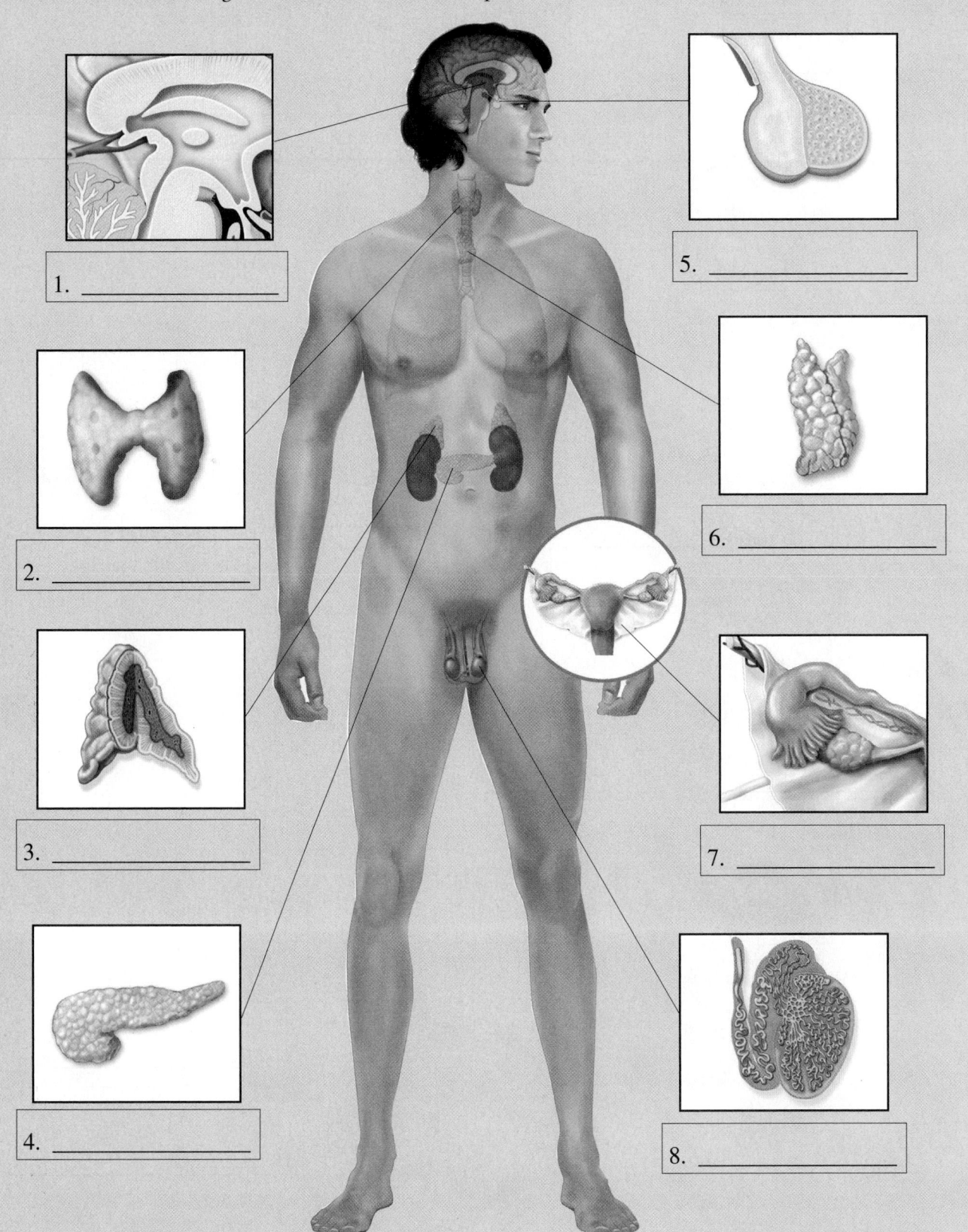

1. _____

2. _____

3. _____

4. _____

5. _____

6. _____

7. _____

8. _____

Image B

Write the labels for this figure on the numbered lines provided.

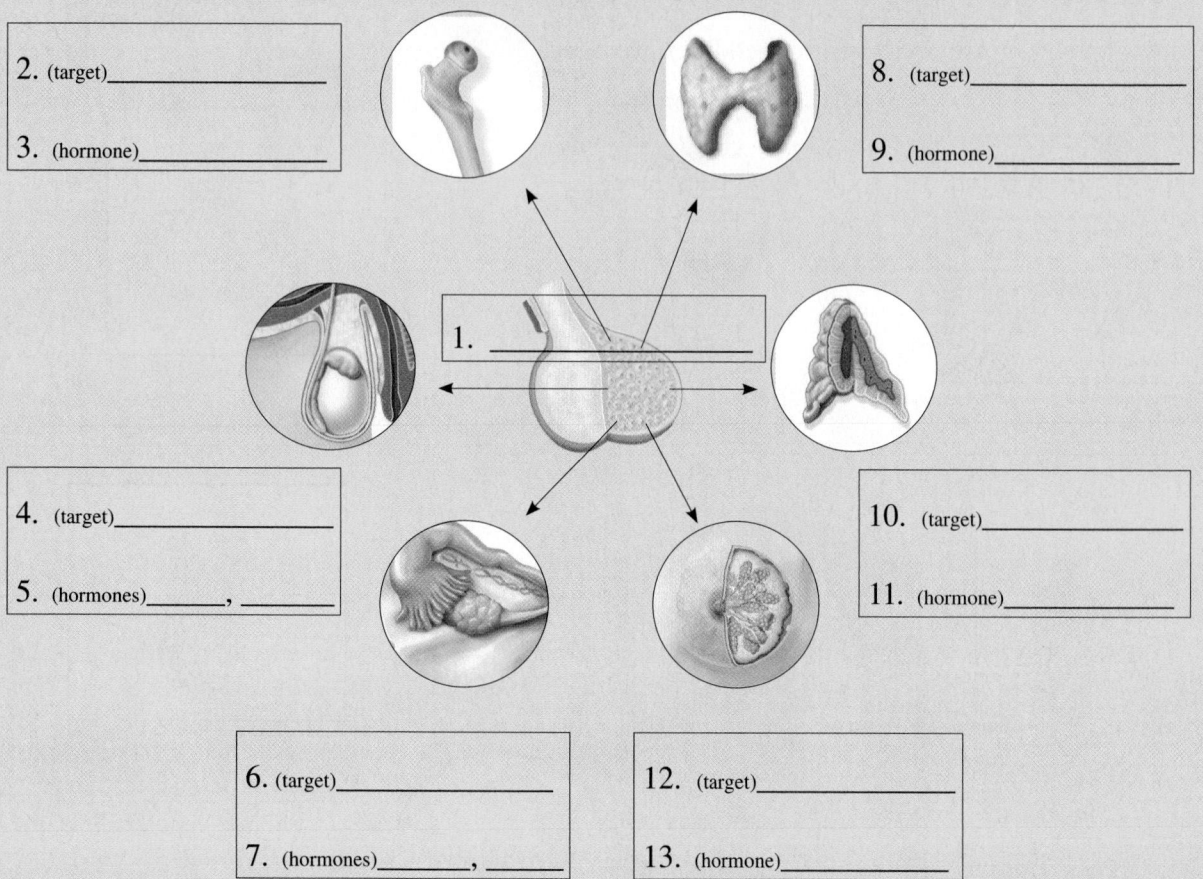

2. (target)_____

3. (hormone)_____

8. (target)_____

9. (hormone)_____

1. _____

4. (target)_____

5. (hormones)_____, _____

10. (target)_____

11. (hormone)_____

6. (target)_____

7. (hormones)_____, _____

12. (target)_____

13. (hormone)_____

Image C

Write the labels for this figure on the numbered lines provided.

1. _____

2. _____

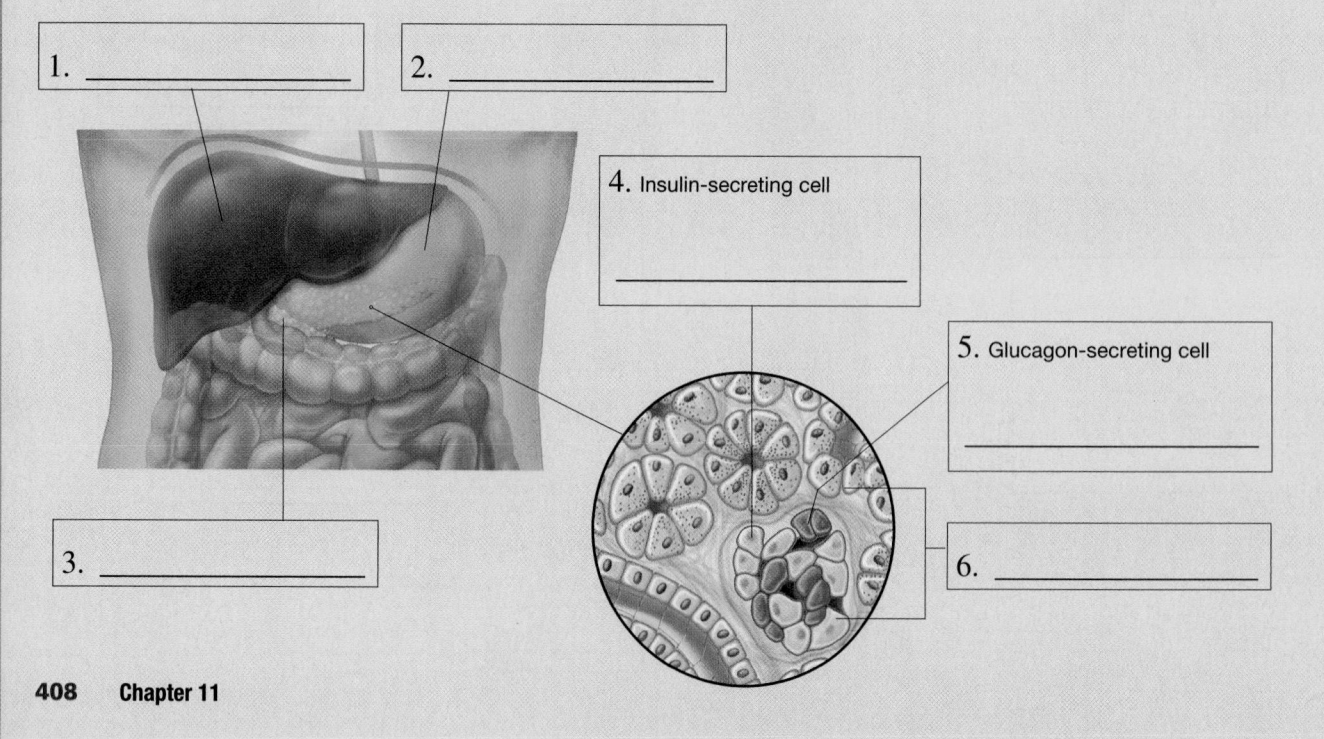

4. Insulin-secreting cell

_____

5. Glucagon-secreting cell

_____

3. _____

6. _____

12

NERVOUS SYSTEM

Learning Objectives

Upon completion of this chapter, you will be able to

- Identify and define the combining forms and suffixes introduced in this chapter.

- Correctly spell and pronounce medical terms and major anatomical structures relating to the nervous system.

- Locate and describe the major organs of the nervous system and their functions.

- Describe the components of a neuron.

- Distinguish between the central nervous system, peripheral nervous system, and autonomic nervous system.

- Identify and define nervous system anatomical terms.

- Identify and define selected nervous system pathology terms.

- Identify and define selected nervous system diagnostic procedures.

- Identify and define selected nervous system therapeutic procedures.

- Identify and define selected medications relating to the nervous system.

- Define selected abbreviations associated with the nervous system.

Nervous System at a Glance

Function

The nervous system coordinates and controls body function. It receives sensory input, makes decisions, and then orders body responses.

Organs

Here are the primary structures that comprise the nervous system.

brain   **spinal cord**
nerves

Word Parts

Here are the most common word parts (with their meanings) used to build nervous system terms. For a more comprehensive list, refer to the Terminology section of this chapter.

Combining Forms

alges/o	sense of pain	mening/o	meninges
astr/o	star	meningi/o	meninges
cephal/o	head	myel/o	spinal cord
cerebell/o	cerebellum	neur/o	nerve
cerebr/o	cerebrum	poli/o	gray matter
clon/o	rapid contracting and relaxing	pont/o	pons
		radicul/o	nerve root
dur/o	dura mater	thalam/o	thalamus
encephal/o	brain	thec/o	sheath (meninges)
esthes/o	sensation, feeling	ton/o	tone
gli/o	glue	ventricul/o	brain ventricle
medull/o	medulla oblongata		

Suffixes

-paresis	weakness	-taxia	muscle coordination
-phasia	speech	-trophic	pertaining to development
-plegia	paralysis		

Nervous System Illustrated

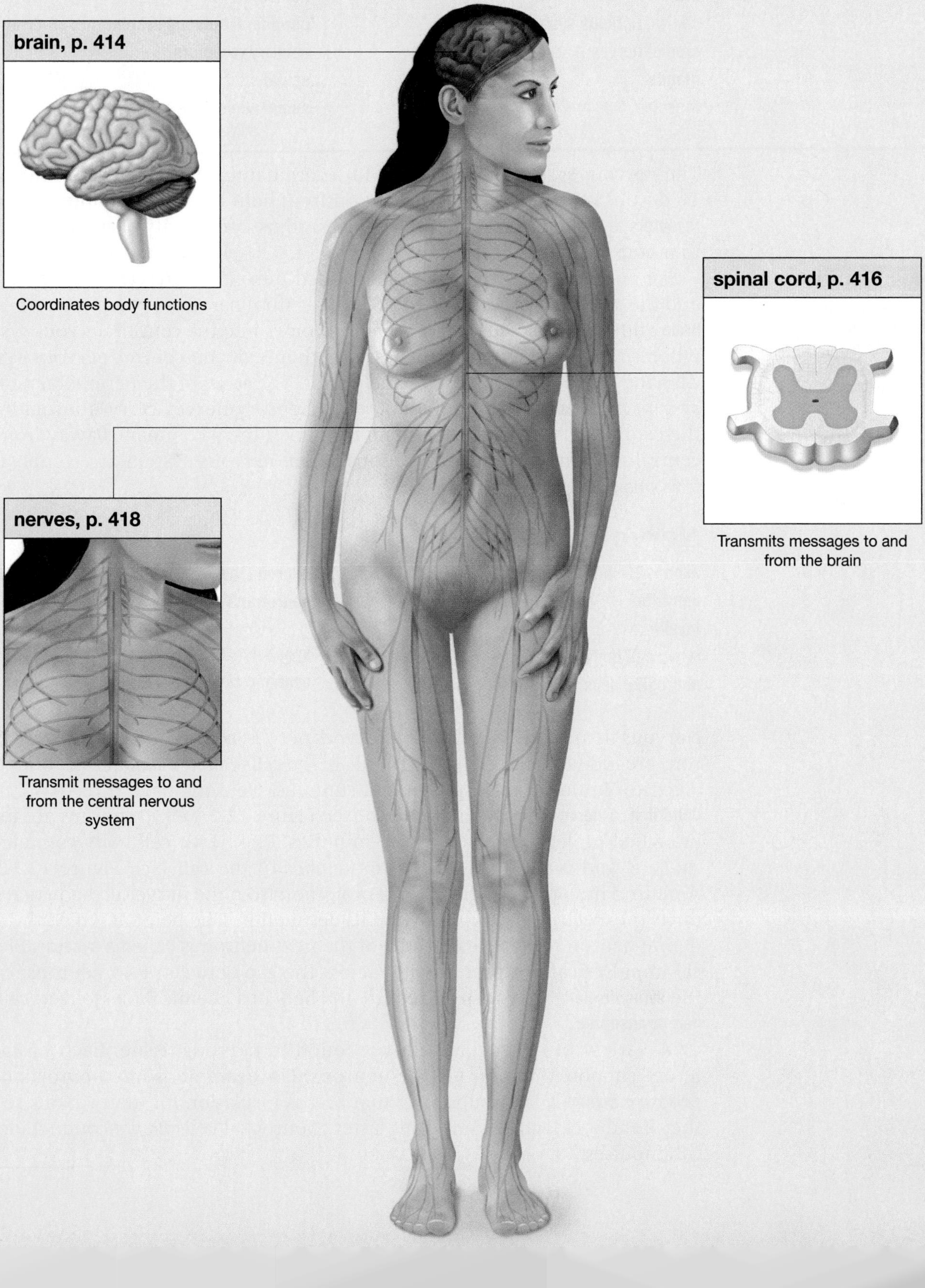

brain, p. 414

Coordinates body functions

spinal cord, p. 416

Transmits messages to and from the brain

nerves, p. 418

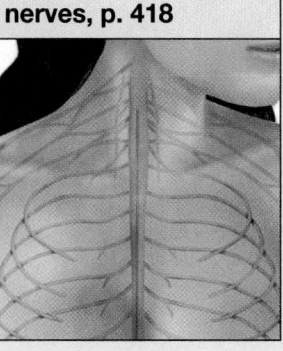

Transmit messages to and from the central nervous system

Anatomy and Physiology of the Nervous System

brain

central nervous system

cranial nerves (KRAY-nee-al)

glands

muscles

nerves

peripheral nervous system (per-IF-er-al)

sensory receptors

spinal cord

spinal nerves

The nervous system is responsible for coordinating all the activity of the body. To do this, it first receives information from both external and internal **sensory receptors** and then uses that information to adjust the activity of **muscles** and **glands** to match the needs of the body.

The nervous system can be subdivided into the **central nervous system** (CNS) and the **peripheral nervous system** (PNS). The central nervous system consists of the **brain** and **spinal cord.** Sensory information comes into the central nervous system, where it is processed. Motor messages then exit the central nervous system carrying commands to muscles and glands. The **nerves** of the peripheral nervous system are **cranial nerves** and **spinal nerves.** Sensory nerves carry information to the central nervous system, and motor nerves carry commands away from the central nervous system. All portions of the nervous system are composed of nervous tissue.

Nervous Tissue

axon (AK-son)

dendrites (DEN-drights)

myelin (MY-eh-lin)

nerve cell body

neuroglial cells (noo-ROH-glee-all)

neuron (NOO-ron)

neurotransmitter
  (noo-roh-TRANS-mit-ter)

synapse (sih-NAPSE)

synaptic cleft (sih-NAP-tik)

Nervous tissue consists of two basic types of cells: **neurons** and **neuroglial cells.** Neurons are individual nerve cells. These are the cells that are capable of conducting electrical impulses in response to a stimulus. Neurons have three basic parts: **dendrites,** a **nerve cell body,** and an **axon** (see Figure 12.1A ■). Dendrites are highly branched projections that receive impulses. The nerve cell body contains the nucleus and many of the other organelles of the cell (see Figure 12.1B ■). A neuron has only a single axon, a projection from the nerve cell body that conducts the electrical impulse toward its destination. The point at which the axon of one neuron meets the dendrite of the next neuron is called a **synapse.** Electrical impulses cannot pass directly across the gap between two neurons, called the **synaptic cleft.** They instead require the help of a chemical messenger, called a **neurotransmitter.**

A variety of neuroglial cells are found in nervous tissue. Each has a different support function for the neurons. For example, some neuroglial cells produce **myelin,** a fatty substance that acts as insulation for many axons so that they conduct electrical impulses faster. Neuroglial cells *do not* conduct electrical impulses.

MED TERM TIP

Neuroglial tissue received its name as a result of its function. This tissue holds neurons together. Therefore, it was called *neuroglial,* a term literally meaning "nerve glue."

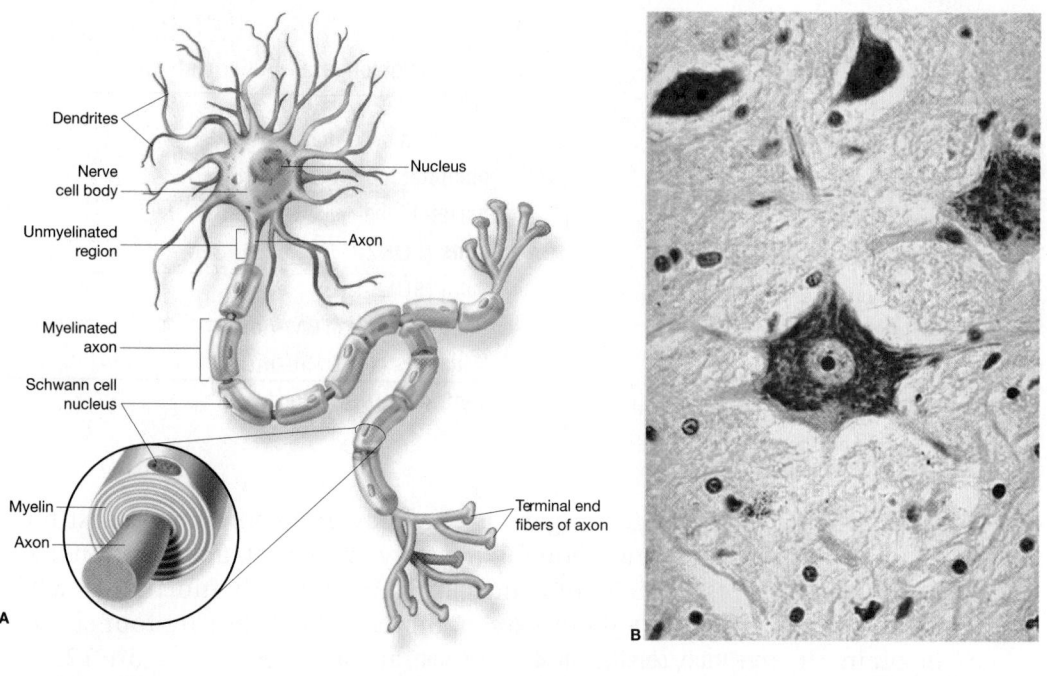

Figure 12.1 (A) The structure of a neuron, showing the dendrites, nerve cell body, and axon. (B) Photomicrograph of typical neuron showing the nerve cell body, nucleus, and dendrites.

Central Nervous System

gray matter

meninges (men-IN-jeez)

myelinated (MY-eh-lih-nayt-ed)

tract

white matter

Because the central nervous system is a combination of the brain and spinal cord, it is able to receive impulses from all over the body, process this information, and then respond with an action. This system consists of both **gray** and **white matter.** Gray matter is comprised of unsheathed or uncovered cell bodies and dendrites. White matter is **myelinated** nerve fibers (see Figure 12.2 ■). The myelin sheath makes the nervous tissue appear white. Bundles of nerve fibers interconnecting different parts of the central nervous system are called **tracts.** The central nervous system is encased and protected by three membranes known as the **meninges.**

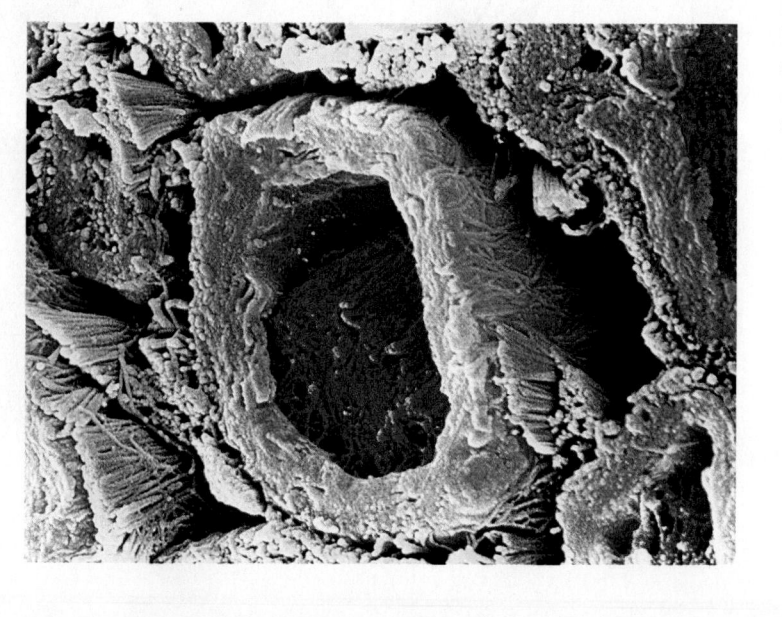

Figure 12.2 Electronmicrograph illustrating an axon (red) wrapped in its myelin sheath (blue). *(Quest/Science Photo Library/Photo Researchers, Inc.)*

The Brain

brain stem
cerebellum (ser-eh-BELL-um)
cerebral cortex (seh-REE-bral / KOR-teks)
cerebral hemisphere
cerebrospinal fluid (ser-eh-broh-SPY-nal)
cerebrum (SER-eh-brum)
diencephalon (dye-en-SEFF-ah-lon)
frontal lobe
gyri (JYE-rye)
hypothalamus (high-poh-THAL-ah-mus)

medulla oblongata (meh-DULL-ah / ob-long-GAH-tah)
midbrain
occipital lobe (ock-SIP-ih-tal)
parietal lobe (pah-RYE-eh-tal)
pons (PONZ)
sulci (SULL-kye)
temporal lobe (TEM-por-al)
thalamus (THAL-ah-mus)
ventricles (VEN-trik-lz)

The brain is one of the largest organs in the body and coordinates most body activities. It is the center for all thought, memory, judgment, and emotion. Each part of the brain is responsible for controlling different body functions, such as temperature regulation, blood pressure, and breathing. There are four sections to the brain: the **cerebrum, cerebellum, diencephalon,** and **brain stem** (see Figure 12.3 ■).

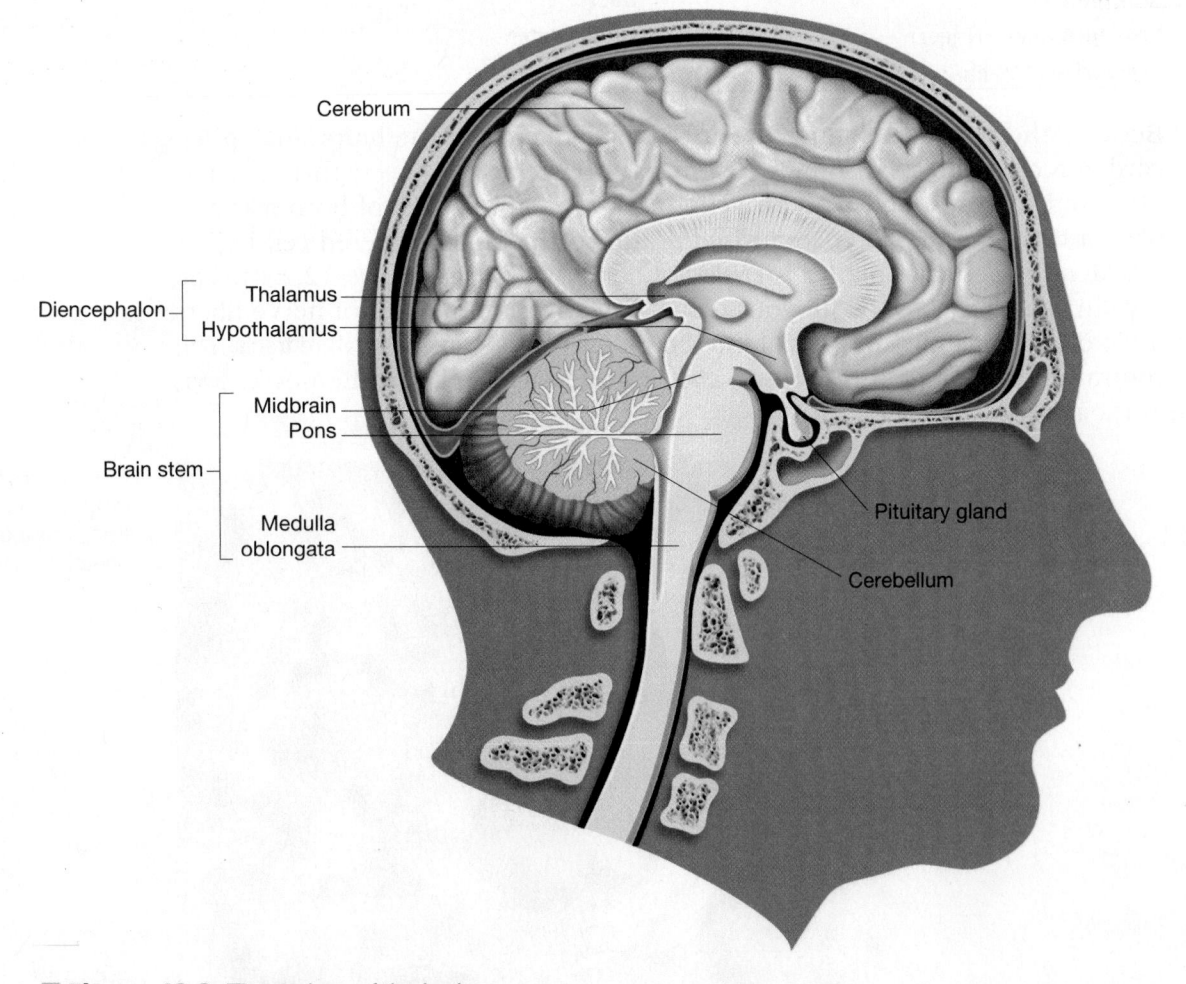

■ **Figure 12.3** The regions of the brain.

The largest section of the brain is the cerebrum. It is located in the upper portion of the brain and is the area that processes thoughts, judgment, memory, problem solving, and language. The outer layer of the cerebrum is the **cerebral cortex,** which is composed of folds of gray matter. The elevated portions of the cerebrum, or convolutions, are called **gyri** and are separated by fissures, or valleys, called **sulci.** The cerebrum is subdivided into left and right halves called **cerebral hemispheres.** Each hemisphere has four lobes. The lobes and their locations and functions are as follows (see Figure 12.4 ▪):

1. **Frontal lobe:** Most anterior portion of the cerebrum; controls motor function, personality, and speech
2. **Parietal lobe:** Most superior portion of the cerebrum; receives and interprets nerve impulses from sensory receptors and interprets language
3. **Occipital lobe:** Most posterior portion of the cerebrum; controls vision
4. **Temporal lobe:** Left and right lateral portion of the cerebrum; controls hearing and smell

The diencephalon, located below the cerebrum, contains two of the most critical areas of the brain, the **thalamus** and the **hypothalamus.** The thalamus is composed of gray matter and acts as a center for relaying impulses from the eyes, ears, and skin to the cerebrum. Our pain perception is controlled by the thalamus. The hypothalamus located just below the thalamus controls body temperature, appetite, sleep, sexual desire, and emotions. The hypothalamus is actually responsible for controlling the autonomic nervous system, cardiovascular system, digestive system, and the release of hormones from the pituitary gland.

The cerebellum, the second largest portion of the brain, is located beneath the posterior part of the cerebrum. This part of the brain aids in coordinating voluntary body movements and maintaining balance and equilibrium. The cerebellum refines the muscular movement that is initiated in the cerebrum.

The final portion of the brain is the brain stem. This area has three components: **midbrain, pons,** and **medulla oblongata.** The midbrain acts as a pathway for

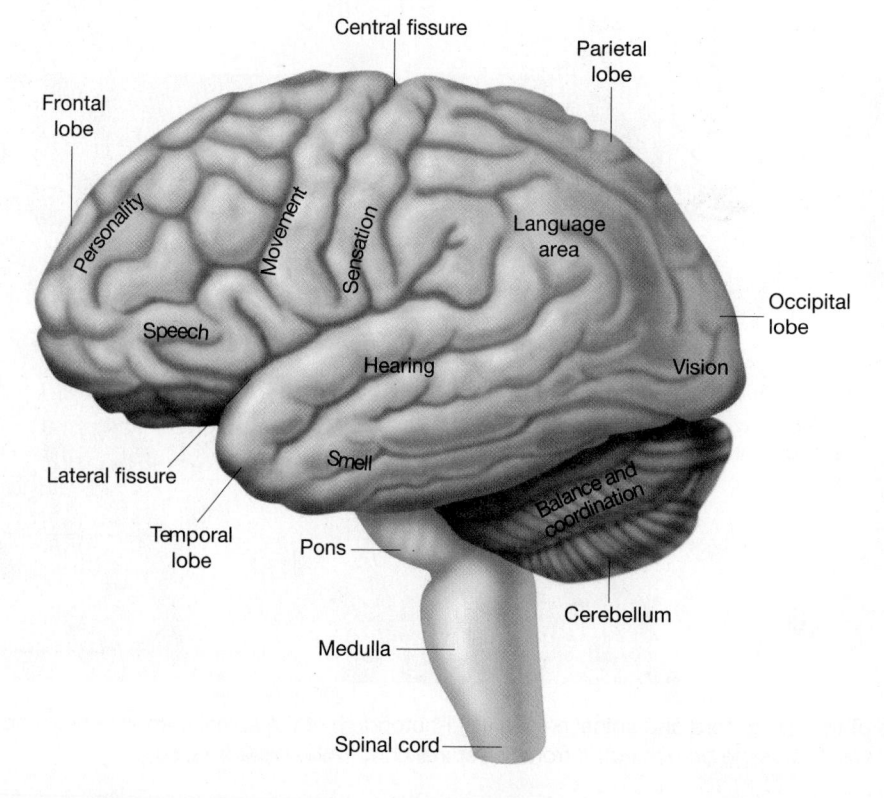

▪ **Figure 12.4** The functional regions of the cerebrum.

impulses to be conducted between the brain and the spinal cord. The pons—a term meaning bridge—connects the cerebellum to the rest of the brain. The medulla oblongata is the most inferior positioned portion of the brain; it connects the brain to the spinal cord. However, this vital area contains the centers that control respiration, heart rate, temperature, and blood pressure. Additionally, this is the site where nerve tracts cross from one side of the brain to control functions and movement on the other side of the body. In other words, with few exceptions, the left side of the brain controls the right side of the body and vice versa.

The brain has four interconnected cavities called **ventricles:** one in each cerebral hemisphere, one in the thalamus, and one in front of the cerebellum. These contain **cerebrospinal fluid** (CSF), which is the watery, clear fluid that provides protection from shock or sudden motion to the brain and spinal cord.

Spinal Cord

ascending tracts	**spinal cavity**
central canal	**vertebral canal**
descending tracts	**vertebral column**

The function of the spinal cord is to provide a pathway for impulses traveling to and from the brain. The spinal cord is actually a column of nervous tissue extending from the medulla oblongata of the brain down to the level of the second lumbar vertebra within the **vertebral column.** The 33 vertebrae of the backbone line up to form a continuous canal for the spinal cord called the **spinal cavity** or **vertebral canal** (see Figure 12.5 ■).

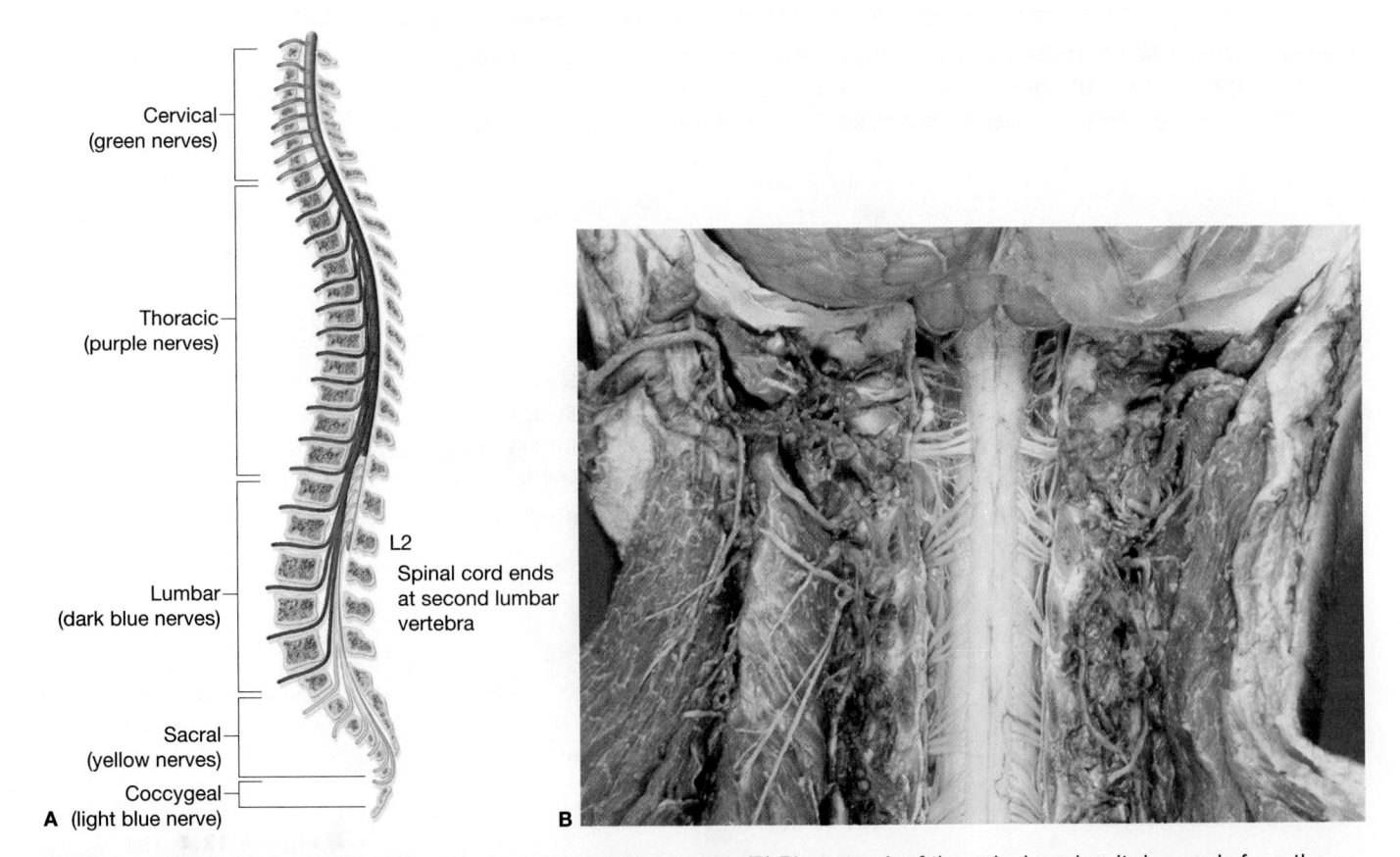

Cervical (green nerves)

Thoracic (purple nerves)

L2
Spinal cord ends at second lumbar vertebra

Lumbar (dark blue nerves)

Sacral (yellow nerves)

Coccygeal
A (light blue nerve)

B

■ **Figure 12.5** (A) The levels of the spinal cord and spinal nerves. (B) Photograph of the spinal cord as it descends from the brain. The spinal nerve roots are clearly visible branching off from the spinal cord. *(Photo Researchers, Inc.)*

Similar to the brain, the spinal cord is also protected by cerebrospinal fluid. It flows down the center of the spinal cord within the **central canal.** The inner core of the spinal cord consists of cell bodies and dendrites of peripheral nerves and therefore is gray matter. The outer portion of the spinal cord is myelinated white matter. The white matter is either **ascending tracts** carrying sensory information up to the brain or **descending tracts** carrying motor commands down from the brain to a peripheral nerve.

Meninges

arachnoid layer (ah-RAK-noyd)

dura mater (DOO-rah / MATE-er)

pia mater (PEE-ah / MATE-er)

subarachnoid space (sub-ah-RAK-noyd)

subdural space (sub-DOO-ral)

MED TERM TIP

Certain disease processes attack the gray matter and the white matter of the central nervous system. For instance, *poliomyelitis* is a viral infection of the gray matter of the spinal cord. The combining term *poli/o* means "gray matter." This disease has almost been eradicated, due to the polio vaccine.

The meninges are three layers of connective tissue membranes surrounding the brain and spinal cord (see Figure 12.6 ■). Moving from external to internal, the meninges are:

1. **Dura mater:** Meaning *tough mother;* it forms a tough, fibrous sac around the central nervous system
2. **Subdural space:** Actual space between the dura mater and arachnoid layers
3. **Arachnoid layer:** Meaning *spiderlike;* it is a thin, delicate layer attached to the pia mater by weblike filaments
4. **Subarachnoid space:** Space between the arachnoid layer and the pia mater; it contains cerebrospinal fluid that cushions the brain from the outside
5. **Pia mater:** Meaning *soft mother;* it is the innermost membrane layer and is applied directly to the surface of the brain and spinal cord

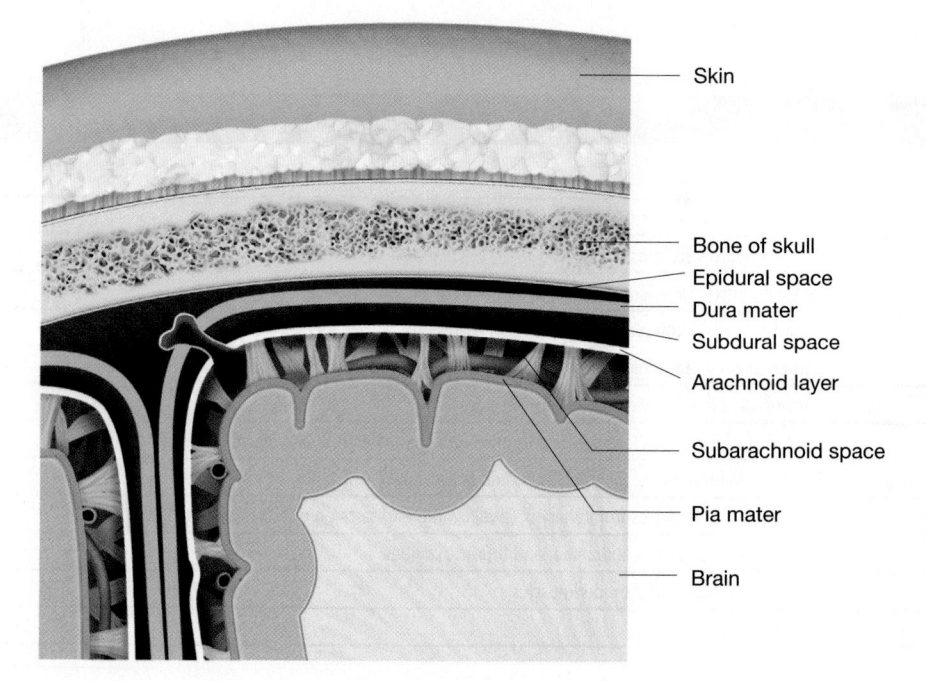

- Skin
- Bone of skull
- Epidural space
- Dura mater
- Subdural space
- Arachnoid layer
- Subarachnoid space
- Pia mater
- Brain

■ **Figure 12.6** The meninges. This figure illustrates the location and structure of each layer of the meninges and their relationship to the skull and brain.

Peripheral Nervous System

afferent neurons (AFF-er-ent)
autonomic nervous system (aw-toh-NOM-ik)
efferent neurons (EFF-er-ent)
ganglion (GANG-lee-on)

motor neurons
nerve root
sensory neurons
somatic nerves

The peripheral nervous system (PNS) includes both the 12 pairs of cranial nerves and the 31 pairs of spinal nerves. A nerve is a group or bundle of axon fibers located outside the central nervous system that carries messages between the central nervous system and the various parts of the body. Whether a nerve is cranial or spinal is determined by where the nerve originates. Cranial nerves arise from the brain, mainly at the medulla oblongata. Spinal nerves split off from the spinal cord, and one pair (a left and a right) exits between each pair of vertebrae. The point where either type of nerve is attached to the central nervous system is called the **nerve root.** The names of most nerves reflect either the organ the nerve serves or the portion of the body the nerve is traveling through. The entire list of cranial nerves is found in Table 12.1 ■. Figure 12.7 ■ illustrates some of the major spinal nerves in the human body.

Although most nerves carry information to and from the central nervous system, individual neurons carry information in only one direction. **Afferent neurons,** also called **sensory neurons,** carry sensory information from a sensory receptor to the central nervous system. **Efferent neurons,** also called **motor neurons,** carry activity instructions from the central nervous system to muscles or glands out in the body (see Figure 12.8 ■). The nerve cell bodies of the neurons forming the nerve are grouped together in a knot-like mass, called a **ganglion,** located outside the central nervous system.

The nerves of the peripheral nervous system are subdivided into two divisions, the **autonomic nervous system** (ANS) and **somatic nerves,** each serving a different area of the body.

MED TERM TIP

Because nerve tracts cross from one side of the body to the other side of the brain, damage to one side of the brain results in symptoms appearing on the opposite side of the body. Since nerve cells that control the movement of the right side of the body are located in the left side of the medulla oblongata, a stroke that paralyzed the right side of the body would actually have occurred in the left side of the brain.

Table 12.1	Cranial Nerves	
NUMBER	**NAME**	**FUNCTION**
I	Olfactory	Transports impulses for sense of smell
II	Optic	Carries impulses for sense of sight
III	Oculomotor	Motor impulses for eye muscle movement and the pupil of the eye
IV	Trochlear	Controls superior oblique muscle of eye on each side
V	Trigeminal	Carries sensory facial impulses and controls muscles for chewing; branches into eyes, forehead, upper and lower jaw
VI	Abducens	Controls an eyeball muscle to turn eye to side
VII	Facial	Controls facial muscles for expression, salivation, and taste on two-thirds of tongue (anterior)
VIII	Vestibulocochlear	Responsible for impulses of equilibrium and hearing; also called auditory nerve
IX	Glossopharyngeal	Carries sensory impulses from pharynx (swallowing) and taste on one-third of tongue
X	Vagus	Supplies most organs in abdominal and thoracic cavities
XI	Accessory	Controls the neck and shoulder muscles
XII	Hypoglossal	Controls tongue muscles

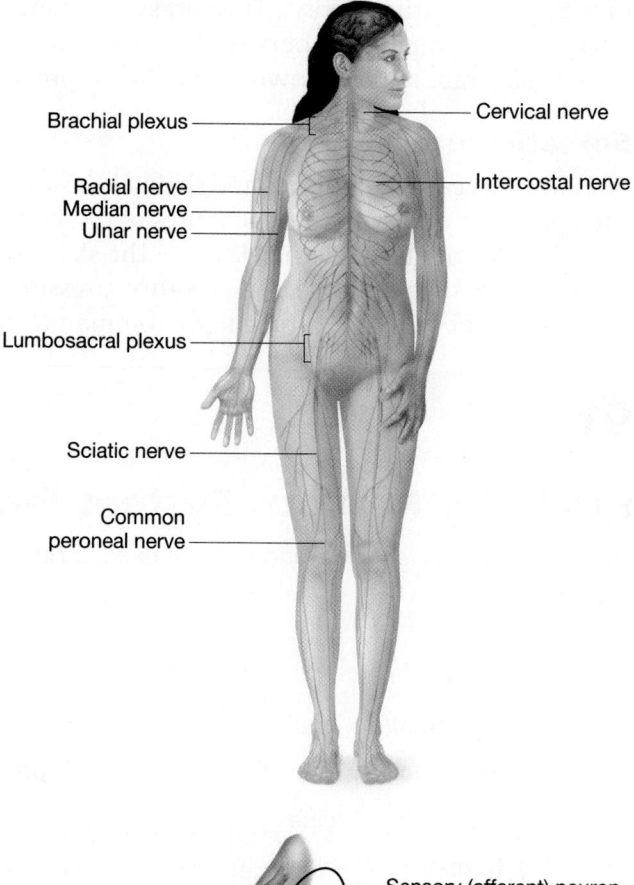

Brachial plexus ——

—— Cervical nerve

Radial nerve ——
Median nerve ——
Ulnar nerve ——

—— Intercostal nerve

Lumbosacral plexus ——

Sciatic nerve ——

Common
peroneal nerve ——

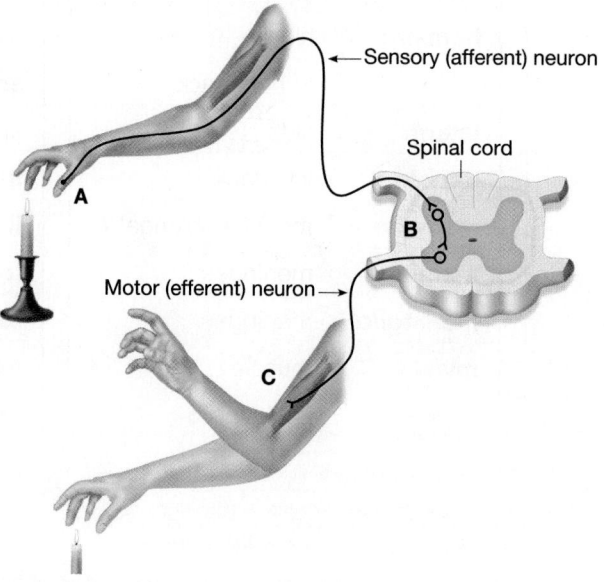

←— Sensory (afferent) neuron

Spinal cord

A

B

Motor (efferent) neuron →

C

■ **Figure 12.8** The functional structure of the peripheral nervous system. (A) Afferent or sensory neurons carry sensory information to the spinal cord; (B) the spinal cord receives incoming sensory information and delivers motor messages; (C) efferent or motor neurons deliver motor commands to muscles and glands.

Autonomic Nervous System

parasympathetic branch
  (pair-ah-sim-pah-THET-ik)

sympathetic branch (sim-pah-THET-ik)

The autonomic nervous system is involved with the control of involuntary or unconscious bodily functions. It may increase or decrease the activity of the smooth muscle found in viscera and blood vessels, cardiac muscle, and glands. The autonomic nervous system is divided into two branches: **sympathetic branch** and **parasympathetic branch.** The sympathetic nerves control the "fight or flight" reaction during times of stress and crisis. These nerves increase heart rate, dilate airways, increase blood pressure, inhibit digestion, and stimulate the production of adrenaline during a crisis. The parasympathetic nerves serve as a counterbalance for the sympathetic nerves, the "rest and digest" reaction. Therefore, they cause heart rate to slow down, lower blood pressure, and stimulate digestion.

Somatic Nerves

Somatic nerves serve the skin and skeletal muscles and are mainly involved with the conscious and voluntary activities of the body. The large variety of sensory receptors found in the dermis layer of the skin use somatic nerves to send their information, such as touch, temperature, pressure, and pain, to the brain. These are also the nerves that carry motor commands to skeletal muscles.

 # Terminology

Word Parts Used to Build Nervous System Terms

The following lists contain the combining forms, suffixes, and prefixes used to build terms in the remaining sections of this chapter.

Combining Forms

alges/o	sense of pain	**encephal/o**	brain	**neur/o**	nerve
angi/o	vessel	**esthes/o**	sensation, feeling	**poli/o**	gray matter
arteri/o	artery	**gli/o**	glue	**pont/o**	pons
astr/o	star	**hemat/o**	blood	**radicul/o**	nerve root
cephal/o	head	**isch/o**	to hold back	**scler/o**	hard
cerebell/o	cerebellum	**later/o**	side	**spin/o**	spine
cerebr/o	cerebrum	**lumb/o**	low back	**thalam/o**	thalamus
clon/o	rapid contracting and relaxing	**medull/o**	medulla oblongata	**thec/o**	sheath
cyt/o	cell	**mening/o**	meninges	**tom/o**	to cut
dur/o	dura mater	**meningi/o**	meninges	**ton/o**	muscle tone
electr/o	electricity	**my/o**	muscle	**vascul/o**	blood vessel
		myel/o	spinal cord	**ventricul/o**	ventricle

Suffixes

-al	pertaining to	**-ia**	condition, state	**-pathy**	disease
-algia	pain	**-ic**	pertaining to	**-phasia**	speech
-ar	pertaining to	**-ine**	pertaining to	**-plasty**	surgical repair
-ary	pertaining to	**-itis**	inflammation	**-plegia**	paralysis
-asthenia	weakness	**-logy**	study of	**-rrhaphy**	suture
-cele	protrusion	**-nic**	pertaining to	**-taxia**	muscle coordination
-eal	pertaining to	**-oma**	tumor, swelling	**-tic**	pertaining to
-ectomy	surgical removal	**-osis**	abnormal condition	**-trophic**	pertaining to development
-gram	record	**-otomy**	cutting into		
-graphy	process of recording	**-paresis**	weakness		

Prefixes

a-	without	hemi-	half	poly-	many
an-	without	hydro-	water	quadri-	four
anti-	against	hyper-	excessive	semi-	partial
bi-	two	intra-	within	sub-	below
dys-	abnormal, difficult	mono-	one	un-	not
endo-	within	para-	abnormal, two like parts of a pair		
epi-	above				

Anatomical Terms

TERM	WORD PARTS	DEFINITION
cerebellar (ser-eh-BELL-ar)	cerebell/o = cerebellum -ar = pertaining to	Pertaining to the cerebellum.
cerebral (seh-REE-bral)	cerebr/o = cerebrum -al = pertaining to	Pertaining to the cerebrum.
cerebrospinal (ser-eh-broh-SPY-nal)	cerebr/o = cerebrum spin/o = spine -al = pertaining to	Pertaining to the cerebrum and spine.
encephalic (IN-seh-FAL-ik)	encephal/o = brain -ic = pertaining to	Pertaining to the brain.
intrathecal (in-tra-THEE-kal)	intra- = within thec/o = sheath -al = pertaining to	Pertaining to within the meninges, specifically the subdural or subarachnoid space.
medullary (MED-yoo-lair-ee)	medull/o = medulla oblongata -ary = pertaining to	Pertaining to the medulla oblongata.
myelonic (MY-eh-LON-ik)	myel/o = spinal cord -nic = pertaining to	Pertaining to the spinal cord.
meningeal (meh-NIN-jee-all)	mening/o = meninges -eal = pertaining to	Pertaining to the meninges.
neural (NOO-rall)	neur/o = nerve -al = pertaining to	Pertaining to nerves.
neuroglial (noo-RIG-lee-al)	neur/o = nerve gli/o = glue -al = pertaining to	Pertaining to the support cells, glial cells, of nerves.
pontine (pon-TEEN)	pont/o = pons -ine = pertaining to	Pertaining to the pons.
thalamic (tha-LAM-ik)	thalam/o = thalamus -ic = pertaining to	Pertaining to the thalamus.
ventricular (ven-TRIK-yoo-lar)	ventricul/o = ventricle -ar = pertaining to	Pertaining to the ventricles.

Pathology

TERM	WORD PARTS	DEFINITION
Medical Specialties		
anesthesiology (an-es-thee-zee-ol-oh-jee)	an- = without esthes/o = sensation, feeling -logy = study of	Branch of medicine specializing in all aspects of anesthesia, including for surgical procedures, resuscitation measures, and the management of acute and chronic pain. Physician is an *anesthesiologist*.
neurology (noo-rol-oh-jee)	neur/o = nerve -logy = study of	Branch of medicine concerned with diagnosis and treatment of diseases and conditions of the nervous system. Physician is a *neurologist*.
neurosurgery (noo-roh-SIR-jury)	neur/o = nerve	Branch of medicine concerned with treating conditions and diseases of the nervous systems by surgical means. Physician is a *neurosurgeon*.
Signs and Symptoms		
absence seizure		Type of epileptic seizure that lasts only a few seconds to half a minute, characterized by a loss of awareness and an absence of activity. It is also called a *petit mal seizure*.
analgesia (an-al-JEE-zee-ah)	an- = without alges/o = sense of pain -ia = state	Absence of pain.
anesthesia (an-ess-THEE-zee-ah)	an- = without esthes/o = feeling, sensations -ia = condition	Lack of feeling or sensation.
aphasia (ah-FAY-zee-ah)	a- = without -phasia = speech	Inability to communicate verbally or in writing due to damage of the speech or language centers in the brain.
ataxia (ah-TAK-see-ah)	a- = without -taxia = muscle coordination	Lack of muscle coordination.
aura (AW-ruh)		Sensations, such as seeing colors or smelling an unusual odor, that occur just prior to an epileptic seizure or migraine headache.
cephalalgia (seff-al-AL-jee-ah)	cephal/o = head -algia = pain	Headache.
coma (COH-mah)		Profound unconsciousness resulting from an illness or injury.
conscious (KON-shus)		Condition of being awake and aware of surroundings.
convulsion (kon-VULL-shun)		Severe involuntary muscle contractions and relaxations. These have a variety of causes, such as epilepsy, fever, and toxic conditions.

◼ Pathology *(continued)*

TERM	WORD PARTS	DEFINITION
delirium (dee-LEER-ee-um)		Abnormal mental state characterized by confusion, disorientation, and agitation.
dementia (dee-MEN-she-ah)		Progressive impairment of intellectual function that interferes with performing activities of daily living. Patients have little awareness of their condition. Found in disorders such as Alzheimer's.
dysphasia (dis-FAY-zee-ah)	dys- = abnormal, difficult -phasia = speech	Difficulty communicating verbally or in writing due to damage of the speech or language centers in the brain.
focal seizure (FOE-kal)	-al = pertaining to	Localized seizure often affecting one limb.
hemiparesis (hem-ee-par-EE-sis)	hemi- = half -paresis = weakness	Weakness or loss of motion on one side of the body.
hemiplegia (hem-ee-PLEE-jee-ah)	hemi- = half -plegia = paralysis	Paralysis on only one side of the body.
hyperesthesia (high-per-ess-THEE-zee-ah)	hyper- = excessive esthes/o = feeling, sensations -ia = condition	Abnormally heightened sense of feeling, sense of pain, or sensitivity to touch.
monoparesis (mon-oh-pah-REE-sis)	mono- = one -paresis = weakness	Muscle weakness in one limb.
monoplegia (mon-oh-PLEE-jee-ah)	mono- = one -plegia = paralysis	Paralysis of one limb.
neuralgia (noo-RAL-jee-ah)	neur/o = nerve -algia = pain	Nerve pain.
palsy (PAWL-zee)		Temporary or permanent loss of the ability to control movement.
paralysis (pah-RAL-ih-sis)		Temporary or permanent loss of function or voluntary movement.
paraplegia (pair-ah-PLEE-jee-ah)	para- = two like parts of a pair -plegia = paralysis	Paralysis of the lower portion of the body and both legs.
paresthesia (par-es-THEE-zee-ah)	para- = abnormal esthes/o = sensation, feeling -ia = condition	Abnormal sensation such as burning or tingling.
quadriplegia (kwod-rih-PLEE-jee-ah)	quadri- = four -plegia = paralysis	Paralysis of all four limbs.
seizure (SEE-zyoor)		Sudden, uncontrollable onset of symptoms, such as in an epileptic seizure.
semiconscious (sem-ee-KON-shus)	semi- = partial	State of being aware of surroundings and responding to stimuli only part of the time.

■ **Pathology** *(continued)*

TERM	WORD PARTS	DEFINITION
syncope (SIN-koh-pee)		Fainting.
tonic-clonic seizure	ton/o = muscle tone clon/o = rapid contracting and relaxing -ic = pertaining to	Type of severe epileptic seizure characterized by a loss of consciousness and convulsions. The seizure alternates between strong continuous muscle spasms (tonic) and rhythmic muscle contraction and relaxation (clonic). It is also called a *grand mal seizure.*
tremor (TREM-or)		Involuntary repetitive alternating movement of a part of the body.
unconscious (un-KON-shus)	un- = not	State of being unaware of surroundings, with the inability to respond to stimuli.
Brain		
Alzheimer's disease (ALTS-high-merz)		Chronic, organic mental disorder consisting of dementia, which is more prevalent in adults after 65 years of age. Involves progressive disorientation, apathy, speech and gait disturbances, and loss of memory. Named for German neurologist Alois Alzheimer.
astrocytoma (ass-troh-sigh-TOH-mah)	astr/o = star cyt/o = cell -oma = tumor	Tumor of the brain or spinal cord composed of astrocytes, one type of neuroglial cells.
brain tumor		Intracranial mass, either benign or malignant. A benign tumor of the brain can still be fatal since it will grow and cause pressure on normal brain tissue.

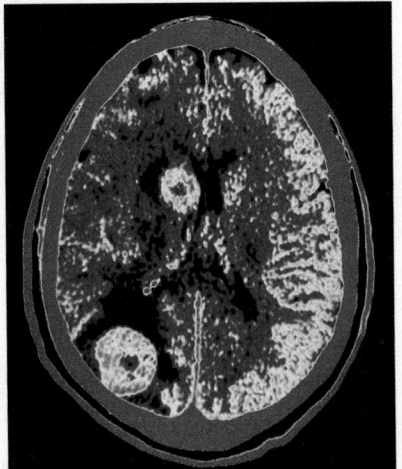

■ **Figure 12.9** Color-enhanced CT scan showing two malignant tumors in the brain. *(Scott Camazine/Photo Researchers, Inc.)*

TERM	WORD PARTS	DEFINITION
cerebellitis (ser-eh-bell-EYE-tis)	cerebell/o = cerebellum -itis = inflammation	Inflammation of the cerebellum.

Pathology *(continued)*

TERM	WORD PARTS	DEFINITION
cerebral aneurysm (AN-yoo-rizm)	cerebr/o = cerebrum -al = pertaining to	Localized abnormal dilation of a blood vessel, usually an artery; the result of a congenital defect or weakness in the wall of the vessel. A ruptured aneurysm is a common cause of a hemorrhagic cerebrovascular accident.

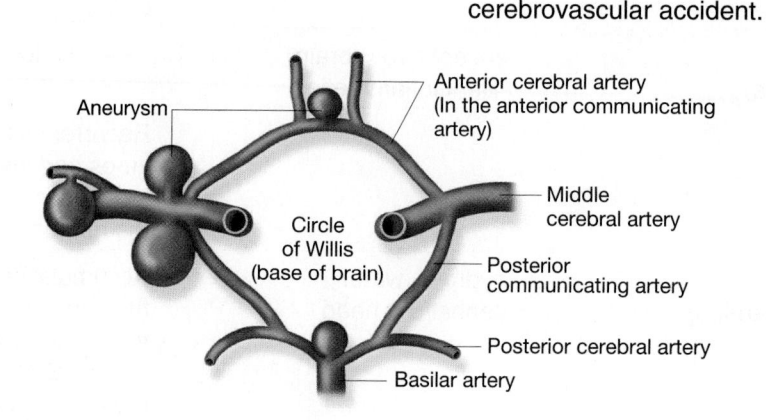

Aneurysm

Anterior cerebral artery (In the anterior communicating artery)

Middle cerebral artery

Circle of Willis (base of brain)

Posterior communicating artery

Posterior cerebral artery

Basilar artery

■ **Figure 12.10** Common locations for cerebral artery aneurysms in the Circle of Willis.

TERM	WORD PARTS	DEFINITION
cerebral contusion (kon-TOO-shun)	cerebr/o = cerebrum -al = pertaining to	Bruising of the brain from a blow or impact.
cerebral palsy (CP) (ser-REE-bral / PAWL-zee)	cerebr/o = cerebrum -al = pertaining to	Nonprogressive brain damage resulting from a defect, trauma, or oxygen deprivation at the time of birth.
cerebrovascular accident (CVA) (ser-eh-broh-VASS-kyoo-lar)	cerebr/o = cerebrum vascul/o = blood vessel -ar = pertaining to	Development of an infarct due to loss in the blood supply to an area of the brain. Blood flow can be interrupted by a ruptured blood vessel (hemorrhage), a floating clot (embolus), a stationary clot (thrombosis), or compression. The extent of damage depends on the size and location of the infarct and often includes dysphasia and hemiplegia. Commonly called a *stroke*.

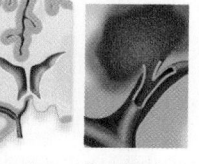

Cerebral hemorrhage: Cerebral artery ruptures and bleeds into brain tissue.

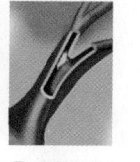

Cerebral embolism: Embolus from another area lodges in cerebral artery and blocks blood flow.

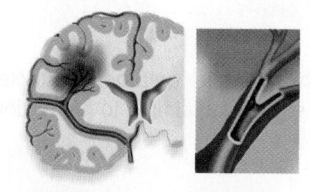

■ **Figure 12.11** The four common causes for cerebrovascular accidents.

Cerebral thrombosis: Blood clot forms in cerebral artery and blocks blood flow.

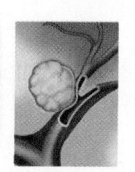

Compression: Pressure from tumor squeezes adjacent blood vessel and blocks blood flow.

■ Pathology *(continued)*

TERM	WORD PARTS	DEFINITION
concussion (kon-KUSH-un)		Injury to the brain resulting from the brain being shaken inside the skull from a blow or impact. Symptoms vary and may include: headache, blurred vision, nausea or vomiting, dizziness, and balance problems. Also called *mild traumatic brain injury* (TBI).
encephalitis (en-seff-ah-LYE-tis)	encephal/o = brain -itis = inflammation	Inflammation of the brain.
epilepsy (EP-ih-lep-see)		Recurrent disorder of the brain in which seizures and loss of consciousness occur as a result of uncontrolled electrical activity of the neurons in the brain.
hydrocephalus (high-droh-SEFF-ah-lus)	hydro- = water cephal/o = head	Accumulation of cerebrospinal fluid within the ventricles of the brain, causing the head to be enlarged. It is treated by creating an artificial shunt for the fluid to leave the brain. If left untreated, it may lead to seizures and mental retardation.

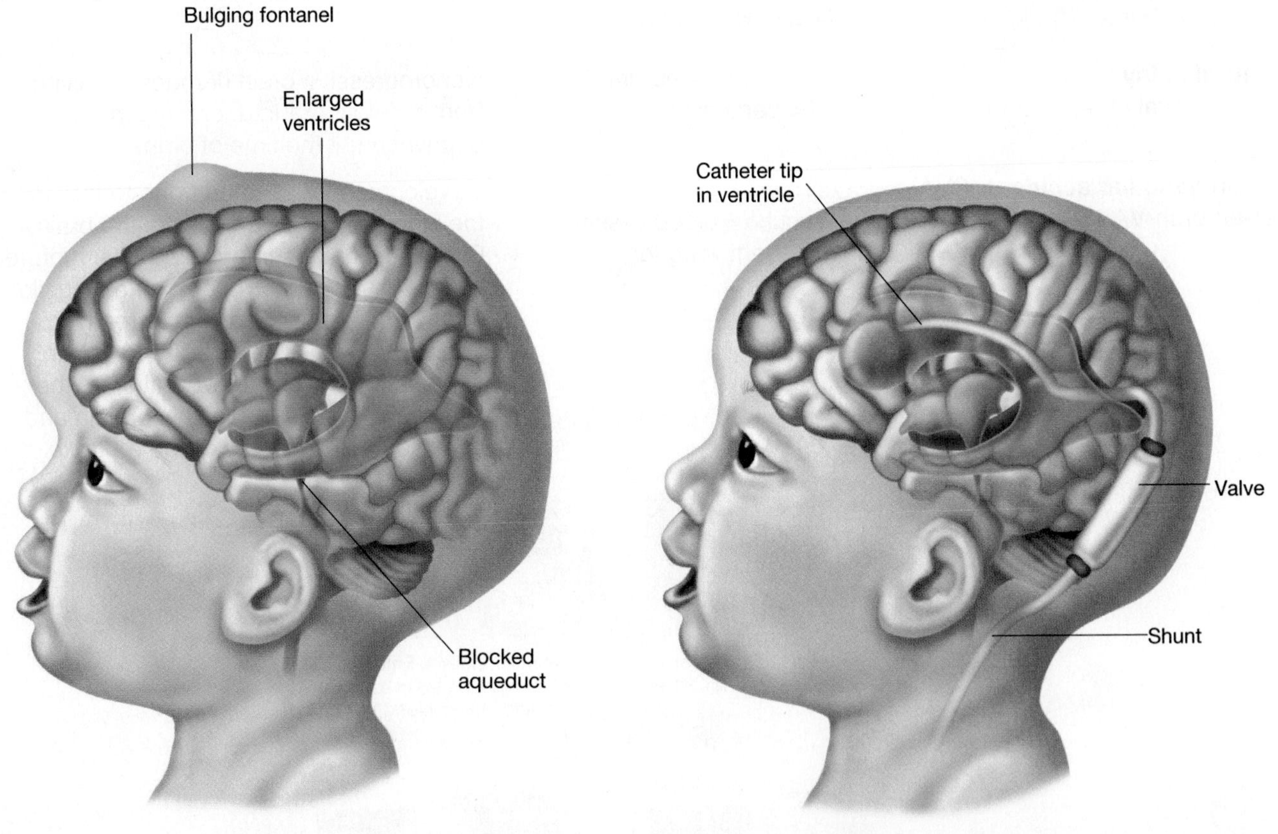

Bulging fontanel

Enlarged ventricles

Catheter tip in ventricle

Valve

Blocked aqueduct

Shunt

■ **Figure 12.12** Hydrocephalus. The figure on the left is a child with the enlarged ventricles of hydrocephalus. The figure on the right is the same child with a shunt to send the excess cerebrospinal fluid to the abdominal cavity.

Pathology *(continued)*

TERM	WORD PARTS	DEFINITION
migraine (MY-grain)		Specific type of headache characterized by severe head pain, sensitivity to light, dizziness, and nausea.
Parkinson's disease (PARK-in-sons)		Chronic disorder of the nervous system with fine tremors, muscular weakness, rigidity, and a shuffling gait. Named for British physician Sir James Parkinson.
Reye syndrome (RISE / SIN-drohm)		Combination of symptoms first recognized by Australian pathologist R. D. K. Reye that includes acute encephalopathy and damage to various organs, especially the liver. This occurs in children under age 15 who have had a viral infection. It is also associated with taking aspirin. For this reason, it's not recommended for children to use aspirin.
transient ischemic attack (TIA) (TRAN-shent / iss-KEM-ik)	isch/o = to hold back hem/o = blood -ic = pertaining to	Temporary interference with blood supply to the brain, causing neurological symptoms such as dizziness, numbness, and hemiparesis. May eventually lead to a full-blown stroke (cerebrovascular accident).
Spinal Cord		
amyotrophic lateral sclerosis (ALS) (ah-my-oh-TROFF-ik / LAT-er-al / skleh-ROH-sis)	a- = without my/o = muscle -trophic = pertaining to development later/o = side -al = pertaining to scler/o = hard -osis = abnormal condition	Disease with muscular weakness and atrophy due to degeneration of motor neurons of the spinal cord. Also called *Lou Gehrig's disease,* after the New York Yankees baseball player who died from the disease.
meningocele (men-IN-goh-seel)	mening/o = meninges -cele = protrusion	Congenital condition in which the meninges protrude through an opening in the vertebral column (see Figure 12.13B ■). See *spina bifida.*
myelitis (my-eh-LYE-tis)	myel/o = spinal cord -itis = inflammation	Inflammation of the spinal cord.
myelomeningocele (my-eh-loh-meh-NIN-goh-seel)	myel/o = spinal cord mening/o = meninges -cele = protrusion	Congenital condition in which the meninges and spinal cord protrude through an opening in the vertebral column (see Figure 12.13C ■). See *spina bifida.*
poliomyelitis (poh-lee-oh-my-eh-lye-tis)	poli/o = gray matter myel/o = spinal cord -itis = inflammation	Viral inflammation of the gray matter of the spinal cord. Results in varying degrees of paralysis; may be mild and reversible or may be severe and permanent. This disease has been almost eliminated due to the discovery of a vaccine in the 1950s.

Pathology *(continued)*

TERM	WORD PARTS	DEFINITION
spina bifida (SPY-nah / BIFF-ih-dah)	spin/o = spine bi- = two	Congenital defect in the walls of the spinal canal in which the laminae of the vertebra do not meet or close (see Figure 12.13A ■). May result in a meningocele or a myelomeningocele—meninges or the spinal cord being pushed through the opening.

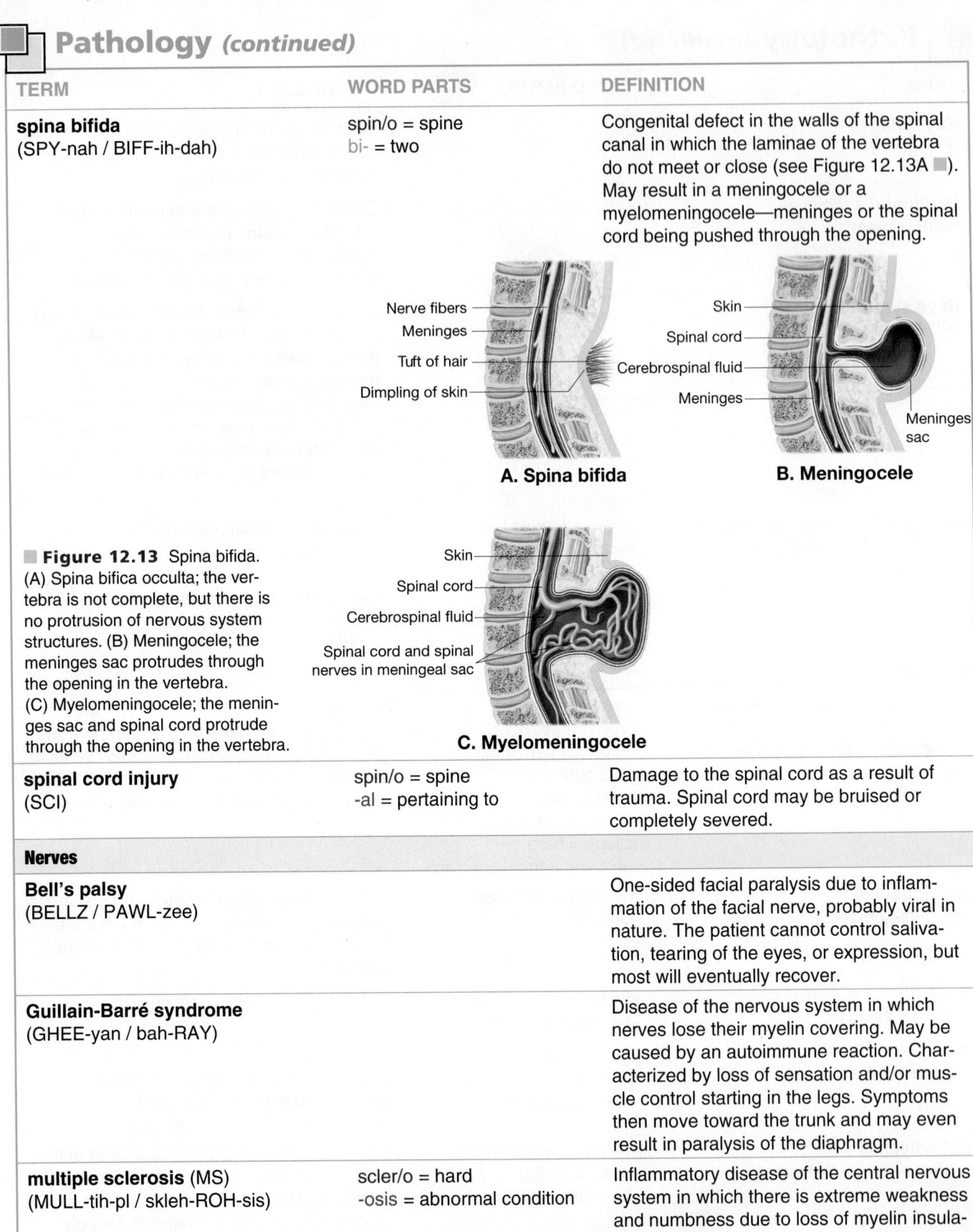

A. Spina bifida   **B. Meningocele**

Nerve fibers — Meninges — Tuft of hair — Dimpling of skin

Skin — Spinal cord — Cerebrospinal fluid — Meninges — Meninges sac

C. Myelomeningocele

Skin — Spinal cord — Cerebrospinal fluid — Spinal cord and spinal nerves in meningeal sac

■ **Figure 12.13** Spina bifida. (A) Spina bifica occulta; the vertebra is not complete, but there is no protrusion of nervous system structures. (B) Meningocele; the meninges sac protrudes through the opening in the vertebra. (C) Myelomeningocele; the meninges sac and spinal cord protrude through the opening in the vertebra.

TERM	WORD PARTS	DEFINITION
spinal cord injury (SCI)	spin/o = spine -al = pertaining to	Damage to the spinal cord as a result of trauma. Spinal cord may be bruised or completely severed.

Nerves

TERM	WORD PARTS	DEFINITION
Bell's palsy (BELLZ / PAWL-zee)		One-sided facial paralysis due to inflammation of the facial nerve, probably viral in nature. The patient cannot control salivation, tearing of the eyes, or expression, but most will eventually recover.
Guillain-Barré syndrome (GHEE-yan / bah-RAY)		Disease of the nervous system in which nerves lose their myelin covering. May be caused by an autoimmune reaction. Characterized by loss of sensation and/or muscle control starting in the legs. Symptoms then move toward the trunk and may even result in paralysis of the diaphragm.
multiple sclerosis (MS) (MULL-tih-pl / skleh-ROH-sis)	scler/o = hard -osis = abnormal condition	Inflammatory disease of the central nervous system in which there is extreme weakness and numbness due to loss of myelin insulation from nerves.
myasthenia gravis (my-ass-THEE-nee-ah / GRAV-iss)	my/o = muscle -asthenia = weakness	Disease with severe muscular weakness and fatigue due to insufficient neurotransmitter at a synapse.

■ Pathology (continued)

TERM	WORD PARTS	DEFINITION
neuroma (noo-ROH-mah)	neur/o = nerve -oma = tumor	Nerve tumor or tumor of the connective tissue sheath around a nerve.
neuropathy (noo-ROP-ah-thee)	neur/o = nerve -pathy = disease	General term for disease or damage to a nerve.
polyneuritis (pol-ee-noo-RYE-tis)	poly- = many neur/o = nerve -itis = inflammation	Inflammation of two or more nerves.
radiculitis (rah-dick-yoo-LYE-tis)	radicul/o = nerve root -itis = inflammation	Inflammation of a nerve root; may be caused by a herniated nucleus pulposus.
radiculopathy (rah-dick-yoo-LOP-ah-thee)	radicul/o = nerve root -pathy = disease	Refers to the condition that occurs when a herniated nucleus pulposus puts pressure on a nerve root. Symptoms include pain and numbness along the path of the affected nerve.
shingles (SHING-lz)		Eruption of painful blisters on the body along a nerve path. Thought to be caused by a *Herpes zoster* virus infection of the nerve root.

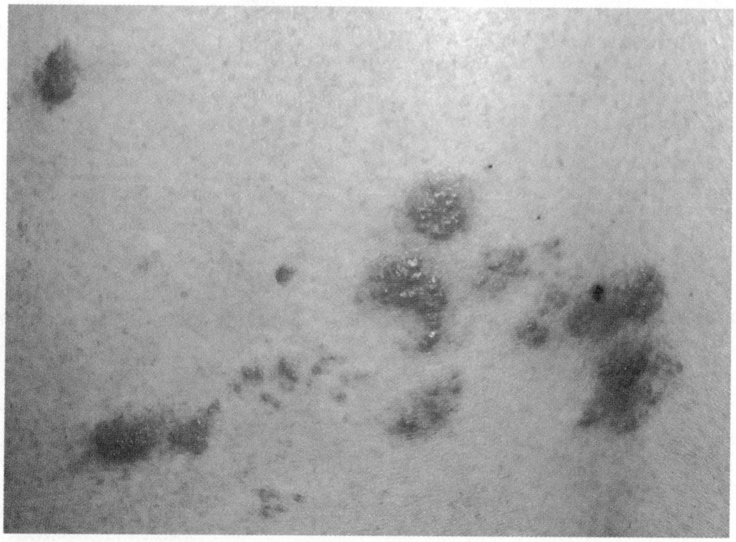

■ **Figure 12.14** Photograph of the skin eruptions associated with shingles. *(Stephen VanHorn/Shutterstock)*

Meninges

TERM	WORD PARTS	DEFINITION
epidural hematoma (ep-ih-DOO-ral / hee-mah-TOH-mah)	epi- = above dur/o = dura mater -al = pertaining to hemat/o = blood -oma = swelling	Mass of blood in the space outside the dura mater of the brain and spinal cord.
meningioma (meh-nin-jee-OH-mah)	meningi/o = meninges -oma = tumor	A tumor in the meninges.
meningitis (men-in-JYE-tis)	mening/o = meninges -itis = inflammation	Inflammation of the meninges around the brain or spinal cord caused by bacterial or viral infection. Symptoms include fever, headache, neck stiffness, lethargy, vomiting, irritability, and photophobia.

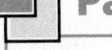 Pathology *(continued)*

TERM	WORD PARTS	DEFINITION
subdural hematoma (sub-DOO-ral / hee-mah-TOH-mah)	sub- = below dur/o = dura mater -al = pertaining to hemat/o = blood -oma = swelling	Mass of blood forming beneath the dura mater if the meninges are torn by trauma. May exert fatal pressure on the brain if the hematoma is not drained by surgery.

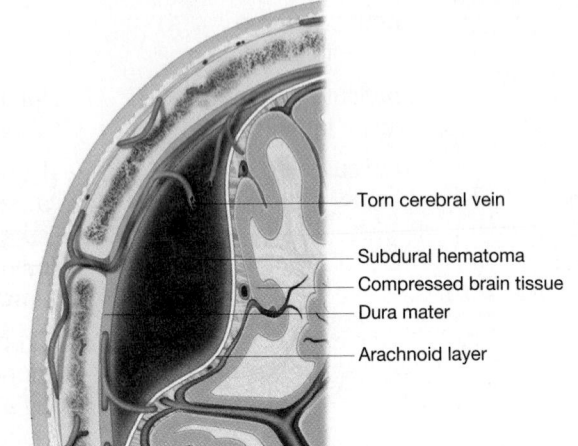

■ **Figure 12.15** A subdural hematoma. A meningeal vein is ruptured and blood has accumulated in the subdural space, producing pressure on the brain.

- Torn cerebral vein
- Subdural hematoma
- Compressed brain tissue
- Dura mater
- Arachnoid layer

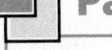 Diagnostic Procedures

TERM	WORD PARTS	DEFINITION
Clinical Laboratory Tests		
cerebrospinal fluid analysis (ser-eh-broh-SPY-nal / an-NAL-ih-sis)	cerebr/o = cerebrum spin/o = spine -al = pertaining to	Laboratory examination of the clear, watery, colorless fluid from within the brain and spinal cord. Infections and the abnormal presence of blood can be detected in this test.
Diagnostic Imaging		
brain scan		Image of the brain taken after injection of radioactive isotopes into the circulation.
cerebral angiography (seh-REE-bral / an-jee-OG-rah-fee)	cerebr/o = cerebrum -al = pertaining to angi/o = vessel -graphy = process of recording	X-ray of the blood vessels of the brain after the injection of radiopaque dye.
echoencephalography (ek-oh-en-SEFF-ah-log-rah-fee)	encephal/o = brain -graphy = process of recording	Recording of the ultrasonic echoes of the brain. Useful in determining abnormal patterns of shifting in the brain.
myelogram (MY-eh-loh-gram)	myel/o = spinal cord -gram = record	X-ray record of the spinal cord.

MED TERM TIP

The combining form *myel/o* means "marrow" and is used for both the spinal cord and bone marrow. To the ancient Greek philosophers and physicians, the spinal cord appeared to be much like the marrow found in the medullary cavity of a long bone.

Diagnostic Procedures *(continued)*

TERM	WORD PARTS	DEFINITION
myelography (my-eh-LOG-rah-fee)	myel/o = spinal cord -graphy = process of recording	Injection of radiopaque dye into the spinal canal. An X-ray is then taken to examine the normal and abnormal outlines made by the dye.
positron emission tomography (PET) (PAHZ-ih-tron / ee-MISH-un / toh-MOG-rah-fee)	tom/o = to cut -graphy = process of recording	Image of the brain produced by measuring gamma rays emitted from the brain after injecting glucose tagged with positively charged isotopes. Measurement of glucose uptake by the brain tissue indicates how metabolically active the tissue is.

Additional Diagnostic Tests

TERM	WORD PARTS	DEFINITION
Babinski reflex (bah-BIN-skeez)		Reflex test developed by French neurologist Joseph Babinski to determine lesions and abnormalities in the nervous system. The Babinski reflex is present if the great toe extends instead of flexes when the lateral sole of the foot is stroked. The normal response to this stimulation is flexion of the toe.
electroencephalogram (EEG) (ee-lek-troh-en-SEFF-ah-loh-gram)	electr/o = electricity encephal/o = brain -gram = record	Record of the brain's electrical patterns.
electroencephalography (EEG) (ee-lek-troh-en-SEFF-ah-LOG-rah-fee)	electr/o = electricity encephal/o = brain -graphy = process of recording	Recording the electrical activity of the brain by placing electrodes at various positions on the scalp. Also used in sleep studies to determine if there is a normal pattern of activity during sleep.
lumbar puncture (LP) (LUM-bar / PUNK-chur)	lumb/o = low back -ar = pertaining to	Puncture with a needle into the lumbar area (usually the fourth intervertebral space) to withdraw fluid for examination and for the injection of anesthesia. Also called *spinal puncture* or *spinal tap*.

L1 vertebra
Lumbar puncture needle
Coccyx
Skin
Fat
Interspinous ligament
L4
L5
Extradural "space"
Tip end of spinal cord
CSF in lumbar cistern
Dura mater
Sacrum

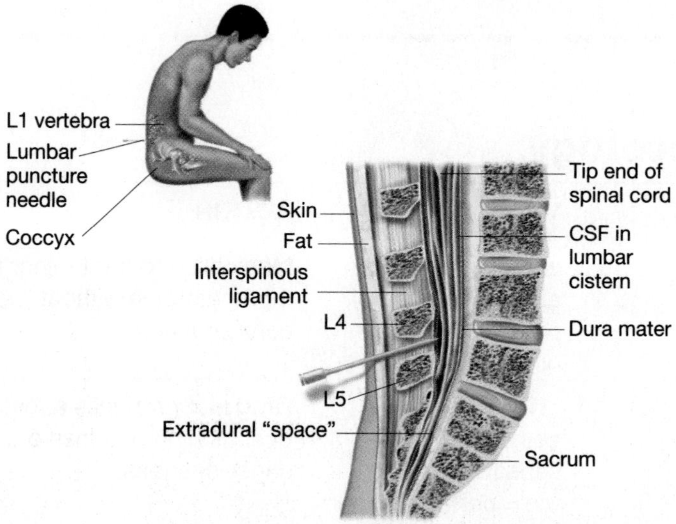

■ **Figure 12.16** A lumbar puncture. The needle is inserted between the lumbar vertebrae and into the spinal canal.

TERM	WORD PARTS	DEFINITION
nerve conduction velocity		Test that measures how fast an impulse travels along a nerve. Can pinpoint an area of nerve damage.

Therapeutic Procedures

TERM	WORD PARTS	DEFINITION
Medical Procedures		
nerve block		Injection of regional anesthetic to stop the passage of sensory or pain impulses along a nerve path.
Surgical Procedures		
carotid endarterectomy (kah-ROT-id / end-ar-ter-EK-toh-mee)	endo- = within arteri/o = artery -ectomy = surgical removal	Surgical procedure for removing an obstruction within the carotid artery, a major artery in the neck that carries oxygenated blood to the brain. Developed to prevent strokes, but is found to be useful only in severe stenosis with transient ischemic attack.
cerebrospinal fluid shunts (ser-eh-bro-SPY-nal)	cerebr/o = cerebrum spin/o = spine -al = pertaining to	Surgical procedure in which a bypass is created to drain cerebrospinal fluid. It is used to treat hydrocephalus by draining the excess cerebrospinal fluid from the brain and diverting it to the abdominal cavity.
laminectomy (lam-ih-NEK-toh-mee)	-ectomy = surgical removal	Removal of a portion of a vertebra, called the lamina, in order to relieve pressure on the spinal nerve.
neurectomy (noo-REK-toh-mee)	neur/o = nerve -ectomy = surgical removal	Surgical removal of a nerve.
neuroplasty (NOOR-oh-plas-tee)	neur/o = nerve -plasty = surgical repair	Surgical repair of a nerve.
neurorrhaphy (noo-ROR-ah-fee)	neur/o = nerve -rrhaphy = suture	To suture a nerve back together. Actually refers to suturing the connective tissue sheath around the nerve.
tractotomy (track-OT-oh-mee)	-otomy = cutting into	Surgical interruption of a nerve tract in the spinal cord. Used to treat intractable pain or muscle spasms.

Pharmacology

CLASSIFICATION	WORD PARTS	ACTION	EXAMPLES
analgesic (an-al-JEE-zik)	an- = without alges/o = sense of pain -ic = pertaining to	Medication to treat minor to moderate pain without loss of consciousness.	aspirin, Bayer, Ecotrin; acetaminophen, Tylenol; ibuprofen, Motrin
anesthetic (an-ess-THET-ik)	an- = without esthes/o = feeling, sensation -tic = pertaining to	Drug that produces a loss of sensation or a loss of consciousness.	lidocaine, Xylocaine; pentobarbital, Nembutal; propofol, Diprivan; procaine, Novocain

■ Pharmacology *(continued)*

CLASSIFICATION	WORD PARTS	ACTION	EXAMPLES
anticonvulsant (an-tye-kon-VULL-sant)	anti- = against	Substance that reduces the excitability of neurons and therefore prevents the uncontrolled neuron activity associated with seizures.	carbamazepine, Tegretol; phenobarbital, Nembutal
dopaminergic drugs (dope-ah-men-ER-gik)	-ic = pertaining to	Group of medications to treat Parkinson's disease by either replacing the dopamine that is lacking or increasing the strength of the dopamine that is present.	levodopa; L-dopa, Larodopa; levodopa/carbidopa, Sinemet
hypnotic (hip-NOT-tik)	-ic = pertaining to	Drug that promotes sleep.	secobarbital, Seconal; temazepam, Restoril
narcotic analgesic (nar-KOT-tik)	-ic = pertaining to an- = without alges/o = sense of pain -ic = pertaining to	Drug used to treat severe pain; has the potential to be habit forming if taken for a prolonged time. Also called *opiates*.	morphine, MS Contin; oxycodone, OxyContin; meperidine, Demerol
sedative (SED-ah-tiv)		Drug that has a relaxing or calming effect.	amobarbital, Amytal; butabarbital, Butisol

■ Abbreviations

ALS	amyotrophic lateral sclerosis		**HA**	headache
ANS	autonomic nervous system		**ICP**	intracranial pressure
CNS	central nervous system		**LP**	lumbar puncture
CP	cerebral palsy		**MS**	multiple sclerosis
CSF	cerebrospinal fluid		**PET**	positron emission tomography
CVA	cerebrovascular accident		**PNS**	peripheral nervous system
CVD	cerebrovascular disease		**SCI**	spinal cord injury
EEG	electroencephalogram, electroencephalography		**TBI**	traumatic brain injury
			TIA	transient ischemic attack

Chapter Review

Real-World Applications

Medical Record Analysis

This Discharge Summary contains 12 medical terms. Underline each term and write it in the list below the report. Then define each term.

Discharge Summary

Admitting Diagnosis:	Paraplegia following motorcycle accident.
Final Diagnosis:	Comminuted L2 fracture with epidural hematoma and spinal cord injury resulting in complete paraplegia at the L2 level.
History of Present Illness:	Patient is a 23-year-old male who was involved in a motorcycle accident. He was unconscious for 35 minutes but was fully aware of his surroundings upon regaining consciousness. He was immediately aware of total anesthesia and paralysis below the waist.
Summary of Hospital Course:	CT scan revealed extensive bone destruction at the fracture site and that the spinal cord was severed. Patient was unable to voluntarily contract any lower extremity muscles and was not able to feel touch or pinpricks. Lumbar laminectomy with spinal fusion was performed to stabilize the fracture and remove the epidural hematoma. The immediate postoperative recovery period proceeded normally. Patient began physical therapy and occupational therapy. After 2 months, X-rays indicated full healing of the spinal fusion and patient was transferred to a rehabilitation institute.
Discharge Plans:	Patient was transferred to a rehabilitation institute to continue intensive PT and OT.

	Term	Definition
1	_____	_____
2	_____	_____
3	_____	_____
4	_____	_____
5	_____	_____
6	_____	_____
7	_____	_____
8	_____	_____
9	_____	_____
10	_____	_____
11	_____	_____
12	_____	_____

Chart Note Transcription

The chart note below contains 11 phrases that can be reworded with a medical term that you learned in this chapter. Each phrase is identified with an underline. Determine the medical term and write your answers in the space provided.

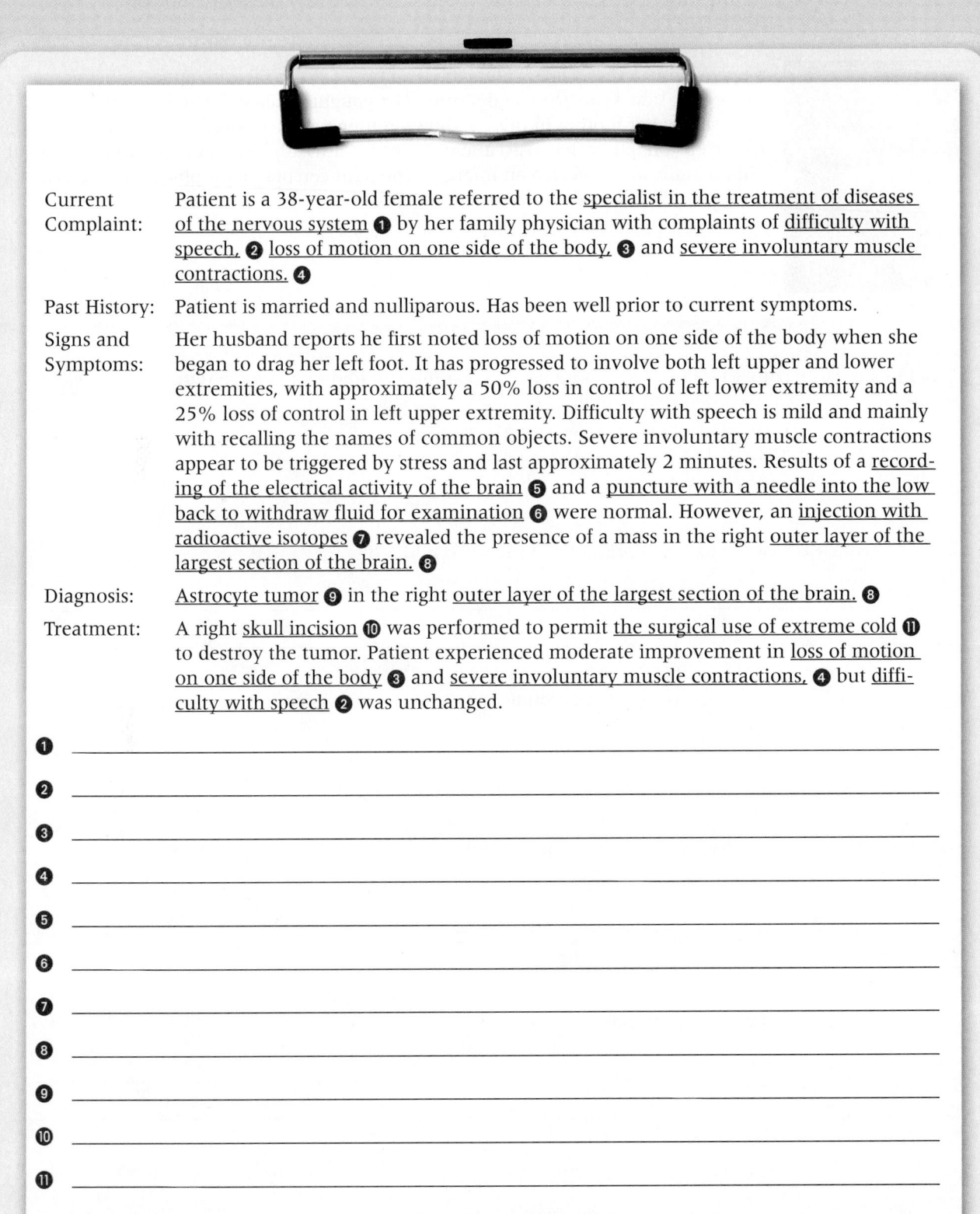

Current Complaint: Patient is a 38-year-old female referred to the <u>specialist in the treatment of diseases of the nervous system</u> ❶ by her family physician with complaints of <u>difficulty with speech,</u> ❷ <u>loss of motion on one side of the body,</u> ❸ and <u>severe involuntary muscle contractions.</u> ❹

Past History: Patient is married and nulliparous. Has been well prior to current symptoms.

Signs and Symptoms: Her husband reports he first noted loss of motion on one side of the body when she began to drag her left foot. It has progressed to involve both left upper and lower extremities, with approximately a 50% loss in control of left lower extremity and a 25% loss of control in left upper extremity. Difficulty with speech is mild and mainly with recalling the names of common objects. Severe involuntary muscle contractions appear to be triggered by stress and last approximately 2 minutes. Results of a <u>recording of the electrical activity of the brain</u> ❺ and a <u>puncture with a needle into the low back to withdraw fluid for examination</u> ❻ were normal. However, an <u>injection with radioactive isotopes</u> ❼ revealed the presence of a mass in the right <u>outer layer of the largest section of the brain.</u> ❽

Diagnosis: <u>Astrocyte tumor</u> ❾ in the right <u>outer layer of the largest section of the brain.</u> ❽

Treatment: A right <u>skull incision</u> ❿ was performed to permit <u>the surgical use of extreme cold</u> ⓫ to destroy the tumor. Patient experienced moderate improvement in <u>loss of motion on one side of the body</u> ❸ and <u>severe involuntary muscle contractions,</u> ❹ but <u>difficulty with speech</u> ❷ was unchanged.

❶ _____

❷ _____

❸ _____

❹ _____

❺ _____

❻ _____

❼ _____

❽ _____

❾ _____

❿ _____

⓫ _____

Case Study

Below is a case study presentation of a patient with a condition covered in this chapter. Read the case study and answer the questions below. Some questions will ask for information not included within this chapter. Use your text, a medical dictionary, or any other reference material you choose to answer these questions.

Anna Moore, an 83-year-old female, is admitted to the ER with aphasia, hemiparesis on her left side, syncope, and delirium. Her daughter called the ambulance after discovering her mother in this condition at home. Mrs. Moore has a history of hypertension, atherosclerosis, and diabetes mellitus. She was admitted to the hospital after a brain scan revealed an infarct in the right cerebral hemisphere leading to a diagnosis of CVA of the middle cerebral artery.

(iofoto/Shutterstock)

1. What pathological condition does Ms. Moore have? Look this condition up in a reference source and include a short description of it.

_____

_____

2. List and define each of the patient's presenting symptoms in the ER.

_____

_____

3. The patient has a history of three significant conditions. Describe each in your own words.

_____

_____

4. What diagnostic test did the physician perform? Describe this test and the results in your own words.

_____

_____

5. What is an infarct and what causes it?

_____

_____

6. List and describe the four common causes of a CVA.

_____

_____

Practice Exercises

A. Complete the Statement

1. The study of the nervous system is called _____.

2. The organs of the nervous system are the _____, _____, and

   _____.

3. The two divisions of the nervous system are the _____ and _____.

4. The neurons that carry impulses away from the brain and spinal cord are called _____ neurons.

5. The neurons that carry impulses to the brain and spinal cord are called _____ neurons.

6. The largest portion of the brain is the _____.

7. The second largest portion of the brain is the _____.

8. The occipital lobe controls _____.

9. The temporal lobe controls _____ and _____.

10. The two divisions of the autonomic nervous system are the _____ and _____.

B. Terminology Matching

Match each term to its definition.

1. _____ olfactory
2. _____ optic
3. _____ oculomotor
4. _____ trochlear
5. _____ trigeminal
6. _____ abducens
7. _____ facial
8. _____ vestibulocochlear
9. _____ glossopharyngeal
10. _____ vagus
11. _____ accessory
12. _____ hypoglossal

a. carries facial sensory impulses
b. turns eye to side
c. controls tongue muscles
d. controls eye muscles and pupils
e. swallowing
f. controls facial muscles
g. controls oblique eye muscles
h. smell
i. controls neck and shoulder muscles
j. hearing and equilibrium
k. vision
l. organs in lower body cavities

C. Combining Form Practice

The combining form **neur/o** refers to the nerve. Use it to write a term that means:

1. inflammation of the nerve _____

2. specialist in nerves _____

3. pain in the nerve _____

4. inflammation of many nerves _____

5. removal of a nerve _____

6. surgical repair of a nerve _____

7. nerve tumor _____

8. suture of a nerve _____

The combining form **mening/o** refers to the meninges or membranes. Use it to write a term that means:

9. inflammation of the meninges _____

10. protrusion of the meninges _____

11. protrusion of the spinal cord and the meninges _____

The combining form **encephal/o** refers to the brain. Use it to write a term that means:

12. X-ray record of the brain _____

13. disease of the brain _____

14. inflammation of the brain _____

15. protrusion of the brain _____

The combining form **cerebr/o** refers to the cerebrum. Use it to write a term that means:

16. pertaining to the cerebrum and spinal cord _____

17. pertaining to the cerebrum _____

D. What Does it Stand For?

1. TIA _____

2. MS _____

3. SCI _____

4. CNS _____

5. PNS _____

6. HA _____

7. CP _____

8. LP _____

9. ALS _____

E. Terminology Matching

Match each term to its definition.

1. _____ aura

2. _____ meningitis

3. _____ coma

4. _____ shingles

5. _____ syncope

6. _____ palsy

7. _____ absence seizure

8. _____ tonic-clonic seizure

9. _____ meningocele

a. loss of ability to control movement

b. sensations before a seizure

c. seizure with convulsions

d. congenital hernia of meninges

e. seizure without convulsion

f. inflammation of meninges

g. profound unconsciousness

h. *Herpes zoster* infection

i. fainting

F. What's the Abbreviation?

1. cerebrospinal fluid _____

2. cerebrovascular disease _____

3. electroencephalogram _____

4. intracranial pressure _____

5. positron emission tomography _____

6. cerebrovascular accident _____

7. subarachnoid hemorrhage _____

8. autonomic nervous system _____

G. Define the Procedures and Tests

1. myelography _____

2. cerebral angiography _____

3. Babinski's reflex _____

4. nerve conduction velocity _____

5. cerebrospinal fluid analysis _____

6. PET scan _____

7. echoencephalography _____

8. lumbar puncture _____

H. Define the Suffix

	Definition	Example from Chapter
1. -plegia		
2. -taxia		
3. -trophic		
4. -paresis		
5. -phasia		

I. Define the Combining Form

	Definition	Example from Chapter Term
1. mening/o		
2. encephal/o		
3. cerebell/o		
4. myel/o		
5. cephal/o		
6. thalam/o		
7. neur/o		
8. radicul/o		
9. cerebr/o		
10. pont/o		

J. Define the Term

1. astrocytoma _____

2. epilepsy _____

3. anesthesia _____

4. hemiparesis _____

5. neurosurgeon _____

6. analgesia _____

7. focal seizure _____

8. quadriplegia _____

9. subdural hematoma _____

10. intrathecal _____

K. Terminology Matching

Match each term to its definition.

1. _____ neurologist
2. _____ cerebrovascular accident
3. _____ concussion
4. _____ aphasia
5. _____ migraine
6. _____ seizure
7. _____ dementia
8. _____ ataxia
9. _____ spina bifida
10. _____ unconscious

a. sudden attack
b. a type of severe headache
c. loss of intellectual ability
d. physician who treats nervous problem
e. stroke
f. mild traumatic brain injury
g. loss of ability to speak
h. congenital anomaly
i. state of being unaware
j. lack of muscle coordination

L. Fill in the Blank

Parkinson's disease	transient ischemic attack	cerebral palsy	cerebrospinal fluid shunt
Bell's palsy	subdural hematoma	amyotrophic lateral sclerosis	nerve conduction velocity
delirium	cerebral aneurysm		

1. Dr. Martin noted that the 96-year-old patient suffered from _____ when she determined that he was confused, disoriented, and agitated.

2. Lucinda's _____ resulted in increasing muscle weakness as the motor neurons in her spinal cord degenerated.

3. The diagnosis of _____ was correct because the weakness affected only one side of Charles's face.

4. A cerebral angiogram was ordered because Dr. Larson suspected Mrs. Constantine had a(n) _____.

5. Roberta's symptoms included fine tremors, muscular weakness, rigidity, and a shuffling gait, leading to a diagnosis of _____.

6. Matthew's hydrocephalus required the placement of a(n) _____.

7. Because Mae's hemiparesis was temporary, the final diagnosis was _____.

8. Following the car accident, a CT scan showed a(n) _____ was putting pressure on the brain, necessitating immediate neurosurgery.

9. Birth trauma resulted in the newborn developing _____.

10. A(n) _____ test was performed in order to pinpoint the exact position of the nerve damage.

M. Pharmacology Challenge

Fill in the classification for each drug description, then match the brand name.

Drug Description	Classification	Brand Name
1. _____ produces loss of sensation	_____	a. L-Dopa
2. _____ treats Parkinson's disease	_____	b. Amytal
3. _____ promotes sleep	_____	c. OxyContin
4. _____ medication for mild pain	_____	d. Seconal
5. _____ produces a calming effect	_____	e. Xylocaine
6. _____ treats severe pain	_____	f. Tegretol
7. _____ treats seizures	_____	g. Motrin

Labeling Exercise

Image A

Write the labels for this figure on the numbered lines provided.

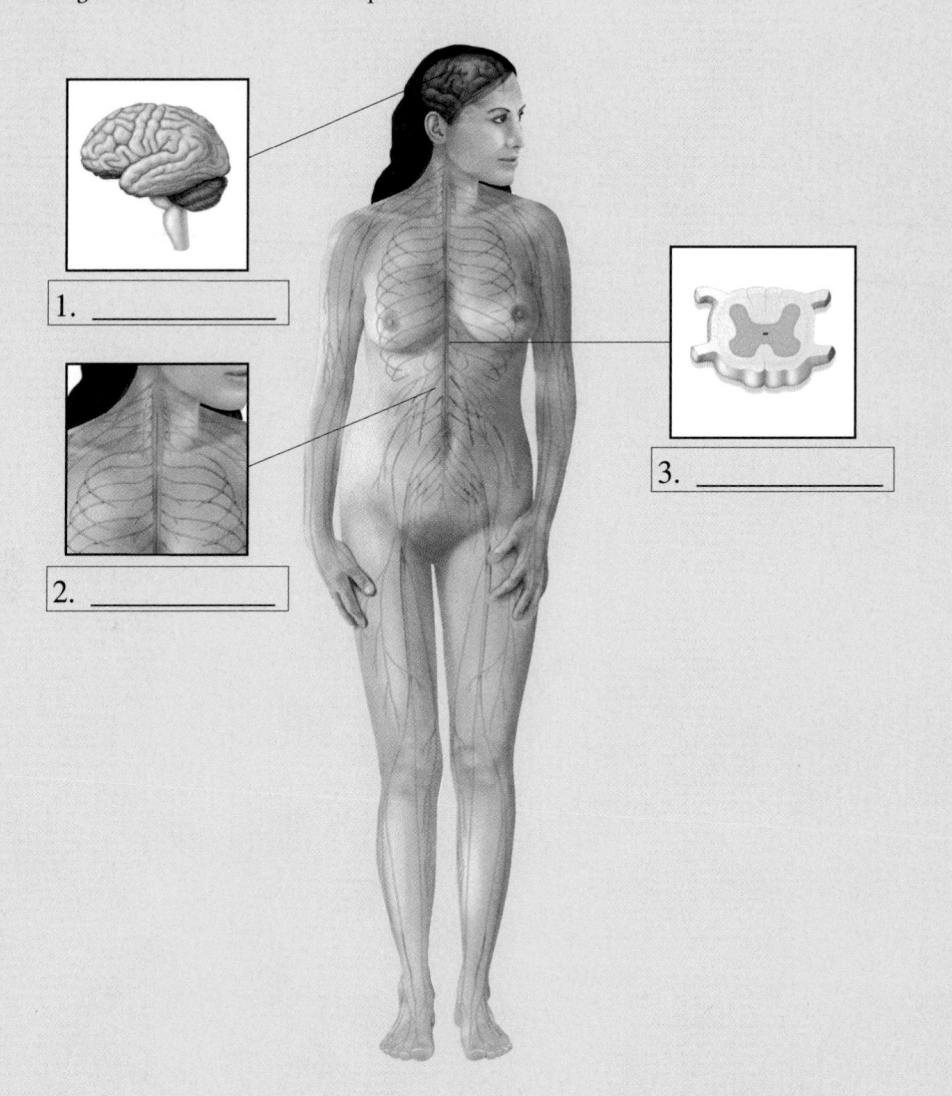

1. _____

2. _____

3. _____

Image B

Write the labels for this figure on the numbered lines provided.

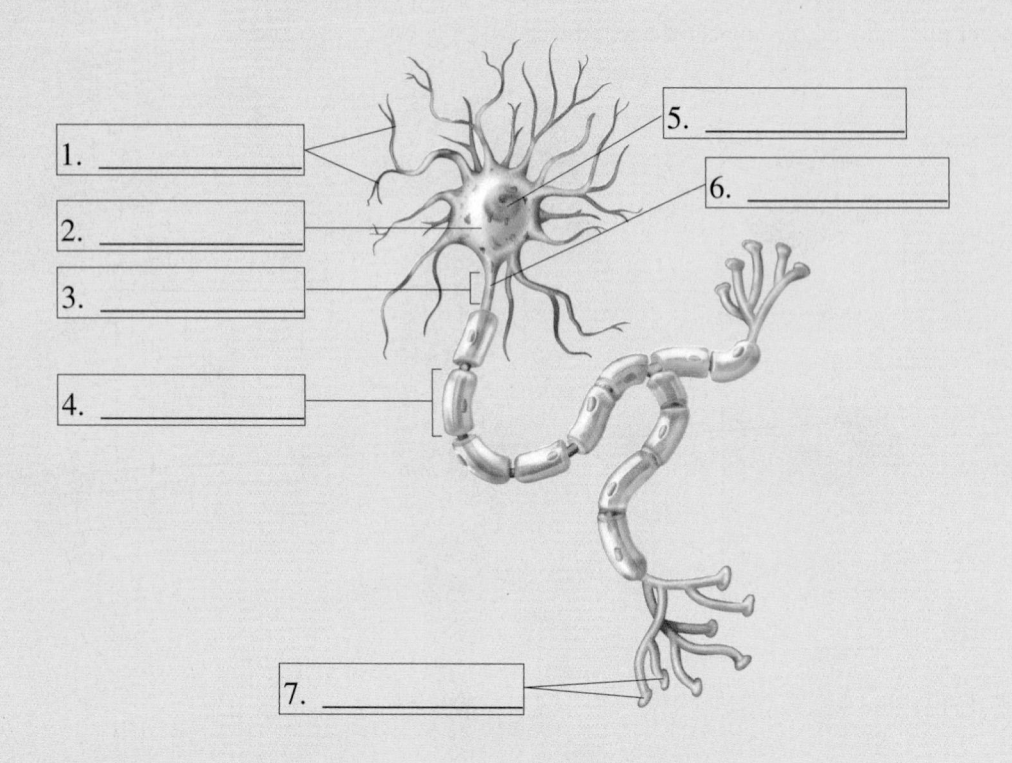

1. _____

2. _____

3. _____

4. _____

5. _____

6. _____

7. _____

Image C

Write the labels for this figure on the numbered lines provided.

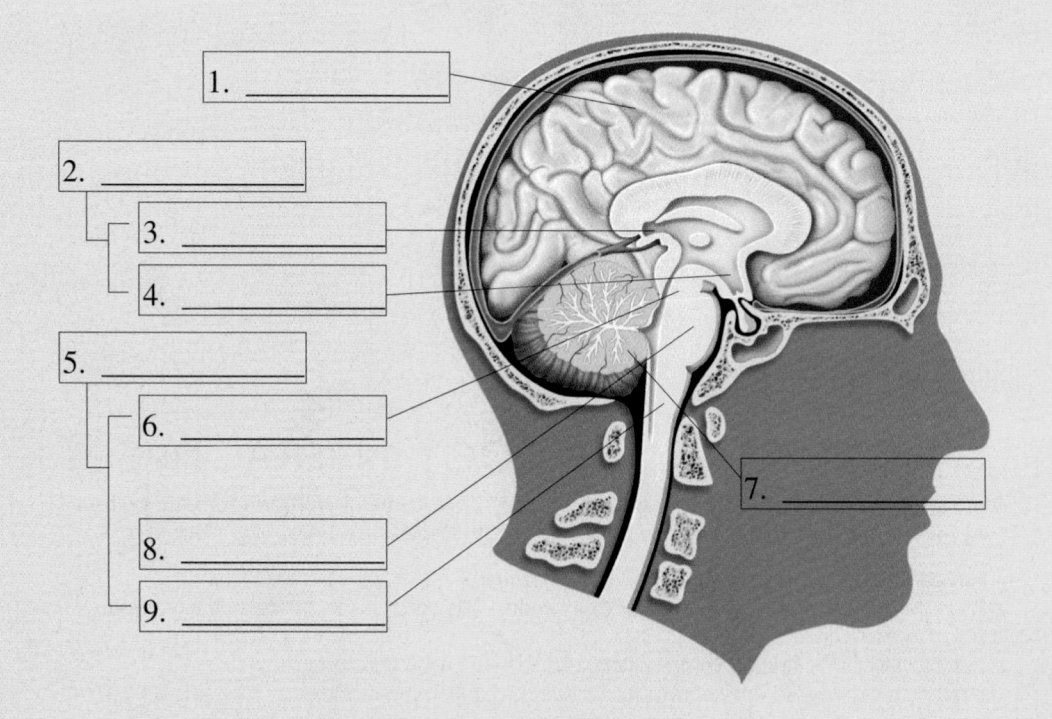

1. _____

2. _____

3. _____

4. _____

5. _____

6. _____

7. _____

8. _____

9. _____

13

Learning Objectives

Upon completion of this chapter, you will be able to

- Identify and define the combining forms and suffixes introduced in this chapter.

- Correctly spell and pronounce medical terms and major anatomical structures relating to the eye and ear.

- Locate and describe the major structures of the eye and ear and their functions.

- Describe how we see.

- Describe the path of sound vibration.

- Identify and define eye and ear anatomical terms.

- Identify and define selected eye and ear pathology terms.

- Identify and define selected eye and ear diagnostic procedures.

- Identify and define selected eye and ear therapeutic procedures.

- Identify and define selected medications relating to the eye and ear.

- Define selected abbreviations associated with the eye and ear.

SPECIAL SENSES: THE EYE AND EAR

Section I: The Eye at a Glance

Function

The eye contains the sensory receptor cells for vision.

Structures

Here are the primary structures that comprise the eye.

choroid	eyelids
conjunctiva	lacrimal apparatus
eye muscles	retina
eyeball	sclera

Word Parts

Here are the most common word parts (with their meanings) used to build eye terms. For a more comprehensive list, refer to the Terminology section of this chapter.

Combining Forms

ambly/o	dull, dim	mi/o	lessening
aque/o	water	mydr/i	widening
blast/o	immature, embryonic	nyctal/o	night
blephar/o	eyelid	ocul/o	eye
chromat/o	color	ophthalm/o	eye
conjunctiv/o	conjunctiva	opt/o	eye, vision
corne/o	cornea	optic/o	eye, vision
cycl/o	ciliary muscle	papill/o	optic disk
dacry/o	tear, tear duct	phac/o	lens
dipl/o	double	phot/o	light
emmetr/o	correct, proper	presby/o	old age
glauc/o	gray	pupill/o	pupil
ir/o	iris	retin/o	retina
irid/o	iris	scler/o	sclera
kerat/o	cornea	stigmat/o	point
lacrim/o	tears	uve/o	choroid
macul/o	macula lutea	vitre/o	glassy

Suffixes

-ician	specialist	-opsia	vision condition
-metrist	specialist in measuring	-tropia	turned condition
-opia	vision condition		

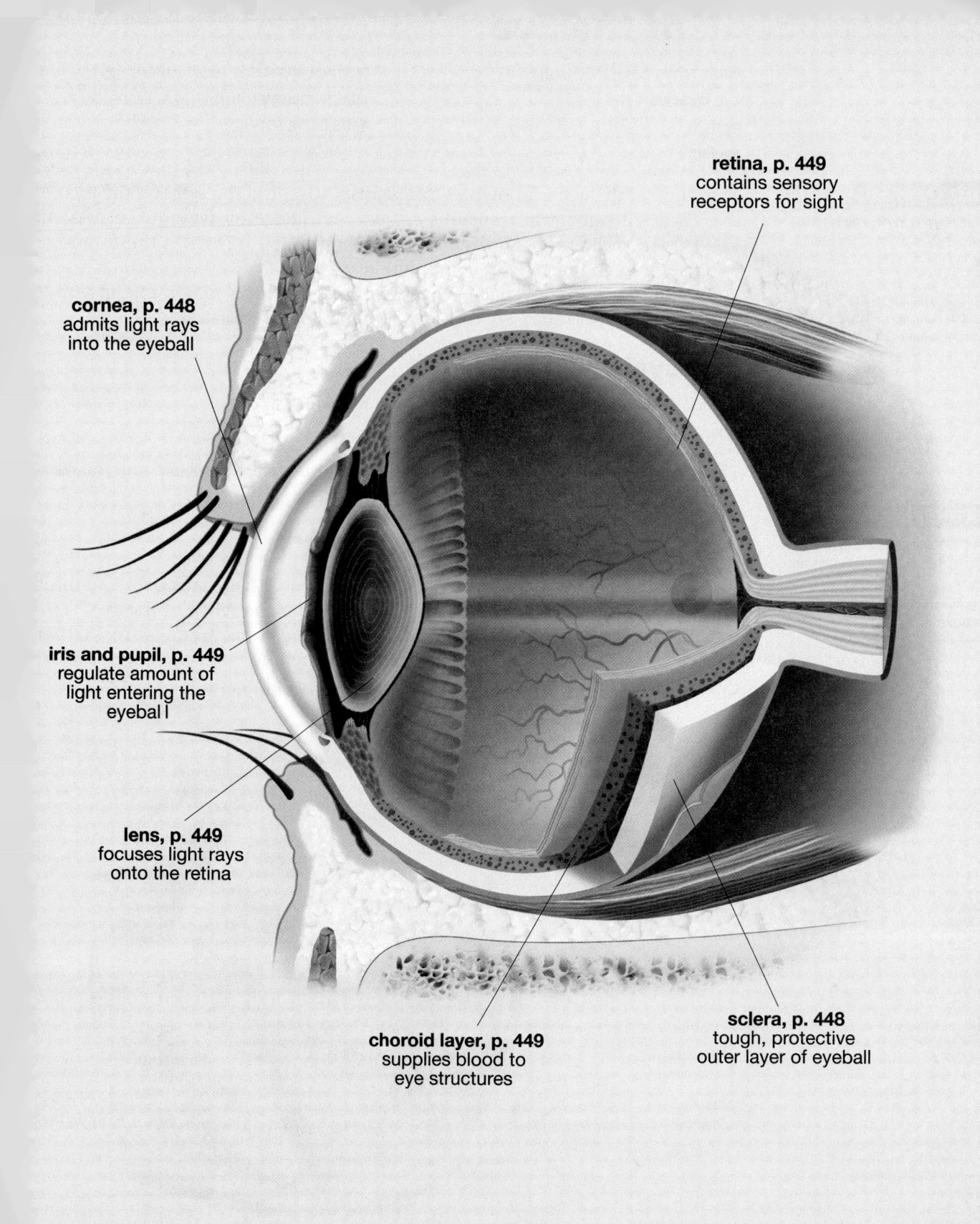

retina, p. 449
contains sensory
receptors for sight

cornea, p. 448
admits light rays
into the eyeball

iris and pupil, p. 449
regulate amount of
light entering the
eyebal l

lens, p. 449
focuses light rays
onto the retina

choroid layer, p. 449
supplies blood to
eye structures

sclera, p. 448
tough, protective
outer layer of eyeball

Anatomy and Physiology of the Eye

conjunctiva (kon-JUNK-tih-vah)
eye muscles
eyeball
eyelids
lacrimal apparatus (LAK-rim-al)
ophthalmology (off-thal-MALL-oh-gee)
optic nerve (OP-tik)

The study of the eye is known as **ophthalmology** (Ophth). The **eyeball** is the incredible organ of sight that transmits an external image by way of the nervous system—the **optic nerve**—to the brain. The brain then translates these sensory impulses into an image with computerlike accuracy.

In addition to the eyeball, several external structures play a role in vision. These are the **eye muscles, eyelids, conjunctiva,** and **lacrimal apparatus.**

MED TERM TIP

When studying the functions and terminology of the eye, it is helpful to know the meanings of the terms *opaque* and *transparent.* Opaque means that light is unable to pass through. Transparent, however, means that light is permitted through.

The Eyeball

choroid (KOR-oyd)
sclera (SKLAIR-ah)
retina (RET-in-ah)

The actual eyeball is composed of three layers: the **sclera,** the **choroid,** and the **retina.**

Sclera

cornea (COR-nee-ah)
refracts

The outer layer, the sclera, provides a tough protective coating for the inner structures of the eye. Another term for the sclera is the white of the eye.

The anterior portion of the sclera is called the **cornea** (see Figure 13.1 ■). This clear, transparent area of the sclera allows light to enter the interior of the eyeball. The cornea actually bends, or **refracts,** the light rays.

MED TERM TIP

The color of the sclera may indicate the presence of disease. For instance, a yellowish cast to the sclera can be present in liver disease and certain anemias.

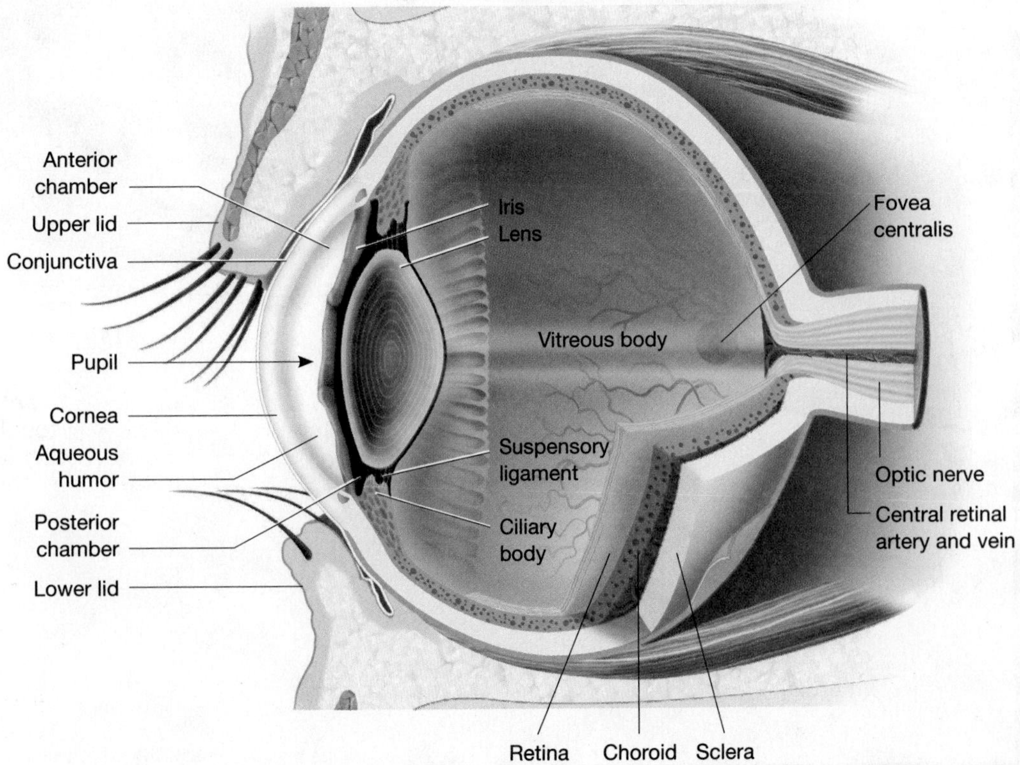

■ **Figure 13.1** The internal structures of the eye.

Choroid

ciliary body (SIL-ee-ar-ee)   **iris**
lens   **pupil**

The second or middle layer of the eyeball is called the choroid. This opaque layer provides the blood supply for the eye.

The anterior portion of the choroid layer consists of the **iris, pupil,** and **ciliary body** (see again Figure 13.1). The iris is the colored portion of the eye and contains smooth muscle. The pupil is the opening in the center of the iris that allows light rays to enter the eyeball. The iris muscle contracts or relaxes to change the size of the pupil, thereby controlling how much light enters the interior of the eyeball. Behind the iris is the **lens.** The lens is not actually part of the choroid layer, but it is attached to the muscular ciliary body. By pulling on the edge of the lens, these muscles change the shape of the lens so it can focus incoming light onto the retina.

Retina

aqueous humor (AY-kwee-us)   **optic disk**
cones   **retinal blood vessels** (RET-in-al)
fovea centralis (FOH-vee-ah / sen-TRAH-lis)   **rods**
macula lutea (MAK-yoo-lah / loo-TEE-ah)   **vitreous humor** (VIT-ree-us)

The third and innermost layer of the eyeball is the retina. It contains the sensory receptor cells (**rods** and **cones**) that respond to light rays. Rods are active in dim light and help us to see in gray tones. Cones are active only in bright light and are responsible for color vision. When the lens projects an image onto the retina, it strikes an area called the **macula lutea,** or yellow spot (see Figure 13.1). In the center of the macula lutea is a depression called the **fovea centralis,** meaning central pit. This pit contains a high concentration of sensory receptor cells and, therefore, is the point of clearest vision. Also visible on the retina is the **optic disk.** This is the point where the **retinal blood vessels** enter and exit the eyeball and where the optic nerve leaves the eyeball (see Figure 13.2 ■). There are no sensory receptor cells in the optic disk and therefore it causes a blind spot in each eye's field of vision. The interior spaces of the eyeball are not empty. The spaces between the cornea and lens are filled with **aqueous humor,** a watery fluid, and the large open area between the lens and retina contains **vitreous humor,** a semisolid gel.

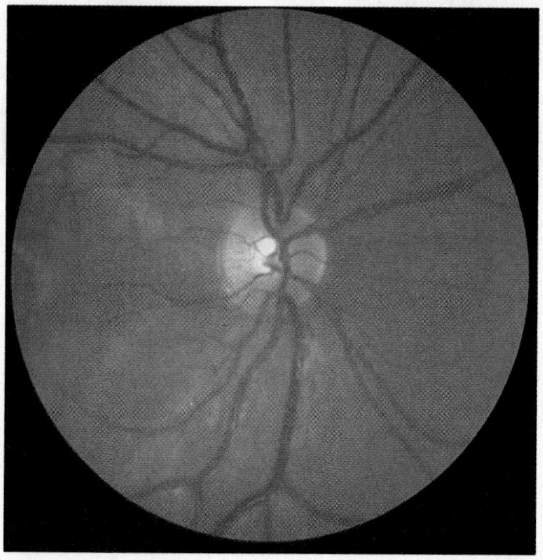

> **MED TERM TIP**
>
> The function of the choroid, to provide the rest of the eyeball with blood, is responsible for an alternate name for this layer—*uvea.* The combining form *uve/o* means "vascular."

■ **Figure 13.2**
Photograph of the retina of the eye. The optic disk appears yellow and the retinal arteries radiate out from it.
(Photo Researchers, Inc.)

Muscles of the Eye

oblique muscles (oh-BLEEK)   **rectus muscles** (REK-tus)

Six muscles connect the actual eyeball to the skull (see Figure 13.3 ■). These muscles allow for change in the direction of each eye's sightline. In addition, they provide support for the eyeball in the eye socket. Children may be born with a weakness in some of these muscles and may require treatments such as eye exercises or even surgery to correct this problem commonly referred to as crossed eyes or *strabismus* (see Figure 13.4 ■). The muscles involved are the four **rectus** and two **oblique muscles.** Rectus muscles (meaning straight) pull the eye up, down, left, or right in a straight line. Oblique muscles are on an angle and produce diagonal eye movement.

Tendinous sling (trochlea)

Superior oblique

Superior rectus

Conjunctiva

Lateral rectus

Inferior rectus

Inferior oblique

A

Tendinous sling (trochlea)

Superior oblique

Superior rectus

Medial rectus

Lateral rectus

Inferior rectus

Inferior oblique

B

■ **Figure 13.3**   The arrangement of the external eye muscles: (A) lateral and (B) anterior views.

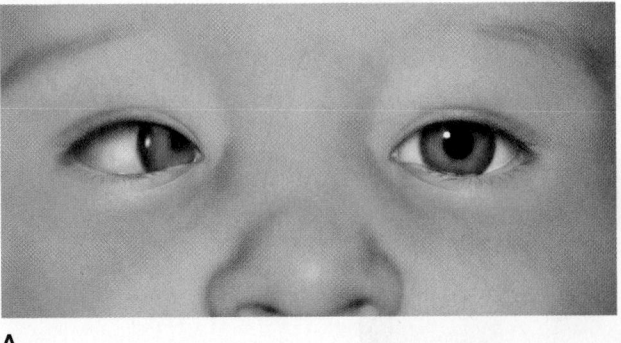
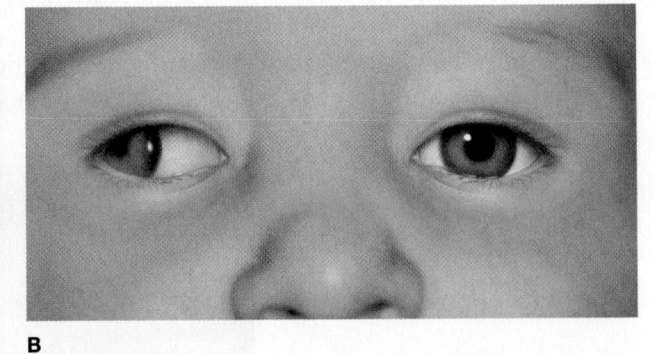

A   **B**

■ **Figure 13.4**   Examples of common forms of strabismus: (A) esotropia with the right eye turning inward and (B) exotropia with the right eye turning outward.

The Eyelids

cilia (SIL-ee-ah)   **eyelashes**
sebaceous glands (see-BAY-shus)

A pair of eyelids over each eyeball provides protection from foreign particles, injury from the sun and intense light, and trauma (see Figure 13.1). Both the upper and lower edges of the eyelids have **eyelashes** or **cilia** that protect the eye from foreign particles. In addition, **sebaceous glands** located in the eyelids secrete lubricating oil onto the eyeball.

Conjunctiva

mucous membrane

The conjunctiva of the eye is a **mucous membrane** lining. It forms a continuous covering on the underside of each eyelid and across the anterior surface of each eyeball (see again Figure 13.1). This serves as protection for the eye by sealing off the eyeball in the socket.

Lacrimal Apparatus

lacrimal ducts   **lacrimal gland**
nasal cavity   **nasolacrimal duct** (naz-oh-LAK-rim-al)
tears

The **lacrimal gland** is located under the outer upper corner of each eyelid. These glands produce **tears.** Tears serve the important function of washing and lubricating the anterior surface of the eyeball. **Lacrimal ducts** located in the inner corner of the eye socket then collect the tears and drain them into the **nasolacrimal duct.** This duct ultimately drains the tears into the **nasal cavity** (see Figure 13.5 ■).

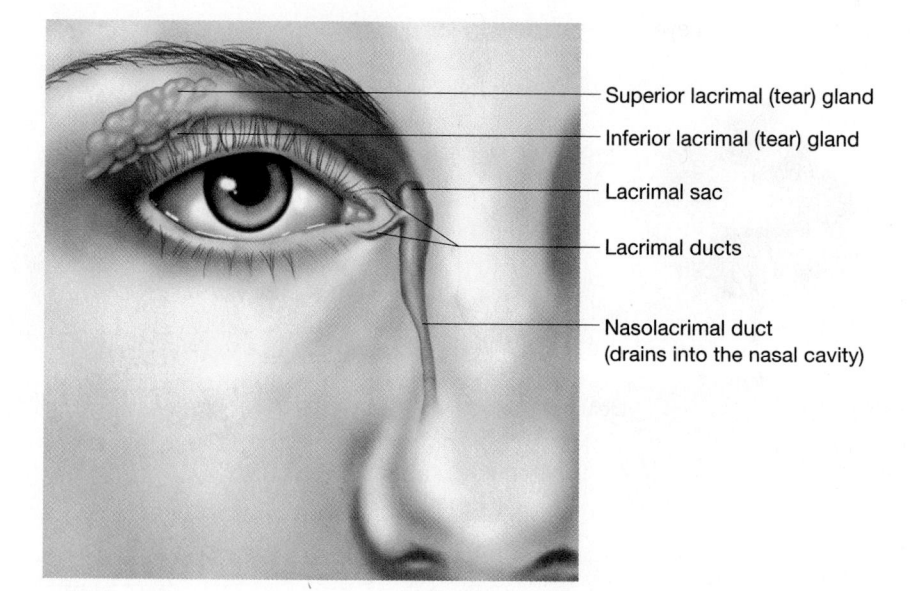

- Superior lacrimal (tear) gland
- Inferior lacrimal (tear) gland
- Lacrimal sac
- Lacrimal ducts
- Nasolacrimal duct
  (drains into the nasal cavity)

■ **Figure 13.5**
The structure of the lacrimal apparatus.

■ Figure 13.6 The path of light through the cornea, iris, lens, and striking the retina.

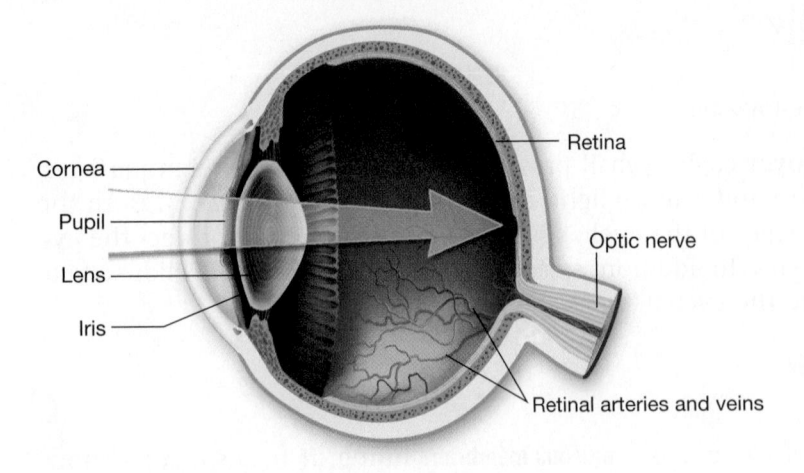

How We See

When light rays strike the eye, they first pass through the cornea, pupil, aqueous humor, lens, and vitreous humor (see Figure 13.6 ■). They then strike the retina and stimulate the rods and cones. When the light rays hit the retina, an upside-down image is sent along nerve impulses to the optic nerve (see Figure 13.7 ■). The optic nerve transmits these impulses to the brain, where the upside-down image is translated into the right-side-up image we are looking at.

Vision requires proper functioning of four mechanisms:

1. Coordination of the external eye muscles so that both eyes move together.
2. The correct amount of light admitted by the pupil.
3. The correct focus of light on the retina by the lens.
4. The optic nerve transmitting sensory images to the brain.

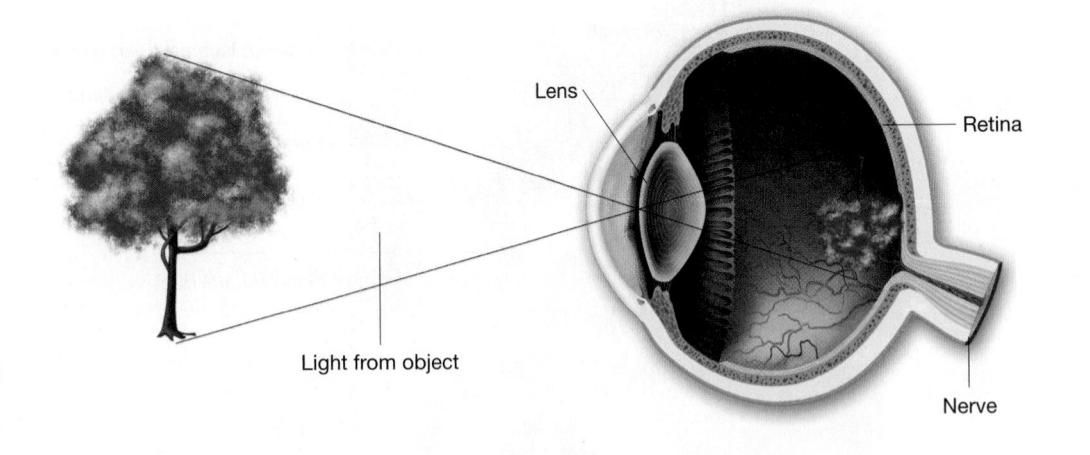

■ Figure 13.7 The image formed on the retina is inverted. The brain rights the image as part of the interpretation process.

Terminology

Word Parts Used to Build Eye Terms

The following lists contain the combining forms, suffixes, and prefixes used to build terms in the remaining sections of this chapter.

Combining Forms

aden/o	gland	**emmetr/o**	correct, proper	**optic/o**	eye, vision
ambly/o	dull, dim	**esthes/o**	sensation, feeling	**papill/o**	optic disc
angi/o	vessel	**glauc/o**	gray	**phac/o**	lens
aque/o	water	**ir/o**	iris	**phot/o**	light
bi/o	life	**irid/o**	iris	**presby/o**	old age
blast/o	immature, embryonic	**kerat/o**	cornea	**pupill/o**	pupil
blephar/o	eyelid	**lacrim/o**	tears	**retin/o**	retina
chromat/o	color	**macul/o**	macula lutea	**scler/o**	sclera
conjuctiv/o	conjunctiva	**mi/o**	lessening	**stigmat/o**	point
corne/o	cornea	**myc/o**	fungus	**ton/o**	tone
cry/o	cold	**mydr/i**	widening	**uve/o**	choroid
cycl/o	ciliary body	**nyctal/o**	night	**vitre/o**	glassy
cyst/o	sac	**ocul/o**	eye	**xer/o**	dry
dacry/o	tears	**ophthalm/o**	eye		
dipl/o	double	**opt/o**	eye, vision		

Suffixes

-al	pertaining to	-logist	one who studies	-pathy	disease
-algia	pain	-logy	study of	-pexy	surgical fixation
-ar	pertaining to	-malacia	softening	-phobia	fear
-ary	pertaining to	-meter	instrument to measure	-plasty	surgical repair
-atic	pertaining to	-metrist	specialist in measuring	-plegia	paralysis
-ectomy	surgical removal			-ptosis	drooping
-edema	swelling	-metry	process of measuring	-rrhagia	abnormal flow condition
-graphy	process of recording	-oma	tumor		
-ia	condition	-opia	vision condition	-scope	instrument for viewing
-ic	pertaining to	-opsia	vision condition		
-ician	specialist	-osis	abnormal condition	-scopy	process of visually examining
-ism	state of	-otomy	cutting into	-tic	pertaining to
-itis	inflammation	-ous	pertaining to	-tropia	turned condition

Prefixes

a-	without
an-	without
anti-	against
de-	without
eso-	inward

exo-	outward
extra-	outside of
hemi-	half
hyper-	excessive

intra-	within
micro-	small
mono-	one
myo-	to shut

Anatomical Terms

TERM	WORD PARTS	DEFINITION
aqueous (AK-wee-us)	aque/o = water -ous = pertaining to	Pertaining to water or being water-like.
conjunctival (kon-JUNK-tih-vall)	conjuctiv/o = conjunctiva -al = pertaining to	Pertaining to the conjunctiva.
corneal (KOR-nee-all)	corne/o = cornea -al = pertaining to	Pertaining to the cornea. **MED TERM TIP** Word Watch: Be careful using the combining forms *core/o* meaning "pupil" and *corne/o* meaning "cornea."
extraocular (EKS-truh-OK-yoo-lar)	extra- = outside of ocul/o = eye -ar = pertaining to	Pertaining to being outside the eyeball; for example, the extraocular eye muscles.
iridal (ir-id-al)	irid/o = iris -al = pertaining to	Pertaining to the iris.
lacrimal (LAK-rim-al)	lacrim/o = tears -al = pertaining to	Pertaining to tears.
macular (MACK-uoo-lar)	macul/o = macula lutea -ar = pertaining to	Pertaining to the macula lutea.
ocular (OCK-yoo-lar)	ocul/o = eye -ar = pertaining to	Pertaining to the eye.
intraocular (in-trah-OCK-yoo-lar)	intra- = within ocul/o = eye -ar = pertaining to	Pertaining to within the eye.
ophthalmic (off-THAL-mik)	ophthalm/o = eye -ic = pertaining to	Pertaining to the eye.
optic (OP-tik)	opt/o = eye, vision -ic = pertaining to	Pertaining to the eye or vision.
optical (OP-tih-kal)	optic/o = eye, vision -al = pertaining to	Pertaining to the eye or vision.
pupillary (PYOO-pih-lair-ee)	pupill/o = pupil -ary = pertaining to	Pertaining to the pupil.
retinal (RET-in-al)	retin/o = retina -al = pertaining to	Pertaining to the retina.
scleral (SKLAIR-all)	scler/o = sclera -al = pertaining to	Pertaining to the sclera.
uveal (YOO-vee-al)	uve/o = choroid -al = pertaining to	Pertaining to the choroid layer of the eye.
vitreous (VIT-ree-us)	vitre/o = glass -ous = pertaining to	Pertaining to the vitreous humor.

Pathology

TERM	WORD PARTS	DEFINITION
Medical Specialties		
ophthalmologist (opf-thal-MOLL-oh-jist)	ophthalm/o = eye -logist = one who studies	Medical doctor who has specialized in the diagnosis and treatment of eye conditions and diseases.
ophthalmology (opf-thal-MOLL-oh-jee)	ophthalm/o = eye -logy = study of	Branch of medicine involving the diagnosis and treatment of conditions and diseases of the eye and surrounding structures.
optician (op-TISH-an)	opt/o = vision -ician = specialist	Person trained in grinding and fitting corrective lenses.
optometrist (op-TOM-eh-trist)	opt/o = vision -metrist = specialist in measuring	Doctor of optometry.
optometry (op-TOM-eh-tree)	opt/o = vision -metry = process of measuring	Medical profession specializing in examining the eyes, testing visual acuity, and prescribing corrective lenses.
Signs and Symptoms		
blepharoptosis (blef-ah-rop-TOH-sis)	blephar/o = eyelid -ptosis = drooping	Drooping eyelid.
cycloplegia (sigh-kloh-PLEE-jee-ah)	cycl/o = ciliary body -plegia = paralysis	Paralysis of the ciliary body. This affects changing the shape of the lens to bring images into focus.
diplopia (dip-LOH-pee-ah)	dipl/o = double -opia = vision condition	Condition of seeing double.
emmetropia (EM) (em-eh-TROH-pee-ah)	emmetr/o = correct, proper -opia = vision condition	State of normal vision.
iridoplegia (ir-id-oh-PLEE-jee-ah)	irid/o = iris -plegia = paralysis	Paralysis of the iris. This affects changing the size of the pupil to regulate the amount of light entering the eye.
nyctalopia (nik-tah-LOH-pee-ah)	nyctal/o = night -opia = vision condition	Difficulty seeing in dim light; also called *night-blindness.* Usually due to damaged rods.

> **MED TERM TIP**
>
> The simple translation of *nyctalopia* is "night vision." However, it is used to mean "night blindness."

TERM	WORD PARTS	DEFINITION
ophthalmalgia (off-thal-MAL-jee-ah)	ophthalm/o = eye -algia = pain	Eye pain.
ophthalmoplegia (off-thal-moh-PLEE-jee-ah)	ophthalm/o = eye -plegia = paralysis	Paralysis of one or more of the extraocular eye muscles.
ophthalmorrhagia (off-thal-moh-RAH-jee-ah)	ophthalm/o = eye -rrhagia = abnormal flow condition	Bleeding from the eye.
papilledema (pah-pill-eh-DEEM-ah)	papill/o = optic disc -edema = swelling	Swelling of the optic disk. Often as a result of increased intraocular pressure. Also called *choked disk.*

■ Pathology (continued)

TERM	WORD PARTS	DEFINITION
photophobia (foh-toh-FOH-bee-ah)	phot/o = light -phobia = fear	Although the term translates into *fear of light,* it actually means a strong sensitivity to bright light.
presbyopia (prez-bee-OH-pee-ah)	presby/o = old age -opia = vision condition	Visual loss due to old age, resulting in difficulty in focusing for near vision (such as reading).
scleromalacia (sklair-oh-mah-LAY-she-ah)	scler/o = sclera -malacia = softening	Softening of the sclera.
xerophthalmia (zee-ROP-thal-mee-ah)	xer/o = dry ophthalm/o = eye -ia = condition	Dry eyes.
Eyeball		
achromatopsia (ah-kroh-mah-TOP-see-ah)	a- = without chromat/o = color -opsia = vision condition	Condition of color blindness—unable to perceive one or more colors; more common in males.
amblyopia (am-blee-OH-pee-ah)	ambly/o = dull, dim -opia = vision condition	Loss of vision not as a result of eye pathology. Usually occurs in patients who see two images. In order to see only one image, the brain will no longer recognize the image being sent to it by one of the eyes. May occur if strabismus is not corrected. This condition is not treatable with a prescription lens. Commonly referred to as *lazy eye.*
astigmatism (Astigm) (ah-STIG-mah-tizm)	a- = without stigmat/o = point -ism = state of	Condition in which light rays are focused unevenly on the retina, causing a distorted image, due to an abnormal curvature of the cornea.
cataract (KAT-ah-rakt)		Damage to the lens causing it to become opaque or cloudy, resulting in diminished vision. Treatment is usually surgical removal of the cataract or replacement of the lens.

MED TERM TIP

The term *cataract* comes from the Latin word meaning "waterfall." This refers to how a person with a cataract sees the world—as if looking through a waterfall.

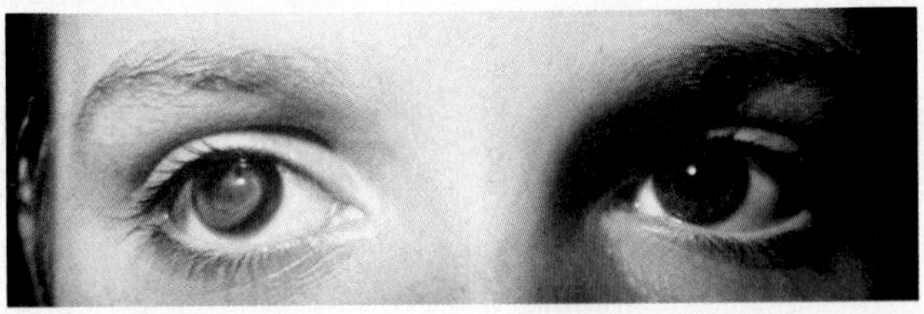

■ **Figure 13.8** Photograph of a person with a cataract in the right eye.

TERM	WORD PARTS	DEFINITION
corneal abrasion	corne/o = cornea -al = pertaining to	Scraping injury to the cornea. If it does not heal, it may develop into an ulcer.
glaucoma (glau-KOH-mah)	glauc/o = gray -oma = mass	Increase in intraocular pressure, which, if untreated, may result in atrophy (wasting away) of the optic nerve and blindness. Glaucoma is treated with medication and surgery. There is an increased risk of developing glaucoma in persons over age 60, of African ancestry, who have sustained a serious eye injury, and in anyone with a family history of diabetes or glaucoma.

Pathology *(continued)*

TERM	WORD PARTS	DEFINITION
hyperopia (high-per-OH-pee-ah)	hyper- = excessive -opia = vision condition	With this condition a person can see things in the distance but has trouble reading material at close range. Also known as *far-sightedness.* This condition is corrected with converging or biconvex lenses.

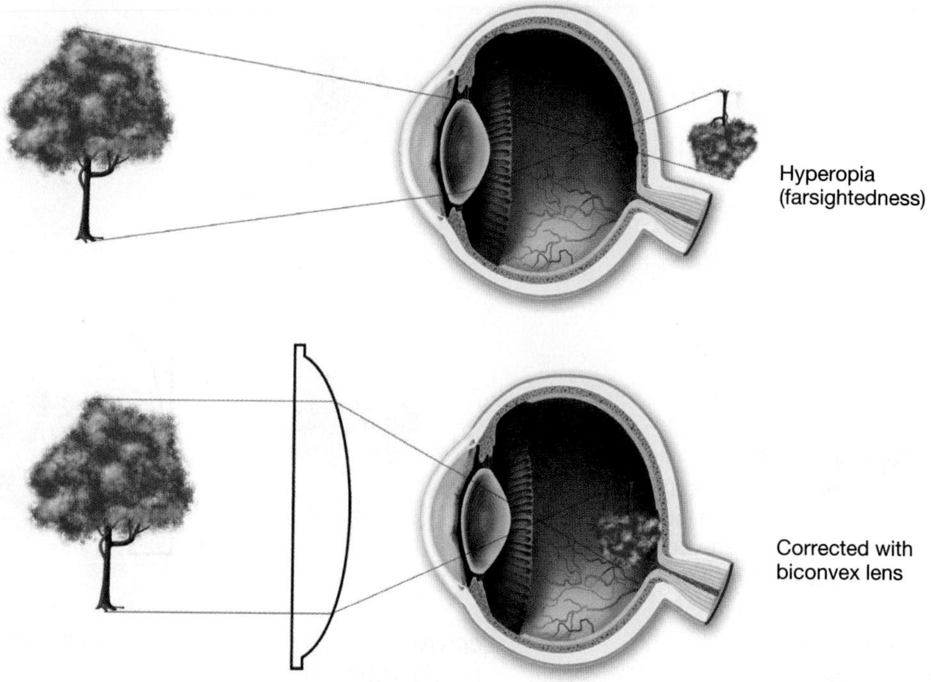

■ Figure 13.9 Hyperopia (farsightedness). In the uncorrected top figure, the image would come into focus behind the retina, making the image on the retina blurry. The bottom image shows how a biconvex lens corrects this condition.

Hyperopia (farsightedness)

Corrected with biconvex lens

TERM	WORD PARTS	DEFINITION
iritis (eye-RYE-tis)	ir/o = iris -itis = inflammation	Inflammation of the iris.
keratitis (kair-ah-TYE-tis)	kerat/o = cornea -itis = inflammation	Inflammation of the cornea. **MED TERM TIP** Word Watch: Be careful using the combining form *kerat/o,* which means both "cornea" and "hard protein keratin."
legally blind		Describes a person who has severely impaired vision. Usually defined as having visual acuity of 20/200 that cannot be improved with corrective lenses or having a visual field of less than 20 degrees.
macular degeneration (MAK-yoo-lar)	macul/o = macula lutea -ar = pertaining to	Deterioration of the macular area of the retina of the eye. May be treated with laser surgery to destroy the blood vessels beneath the macula.
monochromatism (mon-oh-KROH-mah-tizm)	mono- = one chromat/o = color -ism = state of	Unable to perceive one color.

Pathology *(continued)*

TERM	WORD PARTS	DEFINITION
myopia (MY) (my-OH-pee-ah)	myo- = to shut -opia = vision condition	With this condition a person can see things close up but distance vision is blurred. Also known as *nearsightedness*. This condition is corrected with diverging or biconcave lenses. Named because persons with myopia often partially shut their eyes, squint, in order to see better.

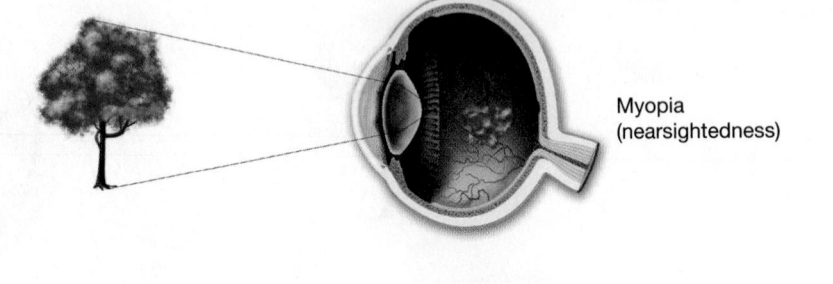

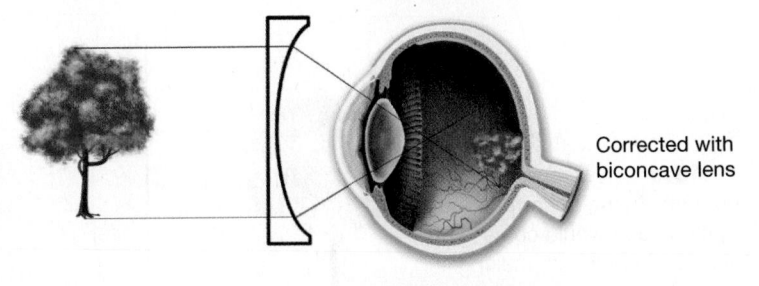

■ **Figure 13.10** Myopia (nearsightedness). In the uncorrected top figure, the image comes into focus in front of the lens, making the image on the retina blurry. The bottom image shows how a biconcave lens corrects this condition.

Myopia (nearsightedness)

Corrected with biconcave lens

TERM	WORD PARTS	DEFINITION
oculomycosis (ok-yoo-loh-my-KOH-sis)	ocul/o = eye myc/o = fungus -osis = abnormal condition	Fungus infection of the eye.
retinal detachment (RET-in-al)	retin/o = retina -al = pertaining to	Occurs when the retina becomes separated from the choroid layer. This separation seriously damages blood vessels and nerves, resulting in blindness. May be treated with surgical or medical procedures to stabilize the retina and prevent separation.
retinitis pigmentosa (ret-in-EYE-tis / pig-men-TOH-sah)	retin/o = retina -itis = inflammation	Progressive disease of the eye resulting in the retina becoming hard (sclerosed), pigmented (colored), and atrophying (wasting away). There is no known cure for this condition.
retinoblastoma (RET-in-noh-blast-OH-mah)	retin/o = retina blast/o = immature, embryonic -oma = tumor	Malignant eye tumor occurring in children, usually under the age of 3. Requires enucleation.
retinopathy (ret-in-OP-ah-thee)	retin/o = retina -pathy = disease	General term for disease affecting the retina.
scleritis (skler-EYE-tis)	scler/o = sclera -itis = inflammation	Inflammation of the sclera.

Pathology *(continued)*

TERM	WORD PARTS	DEFINITION
uveitis (yoo-vee-EYE-tis)	uve/o = choroid -itis = inflammation	Inflammation of the choroid layer.
Conjunctiva		
conjunctivitis (kon-junk-tih-VYE-tis)	conjuctiv/o = conjunctiva -itis = inflammation	Inflammation of the conjunctiva usually as the result of a bacterial infection. Commonly called pink eye.
pterygium (the-RIJ-ee-um)		Hypertrophied conjunctival tissue in the inner corner of the eye.
Eyelids		
blepharitis (blef-ah-RYE-tis)	blephar/o = eyelid -itis = inflammation	Inflammation of the eyelid.
hordeolum (hor-DEE-oh-lum)		Refers to a *stye* (or *sty*), a small purulent inflammatory infection of a sebaceous gland of the eyelid; treated with hot compresses and/or surgical incision.
Lacrimal Apparatus		
dacryoadenitis (dak-ree-oh-ad-eh-NYE-tis)	dacry/o = tears aden/o = gland -itis = inflammation	Inflammation of the lacrimal gland.
dacryocystitis (dak-ree-oh-sis-TYE-tis)	dacry/o = tears cyst/o = sac -itis = inflammation	Inflammation of the lacrimal sac.
Eye Muscles		
esotropia (ST) (ess-oh-TROH-pee-ah)	eso- = inward -tropia = turned condition	Inward turning of the eye; also called *cross-eyed*. An example of a form of strabismus (muscle weakness of the eye).
exotropia (XT) (eks-oh-TROH-pee-ah)	exo- = outward -tropia = turned condition	Outward turning of the eye; also called *wall-eyed*. Also an example of strabismus (muscle weakness of the eye).
strabismus (strah-BIZ-mus)		Eye muscle weakness commonly seen in children resulting in the eyes looking in different directions at the same time. May be corrected with glasses, eye exercises, and/or surgery.
Brain-Related Vision Pathologies		
hemianopia (hem-ee-ah-NOP-ee-ah)	hemi- = half a- = without -opia = vision condition	Loss of vision in half of the visual field. A stroke patient may suffer from this disorder.
nystagmus (niss-TAG-mus)		Jerky-appearing involuntary eye movements, usually left and right. Often an indication of brain injury.

Diagnostic Procedures

TERM	WORD PARTS	DEFINITION
Eye Examination Tests		
color vision tests		Use of polychromic (multicolored) charts to determine the ability of the patient to recognize color.

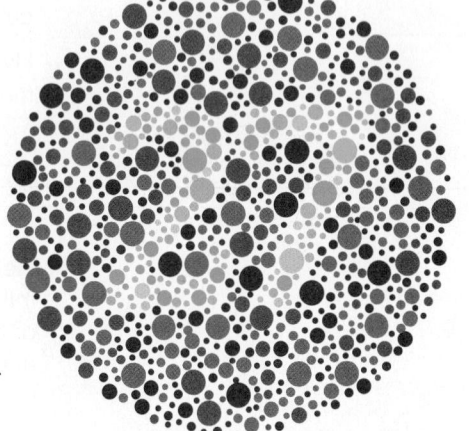

■ **Figure 13.11** An example of color blindness test. A person with red-green color blindness would not be able to distinguish the green 27 from the surrounding red circles.

TERM	WORD PARTS	DEFINITION
fluorescein angiography (floo-oh-RESS-ee-in / an-jee-OG-rah-fee)	angi/o = vessel -graphy = process of recording	Process of injecting a dye (fluorescein) to observe the movement of blood and detect lesions in the macular area of the retina. Used to determine if there is a detachment of the retina.
fluorescein staining (floo-oh-RESS-ee-in)		Applying dye eye drops that are a bright green fluorescent color. Used to look for corneal abrasions or ulcers.
keratometer (KAIR-ah-toh-mee-ter)	kerat/o = cornea -meter = instrument to measure	An instrument used to measure the curvature of the cornea.
keratometry (kair-ah-TOM-eh-tree)	kerat/o = cornea -metry = process of measuring	Measurement of the curvature of the cornea using an instrument called a *keratometer*.
ophthalmoscope (off-THAL-moh-scope)	ophthalm/o = eye -scope = instrument for viewing	Instrument used to examine the inside of the eye through the pupil.
ophthalmoscopy (off-thal-MOSS-koh-pee)	ophthalm/o = eye -scopy = process of visually examining	Examination of the interior of the eyes using an instrument called an *ophthalmoscope* (see Figure 13.12 ■). The physician dilates the pupil in order to see the cornea, lens, and retina. Used to identify abnormalities in the blood vessels of the eye and some systemic diseases.

Diagnostic Procedures *(continued)*

TERM	WORD PARTS	DEFINITION

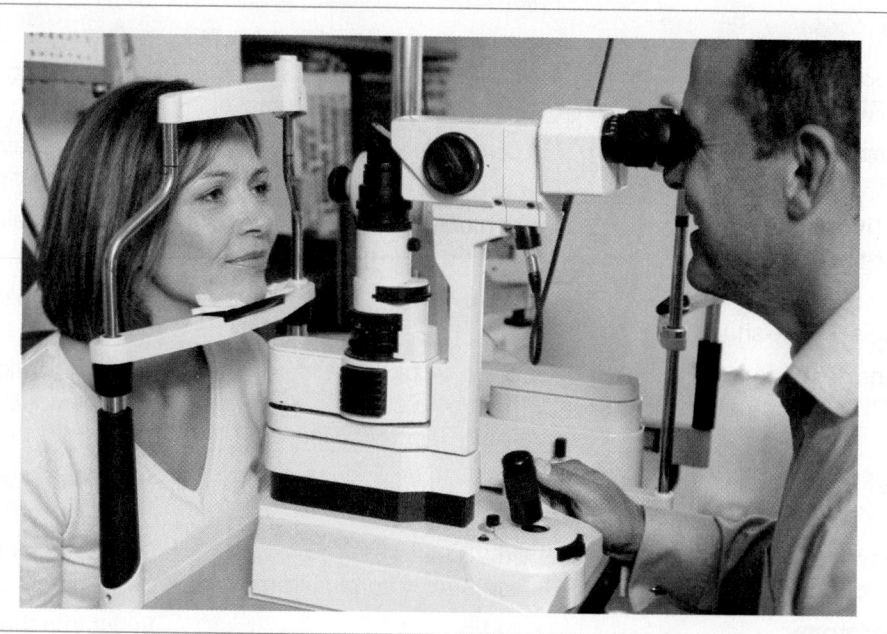

■ **Figure 13.12** Examination of the interior of the eye using an ophthalmoscope. *(Monkey Business Images/Shutterstock)*

TERM	WORD PARTS	DEFINITION
optometer (op-TOM-eh-ter)	opt/o = vision -meter = instrument to measure	Instrument used to measure how well the eye is able to focus images clearly on the retina.
refractive error test (ree-FRAK-tiv)		Vision test for a defect in the ability of the eye to accurately focus the image that is hitting it. Refractive errors result in myopia and hyperopia.
slit lamp microscopy	micro- = small -scopy = process of visually examining	Examining the posterior surface of the cornea.
Snellen chart (SNEL-enz)		Chart used for testing distance vision named for Dutch ophthalmologist Hermann Snellen. It contains letters of varying size and is administered from a distance of 20 feet. A person who can read at 20 feet what the average person can read at this distance is said to have 20/20 vision.
tonometry (tohn-OM-eh-tree)	ton/o = tone -metry = process of measuring	Measurement of the intraocular pressure of the eye using a *tonometer* to check for the condition of glaucoma. The physician places the tonometer lightly on the eyeball and a pressure measurement is taken. Generally part of a normal eye exam for adults.
visual acuity (VA) **test** (VIZH-oo-al / ah-KYOO-ih-tee)	-al = pertaining to	Measurement of the sharpness of a patient's vision. Usually, a Snellen chart is used for this test in which the patient identifies letters from a distance of 20 feet.

Therapeutic Procedures

TERMS	WORD PARTS	DEFINITION
Surgical Procedures		
blepharectomy (blef-ah-REK-toh-mee)	blephar/o = eyelid -ectomy = surgical removal	Surgical removal of the eyelid.
blepharoplasty (BLEF-ah-roh-plass-tee)	blephar/o = eyelid -plasty = surgical repair	Surgical repair of the eyelid. A common plastic surgery to correct blepharoptosis.
conjunctivoplasty (kon-junk-tih-VOH-plas-tee)	conjuctiv/o = conjunctiva -plasty = surgical repair	Surgical repair of the conjunctiva.
cryoextraction (cry-oh-eks-TRAK-shun)	cry/o = cold	Procedure in which cataract is lifted from the lens with an extremely cold probe.
cryoretinopexy (cry-oh-RET-ih-noh-pek-see)	cry/o = cold retin/o = retina -pexy = surgical fixation	Surgical fixation of the retina by using extreme cold.
enucleation (ee-new-klee-AH-shun)		Surgical removal of an eyeball.
iridectomy (ir-id-EK-toh-mee)	irid/o = iris -ectomy = surgical removal	Surgical removal of the iris.
iridosclerotomy (ir-ih-doh-skleh-ROT-oh-mee)	irid/o = iris scler/o = sclera -otomy = cutting into	To cut into the iris and sclera.
keratoplasty (KAIR-ah-toh-plass-tee)	kerat/o = cornea -plasty = surgical repair	Surgical repair of the cornea is the simple translation of this term that is utilized to mean corneal transplant.
laser-assisted in-situ keratomileusis (LASIK) (in-SIH-tyoo / kair-ah-toh-mih-LOO-sis)	kerat/o = cornea	Correction of myopia using laser surgery to remove corneal tissue.

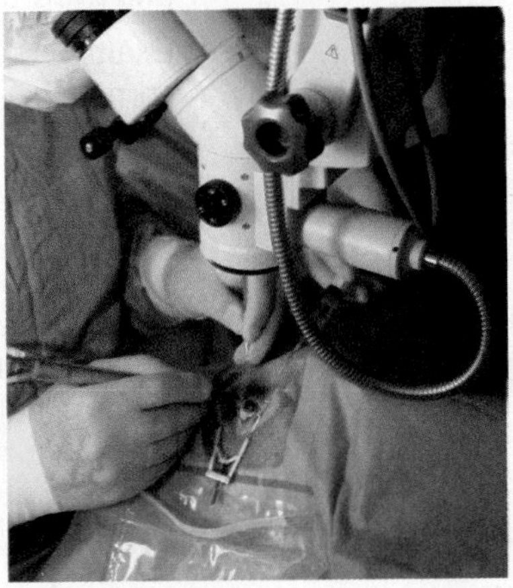

Figure 13.13 LASIK surgery uses a laser to reshape the cornea. *(mehmetcan/Shutterstock)*

TERMS	WORD PARTS	DEFINITION
laser photocoagulation (LAY-zer / foh-toh-koh-ag-yoo-LAY-shun)	phot/o = light	Use of a laser beam to destroy very small precise areas of the retina. May be used to treat retinal detachment or macular degeneration.
phacoemulsification (fak-oh-ee-mull-sih-fih-KAY-shun)	phac/o = lens	Use of high-frequency sound waves to emulsify (liquefy) a lens with a cataract, which is then aspirated (removed by suction) with a needle.
photorefractive keratectomy (PRK) (foh-toh-ree-FRAK-tiv / kair-ah-TEK-toh-mee)	phot/o = light kerat/o = cornea -ectomy = surgical removal	Use of a laser to reshape the cornea and correct errors of refraction.
prosthetic lens implant (pros-THET-ik)		Use of an artificial lens to replace the lens removed during cataract surgery.

Therapeutic Procedures *(continued)*

TERMS	WORD PARTS	DEFINITION
radial keratotomy (RK) (RAY-dee-all / kair-ah-TOT-oh-mee)	-al = pertaining to kerat/o = cornea -otomy = cutting into	Spokelike incisions around the cornea that result in it becoming flatter. A surgical treatment for myopia.
retinopexy (ret-ih-noh-PEX-ee)	retin/o = retina -pexy = surgical fixation	Surgical fixation of the retina. One treatment for a detaching retina.
scleral buckling (SKLAIR-al)	scler/o = sclera -al = pertaining to	Placing a band of silicone around the outside of the sclera that stabilizes a detaching retina.
sclerotomy (skleh-ROT-oh-mee)	scler/o = sclera -otomy = cutting into	To cut into the sclera.
strabotomy (strah-BOT-oh-mee)	-otomy = cutting into	Incision into the eye muscles in order to correct strabismus.

Pharmacology

CLASSIFICATION	WORD PARTS	ACTION	EXAMPLES
anesthetic ophthalmic solution (off-THAL-mik)	an- = without esthes/o = sensation, feeling -ic = pertaining to ophthalm/o = eye -ic = pertaining to	Eye drops for pain relief associated with eye infections, corneal abrasions, or surgery.	proparacain, Ak-Taine, Ocu-Caine; tetracaine, Opticaine, Pontocaine
antibiotic ophthalmic solution (off-THAL-mik)	anti- = against bi/o = life -ic = pertaining to ophthalm/o = eye -ic = pertaining to	Eye drops for the treatment of bacterial eye infections.	erythromycin, Del-Mycin, Ilotycin Ophthalmic
antiglaucoma medications (an-tye-glau-KOH-mah)	anti- = against glauc/o = gray -oma = mass	Group of drugs that reduce intraocular pressure by lowering the amount of aqueous humor in the eyeball. May achieve this by either reducing the production of aqueous humor or increasing its outflow.	timolol, Betimol, Timoptic; acetazolamide, Ak-Zol, Dazamide; prostaglandin analogs, Lumigan, Xalatan
artificial tears		Medications, many of them over the counter, to treat dry eyes.	buffered isotonic solutions, Akwa Tears, Refresh Plus, Moisture Eyes
miotic drops (my-OT-ik)	mi/o = lessening -tic = pertaining to	Any substance that causes the pupil to constrict. These medications may also be used to treat glaucoma.	physostigmine, Eserine Sulfate, Isopto Eserine; carbachol, Carbastat, Miostat
mydriatic drops (mid-ree-AT-ik)	mydr/i = widening -atic = pertaining to	Any substance that causes the pupil to dilate by paralyzing the iris and/or ciliary body muscles. Particularly useful during eye examinations and eye surgery.	atropine sulfate, Atropine-Care Ophthalmic, Atropisol Ophthalmic
ophthalmic decongestants	ophthalm/o = eye -ic = pertaining to de- = without	Over-the-counter medications that constrict the arterioles of the eye and reduce redness and itching of the conjunctiva.	tetrahydrozoline, Visine, Murine

Abbreviations

ARMD	age-related macular degeneration	**Ophth.**	ophthalmology
Astigm	astigmatism	**OS**	left eye
c.gl.	correction with glasses	**OU**	each eye/both eyes
D	diopter (lens strength)	**PERRLA**	pupils equal, round, react to light and accommodation
DVA	distance visual acuity		
ECCE	extracapsular cataract extraction	**PRK**	photorefractive keratectomy
EENT	eye, ear, nose, and throat	**REM**	rapid eye movement
EM	emmetropia	**s.gl.**	without correction or glasses
EOM	extraocular movement	**SMD**	senile macular degeneration
ICCE	intracapsular cataract extraction	**ST**	esotropia
IOP	intraocular pressure	**VA**	visual acuity
LASIK	laser-assisted in-situ keratomileusis	**VF**	visual field
OD	right eye	**XT**	exotropia

MED TERM TIP

The abbreviations for right eye (OD) and left eye (OS) are easy to remember when we know their origins. OD stands for *oculus* (eye) *dexter* (right). OS has its origin in *oculus* (eye) *sinister* (left). At one time in history it was considered to be sinister if a person looked at another from only the left side. Hence the term *oculus sinister* (OS) means left eye.

Section II: The Ear at a Glance

Function

The ear contains the sensory receptors for hearing and equilibrium (balance).

Structures

Here are the primary structures that comprise the ear.

auricle	external ear
inner ear	middle ear

Word Parts

Here are the most common word parts (with their meanings) used to build ear terms. For a more comprehensive list, refer to the Terminology section of this chapter.

Combining Forms

acous/o	hearing	myring/o	tympanic membrane (eardrum)
audi/o	hearing		
audit/o	hearing	ot/o	ear
aur/o	ear	salping/o	auditory tube (eustachian tube)
auricul/o	ear		
cerumin/o	cerumen	staped/o	stapes
cochle/o	cochlea	tympan/o	tympanic membrane (eardrum)
labyrinth/o	labyrinth (inner ear)		

Suffixes

-cusis	hearing
-otia	ear condition

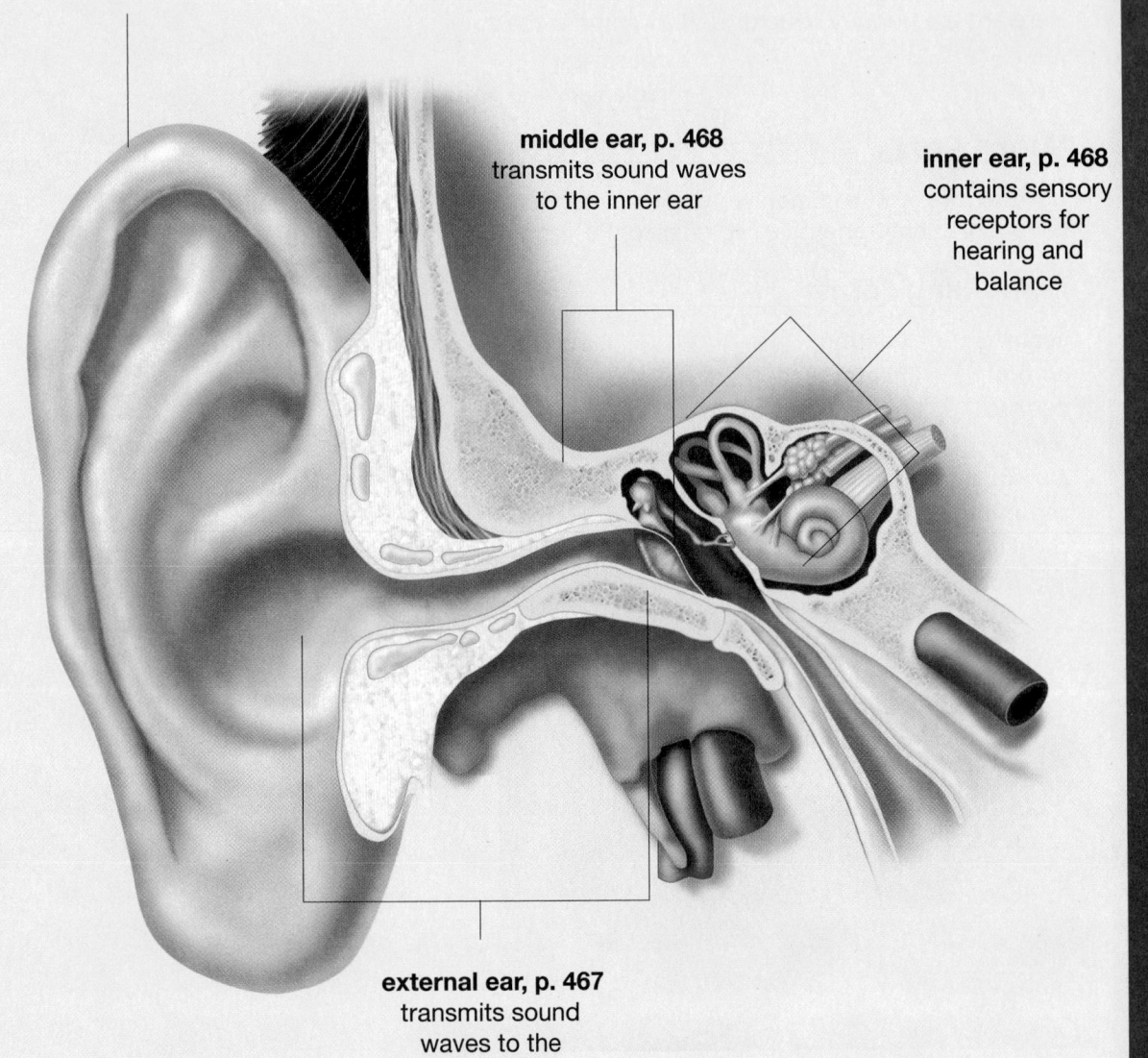

auricle, p. 467
directs sound
waves into the
ear canal

middle ear, p. 468
transmits sound waves
to the inner ear

inner ear, p. 468
contains sensory
receptors for
hearing and
balance

external ear, p. 467
transmits sound
waves to the
middle ear

Anatomy and Physiology of the Ear

audiology (aw-dee-OL-oh-jee)

cochlear nerve (KOK-lee-ar)

equilibrium (ee-kwih-LIB-ree-um)

external ear

hearing

inner ear

middle ear

otology (oh-TOL-oh-jee)

vestibular nerve (ves-TIB-yoo-lar)

vestibulocochlear nerve
(ves-tib-yoo-loh-KOK-lee-ar)

The study of the ear is referred to as **otology** (Oto), and the study of hearing disorders is called **audiology.** While there is a large amount of overlap between these two areas, there are also examples of ear problems that do not affect hearing. The ear is responsible for two senses: **hearing** and **equilibrium,** or our sense of balance. Hearing and equilibrium sensory information is carried to the brain by cranial nerve VIII, the **vestibulocochlear nerve.** This nerve is divided into two major branches. The **cochlear nerve** carries hearing information, and the **vestibular nerve** carries equilibrium information.

The ear is subdivided into three areas: **external ear, middle ear,** and **inner ear.**

External Ear

auditory canal (AW-dih-tor-ee)

auricle (AW-rih-k'l)

cerumen (seh-ROO-men)

external auditory meatus
(AW-dih-tor-ee / me-A-tus)

pinna (PIN-ah)

tympanic membrane (tim-PAN-ik)

The external ear consists of three parts: the **auricle,** the **auditory canal,** and the **tympanic membrane** (see Figure 13.14 ■). The auricle or **pinna** is what is commonly referred to as the *ear* because this is the only visible portion. The auricle with its

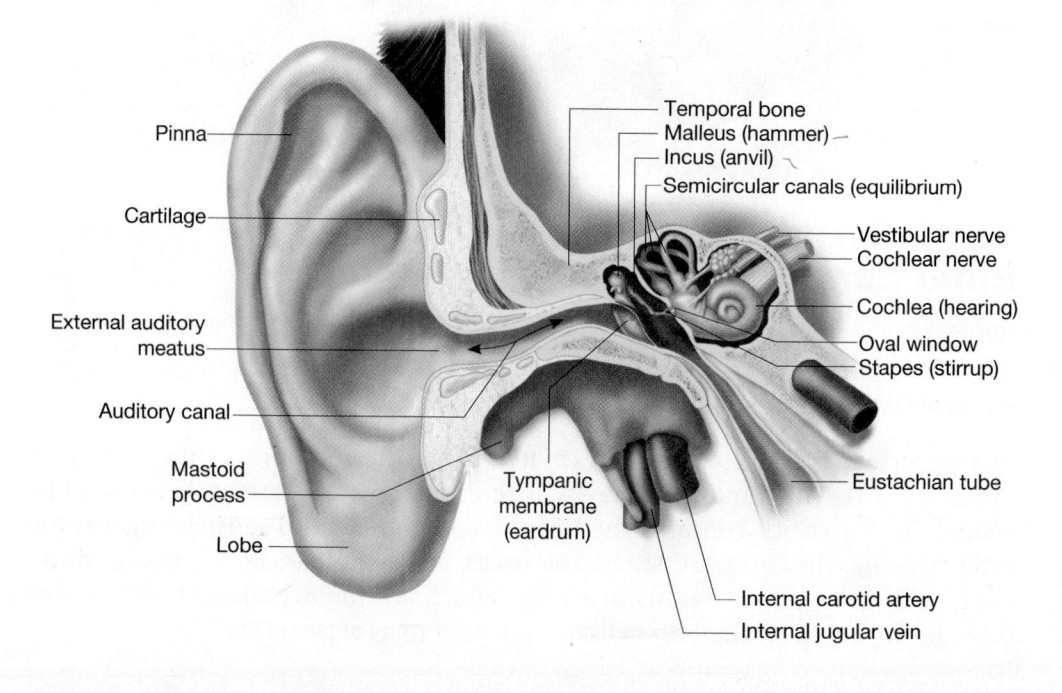

■ **Figure 13.14** The internal structures of the outer, middle, and inner ear.

earlobe has a unique shape in each person and functions like a funnel to capture sound waves as they go past the outer ear and channel them through the **external auditory meatus.** The sound then moves along the auditory canal and causes the tympanic membrane (eardrum) to vibrate. The tympanic membrane actually separates the external ear from the middle ear. Ear wax or **cerumen** is produced in oil glands in the auditory canal. This wax helps to protect and lubricate the ear. It is also just barely liquid at body temperature. This causes cerumen to slowly flow out of the auditory canal, carrying dirt and dust with it. Therefore, the auditory canal is self-cleaning.

Middle Ear

auditory tube (AW-dih-tor-ee)

eustachian tube (yoo-STAY-she-en)

incus (ING-kus)

malleus (MAL-ee-us)

ossicles (OSS-ih-kls)

oval window

stapes (STAY-peez)

The middle ear is located in a small cavity in the temporal bone of the skull. This air-filled cavity contains three tiny bones called **ossicles** (see Figure 13.15 ■). These three bones, the **malleus, incus,** and **stapes,** are vital to the hearing process. They amplify the vibrations in the middle ear and transmit them to the inner ear from the malleus to the incus and finally to the stapes. The stapes, the last of the three ossicles, is attached to a very thin membrane that covers the opening to the inner ear called the **oval window.**

The **eustachian tube** or **auditory tube** connects the nasopharynx with the middle ear (see Figure 13.14). Each time you swallow the eustachian tube opens. This connection allows pressure to equalize between the middle ear cavity and the atmospheric pressure.

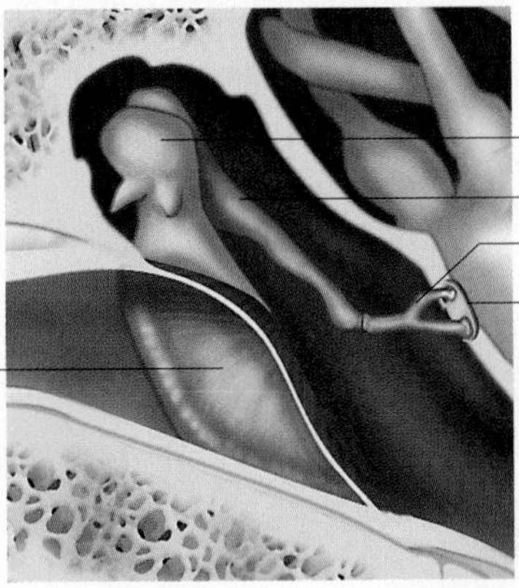

■ **Figure 13.15** Closeup view of the ossicles within the middle ear. These three bones extend from the tympanic membrane to the oval window.

Inner Ear

cochlea (KOK-lee-ah)

labyrinth (LAB-ih-rinth)

organs of Corti (KOR-tee)

saccule (SAK-yool)

semicircular canals

utricle (YOO-trih-k'l)

The inner ear is also located in a cavity within the temporal bone (see again Figure 13.14). This fluid-filled cavity is referred to as the **labyrinth** because of its shape. The labyrinth contains the hearing and equilibrium sensory organs: the **cochlea** for hearing and the **semicircular canals, utricle,** and **saccule** for equilibrium. Each of these organs contains hair cells, which are the actual sensory receptor cells. In the cochlea, the hair cells are referred to as **organs of Corti.**

MED TERM TIP

The term *tympanic membrane* comes from the Greek word for "drumhead." The tympanic membrane or eardrum vibrates to sound waves like a drum head.

MED TERM TIP

The three bones in the middle ear are referred to by terms that are similar to their shape. Thus, the malleus is called the hammer, the incus is the anvil, and the stapes is the stirrup (see Figure 13.15).

MED TERM TIP

Frequently, children will twirl in circles and fall or stumble from dizziness when they stop. This is caused from a temporary imbalance in the inner ear.

How We Hear

conductive hearing loss (kon-DUK-tiv)
sensorineural hearing loss (sen-soh-ree-NOO-ral)

Figure 13.16 ■ outlines the path of sound through the outer ear and middle ear and into the cochlea of the inner ear. Sound waves traveling down the external auditory canal strike the eardrum, causing it to vibrate. The ossicles conduct these vibrations across the middle ear from the eardrum to the oval window. Oval window movements initiate vibrations in the fluid that fills the cochlea. As the fluid vibrations strike a hair cell, they bend the small hairs and stimulate the nerve ending. The nerve ending then sends an electrical impulse to the brain on the cochlear portion of the vestibulocochlear nerve.

Hearing loss can be divided into two main categories: **conductive hearing loss** and **sensorineural hearing loss.** Conductive refers to disease or malformation of the outer or middle ear. All sound is weaker and muffled in conductive hearing loss since it is not conducted correctly to the inner ear. Sensorineural hearing loss is the result of damage or malformation of the inner ear (cochlea) or the cochlear nerve. In this hearing loss, some sounds are distorted and heard incorrectly. There can also be a combination of both conductive and sensorineural hearing loss.

MED TERM TIP

Hearing impairment is becoming a greater problem for the general population for several reasons. First, people are living longer. Hearing loss can accompany old age, and there are a greater number of people over 50 years of age requiring hearing assistance. In addition, sound technology has produced music quality that was never available before. However, listening to loud music either naturally or through earphones can cause gradual damage to the hearing mechanism.

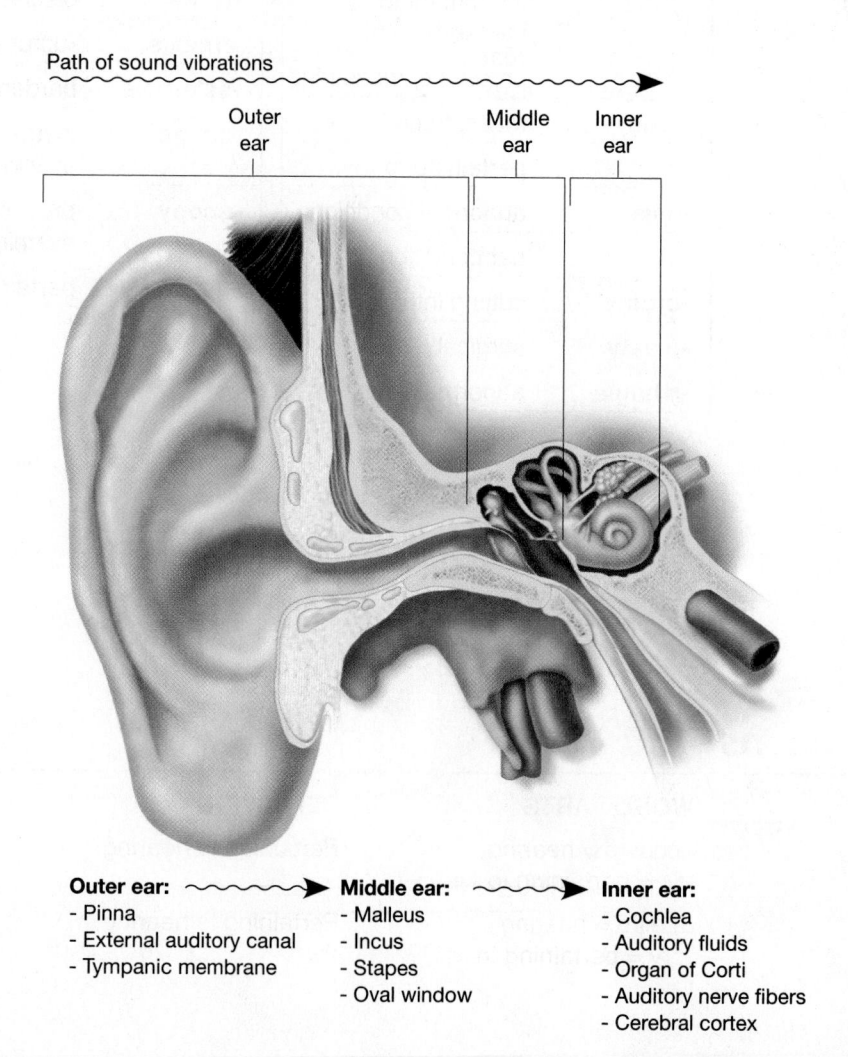

Path of sound vibrations

| Outer ear | Middle ear | Inner ear |

Outer ear:
- Pinna
- External auditory canal
- Tympanic membrane

Middle ear:
- Malleus
- Incus
- Stapes
- Oval window

Inner ear:
- Cochlea
- Auditory fluids
- Organ of Corti
- Auditory nerve fibers
- Cerebral cortex

■ **Figure 13.16** The path of sound waves through the outer, middle, and inner ear.

Terminology

Word Parts Used to Build Ear Terms

The following lists contain the combining forms, suffixes, and prefixes used to build terms in the remaining sections of this chapter.

Combining Forms

acous/o	hearing	**cochle/o**	cochlea	**presby/o**	old age
audi/o	hearing	**labyrinth/o**	labyrinth	**py/o**	pus
audit/o	hearing	**laryng/o**	larynx	**rhin/o**	nose
aur/o	ear	**myc/o**	fungus	**salping/o**	auditory tube
auricul/o	ear	**myring/o**	tympanic membrane	**staped/o**	stapes
bi/o	life	**neur/o**	nerve	**tympan/o**	tympanic membrane
cerumin/o	cerumen	**ot/o**	ear		

Suffixes

-al	pertaining to	-meter	instrument to measure	-rrhea	discharge
-algia	pain			-rrhexis	rupture
-ar	pertaining to	-metry	process of measuring	-sclerosis	hardening
-cusis	hearing	-oma	mass, tumor	-scope	instrument to visually examine
-ectomy	pertaining to	-ory	pertaining to		
-emesis	vomiting	-osis	abnormal condition	-scopy	process of visually examining
-gram	record	-otia	ear condition		
-ic	pertaining to	-otomy	cutting into	-tic	pertaining to
-itis	inflammation	-plasty	surgical repair		
-logy	study of	-rrhagia	abnormal flow		

Prefixes

an- = without	bi- = two	micro- = small
anti- = against	macro- = large	mono- = one

Anatomical Terms

TERM	WORD PARTS	DEFINITION
acoustic (ah-KOOS-tik)	acous/o = hearing -tic = pertaining to	Pertaining to hearing.
auditory (AW-dih-tor-ee)	audit/o = hearing -ory = pertaining to	Pertaining to hearing.

Anatomical Terms (continued)

TERM	WORD PARTS	DEFINITION
aural (AW-ral)	aur/o = ear -al = pertaining to	Pertaining to the ear. **MED TERM TIP** Word Watch: Be careful when using two terms that sound the same—*aural* meaning "pertaining to the ear" and *oral* meaning "pertaining to the mouth."
auricular (aw-RIK-cu-lar)	auricul/o = ear -ar = pertaining to	Pertaining to the ear.
binaural (bin-AW-rall)	bi- = two aur/o = ear -al = pertaining to	Pertaining to both ears.
cochlear (KOK-lee-ar)	cochle/o = cochlea -ar = pertaining to	Pertaining to the cochlea.
monaural (mon-AW-rall)	mono- = one aur/o = ear -al = pertaining to	Pertaining to one ear.
otic (OH-tik)	ot/o = ear -ic = pertaining to	Pertaining to the ear.
tympanic (tim-PAN-ik)	tympan/o = tympanic membrane -ic = pertaining to	Pertaining to the tympanic membrane.

Pathology

TERM	WORD PARTS	DEFINITION
Medical Specialties		
audiology (aw-dee-OL-oh-jee)	audi/o = hearing -logy = study of	Medical specialty involved with measuring hearing function and identifying hearing loss. Specialist is an *audiologist*.
otorhinolaryngology (ENT) (oh-toh-rye-noh-lair-in-GOL-oh-jee)	ot/o = ear rhin/o = nose laryng/o = larynx -logy = study of	Branch of medicine involving the diagnosis and treatment of conditions and diseases of the ear, nose, and throat. Also referred to as *ENT*. Physician is an *otorhinolaryngologist*.
Signs and Symptoms		
macrotia (mah-KROH-she-ah)	macro- = large -otia = ear condition	Condition of having abnormally large ears.
microtia (my-KROH-she-ah)	micro- = small -otia = ear condition	Condition of having abnormally small ears.
otalgia (oh-TAL-jee-ah)	ot/o = ear -algia = pain	Ear pain.
otopyorrhea (oh-toh-pye-oh-REE-ah)	ot/o = ear py/o = pus -rrhea = discharge	Discharge of pus from the ear.
otorrhagia (oh-toh-RAH-jee-ah)	ot/o = ear -rrhagia = abnormal flow	Bleeding from the ear.

Pathology *(continued)*

TERM	WORD PARTS	DEFINITION
presbycusis (pres-bih-KOO-sis)	presby/o = old age -cusis = hearing condition	Normal loss of hearing that can accompany the aging process.
residual hearing (rih-ZID-yoo-al)	-al = pertaining to	Amount of hearing that is still present after damage has occurred to the auditory mechanism.
tinnitus (tin-EYE-tus)		Ringing in the ears.
tympanorrhexis (tim-pan-oh-REK-sis)	tympan/o = tympanic membrane -rrhexis = rupture	Rupture of the tympanic membrane.
vertigo (VER-tih-goh)		Dizziness caused by the sensation that the room is spinning.

Hearing Loss

TERM	WORD PARTS	DEFINITION
anacusis (an-ah-KOO-sis)	an- = without -cusis = hearing	Total absence of hearing; inability to perceive sound. Also called *deafness*.
deafness		Inability to hear or having some degree of hearing impairment.

External Ear

TERM	WORD PARTS	DEFINITION
ceruminoma (seh-roo-men-oh-ma)	cerumin/o = cerumen -oma = mass	Excessive accumulation of ear wax resulting in a hard wax plug. Sound becomes muffled.
otitis externa (OE) (oh-TYE-tis / ex-TERN-ah)	ot/o = ear -itis = inflammation	External ear infection. May be caused by bacteria or fungus. Also called *otomycosis* and commonly referred to as *swimmer's ear*.
otomycosis (oh-toh-my-KOH-sis)	ot/o = ear myc/o = fungus -osis = abnormal condition	Fungal infection of the ear. One type of otitis externa.

Middle Ear

TERM	WORD PARTS	DEFINITION
myringitis (mir-ing-JYE-tis)	myring/o = tympanic membrane -itis = inflammation	Inflammation of the tympanic membrane.
otitis media (OM) (oh-TYE-tis / MEE-dee-ah)	ot/o = ear -itis = inflammation	Seen frequently in children; commonly referred to as a *middle ear infection*. Often preceded by an upper respiratory infection during which pathogens move from the pharynx to the middle ear via the eustachian tube. Fluid accumulates in the middle ear cavity. The fluid may be watery, *serous otitis media,* or full of pus, *purulent otitis media.*
otosclerosis (oh-toh-sklair-OH-sis)	ot/o = ear -sclerosis = hardening	Loss of mobility of the stapes bone, leading to progressive hearing loss.
salpingitis (sal-pin-JIH-tis)	salping/o = auditory tube -itis = inflammation	Inflammation of the auditory tube.

> **MED TERM TIP**
>
> Word Watch: Be careful using the combining form *salping/o,* which can mean either "Eustachian tube" or "fallopian tube."

TERM	WORD PARTS	DEFINITION
tympanitis (tim-pan-EYE-tis)	tympan/o = tympanic membrane -itis = inflammation	Inflammation of the tympanic membrane.

Pathology (continued)

TERM	WORD PARTS	DEFINITION
Inner Ear		
acoustic neuroma (ah-KOOS-tik / noor-OH-mah)	acous/o = hearing -tic = pertaining to neur/o = nerve -oma = tumor	Benign tumor of the eighth cranial nerve sheath. The pressure causes symptoms such as tinnitus, headache, dizziness, and progressive hearing loss.
labyrinthitis (lab-ih-rin-THIGH-tis)	labyrinth/o = labyrinth -itis = inflammation	May affect both the hearing and equilibrium portions of the inner ear. Also referred to as an *inner ear infection*.
Ménière's disease (may-nee-ARZ)		Abnormal condition within the labyrinth of the inner ear that can lead to a progressive loss of hearing. The symptoms are dizziness or vertigo, hearing loss, and tinnitus (ringing in the ears). Named for French physician Prosper Ménière.

Diagnostic Procedures

TERM	WORD PARTS	DEFINITION
Audiology Tests		
audiogram (AW-dee-oh-gram)	audi/o = hearing -gram = record	Graphic record that illustrates the results of audiometry.
audiometer (aw-dee-OM-eh-ter)	audi/o = hearing -meter = instrument to measure	Instrument to measure hearing.
audiometry (aw-dee-OM-eh-tree)	audi/o = hearing -metry = process of measuring	Test of hearing ability by determining the lowest and highest intensity (decibels) and frequencies (hertz) that a person can distinguish. The patient may sit in a sound-proof booth and receive sounds through earphones as the technician decreases the sound or lowers the tones.

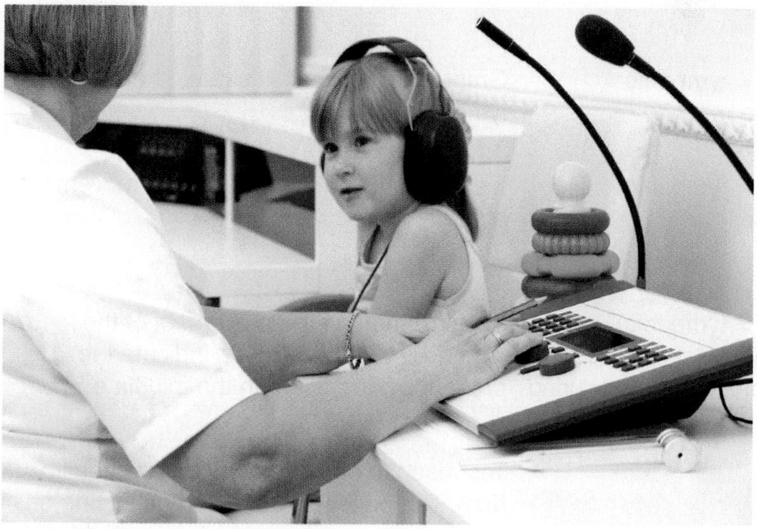

■ **Figure 13.17** Audiometry exam being administered to a young child who is wearing the ear phones through which sounds are given. *(Capifrutta/Shutterstock)*

decibel (dB) (DES-ih-bel)		Measures the intensity or loudness of a sound. Zero decibels is the quietest sound measured and 120 dB is the loudest sound commonly measured.

Diagnostic Procedures (continued)

TERM	WORD PARTS	DEFINITION
hertz (Hz)		Measurement of the frequency or pitch of sound. The lowest pitch on an audiogram is 250 Hz. The measurement can go as high as 8000 Hz, which is the highest pitch measured.
Rinne and Weber tuning-fork tests (RIN-eh)		Tests that assess both nerve and bone conduction of sound. The physician holds a tuning fork, an instrument that produces a constant pitch when it is struck, against or near the bones on the side of the head.

Otology Tests

TERM	WORD PARTS	DEFINITION
otoscope (OH-toh-scope)	ot/o = ear -scope = instrument to visually examine	Instrument to view inside the ear canal.
otoscopy (oh-TOSS-koh-pee)	ot/o = ear -scopy = process of visually examining	Examination of the ear canal, eardrum, and outer ear using an *otoscope*.

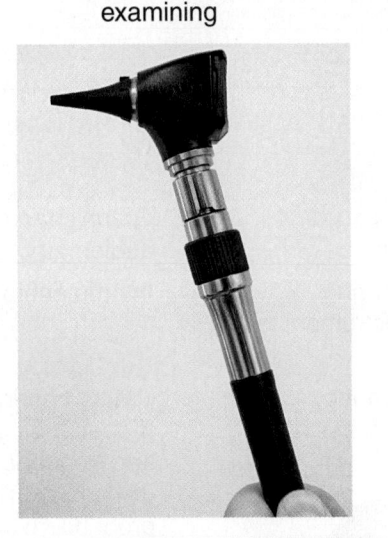

Figure 13.18 An otoscope, used to visually examine the external auditory ear canal and tympanic membrane.

> **MED TERM TIP**
>
> Small children are prone to placing objects in their ears. In some cases, as with peas and beans, these become moist in the ear canal and swell, which makes removal difficult. *Otoscopy*, or the examination of the ear using an *otoscope*, can aid in identifying and removing the cause of hearing loss if it is due to foreign bodies.

TERM	WORD PARTS	DEFINITION
tympanogram (TIM-pah-no-gram)	tympan/o = tympanic membrane -gram = record	Graphic record that illustrates the results of tympanometry.
tympanometer (tim-pah-NOM-eh-ter)	tympan/o = tympanic membrane -meter = instrument to measure	Instrument used to measure the movement of the tympanic membrane.
tympanometry (tim-pah-NOM-eh-tree)	tympan/o = tympanic membrane -metry = process of measuring	Measurement of the movement of the tympanic membrane. Can indicate the presence of pressure in the middle ear.

Balance Tests

TERM	WORD PARTS	DEFINITION
falling test		Test used to observe balance and equilibrium. The patient is observed balancing on one foot, then with one foot in front of the other, and then walking forward with eyes open. The same test is conducted with the patient's eyes closed. Swaying and falling with the eyes closed can indicate an ear and equilibrium malfunction.

Diagnostic Procedures (continued)

Therapeutic Procedures

TERM	WORD PARTS	DEFINITION
Audiology Procedures		
American Sign Language (ASL)		Nonverbal method of communicating in which the hands and fingers are used to indicate words and concepts. Used by both persons who are deaf and persons with speech impairments.

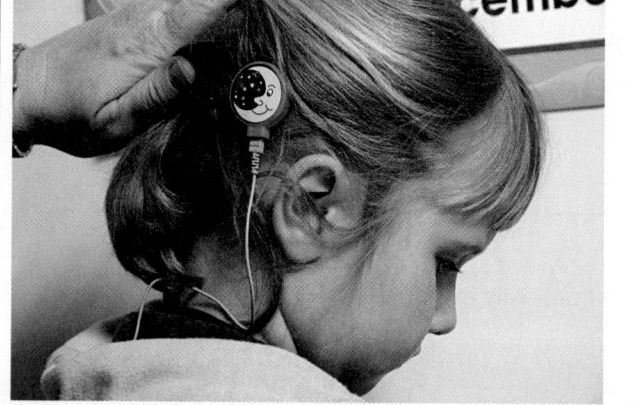

■ **Figure 13.19** Two women having a conversation using American Sign Language. *(Vladimir Mucibabic/Shutterstock)*

TERM	WORD PARTS	DEFINITION
hearing aid		Apparatus or mechanical device used by persons with impaired hearing to amplify sound. Also called an *amplification device*.
Surgical Procedures		
cochlear implant (KOK-lee-ar)	cochle/o = cochlea -ar = pertaining to	Mechanical device surgically placed under the skin behind the outer ear (pinna) that converts sound signals into magnetic impulses to stimulate the auditory nerve. Can be beneficial for those with profound sensorineural hearing loss.

■ **Figure 13.20** Photograph of a child with a cochlear implant. This device sends electrical impulses directly to the brain.

TERM	WORD PARTS	DEFINITION
labyrinthectomy (lab-ih-rin-THEK-toh-mee)	labyrinth/o = labyrinth -ectomy = surgical removal	Surgical removal of the labyrinth.
labyrinthotomy (lab-ih-rinth-OT-oh-mee)	labyrinth/o = labyrinth -otomy = cutting into	To cut into the labyrinth.
myringectomy (mir-in-GEK-toh-mee)	myring/o = tympanic membrane -ectomy = surgical removal	Surgical removal of the tympanic membrane.
myringoplasty (mir-IN-goh-plass-tee)	myring/o = tympanic membrane -plasty = surgical repair	Surgical repair of the tympanic membrane.

Therapeutic Procedures (continued)

TERM	WORD PARTS	DEFINITION
myringotomy (mir-in-GOT-oh-mee)	myring/o = tympanic membrane -otomy = cutting into	Surgical puncture of the eardrum with removal of fluid and pus from the middle ear to eliminate a persistent ear infection and excessive pressure on the tympanic membrane. A pressure equalizing tube is placed in the tympanic membrane to allow for drainage of the middle ear cavity; this tube typically falls out on its own.
otoplasty (OH-toh-plas-tee)	ot/o = ear -plasty = surgical repair	Surgical repair of the external ear.
pressure equalizing tube (PE tube)		Small tube surgically placed in a child's eardrum to assist in drainage of trapped fluid and to equalize pressure between the middle ear cavity and the atmosphere.
salpingotomy (sal-pin-GOT-oh-mee)	salping/o = auditory tube -otomy = cutting into	To cut into the auditory tube.
stapedectomy (stay-pee-DEK-toh-mee)	staped/o = stapes -ectomy = pertaining to	Removal of the stapes bone to treat otosclerosis (hardening of the bone). A prosthesis or artificial stapes may be implanted.
tympanectomy (tim-pan-EK-toh-mee)	tympan/o = tympanic membrane -ectomy = surgical removal	Surgical removal of the tympanic membrane.
tympanoplasty (tim-pan-oh-PLASS-tee)	tympan/o = tympanic membrane -plasty = surgical repair	Surgical repair of the tympanic membrane.
tympanotomy (tim-pan-OT-oh-mee)	tympan/o = tympanic membrane -otomy = cutting into	To cut into the tympanic membrane.

Pharmacology

CLASSIFICATION	WORD PARTS	ACTION	EXAMPLES
antibiotic otic solution (OH-tik)	anti- = against bi/o = life -tic = pertaining to ot/o = ear -ic = pertaining to	Eardrops to treat otitis externa.	Neomycin, polymyxin B and hydrocortisone solution, Otocort, Cortisporin, Otic Care
antiemetics (an-tye-ee-mit-tiks)	anti- = against -emesis = vomiting -tic = pertaining to	Medications effective in treating the nausea associated with vertigo.	meclizine, Antivert, Meni-D; prochlorperazine, Compazine
anti-inflammatory otic solution (OH-tik)	anti- = against -ory = pertaining to ot/o = ear -ic = pertaining to	Reduces inflammation, itching, and edema associated with otitis externa.	antipyrine and benzoaine, Allergan Ear Drops, A/B Otic
wax emulsifiers		Substances used to soften ear wax to prevent buildup within the external ear canal.	carbamide peroxide, Debrox Drops, Murine Ear Drops

Abbreviations

AD	right ear		**HEENT**	head, ears, eyes, nose, throat
AS	left ear		**Hz**	hertz
ASL	American Sign Language		**OM**	otitis media
AU	both ears		**Oto**	otology
BC	bone conduction		**PE tube**	pressure equalizing tube
dB	decibel		**PORP**	partial ossicular replacement prosthesis
EENT	eyes, ears, nose, throat		**SOM**	serous otitis media
ENT	ear, nose, and throat		**TORP**	total ossicular replacement prosthesis

Chapter Review

Real-World Applications

Medical Record Analysis

This Ophthalmology Consultation Report contains 11 medical terms. Underline each term and write it in the list below the report. Then define each term.

Ophthalmology Consultation Report

Reason for Consultation:	Evaluation of progressive loss of vision in right eye.
History of Present Illness:	Patient is a 79-year-old female who has noted gradual deterioration of vision and increasing photophobia during the past year, particularly in the right eye. She states that it feels like there is a film over her right eye. She denies any change in vision in her left eye. Patient has used corrective lenses her entire adult life for hyperopia.
Results of Physical Examination:	Visual acuity test showed no change in this patient's long-standing hyperopia. The pupils react properly to light. Intraocular pressure is normal. Ophthalmoscopy after application of mydriatic drops revealed presence of large opaque cataract in lens of right eye. There is a very small cataract forming in the left eye. There is no evidence of retinopathy, macular degeneration, or keratitis.
Assessment:	Diminished vision in right eye secondary to cataract.
Recommendations:	Phacoemulsification of cataract followed by prosthetic lens implant.

	Term	Definition
1	_____	_____
2	_____	_____
3	_____	_____
4	_____	_____
5	_____	_____
6	_____	_____
7	_____	_____
8	_____	_____
9	_____	_____
10	_____	_____
11	_____	_____

Chart Note Transcription

The chart note below contains 10 phrases that can be reworded with a medical term that you learned in this chapter. Each phrase is identified with an underline. Determine the medical term and write your answers in the space provided.

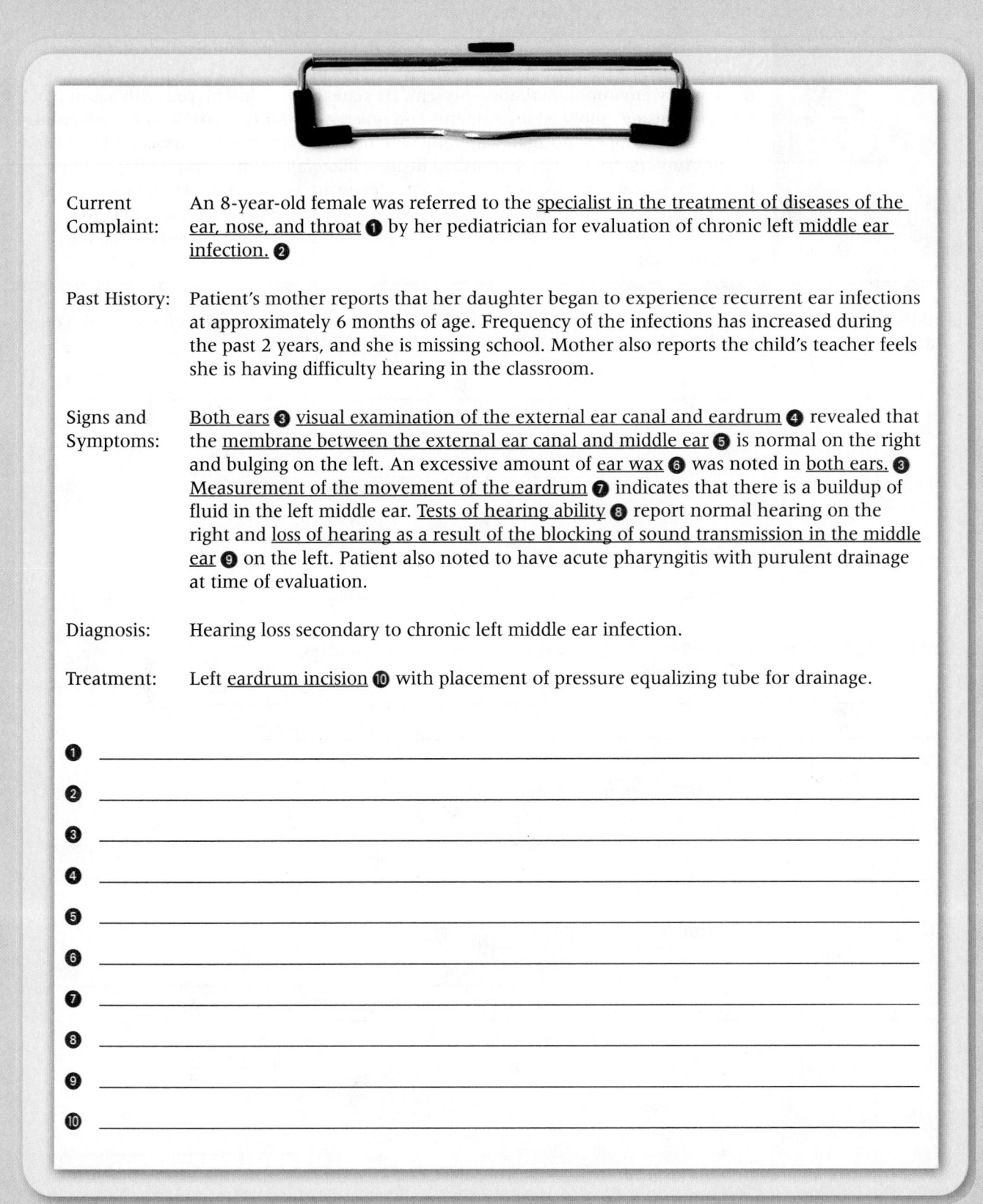

Current Complaint: An 8-year-old female was referred to the <u>specialist in the treatment of diseases of the ear, nose, and throat</u> ❶ by her pediatrician for evaluation of chronic left <u>middle ear infection.</u> ❷

Past History: Patient's mother reports that her daughter began to experience recurrent ear infections at approximately 6 months of age. Frequency of the infections has increased during the past 2 years, and she is missing school. Mother also reports the child's teacher feels she is having difficulty hearing in the classroom.

Signs and Symptoms: <u>Both ears</u> ❸ <u>visual examination of the external ear canal and eardrum</u> ❹ revealed that the <u>membrane between the external ear canal and middle ear</u> ❺ is normal on the right and bulging on the left. An excessive amount of <u>ear wax</u> ❻ was noted in <u>both ears.</u> ❸ <u>Measurement of the movement of the eardrum</u> ❼ indicates that there is a buildup of fluid in the left middle ear. <u>Tests of hearing ability</u> ❽ report normal hearing on the right and <u>loss of hearing as a result of the blocking of sound transmission in the middle ear</u> ❾ on the left. Patient also noted to have acute pharyngitis with purulent drainage at time of evaluation.

Diagnosis: Hearing loss secondary to chronic left middle ear infection.

Treatment: Left <u>eardrum incision</u> ❿ with placement of pressure equalizing tube for drainage.

❶ _____

❷ _____

❸ _____

❹ _____

❺ _____

❻ _____

❼ _____

❽ _____

❾ _____

❿ _____

Case Study

Below is a case study presentation of a patient with a condition covered in this chapter. Read the case study and answer the questions below. Some questions will ask for information not included within this chapter. Use your text, a medical dictionary, or any other reference material you choose to answer these questions.

(© My-Music/Alamy)

This 35-year-old male musician was seen in the EENT clinic complaining of a progressive hearing loss over the past 15 years. He is now unable to hear what is being said if there is any environmental noise present. He states that he has played with a group of musicians using amplified instruments and no earplugs for the past 20 years. External ear structures appear normal bilaterally with otoscopy. Tympanometry is normal bilaterally. Audiometry reveals diminished hearing bilaterally. Rinne and Weber tuning-fork tests indicate that the patient has a moderate amount of conductive hearing loss but rule out sensorineural hearing loss. Diagnosis is moderate bilateral conductive hearing loss as a result of prolonged exposure to loud noise. Patient is referred for evaluation for a hearing aid.

1. Which type of hearing loss does this patient appear to have? Look this condition up in a reference source and include a short description of it.

   _____

   _____

2. Explain how the other type of hearing loss (the type ruled out by the Rinne and Weber tuning-fork tests) is different from what this patient has.

   _____

   _____

3. What diagnostic tests did the physician perform? Describe them in your own words.

   _____

   _____

4. Explain the difference between a hearing aid and a cochlear implant.

   _____

   _____

5. How do you think this patient could have avoided this hearing loss?

   _____

   _____

Practice Exercises

A. Complete the Statement

1. The study of the eye is _____.

2. Another term for eyelashes is _____.

3. The glands responsible for tears are called _____ glands.

4. The clear, transparent portion of the sclera is called the _____.

5. The innermost layer of the eye, which is composed of sensory receptors, is the _____.

6. The pupil of the eye is actually a hole in the _____.

7. The three bones in the middle ear are the _____, _____, and _____.

8. The study of the ear is called _____.

9. Another term for the eardrum is _____.

10. _____ is produced in the oil glands in the auditory canal.

11. The _____ tube connects the nasopharynx with the middle ear.

12. The _____ is responsible for conducting impulses from the ear to the brain.

B. Pharmacology Challenge

Fill in the classification for each drug description, then match the brand name.

Drug Description	Classification	Brand Name
1. _____ treats dry eyes	_____	a. Atropine-Care
2. _____ reduces intraocular pressure	_____	b. Allergan Ear Drops
3. _____ ear drops for ear infection	_____	c. Timoptic
4. _____ dilates pupil	_____	d. Opticaine
5. _____ treats nausea from vertigo	_____	e. Debrox Drops
6. _____ eye drops for bacterial infection	_____	f. Eserine Sulfate
7. _____ treats ear itching	_____	g. Antivert
8. _____ constricts pupil	_____	h. Refresh Plus
9. _____ softens cerumen	_____	i. Otocort
10. _____ eye drops for pain	_____	j. Del-Mycin

C. Combining Form Practice

The combining form **blephar/o** refers to the eyelid. Use it to write a term that means:

1. inflammation of the eyelid _____

2. surgical repair of the eyelid _____

3. drooping of the upper eyelid _____

The combining form **retin/o** refers to the retina. Use it to write a term that means:

4. a disease of the retina _____

5. surgical fixation of the retina _____

The combining form **ophthalm/o** refers to the eye. Use it to write a term that means:

6. the study of the eye _____

7. pertaining to the eye _____

8. an eye examination using a scope _____

The combining form **irid/o** refers to the iris. Use it to write a term that means:

9. iris paralysis _____

10. removal of the iris _____

The combining form **ot/o** refers to the ear. Write a word that means:

11. ear surgical repair _____

12. pus flow from the ear _____

13. pain in the ear _____

14. inflammation of the ear _____

The combining form **tympan/o** refers to the eardrum. Write a word that means:

15. eardrum rupture _____

16. eardrum incision _____

17. eardrum inflammation _____

The combining form **audi/o** refers to hearing. Write a word that means:

18. record of hearing _____

19. instrument to measure hearing _____

20. study of hearing _____

D. Name That Suffix

	Suffix	Example from Chapter
1. to turn		
2. vision		
3. inflammation of		
4. the study of		
5. cutting into		
6. surgical repair		
7. surgical fixation		
8. pain		
9. ear condition		
10. hearing		

E. Define the Combining Form

	Definition	Example from Chapter
1. **dacry/o**		
2. **uve/o**		
3. **aque/o**		
4. **phot/o**		
5. **kerat/o**		
6. **vitre/o**		
7. **dipl/o**		
8. **glauc/o**		
9. **presby/o**		
10. **ambly/o**		
11. **aur/o**		
12. **staped/o**		
13. **acous/o**		
14. **salping/o**		
15. **myring/o**		

F. Answer the Question

1. Describe the difference between conductive hearing loss and sensorineural hearing loss. _____

_____

2. List in order the eyeball structures light rays pass through: _____, _____,

_____, _____

3. Describe the role of the conjunctiva. _____

_____

4. List the ossicles and what they do. _____

_____

G. Terminology Matching

Match each term to its definition.

1.	_____ emmetropia		a.	opacity of the lens
2.	_____ sclera		b.	muscle regulating size of pupil
3.	_____ cataract		c.	nearsightedness
4.	_____ conjunctiva		d.	protective membrane of eye
5.	_____ iris		e.	blind spot
6.	_____ xerophthalmia		f.	involuntary movements of eye
7.	_____ myopia		g.	white of eye
8.	_____ nystagmus		h.	normal vision
9.	_____ optic disk		i.	dry eyes
10.	_____ vitreous humor		j.	material filling eyeball

H. What Does it Stand For?

1. Oto _____

2. OU _____

3. REM _____

4. Hz _____

5. SMD _____

6. PERRLA _____

7. IOP _____

8. dB _____

9. OD _____

10. VF _____

I. Terminology Matching

Match each term to its definition.

1. _____ myringotomy   a. removal of stapes bone

2. _____ tympanoplasty   b. reconstruction of eardrum

3. _____ otoplasty   c. surgical puncture of eardrum

4. _____ stapedectomy   d. change size of pinna

5. _____ anacusis   e. absence of hearing

6. _____ falling test   f. treats sensorineural hearing loss

7. _____ PE tube   g. tuning fork tests

8. _____ cochlear implant   h. swimmer's ear

9. _____ otitis externa   i. drains off fluid

10. _____ Rinne & Weber   j. balance test

J. What's the Abbreviation?

1. pressure equalizing tube _____

2. eye, ear, nose, and throat _____

3. bone conduction _____

4. both ears _____

5. otitis media _____

6. emmetropia _____

7. exotropia _____

8. left eye _____

9. extraocular movement _____

10. visual acuity _____

K. Fill in the Blank

emmetropia	tonometry	Ménière's disease
hyperopia	cataract	hordeolum
acoustic neuroma	strabismus	myopia
otorhinolaryngologist	presbycusis	
conjunctivitis	inner ear	

1. Cheri is having a regular eye checkup. The pressure reading test that the physician will do to detect glaucoma is

   _____.

2. Carlos's ophthalmologist tells him that he has normal vision. This is called _____.

3. Ana has been given an antibiotic eye ointment for pink eye. The medical term for this condition is _____.

4. Adrian is nearsighted and cannot read signs in the distance. This is called _____.

5. Ivan is scheduled to have surgery to have the opaque lens of his right eye removed. This condition is a(n)

   _____.

6. Roberto has developed a stye on the corner of his left eye. He has been told to treat it with hot compresses. This condition

   is called a(n) _____.

7. Judith has twin boys with crossed eyes that will require surgical correction. The medical term for this condition is

   _____.

8. Beth is farsighted and has difficulty reading textbooks. Her eyeglass correction will be for _____.

9. Grace was told by her physician that her hearing loss was a part of the aging process. The term for this is

   _____.

10. Stacey is having frequent middle ear infections and wishes to be treated by a specialist. She would go to a(n)

    _____.

11. Warren was told that his dizziness may be caused by a problem in the _____ area.

12. Shantel is suffering from an abnormal condition of the inner ear, vertigo, and tinnitus. She may have

    _____.

13. Keisha was told that her tumor of the eighth cranial nerve was benign, but she still experienced a hearing loss as a result

    of the tumor. This tumor is called a(n) _____.

L. Define the Term

1. amblyopia _____

2. diplopia _____

3. mydriatic _____

4. miotic _____

5. presbyopia _____

6. tinnitus _____

7. stapes _____

8. tympanometry _____

9. eustachian tube _____

10. labyrinth _____

11. audiogram _____

12. otitis media _____

Labeling Exercise

Image A

Write the labels for this figure on the numbered lines provided.

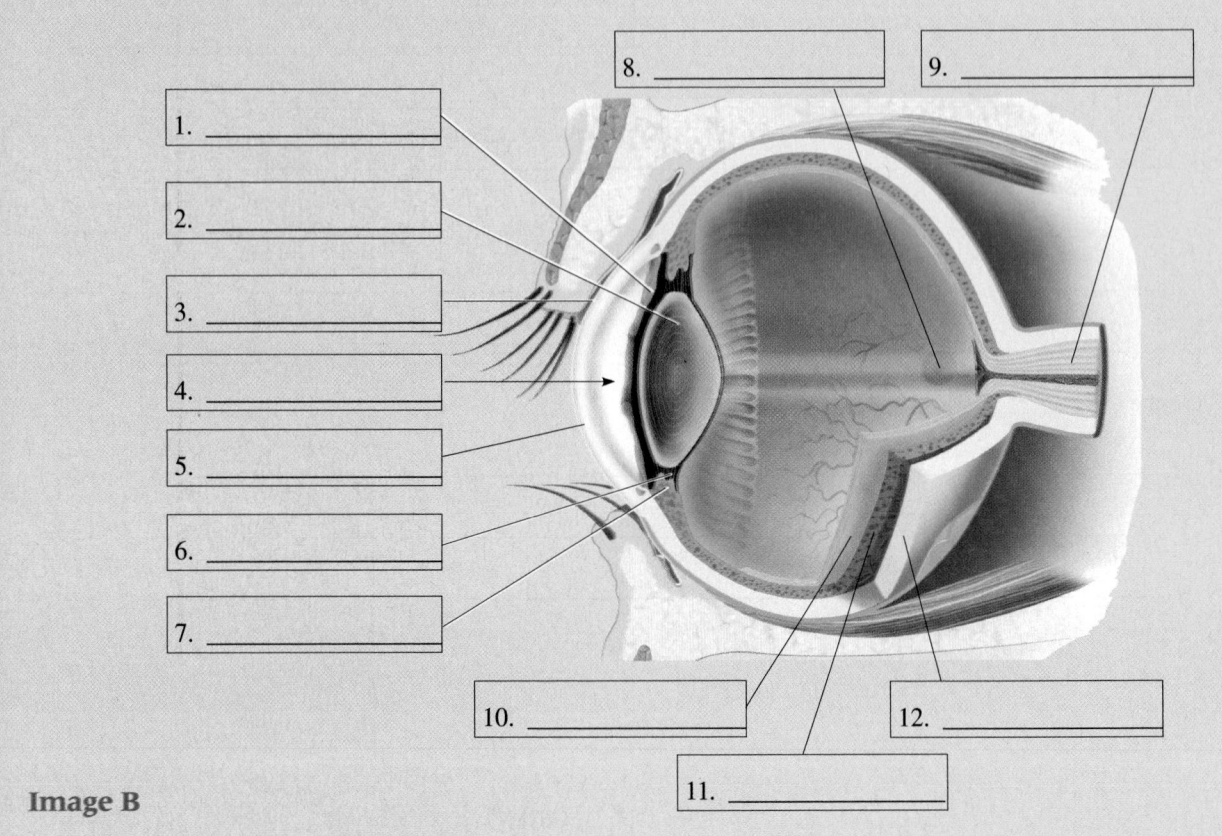

8. _____

9. _____

1. _____

2. _____

3. _____

4. _____

5. _____

6. _____

7. _____

10. _____

11. _____

12. _____

Image B

Write the labels for this figure on the numbered lines provided.

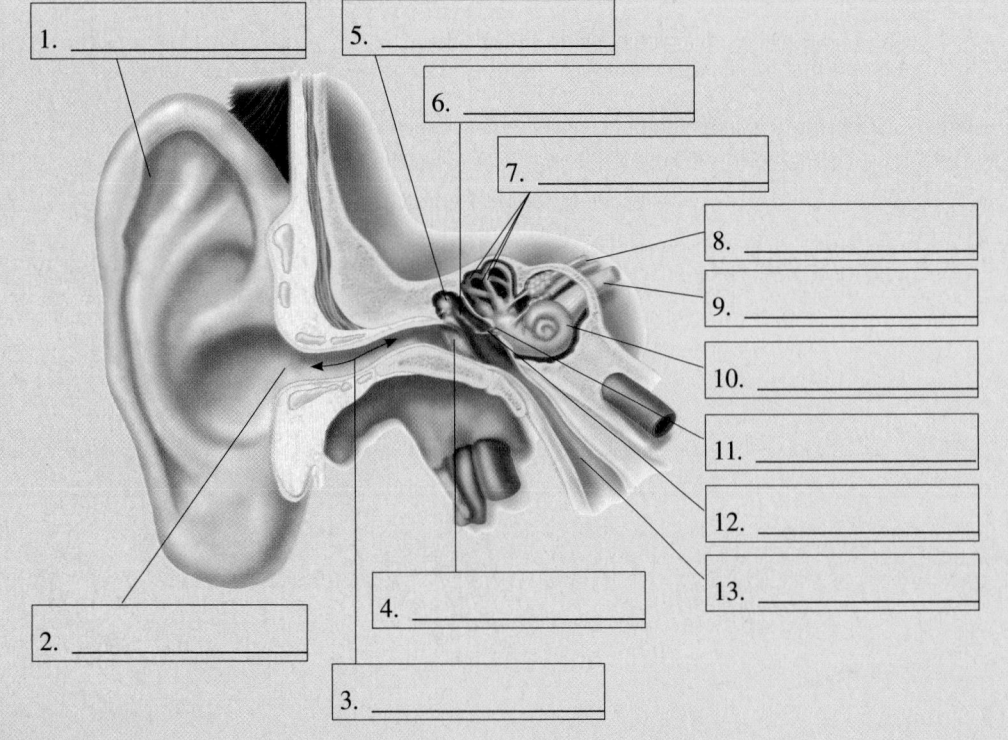

1. _____

5. _____

6. _____

7. _____

8. _____

9. _____

10. _____

11. _____

12. _____

13. _____

2. _____

3. _____

4. _____

Appendices

Appendix I
Word Parts Arranged Alphabetically and Defined

The word parts that have been presented in this textbook are summarized with their definitions for quick reference. Prefixes are listed first, followed by combining forms and suffixes.

Prefix	Definition	Prefix	Definition
a-	without, away from	intra-	inside, within
ab-	away from	macro-	large
ad-	toward	micro-	small
allo-	other, different from usual	mono-	one
an-	without	multi-	many
ante-	before, in front of	myo-	to shut
anti-	against	neo-	new
auto-	self	nulli-	none
bi-	two	pan-	all
brady-	slow	para-	abnormal, two like parts of a pair, beside, near
circum-	around		
contra-	against	per-	through
de-	without	peri-	around
dis-	apart	poly-	many
dys-	abnormal, difficult, painful	post-	after
e-	outward, without	pre-	before, in front of
en-	inward	primi-	first
endo-	inner, within	pro-	before
epi-	upon, over, above	pseudo-	false
eso-	inward	quadri-	four
eu-	normal, good	re-	again
ex-	external, outward	retro-	backward, behind
exo-	outward	semi-	partial, half
extra-	outside of	sub-	below, under
hemi-	half	supra-	above
hetero-	different	tachy-	fast, rapid
homo-	same	tetra-	four
hydro-	water	trans-	across, through
hyper-	excessive, over, above	tri-	three
hypo-	below, under	ultra-	beyond, excess
in-	inward, without, not, within	un-	not
inter-	among, between	xeno-	strange, foreign

Combining Form	Definition	Combining Form	Definition
abdomin/o	abdomen	aden/o	gland
acous/o	hearing	adenoid/o	adenoids
acr/o	extremities	adip/o	fat

Combining Form	Definition	Combining Form	Definition
adren/o	adrenal glands	cephal/o	head
adrenal/o	adrenal glands	cerebell/o	cerebellum
aer/o	air	cerebr/o	cerebrum
agglutin/o	clumping	cerumin/o	cerumen
albin/o	white	cervic/o	neck, cervix
alges/o	sense of pain	chem/o	chemical, drug
alveol/o	alveolus; air sac	chol/e	bile, gall
ambly/o	dull, dim	cholangi/o	bile duct
amnes/o	forgetfulness	cholecyst/o	gallbladder
amni/o	amnion	choledoch/o	common bile duct
an/o	anus	chondr/o	cartilage
andr/o	male	chori/o	chorion
angi/o	vessel	chrom/o	color
ankyl/o	stiff joint	chromat/o	color
anter/o	front	cirrh/o	yellow
anthrac/o	coal	cis/o	to cut
anxi/o	fear, worry	clavicul/o	clavicle
aort/o	aorta	clon/o	rapid contracting and relaxing
append/o	appendix	coagul/o	clotting
appendic/o	appendix	coccyg/o	coccyx
aque/o	water	cochle/o	cochlea
arteri/o	artery	col/o	colon
arthr/o	joint	colon/o	colon
articul/o	joint	colp/o	vagina
aspir/o	to breathe in	compuls/o	drive, compel
astr/o	star	coni/o	dust
atel/o	incomplete	conjunctiv/o	conjunctiva
ather/o	fatty substance	corne/o	cornea
atri/o	atrium	coron/o	heart
audi/o	hearing	corpor/o	body
audit/o	hearing	cortic/o	outer portion, cortex
aur/o	ear	cost/o	rib
auricul/o	ear	crani/o	skull
axill/o	axilla, underarm	crin/o	to secrete
azot/o	nitrogenous waste	crur/o	leg
bacteri/o	bacteria	cry/o	cold
balan/o	glans penis	crypt/o	hidden
bar/o	weight	culd/o	cul-de-sac
bas/o	base	cutane/o	skin
bi/o	life	cyan/o	blue
blast/o	immature, embryonic	cycl/o	ciliary body, ciliary muscle
blephar/o	eyelid	cyst/o	bladder, pouch, sac
brachi/o	arm	cyt/o	cell
bronch/o	bronchus	dacry/o	tear duct, tears
bronchi/o	bronchus	deluss/o	false belief
bronchiol/o	bronchiole	dent/o	tooth
bucc/o	cheek	depress/o	to press down
burs/o	bursa, sac	derm/o	skin
calc/o	calcium	dermat/o	skin
capsul/o	to box	diaphor/o	profuse sweating
carcin/o	cancer	diaphragmat/o	diaphragm
cardi/o	heart	dilat/o	to widen
carp/o	carpus, wrist	dipl/o	double
caud/o	tail	dist/o	away from
cec/o	cecum	diverticul/o	pouch

Combining Form	Definition
dors/o	back of body
duct/o	to bring
duoden/o	duodenum
dur/o	dura mater
electr/o	electricity
embol/o	plug
embry/o	embryo
emmetr/o	correct, proper
encephal/o	brain
enter/o	small intestine
eosin/o	rosy red
epididym/o	epididymis
epiglott/o	epiglottis
episi/o	vulva
epitheli/o	epithelium
erg/o	work
erythr/o	red
esophag/o	esophagus
esthes/o	sensation, feeling
estr/o	female
extens/o	to stretch out
factiti/o	artificial, contrived
fasci/o	fibrous band
femor/o	femur
fet/o	fetus
fibr/o	fibers
fibrin/o	fibers, fibrous
fibul/o	fibula
flex/o	to bend
fluor/o	fluorescence, luminous
fus/o	pouring
gastr/o	stomach
genit/o	genitals
gingiv/o	gums
glauc/o	gray
gli/o	glue
glomerul/o	glomerulus
gloss/o	tongue
gluc/o	glucose
glute/o	buttock
glyc/o	sugar
glycos/o	sugar, glucose
gonad/o	sex glands
granul/o	granules
gynec/o	female, woman
habilitat/o	ability
hal/o	to breathe
hallucin/o	imagined perception
hem/o	blood
hemat/o	blood
hepat/o	liver
hidr/o	sweat
hist/o	tissue
home/o	sameness
humer/o	humerus

Combining Form	Definition
hydr/o	water
hymen/o	hymen
hyster/o	uterus
iatr/o	physician, medicine, treatment
ichthy/o	scaly, dry
idi/o	distinctive
ile/o	ileum
ili/o	ilium
immun/o	immunity, protection
infer/o	below
inguin/o	groin region
iod/o	iodine
ir/o	iris
irid/o	iris
isch/o	to hold back
ischi/o	ischium
jejun/o	jejunum
kal/i	potassium
kerat/o	cornea, hard, horny
ket/o	ketones
keton/o	ketones
kinesi/o	movement
klept/o	to steal
kyph/o	hump
labi/o	lip
labyrinth/o	labyrinth (inner ear)
lacrim/o	tears
lact/o	milk
lamin/o	lamina, part of vertebra
lapar/o	abdomen
laps/o	to slide back
laryng/o	larynx, voice box
later/o	side
leuk/o	white
lingu/o	tongue
lip/o	fat
lith/o	stone
lob/o	lobe
lord/o	bent backwards
lumb/o	loin, low back
lymph/o	lymph
lymphaden/o	lymph node
lymphangi/o	lymph vessel
macul/o	macula lutea
mamm/o	breast
mandibul/o	mandible
mast/o	breast
maxill/o	maxilla
meat/o	meatus
medi/o	middle
medull/o	inner portion, medulla, oblongata
melan/o	black
men/o	menses, menstruation
mening/o	meninges

Combining Form	Definition	Combining Form	Definition
meningi/o	meninges	parathyroid/o	parathyroid gland
ment/o	mind	patell/o	patella
metacarp/o	metacarpals	path/o	disease
metatars/o	metatarsals	pect/o	chest
metr/o	uterus	ped/o	child, foot
mi/o	lessening	pedicul/o	lice
mineral/o	minerals, electrolytes	pelv/o	pelvis
miss/o	to send back	pen/o	penis
morbid/o	ill	perine/o	perineum
morph/o	shape	peritone/o	peritoneum
mort/o	death	phac/o	lens
muc/o	mucus	phag/o	eat, swallow
muscul/o	muscles	phalang/o	phalanges
mutat/o	to change	pharmac/o	drug
my/o	muscle	pharyng/o	pharynx (throat)
myc/o	fungus	phleb/o	vein
mydr/i	widening	phob/o	irrational fear
myel/o	bone marrow, spinal cord	phon/o	sound
myocardi/o	heart muscle	phot/o	light
myos/o	muscle	phren/o	mind
myring/o	tympanic membrane (eardrum)	physic/o	body
		pineal/o	pineal gland
nas/o	nose	pituitar/o	pituitary gland
nat/o	birth	plant/o	sole of foot
natr/o	sodium	pleur/o	pleura
necr/o	death	pneum/o	lung, air
nephr/o	kidney	pneumon/o	lung, air
neur/o	nerve	pod/o	foot
neutr/o	neutral	poli/o	gray matter
noct/i	night	polyp/o	polyp
nucle/o	nucleus	pont/o	pons
nyctal/o	night	poster/o	back
o/o	egg	presby/o	old age
obsess/o	besieged by thoughts	proct/o	rectum and anus
ocul/o	eye	prostat/o	prostate gland
odont/o	tooth	prosthet/o	addition
olig/o	scanty	protein/o	protein
onc/o	tumor	proxim/o	near to
onych/o	nail	psych/o	mind
oophor/o	ovary	pub/o	genital region, pubis
ophthalm/o	eye	pulmon/o	lung
opt/o	eye, vision	pupill/o	pupil
optic/o	eye, vision	py/o	pus
or/o	mouth	pyel/o	renal pelvis
orch/o	testes	pylor/o	pylorus
orchi/o	testes	pyr/o	fire
orchid/o	testes	radi/o	radius, ray (X-ray)
orth/o	straight, correct, upright	radic/o	root
oste/o	bone	radicul/o	nerve root
ot/o	ear	rect/o	rectum
ovari/o	ovary	recumb/o	to lie back
ox/o, ox/i	oxygen	ren/o	kidney
palat/o	palate	retin/o	retina
pancreat/o	pancreas	rhin/o	nose
papill/o	optic disc	rhytid/o	wrinkle

Combining Form	Definition
roentgen/o	X-ray
rotat/o	to revolve
sacr/o	sacrum
salping/o	auditory tube (eustachian tube), uterine tubes, fallopian tubes
sanguin/o	blood
sarc/o	flesh (muscular substance)
scapul/o	scapula
schiz/o	split
scler/o	hard, sclera
scoli/o	crooked, bent
seb/o	oil
sect/o	to cut
sept/o	a wall
septic/o	infection
sialaden/o	salivary gland
sigmoid/o	sigmoid colon
sinus/o	sinus, cavity
soci/o	society
somat/o	body
somn/o	sleep
son/o	sound
specul/o	to look at
spermat/o	sperm
sphygm/o	pulse
spin/o	spine
spir/o	breathing
splen/o	spleen
spondyl/o	vertebrae
staped/o	stapes
stern/o	sternum
steth/o	chest
stigmat/o	point
super/o	above
synov/o	synovial membrane
synovi/o	synovial membrane
system/o	systems
tars/o	ankle, tarsus
ten/o	tendon
tenacul/o	to hold
tend/o	tendon
tendin/o	tendon
testicul/o	testes, testicle
thalam/o	thalamus

Combining Form	Definition
thec/o	sheath (meninges)
therm/o	heat
thorac/o	chest, thorax
thromb/o	clot
thym/o	thymus gland
thyr/o	thyroid gland
thyroid/o	thyroid gland
tibi/o	tibia
tom/o	to cut
ton/o	tone
tonsill/o	tonsils
topic/o	a specific area
tox/o	poison
toxic/o	poison
trache/o	trachea, windpipe
trich/o	hair
tuss/o	cough
tympan/o	tympanic membrane (eardrum)
uln/o	ulna
ungu/o	nail
ur/o	urine
ureter/o	ureter
urethr/o	urethra
urin/o	urine
uter/o	uterus
uve/o	choroid
vagin/o	vagina
valv/o	valve
valvul/o	valve
varic/o	dilated vein
vas/o	vas deferens, vessel, duct
vascul/o	blood vessel
ven/o	vein
ventr/o	belly
ventricul/o	brain ventricle, ventricle
vers/o	to turn
vertebr/o	vertebra
vesic/o	bladder
vesicul/o	seminal vesicle
viscer/o	internal organ
vitre/o	glassy
vulv/o	vulva
xer/o	dry

Suffix	Definition
-ac	pertaining to
-al	pertaining to
-algia	pain
-an	pertaining to
-apheresis	removal, carry away
-ar	pertaining to
-arche	beginning
-ary	pertaining to

Suffix	Definition
-asthenia	weakness
-atic	pertaining to
-blast	immature, embryonic
-capnia	carbon dioxide
-cele	hernia, protrusion
-centesis	puncture to withdraw fluid
-cide	to kill
-clasia	to surgically break

Suffix	Definition	Suffix	Definition
-crit	separation of	-manometer	instrument to measure pressure
-cusis	hearing	-megaly	enlargement, large
-cyesis	state of pregnancy	-meter	instrument for measuring
-cyte	cell	-metrist	specialist in measuring
-cytosis	more than the normal number of cells	-metry	process of measuring
-derma	skin condition	-nic	pertaining to
-desis	fuse, stabilize	-nomics	pertaining to laws
-dipsia	thirst	-oid	resembling
-dynia	pain	-ole	small
-eal	pertaining to	-oma	mass, tumor, swelling
-ectasis	dilation	-opaque	nontransparent
-ectomy	surgical removal	-opia	vision condition
-edema	swelling	-opsia	vision condition
-emesis	vomit	-opsy	view of
-emia	blood condition	-orexia	appetite
-gen	that which produces	-ory	pertaining to
-genesis	produces, generates	-ose	pertaining to
-genic	producing, produced by	-osis	abnormal condition
-globin	protein	-osmia	smell
-globulin	protein	-ostomy	surgically create an opening,
-gram	record or picture	-otia	ear condition
-graph	instrument for recording	-otomy	cutting into
-graphy	process of recording	-ous	pertaining to
-gravida	pregnancy	-para	to bear (offspring)
-ia	condition, state	-paresis	weakness
-iac	pertaining to	-partum	childbirth
-iasis	abnormal condition	-pathy	disease
-iatrist	physician	-penia	abnormal decrease, too few
-iatry	medical treatment	-pepsia	digestion
-ic	pertaining to	-pexy	surgical fixation
-ical	pertaining to	-phagia	eat, swallow
-ician	specialist	-phasia	speech
-ile	pertaining to	-phil	attracted to
-ine	pertaining to	-philia	attracted to
-ion	action, condition	-phobia	fear
-ior	pertaining to	-phonia	voice
-ism	state of	-phoresis	carrying
-ist	specialist	-phylaxis	protection
-istry	specialty of	-plasia	development, growth, formation
-itis	inflammation	-plasm	formation, development, growth
-kinesia	movement		
-listhesis	slipping		
-lith	stone	-plastic	pertaining to development
-lithiasis	condition of stones	-plasty	surgical repair
-logic	pertaining to studying	-plegia	paralysis
-logical	pertaining to the study of	-pnea	breathing
-logist	one who studies	-poiesis	formation
-logy	study of	-porosis	porous
-lucent	to shine through	-prandial	pertaining to a meal
-lysis	destruction	-pressin	to press down
-lytic	destruction	-ptosis	drooping
-malacia	abnormal softening	-ptysis	spitting
-mania	frenzy	-rrhage	abnormal flow, excessive

Suffix	Definition	Suffix	Definition
-rrhagia	abnormal flow condition	-taxia	muscle coordination
-rrhagic	pertaining to abnormal flow	-tension	pressure
-rrhaphy	suture	-therapy	treatment
-rrhea	discharge, flow	-thorax	chest
-rrhexis	rupture	-tic	pertaining to
-salpinx	uterine tube	-tocia	labor, childbirth
-sclerosis	hardening	-tome	instrument to cut
-scope	instrument for viewing	-tonia	tone
-scopic	pertaining to visually examining	-tonic	pertaining to tone
		-tripsy	surgical crushing
-scopy	process of visually examining	-trophic	pertaining to development
-spasm	involuntary muscle contraction	-trophy	nourishment, development
-spermia	condition of sperm	-tropia	turned condition
-stasis	standing still	-tropin	to stimulate
-stat	standing still	-ule	small
-stenosis	narrowing	-uria	condition of the urine

Appendix II
Word Parts Arranged Alphabetically by Definition

The definitions of the word parts that have been presented in this textbook are presented here and are arranged alphabetically. Prefixes are listed first, followed by combining forms and suffixes.

Definition	Prefix	Definition	Prefix
abnormal	dys-, para-	inside	intra-
above	hyper-, epi-, supra-	inward	en-, eso-, in-
across	trans-	large	macro-
after	post-	many	multi-, poly-
again	re-	near	para-
against	anti-, contra-	new	neo-
all	pan-	none	nulli-
among	inter-	normal	eu-
apart	dis-	not	in-, un-
around	circum-, peri-	one	mono-
away from	a-, ab-	other	allo-
backward	retro-	outside of	extra-
before	ante-, pre-, pro-	outward	ex-, exo-, e-
behind	retro-	over	epi-, hyper-
below	hypo-, sub-	painful	dys-
beside	para-	partial	semi-
between	inter-	same	homo-
beyond	ultra-	self	auto-
different from usual	allo-	to shut	myo-
different	hetero-	slow	brady-
difficult	dys-	small	micro-
excess	ultra-	strange	xeno-
excessive	hyper-	three	tri-
external	ex-	through	trans-, per-
false	pseudo-	toward	ad-
fast	tachy-	two	bi-
first	primi-	two like parts of a pair	para-
foreign	xeno-	under	hypo-, sub-
four	quadri-, tetra-	upon	epi-
good	eu-	water	hydro-
half	semi-, hemi-	within	endo-, in-, intra-
in front of	ante-, pre-	without	e-, a-, an-, de-, in-
inner	endo-		

Definition	Combining Form	Definition	Combining Form
abdomen	abdomin/o, lapar/o	air	aer/o, pneum/o, pneumon/o
ability	habilitat/o		
above	super/o	air sac	alveol/o
addition	prosthet/o	alveolus	alveol/o
adenoids	adenoid/o	amnion	amni/o
adrenal glands	adren/o, adrenal/o	ankle	tars/o

Definition	Combining Form	Definition	Combining Form
anus	an/o	cartilage	chondr/o
aorta	aort/o	cavity	sinus/o
appendix	append/o, appendic/o	cecum	cec/o
		cell	cyt/o
arm	brachi/o	cerebellum	cerebell/o
artery	arteri/o	cerebrum	cerebr/o
artificial	factiti/o	cerumen	cerumin/o
atrium	atri/o	cervix	cervic/o
auditory tube	salping/o	to change	mutat/o
away from	dist/o	cheek	bucc/o
axilla	axill/o	chemical	chem/o
back	poster/o	chest	pect/o, steth/o, thorac/o
back of body	dors/o		
bacteria	bacteri/o	child	ped/o
base	bas/o	chorion	chori/o
belly	ventr/o	choroid	uve/o
below	infer/o	ciliary body	cycl/o
to bend	flex/o	ciliary muscle	cycl/o
bent	scoli/o	clavicle	clavicul/o
bent backwards	lord/o	clot	thromb/o
besieged by thoughts	obsess/o	clotting	coagul/o
bile duct	cholangi/o	clumping	agglutin/o
bile	chol/e	coal	anthrac/o
birth	nat/o	coccyx	coccyg/o
black	melan/o	cochlea	cochle/o
bladder	vesic/o, cyst/o	cold	cry/o
blood	hem/o, hemat/o, sanguin/o	colon	col/o, colon/o
		color	chrom/o, chromat/o
blood vessel	vascul/o	common bile duct	choledoch/o
blue	cyan/o	compel	compuls/o
body	corpor/o, physic/o, somat/o	conjunctiva	conjunctiv/o
		contrived	factiti/o
bone	oste/o	cornea	corne/o, kerat/o
bone marrow	myel/o	correct	emmetr/o, orth/o
to box	capsul/o	cortex	cortic/o
brain	encephal/o	cough	tuss/o
brain ventricle	ventricul/o	crooked	scoli/o
breast	mamm/o, mast/o	cul-de-sac	culd/o
to breathe	hal/o	to cut	cis/o, sect/o, tom/o
to breathe in	aspir/o	death	mort/o, necr/o
breathing	spir/o	diaphragm	diaphragmat/o
to bring	duct/o	dilated vein	varic/o
bronchiole	bronchiol/o	dim	ambly/o
bronchus	bronch/o, bronchi/o	disease	path/o
bursa	burs/o	distinctive	idi/o
buttock	glute/o	double	dipl/o
calcium	calc/o	drive	compuls/o
cancer	carcin/o	drug	chem/o, pharmac/o
carpus	carp/o	dry	ichthy/o, xer/o

Definition	Combining Form	Definition	Combining Form
duct	vas/o	glassy	vitre/o
dull	ambly/o	glomerulus	glomerul/o
duodenum	duoden/o	glucose	glycos/o, gluc/o
dura mater	dur/o	glue	gli/o
dust	coni/o	granules	granul/o
ear	aur/o, auricul/o, ot/o	gray	glauc/o
		gray matter	poli/o
eardrum	myring/o, tympan/o	groin region	inguin/o
eat	phag/o	gums	gingiv/o
egg	o/o	hair	trich/o
electricity	electr/o	hard	kerat/o, scler/o
electrolytes	mineral/o	head	cephal/o
embryo	embry/o	hearing	audi/o, audit/o, acous/o
embryonic	blast/o		
epididymis	epididym/o	heart	cardi/o, coron/o
epiglottis	epiglott/o	heart muscle	myocardi/o
epithelium	epitheli/o	heat	therm/o
esophagus	esophag/o	hidden	crypt/o
eustachian tube	salping/o	to hold	tenacul/o
extremities	acr/o	to hold back	isch/o
eye	ocul/o, ophthalm/o, opt/o, optic/o	horny	kerat/o
		humerus	humer/o
eyelid	blephar/o	hump	kyph/o
fallopian tubes	salping/o	hymen	hymen/o
false belief	deluss/o	ileum	ile/o
fat	adip/o, lip/o	ilium	ili/o
fatty substance	ather/o	ill	morbid/o
fear	anxi/o	imagined perception	hallucin/o
feeling	esthes/o	immature	blast/o
female	estr/o, gynec/o	immunity	immun/o
femur	femor/o	incomplete	atel/o
fetus	fet/o	infection	septic/o
fibers	fibr/o, fibrin/o	inner portion	medull/o
fibrous	fibrin/o	internal organ	viscer/o
fibrous band	fasci/o	iodine	iod/o
fibula	fibul/o	iris	ir/o, irid/o
fire	pyr/o	irrational fear	phob/o
flesh (muscular substance)	sarc/o	ischium	ischi/o
fluorescence	fluor/o	jejunum	jejun/o
foot	ped/o, pod/o	joint	arthr/o, articul/o
forgetfulness	amnes/o	ketones	ket/o, keton/o
front	anter/o	kidney	nephr/o, ren/o
fungus	myc/o	labyrinth	labyrinth/o
gall	chol/e	inner ear	labyrinth/o
gallbladder	cholecyst/o	lamina	lamin/o
genital region	pub/o	larynx	laryng/o
genitals	genit/o	leg	crur/o
gland	aden/o	lens	phac/o
glans penis	balan/o	lessening	mi/o

Definition	Combining Form	Definition	Combining Form
lice	pedicul/o	nucleus	nucle/o
to lie back	recumb/o	oil	seb/o
life	bi/o	old age	presby/o
light	phot/o	outer portion	cortic/o
lip	labi/o	ovary	oophor/o, ovari/o
liver	hepat/o	oxygen	ox/o, ox/i
lobe	lob/o	palate	palat/o
loin	lumb/o	pancreas	pancreat/o
to look at	specul/o	parathyroid gland	parathyroid/o
low back	lumb/o	part of vertebra	lamin/o
luminous	fluor/o	patella	patell/o
lung	pulmon/o, pneum/o, pneumon/o	pelvis	pelv/o
		penis	pen/o
		perineum	perine/o
lymph	lymph/o	peritoneum	peritone/o
lymph node	lymphaden/o	phalanges	phalang/o
lymph vessel	lymphangi/o	pharynx	pharyng/o
macula lutea	macul/o	physician	iatr/o
male	andr/o	pineal gland	pineal/o
mandible	mandibul/o	pituitary gland	pituitar/o
maxilla	maxill/o	pleura	pleur/o
meatus	meat/o	plug	embol/o
medicine	iatr/o	point	stigmat/o
medulla oblongata	medull/o	poison	tox/o, toxic/o
meninges	mening/o, meningi/o, thec/o	polyp	polyp/o
		pons	pont/o
menses	men/o	potassium	kal/i
menstruation	men/o	pouch	diverticul/o, cyst/o
metacarpals	metacarp/o	pouring	fus/o
metatarsals	metatars/o	to press down	depress/o
middle	medi/o	profuse sweating	diaphor/o
milk	lact/o	proper	emmetr/o
mind	ment/o, phren/o, psych/o	prostate gland	prostat/o
		protection	immun/o
minerals	mineral/o	protein	protein/o
mouth	or/o	pubis	pub/o
movement	kinesi/o	pulse	sphygm/o
mucus	muc/o	pupil	pupill/o
muscle	my/o, myos/o, muscul/o	pus	py/o
		pylorus	pylor/o
nail	onych/o, ungu/o	radius	radi/o
near to	proxim/o	rapid contracting and relaxing	clon/o
neck	cervic/o		
nerve	neur/o	ray (X-ray)	radi/o
nerve root	radicul/o	rectum	rect/o
neutral	neutr/o	rectum and anus	proct/o
night	noct/l, nyctal/o	red	erythr/o
nitrogenous waste	azot/o	renal pelvis	pyel/o
nose	nas/o, rhin/o	retina	retin/o

Definition	Combining Form	Definition	Combining Form
to revolve	rotat/o	swallow	phag/o
rib	cost/o	sweat	hidr/o
root	radic/o	synovial membrane	synov/o, synovi/o
rosy red	eosin/o	systems	system/o
sac	burs/o, cyst/o	tail	caud/o
sacrum	sacr/o	tarsus	tars/o
salivary gland	sialaden/o	tear duct	dacry/o
sameness	home/o	tears	dacry/o, lacrim/o
scaly	ichthy/o	tendon	ten/o, tend/o,
scanty	olig/o		tendin/o
scapula	scapul/o	testes	orch/o, orchi/o,
sclera	scler/o		orchid/o, testicul/o
to secrete	crin/o	thalamus	thalam/o
seminal vesicle	vesicul/o	thorax	thorac/o
to send back	miss/o	throat	pharyng/o
sensation	esthes/o	thymus gland	thym/o
sense of pain	alges/o	thyroid gland	thyr/o, thyroid/o
sex glands	gonad/o	tibia	tibi/o
shape	morph/o	tissue	hist/o
sheath (meninges)	thec/o	tone	ton/o
side	later/o	tongue	gloss/o, lingu/o
sigmoid colon	sigmoid/o	tonsils	tonsill/o
sinus	sinus/o	tooth	dent/o, odont/o
skin	cutane/o, derm/o,	trachea	trache/o
	dermat/o	treatment	iatr/o
skull	crani/o	tumor	onc/o
sleep	somn/o	to turn	vers/o
to slide back	laps/o	tympanic membrane	myring/o, tympan/o
small intestine	enter/o	ulna	uln/o
society	soci/o	underarm	axill/o
sodium	natr/o	upright	orth/o
sole of foot	plant/o	ureter	ureter/o
sound	phon/o, son/o	urethra	urethr/o
specific area	topic/o	urine	ur/o, urin/o
sperm	spermat/o	uterine tubes	salping/o
spinal cord	myel/o	uterus	hyster/o, metr/o,
spine	spin/o		uter/o
spleen	splen/o	vagina	colp/o, vagin/o
split	schiz/o	valve	valv/o, valvul/o
stapes	staped/o	vas deferens	vas/o
star	astr/o	vein	phleb/o, ven/o
to steal	klept/o	ventricle	ventricul/o
sternum	stern/o	vertebra	vertebr/o,
stiff joint	ankyl/o		spondyl/o
stomach	gastr/o	vessel	angi/o, vas/o
stone	lith/o	vision	opt/o, optic/o
straight	orth/o	voice box	laryng/o
to stretch out	extens/o	vulva	episi/o, vulv/o
sugar	glyc/o, glycos/o	wall	sept/o
		water	aque/o, hydr/o

Definition	Combining Form	Definition	Combining Form
weight	bar/o	work	erg/o
white	albin/o, leuk/o	worry	anxi/o
to widen	dilat/o	wrinkle	rhytid/o
widening	mydr/i	wrist	carp/o
windpipe	trache/o	X-ray	roentgen/o
woman	gynec/o	yellow	cirrh/o

Definition	Suffix	Definition	Suffix
abnormal condition	-iasis, -osis	fear	-phobia
abnormal decrease	-penia	flow	-rrhea
abnormal flow condition	-rrhagia	formation	-poiesis, -plasia, -plasm
abnormal flow	-rrhage	frenzy	-mania
abnormal flow (pertaining to)	-rrhagic	fuse	-desis
abnormal softening	-malacia	generates	-genesis
action	-ion	growth	-plasia, -plasm
appetite	-orexia	hardening	-sclerosis
attracted to	-phil, -philia	hearing	-cusis
to bear (offspring)	-para	hernia	-cele
beginning	-arche	immature	-blast
blood condition	-emia	inflammation	-itis
breathing	-pnea	pressure (instrument to measure)	-manometer
carbon dioxide	-capnia	involuntary muscle contraction	-spasm
carry away	-apheresis	to kill	-cide
carrying	-phoresis	labor	-tocia
cell	-cyte	large	-megaly
chest	-thorax	laws (pertaining to)	-nomics
childbirth	-partum, -tocia	mass	-oma
condition	-ion, -ia	meal (pertaining to a)	-prandial
condition of sperm	-spermia	measuring (instrument for)	-meter
condition of stones	-lithiasis	measuring (process of)	-metry
condition of the urine	-uria	medical treatment	-iatry
cut (instrument to)	-tome	more than the normal number of cells	-cytosis
cutting into	-otomy	movement	-kinesia
destruction	-lytic, -lysis	muscle coordination	-taxia
development	-plasia, -trophy, -plasm	narrowing	-stenosis
development (pertaining to)	-plastic, -trophic	nontransparent	-opaque
digestion	-pepsia	nourishment	-trophy
dilation	-ectasis	one who studies	-logist
discharge	-rrhea	pain	-algia, -dynia
disease	-pathy	paralysis	-plegia
drooping	-ptosis	pertaining to	-ac, -al, -an, -ar, -ary, -atic, -eal, -ia, -iac, -ic, -ical, -ile, -ine, -ior, -nic, -ory, -ose, -ous, -tic
ear condition	-otia		
eat	-phagia		
embryonic	-blast		
enlargement	-megaly		
excessive flow	-rrhage		
fallopian tube	-salpinx	physician	-iatrist

Definition	Suffix	Definition	Suffix
porous	-porosis	to stimulate	-tropin
pregnancy	-gravida	stone	-lith
pregnancy (state of)	-cyesis	studying (pertaining to)	-logic
pressure	-tension	study of	-logy
to press down	-pressin	study of (pertaining to the)	-logical
produced by	-genic	surgical fixation	-pexy
produces	-genesis	surgical removal	-ectomy
producing	-genic	surgical repair	-plasty
protection	-phylaxis	to surgically break	-clasia
protein	-globin, -globulin	surgically create an opening	-ostomy
protrusion	-cele	suture	-rrhaphy
puncture to withdraw fluid	-centesis	swallow	-phagia
record or picture	-gram	swelling	-edema, -oma
recording (instrument for)	-graph	that which produces	-gen
recording (process of)	-graphy	thirst	-dipsia
removal	-apheresis	tone	-tonia
resembling	-oid	tone (pertaining to)	-tonic
rupture	-rrhexis	too few	-penia
separation of	-crit	treatment	-therapy
to shine through	-lucent	tumor	-oma
skin condition	-derma	turned condition	-tropia
slipping	-listhesis	uterine tube	-salpinx
small	-ole, -ule	viewing (instrument for)	-scope
smell	-osmia	view of	-opsy
specialist	-ician, -ist	vision condition	-opia, -opsia
specialist in measuring	-metrist	visually examining (pertaining to)	-scopic
specialty of	-istry	visually examining (process of)	-scopy
speech	-phasia		
spitting	-ptysis	voice	-phonia
stabilize	-desis	vomit	-emesis
standing still	-stasis, -stat	weakness	-asthenia, -paresis
state	-ia		
state of	-ism		

Appendix III
Abbreviations

Abbreviation	Meaning	Abbreviation	Meaning
@	at	ASL	American Sign Language
5-FU	5-fluorouracil	AST	aspartate transaminase
^{67}Ga	radioactive gallium	Astigm	astigmatism
^{99m}Tc	radioactive technetium	ATN	acute tubular necrosis
^{131}I	radioactive iodine	AU	both ears
^{133}Xe	radioactive xenon	AV, A-V	atrioventricular
^{201}Tl	radioactive thallium	β	beta
α	alpha	Ba	barium
$\bar{a}$	before	BaE	barium enema
AAROM	active assistive range of motion	basos	basophils
AB	abortion	BBB	bundle branch block (L for left; R for right)
ABGs	arterial blood gases	BC	bone conduction
ac	before meals	BCC	basal cell carcinoma
ACTH	adrenocorticotropin hormone	BDT	bone density testing
ad lib	as desired	BE	barium enema, below elbow
AD	Alzheimer's disease, right ear	bid	twice a day
ADD	attention-deficit disorder	BK	below knee
ADH	antidiuretic hormone	BM	bowel movement
ADHD	attention-deficit/hyperactivity disorder	BMD	bone mineral density
ADL	activities of daily living	BMR	basal metabolic rate
AE	above elbow	BMT	bone marrow transplant
AF	atrial fibrillation	BNO	bladder neck obstruction
AGN	acute glomerulonephritis	BP	blood pressure
AI	artificial insemination	BPD	bipolar disorder
AIDS	acquired immunodeficiency syndrome	BPH	benign prostatic hyperplasia
AK	above knee	bpm	beats per minute
ALL	acute lymphocytic leukemia	Bronch	bronchoscopy
ALS	amyotrophic lateral sclerosis	BS	bowel sounds
ALT	alanine transaminase	BSE	breast self-examination
AMI	acute myocardial infarction	BUN	blood urea nitrogen
AML	acute myelogenous leukemia	BX, bx	biopsy
Angio	angiography	$\bar{c}$	with
ANS	autonomic nervous system	C1, C2, etc.	first cervical vertebra, second cervical vertebra, etc.
ante	before	Ca	calcium, cancer
AP	anteroposterior	CA	chronological age
APAP	acetaminophen (Tylenol™)	CABG	coronary artery bypass graft
aq	aqueous (water)	CAD	coronary artery disease
ARC	AIDS-related complex	cap(s)	capsule(s)
ARDS	adult (or acute) respiratory distress syndrome	CAPD	continuous ambulatory perito-neal dialysis
ARF	acute renal failure	CAT	computerized axial tomography
ARMD	age-related macular degeneration	cath	catheterization
AROM	active range of motion	CBC	complete blood count
AS	arteriosclerosis, left ear	CBD	common bile duct
ASA	aspirin	CC	cardiac catheterization, chief complaint, clean catch urine specimen
ASD	atrial septal defect		
ASHD	arteriosclerotic heart disease	CCU	coronary care unit

Abbreviation	Meaning	Abbreviation	Meaning
c.gl.	correction with glasses	DSM	*Diagnostic and Statistical Manual of Mental Disorders*
chemo	chemotherapy		
CHF	congestive heart failure	dtd	give of such a dose
Ci	curie	DTR	deep tendon reflex
CIS	carcinoma in situ	DVA	distance visual acuity
Cl⁻	chloride	DVT	deep vein thrombosis
CLL	chronic lymphocytic leukemia	Dx	diagnosis
CML	chronic myelogenous leukemia	DXA	dual-energy absorptiometry
		e-stim	electrical stimulation
CNS	central nervous system	ECC	extracorporeal circulation
CO₂	carbon dioxide	ECCE	extracapsular cataract extraction
CoA	coarctation of the aorta		
COPD	chronic obstructive pulmonary disease	ECG, EKG	electrocardiogram
		ECHO	echocardiogram
CP	cerebral palsy, chest pain	ECT	electroconvulsive therapy
CPK	creatine phosphokinase	ED	erectile dysfunction
CPR	cardiopulmonary resuscitation	EDC	estimated date of confinement
CRF	chronic renal failure		
C&S	culture and sensitivity	EEG	electroencephalogram, electroencephalography
CS, C-section	cesarean section		
CSD	congenital septal defect	EENT	eye, ear, nose, and throat
CSF	cerebrospinal fluid	EGD	esophagogastroduodenoscopy
CT	calcitonin, computerized tomography	ELISA	enzyme-linked immunosorbent assay
CTA	clear to auscultation	EM	emmetropia
CTS	carpal tunnel syndrome	EMB	endometrial biopsy
CV	cardiovascular	EMG	electromyogram
CVA	cerebrovascular accident	Endo	endoscopy
CVD	cerebrovascular disease	ENT	ear, nose, and throat
CVS	chorionic villus sampling	EOM	extraocular movement
Cx	cervix	eosins, eos	eosinophils
CXR	chest X-ray	ERCP	endoscopic retrograde cholangiopancreatography
cysto	cystoscopy		
d	day	ERT	estrogen replacement therapy
D	diopter (lens strength)	ERV	expiratory reserve volume
dB	decibel	ESR, SR, sed rate	erythrocyte sedimentation rate
D & C	dilation and curettage		
d/c, DISC	discontinue	ESRD	end-stage renal disease
DC, disc	discontinue	ESWL	extracorporeal shockwave lithotripsy
DEA	Drug Enforcement Agency		
decub	decubitus ulcer, lying down	et	and
Derm, derm	dermatology	EU	excretory urography
DI	diabetes insipidus, diagnostic imaging	EUA	exam under anesthesia
		FBS	fasting blood sugar
diff	differential	FDA	Federal Drug Administration
dil	dilute	FEKG	fetal electrocardiogram
disp	dispense	FHR	fetal heart rate
DJD	degenerative joint disease	FHT	fetal heart tone
DM	diabetes mellitus	FOBT	fecal occult blood test
DOE	dyspnea on exertion	FRC	functional residual capacity
DPT	diphtheria, pertussis, tetanus injection	FS	frozen section
		FSH	follicle-stimulating hormone
DRE	digital rectal exam	FTND	full-term normal delivery
DSA	digital subtraction angiography	FX, Fx	fracture
		GA	gallium, general anesthesia

Abbreviation	Meaning	Abbreviation	Meaning
GB	gallbladder, gallbladder X-ray	ICP	intracranial pressure
GC	gonorrhea	ICU	intensive care unit
GERD	gastroesophageal reflux disease	I&D	incision and drainage
GH	growth hormone	ID	intradermal
GI, grav I	first pregnancy	IDDM	insulin-dependent diabetes mellitus
GI	gastrointestinal	Ig	immunoglobulins (IgA, IgD, IgE, IgG, IgM)
gm	gram		
GOT	glutamic oxaloacetic transaminase	IM	intramuscular
gr	grain	inj	injection
gt	drop	I&O	intake and output
gtt	drops	IOP	intraocular pressure
GTT	glucose tolerance test	IPD	intermittent peritoneal dialysis
GU	genitourinary	IPPB	intermittent positive pressure breathing
GVHD	graft versus host disease	IRDS	infant respiratory distress syndrome
GYN, gyn	gynecology		
H_2O	water	IRV	inspiratory reserve volume
HA	headache	IU	international unit
HAV	hepatitis A virus	IUD	intrauterine device
HBV	hepatitis B virus	IV	intravenous
HCG, hCG	human chorionic gonadotropin	IVC	intravenous cholangiogram, intravenous cholangiography
HCl	hydrochloric acid	IVF	*in vitro* fertilization
HCO_3^-	bicarbonate	IVP	intravenous pyelogram
HCT, Hct, crit	hematocrit	JRA	juvenile rheumatoid arthritis
HCV	hepatitis C virus	K^+	potassium
HD	Hodgkin's disease, hemodialysis	kg	kilogram
		KS	Kaposi's sarcoma
HDN	hemolytic disease of the newborn	KUB	kidney, ureter, bladder
		L1, L2, etc.	first lumbar vertebra, second lumbar vertebra, etc.
HDV	hepatitis D virus		
HEENT	head, ears, eyes, nose, throat	L	liter
HEV	hepatitis E virus	LASIK	laser-assisted in-situ keratomileusis
Hgb, Hb, HGB	hemoglobin		
HIV	human immunodeficiency virus	LAT, lat	lateral
		LBW	low birth weight
HMD	hyaline membrane disease	LE	lower extremity
HNP	herniated nucleus pulposus	LGI	lower gastrointestinal series
HPV	human papilloma virus	LH	luteinizing hormone
HRT	hormone replacement therapy	LL	left lateral
hs	at bedtime	LLE	left lower extremity
HSG	hysterosalpingography	LLL	left lower lobe
HSV-1	herpes simplex virus type 1	LLQ	left lower quadrant
HSV	herpes simplex virus	LMP	last menstrual period
HTN	hypertension	LP	lumbar puncture
Hz	hertz	LUE	left upper extremity
ī	one	LUL	left upper lobe
ī ī	two	LUQ	left upper quadrant
ī ī ī	three	LVAD	left ventricular assist device
IBD	inflammatory bowel disease	LVH	left ventricular hypertrophy
IBS	irritable bowel syndrome	lymphs	lymphocytes
IC	inspiratory capacity	MA	mental age
ICCE	intracapsular cataract extraction	mA	milliampere
		MAO	monoamine oxidase

Abbreviation	Meaning
mcg	microgram
mCi	millicurie
MD	muscular dystrophy
MDI	metered-dose inhaler
mEq	milliequivalent
mets	metastases
mg	milligram
MI	myocardial infarction, mitral insufficiency
mL	milliliter
mm Hg	millimeters of mercury
MM	malignant melanoma
MMPI	Minnesota Multiphasic Personality Inventory
mono	mononucleosis
monos	monocytes
MR	mitral regurgitation
MRA	magnetic resonance angiography
MRI	magnetic resonance imaging
MS	mitral stenosis, multiple sclerosis, musculoskeletal
MSH	melanocyte-stimulating hormone
MTX	methotrexate
MUA	manipulation under anesthesia
MVP	mitral valve prolapse
Na$^+$	sodium
NB	newborn
NG	nasogastric (tube)
NHL	non-Hodgkin's lymphoma
NIDDM	non-insulin-dependent diabetes mellitus
NK	natural killer cells
NMR	nuclear magnetic resonance
no sub	no substitute
noc	night
non rep	do not repeat
NPH	neutral protamine Hagedorn (insulin)
NPO	nothing by mouth
NS	nephrotic syndrome, normal saline
NSAID	nonsteroidal anti-inflammatory drug
n&v	nausea and vomiting
O$_2$	oxygen
OA	osteoarthritis
OB	obstetrics
OCD	obsessive–compulsive disorder
OCPs	oral contraceptive pills
od	overdose
OD	right eye
oint	ointment

Abbreviation	Meaning
OM	otitis media
O&P	ova and parasites
Ophth.	ophthalmology
OR	operating room
ORIF	open reduction–internal fixation
Orth, ortho	orthopedics
OS	left eye
OT	occupational therapy
OTC	over the counter
Oto	otology
OU	each eye/both eyes
oz	ounce
$\bar{p}$	after
P	pulse
PA	pernicious anemia, posteroanterior
PAC	premature atrial contraction
PAP	Papanicolaou test
PARR	postanesthetic recovery room
PBI	protein-bound iodine
pc	after meals
PCA	patient-controlled administration
PCP	pneumocystis pneumonia
PCV	packed cell volume
PDA	patent ductus arteriosus
PDR	*Physician's Desk Reference*
PE tube	pressure equalizing tube
per	with
PERRLA	pupils equal, round, react to light and accommodation
PET	positron emission tomography
PFT	pulmonary function test
pH	acidity or alkalinity of urine
PI, para I	first delivery
PID	pelvic inflammatory disease
PMN, polys	polymorphonuclear neutrophil
PMS	premenstrual syndrome
PNS	peripheral nervous system
PO, po	by mouth
PORP	partial ossicular replacement prosthesis
pp	postprandial
PPD	purified protein derivative
preop, pre-op	preoperative
prep	preparation, prepared
PRK	photorefractive keratectomy
PRL	prolactin
prn	as needed
PROM	passive range of motion
prot	protocol
PSA	prostate-specific antigen
PT, pro-time	prothrombin time
pt	patient

Abbreviation	Meaning	Abbreviation	Meaning
PT	physical therapy	SCIDS	severe combined immunodeficiency syndrome
PTC	percutaneous transhepatic cholangiography	segs	segmented neutrophils
PTCA	percutaneous transluminal coronary angioplasty	s.gl.	without correction or glasses
		SG, sp. gr.	specific gravity
PTH	parathyroid hormone	SG	skin graft
PUD	peptic ulcer disease	SIDS	sudden infant death syndrome
PVC	premature ventricular contraction	Sig	label as follows/directions
		SK	streptokinase
q	every	sl	under the tongue
qam	every morning	SLE	systemic lupus erythematosus
qh	every hour	SMAC	sequential multiple analyzer computer
qhs	at bedtime		
qid	four times a day	SMD	senile macular degeneration
qs	quantity sufficient	SOB	shortness of breath
R	respiration, roentgen	sol	solution
Ra	radium	SOM	serous otitis media
RA	rheumatoid arthritis, room air	SPP	suprapubic prostatectomy
rad	radiation-absorbed dose	ST	esotropia
RAI	radioactive iodine	st	stage
RBC	red blood cell	stat	at once/immediately
RDS	respiratory distress syndrome	STD	sexually transmitted disease
REM	rapid eye movement	STSG	split-thickness skin graft
Rh+	Rh-positive	Subc, SubQi	subcutaneous
Rh−	Rh-negative	subcu, SC, sc,	
RIA	radioimmunoassay	subq	
RL	right lateral	suppos, supp	suppository
RLE	right lower extremity	susp	suspension
RLL	right lower lobe	syr	syrup
RLQ	right lower quadrant	T & A	tonsillectomy and adenoidectomy
RML	right middle lobe		
ROM	range of motion	T, tbsp	tablespoon
RP	retrograde pyelogram	t, tsp	teaspoon
RPR	rapid plasma reagin (test for syphilis)	T1, T2, etc.	first thoracic vertebra, second thoracic vertebra, etc.
RRT	registered radiologic technologist, registered respiratory therapist	T_3	triiodothyronine
		T_4	thyroxine
		tab	tablet
RUE	right upper extremity	TAH-BSO	total abdominal hysterectomy–bilateral salpingo-oophorectomy
RUL	right upper lobe		
RUQ	right upper quadrant		
RV	reserve volume	TAH	total abdominal hysterectomy
Rx	take	TB	tuberculosis
$\bar{s}$	without	TENS	transcutaneous electrical stimulation
$\overline{ss}$	one-half		
S1	first heart sound	TFT	thyroid function test
S2	second heart sound	THA	total hip arthroplasty
SA, S-A	sinoatrial	THR	total hip replacement
SAD	seasonal affective disorder	TIA	transient ischemic attack
SARS	severe acute respiratory syndrome	tid	three times a day
		TKA	total knee arthroplasty
SC	subcutaneous	TKR	total knee replacement
SCC	squamous cell carcinoma	TLC	total lung capacity
SCI	spinal cord injury	TNM	tumor, nodes, metastases

Abbreviation	Meaning	Abbreviation	Meaning
TO	telephone order	UE	upper extremity
top	apply topically	UGI	upper gastrointestinal series
TORP	total ossicular replacement prosthesis	URI	upper respiratory infection
		US	ultrasound
tPA	tissue-type plasminogen activator	UTI	urinary tract infection
		UV	ultraviolet
TPN	total parenteral nutrition	VA	visual acuity
TPR	temperature, pulse, and respiration	VC	vital capacity
		VCUG	voiding cystourethrography
TSH	thyroid-stimulating hormone	VD	venereal disease
TSS	toxic shock syndrome	VF	visual field
TUR	transurethral resection	Vfib	ventricular fibrillation
TURP	transurethral resection of the prostate	VO	verbal order
		VSD	ventricular septal defect
TV	tidal volume	VT	ventricular tachycardia
u	unit	WBC	white blood cell
U/A, UA	urinalysis	wt	weight
UC	urine culture, uterine contractions	x	times
		XT	exotropia

Chapter Review Answers

Chapter 1 Answers
Practice Exercises

A. 1. combining form 2. o 3. suffix 4. prefix
   5. spelling 6. word root, combining vowel, prefix, suffix
B. 1. l 2. e 3. j 4. f 5. d 6. k 7. m 8. o 9. g 10. n 11. b
   12. h 13. a 14. c 15. i
C. 1. surgical repair 2. narrowing 3. inflammation
   4. pertaining to 5. pain 6. cutting into
   7. enlargement 8. surgical removal of
   9. excessive, abnormal flow 10. puncture to
   remove fluid 11. record or picture 12. pertaining to 13. abnormal softening 14. state of
   15. to suture 16. surgical creation of opening
   17. surgical fixation 18. discharge or flow
   19. process of visually examining 20. tumor, mass
D. 1. pulmonology 2. neuralgia or neurodynia
   3. rhinorrhea 4. nephromalacia 5. cardiomegaly
   6. gastrotomy 7. dermatitis 8. laryngectomy
   9. arthroplasty 10. adenopathy
E. 1. intra-/endo- 2. macro- 3. pre-/ante- 4. peri-
   5. neo- 6. a-/an-/de- 7. hemi-/semi- 8. dys-
   9. supra-/ hyper- 10. hyper- 11. poly-/multi-
   12. brady- 13. auto- 14. trans- 15. bi-
F. 1. tachy-, fast 2. pseudo-, false 3. hypo-, under/
   below 4. inter-, among/between 5. eu-, normal/
   good 6. post-, after 7. mono-, one 8. sub-,
   below/under
G. 1. metastases 2. ova 3. diverticula 4. atria
   5. di agnoses 6. vertebrae
H. 1. cardiology 2. gastrology 3. dermatology
   4. ophthalmology 5. immunology 6. nephrology 7. hematology 8. gynecology 9. neurology
   10. pathology
I. 1. cardiomalacia 2. gastrostomy 3. rhinoplasty
   4. hypertrophy 5. pathology 6. adenoma
   7. gastroenterology 8. otitis 9. hydrotherapy
   10. carcinogen
J. 1. gland 2. cancer 3. heart 4. chemical 5. to cut
   6. skin 7. small intestine 8. stomach 9. female
   10. blood 11. water 12. immunity 13. voice box
   14. disease 15. kidney 16. nerve 17. eye 18. ear
   19. lung 20. nose

Chapter 2 Answers
Practice Exercises

A. 1. cells, tissues, organs, systems, body 2. cell
   membrane, cytoplasm, nucleus 3. histology
   4. epithelial 5. anatomical 6. right lower
   7. cranial, spinal 8. nine 9. right iliac 10. pleural,
   pericardial
B. 1. c 2. a 3. b
C. 1. epi-; above 2. peri-; around or about
   3. hypo-; under or below 4. retro-; behind or
   backward
D. 1. n 2. f 3. k 4. d 5. a 6. e 7. m 8. i 9. b 10. j 11. h
   12. l 13. c 14. g
E. 1. MS 2. lat 3. RUQ 4. CV 5. GI 6. AP 7. OB
   8. LLQ
F. 1. dorsal 2. thoracic 3. superior 4. caudal
   5. visceral 6. lateral 7. distal 8. neural
   9. pulmonology 10. muscular 11. ventral
   12. anterior 13. cephalic 14. medial
G. 1. internal organ 2. back 3. abdomen 4. chest
   5. middle 6. belly 7. front 8. tissues 9. epithelium
   10. skull 11. cell 12. near to 13. head
H. 1. integumentary, d 2. cardiovascular, i
   3. digestive, g 4. female reproductive, b
   5. musculoskeletal (skeletal), a 6. respiratory, j
   7. urinary, c 8. male reproductive, f 9. nervous, h
   10. musculoskeletal (muscular), e
I. 1. cephalic 2. pubic 3. crural 4. gluteal
   5. cervical 6. brachial 7. dorsum 8. thoracic
J. 1. a 2. c 3. f 4. e 5. a 6. d 7. b 8. e 9. c 10. b
K. 1. otorhinolaryngology 2. cardiology
   3. gynecology 4. orthopedics
   5. ophthalmology 6. urology
   7. dermatology 8. gastroenterology

Labeling Exercises

A. 1. cephalic 2. cervical 3. thoracic 4. brachial
   5. abdominal 6. pelvic 7. pubic 8. crural 9. trunk
   10. vertebral 11. dorsum 12. gluteal
B. 1. frontal or coronal plane 2. sagittal or median
   plane 3. transverse or horizontal plane

Chapter 3 Answers
Real World Applications

Medical Record Analysis

1. basal cell carcinoma—Cancerous tumor of the basal cell layer of the epidermis. A frequent type of skin cancer that rarely metastasizes or spreads. These cancers can arise on sun exposed skin.
2. lesions—A general term for a wound, injury, or abnormality.
3. biopsies—A piece of tissue is removed by syringe and needle, knife, punch, or brush to examine under a microscope. Used to aid in diagnosis.
4. excised—to surgically cut out.
5. pruritus—Severe itching.
6. anterior—Pertaining to the front side of the body.
7. erythema—Redness or flushing of the skin.
8. depigmentation—Loss of normal skin color or pigment.
9. epidermis—The superficial layer of the skin.
10. dermis—The middle layer of the skin.
11. dermatoplasty—Skin grafting; transplantation of skin.

Chart Note Transcription

1. ulcer 2. dermatologist 3. pruritus 4. erythema 5. pustules 6. dermis 7. necrosis 8. culture and sensitivity 9. cellulitis 10. debridement

Case Study

1. Systemic lupus erythematosus; another example is rheumatoid arthritis
2. Erythema—skin redness; photosensitivity—intolerance to strong light; alopecia—baldness; stiffness in joints
3. Exfoliative cytology and fungal scrapings—in both tests cells are scraped away from the skin and examined under a microscope in order to make a diagnosis; in order to make sure the rash was not caused by something else like a fungal infection
4. Internist—anti-inflammatory—to reduce pain, swelling, and stiffness in joints; dermatologist—corticosteroid cream to anti-inflammatory to reduce the red rash
5. Completing examinations and various diagnostic tests in order to collect information necessary for a diagnosis

Practice Exercises

A. 1. epidermis, dermis, subcutaneous layer 2. basal cell 3. adipose 4. dermis 5. keratin 6. melanin 7. corium 8. nail bed 9. sebaceous, sweat 10. apocrine

B. 1. cold 2. skin 3. profuse sweating 4. pus 5. blue 6. nail 7. fat 8. sweat 9. wrinkles 10. oil 11. hair 12. death
C. 1. redness involving superficial layer of skin 2. burn damage through epidermis and into dermis causing vesicles 3. burn damage to full thickness of epidermis and dermis
D. 1. e 2. f 3. i 4. j 5. a 6. c 7. l 8. g 9. k 10. h 11. d 12. b
E. 1. flat, discolored area 2. small solid raised spot less than 0.5 cm 3. fluid filled sac 4. crack-like lesion 5. raised spot containing pus 6. small, round swollen area 7. fluid-filled blister 8. open sore 9. firm, solid mass larger than 0.5 cm 10. torn or jagged wound
F. 1. dermatitis 2. dermatosis 3. dermatome 4. dermatologist 5. dermatoplasty 6. dermatology 7. melanoma 8. melanocyte 9. ichthyoderma 10. leukoderma 11. erythroderma 12. onychomalacia 13. paronychia 14. onychophagia 15. onychectomy
G. 1. h 2. i 3. j 4. e 5. c 6. a 7. f 8. g 9. b 10. d
H. 1. FS 2. I & D 3. ID 4. subq, subcu, SC, sc 5. UV 6. BX, bx
I. 1. culture and sensitivity 2. basal cell carcinoma 3. dermatology 4. skin graft 5. decubitus ulcer 6. malignant melanoma
J. 1. xeroderma 2. petechiae 3. tinea 4. scabies 5. paronychia 6. Kaposi's sarcoma 7. impetigo 8. keloid 9. exfoliative cytology 10. frozen section
K. 1. antifungal, f 2. antipruritic, d 3. antiparasitic, a 4. antiviral, c 5. corticosteroid cream, b 6. anesthetic, g 7. antibiotic, e

Labeling Exercise

A. 1. epidermis 2. dermis 3. subcutaneous layer 4. sweat gland 5. sweat duct 6. hair shaft 7. sebaceous gland 8. arrector pili muscle 9. sensory receptors
B. 1. epidermis 2. dermis 3. subcutaneous layer 4. sebaceous gland 5. arrector pili muscle 6. hair shaft 7. hair follicle 8. hair root 9. papilla
C. 1. free edge 2. lateral nail groove 3. lunula 4. nail bed 5. nail body 6. cuticle 7. nail root

Chapter 4 Answers
Real World Applications

Medical Record Analysis

1. osteoarthritis—Joint inflammation resulting in degeneration of the bones and joints, especially those bearing weight. Results in bone rubbing against bone; 2. bilateral—pertaining to both sides; 3. TKA—Surgical reconstruction of a knee joint by implanting a prosthetic knee joint. Also called *total*

knee replacement (TKR); 4. orthopedic surgeon—Physician that specializes in the diagnosis and treatment of conditions of the musculoskeletal system using surgical means; 5. CT scan—computed tomography scan—imaging technique that produces cross-sectional view of the body; 6. physical therapy—treats disorders using physical means and methods; includes joint motion and muscle strength; 7. ROM—range of movement of a joint, from maximum flexion through maximum extension; it is measure das degrees of a circle; 8. gait training—learning how to walk; 9. occupational therapy—assists patients to regain, develop, and improve skills that are important for independent functioning; 10. ADLs—activities of daily living

Chart Note Transcription

1. Colles' fracture (fx) 2. cast 3. fracture 4. orthopedist 5. osteoporosis 6. computerized axial tomography (CT or CAT scan) 7. flexion 8. extension 9. comminuted fracture (fx) 10. femur 11. total hip arthroplasty (THA)

Case Study

1. Rheumatoid arthritis; 2. Cartilage damage and crippling deformities; 3. Osteoarthritis; 4. Bone scan—radioactive dye is used to visualize the body; erythrocyte sedimentation rate—a blood test that can determine if a person has an inflammatory disease; 5. Anti-inflammatory medication to reduce inflammation and provide some pain relief; physical therapy—treatment using warm water and exercises to maintain the flexibility of the joints; 6. Acute—brief disease, also used to mean sudden and severe disease; Chronic—disease of a long duration

Practice Exercises

A. 1. axial, appendicular 2. smooth 3. frame, protect vital organs, work with muscles for movement, store minerals, red blood cell production 4. myoneural 5. short 6. periosteum 7. wrist 8. cancellous 9. synovial 10. skeletal, smooth, cardiac 11. foramen 12. diaphysis

B. 1. femoral 2. sternal 3. clavicular 4. coccygeal 5. maxillary 6. tibial 7. patellar 8. phalangeal 9. humeral 10. pubic

C. 1. osteocyte 2. osteoblast 3. osteoporosis 4. osteopathy 5. osteotomy 6. osteotome 7. osteomyelitis 8. osteomalacia 9. osteochondroma 10. myopathy 11. myoplasty 12. myorrhaphy 13. electromyogram 14. myasthenia 15. tenodynia 16. tenorrhaphy 17. arthrodesis 18. arthroplasty 19. arthrotomy 20. arthritis 21. arthrocentesis 22. arthralgia 23. chondrectomy 24. chondroma 25. chondromalacia

D. 1. -desis 2. -asthenia 3. -listhesis 4. -clasia 5. -kinesia 6. -porosis

E. 1. cervical, 7 2. thoracic, 12 3. lumbar, 5 4. sacrum, 1 (5 fused) 5. coccyx, 1 (3–5 fused)

F. 1. S = -scopy; visual examination of inside of a joint 2. P = inter-, S = -al; pertaining to between vertebrae 3. S = -malacia; softening of cartilage 4. S = -ectomy; surgical removal of disk 5. P = intra- S = -al; pertaining to inside the skull 6. P = sub-, -ar = pertaining to; pertaining to under the scapula

G. 1. lamina, part of vertebra 2. stiff joint 3. cartilage 4. vertebrae 5. muscle 6. straight 7. hump 8. tendon 9. bone marrow 10. joint

H. 1. IM 2. TKR 3. HNP 4. DTR 5. UE 6. L5 7. BDT 8. AK 9. fx/FX 10. NSAID

I. 1. medical doctor who treats musculoskeletal system 2. uses manipulation of vertebral column 3. specialty that treats disorders of feet 4. fitting of braces and splints 5. fabricates and fits artificial limbs

J. 1. e 2. d 3. b 4. c 5. a 6. h 7. g 8. f

K. 1. osteoporosis 2. rickets 3. lateral epicondylitis 4. herniated nucleus pulposus 5. osteogenic sarcoma 6. scoliosis 7. pseudotrophic muscular dystrophy 8. systemic lupus erythematosus 9. spondylolisthesis 10. carpal tunnel syndrome

L. 1. c 2. h 3. f 4. g 5. d 6. e 7. a 8. b

M. 1. patella 2. tarsals 3. clavicle 4. femur 5. phalanges 6. carpals 7. tibia 8. scapula 9. phalanges

N. 1. degenerative joint disease 2. electromyogram 3. first cervical vertebra 4. sixth thoracic vertebra 5. intramuscular 6. deep tendon reflexes 7. juvenile rheumatoid arthritis 8. left lower extremity 9. orthopedics 10. carpal tunnel syndrome

O. 1. surgical repair of cartilage 2. slow movement 3. porous bone 4. abnormal increase in lumbar spine curve (swayback) 5. lack of development/nourishment 6. bone marrow tumor 7. artificial substitute for a body part 8. cutting into skull 9. puncture of a joint to withdraw fluid 10. bursa inflammation

P. 1. nonsteroidal anti-inflammatory drugs, b 2. corticosteroids, e 3. skeletal muscle relaxants, a 4. bone reabsorption inhibitors, c 5. calcium supplements, d

Labeling Exercise

A. 1. skull 2. cervical vertebrae 3. sternum 4. ribs 5. thoracic vertebrae 6. lumbar vertebrae 7. ilium 8. pubis 9. ischium 10. femur 11. patella 12. tibia 13. fibula 14. tarsals 15. metatarsals 16. phalanges 17. maxilla 18. mandible 19. scapula 20. humerus 21. ulna 22. radius 23. sacrum 24. coccyx 25. carpals 26. metacarpals 27. phalanges

B. 1. proximal epiphysis 2. diaphysis 3. distal epiphysis 4. articular cartilage 5. epiphyseal line 6. spongy or cancellous bone 7. compact or cortical bone 8. medullary cavity

C. 1. periosteum 2. synovial membrane 3. articular cartilage 4. joint cavity 5. joint capsule

Chapter 5 Answers
Real World Applications

Medical Record Analysis

1. hypertension—Blood pressure above the normal range. 2. tachycardia—The condition of having a fast heart rate; typically more than 100 beats/minute while at rest. 3. congestive heart failure (CAD)—Pathological condition of the heart in which there is a reduced outflow of blood from the left side of the heart because the left ventricle myocardium has become too weak to efficiently pump blood. Results in weakness, breathlessness, and edema. 4. mitral valve prolapse—Condition in which the cusps or flaps of the heart valve are too loose and fail to shut tightly, allowing blood to flow backward through the valve when the heart chamber contracts. Most commonly occurs in the mitral valve, but may affect any of the heart valves. 5. palpitations—Pounding, racing heartbeats. 6. electrocardiography (EKG)—Process of recording the electrical activity of the heart. Useful in the diagnosis of abnormal cardiac rhythm and heart muscle (myocardium) damage. 7. cardiac enzymes—Blood test to determine the level of enzymes specific to heart muscles in the blood. An increase in the enzymes may indicate heart muscle damage such as a myocardial infarction. These enzymes include creatine phosphokinase (CPK), lactate dehydrogenase (LDH), and glutamic oxaloacetic transaminase (GOT). 8. echocardiography—Noninvasive diagnostic method using ultrasound to visualize internal cardiac structures. Cardiac valve activity can be evaluated using this method. 9. stress test—Method for evaluating cardiovascular fitness. The patient is placed on a treadmill or a bicycle and then subjected to steadily increasing levels of work. An EKG and oxygen levels are taken while the patient exercises. The test is stopped if abnormalities occur on the EKG. Also called an *exercise test* or a *treadmill test*. 10. angiocardiography—X-rays taken after the injection of an opaque material into a blood vessel. Can be performed on the aorta as an aortic angiogram, on the heart as an angiocardiogram, and on the brain as a cerebral angiogram. 11. coronary artery disease (CAD)—Insufficient blood supply to the heart muscle due to an obstruction of one or more coronary arteries. May be caused by atherosclerosis and may cause angina pectoris and myocardial infarction. 12. myocardial infarction—Condition caused by the partial or complete occlusion or closing of one or more of the coronary arteries. Symptoms include a squeezing pain or heavy pressure in the middle of the chest (angina pectoris). A delay in treatment could

result in death. Also referred to as a *heart attack*. 13. mitral valve replacement—Removal of a diseased heart valve and replacement with an artificial valve.

Chart Note Transcription

1. angina pectoris 2. bradycardia 3. hyper tension 4. myocardial infarction (MI) 5. electrocardiogram (EKG, ECG) 6. cardiac enzymes 7. coronary artery disease (CAD) 8. cardiac catheterization 9. stress test (treadmill test) 10. percutaneous transluminal coronary angioplasty (PTCA) 11. coronary artery bypass graft (CABG)

Case Study

1. Heart attack; condition caused by the partial or complete occlusion or closing of one or more of the coronary arteries. Symptoms include a squeezing pain or heavy pressure in the middle of the chest (angina pectoris). A delay in treatment could result in death. 2. The main complaint, the one the patient is most aware of or most anxious about. 3. Angina pectoris—Condition in which there is severe pain with a sensation of constriction around the heart; caused by a deficiency of oxygen to the heart muscle. 4. Nausea—feeling of need to vomit; dyspnea–difficulty breathing; diaphoresis–profuse sweating 5. Cardiac enzymes; angiocardiography; cardiac scan; electrocardiography; stress testing; cardiac catheterization; Holter monitor 6. Smokes; overweight; family history; sedentary lifestyle. He can stop smoking, lose weight, and become more active.

Practice Exercises

A. 1. cardiology 2. endocardium, myocardium, epicardium 3. sinoatrial node 4. away from 5. tricuspid, pulmonary, mitral (bicuspid), aortic 6. atria, ventricles 7. pulmonary 8. apex 9. septum 10. systole, diastole

B. 1. cardiac 2. cardiomyopathy 3. cardiomegaly 4. tachycardia 5. bradycardia 6. electrocardiogram 7. angiostenosis 8. angiitis 9. angiospasm 10. arterial 11. arteriosclerosis 12. arteriole

C. 1. endocarditis 2. epicarditis 3. myocarditis

D. 1. heart 2. valve 3. chest 4. artery 5. vein 6. vessel 7. ventricle 8. clot 9. atrium 10. fatty substance

E. 1. venous 2. cardiology 3. venogram 4. electro cardiography 5. hypertension 6. hypotension 7. valvoplasty 8. interventricular 9. atherectomy 10. arteriostenosis

F. 1. -tension 2. -stenosis 3. -manometer 4. -ule, -ole 5. -sclerosis

G. 1. f 2. h 3. d 4. g 5. b 6. i 7. a 8. c 9. e 10. j

H. 1. blood pressure 2. congestive heart failure 3. myocardial infarction 4. coronary care unit 5. premature ventricular contraction 6. cardiopulmonary resuscitation 7. coronary artery

disease 8. chest pain 9. electrocardiogram
10. first heart sound

I. 1. MVP 2. VSD 3. PTCA 4. Vfib 5. DVT 6. LDH
    7. CoA 8. tPA 9. CV 10. ECC

J. 1. c 2. g 3. j 4. a 5. d 6. b 7. i 8. e 9. f 10. h

K. 1. thin flexible tube 2. an area of dead tissue
    3. a blood clot 4. pounding heartbeat 5. back-
    flow 6. weakened and ballooning arterial wall
    7. complete stoppage of heart activity 8. serious
    cardiac arrhythmia 9. heart attack 10. varicose
    veins in anal region

L. 1. murmur 2. defibrillation 3. hypertension
    4. pacemaker 5. varicose veins 6. angina
    pectoris 7. CCU 8. MI 9. angiography
    10. echocardiogram 11. Holter monitor 12. CHF

M. 1. antiarrhythmic, e 2. antilipidemic, g
    3. cardiotonic, f 4. diuretic, h 5. anticoagu-
    lant, b 6. thrombolytic, a 7. vasodilator, d
    8. calcium channel blocker, c

Labeling Exercise

A. 1. pulmonary arteries 2. vena cavae 3. right
    atrium 4. right ventricle 5. systemic veins 6. cap-
    illary bed lungs 7. pulmonary veins 8. aorta
    9. left atrium 10. left ventricle 11. systemic
    arteries 12. systemic capillary beds

B. 1. superior vena cava 2. aorta 3. pulmonary
    trunk 4. pulmonary valve 5. right atrium 6. tri-
    cuspid valve 7. right ventricle 8. inferior vena
    cava 9. pulmonary artery 10. pulmonary vein
    11. left atrium 12. aortic valve 13. mitral or
    bicuspid valve 14. left ventricle 15. endocar-
    dium 16. myocardium 17. pericardium

Chapter 6 Answers
Real World Applications

Medical Record Analysis

1. splenomegaly—An enlarged spleen.
2. non-Hodgkin's lymphoma—Cancer of the lym-
    phatic tissues other than Hodgkin's lymphoma.
3. spleen—An organ located in the upper
    left quadrant of the abdomen. Consists of
    lymphatic tissue that is highly infiltrated with
    blood vessels. It filters out and destroys old red
    blood cells.
4. splenectomy—The surgical removal of the
    spleen.
5. Monospot—A blood test for infectious
    mononucleosis.
6. enzyme-linked immunosorbent assay (ELISA)—
    A blood test for an antibody to the AIDS virus.
    A positive test means that the person has been
    exposed to the virus. There may be a false-

positive reading, and then the Western blot
test would be used to verify the results.

7. Magnetic resonance imaging (MRI)—Medical
    imaging that uses radio-frequency radiation
    as its source of energy. It does not require the
    injection of contrast medium or exposure to
    ionizing radiation. The technique is useful for
    visualizing large blood vessels, the heart, the
    brain, and soft tissues
8. tumor—Abnormal growth of tissue that may
    be benign or malignant.
9. biopsy—A piece of tissue is removed by syringe
    and needle, knife, punch, or brush to examine
    under a microscope. Used to aid in diagnosis.
10. oncologist—A physician who specializes in the
    treatment of cancer.
11. metastases—The spreading of a cancerous
    tumor from its original site to different loca-
    tions of the body.

Chart Note Transcription

1. hematologist 2. ELISA 3. prothrombin time
4. complete blood count (CBC) 5. erythropenia
6. thrombopenia 7. leukocytosis 8. bone marrow
aspiration 9. leukemia 10. homologous transfusion

Case Study

1. Acute lymphocytic leukemia
2. High fever; thrombopenia—too few platelets;
    epistaxis—nose bleed; gingival bleeding—
    gums bleeding; petechiae—pinpoint bruises;
    ecchymoses—large black and blue bruises
3. Bone marrow aspiration—sample of bone
    marrow is removed by aspiration with a needle
    and examined for diseases.
4. A diagnosis based on the results of the physi-
    cian's direct examination rather than based on
    other tests like x-rays and lab work
5. Chemotherapy—treating disease by using
    chemicals that have a toxic effect upon the
    body, especially cancerous tissue
6. Remission—a period during which the symptoms
    of a disease or disorder leave. Can be temporary.

Practice Exercises

A. 1. hematology 2. spleen, tonsils, thymus
    3. thoracic duct, right lymphatic duct 4. axillary,
    cervical, mediastinal, inguinal 5. phagocytosis
    6. erythrocytes (red blood cells), leukocytes
    (white blood cells), platelets (thrombocytes)
    7. plasma 8. active acquired 9. antibody-
    mediated 10. hemostasis

B. 1. leukopenia 2. erythropenia 3. thrombopenia
    4. pancytopenia 5. leukocytosis 6. erythrocytosis
    7. thrombocytosis 8. hemoglobin 9. immu-
    noglobulin 10. erythrocyte 11. leukocyte
    12. lymphocyte

C. 1. splenomegaly 2. splenectomy
    3. splenotomy 4. lymphocytes 5. lymphoma
    6. lymphadenopathy 7. lymphadenoma
    8. lymphadenitis 9. immunologist 10. immu-
    noglobulin 11. immunology 12. hematic
    13. hematoma 14. hematopoiesis 15. hemo-
    lytic 16. hemoglobin
D. 1. basophil 2. complete blood count
    3. hemoglobin 4. prothrombin time 5. graft
    vs. host disease 6. red blood count/red blood
    cell 7. packed cell volume 8. erythrocyte
    sedimentation rate 9. differential
    10. lymphocyte
E. 1. g 2. i 3. e 4. a 5. h 6. d 7. c 8. j 9. b 10. f
F. 1. AIDS 2. ARC 3. HIV 4. ALL 5. BMT 6. mono
    7. KS 8. eosins, eos 9. IG 10. SCIDS
G. 1. lymphaden/o 2. thromb/o 3. sanguin/o,
    hem/o, hemat/o 4. tonsill/o 5. tox/o 6. phag/o
    7. lymphangi/o 8. path/o 9. splen/o
    10. lymph/o
H. 1. polycythemia vera 2. mononucleosis 3. ana-
    phylac tic shock 4. HIV 5. Kaposi's sarcoma
    6. AIDS 7. Hodgkin's disease 8. Pneumocystis
    9. aplastic 10. pernicious
I. 1. c 2. h 3. d 4. a 5. e 6. b 7. f 8. g 9. j 10. i
J. 1. reverse transcriptase inhibitor, e 2. anticoagu-
    lant, a 3. antihemorrhagic, d 4. antihistamine, h
    5. immunosuppresant, f 6. thrombolytic, b
    7. hematinic, g 8. corticosteroid, c 9. antiplate-
    let agent, i
K. 1. d 2. f 3. b 4. g 5. a 6. e 7. c

Labeling Exercise

A. 1. plasma 2. red blood cells or erythrocytes
    3. platelets or thrombocytes 4. white blood
    cells or leukocytes
B. 1. cervical nodes 2. mediastinal nodes 3. axillary
    nodes 4. inguinal nodes
C. 1. thymus gland 2. lymph node 3. tonsil
    4. spleen 5. lymphatic vessels

Chapter 7 Answers
Real World Applications

Medical Record Analysis

1. asthma—Disease caused by various conditions,
    like allergens, and resulting in constriction of
    the bronchial airways, dyspnea, coughing, and
    wheezing. Can cause violent spasms of the
    bronchi (bronchospasms) but is generally not a
    life-threatening condition. Medication can be
    very effective.
2. dyspnea—Term describing difficult or labored
    breathing.

3. cyanosis—Refers to the bluish tint of skin that
    is receiving an insufficient amount of oxygen or
    circulation.
4. expiration—To breath out; exhale or expiration
5. phlegm—Thick mucus secreted by the mem-
    branes that line the respiratory tract. When
    phlegm is coughed through the mouth, it is
    called *sputum*. Phlegm is examined for color,
    odor, and consistency.
6. auscultation—To listen to body sounds, usually
    using a stethoscope.
7. rhonchi—Somewhat musical sound during
    expiration, often found in asthma or infection.
    Caused by spasms of the bronchial tubes. Also
    called *wheezing*.
8. arterial blood gases (ABGs)—Testing for the
    gases present in the blood. Generally used to
    assist in determining the levels of oxygen (O_2)
    and carbon dioxide (CO_2) in the blood.
9. hypoxemia—The condition of having an insuf-
    ficient amount of oxygen in the bloodstream.
10. spirometry—Procedure to measure lung capac-
    ity using a *spirometer*.
11. Proventil—Medication that elaxes muscle
    spasms in bronchial tubes. Used to treat asthma.
12. bronchospasms—An involuntary muscle
    spasm of the smooth muscle in the wall of the
    bronchus.

Chart Note Transcription

1. dyspnea 2. tachyp nea 3. arterial blood gases
(ABGs) 4. hypoxemia 5. auscultation 6. crackles
7. purulent 8. sputum 9. CXR 10. pneumonia
11. endotracheal intubation

Case Study

1. Pneumonia
2. dyspnea-difficulty breathing; dizziness;
    orthopnea-comfortable breathing only while
    sitting up; elevated temperature, cough
3. Auscultation (listening to the body sounds)
    revealed crackles (abnormal sound); chest x-ray
    revealed fluid in the upper lobe of the right
    lung.
4. A method of determining a patient's general
    health and heart and lung function by measur-
    ing pulse (100 BPM and rapid), respiratory rate
    (24 breaths/min and labored), temperature
    (102°F), and blood pressure (180/110)
5. IV antibiotics—medicine to kill bacteria given
    into a vein; intermittent positive pressure
    breathing—method of assisting patients in
    breathing by using a machine that produces an
    increased pressure
6. The IV antibiotics were changed to oral
    antibiotics—she started taking pills.

Practice Exercises

A. 1. exchange of O_2 and CO_2 2. ventilation
3. exchange of O_2 and CO_2 in the lungs
4. exchange of O_2 and CO_2 at cellular level
5. nasal cavity, pharynx, larynx, trachea, bronchial tubes, lungs 6. pharynx 7. epiglottis
8. filter out dust 9. diaphragm 10. 12–20
11. 30–60 12. 3; 2 13. alveoli 14. pleura
15. palate 16. bronchioles

B. 1. dilation 2. carbon dioxide 3. voice 4. chest
5. breathing 6. spitting 7. smell

C. 1. rhinitis 2. rhinorrhagia 3. rhinorrhea
4. rhinoplasty 5. laryngitis 6. laryngospasm
7. laryngoscopy 8. laryngeal 9. laryngotomy 10. laryngectomy 11. laryngoplasty
12. laryngoplegia 13. bronchial 14. bronchitis
15. bronchoscopy 16. bronchogenic 17. bronchospasm 18. thoracoplasty 19. thoracotomy
20. thoracalgia 21. thoracic 22. tracheotomy
23. tracheoplasty 24. tracheostenosis 25. endotracheal 26. tracheitis

D. 1. trachea or windpipe 2. larynx 3. bronchus
4. breathing 5. lung or air 6. nose 7. dust
8. pleura 9. epiglottis 10. alveolus or air sac
11. lung 12. oxygen 13. sinus 14. lobe 15. nose

E. 1. eupnea 2. dyspnea 3. tachypnea
4. orthopnea 5. apnea

F. 1. inhalation or inspiration 2. hemoptysis
3. pulmonary emboli 4. sinusitis 5. pharyngitis
6. pneumothorax 7. pertussis 8. pleurotomy
9. pleurodynia 10. nasopharyngitis

G. 1. URI 2. PFT 3. LLL 4. O_2 5. CO_2 6. IPPB 7. COPD
8. Bronch 9. TLC 10. TB 11. IRDS

H. 1. chest X-ray 2. tidal volume 3. temperature,
pulse, respirations 4. arterial blood gases
5. dyspnea on exertion 6. right upper lobe
7. sudden infant death syndrome 8. total lung
capacity 9. adult respiratory distress syndrome
10. metered dose inhaler 11. clear to auscultation 12. severe acute respiratory syndrome

I. 1. e 2. k 3. h 4. a 5. j 6. l 7. c 8. g 9. f 10. b 11. d
12. i

J. 1. volume of air in the lungs after a maximal
inhalation or inspiration 2. amount of air entering lungs in a single inspiration or leaving air
in single expiration of quiet breathing 3. air
remaining in the lungs after a forced expiration

K. 1. cardiopulmonary resuscitation 2. thoracentesis 3. respirator 4. supplemental oxygen
5. patent 6. ventilation-perfusion scan 7. sputum cytology 8. hyperventilation 9. rhonchi
10. anthracosis

L. 1. decongestant, f 2. antitussive, a 3. antibiotic,
c 4. expectorant, g 5. mucolytic, h 6. bronchodilator, d 7. antihistamine, e 8. corticosteroid, b

Labeling Exercise

A. 1. pharynx and larynx 2. trachea 3. nasal cavity
4. bronchial tubes 5. lungs

B. 1. nares 2. paranasal sinuses 3. nasal cavity
4. hard palate 5. soft palate 6. palatine tonsil
7. epiglottis 8. vocal cords 9. esophagus
10. trachea

C. 1. trachea 2. right upper lobe 3. right middle
lobe 4. right lower lobe 5. apex of lung 6. left
upper lobe 7. left lower lobe 8. diaphragm

Chapter 8 Answers
Real World Applications

Medical Record Analysis

1. epigastric—Pertaining to the area above the
stomach.
2. anemia—A large group of conditions characterized by a reduction in the number of red
blood cells or the amount of hemoglobin in
the blood; results in less oxygen reaching the
tissues.
3. melena—Passage of dark tarry stools. Color
is the result of digestive enzymes working on
blood in the gastrointestinal tract.
4. dyspepsia—An "upset stomach"
5. antacids—Medication to neutralize stomach
acid
6. complete blood count (CBC)—A combination
of blood tests including: red blood cell count,
white blood cell count, hemoglobin, hematocrit, white blood cell differential, and platelet
count.
7. fecal occult blood—Laboratory test on the
feces to determine if microscopic amounts of
blood are present. Also called *hemoccult* or
stool guaiac.
8. *Helicobacter pylori*—A bacteria that may damage the lining of the stomach setting up the
conditions for peptic ulcer disease to develop
9. gastroscopy—Procedure in which a flexible
gastroscope is passed through the mouth and
down the esophagus in order to visualize inside
the stomach. Used to diagnose peptic ulcers
and gastric carcinoma.
10. ulcer—An open sore or lesion in the skin or
mucous membrane.
11. peptic ulcer disease—Ulcer occurring in the
lower portion of the esophagus, stomach, and/
or duodenum; thought to be caused by the
acid of gastric juices. Initial damage to the protective lining of the stomach may be caused
by a *Helicobacter pylori* (*H. pylori*) bacterial

infection. If the ulcer extends all the way through the wall of the stomach, it is called a *perforated ulcer* which requires immediate surgery to repair.

12. gastrectomy—surgical removal of the stomach

Chart Note Transcription

1. gastroenterologist 2. constipation 3. cholelithiasis 4. cholecystectomy 5. gastroesophageal reflux disease 6. ascites 7. lower gastrointestinal series 8. polyposis 9. colonoscopy 10. sigmoid colon 11. colectomy 12. colostomy

Case Study

1. severe RUQ pain-severe pain is located in the upper right corner of the abdomen; nausea-feeling the urge to vomit; emesis-vomiting; scleral jaundice-the whites of the eye have a yellowish cast to them
2. gallbladder, right kidney, majority of the liver, a small portion of the pancreas, portion of colon and small intestine
3. gallstones blocking the common bile duct so bile can't drain into the small intestine
4. abdominal ultrasound- The use of high frequency sound waves to produce an image of an organ, such as the uterus and ovaries or a fetus; percutaneous transhepatic cholangiography (PTC)- Procedure in which contrast medium is injected directly into the liver to visualize the bile ducts; used to detect obstructions such as gallstones in the common bile duct.
5. cholelithiasis is the condition of having gallstones present in the gallbladder, they may not be causing any symptoms; cholecystitis is the inflammation of the gallbladder that occurs when gallstones block the flow of bile out of the gallbladder
6. laparoscopic cholecystectomy- The gallbladder was removed through a very small abdominal incision with the assistance of a laparoscope.

Practice Exercises

A. 1. gastrointestinal 2. gut, alimentary canal, mouth, anus 3. salivary glands, liver, gallbladder, pancreas 4. digesting food, absorbing nutrients, eliminating waste 5. cutting, grinding 6. peristalsis 7. hydrochloric acid, chyme 8. duodenum, jejunum, ileum 9. sigmoid 10. bile, eumulsification, gallbladder

B. 1. gastritis 2. gastroenterology 3. gastrectomy 4. gastroscopy 5. gastralgia 6. gastromegaly 7. gastrotomy 8. esophagitis 9. esophagoscopy 10. esophagoplasty 11. esophageal

12. esophagectasis 13. proctopexy 14. proctoptosis 15. proctitis 16. proctologist 17. cholecystectomy 18. cholecystolithiasis 19. cholecystolithotripsy 20. cholecystitis 21. laparoscope 22. laparotomy 23. laparoscopy 24. hepatoma 25. hepatomegaly 26. hepatic 27. hepatitis 28. pancreatitis 29. pancreatic 30. colostomy 31. colitis

C. 1. esophagus 2. liver 3. ileum 4. anus and rectum 5. tongue 6. lip 7. jejunum 8. sigmoid colon 9. rectum 10. gum 11. gallbladder 12. duodenum 13. anus 14. small intestine 15. tooth

D. 1. postprandial 2. cholelithiasis 3. anorexia 4. dysphagia 5. hematemesis 6. bradypepsia

E. 1. bowel movement 2. upper gastrointestinal series 3. barium enema 4. bowel sounds 5. nausea and vomiting 6. ova and parasites 7. by mouth 8. common bile duct 9. nothing by mouth 10. postprandial

F. 1. h 2. i 3. f 4. c 5. a 6. j 7. l 8. e 9. b 10. k 11. d 12. g 13. o 14. p 15. n 16. m

G. 1. NG 2. GI 3. HBV 4. FOBT 5. IBD 6. HSV-1 7. AST 8. pc 9. PUD 10. GERD

H. 1. visual exam of the colon 2. tooth X-ray 3. bright red blood in the stools 4. blood test to determine amount of waste product in the bloodstream 5. weight loss and wasting from a chronic illness 6. use NG tube to wash out stomach 7. surgical repair of hernia 8. pulling teeth 9. surgical crushing of common bile duct stone 10. surgically create a connection between two organs

I. 1. liver biopsy 2. colostomy 3. barium swallow 4. lower GI series 5. colectomy 6. fecal occult blood test 7. choledocholithotripsy 8. total parenteral nutrition 9. gastric stapling 10. intravenous cholecystography 11. colonoscopy 12. ileostomy

J. 1. d 2. g 3. h 4. e 5. f 6. b 7. c 8. a

K. 1. antidiarrheal, f 2. proton pump inhibitor, g 3. antiemetic, d 4. H$_2$-receptor antagonist, a 5. anorexiant, b 6. laxative, c 7. antacid, e

Labeling Exercise

A. 1. salivary glands 2. esophagus 3. pancreas 4. small intestine 5. oral cavity 6. stomach 7. liver and gallbladder 8. colon

B. 1. esophagus 2. cardiac or lower esophageal sphincter 3. pyloric sphincter 4. duodenum 5. antrum 6. fundus of stomach 7. rugae 8. body of stomach

C. 1. cystic duct 2. common bile duct 3. gallbladder 4. duodenum 5. liver 6. hepatic duct 7. pancreas 8. pancreatic duct

Chapter 9 Answers
Real World Applications

Medical Record Analysis

1. hematuria—The presence of blood in the urine.
2. pyelonephritis—Inflammation of the renal pelvis and the kidney. One of the most common types of kidney disease. It may be the result of a lower urinary tract infection that moved up to the kidney by way of the ureters. There may be large quantities of white blood cells and bacteria in the urine. Blood (hematuria) may even be present in the urine in this condition. Can occur with any untreated or persistent case of cystitis.
3. chronic cystitis—Urinary bladder inflammation
4. dysuria—Difficult or painful urination
5. clean catch urinalysis—Laboratory test that consists of the physical, chemical, and microscopic examination of urine. Laboratory test that consists of the physical, chemical, and microscopic examination of urine.
6. pyuria—The presence of pus in the urine.
7. culture and sensitivity—Laboratory test of urine for bacterial infection. Attempt to grow bacteria on a culture medium in order to identify it and determine which antibiotics it is sensitive to.
8. pathogen—Anything, such as bacteria, viruses, fungi, or toxins, that may cause disease
9. antibiotic—Medication used to treat bacterial infections of the urinary tract.
10. cystoscopy—Visual examination of the urinary bladder using an instrument called a *cystoscope*.
11. bladder neck obstruction—Blockage of the bladder outlet. Often caused by an enlarged prostate gland in males.
12. congenital present from birth
13. catheterized—Insertion of a tube through the urethra and into the urinary bladder for the purpose of withdrawing urine or inserting dye.

Chart Note Transcription

1. urologist 2. hematuria 3. cystitis 4. clean-catch specimen 5. urinalysis (U/A, UA) 6. pyuria 7. retrograde pyelogram 8. ureter 9. ureterolith 10. extracorporeal shockwave lithotripsy (ESWL) 11. calculi

Case Study

1. Cystitis—Inflammation of the urinary bladder; pyelonephritis–Inflammation of the renal pelvis and the kidney. One of the most common types of kidney disease. It may be the result of a lower urinary tract infection that moved up to the kidney by way of the ureters. There may be large quantities of white blood cells and bacteria in the urine. Blood (hematuria) may even be present in the urine in this condition. Can occur with any untreated or persistent case of cystitis.
2. Fever; chills; fatigue; urgency—Feeling the need to urinate immediately; frequency—Urge to urinate more often than normal; dysuria—Difficult or painful urination; hematuria—Blood in the urine; cloudy urine with a fishy smell—Urine was not clear and smelled bad
3. Clean catch specimen—Urine sample obtained after cleaning off the urinary opening and catching or collecting a urine sample in midstream (halfway through the urination process) to minimize contamination from the genitalia.; U/A (urinalysis)—A physical, chemical, and microscopic examination of the urine; urine C&S (culture & sensitivity)—Test for the presence and identification of bacteria in the urine; KUB (kidney, ureters, and bladder)—An x-ray of the urinary organs
4. Pyuria—Pus in the urine; bacteriuria—Bacteria in the urine; acidic pH—Indicates a urinary tract infection; culture and sensitivity—Revealed a common type of bacteria; KUB—Pyelonephritis
5. antibiotic—To kill the bacteria; push fluids—To flush out the bladder.
6. Clear yellow to deep gold color, aromatic odor, specific gravity between 1.010–1.030, pH between 5.0–8.0, very little protein, no glucose, ketones, or blood

Practice Exercises

A. 1. nephrons 2. filtration, reabsorption, secretion 3. electrolytes 4. retroperitoneal 5. hilum 6. glomerulus 7. calyx 8. two, one 9. micturition, voiding 10. urinalysis
B. 1. nephropexy 2. nephrogram 3. nephrolithiasis 4. nephrectomy 5. nephritis 6. nephropathy 7. nephrosclerosis 8. cystitis 9. cystorrhagia 10. cystoplasty 11. cystoscope 12. cystalgia 13. pyeloplasty 14. pyelitis 15. pyelogram 16. ureterolith 17. ureterectasis 18. ureterostenosis 19. urethritis 20. urethroscope
C. 1. urine 2. meatus 3. urinary bladder 4. kidney 5. renal pelvis 6. sugar 7. night 8. scanty 9. ureter 10. glomerulus
D. 1. antispasmodic, b 2. antibiotic, c 3. diuretic, a
E. 1. urination, voiding 2. increases urine production 3. pain associated with kidney stone 4. inserting a tube through urethra into the bladder 5. inflammation of renal pelvis 6. inflammation of glomeruli in the kidney 7. cutting into an organ to remove stone 8. bedwetting 9. enlargement of urethral opening 10. damage to glomerulus secondary to diabetes mellitus 11. lab test of chemical

composition of urine 12. decrease in force of urine stream

F.   1. anuria 2. hematuria 3. calculus/nephrolith 4. lithotripsy 5. urethritis 6. pyuria 7. bacteriuria 8. dysuria 9. ketonuria 10. proteinuria 11. polyuria

G.   1. K+ 2. Na+ 3. UA 4. BUN 5. SG, sp.gr. 6. IVP 7. BNO 8. I & O 9. ATN 10. ESRD

H.   1. kidneys, ureters, bladder 2. catheter/catheterization 3. cystoscopy 4. genitourinary 5. extracorporeal shockwave lithotripsy 6. urinary tract infection 7. urine culture 8. retrograde pyelogram 9. acute renal failure 10. blood urea nitrogen 11. chronic renal failure 12. water

I.   1. c 2. g 3. h 4. i 5. f 6. e 7. d 8. b 9. a 10. j

J.   1. drooping 2. condition of the urine 3. stone 4. surgical crushing 5. condition of stones

K.   1. renal transplant 2. nephropexy 3. urinary tract infection 4. pyelolithectomy 5. renal biopsy 6. ureterectomy 7. cystostomy 8. cystoscopy 9. IVP

Labeling Exercise

A.   1. kidney 2. urinary bladder 3. ureter 4. male urethra 5. female urethra

B.   1. cortex 2. medulla 3. calyx 4. renal pelvis 5. renal papilla 6. renal pyramid 7. ureter

C.   1. efferent arteriole 2. glomerular (Bowman's) capsule 3. glomerulus 4. afferent arteriole 5. proximal convoluted tubule 6. descending nephron loop 7. distal convoluted tubule 8. collecting tubule 9. ascending nephron loop 10. peritubular capillaries

Chapter 10 Answers
Real World Applications

Medical Chart Analysis

1.   gestation—The length of time of pregnancy, normally about 40 weeks.

2.   amniocentesis—Puncturing of the amniotic sac using a needle and syringe for the purpose of withdrawing amniotic fluid for testing. Can assist in determining fetal maturity, development, and genetic disorders.

3.   fetus—The unborn infant from approximately week 9 until birth.

4.   obstetrician—Branch of medicine specializing in the diagnosis and treatment of women during pregnancy and childbirth, and immediately after childbirth. Physician is called an obstetrician.

5.   multigravida—A woman who has not been pregnant.

6.   nullipara—A woman who has not given birth to a live infant.

7.   miscarriage—Unplanned loss of a pregnancy due to the death of the embryo or fetus before the time it is viable, also referred to as a spontaneous abortion.

8.   pelvic ultrasound—Use of high frequency sound waves to produce an image or photograph of an organ, such as the uterus, ovaries, or fetus.

9.   placenta previa—A placenta that is implanted in the lower portion of the uterus and, in turn, blocks the birth canal.

10. abruptio placentae—Emergency condition in which the placenta tears away from the uterine wall prior to delivery of the infant. Requires immediate delivery of the baby.

11. placenta—The organ than connects the fetus to the mothers uterus, supplies fetus with oxygen and nutrients.

12. C-section—Surgical delivery of a baby through an incision into the abdominal and uterine walls.

Chart Note Transcription

1. ejaculation 2. cryptorchidism 3. orchidopexy 4. vasectomy 5. ejaculation 6. digital rectal exam (DRE) 7. prostate cancer 8. prostate-specific antigen (PSA) 9. benign prostatic hyperplasia (BPH) 10. transurethral resection (TUR)

Case Study

1.   Genital herpes.

2.   Fever—she has a temperature; malaise–a feeling of general discomfort; dysuria–painful urination; vaginal leukorrhea–a white discharge or flow from the vagina

3.   Vesicles—small fluid-filled blisters; ulcers–crater like erosions of the skin; erythema–redness; edema–swelling

4.   An abnormality located on the body in some area outside of the genital region

5.   To feel with your hands

6.   There is a risk of passing the virus to the baby as it passes through the birth canal.

Practice Exercises

A.   1. gynecology 2. gynecologist 3. dilation, expulsion, placental 4. gestation 5. menopause 6. ovum 7. endometrium 8. uterus 9. uterine tubes 10. total abdominal hysterectomy–bilateral salpingo-oophorectomy

B.   1. suprapubic prostatectomy 2. transurethral resection 3. genitourinary 4. benign prostatic hyperplasia 5. digital rectal exam 6. prostate-specific antigen

C.   1. the formation of mature sperm 2. accumulation of fluid within the testes 3. surgical removal of the prostate gland by inserting a device through the urethra and removing prostate tissue 4. inability to father children due to a problem with spermatogenesis 5. surgical removal of the testes 6. surgical removal of part or all of the vas deferens 7. Removal of the testicles in the male or the ovaries in the female.

D. 1. colposcopy 2. colposcope 3. cervicectomy 4. cervicitis 5. cervical 6. hysteropexy 7. hysterectomy 8. hysterorrhexis 9. oophoritis 10. oophorectomy 11. mammary 12. mammogram 13. mammoplasty 14. amniotic 15. amniotomy 16. amniorrhea

E. 1. cervix 2. last menstrual period 3. fetal heart rate 4. pelvic inflammatory disease 5. gynecology 6. cesarean section 7. newborn 8. premenstrual syndrome 9. toxic shock syndrome 10. low birth weight

F. 1. GI, grav I 2. AI 3. UC 4. FTND 5. IUD 6. D & C 7. HRT 8. gyn/GYN 9. AB 10. OCPs

G. 1. uterus 2. uterus 3. female 4. vulva 5. ovary 6. ovary 7. uterine tube 8. menstruation or menses 9. vagina 10. breast

H. 1. b 2. e 3. h 4. c 5. i 6. j 7. d 8. n 9. l 10. f 11. o 12. g 13. k 14. m 15. a

I. 1. labor, childbirth 2. pregnancy 3. beginning 4. pregnancy 5. childbirth 6. to bear (offspring) 7. uterine tube 8. sperm condition

J. 1. conization 2. stillbirth 3. puberty 4. premenstrual syndrome 5. laparoscopy 6. fibroid tumor 7. D & C 8. eclampsia 9. endometriosis 10. cesarean section

K. 1. urinary, reproductive 2. testes, epididymis, penis 3. foreskin 4. testes 5. bulbourethral glands 6. testosterone 7. perineum

L. 1. e 2. i 3. h 4. c 5. a 6. d 7. g 8. b 9. f

M. 1. prostatectomy 2. prostatic 3. prostatitis 4. orchiectomy 5. orchioplasty 6. orchiotomy 7. aspermia 8. oligospermia 9. spermatogenesis 10. spermatolysis

N. 1. androgen therapy, f 2. oxytocin, a 3. antiprostatic agent, b 4. birth control pills, g 5. spermatocide, d 6. erectile dysfunction agent, h 7. hormone replacement therapy, i 8. abortifacient, e 9. fertility drug, c

Labeling Exercise

A. 1. uterine tube 2. ovary 3. fundus of uterus 4. corpus (body) of uterus 5. cervix 6. vagina 7. clitoris 8. labium majora 9. labium minora

B. 1. seminal vesicle 2. vas deferens 3. prostate gland 4. bulbourethral gland 5. urethra 6. epididymis 7. glans penis 8. testis

C. 1. areola 2. nipple 3. lactiferous gland 4. lactiferous duct 5. fat

Chapter 11 Answers
Real World Applications

Medical Record Analysis

1. hyperglycemia—The condition of having a high level of sugar in the blood; associated with diabetes mellitus.
2. ketoacidosis—Acidosis due to an excess of acidic ketone bodies (waste products). A serious condition requiring immediate treatment that can result in death for the diabetic patient if not reversed. Also called *diabetic acidosis*.
3. glycosuria—Having a high level of sugar excreted in the urine.
4. type 1 diabetes mellitus—Also called *insulin-dependent diabetes mellitus*. It develops early in life when the pancreas stops insulin production. Patient must take daily insulin injections.
5. polyuria—The condition of producing and excessive amount of urine.
6. polydipsia—Excessive feeling of thirst.
7. fasting blood sugar–Blood test to measure the amount of sugar circulating throughout the body after a 12-hour fast.
8. insulin—Medication administered to replace insulin for type 1 diabetics or to treat severe type 2 diabetics.
9. glucose tolerance test—Test to determine the blood sugar level. A measured dose of glucose is given to a patient either orally or intravenously. Blood samples are then drawn at certain intervals to determine the ability of the patient to use glucose. Used for diabetic patients to determine their insulin response to glucose.
10. glucometer—A device that is designed for a diabetic to use at home to measure the level of glucose in the bloodstream.

Chart Note Transcription

1. endocrinologist 2. obesity 3. hirsutism 4. radio immunoassay (RIA) 5. cortisol 6. adenoma 7. adrenal cortex 8. Cushing's syndrome 9. adenoma 10. adrenal cortex 11. adrenalectomy

Case Study

1. Diabetes mellitus
2. Diaphoresis—Profuse sweating; rapid respirations—Breathing fast; rapid pulse—Fast heart rate; disorientation—Confused about his surroundings
3. Blood serum test—Lab test to measure the levels of different substances in the blood, used to determine the function of endocrine glands

4. Hyperglycemia—blood level of glucose is too high; ketoacidosis–an excessive amount of acidic ketone bodies in the body
5. Type 1, insulin-dependent, or juvenile diabetes mellitus because he has had it since childhood and he is taking insulin shots.
6. Type 2, non-insulin-dependent diabetes mellitus typically develops later in life. The pancreas produces normal to high levels of insulin, but the cells fail to respond to it. Patients may take oral hypoglycemic agents to improve insulin function, or may eventually have to take insulin.

Practice Exercises

A. 1. endocrinology 2. pituitary 3. gonads 4. corticosteroids 5. testosterone 6. estrogen, progesterone 7. antidiuretic hormone (ADH) 8. thymus gland 9. exophthalmos 10. adenocarcinoma
B. 1. thyroidectomy 2. thyroidal 3. hyperthyroidism 4. pancreatic 5. pancreatitis 6. pancreatectomy 7. pancreatotomy 8. adrenal 9. adrenomegaly 10. adrenopathy 11. thymoma 12. thymectomy 13. thymic 14. thymitis
C. 1. sodium 2. female 3. pineal gland 4. pituitary gland 5. potassium 6. calcium 7. parathyroid glands 8. extremities 9. sugar 10. sex glands
D. 1. e 2. d 3. a 4. f 5. c 6. b
E. 1. NIDDM 2. IDDM 3. ACTH 4. PTH 5. T_3 6. TSH 7. FBS 8. PRL
F. 1. b 2. a 3. e 4. k 5. h 6. j 7. i 8. f 9. g 10. c 11. d
G. 1. protein-bound iodine 2. potassium 3. thyroxine 4. glucose tolerance test 5. diabetes mellitus 6. basal metabolic rate 7. sodium 8. antidiuretic hormone
H. 1. glycosuria 2. vasopressin 3. polyuria 4. hypercalcemia 5. polydipsia 6. adrenocorticotropin 7. postprandial
I. 1. hormone obtained from cortex of adrenal gland 2. having excessive hair 3. a nerve condition characterized with spasms of extremities; can occur from imbalance of pH and calcium or disorder of parathyroid gland 4. disorder of the retina occurring with diabetes mellitus 5. increase in blood sugar level 6. decrease in blood sugar level 7. another term for epinephrine; produced by inner portion of adrenal gland 8. hormone produced by pancreas; essential for metabolism of blood sugar 9. toxic condition due to hyperactivity of thyroid gland 10. a condition resulting when the endocrine gland secretes more hormone than is needed by the body
J. 1. insulinoma 2. ketoacidosis 3. panhypopituitarinism 4. pheochromocytoma 5. Hashimoto's thyroiditis 6. gynecomastia
K. 1. corticosteroids, e 2. human growth hormone therapy, a 3. oral hypoglycemic agent, d 4. antithyroid agent, c 5. insulin, f 6. vasopressin, b

Labeling Exercise

A. 1. pineal gland 2. thyroid and parathyroid glands 3. adrenal glands 4. pancreas 5. pituitary gland 6. thymus gland 7. ovary 8. testis
B. 1. pituitary gland 2. bone and soft tissue 3. GH 4. testes 5. FSH, LH 6. ovary 7. FSH, LH 8. thyroid gland 9. TSH 10. adrenal cortex 11. ACTH 12. breast 13. PRL
C. 1. liver 2. stomach 3. pancreas 4. beta cell 5. alpha cell 6. islet of Langerhans

Chapter 12 Answers
Real World Applications

Medical Chart Analysis

1. paraplegia—Paralysis of the lower portion of the body and both legs.
2. comminuted fracture—Fracture in which the bone is shattered, splintered, or crushed into many small pieces or fragments.
3. epidural hematoma—Mass of blood in the space outside the dura mater of the brain and spinal cord.
4. spinal cord injury—Damage to the spinal cord as a result of trauma. Spinal cord may be bruised or completely severed.
5. unconscious—State of being unaware of surroundings, with the inability to respond to stimuli.
6. anesthesia—The lack of feeling or sensation.
7. paralysis—Temporary or permanent loss of function or voluntary movement.
8. computed tomography scan (CT scan)—An imaging technique that is able to produce a cross-sectional view of the body.
9. laminectomy—Removal of a portion of a vertebra, called the lamina, in order to relieve pressure on the spinal nerve.
10. spinal fusion—Surgical immobilization of adjacent vertebrae. This may be done for several reasons, including correction for a herniated disk.
11. physical therapy (PT)—treats disorders using physical means and methods; includes joint motion and muscle strength
12. occupational therapy (OT)—assists patients to regain, develop, and improve skills that are important for independent functioning

Chart Note Transcription

1. neurologist 2. dysphasia 3. hemiplegia 4. convulsions 5. electroencephalography (EEG) 6. lumbar puncture (LP) 7. brain scan 8. cerebral cortex 9. astrocytoma 10. craniotomy 11. cryosurgery

Case Study

1. Cerebrovascular Accident (CVA or stroke)
2. aphasia—Inability to speak; hemiparesis—Weakness on one side of the body; syncope—Fainting; delirium—Abnormal mental state with confusion, disorientation, and agitation
3. hypertension—High blood pressure; atherosclerosis—Hardening of arteries due to build up of yellow fatty substances; diabetes mellitus—Inability to make or use insulin properly to control blood sugar levels
4. brain scan—An image of the brain after injection of radioactive isotopes into the circulation; revealed an infarct in the right cerebral hemisphere
5. infarct—An area of tissue within an organ that undergoes necrosis (death) following the loss of its blood supply
6. hemorrhage—Ruptured blood vessel; thrombus—Stationary clot; embolus—Floating clot; compression—Pinching off a blood vessel

Practice Exercises

A. 1. neurology 2. brain, spinal cord, nerves 3. peripheral nervous system, central nervous system 4. efferent or motor 5. afferent or sensory 6. cerebrum 7. cerebellum 8. eyesight 9. hearing, smell 10. parasympathetic, sympathetic
B. 1. h 2. k 3. d 4. g 5. a 6. b 7. f 8. j 9. e 10. l 11. i 12. c
C. 1. neuritis 2. neurologist 3. neuralgia 4. polyneuritis 5. neurectomy 6. neuroplasty 7. neuroma 8. neurorrhaphy 9. meningitis 10. meningocele 11. myelomeningocele 12. encephalogram 13. encephalopathy 14. encephalitis 15. encephalocele 16. cerebrospinal 17. cerebral
D. 1. transient ischemic attack 2. multiple sclerosis 3. spinal cord injury 4. central nervous system 5. peripheral nervous system 6. headache 7. cerebral palsy 8. lumbar puncture 9. amyotrophic lateral sclerosis
E. 1. b 2. f 3. g 4. h 5. i 6. a 7. e 8. c 9. d
F. 1. CSF 2. CVD 3. EEG 4. ICP 5. PET 6. CVA 7. SAH 8. ANS
G. 1. injecting radiopaque dye into spinal canal to examine under X-ray the outlines made by the dye 2. X-ray of the blood vessels of the brain after the injection of radiopaque dye 3. reflex test on bottom of foot to detect lesion and abnormalities of nervous system 4. test that measures how fast an impulse travels along a nerve to pinpoint an area of nerve damage 5. laboratory examination of fluid taken from the brain and spinal cord 6. positron emission tomography to measure cerebral blood flow, blood volume, oxygen, and glucose uptake 7. recording the ultrasonic echoes of the brain 8. needle puncture into the spinal cavity to withdraw fluid
H. 1. paralysis 2. muscular coordination 3. pertaining to development 4. weakness 5. speech
I. 1. meninges 2. brain 3. cerebellum 4. spinal cord 5. head 6. thalamus 7. nerve 8. nerve root 9. cerebrum 10. pons
J. 1. tumor of astrocyte cells 2. seizure 3. without sensation 4. weakness of one-half of body 5. physician that treats nervous system with surgery 6. without sense of pain 7. localized seizure of one limb 8. paralysis of all four limbs 9. accumulation of blood in the subdural space 10. within the meninges
K. 1. d 2. e 3. f 4. g 5. b 6. a 7. c 8. j 9. h 10. i
L. 1. delirium 2. amyotrophic lateral sclerosis 3. Bell's palsy 4. cerebral aneurysm 5. Parkinson's disease 6. cerebrospinal fluid shunt 7. transient ischemic attack 8. subdural hematoma 9. cerebral palsy 10. nerve conduction velocity
M. 1. anesthetic, e 2. dopaminergic drugs, a 3. hypnotic, d 4. analgesic, g 5. sedative, b 6. narcotic analgesic, c 7. anticonvulsant, f

Labeling Exercise

A. 1. brain 2. spinal nerves 3. spinal cord
B. 1. dendrites 2. nerve cell body 3. unmyelinated region 4. myelinated axon 5. nucleus 6. axon 7. terminal end fibers
C. 1. cerebrum 2. diencephalon 3. thalamus 4. hypothalamus 5. brain stem 6. midbrain 7. cerebellum 8. pons 9. medulla oblongata

Chapter 13 Answers
Real World Applications

Medical Record Analysis

1. photophobia—Although the term translates into *fear of light,* it actually means a strong sensitivity to bright light.
2. hyperopia—With this condition a person can see things in the distance but has trouble reading material at close range. Also known as *farsightedness.* This condition is corrected with converging or biconvex lenses.

3. visual acuity test—Measurement of the sharpness of a patient's vision. Usually, a Snellen chart is used for this test in which the patient identifies letters from a distance of 20 feet.

4. intraocular—Pertaining to inside the eye.

5. ophthalmoscopy—Examination of the interior of the eyes using an instrument called an *ophthalmoscope*. The physician dilates the pupil in order to see the cornea, lens, and retina. Used to identify abnormalities in the blood vessels of the eye and some systemic diseases.

6. mydriatic drops—Any substance that causes the pupil to dilate by paralyzing the iris and/or ciliary body muscles. Particularly useful during eye examinations and eye surgery.

7. cataract—Damage to the lens causing it to become opaque or cloudy, resulting in diminished vision. Treatment is usually surgical removal of the cataract or replacement of the lens.

8. retinopathy—A general term for disease affecting the retina

9. macular degeneration—Deterioration of the macular area of the retina of the eye. May be treated with laser surgery to destroy the blood vessels beneath the macula.

10. phacoemulsification—Use of high-frequency sound waves to emulsify (liquefy) a lens with a cataract, which is then aspirated (removed by suction) with a needle.

11. prosthetic lens implant—The use of an artificial lens to replace the lens removed during cataract surgery.

Chart Note Transcription

1. otorhinolaryngologist (ENT) 2. otitis media (OM) 3. AU, binaural 4. otoscopy 5. tympanic membrane 6. cerumen 7. tympanometry 8. audiometric test 9. conductive hearing loss 10. myringotomy

Case Study

1. conductive hearing loss results from disease or malformation of the outer or middle ear; all sound is weaker because it is not conducted correctly to the inner ear.

2. sensorineural hearing loss result of damage or malformation of the inner ear or the cochlear nerve

3. otoscopy examination of the auditory canal and middle ear; tympanometry measurement of the movement of the tympanic membrane; audiometry test for hearing ability; Rinne and Weber tuning-fork tests assess both the nerve and bone conduction of

4. Hearing aids or amplification devices amplify sound and will work best for conductive hearing loss; cochlear implant is a device that converts sound signals into magnetic impulses to stimulate the auditory nerve and is used to treat profound sensorineural hearing loss.

5. Protect his ears better during playing music by wearing earplugs

Practice Exercises

A. 1. ophthalmology 2. cilia 3. lacrimal 4. cornea 5. retina 6. iris 7. malleus, incus, stapes 8. otology 9. tympanic membrane 10. cerumen 11. eustachian or auditory 12. vestibulocochlear nerve

B. 1. artificial tears, h 2. antiglaucoma medication, c 3. antibiotic otic solution, i 4. mydriatic, a 5. antiemetic, g 6. antibiotic ophthalmic solution, j 7. anti-inflammatory otic solution, b 8. miotic, f 9. wax emulsifier, e 10. anesthetic ophthalmic solution, d

C. 1. blepharitis 2. blepharoplasty 3. blepharoptosis 4. retinopathy 5. retinopexy 6. ophthalmology 7. ophthalmic 8. ophthalmoscopy 9. iridoplegia 10. iridectomy 11. otoplasty 12. otopyorrhea 13. otalgia 14. otitis 15. tympanorrhexis 16. tympanotomy 17. tympanitis 18. audiogram 19. audiometer 20. audiology

D. 1. -tropia 2. -opia 3. -itis 4. -logy 5. -otomy 6. -plasty 7. -pexy 8. -algia 9. -otia 10. -cusis

E. 1. tear or tear duct 2. choroid 3. water 4. light 5. cornea 6. glassy 7. double 8. gray 9. old age 10. dull or dim 11. ear 12. stapes 13. hearing 14. eustachian or auditory tube 15. eardrum or tympanic membrane

F. 1. conductive—problem with outer or middle ear, muffles sound; sensorineural—damage of inner ear or nerve 2. cornea, pupil, lens, retina 3. mucous membrane that covers and protects front of eyeball 4. incus, malleus, stapes, vibrate to amplify and conduct sound waves from outer ear to inner ear

G. 1. h 2. g 3. a 4. d 5. b 6. i 7. c 8. f 9. e 10. j

H. 1. otology 2. both eyes 3. rapid eye movement 4. hertz 5. senile macular degeneration 6. pupils equal, round, react to light and accommodation 7. intraocular pressure 8. decibel 9. right eye 10. visual field

I. 1. c 2. b 3. d 4. a 5. e 6. j 7. i 8. f 9. h 10. g

J. 1. PE tube 2. EENT 3. BC 4. AU 5. OM 6. EM 7. XT 8. OS 9. EOM 10. VA

K. 1. tonometry 2. emmetropia 3. conjunctivitis 4. myopia 5. cataract 6. hordeolum 7. strabismus 8. hyperopia 9. presbycusis 10. otorhinolaryngologist 11. inner ear 12. Ménière's disease 13. acoustic neuroma

L. 1. dull/dim vision 2. double vision 3. enlarge or widen pupil 4. constrict pupil 5. diminished vision of old age 6. ringing in the ears 7. middle ear bone 8. measure movement in eardrum 9. auditory tube 10. inner ear 11. results of hearing test 12. middle ear infection

Labeling Exercise

A. 1. iris 2. lens 3. conjunctiva 4. pupil 5. cornea
    6. suspensory ligaments 7. ciliary body 8. fovea
    centralis 9. optic nerve 10. retina 11. choroid
    12. sclera

B. 1. pinna 2. external auditory meatus 3. audi-
    tory canal 4. tympanic membrane 5. malleus
    6. incus 7. semicircular canals 8. vestibular nerve
    9. cochlear nerve 10. cochlea 11. round window
    12. stapes 13. Eustachian tube

Glossary/Index

A

Abbreviations, 11. *See also* individual subject headings

Abdomen
  anatomical divisions of, 36*t*
  clinical divisions of, 36*t*

abdominal, pertaining to abdomen, 33, 39

Abdominal aorta, 382*f*

Abdominal cavity, superior portion of abdominopelvic cavity, 34, 34*f*, 35*t*

Abdominal region, 33, 33*f*

Abdominopelvic cavity, ventral cavity consisting of abdominal and pelvic cavities; contains digestive, urinary, and reproductive organs, 34, 35, 36*t*

Abducens nerve, 418*t*

Abduction, directional term meaning to move away from median or middle line of body, 9, 116, 116*f*

Abnormal psychology, study and treatment of behaviors outside of normal and detrimental to person or society; these maladaptive behaviors range from occasional difficulty coping with stress, to bizarre actions and beliefs, to total withdrawal, 500

ABO system, major system of blood typing, 182

Abortifacient, medication that terminates a pregnancy, 351

Abortion (AB), 336

Abrasion, scraping away a portion of skin surface; performed to remove acne scars, tattoos, and scar tissue, 58

Abruptio placentae, emergency condition in which placenta tears away from uterine wall before twentieth week of pregnancy; requires immediate delivery of baby, 345

Abscess, a collection of pus in skin, 63

Absence seizure, type of epileptic seizure that lasts only a few seconds to half a minute, characterized by loss of awareness and absence of activity; also called *petit mal seizure,* 422

Acapnia, lack of carbon dioxide, 218

Accessory nerve, 418*t*

Accessory organs, accessory organs to digestive system consist of organs that are part of system, but not part of continuous tube from mouth to anus; accessory organs are liver, pancreas, gallbladder, and salivary glands, 258, 264–65

ACE inhibitor drugs, medication that produces vasodilation and decreases blood pressure, 163

Achromatopsia, condition of color blindness; more common in males, 456

Acidosis, excessive acidity of body fluids due to accumulation of acids, as in diabetic acidosis, 392

Acne, inflammatory disease of sebaceous glands and hair follicles resulting in papules and pustules, 63

Acne rosacea, hypertrophy of sebaceous glands causing thickened skin generally on nose, forehead, and cheeks, 63

Acne vulgaris, common form of acne occurring in adolescence from oversecretion of oil glands; characterized by papules, pustules, blackheads, and whiteheads, 63

Acoustic, pertaining to hearing, 470

Acoustic neuroma, benign tumor of eighth cranial nerve sheath, which can cause symptoms from pressure being exerted on tissues, 473

Acquired immunity, protective response of body to a specific pathogen, 197

Acquired immunodeficiency syndrome (AIDS), disease involving a defect in cell-mediated immunity system; syndrome of opportunistic infections occurring in final stages of infection with human immunodeficiency virus (HIV); virus attacks T_4 lymphocytes and destroys them, which reduces person's ability to fight infection, 66, 202

Acromegaly, chronic disease of adults resulting in elongation and enlargement of bones of head and extremities, 393, 393*f*

Action, type of movement a muscle produces, 115

Active acquired immunity, immunity developing after direct exposure to a pathogen, 196, 197

Active exercises, exercises that a patient performs without assistance, 516

Active range of motion (AROM), range of motion for joints that a patient is able to perform without assistance of someone else, 516

Anterior lobe, anterior portion of pituitary gland; secretes adrenocorticotropin hormone, follicle-stimulating hormone, growth hormone, luteinizing hormone, melanocyte-stimulating hormone, prolactin, and thyroid-stimulating hormone, 385

Anterior pituitary gland, 385*f*, 386*f*

Anterior tibial artery, 148*f*

Anterior tibial vein, 150*f*

Anteroposterior view (AP), positioning patient so that X-rays pass through body from anterior side to posterior side, 507

Anthracosis, type of pneumoconiosis that develops from collection of coal dust in lung; also called black lung or miner's lung, 234

Anti-inflammatory otic solution, reduces inflammation, itching, and edema associated with otitis externa, 476

Anti-virals, substance that weakens viral infection in body, often by interfering with virus's ability to replicate, 72

Antiarrhythmic, controls cardiac arrhythmias by altering nerve impulses within heart, 163

Antibiotic, substance that destroys or prohibits growth of microorganisms; used to treat bacterial infections; not found effective in treating viral infections; to be effective, it must be taken regularly for specified period, 72, 242, 315

Antibiotic ophthalmic solution, eyedrops for treatment of bacterial eye infections, 463

Antibiotic otic solution, eardrops to treat otitis externa, 476

Antibody, protein material produced in body as a response to invasion of foreign substance, 198

Antibody-mediated immunity, production of antibodies by B cells in response to an antigen; also called *humoral immunity,* 197

Anticoagulant, substance that prevents or delays clotting or coagulation of blood, 163, 189

Anticonvulsant, prevents or relieves convulsions; drugs such as phenobarbital reduce excessive stimulation in brain to control seizures and other symptoms of epilepsy, 433

Antidepressant drugs, medications classified as stimulants that alter patient's mood by affecting levels of neurotransmitters in brain, 504

Antidiarrheal, prevents or relieves diarrhea, 281

Antidiuretic hormone (ADH), hormone secreted by posterior pituitary; promotes water reabsorption by kidney tubules, 381*t*, 385

Antidote, substance that will neutralize poisons or their side effects, 496

Antiemetic, substance that controls nausea and vomiting, 281, 476

Antifungal, substance that kills fungi infecting skin, 72

Antigen, substance capable of inducing formation of antibody; antibody then intereacts with antigen in antigen–antibody reaction, 197

Antigen-antibody complex, combination of antigen with its specific antibody; increases susceptibility to phagocytosis and immunity, 197, 198

Antiglaucoma medications, group of drugs that reduce intraocular pressure by lowering amount of aqueous humor in eyeball; may achieve this by either reducing production of aqueous humor or increasing its outflow, 463

Antihemorrhagic, substance that prevents or stops hemorrhaging, 189

Antihistamine, substance that acts to control allergic symptoms by counteracting histamine, which exists naturally in body, and which is released in allergic reactions, 205, 242

Antilipidemic, substance that reduces amount of cholesterol and lipids in bloodstream; treats hyperlipidemia, 163

Antiparasitic, substance that kills mites or lice, 72

Antiplatelet agent, substance that interferes with action of platelets; prolongs bleeding time; commonly referred to as blood thinner; used to prevent heart attacks and strokes, 163, 189

Antiprostatic agents, medications to treat early cases of benign prostatic hypertrophy; may prevent surgery for mild cases, 362

Antipruritic, substance that reduces severe itching, 72

Antipsychotic drugs, major tranquilizer drugs that have transformed treatment of patients with psychoses and schizophrenia by reducing patient agitation and panic and shortening schizophrenic episodes, 504

Antiseptic, substance used to kill bacteria in skin cuts and wounds or at a surgical site, 72

Antisocial personality disorder, personality disorder in which patient engages in behaviors that are illegal or outside of social norms, 502

Antispasmodic, medication to prevent or reduce bladder muscle spasms, 315

Antithyroid agents, medication given to block production of thyroid hormones in patients with hypersecretion disorders, 397

Antitussive, substance that controls or relieves coughing; codeine is an ingredient in many prescription cough medicines that acts upon the brain to control coughing, 243

Antrum, tapered distal end of the stomach, 262, 262*f*

Anuria, complete suppression of urine formed by kidneys and complete lack of urine excretion, 305

Cytologic testing, examination of cells to determine structure and origin; pap smears are considered a form of cytologic testing, 529

Cytology, study of cells, 24, 39

Cytoplasm, watery internal environment of a cell, 24

Cytotoxic, pertaining to poisoning cells, 197, 198

D

Dacryoadenitis, inflammation of lacrimal gland, 459

Dacryocystitis, inflammation of tear sac, 459

Day surgery, type of outpatient surgery in which patient is discharged on same day he or she is admitted; also called ambulatory surgery, 523

Deafness, inability to hear or having some degree of hearing impairment, 472

Debridement, removal of foreign material and dead or damaged tissue from wound, 71, 516

Decibel (dB), measures intensity or loudness of sound; zero decibels is quietest sound measured and 120 dB is loudest sound commonly measured, 473

Deciduous teeth, 20 teeth that begin to erupt around age of 6 months; eventually pushed out by permanent teeth, 260, 261

Decongestant, substance that reduces nasal congestion and swelling, 243

Decubitus ulcer (decub), bedsore or pressure sore caused by pressure over bony prominences on body; caused by lack of blood flow, 65

Deep, directional term meaning away from surface of body, 37t

Deep tendon reflex (DTR), muscle contraction in response to stretch caused by striking muscle tendon with reflex hammer; test used to determine if muscles are responding properly, 122

Defecation, evacuation of feces from rectum, 263

Defibrillation, procedure that converts serious irregular heartbeats, such as fibrillation, by giving electric shocks to heart, 161, 161f

Delirium, state of mental confusion with lack of orientation to time and place, 423

Delivery, emergence of baby from birth canal, 338, 338f

Delusions, false belief held with conviction even in face of strong evidence to contrary, 503

Dementia, progressive impairment of intellectual function that interferes with performing activities of daily living; patients have little awareness of their condition; found in disorders such as Alzheimer's, 423, 521

Dendrite, branched process off a neuron that receives impulses and carries them to cell body, 412, 413f

Dental, pertaining to teeth 267

Dental caries, gradual decay and disintegration of teeth caused by bacteria that can result in inflamed tissue and abscessed teeth; commonly called a *tooth cavity,* 270

Dentalgia, tooth pain, 269

Dentin, main bulk of tooth; is covered by enamel, 260, 261, 261f

Dentist, practitioner of dentistry, 268

Dentistry, branch of healthcare involved with prevention, diagnosis, and treatment of conditions involving teeth, jaw, and mouth; dentistry is practiced by *dentist* or *oral surgeon,* 268

Denture, partial or complete set of artificial teeth that are set in plastic materials; substitute for natural teeth and related structures, 279

Deoxygenated, blood in veins that is low in oxygen content, 140

Depigmentation, loss of normal skin color or pigment, 59

Depression, downward movement, as in dropping shoulders, 88–89, 118t

Dermabrasion, abrasion or rubbing using wire brushes or sandpaper, 71

Dermal, pertaining to skin, 57

Dermatitis, inflammation of skin, 65

Dermatologist, physician specialized in diagnosis and treatment of diseases of integumentary system, 58

Dermatology (Derm, derm), branch of medicine specializing in conditions of integumentary system, 27t, 39, 58

Dermatome, instrument for cutting skin or thin transplants of skin, 70

Dermatoplasty, surgical repair of skin, 71, 520

Dermatosis, abnormal condition of skin, 65

Dermis, living layer of skin located between epidermis and subcutaneous tissue; also referred to as corium or *true skin;* contains hair follicles, sweat glands, sebaceous glands, blood vessels, lymph vessels, nerve fibers, and muscle fibers, 52, 53f, 54

Descending aorta, 145f

Descending colon, section of colon that descends left side of abdomen, 263, 263f, 264f

Descending tracts, nerve tracts carrying motor signals down spinal cord to muscles, 416, 417

Diabetes insipidus (DI), disorder caused by inadequate secretion of hormone by posterior lobe of pituitary gland; there may be polyuria and polydipsia; is more common in young, 385, 393

Diabetes mellitus (DM), serious disease in which pancreas fails to produce insulin or insulin does not work properly; consequently, patient has very high blood sugar; kidney will attempt to lower high blood sugar level by excreting excess sugar in urine, 385, 392

Glomerular, 300*f*

Glomerular capsule, also called Bowman's capsule; part of renal corpuscle; is a double-walled cuplike structure that encircles glomerulus; in filtration stage of urine production, waste products filtered from blood enter Bowman's capsule as glomerular filtrate, 299, 300*f*, 302*f*

Glomerular filtrate, product of filtration stage of urine production; water, electrolytes, nutrients, wastes, and toxins that are filtered from blood passing through glomerulus; filtrate enters Bowman's capsule, 302

Glomerulonephritis, inflammation of kidney (primarily of glomerulus); since glomerular membrane is inflamed, it becomes more permeable and will allow protein and blood cells to enter filtrate; results in protein in urine (proteinuria) and hematuria, 308

Glomerulus, ball of capillaries encased by Bowman's capsule; in filtration stage of urine production, wastes filtered from blood leave glomerulus capillaries and enter Bowman's capsule, 299, 300*f*, 302*f*

Glossal, pertaining to tongue, 267

Glossopharyngeal nerve, 418*t*

Glottis, opening between vocal cords; air passes through glottis as it moves through larynx; changing tension of vocal cords changes size of opening, 222

Glucagon, hormone secreted by pancreas; stimulates liver to release glucose into blood, 359*t*, 361

Glucocorticoids, group of hormones secreted by adrenal cortex; regulate carbohydrate levels in body; cortisol is an example, 380*t*, 382

Glucose, form of sugar used by cells of body to make energy; transported to cells in blood, 180

Glucose tolerance test (GTT), test to determine blood sugar level; a measured dose of glucose is given to patient either orally or intravenously; blood samples are then drawn at certain intervals to determine ability of patient to utilize glucose; used for diabetic patients to determine their insulin response to glucose, 395

Glutamic oxaloacetic transaminase (GOT), 159

Gluteal, pertaining to buttocks, 40

Gluteal region, refers to buttock region of body, 33, 33*f*

Gluteus maximus, muscle named for its size and location; gluteus means *rump area* and maximus means *large,* 115

Glycosuria, presence of an excess of sugar in urine, 306, 390

Goiter, enlargement of thyroid gland, 394, 394*f*

Gonadotropins, common name for follicle-stimulating hormone and luteinizing hormone, 318*t*, 384, 385

Gonads, organs responsible for producing sex cells; female gonads are ovaries, and they produce ova; male gonads are testes, and they produce sperm, 382

Gonorrhea, sexually transmitted inflammation of mucous membranes of either sex; can be passed on to infant during birth process, 360

Grade, tumor can be graded from grade I through grade IV; grade is based on microscopic appearance of tumor cells; grade I tumor is well differentiated and is easier to treat than more advanced grades, 526, 527, 527*t*

Graft *versus* host disease (GVHD), serious complication of bone marrow transplant; immune cells from donor bone marrow (graft) attack recipient's (host's) tissues, 202

Grand mal seizure, 424

Granulocytes, granular polymorphonuclear leukocyte; there are three types: neutrophil, eosinophil, and basophil, 181, 181*t*

Graves' disease, condition, named for Robert Graves, an Irish physician, resulting in overactivity of thyroid gland and can result in crisis situation; also called *hyperthyroidism,* 394

Gray matter, tissue within central nervous system; consists of unsheathed or uncovered nerve cell bodies and dendrites, 413, 417

Great saphenous vein, 150*f*

Greenstick fracture, fracture in which there is incomplete break; one side of bone is broken and other side is bent; this type of fracture is commonly found in children due to their softer and more pliable bone structure, 102

Gross motor skills, use of large muscle groups that coordinate body movements such as walking, running, jumping, and balance, 515

Growth hormone (GH), hormone secreted by anterior pituitary that stimulates growth of body, 381*t*, 384, 385

Guillain-Barré syndrome, disease of nervous system in which nerves lose their myelin covering; may be caused by autoimmune reaction; characterized by loss of sensation and/or muscle control in arms and legs; symptoms then move toward trunk and may even result in paralysis of diaphragm, 428

Gums, tissue around teeth; also called *gingiva,* 258, 260

L

O

Tubercle, small, rounded process that provides attachment for tendons and muscles, 88

Tuberculin skin tests (TB test), applying chemical agent (Tine or Mantoux tests) under surface of skin to determine if patient has been exposed to tuberculosis, 239

Tuberculosis (TB), infectious disease caused by tubercle bacillus, *Myocobacterium tuberculosis;* most commonly affects respiratory system and causes inflammation and calcification of system; tuberculosis is again on uprise and is seen in many patients who have AIDS, 237

Tuberosity, large, rounded process that provides attachment to tendons and muscles, 83

Tumor, abnormal growth of tissue that may be benign or malignant; also called *neoplasm,* 526, 528

Two-hour postprandial glucose tolerance test, blood test to assist in evaluating glucose metabolism; patient eats high-carbohydrate diet and fasts overnight before test; blood sample is then taken two hours after meal, 396

Tympanectomy, excision of eardrum, 472

Tympanic, pertaining to eardrum, 471

Tympanic membrane, also called eardrum; as sound moves along auditory canal, it strikes tympanic membrane causing it to vibrate; this conducts sound wave into middle ear, 467, 467*f*

Tympanitis, eardrum inflammation, 472

Tympanogram, graphic record that illustrates results ofs tympanometry, 474

Tympanometer, instrument to measure eardrum, 474

Tympanometry, measurement of movement of tympanic membrane; can indicate presence of pressure in middle ear, 474

Tympanoplasty, another term for surgical reconstruction of eardrum; also called *myringoplasty,* 476

Tympanorrhexis, ruptured eardrum, 472

Tympanotomy, incision into eardrum, 476

Type A blood, one of ABO blood types; person with type A markers on his or her RBCs; type A blood will make anti-B antibodies, 182

Type AB blood, one of ABO blood types; person with both type A and type B markers on his or her RBCs; since it has both markers, it will not make antibodies against either A or B blood, 182

Type B blood, one of ABO blood types; person with type B markers on his or her RBCs; type B blood will make anti-A antibodies, 182

Type O blood, one of ABO blood types; person with no markers on his or her RBCs; type O blood will not react with anti-A or anti-B antibodies; therefore, is considered universal donor, 182

Type and cross-match, lab test performed before person receives blood transfusion; double checks blood type of both donor's and recipient's blood, 189

U

Ulcer, open sore or lesion in skin or mucous membrane, 62, 62*f*

Ulcerative colitis, ulceration of unknown origin of mucous membranes of colon; also known as *inflammatory bowel disease* (IBD), 275

Ulna, one of forearm bones in upper extremity, 92, 93*f,* 94, 94*f*

Ulnar, pertaining to ulna, one of lower arm bones, 99

Ulnar artery, 148*f*

Ulnar nerve, 419*f*

Ulnar vein, 150*f*

Ultrasound (US), use of high-frequency sound waves to create heat in soft tissues under skin; particularly useful for treating injuries to muscles, tendons, and ligaments, as well as muscle spasms; in radiology, ultrasound waves can be used to outline shapes of tissues, organs, and fetus, 511, 511*f,* 518

Ultraviolet (UV), 72

Umbilical, anatomical division of abdomen; middle section of middle row, 36*t*

Umbilical cord, cord extending from baby's umbilicus (navel) to placenta; contains blood vessels that carry oxygen and nutrients from mother to baby and carbon dioxide and wastes from baby to mother, 336, 337*f,* 338

Unconscious, condition or state of being unaware of surroundings with inability to respond to stimuli, 424

Ungual, 57

Unit dose, drug dosage system that provides prepackaged, prelabeled, individual medications ready for immediate use by the patient, 497

Universal donor, type O blood is considered universal donor; since it has no markers on RBC surface, it will not trigger reaction with anti-A or anti-B antibodies, 182

Universal recipient, person with type AB blood has no antibodies against other blood types and therefore, in emergency, can receive any type of blood, 182

Upper extremity (UE), the arm, 31, 92, 93*f,* 94, 94*f,* 516

Upper gastrointestinal (UGI) series, administering barium contrast material orally and then taking X-ray to visualize esophagus, stomach, and duodenum, 278

V

Vaccination, providing protection against communicable diseases by stimulating immune system to produce antibodies against that disease; children can now be immunized for: hepatitis B, diphtheria, tetanus, pertussis, *Haemophilus influenzae* type b, polio, measles, mumps, rubella, and chickenpox; also called *immunization,* 196, 197, 204

Vagina, organ in female reproductive system that receives penis and semen, 30*t,* 35*t,* 301*f,* 332, 332*f,* 334*f,* 335, 335*f,* 337*f,* 344

Vaginal, (1) pertaining to vagina; (2) tablets and suppositories inserted vaginally and used to treat vaginal yeast infections and other irritations, 341, 494, 496*t*

Vaginal hysterectomy, removal of uterus through vagina rather than through abdominal incision, 350

Vaginal orifice, external vaginal opening; may be covered by hymen, 335, 335*f*

Vaginitis, inflammation of vagina, 344

Vagus nerve, 418*t*

Valve replacement, excision of diseased heart valve and replacement with artificial valve, 163

Valves, flaplike structures found within tubular organs such as lymph vessels, veins, and heart; function to prevent backflow of fluid, 193, 194, 194*f,*

Valvoplasty, surgical repair of valve, 163

Valvular, pertaining to valve, 152

Valvulitis, inflammation of valve, 157

Varicella, contagious viral skin infection; commonly called *chickenpox,* 68, 68*f*

Varicocele, enlargement of veins of spermatic cord, which commonly occurs on left side of adolescent males; seldom needs treatment, 358

Varicose veins, swollen and distended veins, usually in legs, 158

Vas deferens, also called ductus deferens; vas deferens is long, straight tube that carries sperm from epididymis up into pelvic cavity, where it continues around bladder and empties into urethra; one component, along with nerves and blood vessels, of spermatic cord, 30*t,* 35*t,* 96*f,* 354, 354*f,* 356, 362*f,* 386*f*

Vasal, pertaining to vas deferens, 357

Vascular, pertaining to vessels, 152

Vasectomy, removal of segment or all of vas deferens to prevent sperm from leaving male body; used for contraception purposes, 361, 362*f*

Vasoconstrictor, contracts smooth muscle in walls of blood vessels; raises blood pressure, 164

Vasodilator, produces relaxation of blood vessels to lower blood pressure, 164

Vasopressin, substance given to control diabetes insipidus and promote reabsorption of water in kidney tubules, 398

Vasovasostomy, creation of new opening between two sections of vas deferens; used to reverse vasectomy, 362

Vegetation, 155

Veins, blood vessels of cardiovascular system that carry blood toward heart, 28*t,* 53*f,* 139*f,* 140, 142*f,* 147*f,* 149, 193*f*

Vena cava, 140*f*

Venereal disease (VD), 360

Venipuncture, 188

Venogram, 143

Venous, pertaining to vein, 152

Ventilation, movement of air in and out of lungs, 220

Ventilation-perfusion scan, nuclear medicine diagnostic test especially useful in identifying pulmonary emboli; radioactive air is inhaled for ventilation portion to determine if air is filling entire lung; radioactive intravenous injection shows whether blood is flowing to all parts of lung, 238

Ventilator, machine that provides artificial ventilation for patient unable to breath on his or her own; also called *respirator,* 240

Ventral, directional term meaning near or on front or belly side of body, 34*f,* 37*t*

Ventral cavities, 35*t*

Ventricles, two lower chambers of heart that receive blood from atria and pump it back out of heart; left ventricle pumps blood to body, and right ventricle pumps blood to lungs; also fluid-filled spaces within cerebrum; contain cerebrospinal fluid, which is watery, clear fluid that provides protection from shock or sudden motion to brain, 142, 414, 416

Ventricular, pertaining to ventricle, 152

Ventricular septal defect (VSD), 155

Venules, smallest veins; receive deoxygenated blood leaving capillaries, 149, 152, 192*f*

Vermiform appendix, small outgrowth at end of cecum; function or purpose is unknown, 263

Verruca, warts; benign neoplasm (tumor) caused by virus; has rough surface that is removed by chemicals and/or laser therapy, 68

Vertebrae, 90*f*

Vertebral, pertaining to vertebrae, 41

Vertebral canal, bony canal through vertebrae that contains spinal cord, 416

Vertebral column, part of axial skeleton; a column of 26 vertebrae that forms backbone and protects spinal cord; divided into five sections: cervical, thoracic, and lumbar vertebrae, sacrum, and coccyx; also called *spinal column,* 89, 91, 92*f,* 92*t,* 416